The team

Project Managers: Gill Dawson, Alison Nash

Production & Reprographics: Bill Griffiths, Emma Griffin, Jackie Blizzard

Design & Page Layout: Jackie Blizzard, Kathryn Teece

Researchers: Alana Clogan, James Hollingsworth

Advertising Sales: Jackie Smith, Gill Grimshaw, Debra Greer, Heather Gallimore, Natalie Bunegar, Sarah Wiggett

Editorial Contibutors: Michael Holmes, Jason Orme, Natasha Brinsmead, Melanie Griffiths

Subscriptions: Alexandra Worthington

Marketing: Caroline Hawksworth

Technical & Database Support: Stephen Marks & ICO Solutions Ltd

Publishing Director: Peter Harris

Additional copies of The Homebuilder's Handbook are available priced at £25.00 excluding postage and packaging. To order, please call 01527 834435 or visit www.homebuilding.co.uk/bookshop.

Other titles

From the publishers of Homebuilding & Renovating magazine, Move or Improve? magazine, and Period Living magazine.

www.homebuilding.co.uk, www.moveorimprove.co.uk, www.periodliving.co.uk, www.plotfinder.net, www.propertyfinderfrance.net, www.renovationfrance.net, www.sitefinderireland.com

ISBN 978-0-9552043-0-2

Printed in Italy

Able Skills   Open 7 Days   0808 100 3245
INTENSIVE CONSTRUCTION COURSES

5 Day Courses
- Plastering
- Plumbing
- Tiling
- Bricklaying
- Electrical
- Dry Lining
- Carpentry
- Multi-Skilled

Able Skills is a well established and reputable Construction Training Centre

Able Skills has been specifically set up to help you learn your chosen construction skill in a friendly and spacious environment. No previous experience is required in order to take part in any of our courses; these courses are open to anyone, regardless of gender, age or status.

At Able Skills we can offer training in:

Carpentry

Plumbing

Part P Electrical

Bricklaying

Dry lining

Tiling

Plastering

Kitchen Fitting

These courses are available over 5 or 10 days, which offers you the option to do an intensive or advanced course, or both.

Everyone is welcome to attend training courses at Able Skills and since opening, we have built links with the Princes Trust, various training organisations supported by Job Centre Plus, Housing Associations nationwide, Armed Forces Resettlement and Connexions to name but a few.

These important links have meant that we have been able to train young people, unemployed people, Servicemen for resettlement and have gone some way towards enhancing the skills of those already in employment.

We pride ourselves in the quality of training we deliver, so much so that we have now obtained City & Guilds and NPTC approval which enables us to provide qualifications for those seeking to further their education and career.

For further information visit our website: www.ableskills.co.uk
Tel: 0808 100 3245 Email: info@ableskills.co.uk
Unit K5, Riverside Industrial Estate, Riverside Way, Dartford, Kent DA1 5BS

Foreword

Welcome to the fourth edition of the Homebuilder's Handbook, the largest and most comprehensive directory of manufacturers and suppliers to the UK home building industry. Whether you are a DIYer, self-builder, renovator or construction professional, the Handbook is an essential companion – the definitive guide to what is now a vast marketplace, helping you to find the very best products and services and keeping access to all of your key contacts within easy reach.

This latest edition has been a year in the making and includes over 500 new entries, and an entire new section on suppliers to the rapidly expanding, and increasingly important, smart home market. The Homebuilder's Handbook team have also been busy checking and verifying every one of the 1,000s of existing entries to make sure they are up to date, complete with as many website URLs as possible.

Since the last edition of the Handbook was published I have been busier than ever, completing my third self-build project and overseeing the start of a development of seven new homes. The Handbook has proved an essential component in the success of these projects.

For my last home I found the Handbook especially useful when researching ecological features. The marketplace for green products and services is full of small suppliers, many of which are not well known names and so difficult to track down via the web, so for instance when it came to finding a rainwater harvesting system the Handbook proved the best source of leads. I contacted three suppliers, found the best price and the most convenient delivery date – I was desperate to save my newly planted garden from the drought and the

Thames Water hosepipe ban. Two weeks later the system was up and running and, thanks to the Handbook, I managed to keep my newly laid turf green all summer without having to break the law.

The directory also came to the rescue when it came to finding verge tiles to match the reclaimed handmade clay tiles I have used on the roof of my new home. It is always difficult to find enough specials to match reclaimed tiles and the usual solution is to mix in some new ones, but at 7"x11" rather than the standard 6 1/2" x 10 this was not an option for matching the tiles I had found. By calling every supplier listed in the Handbook, I eventually managed to find a firm who had made a special batch for a client and had sufficient left over for my roof. The specials weren't cheap, but by enabling me to use 7,000 reclaimed tiles each costing 20p less than new, they saved me a small fortune.

These are just two examples of the countless ways that the Handbook has helped me save time and money over the past year. Information is the key to solving problems, and there is no better source of supplier information than the Homebuilder's Handbook.

I wish you the best of luck with your project.

Michael

Michael Holmes
Editor in Chief
Homebuilding & Renovating Magazine

2008 Edition: In a fast changing market full of new ideas and innovation, no directory can be 100% comprehensive, and so work has already started on the Fifth Edition for 2008 (for details visit www.homebuilding.co.uk). If you have any suggestions for improvements, or further contacts you feel should be included in the next edition, please let us know either by writing to us or emailing us as homebuilders.handbook@centaur.co.uk

PRODUCT INDEX

PRODUCT INDEX

Contents

SUBSTRUCTURE & FOUNDATIONS

SPONSORED BY: Homebuilding & Renovating Magazine
Tel: 01527 834435 Web: www.homebuilding.co.uk

Britain's Best Selling Self-Build Magazine

HOMEBUILDING & RENOVATING

Basements

Many older homes, especially those in urban areas, were built with a cellar as it was a handy area for food and fuel storage. Unwilling or unmotivated to use this often dark and damp space, homeowners buying these properties often left their cellars neglected. But today, the cellar – or basement – is enjoying a renaissance, as homebuilders and renovators try to squeeze as many rooms as possible out of their living space.

As the cost of moving house continues to soar, more homeowners are deciding to convert a damp basement into comfortable living space, rather than search for a bigger house.

A basement conversion is treated as an extension by the planners, so if it exceeds the 70ᵐ3 allowed by Permitted Development Right (this figure may be reduced in designated areas, such as Conservation Areas), you will need planning permission. However, as a basement will not have any significant visual impact on the property, planning refusal is unlikely.

Where there isn't an existing cellar space, it is becoming increasingly popular to retro-fit basements under a house. Even though the process requires considerable remedial work to excavate the ground, create new foundations and stabilise the present structure, the state of the current housing market means it may make more financial sense to improve rather than move. After all, much of the cost will be recouped if the property is sold on, and the amount of space gained by adding a basement could be more than enough for your needs.

Admittedly in some cases, particularly when retro-fitting, the creation of living space in a basement can be more costly than simply building an extension or converting a loft. But you could be creating a significant amount of space and you won't be encroaching onto the garden, as with other extensions.

Enlisting the services of a one-stop basement company may be a wise decision. The specialists can help with issues such as waterproofing, and grey areas between the architect's drawings and the builder.

Waterproofing is a particularly important factor to consider. If you get it wrong and water ingress occurs, you'll ruin fittings, fixtures and construction materials, which will have to be replaced.

To assess the best course of action, contact the British Structural Waterproofing Association (www.bswa.co.uk) or the Structural Waterproofing Group (www.structuralwaterproofing.org), and remember that your choice should be dictated by British Standard BS8102 - Code of Practice for Protection of Structures Against Water from the Ground.

Anyone considering improving their home should consult Move or Improve? magazine.

The bible for extenders and remodellers, the magazine provides case studies, tips and practical advice on everything from building a basement, to fitting bathroom taps.

Triton Chemical Engineering Ltd

FOUNDATIONS & PILING

KEY

PRODUCT TYPES: 1= Strip Foundations
2 = Trenchfill Foundations   3 = Piled &
Ringbeam Foundations   4 = Raft Foundations

SEE ALSO: BRICKS, BLOCKS, STONE &
CLADDING - Blocks

OTHER: ▽ Reclaimed   ⏘ On-line shopping
✎ Bespoke ✋Hand-made   ECO Ecological

AARSLEFF PILING
Hawton Lane, Balderton, Newark,
Nottinghamshire, NG24 3BU
Area of Operation: UK (Excluding Ireland)
Tel: 01636 611140
Fax: 01636 611142
Email: piling@aarsleff.co.uk
Web: www.aarsleff.co.uk   **Product Type:** 2

**ABBEY PYNFORD HOUSE
FOUNDATIONS LIMITED**
Second Floor, Hille House, 132 St Albans Road,
Watford, Hertfordshire, WD24 4AQ
Area of Operation: Midlands & Mid Wales, North
West England and North Wales, South West England
and South Wales
Tel: 0870 085 8400   **Fax:** 0870 085 8401
Email: info@abbeypynford.co.uk
Web: www.abbeypynford.co.uk

ACE MINIMIX
Millfields Road, Ettingshall,
Wolverhampton, West Midlands, WV4 6JP
Area of Operation: UK (Excluding Ireland)
Tel: 0121 585 5559   **Fax:** 0121 585 5557
Email: info@tarmac.co.uk   **Web:** www.tarmac.co.uk

ALL FOUNDATIONS LIMITED
Primrose Business Park, White Lane,
Blackwell, Derby, Derbyshire, DE55 5JR
Area of Operation: UK & Ireland
Tel: 0870 350 2050
Email: mail@allfoundations.co.uk
Web: www.allfoundations.co.uk   **Product Type:** 1, 2

ANVIL FOUNDATIONS LTD
8 Beaufort Chase, Dean Row,
Wilmslow, Cheshire, SK9 2BZ
Area of Operation: UK (Excluding Ireland)
Tel: 01625 522800
Fax: 01625 522850
Email: info@minipiling.co.uk
Web: www.minipiling.co.uk   **Product Type:** 1, 2

CEMEX READYMIX
CEMEX House, Rugby, Warwickshire, CV21 2DT
Area of Operation: Worldwide
Tel: 0800 667 827
Fax: 01788 564404
Email: info.readymix@cemex.co.uk
Web: www.cemex.co.uk ⏘   **Product Type:** 1

CENTRAL PILING LTD
Central Park, Colchester Road,
Halstead, Essex, CO9 2EU
Area of Operation: East England, Greater London,
South East England, South West England and
South Wales
Tel: 01787 474000
Fax: 01787 472113
Email: central@piling.uk.com
Web: www.centralpiling.com   **Product Type:** 3

CITIBUILD MINI PILING LTD
Walnut Tree Farm, Swanton Abbott,
Norfolk, NR10 5DL
Area of Operation: UK (Excluding Ireland)
Tel: 01692 538888   **Fax:** 01692 538100
Email: mark@citibuild.co.uk
Web: www.citibuild.co.uk   **Product Type:** 1, 2

CONCEPT ENGINEERING CONSULTANTS LTD
Unit 8 Warple Mews, Warple Way, London, W3 0RF
Area of Operation: East England, Greater London,
South East England, South West England
and South Wales
Tel: 0208 8112880   **Fax:** 0208 8112881
Email: si@conceptconsultants.co.uk
Web: www.conceptconsultants.co.uk
Product Type: 1, 2

CORDEK LIMITED
Spring Copse Business Park,
Slinfold, West Sussex, RH13 0SZ
Area of Operation: UK & Ireland
Tel: 01403 799600   **Fax:** 01403 791718
Email: sales@cordek.com   **Web:** www.cordek.com
Product Type: 2, 3

COUNTY GROUNDWORK SERVICES
6 Middlemarsh Street, Poundbury,
Dorchester, Dorset, DT1 3GD
Area of Operation: South West England/South Wales
Tel: 01305 261976
Email: info@countygroundworkservices.co.uk
Web: www.countygroundworkservices.co.uk

DUFAYLITE
Cromwell Road, St. Neots, Cambridgeshire, PE19 1QW
Area of Operation: Europe
Tel: 01480 215000   **Fax:** 01480 405526
Email: enquiries@dufaylite.com
Web: www.dufaylite.com   **Product Type:** 2, 3

FAIRCLEAR LTD
16 Sibthorpe Drive, Sudbrooke,
Lincoln, Lincolnshire, LN2 2RQ
Area of Operation: East England
Tel: 01522 595189   **Fax:** 01522 595189
Email: enquiries@fairclear.co.uk
Web: www.fairclear.co.uk

FOUNDATION PILING LTD
Ifton Industrial Estate, St.Martins,
Oswestry, Shropshire, SY11 3DA
Area of Operation: UK (Excluding Ireland)
Tel: 0845 803 5116   **Fax:** 0845 803 5117
Email: info@foundation-piling.co.uk
Web: www.foundation-piling.co.uk
Product Type: 1, 2

FOUNDATIONS EASTERN LTD
Moulsham Mill, Parkway, Chelmsford, Essex, CM2 7PX
Area of Operation: East England, Greater London,
Midlands & Mid Wales, South East England, South
West England and South Wales
Tel: 01245 226502   **Fax:** 01245 223967
Email: info@minipiling.com
Web: www.minipiling.com   **Product Type:** 3

FOUNDEX (UK) LTD
Bretby Business Park, Building 1A, Ashby Road,
Burton upon Trent, Staffordshire, DE15 0YZ
Area of Operation: UK (Excluding Ireland)
Tel: 01283 553240   **Fax:** 01283 553242
Email: email@foundex.fsnet.co.uk
Web: www.foundexukltd.co.uk   **Product Type:** 1, 2

H+H CELCON LIMITED
Celcon House, Ightham, Sevenoaks, Kent, TN15 9HZ
Area of Operation: UK (Excluding Ireland)
Tel: 01732 880520   **Fax:** 01732 880531
Email: marketing@celcon.co.uk
Web: www.celcon.co.uk   **Product Type:** 1

HELICAL SYSTEMS LTD
The Old Police Station, 195 Main Road,
Biggin Hill, Westerham, Kent, TN16 3JU
Area of Operation: UK & Ireland
Tel: 01959 541148   **Fax:** 01959 540841
Email: janecannon@helicalsystems.co.uk
Web: www.helicalsystems.co.uk ⏘
Product Type: 3

HOLDEN + PARTNERS
26 High Street, Wimbledon, Greater London, SW19 5BY
Area of Operation: Worldwide
Tel: 0208 946 5502   **Fax:** 0208 879 0310
Email: arch@holdenpartners.co.uk
Web: www.holdenpartners.co.uk

JOE WILLIAMS GROUNDWORK & DEMOLITION
The Holdings, Aston Bury Farm, Aston,
Stevenage, Hertfordshire, SG2 7EG
Area of Operation: East England, South East England
Tel: 01438 880824   **Fax:** 01438 880345
Email: jwgroundworks@yahoo.co.uk
Web: www.joe-williams.co.uk

MAXIT UK
The Heath, Runcorn, Cheshire, WA7 4QX
Area of Operation: UK & Ireland
Tel: 01928 515656   **Fax:** 01928 576792
Email: sales@maxit-uk.co.uk
Web: www.maxit-uk.co.uk   **Product Type:** 1

SAFEGUARD EUROPE LTD
Redkiln Close, Redkiln Way,
Horsham, West Sussex, RH13 5QL
Area of Operation: Worldwide
Tel: 01403 210204   **Fax:** 01403 217529
Email: info@safeguardeurope.com
Web: www.safeguardeurope.com   **Product Type:** 1

**SEVENOAKS ENVIRONMENTAL
CONSULTANCY LTD**
19 Gimble Way, Pembury,
Tunbridge Wells, Kent, TN2 4BX
Area of Operation: East England, Greater London,
Midlands & Mid Wales, North East England, North
West England and North Wales, South East England,
South West England and South Wales
Tel: 01892 822999   **Fax:** 01892 822992
Email: enquires@sevenoaksenvironmental.co.uk
Web: www.sevenoaksenvironmental.co.uk

STRONGBEAM CONSTRUCTION LTD
17 Margam Avenue, Bitterne,
Southampton, Hampshire, S019 2QL
Area of Operation: South East England
Tel: 02380444948   **Fax:** 02380399173
Email: david@strongbeam.co.uk
Product Type: 3, 4

THE BIG BASEMENT COMPANY LIMITED
Trussley Works, Trussley Road,
Shepherds Bush, Greater London, W6 7PR
Area of Operation: Greater London, South East England
Tel: 0700 244 2273
Fax: 0208 748 8957
Email: enquiries@bigbasement.co.uk
Web: www.bigbasement.co.uk
Product Type: 1, 2, 3

URETEK (UK) LTD
Peel House, Peel Road,
Skelmersdale, Lancashire, WN8 9PT
Area of Operation: UK & Ireland
Tel: 01695 50525   **Fax:** 01695 555212
Email: sales@uretek.co.uk **Web:** www.uretek.co.uk

VAN ELLE LIMITED
Kirkby Lane, Pinxton, Nottingham,
Nottinghamshire, NG16 6JA
Area of Operation: UK (Excluding Ireland)
Tel: 01773 580580   **Fax:** 01773 862100
Email: info@van-elle.co.uk
Web: www.van-elle.co.uk   **Product Type:** 3

UNDERPINNING

KEY

OTHER: ▽ Reclaimed ⏘ On-line shopping
✎ Bespoke ✋Hand-made   ECO Ecological

**ABBEY PYNFORD HOUSE FOUNDATIONS
LIMITED**
Second Floor, Hille House, 132 St Albans Road,
Watford, Hertfordshire, WD24 4AQ
Area of Operation: Midlands & Mid Wales, North
West England and North Wales, South West England
and South Wales
Tel: 0870 085 8400   **Fax:** 0870 085 8401
Email: info@abbeypynford.co.uk
Web: www.abbeypynford.co.uk   **Other Info:** ✎

ACE MINIMIX
Millfields Road, Ettingshall,
Wolverhampton, West Midlands, WV4 6JP
Area of Operation: UK (Excluding Ireland)
Tel: 0121 5855559   **Fax:** 0121 585 5557
Email: info@tarmac.co.uk
Web: www.tarmac.co.uk

ALL FOUNDATIONS LIMITED
Primrose Business Park, White Lane,
Blackwell, Derby, Derbyshire, DE55 5JR
Area of Operation: UK & Ireland
Tel: 0870 350 2050
Email: mail@allfoundations.co.uk
Web: www.allfoundations.co.uk

ANVIL FOUNDATIONS LTD
8 Beaufort Chase, Dean Row,
Wilmslow, Cheshire, SK9 2BZ
Area of Operation: UK (Excluding Ireland)
Tel: 01625 522800   **Fax:** 01625 522850
Email: info@minipiling.co.uk
Web: www.minipiling.co.uk
Other Info: ✎ ⏘

CITIBUILD MINI PILING LTD
Walnut Tree Farm, Swanton Abbott,
Norfolk, NR10 5DL
Area of Operation: UK (Excluding Ireland)
Tel: 01692 538888   **Fax:** 01692 538100
Email: mark@citibuild.co.uk
Web: www.citibuild.co.uk

CONCEPT ENGINEERING CONSULTANTS LTD
Unit 8 Warple Mews, Warple Way, London, W3 0RF
Area of Operation: East England, Greater London,
South East England, South West England and
South Wales
Tel: 0208 8112880   **Fax:** 0208 8112881
Email: si@conceptconsultants.co.uk
Web: www.conceptconsultants.co.uk

DUFAYLITE
Cromwell Road, St. Neots,
Cambridgeshire, PE19 1QW
Area of Operation: Europe
Tel: 01480 215000   **Fax:** 01480 405526
Email: enquiries@dufaylite.com
Web: www.dufaylite.com

FOUNDATION PILING LTD
Ifton Industrial Estate, St.Martins,
Oswestry, Shropshire, SY11 3DA
Area of Operation: UK (Excluding Ireland)
Tel: 0845 803 5116   **Fax:** 0845 803 5117
Email: info@foundation-piling.co.uk
Web: www.foundation-piling.co.uk

GUARDIAN PRESERVATION SERVICES LLP
12 Woods Orchard Road, Gloucester,
Gloucestershire, GL4 0BU
Area of Operation: UK (Excluding Ireland)
Tel: 01452 530030   **Fax:** 01452 530031
Email: info@guardianpreservation.co.uk
Web: www.guardianpreservation.co.uk

HELICAL SYSTEMS LTD
The Old Police Station, 195 Main Road,
Biggin Hill, Westerham, Kent, TN16 3JU
Area of Operation: UK & Ireland
Tel: 01959 541148   **Fax:** 01959 540841
Email: janecannon@helicalsystems.co.uk
Web: www.helicalsystems.co.uk ⏘
Other Info: ✎

R E DESIGN
97 Lincoln Avenue, Glasgow, G13 3DH
Area of Operation: Scotland
Tel: 0141 959 1902   **Fax:** 0141 959 3040
Email: mail@r-e-design.co.uk
Web: www.r-e-design.co.uk

STRONGBEAM CONSTRUCTION LTD
17 Margam Avenue, Bitterne,
Southampton, Hampshire, S019 2QL
Area of Operation: South East England
Tel: 02380 444948   **Fax:** 02380 399173
Email: david@strongbeam.co.uk

THE BIG BASEMENT COMPANY LIMITED
Trussley Works, Trussley Road,
Shepherds Bush, Greater London, W6 7PR
Area of Operation: Greater London, South East England
Tel: 0700 244 2273 **Fax:** 0208 748 8957
Email: enquiries@bigbasement.co.uk
Web: www.bigbasement.co.uk

URETEK (UK) LTD
Peel House, Peel Road,
Skelmersdale, Lancashire, WN8 9PT
Area of Operation: UK & Ireland
Tel: 01695 50525 **Fax:** 01695 555212
Email: sales@uretek.co.uk **Web:** www.uretek.co.uk

VAN ELLE LIMITED
Kirkby Lane, Pinxton, Nottingham,
Nottinghamshire, NG16 6JA
Area of Operation: UK (Excluding Ireland)
Tel: 01773 580580 **Fax:** 01773 862100
Email: info@van-elle.co.uk
Web: www.van-elle.co.uk

BASEMENTS

KEY
PRODUCT TYPES: 1= Modular Basements
2 = Basement Tanking   3 = Basement
Specialists   4 = Basement Membranes
5 = Other

OTHER: ▽ Reclaimed 🖰 On-line shopping
✍ Bespoke ✋ Hand-made   ECO Ecological

**ABBEY PYNFORD HOUSE
FOUNDATIONS LIMITED**
Second Floor, Hille House, 132 St Albans Road,
Watford, Hertfordshire, WD24 4AQ
Area of Operation: Midlands & Mid Wales, North
West England and North Wales, South West
England and South Wales
Tel: 0870 085 8400 **Fax:** 0870 085 8401
Email: info@abbeypynford.co.uk
Web: www.abbeypynford.co.uk   **Product Type:** 3

ABTECH (UK) LTD
Sheiling House, Invincible Road,
Farnborough, Hampshire, GU14 7QU
Area of Operation: UK (Excluding Ireland)
Tel: 0800 085 1431 **Fax:** 01252 378665
Email: sales@abtechbasements.co.uk
Web: www.abtechbasements.co.uk
Product Type: 3, 4

AQUATECNIC
211 Heathhall Industrial Estate,
Dumfries, Dumfries & Galloway, DG1 3PH
Area of Operation: UK & Ireland
Tel: 0845 226 8283
Fax: 0845 226 8293
Email: info@aquatecnic.net
Web: www.aquatecnic.net 🖰
Product Type: 2

BASEMENTS UK
Unit 7 Nations Business Park, Curdridge Lane,
Curdridge, Southampton, Hampshire, SO32 2BH
Area of Operation: East England, Greater London,
South East England, South West England and
South Wales
Tel: 0845 060 4488 **Fax:** 01489 786109
Email: info@bukfirst.com
Web: www.basementsuk.co.uk
Product Type: 2, 3, 4

BECO PRODUCTS LTD
Beco House, 6 Exmoor Avenue,
Scunthorpe, Lincolnshire, DN15 8NJ
Area of Operation: UK & Ireland
Tel: 01724 747576 **Fax:** 01724 747579
Email: info@becowallform.co.uk
Web: www.becowallform.co.uk
Product Type: 1, 5   **Materials Type:** G)1, K)11

BILCO UK
Park Farm Business Centre, Fornham St Genevieve,
Bury St Edmunds, Suffolk, IP28 6TS
Area of Operation: UK (Excluding Ireland)
Tel: 01284 701696 **Fax:** 01284 702531
Email: bilcouk@bilco.com
Web: www.bilco.com   **Product Type:** 5

BIOCRAFT LTD
25B Chapel Hill, Reading, Berkshire, RG31 5BT
Area of Operation: East England, Greater London,
South East England, South West England and
South Wales
Tel: 01189 451144   **Email:** info@biocraft.co.uk
Web: www.biocraft.co.uk   **Product Type:** 3, 4

CAVITY TRAYS LTD
New Administration Centre, Boundary Avenue,
Yeovil, Somerset, BA22 8HU
Area of Operation: Worldwide
Tel: 01935 474769 **Fax:** 01935 428223
Email: enquiries@cavitytrays.co.uk
Web: www.cavitytrays.com 🖰 **Product Type:** 4

CORDEK LIMITED
Spring Copse Business Park,
Slinfold, West Sussex, RH13 0SZ
Area of Operation: UK & Ireland
Tel: 01403 799600 **Fax:** 01403 791718
Email: sales@cordek.com
Web: www.cordek.com   **Product Type:** 2, 4

DELTA MEMBRANE SYSTEMS LTD
Bassett Business Centre, Hurricane Way,
North Weald, Epping, Essex, CM16 6AA
Area of Operation: UK & Ireland
Tel: 01992 523811   **Fax:** 01992 524046
Email: info@deltamembranes.com
Web: www.deltamembranes.com
Product Type: 2, 3, 4

FOUNDEX (UK) LTD
Bretby Business Park, Building 1A, Ashby Road,
Burton upon Trent, Staffordshire, DE15 0YZ
Area of Operation: UK (Excluding Ireland)
Tel: 01283 553240   **Fax:** 01283 553242
Email: info@foundex.fsnet.co.uk
Web: www.foundexukltd.co.uk
Product Type: 1, 2, 4

GUARDIAN PRESERVATION SERVICES LLP
12 Woods Orchard Road, Gloucester,
Gloucestershire, GL4 0BU
Area of Operation: UK (Excluding Ireland)
Tel: 01452 530030   **Fax:** 01452 530031
Email: info@guardianpreservation.co.uk
Web: www.guardianpreservation.co.uk
Product Type: 2, 3, 4

HOLDEN + PARTNERS
26 High Street, Wimbledon, Greater London, SW19 5BY
Area of Operation: Worldwide
Tel: 0208 946 5502   **Fax:** 0208 879 0310
Email: arch@holdenpartners.co.uk
Web: www.holdenpartners.co.uk   **Product Type:** 5

INDOOR CLIMATE SOLUTIONS
6 Charlesworth Avenue, Monkspath,
Solihull, West Midlands, B90 4SE
Area of Operation: Midlands & Mid Wales
Tel: 0121 733 2525
Email: info@ics-aircon.com
Web: www.ics-aircon.com   **Product Type:** 2

INDUSTRIAL TEXTILES & PLASTICS LTD
Stillington Road, Easingwold, York, North Yorkshire, YO61 3FA
Area of Operation: Worldwide
Tel: 01347 825200
Email: info@itpltd.com   **Web:** www.itpltd.com
Product Type: 4

MARLEY WATERPROOFING
Covert Road, Aylesham Industrial Estate,
Aylesham, Canterbury, Kent, CT3 3EQ
Area of Operation: UK (Excluding Ireland)
Tel: 01304 843300   **Fax:** 01304 843500
Email: info@marleywaterproofing.co.uk
Web: www.marleywaterproofing.co.uk
Product Type: 2, 4

NEWMIL
17 Arundel Close, New Milton, Hampshire, BH25 5UH
Area of Operation: South East England
Tel: 0845 090 0109
Email: enquiries@newmil.co.uk
Web: www.newmil.co.uk

**PHOENIX WATERPROOFING
(A DIVISION OF CONTITECH UK LTD)**
Chestnut Field House, Chestnut Field,
Rugby, Warwickshire, CU21 2PA
Area of Operation: UK & Ireland
Tel: 01788 571482   **Fax:** 01788 542245
Email: tonyb@phoenix-gb.com
Web: www.phoenix-ag.com   **Product Type:** 2, 4

POLARWALL LIMITED
Unit 3 Old Mill Industrial Estate,
Stoke Canon, Exeter, Devon, EX5 4RJ
Area of Operation: Europe
Tel: 01392 841777   **Fax:** 01392 841936
Email: info@polarwall.co.uk
Web: www.polarwall.co.uk

QUAD-LOCK (ENGLAND) LTD
Unit B3.1, Maws Centre, Jackfield,
Telford, Shropshire, TF8 7LS
Area of Operation: UK (Excluding Ireland)
Tel: 0870 443 1901
Fax: 0870 443 1902
Email: info@quadlock.co.uk
Web: www.quadlock.co.uk
Product Type: 5

QUADRIGA CONCEPTS LTD
Gadbrook House, Gadbrook Business Park,
Rudheath, Northwich, Cheshire, CW9 7RG
Area of Operation: UK & Ireland
Tel: 0808 100 3777
Fax: 01606 330777
Email: info@quadrigaltd.com
Web: www.quadrigaltd.com
Product Type: 2, 4

R E DESIGN
97 Lincoln Avenue, Glasgow, G13 3DH
Area of Operation: Scotland
Tel: 0141 959 1902   **Fax:** 0141 959 3040
Email: mail@r-e-design.co.uk
Web: www.r-e-design.co.uk   **Product Type:** 5

SAFEGUARD EUROPE LTD
Redkiln Close, Redkiln Way,
Horsham, West Sussex, RH13 5QL
Area of Operation: Worldwide
Tel: 01403 210204
Fax: 01403 217529
Email: info@safeguardeurope.com
Web: www.safeguardeurope.com
Product Type: 2, 3, 4

**SAFEGUARD
MAKING BUILDINGS DRY**

SAFEGUARD
Area of Operation: Worldwide
Tel: 01403 210204
Fax: 01403 217529
Email: info@safeguardeurope.com
Web: www.safeguardeurope.com
Product Type: 2, 3, 4

Safeguard supply a choice of systems for
waterproofing and refurbishing existing
basements. CAD drawings can be downloaded
from the company's website.

SPIRAL CELLARS LTD
Waltham Mead, Old London Road,
Pulborough, West Sussex, RH20 1LF
Area of Operation: UK & Ireland
Tel: 0845 241 2768   **Fax:** 0845 241 2767
Email: info@spiralcellars.com
Web: www.spiralcellars.com   **Product Type:** 1, 3, 5

SPRY PRODUCTS LTD
64 Nottingham Road, Long Eaton,
Nottingham, Nottinghamshire, NG10 2AU
Area of Operation: UK & Ireland
Tel: 0115 973 2914   **Fax:** 0115 972 5172
Email: jerspry@aol.com
Web: www.spryproducts.com
Product Type: 2, 3, 4

THE BIG BASEMENT COMPANY LIMITED
Trussley Works, Trussley Road,
Shepherds Bush, Greater London, W6 7PR
Area of Operation: Greater London, South East England
Tel: 0700 244 2273
Fax: 0208 748 8957
Email: enquiries@bigbasement.co.uk
Web: www.bigbasement.co.uk
Product Type: 1, 2, 3, 4, 5

THERMONEX LTD
Delcon House, 65 Manchester Road,
Bolton, Lancashire, BL2 1ES
Area of Operation: UK (Excluding Ireland)
Tel: 01204 559551 **Fax:** 01204 559552
Email: salesadmin@thermonex.co.uk
Web: www.thermonex.co.uk

TIMBERWISE (UK) LTD
1 Drake Mews, Gadbrook Park,
Northwich, Cheshire, CW9 7XF
Area of Operation: UK (Excluding Ireland)
Tel: 0800 991100   **Fax:** 01606 330999
Email: hq@timberwise.co.uk
Web: www.timberwise.co.uk   **Product Type:** 3, 4

TRACE BASEMENT SYSTEMS
Unit 8, Hurst Mill, Hurst Road, Glossop, Derbyshire, SK13 7QB
Area of Operation: East England, Greater London,
Midlands & Mid Wales, North East England, North
West England and North Wales
Tel: 01457 865165   **Fax:** 01457 866253
Email: enquiries@traceremedial.co.uk
Web: www.tracebasementsystems.co.uk
Product Type: 3

TRITON CHEMICAL MANUFACTURING LTD
129 Felixstowe Road, Abbey Wood, London, SE2 9SG
Area of Operation: Worldwide
Tel: 0208 310 3929   **Fax:** 0208 312 0349
Email: neil@triton-chemicals.com
Web: www.triton-chemicals.com
Product Type: 2, 3, 4

WISE PROPERTY CARE
8 Muriel Street, Barrhead, Glasgow, G78 1QB
Area of Operation: Scotland
Tel: 0141 876 0300   **Fax:** 0141 876 0301
Email: les@wisepropertycare.com
Web: www.wisepropertycare.com 🖰
Product Type: 2

GROUND PREPARATION & DEMOLITION

KEY
OTHER: ▽ Reclaimed 🖰 On-line shopping
✍ Bespoke ✋ Hand-made   ECO Ecological

A PROCTOR GROUP LTD
The Haugh, Blairgowrie, Perth and Kinross, PH10 7ER
Area of Operation: Worldwide
Tel: 01250 872261
Fax: 01250 872727
Email: lynsay.johnston@proctorgroup.com
Web: www.proctorgroup.com

ABBEY PYNFORD HOUSE FOUNDATIONS LTD
Second Floor, Hille House, 132 St Albans Road,
Watford, Hertfordshire, WD24 4AQ
Area of Operation: Midlands & Mid Wales, North
West England and North Wales, South West England
and South Wales
Tel: 0870 085 8400   **Fax:** 0870 085 8401
Email: info@abbeypynford.co.uk
Web: www.abbeypynford.co.uk   **Other Info:**

ACE MINIMIX
Millfields Road, Ettingshall, Wolverhampton, WV4 6JP
Area of Operation: UK (Excluding Ireland)
Tel: 0121 5855559   **Fax:** 0121 585 5557
Email: info@tarmac.co.uk   **Web:** www.tarmac.co.uk

ALL FOUNDATIONS LIMITED
Primrose Business Park, White Lane,
Blackwell, Derby, Derbyshire, DE55 5JR
Area of Operation: UK & Ireland
Tel: 0870 350 2050   **Web:** www.allfoundations.co.uk
Email: mail@allfoundations.co.uk

CONCEPT ENGINEERING CONSULTANTS LTD
Unit 8 Warple Mews, Warple Way, London, W3 0RF
Area of Operation: East England, Greater London, South
East England, South West England and South Wales
Tel: 0208 8112880   **Fax:** 0208 8112881
Email: si@conceptconsultants.co.uk
Web: www.conceptconsultants.co.uk

COUNTY GROUNDWORK SERVICES
6 Middlemarsh Street, Poundbury,
Dorchester, Dorset, DT1 3GD
Area of Operation: South West England/South Wales
Tel: 01305 261976
Email: info@countygroundworkservices.co.uk
Web: www.countygroundworkservices.co.uk

GEOINVESTIGATE LTD
Units 4-5 Terry Dicken Industrial Estate,
Ellerbeck Way, Stokesley, North Yorkshire, TS9 7AE
Area of Operation: UK (Excluding Ireland)
Tel: 01642 713779   **Fax:** 01642 719923
Email: geoinvestigate@qnetadsl.com

HB INSULATIONS
Unit 3 Falcon Court, Manners Industrial Estate,
Ilkeston, Derbyshire, DE7 8EF
Area of Operation: UK (Excluding Ireland)
Tel: 0115 944 0244   **Fax:** 0115 944 0244
Web: www.hbinsulations.com

JOE WILLIAMS GROUNDWORK & DEMOLITION
The Holdings, Aston Bury Farm, Aston,
Stevenage, Hertfordshire, SG2 7EG
Area of Operation: East England, South East England
Tel: 01438 880824   **Fax:** 01438 880345
Email: jwgroundworks@yahoo.co.uk
Web: www.joe-williams.co.uk

JP DEMOLITION LTD
Green Lane Business Park, Green Lane,
Tewkesbury, Gloucestershire, GL20 8SJ
Area of Operation: UK (Excluding Ireland)
Tel: 01684 271200   **Web:** www.jp-group.co.uk
Email: tim.deeks@jpconstruction.co.uk

PHI GROUP LTD
Harcourt House, Royal Crescent,
Cheltenham, Gloucestershire, GL50 3DA
Area of Operation: UK (Excluding Ireland)
Tel: 0870 333 4126   **Fax:** 0870 333 4127
Email: marketing@phigroup.co.uk
Web: www.phigroup.co.uk

R E DESIGN
97 Lincoln Avenue, Glasgow, G13 3DH
Area of Operation: Scotland
Tel: 0141 959 1902   **Fax:** 0141 959 3040
Email: mail@r-e-design.co.uk **Web:** www.r-e-design.co.uk

**SEVENOAKS ENVIRONMENTAL
CONSULTANCY LTD**
19 Gimble Way, Pembury, Tunbridge Wells, Kent, TN2 4BX
Area of Operation: England & Wales
Tel: 01892 822999   **Fax:** 01892 822992
Email: enquires@sevenoaksenvironmental.co.uk
Web: www.sevenoaksenvironmental.co.uk

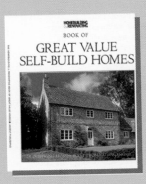
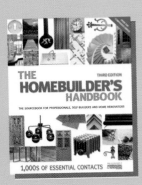

COMPLETE STRUCTURAL SYSTEMS

Image courtesy of Potton (01480 401333)

SPONSORED BY Potton Limited
Tel: 01480 401333 Web: www.potton.co.uk

Timber Frame

One of the self-builder's most frequently asked questions is, "Which is better - brick and block or timber frame?" You won't be surprised to learn that there is no easy answer. But if you are going for a timber frame, here are a few pointers to help you along the way.

A key point to grasp is that the phrase 'timber frame' usually applies only to the internal, structural parts of a house. It's virtually impossible to tell from the outside whether a house is built with a masonry blockwork or timber walls – because your choice of external walling material is unaffected by the type of internal walls you use. So using timber does not limit your choices as to how your home should look.

Construction

During construction of a timber-framed house, all the structural elements – with exception of the chimney – are built using timber. In British house building, almost all timber framed homes are built in factories. This greatly reduces the work of the on-site carpentry team, which has to do little more than assemble the panels – a task that typically takes no more than a few days (as opposed to the several weeks needed to build a masonry superstructure).

The panels often have the windows and doors already in place. Some methods supply fully finished walls and roofs, but the typical British timber frame house has open panels – a semi-finished state that has to be insulated and cabled on site before the plasterers cover the inner walls with a wall-lining board.

If the house requires a brick or blockwork facing, the bricklayers come on site after the timber frame is fully erected. They can work on the outside whilst the finishing trades go on inside and the roofers work overhead.

A typical timber frame wall consists of a framework of timber studs, frequently 90mm deep, boxed over with a sheet of plywood, which is covered with a layer of waterproof building paper – this deflects rainwater away from the frame. The voids between the timber studwork are filled with insulation, and on the inside a sheet of polythene known as a vapour control layer is fixed before the whole thing is faced with plasterboard.

Top tips

- Timber frames are (relatively) quick and easy to erect – prefabricated superstructures can go up quickly once on site and they tend to be built to far tighter tolerances, making fitting out quicker and easier too

- There is less shrinkage and settlement with timber frames which have inherently good thermal insulation

- It's easier to run services through timber frames

- Additional materials are required for adequate soundproofing, so bear this in mind.

Potton

TIMBER FRAME

KEY

PRODUCT TYPES: 1= Post and Beam
2 = Open Panel   3 = Closed Panel
4 = Green Oak   5 = Log Homes
6 = Barn Frames   7 = Other

SEE ALSO: MERCHANTS - Timber Merchants

OTHER: ▽ Reclaimed   On-line shopping
Bespoke   Hand-made   ECO Ecological

AC ROOF TRUSSES LTD
Severn Farm Industrial Estate,
Welshpool, Powys, SY21 7DF
Area of Operation: UK & Ireland
Tel: 01938 554881   **Fax:** 01938 556265
Email: info@acrooftrusses.co.uk
Web: www.acrooftrusses.co.uk

ALLWOOD BUILDINGS LTD
Talewater Works, Talaton, Exeter, Devon, EX5 2RT
Area of Operation: UK (Excluding Ireland)
Tel: 01404 850977
Fax: 01404 850946
Email: frames@allwoodtimber.co.uk
Web: www.allwoodtimber.co.uk
Product Type: 1, 2, 3

ANIRINA OY (FINLAND) - LOG HOME SUPPLIERS & BUILDERS UK
The Gate House, Home Park Terrace,
Hampton Court Road, Hampton Wick,
Kingston upon Thames, Surrey, KT1 4AE
Area of Operation: Europe
Tel: 0208 943 0430   **Fax:** 0208 943 0430
Email: chris.drayson@virgin.net   **Product Type:** 5

ANTIQUE BUILDINGS LTD
Dunsfold, Godalming, Surrey, GU8 4NP
Area of Operation: UK & Ireland
Tel: 01483 200477
Email: info@antiquebuildings.com
Web: www.antiquebuildings.com
Product Type: 6   **Material Type:** A) 2

ARTICHOUSE IRELAND, LOGART HOMES
Arva, Tivoli Terrace North,
Dun Laoghaire, Co Dublin, Ireland
Area of Operation: UK & Ireland
Tel: 00353 1 2802879
Fax: 00353 1 2800955
Email: info@logart.ie   **Web:** www.logart.ie
Product Type: 5   **Other Info:** ECO

AXIS TIMBER LTD
9 Chapel Road, Sarisbury Green,
Southampton, Hampshire, S031 7FB
Area of Operation: UK & Ireland
Tel: 01489 575073   **Fax:** 01489 571607
Email: douglas@axistimber.com
Web: www.axistimber.co.uk
Product Type: 1, 7
Material Type: B) 1, 2, 5, 7, 8, 9, 10, 12

BEAVER TIMBER COMPANY
Barcaldine, Argyll & Bute, PA37 1SG
Area of Operation: UK (Excluding Ireland)
Tel: 01631 720353
Fax: 01631 720430
Email: info@beavertimber.co.uk
Web: www.beavertimber.co.uk
Product Type: 5

BENFIELD ATT
Castle Way, Caldicot, Monmouthshire, NP26 5PR
Area of Operation: UK & Ireland
Tel: 01291 437050
Fax: 01291 437051
Email: info@benfieldatt.co.uk
Web: www.benfieldatt.co.uk
Product Type: 2, 3

BORDER OAK DESIGN & CONSTRUCTION
Kingsland Sawmills, Kingsland,
Leominster, Herefordshire, HR6 9SF
Area of Operation: Worldwide
Tel: 01568 708752   **Fax:** 01568 708295
Email: sales@borderoak.com
Web: www.borderoak.com
Product Type: 4, 6   **Other Info:** ▽ ECO

BROCH LIMITED
Unit 7, Parsons Road, Manor Trading Estate,
South Benfleet, Essex, SS7 4PY
Area of Operation: Europe
Tel: 0870 879 3070   **Fax:** 0870 879 3071
Email: info@brochsolid.com
Web: www.brochsolid.com
Product Type: 1, 2, 3, 4, 5, 6, 7

BUYDIRECT.CO.UK LTD
The Mill, Rough Hill, The Tye,
East Hanningfield, Essex, CM3 8BY
Area of Operation: UK & Ireland
Tel: 01245 400202   **Fax:** 01245 400302
Email: sales@buydirect.co.uk
Web: www.buydirect.co.uk   **Product Type:** 5

CANADA WOOD UK
PO Box 1, Farnborough, Hampshire, GU14 6WE
Area of Operation: UK & Ireland
Tel: 01252 522545   **Fax:** 01252 522546
Email: office@canadawooduk.org
Web: www.canadawood.info
Product Type: 2, 5
Material Type: A) 12

CARPENTER OAK & WOODLAND
Hall Farm, Thickwood Lane, Colerne, Wiltshire, SN14 8BE
Area of Operation: Worldwide
Tel: 01225 743089   **Fax:** 01225 744100
Email: info@carpenteroakandwoodland.com
Web: www.carpenteroakandwoodland.com

Don't Forget !
You can use the materials key at the beginning of the Handbook to get much more information from a company's listing.

Remarkable timber frame homes, share the passion...

Fusion Timber Frame
Tel: 0871 200 2430   Fax: 0871 200 2431
Web: www.fusiontimberframe.com
Email: homes@fusiontimberframe.com

CARPENTER OAK LTD & RODERICK JAMES ARCHITECT LTD
The Framing Yard, East Cornworthy, Totnes, Devon, TQ9 7HF
Area of Operation: Worldwide
Tel: 01803 732900   **Fax:** 01803 732901
Email: enquiries@carpenteroak.com   **Other Info:** ✏
Web: www.carpenteroak.com   **Product Type:** 1, 4, 6

CEDAR SELF-BUILD HOMES
Unit A2, Abbey Close,
Redwither Business Park, Wrexham, LL13 9XG
Area of Operation: Europe
Tel: 01978 664709   **Fax:** 01978 664596
Email: info@cedar-self-build.com
Web: www.cedar-self-build.com
Product Type: 1   **Other Info:** ✏   **Material Type:** A) 12

CJ O'SHEA & CO LTD
Unit 1 Granard Business Centre,
Burns Lane, Mill Hill, London, NW7 2DZ
Area of Operation: East England, Greater London, South East England, South West England, South Wales
Tel: 0208 959 3600   **Fax:** 0208 959 0184
Email: admin@oshea.co.uk   **Web:** www.oshea.co.uk

CLASSICS TIMBERFRAME
The Border Design Centre, Harelaw Moor,
Greenlaw, Borders, TD10 6XT
Tel: 01578 740218   **Fax:** 01578 740218
Email: borderdesign@constructionplus.net
Web: www.borderdesign.co.uk   **Product Type:** 1, 2

CONCEPT TIMBER
35 Lancaster Road, Bowerhill Industrial Estate,
Melksham, Wiltshire, SN12 6SS
Tel: 01225 792939   **Fax:** 01225 792949
Email: enquiries@concept-timber.co.uk
Web: www.concept-timber.co.uk

COWAN JOINERY CONSTRUCTION LTD
3 Clem Attlee Gardens, Larkhall, Lanarkshire, ML9 1HB
Tel: 01698 884362   **Fax:** 01698 883132
Email: office@cowanjoinery.co.uk
Web: www.cowanjoinery.co.uk

CRANNOG HOMES
799a Lordswood Lane, Lordswood, Chatham, Kent, ME5 8JP
Tel: 01634 201143   **Fax:** 01634 201143
Email: johnm@crannoghomes.com
Web: www.crannoghomes.com
Product Type: 1, 5   **Material Type:** A) 12

CREATIVE ESTATES TIMBER FRAME BUILDING
Unit 62, Thornhill Industrial Estate,
South Marston, Swindon, Wiltshire, SN3 4TA
Tel: 0870 432 8268   **Fax:** 0870 432 8269
Email: info@creativeestates.co.uk
Web: www.creativeestates.co.uk   **Product Type:** 2

CSF COUNTRY HOMES LTD
The Mill House, Marsh Farm, Cross Keys,
Withington, Hereford, Herefordshire, HR1 3NN
Tel: 01432 820660   **Fax:** 01432 820404
Email: country_homes@yahoo.co.uk
Web: www.country-homes.org

CUSTOM HOMES
South Suffolk Business Centre,
Alexandra Road, Sudbury, Surrey, CO10 2ZX
Area of Operation: UK & Ireland
Tel: 01787 377388   **Fax:** 01787 377622
Email: admin@customhomes.co.uk
Web: www.customhomes.co.uk   **Product Type:** 2

CUSTOM HOMES
Area of Operation: UK & Ireland
Tel: 01787 377388 **Fax:** 01787 377622
Email: admin@customhomes.co.uk
Web: www.customhomes.co.uk
⌨ : admin__customhomes.co.uk

Custom Homes is the largest self-build homes package company in the UK with offices nationwide offering a complete service from design to construction and finance to plot search.

CUSTOM HOMES
Area of Operation: UK & Ireland
Tel: 01787 377388 **Fax:** 01787 377622
Email: admin@customhomes.co.uk
Web: www.customhomes.co.uk
⌨ : admin__customhomes.co.uk

Custom Homes has built up a reputation the envy of the industry by placing the highest priority on the requirements of its customers right down to the last detail, providing a level of service others just dream about.

Remarkable **timber frame homes**
from concept to completion

Tel: 0871 200 2430
Web: www.fusiontimberframe.com
Email: homes@fusiontimberframe.com

Fusion Timber Frame

CHIPS NOW AVAILABLE TO ALL

CUSTOM HOMES
Area of Operation: UK & Ireland
Tel: 01787 377388 **Fax:** 01787 377622
Email: admin@customhomes.co.uk
Web: www.customhomes.co.uk
: admin_customhomes.co.uk

Independent project managers offer a full turn-key service together with an individual design and planning service with the benefit of local knowledge. Custom Homes leads where others follow.

DEESIDE HOMES TIMBERFRAME
Broomhill Road, Spurryhillock Industrial Estate
Stonehaven, Near Aberdeen, Aberdeenshire, AB39 2NH
Area of Operation: UK (Excluding Ireland)
Tel: 01569 767123 **Fax:** 01569 767766
Email: john.wright@bancon.co.uk
Web: www.bancon.co.uk

DESIGNER HOMES
Pooh Cottage, Minto, Hawick,
Roxburghshire, Borders, TD9 8SB
Area of Operation: UK & Ireland
Tel: 01450 870127 **Fax:** 01450 870127
Product Type: 2, 3 **Other Info:** ✎

DGS CONSTRUCTION LTD
The Glebe, Nash Road, Whaddon,
Milton Keynes, Buckinghamshire, MK17 0NQ
Area of Operation: East England, Greater London,
Midlands & Mid Wales, South East England, South
West England and South Wales
Tel: 01908 503147 **Fax:** 01908 504995
Email: info@dgsconstruction.co.uk
Web: www.dgsconstruction.co.uk
Product Type: 2, 3, 7

ECO SYSTEMS IRELAND LTD
40 Glenshesk Road, Ballycastle, Co Antrim, BT54 6PH
Area of Operation: UK & Ireland
Tel: 02820 768708 **Fax:** 02820 769781
Email: info@ecosystemsireland.com
Web: www.ecosystemsireland.com
Product Type: 3, 7

ENERGY SUPERSTORE
3 Wellington Park, Belfast, BT9 6DJ
Area of Operation: UK & Ireland
Tel: 02890 388391
Email: info@energysuperstore.co.uk
Web: www.energysuperstore.co.uk
Product Type: 3, 7

ENGLISH HERITAGE BUILDINGS
Coldharbour Farm Estate,
Woods Corner, East Sussex, TN21 9LQ
Area of Operation: Europe
Tel: 01424 838643 **Fax:** 01424 838606
Email: info@ehbp.com
Web: www.ehbp.com **Product Type:** 1, 4, 6

EXCEL BUILDING SOLUTIONS
Maerdy Industrial Estate, Gwent, NP22 5PY
Area of Operation: Worldwide
Tel: 01685 845200
Fax: 01685 844106
Email: sales@excelfibre.com
Web: www.excelfibre.com
Product Type: 3 **Other Info:** ECO ✎
Material Type: K) 3

FFOREST TIMBER ENGINEERING LTD
Kestrel Way, Garngoch Industrial Estate,
Gorseinon, Swansea, SA4 9WN
Area of Operation: Midlands & Mid Wales, South
West England and South Wales
Tel: 01792 895620 **Fax:** 01792 893969
Email: info@fforest.co.uk
Web: www.fforest.co.uk **Product Type:** 2

FINNISH WOOD PRODUCTS LTD
Tresparrett Farm Villa, Tresparrett, Cornwall, PL32 9ST
Area of Operation: UK & Ireland
Tel: 01840 261415 **Fax:** 01840 261415
Email: sales@finnishwoodproducts.com
Web: www.finnishwoodproducts.com

FINNISH WOOD PRODUCTS LTD

Area of Operation: UK & Ireland
Tel: 01840 261415
Fax: 01840 261415
Email: sales@finnishwoodproducts.com
Web: www.finnishwoodproducts.com

Timber frame buildings, staircases, external windows and doors all manufactured in Finland. Complete house kits available including, internal doors, kitchens, woodburners even a Finnish Sauna

FIRST LEISURE UK LTD
Oakbank House, Kenmore Street,
Aberfeldy, Perth and Kinross, PH15 2BL
Tel: 01887 829418 **Fax:** 01887 829090
Email: simon@firstleisureuk.co.uk
Web: www.log-buildings.co.uk **Product Type:** 5

FLEMING HOMES
Station Road, Duns, Berwickshire, Borders, TD11 3HS
Area of Operation: UK (Excluding Ireland)
Tel: 01361 883785 **Fax:** 01361 883898
Email: enquiries@fleminghomes.co.uk
Web: www.fleminghomes.co.uk **Other Info:** ✎

FLIGHT TIMBER PRODUCTS
Earls Colne Business Park,
Earls Colne, Essex, CO6 2NS
Area of Operation: East England, Greater London,
South East England
Tel: 01787 222336 **Fax:** 01787 222359
Email: sales@flighttimber.com
Web: www.flighttimber.com

FOUR ACRES CONSTRUCTION
Rannoch Road, Johnstone, Renfrewshire, PA5 0FP
Area of Operation: UK (Excluding Ireland)
Tel: 01505 337788 **Fax:** 01505 337788
Product Type: 2, 3, 5

FRAME UK
Jenson House, Cardrew Industrial Estate,
Redruth, Cornwall, TR15 1SS
Area of Operation: UK (Excluding Ireland)
Tel: 01209 310560 **Fax:** 01209 310561
Email: enquiries@framehomes.co.uk
Web: www.frameuk.com **Product Type:** 2, 3

FRAME WISE
Presteigne Industrial Estate, Presteigne, Powys, LD8 2UF
Area of Operation: UK (Excluding Ireland)
Tel: 01544 260125 **Fax:** 01544 260707
Email: framewise@framewiseltd.co.uk
Web: www.framewiseltd.co.uk

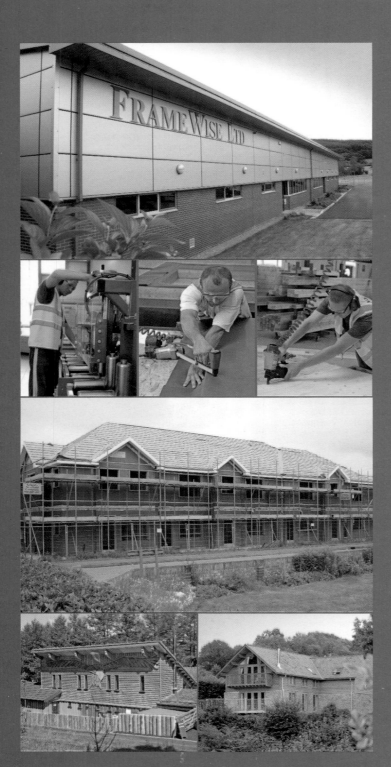

FUSION TIMBER FRAME LTD
First Floor, 18 Keymer Road,
Hassocks, West Sussex, BN6 8AN
Area of Operation: UK (Excluding Ireland)
Tel: 0871 200 2430   **Fax:** 0871 200 2431
Email: homes@fusiontimberframe.com
Web: www.fusiontimberframe.com
Product Type: 1, 2, 3

GREEN OAK STRUCTURES
20 Bushy Coombe Gardens, Glastonbury, Somerset, BA6 8JT
Area of Operation: UK & Ireland
Tel: 01458 833420   **Fax:** 01458 833420
Email: timberframes@greenoakstructures.co.uk
Web: www.greenoakstructures.co.uk
Product Type: 1, 4, 6   **Other Info:** ECO

GRIFFNER COILLTE LTD
Forest Park, Mullingar, Co Westmeath, Ireland
Area of Operation: UK & Ireland
Tel: +353 44 9337800   **Fax:** +353 44 9337888
Email: sales@griffnercoillte.ie
Web: www.griffnercoillte.ie
Product Type: 3   **Other Info:** ECO
Material Type: B) 9

HOBBANS TIMBERWORKS
Old Wythers Farm, King Street,
High Ongar, Essex, CM5 9NR
Area of Operation: UK & Ireland
Tel: 01277 890165   **Fax:** 01277 890165
Email: rupert@hobbanstimberworks.co.uk
Web: www.hobbanstimberworks.co.uk
Product Type: 1, 4, 6

HOMELODGE BUILDINGS LTD
Kingswell Point, Crawley,
Winchester, Hampshire, SO21 2PU
Area of Operation: UK (Excluding Ireland)
Tel: 01962 881480   **Fax:** 01962 889070
Email: info@homelodge.co.uk
Web: www.homelodge.co.uk   **Product Type:** 3

HONEYSUCKLE BOTTOM SAWMILL LTD
Honeysuckle Bottom, Green Dene,
East Horsley, Leatherhead, Surrey, KT24 5TD
Area of Operation: Greater London, South East England
Tel: 01483 282394   **Fax:** 01483 282394
Email: honeysucklemill@aol.com
Web: www.easisites.co.uk/honeysucklebottomsawmill
Product Type: 4

HOUSE - UK
347 Leverington Common, Leverington,
Wisbech, Cambridgeshire, P13 5JR
Area of Operation: UK (Excluding Ireland)
Tel: 01945 410361
Fax: 01945 419038
Email: enquiries@house-uk.co.uk
Web: www.house-uk.co.uk
Product Type: 5, 7   **Other Info:**

INSIDEOUT BUILDINGS LTD
The Green, Over Kellet, Carnforth, Lancashire, LA6 1BU
Area of Operation: UK (Excluding Ireland)
Tel: 01524 737999
Email: lynn@iobuild.co.uk   **Web:** www.iobuild.co.uk
Product Type: 7   **Other Info:**

INTERBILD LTD
2a Ainslie Street, West Pitkerro, Dundee, Angus, DD5 3RR
Area of Operation: UK & Ireland
Tel: 01382 480481   **Fax:** 01382 480482
Email: tpd@interbild.com
Web: www.interbild.com   **Product Type:** 1, 2

JOINERY & TIMBER BUILDINGS
6 Lower Beech Cottages, Off Manchester Road,
Tytherington, Macclesfield, Cheshire, SK10 2ED
Area of Operation: North West England and North Wales
Tel: 07909 907656
Fax: 01625 501655
Email: jim.booth@jandtb.co.uk
Product Type: 1, 4, 6   **Other Info:**

JONES NASH ECO HOMES
12 Lee Street, Louth, Lincolnshire, LN11 9HJ
Area of Operation: UK (Excluding Ireland)
Tel: 01507 609637
Fax: 01507 609637
Email: sd@jones-nash.co.uk
Web: www.eco-houses.co.uk   **Product Type:** 5

KELVA HOMES
Old Brightmoor Farm, Thornborough,
Buckinghamshire, MK18 3EA
Area of Operation: Europe
Tel: 01280 824787   **Fax:** 01280 824288
Email: kelvahomesk@aol.com   **Product Type:** 5

**KINGSPAN CENTURY HOMES
TIMBER FRAME LTD**
Lammas Gate, 84 Meadrow, Godalming, Surrey, GU7 3HT
Area of Operation: Worldwide
Tel: 01483 427733   **Fax:** 01483 418639
Web: www.centuryhomes.co.uk

KINGSTON TIMBER FRAME
14 Mill Hill Drive, Huntington,
York, North Yorkshire, YO32 9PU
Area of Operation: East England, North East
England, North West England and North Wales
Tel: 01904 762589
Fax: 01904 766686
Email: info@kingstontimberframe.co.uk
Web: www.kingstontimberframe.co.uk
Product Type: 3

LAKELAND TIMBER FRAME
Unit 38c, Holme Mills, Holme,
Carnforth, Lancashire, LA6 1RD
Area of Operation: UK (Excluding Ireland)
Tel: 01524 782596
Fax: 01524 784972
Email: tony@lakelandtimberframe.co.uk
Web: www.lakelandtimberframe.co.uk

LAMINATED WOOD LIMITED
Grain Silo Complex, Abbey Road,
Hempsted, Gloucester, Gloucestershire, GL2 5HU
Area of Operation: UK (Excluding Ireland)
Tel: 01452 418000   **Fax:** 01452 418333
Email: mail@lamwood.co.uk
Web: www.lamwood.co.uk
Product Type: 1, 7   **Other Info:**
Material Type: B) 1, 7, 10

LINDISFARNE TIMBER FRAME LTD
197 Rosalind Street, Ashington,
Northumberland, NE63 9BB
Area of Operation: UK (Excluding Ireland)
Tel: 01670 810472   **Fax:** 01670 810472
Email: info@lindisfarnetimberframeltd.co.uk
Web: www.lindisfarnetimberframeltd.co.uk
Product Type: 3

LINWOOD HOMES LTD.
8250 River Road, Delta, British Columbia, Canada , V4G 1B5
Area of Operation: UK & Ireland
Tel: +1 604 946 5430 ext.146
Fax: +1 604 940 6276
Email: pdauphinee@linwoodhomes.com

LINWOOD HOMES LTD

Area of Operation: UK & Ireland
Tel: +1 604 946 5430 ext.146
Fax: +1 604 940 6276
Email: pdauphinee@linwoodhomes.com
Web: www.linwoodhomes.com
Product Type: 1, 2, 5

Craftsmanship in cedar post and beam, log or timber frame. Quality building materials and a custom-designed home package. A complete building solution for your primary residence or vacation home.

LLOYDS TIMBER FRAME LIMITED
Glovers Meadow, Oswestry, Shropshire, SY10 8NH
Area of Operation: Europe
Tel: 01691 656511   **Fax:** 01691 656533
Email: info@lloydstimberframes.co.uk
Web: www.lloydstimberframes.co.uk   **Product Type:** 2, 3

LOG & CEDAR HOMES LTD
10 Birch Court, Doune, Perth and Kinross, FK16 6JD
Area of Operation: North East England, North West England and North Wales, Scotland
Tel: 01786 842216   **Fax:** 01786 842216
Email: enquiries@logandcedarhomes.co.uk
Web: www.logandcedarhomes.co.uk
Product Type: 1, 3, 5, 6

LOG AND CEDAR HOMES LTD
Birch Court, Doune, Perth and Kinross, FK16 6JD
Area of Operation: UK (Excluding Ireland)
Tel: 01786 842216   **Fax:** 01786 842216
Email: enquiries@logandcedarhomes.gotadsl.co.uk
Web: www.logandcedarhomes.co.uk
Product Type: 1, 2, 5, 6, 7

MAPLE TIMBER FRAME
Tarnacre Hall Business Park, Tarnacre Lane, St Michaels, Lancashire, PR3 0SZ
Area of Operation: Worldwide
Tel: 01995 679444   **Fax:** 01995 679769
Email: enquiry@mapletimberframe.com
Web: www.mapletimberframe.com   **Product Type:** 2

MARTIN SILBURN TIMBER FRAMING LIMITED
8 Orchard View, Ham Street, Baltonsborough, Glastonbury, Somerset, BA6 8QH
Area of Operation: UK (Excluding Ireland)
Tel: 01458 835123   **Fax:** 01458 835369
Email: martin@silburn.co.uk
Web: www.silburn.co.uk

NEATWOOD HOMES LTD
Unit 6, Westwood Industrial Estate, Pontrilas, Herefordshire, HR2 0EL
Area of Operation: UK (Excluding Ireland)
Tel: 01981 240860   **Fax:** 01981 240255
Email: sales@neatwoodhomes.co.uk
Web: www.neatwoodhomes.co.uk
Product Type: 2, 3

NEW WORLD TIMBER FRAME
Mitchell Hanger, Audley End Airfield, Saffron Walden, Essex, CB11 4LH
Tel: 01799 513331   **Fax:** 01799 513341
Email: info@newworldtimberframe.co.uk
Web: www.newworldtimberframe.com
Product Type: 1, 2, 3, 4, 6

NORDIC WOOD
21 Tartar Road, Cobham, Surrey, KT11 2AS
Area of Operation: UK & Ireland   **Tel:** 01932 576944
Email: info@nordic-wood.co.uk
Web: www.nordic-wood.co.uk   **Product Type:** 5

OAKMASTERS
The Mill, Isaacs Lane, Haywards Heath, West Sussex, RH16 4RZ
Area of Operation: UK (Excluding Ireland)
Tel: 01444 455455   **Fax:** 01444 455333
Email: oak@oakmasters.co.uk
Web: www.oakmasters.co.uk

POTTON LTD
Eltisley Road, Great Gransden, Bedfordshire, SG19 3AR
Area of Operation: UK & Ireland
Tel: 01767 676400   **Fax:** 01767 676444
Email: contact@potton.co.uk
Web: www.potton.co.uk   **Product Type:** 1, 2, 6

PRYDE HOMES LTD
Whitehall House Estate, Chirnside, Duns, Borders, TD11 3LD
Tel: 01890 818901   **Fax:** 01890 817151
Email: info@prydehomes.co.uk
Web: www.prydehomes.co.uk   **Product Type:** 2, 3, 5

RADNOR TIMBER COMPANY
The Offices, Old Impton Farm, Norton, Presteigne, Powys, LD8 2EN
Tel: 01544 260727   **Fax:** 01544 262113
Email: sales@rtc.enta.net
Web: www.radnortimbercompany

RAYNE CONSTRUCTION
Rayne North, Inverurie, Aberdeenshire, AB51 5DB
Area of Operation: UK & Ireland
Tel: 01464 851518   **Fax:** 01464 851555
Email: info@rayne-construction-ltd.freeserve.co.uk
Web: www.rayne-construction-ltd.freeserve.co.uk
Product Type: 5   **Other Info:** ECO

RAYNE CONSTRUCTION LTD

Area of Operation: UK & Ireland
Tel: 01464 851518
Fax: 01464 851555
Email: info@rayne-construction-ltd.freeserve.co.uk
Web: www.rayne-construction-ltd.freeserve.co.uk
Product Type: 5
Other Info: ECO

Rayne Construction is a small, Scottish company specialising in the design, manufacture, and erection of individual log homes throughout the UK.

ROB ROY HOMES
Dalchonzie, Comrie, Perthshire, PH6 2LB
Tel: 01764 670424   **Fax:** 01764 670419
Email: mail@robroyhomes.co.uk
Web: www.robroyhomes.co.uk   **Product Type:** 2

ROUNDWOOD CONSTRUCTION LTD
The Packhouse, Cryals Farm,
Cryals Road, Matfield, Kent, TN12 7HN
Area of Operation: Europe
Tel: 0800 328 3847   **Fax:** 01892 725416
Email: mary@roundwoodconstruction.com
Web: www.roundwoodconstruction.com

SCANDINAVIAN LOG CABINS DIRECT
6 North End, London Road,
East Grinstead, West Sussex, RH19 1QQ
Area of Operation: UK & Ireland
Tel: 01342 311131   **Fax:** 01342 311131
Email: cabins@slcd.co.uk
Web: www.slcd.co.uk   **Product Type:** 5

SCOTFRAME TIMBER ENGINEERING LIMITED
18 Aghnatrisk Road, Hillsborough, Co Down, BT26 6JJ
Area of Operation: Ireland Only
Tel: 028 9268 8807
Fax: 028 9268 8809
Email: mike.cruickshank@scotframe.co.uk
Web: www.scotframe.co.uk   **Product Type:** 2

SCOTFRAME TIMBER ENGINEERING LIMITED
4 Deerdykes Place, Cumbernauld, Glasgow, G68 9HE
Area of Operation: North East England,
North West England, Scotland
Tel: 01236 861200
Fax: 01236 861201
Email: moira.nicholson@scotframe.co.uk
Web: www.scotframe.co.uk   **Product Type:** 2

SCOTFRAME TIMBER ENGINEERING LIMITED
Inverurie Business Park, Souterford Avenue,
Inverurie, Aberdeenshire, AB51 0ZJ
Area of Operation: Scotland
Tel: 01467 624440
Fax: 01467 624255
Email: martin.johnston@scotframe.co.uk
Web: www.scotframe.co.uk   **Product Type:** 2

SCULPTURE GRAIN LIMITED
Unit 8 Warren Court, Knockholt Road,
Halstead, Sevenoaks, Kent, TN14 7ER
Area of Operation: UK & Ireland
Tel: 01959 534060   **Fax:** 01959 532696
Email: mick.sculpturegrain@virgin.net
Product Type: 1

STRATHCLYDE TIMBER SYSTEMS LTD
Castlecary, Cumbernauld, City of Glasgow, G68 0DT
Area of Operation: UK (Excluding Ireland)
Tel: 01324 840 909   **Fax:** 01324 840 907
Email: sales@strathclydetimbersystems.com
Web: www.strathclydetimbersystems.com
Product Type: 2

SYLVAN STUART LIMITED
Pitmachie Works, Old Rayne, Insch,
Aberdeen, Aberdeenshire, AB52 6RX
Area of Operation: UK & Ireland
Tel: 01464 851208
Fax: 01464 851202
Email: sales@sylvanstuart.com
Web: www.sylvanstuart.com
Product Type: 1, 2, 3, 5   **Other Info:** ECO

T J CRUMP OAKWRIGHTS LIMITED
The Lakes, Swainhill, Hereford, Herefordshire, HR4 7PU
Area of Operation: Worldwide
Tel: 01432 353353   **Fax:** 01432 357733
Email: nick@oakwrights.co.uk
Web: www.oakwrights.co.uk   **Product Type:** 1, 4, 6
Other Info: ✏   **Material Type:** A) 2

TAYLOR LANE TIMBER FRAME LTD
Chapel Road, Rotherwas Industrial Estate,
Hereford, Herefordshire, HR2 6LD
Area of Operation: UK & Ireland
Tel: 01432 271912   **Fax:** 01432 351064
Email: info@taylor-lane.co.uk
Web: www.taylor-lane.co.uk   **Product Type:** 2

TECCO SYSTEMS
1 Elm Close, Hove, East Sussex, BN3 6TG
Tel: 01273 501210   **Fax:** 0207 837 3070
Email: rabernstein@onetel.com
Web: www.teccosystems.co.uk   **Product Type:** 1, 7

THE BEAMLOCK BUILDING COMPANY
Benfield ATT Group, Castle Way,
Caldicot, Monmouthshire, NP26 5PR
Tel: 01291 437050   **Fax:** 01291 437051
Email: beamlock@benfieldatt.co.uk
Web: www.benfieldatt.co.uk/beamlock
Product Type: 1

THE BORDER DESIGN CENTRE
Harelaw Moor, Greenlaw, Borders, TD10 6XT
Tel: 01578 740218   **Fax:** 01578 740218
Email: borderdesign@btconnect.com
Web: www.borderdesign.co.uk
Product Type: 1, 2   **Other Info:** ✏

THE GREEN OAK CARPENTRY CO LTD
Langley Farm, Langley, Rake, Liss, Hampshire, GU33 7JW
Area of Operation: UK & Ireland
Tel: 01730 892049   **Fax:** 01730 895225
Email: enquiries@greenoakcarpentry.co.uk
Web: www.greenoakcarpentry.co.uk

THE GREEN OAK CARPENTRY CO LTD
Area of Operation: UK & Ireland
Tel: 01730 892049   **Fax:** 01730 895225
Email: enquiries@greenoakcarpentry.co.uk
Web: www.greenoakcarpentry.co.uk

The Green Oak Carpentry Company has 15 years experience in the design, engineering and installation of new oak structures such as barns, halls and houses etc. We also restore old timber structures.

THE LOG CABIN COMPANY
Potash Garden Centre, 9 Main Road, Hockley,
Hawkwell, Essex, SS5 4JN   **Tel:** 01702 206012
Email: sales@thelogcabincompany.co.uk
Web: www.thelogcabincompany.co.uk **Product Type:** 5

THE OAK FRAME CARPENTRY CO LTD
Nupend Farm, Nupend,
Stonehouse, Gloucestershire, GL10 3SU
Area of Operation: Midlands & Mid Wales, South
West England and South Wales
Tel: 01453 828788   **Fax:** 01453 825092
Email: simon@oakframecarpentry.co.uk
Product Type: 1, 4, 6

THE PATIO ROOM COMPANY
52 Castlemaine Avenue, South Croydon, Surrey, CR2 7HR
Tel: 0208 406 3001   **Fax:** 0208 686 4928
Email: helpdesk@patioroom.co.uk
Web: www.patioroom.co.uk
Product Type: 1   **Other Info:** ✍

THE SWEDISH HOUSE COMPANY
Seabridge House, 8 St. Johns Road,
Tunbridge Wells, Kent, TN4 9NP
Tel: 0870 770 0760 / 01892 509230
Fax: 0870 770 0759
Email: sales@swedishhouses.com
Web: www.swedishhouses.com
Product Type: 3   **Other Info:** ECO ✍
Material Type: B) 1, 2, 8, 9, 10

THE TIMBER FRAME CO LTD
The Framing Yard, 7 Broadway,
Charlton Adam, Somerset, TA11 7BB
Tel: 01458 224463   **Fax:** 01458 224571
Email: admin@thetimberframe.co.uk
Web: www.thetimberframe.co.uk
Product Type: 1, 4, 6, 7
Other Info: ECO ✍ ✋   **Material Type:** A) 2

THOMAS MITCHELL HOMES LTD
Southend, Thornton, Fife, KY1 4ED
Area of Operation: Worldwide
Tel: 01592 774401   **Fax:** 01592 774088
Email: stuart@tmhomes.co.uk
Web: www.thomasmitchellhomes.com
Product Type: 2

TIMBER DEVELOPMENTS
Unit 13, Stafford Park 12, Telford, Shropshire, TF3 3BJ
Area of Operation: Europe
Tel: 01656 670022   **Fax:** 0870 777 7520
Email: info@timberdevelopments.com
Web: www.timberdevelopments.com

TIMBER ROUTES
42 Armoury Square, Easton, Bristol, BS5 0PT
Area of Operation: UK & Ireland
Tel: 0117 952 2585   **Product Type:** 1, 2, 3, 4, 6
Email: diana@timber-routes.co.uk
Web: www.timber-routes.co.uk

TIMBER ROUTES

Area of Operation: UK & Ireland
Tel: 0117 9522585
Email: diana@timber-routes.co.uk
Web: www.timber-routes.co.uk
Product Type: 1, 2, 3, 4, 6

Quality mortice & tenon timber frames fabricated
from sustainably sourced douglas fir & oak.
Houses, barns, extensions & roofs. Affordable
selfbuild frames. Free first estimate.

TIMBERFRAME WALES
Unit 1 & 5 Maesquarre Road,
Ammanford, Carmarthenshire, SA18 2LF
Tel: 01269 595255   **Fax:** 01269 595305
Email: info@timberframewales.com
Web: www.timberframewales.co.uk

TIMBERPEG HOMES UK LIMITED
PO Box 416, St Albans, Hertfordshire, AL1 1XN
Area of Operation: Europe
Tel: 01727 823032   **Fax:** 01727 823032
Email: jonathan@timberpeg.co.uk
Web: www.timberpeg.co.uk
Product Type: 1, 5
Other Info: ✍   **Material Type:** B) 2, 12

TRUE NORTH LOG HOMES
26 Jennings Road, St Albans, Hertfordshire, AL1 4PD
Area of Operation: UK & Ireland
Tel: 0800 169 6327   **Fax:** 01727 851558
Email: info@pineconeloghomes.co.uk
Web: www.pineconeloghomes.co.uk
Product Type: 5

TURNER TIMBER FRAME
Leven Road, Brandesburton, Nr. Driffield,
East Riding of Yorks, YO25 8RT
Area of Operation: UK (Excluding Ireland)
Tel: 01964 543535
Fax: 01964 543535
Email: info@turnertimberframe.co.uk
Web: www.turnertimberframes.co.uk
Product Type: 1, 2, 5   **Material Type:** B) 2

UK TIMBER FRAME ASSOCIATION
The E Centre, Cooperage Way Business Village,
Alloa, Clackmannanshire, FK10 3LP
Area of Operation: UK (Excluding Ireland)
Tel: 01259 272140   **Fax:** 01259 272141
Email: info@timber-frame.org
Web: www.timber-frame.org ✌

UNIBUD / DAN-WOOD HOUSE
16/4 Timber Bush, Edinburgh, Lothian, EH6 6QH
Area of Operation: UK & Ireland
Tel: 0131 555 1771
Fax: 0131 555 1788
Email: sales@dan-wood.com
Web: www.dan-wood.com   **Product Type:** 3

W.H. COLT SON & CO LTD
Prestige House, Landews Meadow,
Green Lane, Challock, Ashford, Kent, TN25 4BL
Area of Operation: UK & Ireland
Tel: 01233 740074
Fax: 01233 740123
Email: mail@colthouses.co.uk
Web: www.colthouses.co.uk
Product Type: 2   **Material Type:** B) 10

WESTWIND OAK BUILDINGS LTD
Unit 1, Laurel Farm, Streamcross,
Lower Claverham, Nr. Bristol, BS49 4PZ
Area of Operation: Europe
Tel: 01934 877317
Email: judy@westwindoak.com
Web: www.westwindoak.com
Product Type: 4

WOODCO
Tofts of Tain, Castletown, Highlands, KW14 8TB
Area of Operation: Worldwide
Tel: 01847 821418   **Fax:** 01847 821418
Email: woodcoscotland@btconnect.com
Web: www.woodco.clara.net
Product Type: 1, 3, 5

XSPACE
99 Woodlands Avenue, Poole, Dorset, BH15 4EG
Area of Operation: South East England, South West
England and South Wales
Tel: 01202 665387   **Fax:** 01202 380235
Email: design@xspace.biz
Web: www.xspace.biz

STEEL FRAME

KEY

PRODUCT TYPES: 1= Lightweight

2 = Heavyweight

OTHER: ▽ Reclaimed ⏱ On-line shopping

✎ Bespoke ✋ Hand-made ECO Ecological

ALAN BROUGH ASSOCIATES
72 Wilson Street, Derby, Derbyshire, DE1 1PL
Area of Operation: UK (Excluding Ireland)
Tel: 01332 345622 **Fax:** 01332 292994
Email: mail@abaderby.co.uk
Web: www.abstruct.com **Product Type:** 2

ALL FOUNDATIONS LIMITED
Primrose Business Park, White Lane,
Blackwell, Derby, Derbyshire, DE55 5JR
Area of Operation: UK & Ireland
Tel: 0870 350 2050
Email: mail@allfoundations.co.uk
Web: www.allfoundations.co.uk **Product Type:** 1, 2

ANIRINA OY (FINLAND) - LOG HOME SUPPLIERS & BUILDERS UK
The Gate House, Home Park Terrace,
Hampton Court Road, Hampton Wick,
Kingston upon Thames, Surrey, KT1 4AE
Area of Operation: Europe
Tel: 0208 943 0430
Fax: 0208 943 0430
Email: chris.drayson@virgin.net
Product Type: 2

AVON MANUFACTURING LIMITED
Avon House, Kineton Road, Southam,
Leamington Spa, Warwickshire, CV47 0DG
Area of Operation: UK (Excluding Ireland)
Tel: 01926 817292
Fax: 01926 814156
Email: sales@avonmanufacturing.co.uk
Web: www.avonmanufacturing.co.uk
Product Type: 1, 2

CONCEPT ENGINEERING CONSULTANTS LTD
Unit 8 Warple Mews, Warple Way, London, W3 0RF
Area of Operation: East England, Greater London, South
East England, South West England and South Wales
Tel: 0208 8112880
Fax: 0208 8112881
Email: si@conceptconsultants.co.uk
Web: www.conceptconsultants.co.uk

CORUS CONSTRUCTION
Swinden Technology Centre, Moorgate,
Rotherham, South Yorkshire, S60 3AR
Area of Operation: Worldwide
Tel: 01724 405060
Email: corusconstruction@corusgroup.com
Web: www.corusconstruction.com
Product Type: 1, 2

ENGINEERED OFF-SITE SYSTEMS LTD
Heighington Lane, Aycliffe Industrial Park,
Newton Aycliffe, Durham, DL5 6QG
Area of Operation: UK (Excluding Ireland)
Tel: 01325 372739 **Fax:** 01325 370903
Email: enquiries@eosuk.org
Web: www.eosuk.org

JOY STEEL STRUCTURES (LONDON) LTD
London Industrial Park, 1 Whitings Ways, London, E6 6LR
Area of Operation: UK (Excluding Ireland)
Tel: 0207 474 0550 **Fax:** 0207 473 0158
Email: joysteel@dial.pipex.com
Web: www.joysteel.co.uk

LINDAB LTD
Shenstone Trading Estate, Bromsgrove Road,
Halesowen, West Midlands, B63 3XB
Tel: 0121 585 2780 **Fax:** 0121 585 2782
Email: jonathan.fennell@lindab.co.uk
Web: www.lindab.co.uk **Product Type:** 1

PREFAB STEEL CO. LTD
114 Brighton Road, Shoreham, West Sussex, BN43 6RH
Area of Operation: Greater London, South East England
Tel: 01273 597733 **Fax:** 01273 597774
Email: prefabsteel@btinternet.com
Web: www.prefabsteel.co.uk

STEELFRAME BV
Andromedastraat 5, Tilburg, Netherlands, 5015 AV
Area of Operation: Europe
Tel: +31 135 449 859 **Fax:** +31 135 449 860
Email: info@steelframe.nl **Web:** www.steelframe.nl ⏱

TITAN CONTAINERS (UK) LTD
Suite 1, 1 Cecil Court, London Road,
Enfield, Middlesex, Greater London, EN2 6DE
Tel: 0208 362 1444 **Fax:** 0208 362 1555
Email: uk@titancontainer.com
Web: www.titancontainer.com **Product Type:** 2

MASONRY DESIGN & BUILD

KEY

OTHER: ▽ Reclaimed ⏱ On-line shopping

✎ Bespoke ✋ Handmade ECO Ecological

CJ O'SHEA & CO LTD
Unit 1 Granard Business Centre,
Burns Lane, Mill Hill, London, NW7 2DZ
Area of Operation: East England, Greater London, South
East England, South West England and South Wales
Tel: 0208 959 3600 **Fax:** 0208 959 0184
Email: admin@oshea.co.uk **Web:** www.oshea.co.uk

CONCEPT ENGINEERING CONSULTANTS LTD
Unit 8 Warple Mews, Warple Way, London, W3 0RF
Area of Operation: East England, Greater London, South
East England, South West England and South Wales
Tel: 0208 8112880 **Fax:** 0208 8112881
Email: si@conceptconsultants.co.uk
Web: www.conceptconsultants.co.uk

DESIGN AND MATERIALS LTD
Lawn Road, Carlton in Lindrick, Nottinghamshire, S81 9LB
Area of Operation: UK (Excluding Ireland)
Tel: 01909 540123 **Fax:** 01909 730605
Email: enquiries@designandmaterials.uk.com
Web: www.designandmaterials.uk.com ⏱

DESIGN AND MATERIALS LTD

Area of Operation: UK
Tel: 01909 540123
Fax: 01909 730605
Email: enquiries@designandmaterials.uk.com
Web: www.designandmaterials.uk.com

A well established self build company providing a
bespoke home design and materials supply
service using brick and block construction.

FAIRCLEAR LTD
16 Sibthorpe Drive, Sudbrooke,
Lincoln, Lincolnshire, LN2 2RQ
Area of Operation: East England
Tel: 01522 595189 **Fax:** 01522 595189
Email: enquiries@fairclear.co.uk
Web: www.fairclear.co.uk

FELTHAM CONSTRUCTION LTD
Mandarin Court, Hambridge Road,
Newbury, Berkshire, RG14 5SQ
Area of Operation: South East England
Tel: 01635 277100 **Fax:** 01635 277110
Email: info@felthamconstruction.co.uk
Web: www.felthamconstruction.co.uk

GREENERLIVING HOMES LTD
Sussex Innovation Centre, Science Park Square,
Falmer, Brighton, East Sussex, BN1 9SB
Area of Operation: South East England
Tel: 01273 704509 **Fax:** 01273 704499
Email: info@greenerlivinghomes.co.uk
Web: www.greenerlivinghomes.co.uk

MARUN CONSTRUCTION
62 Crofton Park, Yeovil, Somerset, BA21 4EE
Area of Operation: South West England and South Wales
Tel: 01935 426947
Email: marun33@hotmail.com

NORBURY MOOR BUILDING SERVICES LTD
Gawthorne, Hazel Grove, Stockport, Cheshire, SK7 5AB
Area of Operation: North West England and North Wales
Tel: 0800 093 5785 **Fax:** 0161 456 1944
Email: paul@norburymoor.co.uk
Web: www.norburymoor.co.uk ⏱

PLASMOR
P.O. Box 44, Womersley Road,
Knottingley, West Yorkshire, WF11 0DN
Area of Operation: UK (Excluding Ireland)
Tel: 01977 673221 **Fax:** 01977 607071
Email: knott@plasmor.co.uk
Web: www.plasmor.co.uk

PRYDE HOMES LTD
Whitehall House Estate, Chirnside, Duns, Borders, TD11 3LD
Area of Operation: UK (Excluding Ireland)
Tel: 01890 818901 **Fax:** 01890 817151
Email: info@prydehomes.co.uk
Web: www.prydehomes.co.uk

STANCLIFFE STONE
Grange Mill, Matlock, Derbyshire, DE4 4BW
Area of Operation: Worldwide
Tel: 01629 653000 **Fax:** 01629 650996
Email: sales@stancliffe.com
Web: www.stancliffe.com

THIN JOINT TECHNOLOGY LTD
3 Albright Road, Speke Approaches Industrial Estate,
Liverpool, Merseyside, WA8 8FY
Tel: 0151 422 8000 **Fax:** 0151 422 8001
Email: sales@thinjoint.com
Web: www.thinjoint.com **Material Type:** I) 1, 2, 4

XSPACE
99 Woodlands Avenue, Poole, Dorset, BH15 4EG
Area of Operation: South East England, South West
England and South Wales
Tel: 01202 665387 **Fax:** 01202 380235
Email: design@xspace.biz **Web:** www.xspace.biz

ECO STRUCTURES

KEY

PRODUCT TYPES: 1= Cob and Rammed Earth

2 = Straw Bale 3 = Wattle and Daub

4 = Hemp 5 = Other

SEE ALSO: COMPLETE STRUCTURAL SYSTEMS
- Structural Insulated Panels

OTHER: ▽ Reclaimed ⏱ On-line shopping

✎ Bespoke ✋ Hand-made ECO Ecological

ARTIZAN.UK.NET
29 Fore Street, Bradninch, Exeter, Devon, EX5 4NN
Area of Operation: South West England and South Wales
Tel: 01392 882165
Email: info@artizan.uk.net
Web: www.artizan.uk.net **Product Type:** 1, 2

BORDER OAK DESIGN & CONSTRUCTION
Kingsland Sawmills, Kingsland,
Leominster, Herefordshire, HR6 9SF
Area of Operation: Worldwide
Tel: 01568 708752
Fax: 01568 708295
Email: sales@borderoak.com
Web: www.borderoak.com **Product Type:** 5
Other Info: ✳ ECO ✎ ✋

CONCEPT TIMBER
35 Lancaster Road, Bowerhill Industrial Estate,
Melksham, Wiltshire, SN12 6SS
Tel: 01225 792939
Fax: 01225 792949
Email: enquiries@concept-timber.co.uk
Web: www.concept-timber.co.uk **Product Type:** 5

DGS CONSTRUCTION LTD
The Glebe, Nash Road, Whaddon,
Milton Keynes, Buckinghamshire, MK17 0NQ
Area of Operation: East England, Greater London,
Midlands & Mid Wales, South East England, South
West England and South Wales
Tel: 01908 503147 **Fax:** 01908 504995
Email: info@dgsconstruction.co.uk
Web: www.dgsconstruction.co.uk **Product Type:** 5

EARTHA: EAST ANGLIA TELLURIC HOUSES ASSOCIATION
Ivy Green, London Road, Wymondham, Norfolk, NR18 9JD
Area of Operation: East England
Tel: 01 953 601701
Email: dirkbouwens@aol.com
Web: www.eartha.org.uk **Product Type:** 1, 3

ECO SYSTEMS IRELAND LTD
40 Glenshesk Road, Ballycastle, Co Antrim, BT54 6PH
Area of Operation: UK & Ireland
Tel: 02820 768708 **Fax:** 02820 769781
Email: info@ecosystemsireland.com
Web: www.ecosystemsireland.com **Product Type:** 5

ECOHOMES LTD
First Floor, 52 Briggate, Brighouse, West Yorkshire, HD6 1ES
Area of Operation: UK & Ireland
Tel: 01484 402040 **Fax:** 01484 400101
Email: sales@ecohomes.ltd.uk
Web: www.ecohomes.ltd.uk

ENERGY SUPERSTORE
3 Wellington Park, Belfast, BT9 6DJ
Tel: 02890 388391
Email: info@energysuperstore.co.uk
Web: www.energysuperstore.co.uk

EXCEL BUILDING SOLUTIONS
Maerdy Industrial Estate, Gwent, NP22 5PY
Area of Operation: Worldwide
Tel: 01685 845200 **Fax:** 01685 844106
Email: sales@excelfibre.com
Web: www.excelfibre.com **Product Type:** 5
Other Info: ECO **Material Type:** K) 3

GREEN OAK STRUCTURES
20 Bushy Coombe Gardens,
Glastonbury, Somerset, BA6 8JT
Area of Operation: UK & Ireland
Tel: 01458 833420 **Fax:** 01458 833420
Email: timberframes@greenoakstructures.co.uk
Web: www.greenoakstructures.co.uk **Product Type:** 3
Other Info: ECO ✎ **Material Type:** A) 2

GREENERLIVING HOMES LTD
Sussex Innovation Centre, Science Park Square,
Falmer, Brighton, East Sussex, BN1 9SB
Area of Operation: South East England
Tel: 01273 704509
Fax: 01273 704499
Email: info@greenerlivinghomes.co.uk
Web: www.greenerlivinghomes.co.uk

HEMPHAB PRODUCTS
Rusheens, Ballygriffen, Kenmare, Kerry, Ireland
Area of Operation: Ireland Only
Tel: +353 644 1747
Email: hempbuilding@eircom.net
Web: www.hempbuilding.com **Product Type:** 4

LINDAB LTD
Shenstone Trading Estate, Bromsgrove Road,
Halesowen, West Midlands, B63 3XB
Area of Operation: UK & Ireland
Tel: 0121 585 2780   **Fax:** 0121 585 2782
Email: jonathan.fennell@lindab.co.uk
Web: www.lindab.co.uk   **Product Type:** 5

LINDISFARNE TIMBER FRAME LTD
197 Rosalind Street, Ashington,
Northumberland, NE63 9BB
Area of Operation: UK (Excluding Ireland)
Tel: 01670 810472   **Fax:** 01670 810472
Email: info@lindisfarnetimberframeltd.co.uk
Web: www.lindisfarnetimberframeltd.co.uk
Product Type: 5

LOW-IMPACT LIVING INITIATIVE
Redfield Community, Buckingham Road,
Winslow, Buckinghamshire, MK18 3LZ
Area of Operation: UK (Excluding Ireland)
Tel: 01296 714184   **Fax:** 01296 714184
Email: lili@lowimpact.org
Web: www.lowimpact.org

SAFEGUARD EUROPE LTD
Redkiln Close, Redkiln Way,
Horsham, West Sussex, RH13 5QL
Area of Operation: Worldwide
Tel: 01403 210204
Fax: 01403 217529
Email: info@safeguardeurope.com
Web: www.safeguardeurope.com

SAFEGUARD
MAKING BUILDINGS DRY

Area of Operation: Worldwide
Tel: 01403 210204
Fax: 01403 217529
Email: info@safeguardeurope.com
Web: www.safeguardeurope.com

Safeguard supply the Oldroyd Xv Green waterproofing system for green and turf roofs, incorporating 40% recycled material. Manufactured to an ISO14001 environmental management system.

STRAW BALE BUILDING ASSOCIATION
Holinroyd Farm, Butts Lane,
Todmorden, West Yorkshire, OL14 8RJ
Area of Operation: UK & Ireland
Tel: 01706 814696
Email: info@strawbalebuildingassociation.org.uk
Web: www.strawbalebuildingassociation.org.uk
Product Type: 2

STRAWBALE BUILDING COMPANY UK
34 Rosebery Way, Tring,
Hertfordshire, HP23 5DS
Area of Operation: Europe
Tel: 01442 825421
Email: chug@strawbale-building.co.uk
Web: www.strawbale-building.co.uk
Product Type: 1, 2, 3, 4, 5

WOODCO
Tofts of Tain, Castletown,
Highlands, KW14 8TB
Area of Operation: Worldwide
Tel: 01847 821418
Fax: 01847 821418
Email: woodcoscotland@btconnect.com
Web: www.woodco.clara.net

INSULATED CONCRETE FORMWORK

> **KEY**
> **OTHER:** ▽ Reclaimed   🖱 On-line shopping
> ✎ Bespoke   ✋ Handmade   ECO Ecological

BECO PRODUCTS LTD
Beco House, 6 Exmoor Avenue,
Scunthorpe, Lincolnshire, DN15 8NJ
Area of Operation: UK & Ireland
Tel: 01724 747576   **Fax:** 01724 747579
Email: info@becowallform.co.uk
Web: www.becowallform.co.uk
Other Info: ECO ✎   **Material Type:** G) 1, K) 11

FORMWORKS UK LTD
The Pine Barn, Hamsey,
Lewes, East Sussex, BN8 5TB
Area of Operation: Worldwide
Tel: 01273 478110   **Fax:** 01273 471419
Email: sales@formworksuk.com
Web: www.formworksuk.com

STYROFRAME - FORMWORKS UK LTD

Area of Operation: Worldwide
Tel: 01273 478110
Fax: 01273 471419
Email: sales@formworksuk.com
Web: www.formworksuk.com

Insulated concrete formwork panels and floors for the rapid construction of highly insulated, airtight, high mass buildings.

INSULATING CONCRETE FORMWORK ASSOCIATION
PO Box 72, Billingshurst, West Sussex, RH14 0FD
Area of Operation: UK & Ireland
Tel: 01403 701 167
Fax: 01403 701 169
Email: enquiries@icfinfo.org.uk
Web: www.icfinfo.org.uk

KASTELL BUILDING SYSTEMS
The Mansley Business Centre, Timothy's Bridge
Road, Stratford upon Avon, Warwickshire, CV37 9NQ
Area of Operation: UK & Ireland
Tel: 01789 722401   **Fax:** 01789 720914
Email: enquiries@kastell-uk.com
Web: www.kastell-uk.com   **Other Info:** ✎

NEWMIL
17 Arundel Close, New Milton, Hampshire, BH25 5UH
Area of Operation: South East England
Tel: 0845 090 0109
Email: enquiries@newmil.co.uk
Web: www.newmil.co.uk

POLARWALL LIMITED
Unit 3 Old Mill Industrial Estate,
Stoke Canon,
Exeter, Devon, EX5 4RJ
Area of Operation: Europe
Tel: 01392 841777   **Fax:** 01392 841936
Email: info@polarwall.co.uk **Web:** www.polarwall.co.uk

POLYSTEEL UK
Unit 26, Malmesbury Road, Kingsditch Trading
Estate, Cheltenham, Gloucestershire, GL51 9PL
Tel: 0870 382 2229   **Fax:** 0870 169 6869
Email: info@polysteel.co.uk
Web: www.polysteel.co.uk

QUAD-LOCK (ENGLAND) LTD
Unit B3.1, Maws Centre, Jackfield,
Telford, Shropshire, TF8 7LS
Area of Operation: UK (Excluding Ireland)
Tel: 0870 443 1901
Fax: 0870 443 1902
Email: info@quadlock.co.uk
Web: www.quadlock.co.uk

SIPCRETE
PO Box 429, Turvey, MK43 8DT
Area of Operation: Worldwide
Tel: 0870 743 9866   **Fax:** 0870 762 5612
Email: ajp@siptec.com
Web: www.sipcrete.com

STYRO BUILD
16a High Street, Tenterden, Kent, TN30 6AP
Area of Operation: Worldwide
Tel: 01580 767701   **Fax:** 01580 767702
Email: info@styrobuild.com
Web: www.styrobuild.com

STRUCTURAL INSULATED PANELS

> **KEY**
> **OTHER:** ▽ Reclaimed   🖱 On-line shopping
> ✎ Bespoke   ✋ Handmade   ECO Ecological

BALTIC HOMES LTD
59 Downhall Ley, Buntingford, Hertfordshire, SG9 9JT
Area of Operation: Europe
Tel: 01763 272141   **Fax:** 01763 272141
Email: info@baltichomes.co.uk
Web: www.baltichomes.co.uk   **Other Info:** ECO ✎

BUILD EXPRESS (SIPS) LIMITED
3a Beckside North, Beverley, HU17 0PR
Tel: 01482 872726
Email: info@buildexpress.co.uk
Web: www.buildexpress.co.uk

BUILD IT GREEN (UK) LTD
Arena Business Centre, 9 Nimrod Way,
Ferndown, Dorset, BH21 7SH
Tel: 0870 2000358   **Fax:** 0870 2000368
Email: enquiries@builditgreen.co.uk
Web: www.builditgreen.co.uk

GRIFFNER COILLTE LTD
Forest Park, Mullingar, Co Westmeath, Ireland.
Tel: +353 44 9337800   **Fax:** +353 44 9337888
Email: sales@griffnercoillte.ie
Web: www.griffnercoillte.ie   **Other Info:** ECO ✎

INSULATED PANEL CONSTRUCTION LTD
The Grove, Chalton Heights,
Chalton, Luton, Bedfordshire, LU4 9UF
Area of Operation: East England, Midlands & Mid
Wales, South East England
Tel: 01525 877322   **Fax:** 01525 877322
Email: bcipc@aol.com

INTERBILD LTD
2a Ainslie Street, West Pitkerro, Dundee, Angus, DD5 3RR
Tel: 01382 480481   **Fax:** 01382 480482
Email: tpd@interbild.com   **Web:** www.interbild.com

KASTELL BUILDING SYSTEMS
The Mansley Business Centre, Timothy's Bridge
Road, Stratford upon Avon, Warwickshire, CV37 9NQ
Tel: 01789 722401
Fax: 01789 720914
Email: enquiries@kastell-uk.com
Web: www.kastell-uk.com   **Other Info:** ✎

KINGSPAN TEK
Pembridge, Leominster, Herefordshire, HR6 9LA
Area of Operation: UK & Ireland
Tel: 01544 387308   **Fax:** 0870 850 8666
Email: info.uk@tek.kingspan.com
Web: www.tek.kingspan.com
Product Type: 1, 3, 4, 5

MAXIROOF LTD
36 Lower End, Swaffham Prior,
Cambridge, Cambridgeshire, CB5 0HT
Tel: 01638 743380   **Fax:** 01638 743380
Email: info@maxiroof.co.uk
Web: www.maxiroof.co.uk

MILBANK ROOFS
Hargrave Meadow Cottage, Church Lane,
Hargrave, Bury St Edmunds, Suffolk, IP29 5HH
Area of Operation: UK & Ireland
Tel: 01284 852505   **Fax:** 01284 850021
Email: info@milbankroofs.com
Web: www.milbankroofs.com

SIPBUILD LTD
Unit 2 Expressway Industrial Estate,
Turnall Road, Widnes, Merseyside, WA8 8RB
Tel: 0870 850 2264
Fax: 0870 850 2265
Email: sales@sipbuildltd.com
Web: www.sipbuildltd.com   **Other Info:** ▽ ✎

SIPIT (SCOTLAND) LTD
17 Cloberfield, Milngavie, Glasgow, G62 7LN
Tel: 0141 956 2277   **Fax:** 0141 956 2299
Email: enquiries@sipitscotland.co.uk
Web: www.sipitscotland.co.uk

XSPACE
99 Woodlands Avenue, Poole, Dorset, BH15 4EG
Area of Operation: South East England, South West
England and South Wales
Tel: 01202 665387   **Fax:** 01202 380235
Email: design@xspace.biz   **Web:** www.xspace.biz

NOTES

Company Name ....
....
Address ....
....
....
email ....
Web ....

Company Name ....
....
Address ....
....
....
email ....
Web ....

Company Name ....
....
Address ....
....
....
email ....
Web ....

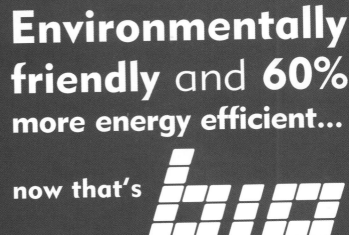
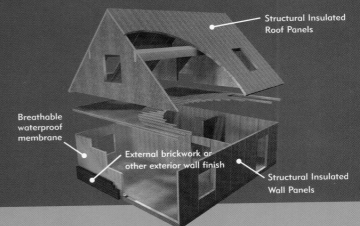

BRICKS, BLOCKS, STONE & CLADDING

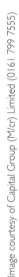

Image courtesy of Capital Group (M/cr) Limited (0161 799 7555)

SPONSORED BY Capital Group (M/cr) Limited
Tel 0161 799 7555 Web www.choosecapital.co.uk

capital
group

Cladding

It can make or break your home, and go out of fashion as quickly as it came in. Cladding is one of those aesthetic choices you will have to live with. So make sure you have a crystal clear idea of how you want your finished home to look.

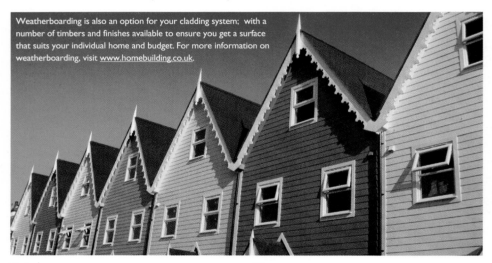

Weatherboarding is also an option for your cladding system; with a number of timbers and finishes available to ensure you get a surface that suits your individual home and budget. For more information on weatherboarding, visit www.homebuilding.co.uk.

Bricks

Bricks are tough, no-nonsense, attractive and cheap to lay. There are thousands of different colours and styles to choose from but your local planning authority may have a say in what bricks you can use.

Your location may also have some influence on the type of brick you use. For example, F-rated bricks should be specified in areas where hard frosts are common. If using reclaimed bricks, make sure they are up to the job before purchasing.

Work out how many bricks you'll need and check that this figure tallies with the amount your supplier has recommended.

- The more bricks you buy, the less you pay per item. Think ahead – will you want to build a garage in the same materials?

- Use cheaper engineering bricks in your foundations, and save the costly, attractive bricks for the visible part of your build.

- Store bricks on a pallet to prevent ground moisture getting in – dry bricks take mortar better than damp ones.

- Ensure your builder takes bricks from different packs simultaneously, to ensure that variations in colour are distributed throughout the wall.

Stone

Stone for building comes in three distinct types: natural, rubble and reconstituted.

Natural stone is often dressed into convenient shapes after being quarried for ease of use. To comply with building regulations, if you are using stone to face an inner block wall, it will need to be at least 100mm thick.

Reconstituted stone is made up of crushed and natural stone bonded together into easy-to-use blocks, and therefore is significantly cheaper than natural stone.

If using natural stone, the type will probably be determined by where you live:

- Granite is found in south-west England, south-west and north Wales, Cumbria and Scotland. It is a tough, zero maintenance choice

- Sandstone is found throughout the UK, but most of it is quarried in the centre of England from Northumberland to Shropshire. It is full of character and colour, and is very durable.

- Limestone is another highly durable stone, predominantly quarried in a strip from Wiltshire to Yorkshire.

- Cotswold stone is a yellow limestone quarried in the Cotswold Hills. When weathered, the colour of buildings made or faced with this stone are often described as 'honey' or 'golden'.

Render

A mix of sand and cement, or sand and lime, render is extremely hard wearing. It is often applied as a quick fix to tidy up crumbling buildings, but remains an attractive option for new homes.

Render is normally applied onto a standard block cavity wall, although some builders like to apply a wire mesh to the blockwork to aid adhesion. A sealant is then applied, followed by a 10-15mm coat of soft sand, sharp sand and cement. The first coat of render is then scored all over and given another application of sealant. The top coat of render goes soft like a sponge when it is ready for finishing with a float – trying to smooth it before this stage will wreck the finish.

Reclaimed bricks add instant character and age to a building. Always ensure that the supplier has enough for your build. Remember there could be around 10% wastage.

BRICKS

KEY

PRODUCT TYPES: 1 = Facing 2 = Engineering
3 = Brick Slips 4 = Specials 5 = Extruded
6 = Glazed 7 = Wire Cut 8 = Reproduction /
Reclaimed 9 = Sand-faced 10 = Stock
11 = Air Bricks

OTHER: ▽ Reclaimed ⌁ On-line shopping
✎ Bespoke ✋ Hand-made ECO Ecological

ABA BUILDING PRODUCTS LTD
Drakes Lodge, 2 Home Farm Lane, Kirklington,
Newark, Nottinghamshire, NG22 8PE
Area of Operation: UK (Excluding Ireland)
Tel: 01636 815491 **Fax:** 01636 812869
Email: sales@ababuildingproducts.com
Web: www.ababuildingproducts.com
Other Info: ▽ ✎ ✋

ADVANCED CONSTRUCTION SYSTEMS
Granite Close, Enderby, Leicester, Leicestershire, LE19 4AE
Area of Operation: Europe
Tel: 0116 272 5133 **Fax:** 0116 272 5131
Email: info@advancedconstructionsystems.co.uk
Web: www.advancedconstructionsystems.co.uk
Product Type: 1, 3, 4, 5, 7, 8, 9, 10
Material Type: E) 1, 2, 4, 7, 11, 13, 14

ALDERSHAW HANDMADE CLAY TILES LTD
Pokehold Wood, Kent Street, Sedlescombe,
Nr Battle, East Sussex, TN33 0SD
Area of Operation: Europe
Tel: 01424 756777 **Fax:** 01424 756888
Email: tiles@aldershaw.co.uk
Web: www.aldershaw.co.uk **Other Info:** ✋
Product Type: 1, 3, 4, 11 **Material Type:** F) 1, 3, 4

BAGGERIDGE BRICK
Fir Street, Sedgley, West Midlands, DY3 4AA
Area of Operation: Worldwide
Tel: 01902 880555 **Fax:** 01902 880432
Email: marketing@baggeridge.co.uk
Web: www.baggeridge.co.uk
Product Type: 1, 2, 3, 4, 5, 6, 7, 8, 9, 10

BANBURY BRICKS LTD
83a Yorke Street, Mansfield Woodhouse,
Nottinghamshire, NG19 9NH
Area of Operation: UK & Ireland
Tel: 0845 230 0941 **Fax:** 0845 230 0942
Email: enquires@banburybricks.co.uk
Web: www.banburybricks.co.uk
Product Type: 1, 2, 3, 4, 5, 6, 7, 8, 9, 10, 11
Other Info: ▽ ECO ✎ ✋

BINGLEY STONE
Cullingworth Mills, Cullingworth,
West Yorkshire, BD13 5AB
Area of Operation: UK (Excluding Ireland)
Tel: 01535 273813
Email: info@bingleystone.co.uk
Web: www.bingleystone.co.uk

BOVINGDON BRICKWORKS LTD
Ley Hill Road, Bovingdon,
Near Hemel Hempstead, Hertfordshire, HP3 0NW
Area of Operation: UK & Ireland
Tel: 01442 833176
Fax: 01442 834539
Email: info@bovingdonbricks.co.uk
Web: www.bovingdonbricks.co.uk
Product Type: 1, 3, 4, 10

BRICK CENTRE LTD
Pottery Lane East, Brimington Road North,
Chesterfield, Derbyshire, S41 9BH
Area of Operation: UK (Excluding Ireland)
Tel: 01246 260001
Fax: 01246 454597
Email: sales@brickcentre.co.uk
Web: www.brickcentre.co.uk

BRICKABILITY
South Road, Bridgend Industrial Estate, Bridgend, CF31 3XG
Area of Operation: UK (Excluding Ireland)
Tel: 01656 645222 **Fax:** 01656 665832
Email: enquiries@brickability.co.uk
Web: www.brickability.co.uk
Product Type: 1, 2, 3, 4, 5, 6, 7, 8, 9, 10, 11

BRIDGE STREET STONE LTD
The Old Gas Works Yard, Knotts Lane,
Colne, Lancashire, BB8 8AA
Area of Operation: UK & Ireland
Tel: 01282 860571 **Fax:** 01282 867446
Email: sales@stonepaving.co.uk
Web: www.stonepaving.co.uk
Product Type: 4 **Other Info:** ✋

BROAD OAK BUILDING PRODUCTS
Unit R3, Elvington Industrial Estate,
Elvington, York, North Yorkshire, YO41 4AR
Area of Operation: UK (Excluding Ireland)
Tel: 01904 607222 **Fax:** 01904 607223
Email: sales@yorkbrick.co.uk
Web: www.yorkbrick.co.uk
Product Type: 1, 2, 3, 4, 5, 7, 8, 9, 10
Other Info: ▽ ✎ ✋

BULMER BRICK CUTTING SERVICES
The Brickfields, Hedingham Road,
Bulmer, Sudbury, Suffolk, CO10 7EF
Area of Operation: UK & Ireland
Tel: 01787 269132 **Fax:** 01787 269044
Email: info@brickcutters.com
Web: www.brickcutters.com **Product Type:** 3, 4

BULMER BRICK CUTTING SERVICES

Area of Operation: UK & Ireland
Tel: 01787 269 132
Fax: 01787 269 044
Email: info@brickcutters.com
Web: www.brickcutters.com

Fully bonded arch lintels, Rubbed & Gauged
Archwork, Hand cutting & Brick Carving.
Cut & Bonded Special Shapes, Refacing,
Herringbone Panels.

CAPITAL GROUP (M/CR) LIMITED
Victoria Mills, Highfield Road,
Little Hulton, Manchester, M38 9ST
Area of Operation: Worldwide
Tel: 0161 799 7555 **Fax:** 0161 799 7666
Email: leigh@choosecapital.co.uk
Web: www.choosecapital.co.uk ⌁

CAWARDEN BRICK & TILE CO. LTD
Cawarden Springs Farm, Blithbury Road,
Rugeley, Staffordshire, WS15 3HL
Tel: 01889 574066 **Fax:** 01889 575695
Email: home-garden@cawardenreclaim.co.uk
Web: www.cawardenreclaim.co.uk

CHESHIRE BRICK & SLATE
Brook House Farm, Salters Bridge,
Tarvin Sands, Tarvin, Cheshire, CH3 8NR
Area of Operation: UK (Excluding Ireland)
Tel: 01829 740883   **Fax:** 01829 740481
Email: enquiries@cheshirebrickandslate.co.uk
Web: www.cheshirebrickandslate.co.uk
Product Type: 1, 2, 3, 4, 7, 8, 10

CLARENDON BRICK
Studio 2, Jennymount Court, Belfast, Co Antrim, BT15 3HN
Area of Operation: Ireland Only
Tel: 028 9075 1751   **Fax:** 028 9075 1155
Email: info@clarendonbrick.com
Web: www.clarendonbrick.com
Product Type: 1, 2, 4, 5, 7, 8, 9, 10
Other Info: ▽ ✎ ✋

COLEFORD BRICK & TILE CO LTD
The Royal Forest of Dean Brickworks,
Cinderford, Gloucestershire, GL14 3JJ
Area of Operation: UK & Ireland
Tel: 01594 822160   **Fax:** 01594 826655
Email: sales@colefordbrick.co.uk
Web: www.colefordbrick.co.uk
Product Type: 4, 8   **Other Info:** ✎ ✋

CREST BRICK, SLATE & TILE LTD
Howdenshire Way, Knedlington Road,
Howden, East Riding of Yorks, DN14 7HZ
Area of Operation: UK (Excluding Ireland)
Tel: 0870 241 1398   **Fax:** 01430 433000
Email: info@crest-bst.co.uk
Web: www.crest-bst.co.uk
Product Type: 1, 2, 3, 4, 8, 9, 10

EUROBRICK SYSTEMS LTD
Unit 7 Wilverley Trading Estate,
Bath Road, Brislington, Bristol, BS4 5NL
Area of Operation: Europe
Tel: 0117 971 7117   **Fax:** 0117 971 7217
Email: info@eurobrick.co.uk
Web: www.eurobrick.co.uk
Product Type: 3

EUROFORM PRODUCTS LIMITED
The Heliport, Lyncastle Road, Appleton,
Warrington, Cheshire, WA4 4SN
Area of Operation: Worldwide
Tel: 01925 860999   **Fax:** 01925 860066
Email: info@euroform.co.uk
Web: www.euroform.co.uk

EUROFORM PRODUCTS LTD
Area of Operation: Worldwide
Tel: 01925 860999
Fax: 01925 860066
Email: info@euroform.co.uk
Web: www.euroform.co.uk

EZ Wall™ real brick thin cladding system.
- Tested & Qualified Wall Assembly
- 2 Hour Fire Test to British Standards
- Brick Matching Service Available
- Lightweight
- Easy to Install

FURNESS BRICK & TILE CO
Askam in Furness, Cumbria, LA16 7HF
Area of Operation: Worldwide
Tel: 01229 462411   **Fax:** 01229 462363
Email: furnessbrick@mac.com
Web: www.furnessbrick.com   **Other Info:** ✎ ✋
Product Type: 1, 4, 8, 10   **Material Type:** F) 1

FYFESTONE
Aquithie Road, Kemnay, Aberdeen,
Aberdeenshire, AB51 5PD
Area of Operation: UK (Excluding Ireland)
Tel: 01467 651000   **Fax:** 01467 642342
Web: www.fyfestone.com   **Product Type:** 1

HANSON BUILDING PRODUCTS
Stewartby, Bedford, Bedfordshire, MK43 9LZ
Area of Operation: Worldwide
Tel: 08705 258258   **Fax:** 01234 762040
Email: info@hansonbp.com   **Web:** www.hanson.biz
Product Type: 1, 2, 3, 4, 5, 6, 7, 8, 9, 10

IBSTOCK BRICK LTD
Leicester Road, Ibstock,
Leicester, Leicestershire, LE67 6HS
Area of Operation: UK & Ireland
Tel: 01530 261999   **Fax:** 01530 263478
Email: marketing@ibstock.co.uk
Web: www.ibstock.com
Product Type: 1, 3, 4, 5, 6, 7, 8, 9, 10, 11

INNOVATIVE BUILDING SOLUTIONS
Mill Green House, 48-50 Mill Green Road,
Mitcham, Surrey, CR4 4HY
Area of Operation: UK & Ireland
Tel: 0208 687 2260   **Fax:** 0208 687 2249
Email: ibs@charterhouseplc.co.uk
Product Type: 1, 2, 3, 4, 5, 6, 7, 8, 9, 10, 11

MANCHESTER BRICK & PRECAST LTD
Haigh Avenue, Whitehill Industrial Estate,
Stockport, Cheshire, SK4 1NU
Area of Operation: UK & Ireland
Tel: 0161 480 2621   **Fax:** 0161 480 0108
Email: sales@manbrick.co.uk
Web: www.manbrick.co.uk

MIDLANDS SLATE & TILE
Units 9-12, Star Industrial Estate,
Chadwell St Mary, Essex, RM16 4LR
Area of Operation: UK & Ireland
Tel: 0871 4743185   **Fax:** 01375 846478
Email: mark@slate-tile-brick.co.uk
Web: www.slate-tile-brick.co.uk
Product Type: 1, 2, 7, 10   **Material Type:** F) 3

NORTHCOT BRICK LTD
Blockley, Moreton-in-Marsh, Gloucestershire, GL56 9LH
Area of Operation: UK & Ireland
Tel: 01386 700551   **Fax:** 01386 700852
Email: info@northcotbrick.co.uk
Web: www.northcotbrick.co.uk
Product Type: 1, 3, 4, 5, 7, 8, 9

PADIPA LIMITED
Unit East 2, Sway Storage and Workshops,
Barrow's Lane, Sway, Lymington, Hampshire, SO41 6DD
Area of Operation: UK & Ireland
Tel: 01590 681710   **Fax:** 01425 616955
Email: enquiries@padipa.co.uk
Web: www.padipa.co.uk   **Product Type:** 3

PENNY BRICKS & TIMBER LIMITED
The Old Timber Yard, York Road, Wetherby,
West Yorkshire, LS22 5EF
Area of Operation: UK (Excluding Ireland)
Tel: 01937 580580   **Fax:** 01937 580587
Email: pw@penny-bricks.co.uk
Web: www.penny-bricks.co.uk
Product Type: 1, 7, 8

SOUTH WEST RECLAMATION LTD
Wireworks Estate, Bristol Road,
Bridgwater, Somerset, TA6 4AP
Area of Operation: South West England and South Wales
Tel: 01278 444141   **Fax:** 01278 444114
Email: info@southwest-rec.co.uk
Web: www.southwest-rec.co.uk   **Other Info:** ▽

SURREY RECLAIMED BRICKS
28C The Plantation, West Park Road,
Newchapel, Lingfield, Surrey, RH7 6HT
Area of Operation: Greater London, South East England
Tel: 01342 714561   **Fax:** 01342 714561
Email: surreybricks@aol.com
Web: www.surreyreclaimedbrickwork.co.uk ✎♦
Product Type: 1, 7, 10   **Other Info:** ▽

TAYLOR MAXWELL & COMPANY LIMITED
4 John Oliver Buildings, 53 Wood Street,
Barnet, Hertfordshire, EN5 4BS
Area of Operation: UK (Excluding Ireland)
Tel: 0208 440 0551   **Fax:** 0208 440 0552
Email: barnet@taylor.maxwell.co.uk
Web: www.taylor.maxwell.co.uk
Product Type: 1, 2, 3, 4, 5, 6, 7, 8, 9, 10

THE BRICK DEVELOPMENT ASSOCIATION LTD.
Woodside House, Winkfield, Windsor, Berkshire, SL4 2DX
Area of Operation: UK (Excluding Ireland)
Tel: 01344 885651   **Fax:** 01344 890129
Email: brick@brick.org.uk
Web: www.brick.org.uk

THE MATCHING BRICK COMPANY
Lockes Yard, Hartcliffe Way, Bedminster, Bristol, BS3 5RJ
Area of Operation: UK (Excluding Ireland)
Tel: 0117 963 7000   **Fax:** 0117 966 4612
Email: matchingbrick@btconnect.com
Web: www.matchingbrick.co.uk
Product Type: 1, 2, 3, 4, 5, 7, 8, 9, 10

THERMOBRICK
20 Underwood Drive, Stoney Stanton,
Leicester, Leicestershire, LE9 4TA
Area of Operation: UK & Ireland
Tel: 01455 272860   **Fax:** 01455 271324
Email: info@rutlandtimber.co.uk
Web: www.rutlandtimber.co.uk   **Product Type:** 1, 3

WETHERBY BUILDING SYSTEMS LIMITED
1 Kidglove Road, Golborne Enterprise Park,
Golborne, Greater Manchester, WA3 3GS
Area of Operation: UK & Ireland
Tel: 01942 717100   **Fax:** 01942 717101
Email: info@wbs-ltd.co.uk
Web: www.wbs-ltd.co.uk   **Product Type:** 3, 7, 9

WIENERBERGER LTD
Wienerberger House, Brooks Drive, Cheadle Royal
Business Park, Cheadle, Cheshire, SK8 3SA
Area of Operation: UK & Ireland
Tel: 0161 491 8200
Fax: 0161 491 6213
Email: nicky.webb@wienerberger.com
Web: www.wienerberger.co.uk
Product Type: 1, 2, 4, 5, 7, 8, 9, 10
Other Info: ✎ ✋

YORK HANDMADE BRICK CO LTD
Forest Lane, Alne, York,
North Yorkshire, YO61 1TU
Area of Operation: Worldwide
Tel: 01347 838881   **Fax:** 01347 838885
Email: sales@yorkhandmade.co.uk
Web: www.yorkhandmade.co.uk
Product Type: 1, 3, 4, 5   **Other Info:** ✋

YORK HANDMADE BRICK CO LTD
Area of Operation: UK
Tel: 01347 838881
Fax: 01347 838885
Email: sales@yorkhandmade.co.uk
Web: www.yorkhandmade.co.uk
Product Type: 1, 3, 4, 5
Other Info: ✋

York Handmade Brick are the largest
independent manufacturer of genuine handmade
bricks in the UK. Also producers of terracotta
floor tiles and landscape products.

PANELS, SECTIONS, SHEETS AND TILES

> ## KEY
> **PRODUCT TYPES:** 1 = Panels   2 = Sections
> 3 = Sheets   4 = Tiles   5 = Other
>
> **OTHER:** ▽ Reclaimed ♦ On-line shopping
> ✎ Bespoke ✋ Hand-made   ECO Ecological

ADVANCED CONSTRUCTION SYSTEMS
Granite Close, Enderby, Leicester, Leicestershire, LE19 4AE
Area of Operation: Europe
Tel: 0116 272 5133   **Fax:** 0116 272 5131
Email: info@advancedconstructionsystems.co.uk
Web: www.advancedconstructionsystems.co.uk
Product Type: 1, 5
Material Type: E) 1, 2, 4, 5, 11, 12, 13, 14

ALMURA BUILDING PRODUCTS LTD
Cantay House, St George's Place,
Cheltenham, Gloucestershire, GL50 3PN
Area of Operation: Europe
Tel: 01242 262900   **Fax:** 01242 221333
Email: philipmarsh@almura.co.uk
Web: www.almuracladdings.co.uk
Product Type: 1, 2, 3, 5   **Material Type:** C) 1

BLANC DE BIERGES
Eastrea Road, Whittlesey, Cambridgeshire, PE7 2AG
Area of Operation: Worldwide
Tel: 01733 202566   **Fax:** 01733 205405
Email: info@blancdebierges.com
Web: www.blancdebierges.com   **Other Info:** ✎ ✋

BOARD CENTRAL
Chiltern Business Centre, Couching Street,
Watlington, Oxfordshire, OX49 5PX
Area of Operation: Greater London, South East England
Tel: 0845 458 8016   **Fax:** 01844 354112
Email: howardmorrice@hotmail.com
Product Type: 1, 3

BORDER CONCRETE PRODUCTS
Jedburgh Road, Kelso, Borders, TD5 8JG
Area of Operation: North East England, North West
England and North Wales, Scotland
Tel: 01573 224393
Fax: 01573 276360
Email: sales@borderconcrete.co.uk
Web: www.borderconcrete.co.uk

CAVALOK BUILDING PRODUCTS LIMITED
Northway Lane, Newtown Industrial Estate,
Tewkesbury, Gloucestershire, GL20 8JG
Area of Operation: UK & Ireland
Tel: 08701 203003   **Fax:** 08701 213003
Email: info@cavalok.com   **Web:** www.cavalok.com
Product Type: 1, 2, 3   **Other Info:** ECO ✎

CEMBRIT BLUNN
6 Coleshill Street, Fazeley, Tamworth, Staffordshire, B78 3XJ
Area of Operation: UK & Ireland
Tel: 01827 288827   **Fax:** 01827 288176
Email: parcher@cembritblunn.co.uk
Web: www.cembritblunn.co.uk
Product Type: 1, 3   **Material Type:** H) 4

CLANCAST CONTRACTS LTD
48 Shaw Street, Glasgow, G51 3BL
Area of Operation: UK (Excluding Ireland)
Tel: 0141 440 2345   **Fax:** 0141 440 2488
Email: info@clancast.co.uk
Product Type: 1   **Material Type:** K) 5

CREST BRICK, SLATE & TILE LTD
Howdenshire Way, Knedlington Road,
Howden, East Riding of Yorks, DN14 7HZ
Area of Operation: UK (Excluding Ireland)
Tel: 0870 241 1398   **Fax:** 01430 433000
Email: info@crest-bst.co.uk
Web: www.crest-bst.co.uk
Product Type: 4

SPONSORED BY: CAPITAL GROUP (M/CR) LIMITED www.choosecapital.co.uk

DELTA MEMBRANE SYSTEMS LTD
Bassett Business Centre, Hurricane Way,
North Weald, Epping, Essex, CM16 6AA
Area of Operation: UK & Ireland
Tel: 01992 523 811   **Fax:** 01992 524046
Email: info@deltamembranes.com
Web: www.deltamembranes.com   **Product Type:** 3

EGGER (UK) LIMITED
Anick Grange Road, Hexham, Northumberland, NE46 4JS
Tel: 01434 602191   **Fax:** 01434 605103
Email: building.uk@egger.com
Web: www.egger.co.uk
Product Type: 1   **Material Type:** H) 1, 6

EUROBRICK SYSTEMS LTD
Unit 7 Wilverley Trading Estate, Bath Road,
Brislington, Bristol, BS4 5NL
Area of Operation: Europe
Tel: 0117 971 7117   **Fax:** 0117 971 7217
Email: info@eurobrick.co.uk
Web: www.eurobrick.co.uk   **Product Type:** 1

EUROFORM PRODUCTS LIMITED
The Heliport, Lyncastle Road,
Appleton, Warrington, Cheshire, WA4 4SN
Area of Operation: Worldwide
Tel: 01925 860999   **Fax:** 01925 860066
Email: info@euroform.co.uk
Web: www.euroform.co.uk   **Product Type:** 1, 3

EXTERIOR IMAGE LTD
5 Hursley Road, Chandlers Ford,
Eastleigh, Hampshire, SO53 2FW
Tel: 02380 271777   **Fax:** 02380 269091
Email: info@exteriorimage.co.uk
Web: www.exteriorimage.co.uk

FRANCIS N. LOWE LTD.
The Marble Works, New Road,
Middleton, Matlock, Derbyshire, DE4 4NA
Area of Operation: Europe
Tel: 01629 822216   **Fax:** 01629 824348
Email: info@lowesmarble.com
Web: www.lowesmarble.com
Product Type: 4   **Material Type:** E) 1, 2, 3, 5, 8, 9

HERAKLITH
Broadway House, 21, Broadway,
Maidenhead, Berkshire, SL6 1NJ
Tel: 01628 784330   **Fax:** 01628 633080
Email: muirwork@btinternet.com
Product Type: 3   **Other Info:** ECO
Material Type: K) 8, 10

IBSTOCK BRICK LTD
Leicester Road, Ibstock, Leicester,
Leicestershire, LE67 6HS
Area of Operation: UK & Ireland
Tel: 01530 261999   **Fax:** 01530 263478
Email: marketing@ibstock.co.uk
Web: www.ibstock.com   **Product Type:** 1, 4

INNOVATIVE BUILDING SOLUTIONS
Mill Green House, 48-50 Mill Green Road,
Mitcham, Surrey, CR4 4HY
Area of Operation: UK & Ireland
Tel: 0208 687 2260   **Fax:** 0208 687 2249
Email: ibs@charterhouseplc.co.uk   **Product Type:** 1

KEYMER TILES LTD
Nye Road, Burgess Hill, West Sussex, RH15 0LZ
Area of Operation: East England, Greater London,
Midlands & Mid Wales, South East England, South
West England and South Wales
Tel: 01444 232931   **Fax:** 01444 871852
Email: info@keymer.co.uk
Web: www.keymer.co.uk
Product Type: 4   **Other Info:** ✍ ✋
Material Type: F) 3

MARLEY ETERNIT LTD
Station Road, Coleshill, Birmingham, West Midlands, B46 1HP
Area of Operation: UK (Excluding Ireland)
Tel: 01763 264686   **Fax:** 01763 262338
Email: cladding@marleyeternit.co.uk or
profile@marleyeternit.co.uk
Web: www.marleyeternit.co.uk
Product Type: 1   **Material Type:** G) 2

NATURAL BUILDING TECHNOLOGIES
The Hangar, Worminghall Road,
Oakley, Buckinghamshire, HP18 9UL
Area of Operation: UK & Ireland
Tel: 01844 338338   **Fax:** 01844 338525
Email: info@natural-building.co.uk
Web: www.natural-building.co.uk
Product Type: 1   **Other Info:** ECO
Material Type: K) 3, 8, 9

NOISE STOP SYSTEMS
Unit 2, Car House Farm, Poole Lane,
Nun Monkton, York, North Yorkshire, YO26 8EH
Area of Operation: UK & Ireland
Tel: 0845 130 6269   **Fax:** 01423 339153
Email: info@noisestopsystems.co.uk
Web: www.noisestopsystems.co.uk ✍
Product Type: 1, 2, 3

PENNINE STONE LTD
Askern Road, Carcroft, Doncaster, DN6 8DH
Area of Operation: UK (Excluding Ireland)
Tel: 01302 729277   **Fax:** 01302 729288
Email: info@penninestone.co.uk
Web: www.penninestone.co.uk
Product Type: 5   **Material Type:** G) 1

SONAE (UK) LTD
Moss Lane, Knowsley Industrial Park,
Knowsley, Liverpool, Merseyside, L33 7XQ
Area of Operation: UK & Ireland
Tel: 0151 545 4000   **Fax:** 0151 545 4090
Email: sonaeuklink@sonae.co.uk
Web: www.sonaeuk.com
Product Type: 1, 3   **Material Type:** H) 1, 2, 5, 6, 7

STANCLIFFE STONE
Grange Mill, Matlock, Derbyshire, DE4 4BW
Area of Operation: Worldwide
Tel: 01629 653000   **Fax:** 01629 650996
Email: sales@stancliffe.com
Web: www.stancliffe.com   **Other Info:** ✍
Product Type: 1   **Material Type:** E) 4, 5

**STRUCTURAL INSULATED PANEL
TECHNOLOGY LTD (SIPTEC)**
PO Box 429, Turvey, Bedfordshire, MK43 8DT
Area of Operation: Europe
Tel: 0870 743 9866
Fax: 0870 762 5612
Email: mail@sips.ws   **Web:** www.sips.ws
Product Type: 1   **Material Type:** H) 4, 6

SURECAV LTD
Holbrook Lodge, Holbrook,
Wincanton, Bath, Somerset, BA9 8BT
Area of Operation: Worldwide
Tel: 01963 34660   **Fax:** 01963 33700
Email: surecavlimited@btconnect.com
Web: www.surecav.com

SWISH BUILDING PRODUCTS LTD
Pioneer House, Mariner, Litchfield Road Industrial
Estate, Tamworth, Staffordshire, B79 7TF
Area of Operation: UK & Ireland
Tel: 01827 317200   **Fax:** 01827 317201
Email: info@swishbp.co.uk
Web: www.swishbp.co.uk
Product Type: 1, 2, 3   **Material Type:** D) 1

TAYLOR MAXWELL & COMPANY LIMITED
4 John Oliver Buildings, 53 Wood Street,
Barnet, Hertfordshire, EN5 4BS
Area of Operation: UK (Excluding Ireland)
Tel: 0208 440 0551   **Fax:** 0208 440 0552
Email: barnet@taylor.maxwell.co.uk
Web: www.taylor.maxwell.co.uk
Product Type: 1, 4, 5

THE EXPANDED METAL COMPANY LIMITED
PO Box 14, Longhill Industrial Estate (North),
Hartlepool, Durham, TS25 1PR
Area of Operation: Worldwide
Tel: 01429 867388
Fax: 01429 866795
Email: paulb@expamet.co.uk
Web: www.expandedmetalcompany.co.uk
Material Type: C) 1, 2, 3, 4, 6, 7, 9, 10, 11, 12, 13, 18

THE GRANITE FACTORY
4 Winchester Drive, Peterlee, Durham, SR8 2RJ
Area of Operation: North East England
Tel: 0191 518 3600   **Fax:** 0191 518 3600
Email: admin@granitefactory.co.uk
Web: www.granitefactory.co.uk ✍
Product Type: 1, 4

TWINFIX
201 Cavendish Place, Birchwood Park,
Birchwood, Warrington, Cheshire, WA3 6WU
Area of Operation: UK & Ireland
Tel: 01925 811311   **Fax:** 01925 852955
Email: enquiries@twinfix.co.uk
Web: www.twinfix.co.uk

VISION ASSOCIATES
Demita House, North Orbital Road,
Denham, Buckinghamshire, UB9 5EY
Area of Operation: UK & Ireland
Tel: 01895 831600   **Fax:** 01895 835323
Email: info@visionassociates.co.uk
Web: www.visionassociates.co.uk
Product Type: 1, 3

WESSEX BUILDING PRODUCTS (MULTITEX)
Dolphin Industrial Estate, Southampton Road,
Salisbury, Wiltshire, SP1 2NB
Area of Operation: UK & Ireland
Tel: 01722 332139   **Fax:** 01722 338458
Email: sales@wessexbuildingproducts.co.uk
Web: www.wessexbuildingproducts.co.uk
Product Type: 1   **Material Type:** D) 6

WETHERBY BUILDING SYSTEMS LIMITED
1 Kidglove Road, Golborne Enterprise Park,
Golborne, Greater Manchester, WA3 3GS
Area of Operation: UK & Ireland
Tel: 01942 717100   **Fax:** 01942 717101
Email: info@wbs-ltd.co.uk
Web: www.wbs-ltd.co.uk   **Product Type:** 1, 4

RENDER

KEY

SEE ALSO: FLOOR AND WALL FINISHES -
Paints, Stains and Varnishes (Exterior Paint)

OTHER: ▽ Reclaimed   ✍ On-line shopping
✍ Bespoke   ✋ Hand-made   ECO Ecological

ALUMASC EXTERIOR BUILDING PRODUCTS
White House Works, Bold Road,
Sutton, St Helens, Merseyside, WA9 4JG
Area of Operation: UK & Ireland
Tel: 01744 648400   **Fax:** 01744 648401
Email: info@alumasc-exteriors.co.uk
Web: www.alumasc-exteriors.co.uk

CASTLE CEMENT LIMITED
Park Square, 3160 Solihull Parkway, Birmingham
Business Park, Birmingham, West Midlands, B37 7YN
Area of Operation: UK (Excluding Ireland)
Tel: 0845 600 1616   **Fax:** 0121 606 1436
Email: customer.services@castlecement.co.uk
Web: www.castlecement.co.uk
Material Type: G) 1, 2

**HEATHFIELD SPECIALIST
FINISHES & COATINGS LTD**
Unit 3, 41 Church Road, Bexleyheath, Kent, DA7 4DD
Area of Operation: UK (Excluding Ireland)
Tel: 0800 019 4718   **Fax:** 0208 303 3072
Email: info@plasterer.co.uk
Web: www.plasterer.co.uk   **Material Type:** I) 1, 4, 7

**INSULATED RENDER &
CLADDING ASSOCIATION**
PO Box 12, Haslemere, Surrey, GU27 3AH
Area of Operation: UK (Excluding Ireland)
Tel: 01428 654011   **Fax:** 01428 651401
Email: incaassociation@aol.com
Web: www.inca-ltd.org.uk

LAFARGE CEMENT
Manor Court, Chilton, Oxfordshire, OX11 0RN
Area of Operation: UK & Ireland
Tel: 01235 448400   **Fax:** 01235 448600
Email: info@lafargecement.co.uk
Web: www.lafargecement.co.uk
Material Type: G) 2

LIME TECHNOLOGY LIMITED
Unit 126, Milton Park, Abingdon, Oxfordshire, OX14 4SA
Area of Operation: Worldwide
Tel: 0845 603 1143   **Fax:** 0845 634 1560
Email: info@limetechnology.co.uk
Web: www.limetechnology.co.uk

LIME TECHNOLOGY LIMITED

Area of Operation: Worldwide
Tel: 0845 603 1143
Fax: 0845 634 1560
Email: info@limetechnology.co.uk
Web: www.limetechnology.co.uk
Other Info: ECO

Limetec hydraulic lime-based plasters and
renders designed for spray or hand application.
Suitable for brickwork, blockwork or concrete.
Enhanced breathability, flexibility and fast
installation. Available in 25kg bags.

NATURAL BUILDING TECHNOLOGIES
The Hangar, Worminghall Road,
Oakley, Buckinghamshire, HP18 9UL
Area of Operation: UK & Ireland
Tel: 01844 338338   **Fax:** 01844 338525
Email: info@natural-building.co.uk
Web: www.natural-building.co.uk
Material Type: I) 2, 3

PERMAROCK PRODUCTS LTD
Jubilee Drive, Loughborough, Leicestershire, LE11 5TW
Area of Operation: UK & Ireland
Tel: 01509 262924   **Fax:** 01509 230063
Email: permarock@permarock.com
Web: www.permarock.com

SURFACE SOLUTIONS
33 Alma Road, Herne Bay, Kent, CT6 6JJ
Area of Operation: UK (Excluding Ireland)
Tel: 01227 362775

THE EXPANDED METAL COMPANY LIMITED
PO Box 14, Longhill Industrial Estate (North),
Hartlepool, Durham, TS25 1PR
Area of Operation: Worldwide
Tel: 01429 867388   **Fax:** 01429 866795
Email: paulb@expamet.co.uk
Web: www.expandedmetalcompany.co.uk

THERMASTEX COATINGS
Rivington House,
82 Great Eastern Street, London, C2A 3JF
Area of Operation: UK (Excluding Ireland)
Tel: 0207 749 7297
Email: thermastex@london.com
Web: www.thermastex.com

WETHERBY BUILDING SYSTEMS LIMITED
1 Kidglove Road, Golborne Enterprise Park,
Golborne, Greater Manchester, WA3 3GS
Area of Operation: UK & Ireland
Tel: 01942 717100   **Fax:** 01942 717101
Email: info@wbs-ltd.co.uk
Web: www.wbs-ltd.co.uk   **Material Type:** G) 5

BUILDING STRUCTURE & MATERIALS - Bricks, Blocks, Stone & Cladding - Shakes & Shingles; Weatherboarding; Stone Cladding

SPONSORED BY: CAPITAL GROUP (M/CR) LIMITED www.choosecapital.co.uk

WETHERTEX UK
Bleakhill Way, Mansfield, Nottinghamshire, NG18 5EZ
Area of Operation: UK (Excluding Ireland)
Tel: 01623 633833   **Fax:** 01623 635551
Email: sales@wethertex.co.uk
Web: www.wethertex.co.uk

SHAKES AND SHINGLES

KEY

SEE ALSO: MERCHANTS - Timber Merchants,
ROOFING - Tiles. Shingles and Slates

OTHER: ▽ Reclaimed ⊕ On-line shopping
✎ Bespoke ✋ Hand-made ECO Ecological

ALMURA BUILDING PRODUCTS LTD
Cantay House, St George's Place,
Cheltenham, Gloucestershire, GL50 3PN
Area of Operation: Europe
Tel: 01242 262900   **Fax:** 01242 221333
Email: philipmarsh@almura.co.uk
Web: www.almuracladdings.co.uk
Material Type: D) 4

CANADA WOOD UK
PO Box 1, Farnborough, Hampshire, GU14 6WE
Area of Operation: UK & Ireland
Tel: 01252 522545   **Fax:** 01252 522546
Email: office@canadawooduk.org
Web: www.canadawood.info   **Material Type:** A) 12

JOHN BRASH LTD
The Old Shipyard, Gainsborough, Lincolnshire, DN21 1NG
Area of Operation: UK & Ireland
Tel: 01427 613858   **Fax:** 01427 810218
Email: info@johnbrash.co.uk
Web: www.johnbrash.co.uk
Material Type: A) 2, 8, 12

PRIORY HARDWOODS LIMITED
Unit 57 Bowers Mill, Branch Road,
Barkisland, West Yorkshire, HX4 0AD
Area of Operation: UK (Excluding Ireland)
Tel: 01422 311 700   **Fax:** 01422 311 118
Email: info@prioryhardwoods.com
Web: www.prioryhardwoods.com
Material Type: A) 12

THE HOMEBUILDER'S HANDBOOK
THE SOURCEBOOK FOR PROFESSIONALS, SELF-BUILDERS AND HOME RENOVATORS

1,000S OF ESSENTIAL CONTACTS

**Don't forget to let us
know about companies
you think should be listed
in the next edition**
email:
customerservice@centaur.co.uk

WEATHERBOARDING

KEY

SEE ALSO: MERCHANTS - Timber Merchants

OTHER: ▽ Reclaimed ⊕ On-line shopping
✎ Bespoke ✋ Hand-made ECO Ecological

ALMURA BUILDING PRODUCTS LTD
Cantay House, St George's Place,
Cheltenham, Gloucestershire, GL50 3PN
Area of Operation: Europe
Tel: 01242 262900   **Fax:** 01242 221333
Email: philipmarsh@almura.co.uk
Web: www.almuracladdings.co.uk   **Material Type:** D) 4

ALMURA BUILDING PRODUCTS LTD

Area of Operation: Europe
Tel: 01242 262 900   **Fax:** 01242 221 333
Email: philipmarsh@alumra.co.uk
Web: www.almuracladdings.co.uk

Almura Supply the highest quality of cladding of
their type in the world. These include
weatherboarding, stone and brick effect boards
and aggregate faced panels.

BOARD CENTRAL
Chiltern Business Centre, Couching Street,
Watlington, Oxfordshire, OX49 5PX
Area of Operation: Greater London, South East England
Tel: 0845 458 8016   **Fax:** 01844 354112
Email: howardmorrice@hotmail.com

CANADA WOOD UK
PO Box 1, Farnborough, Hampshire, GU14 6WE
Area of Operation: UK & Ireland
Tel: 01252 522545   **Fax:** 01252 522546
Email: office@canadawooduk.org
Web: www.canadawood.info   **Material Type:** A) 12

CAVALOK BUILDING PRODUCTS LIMITED
Northway Lane, Newtown Industrial Estate,
Tewkesbury, Gloucestershire, GL20 8JG
Tel: 08701 203003   **Fax:** 08701 213003
Email: info@cavalok.com   **Web:** www.cavalok.com

CEMBRIT BLUNN
6 Coleshill Street, Fazeley, Tamworth, Staffordshire, B78 3XJ
Area of Operation: UK & Ireland
Tel: 01827 288827   **Fax:** 01827 288176
Email: parcher@cembritblunn.co.uk
Web: www.cembritblunn.co.uk

EGGER (UK) LIMITED
Anick Grange Road, Hexham, Northumberland, NE46 4JS
Area of Operation: UK & Ireland
Tel: 01434 602191   **Fax:** 01434 605103
Email: building.uk@egger.com
Web: www.egger.co.uk   **Material Type:** H) 1

EUROFORM PRODUCTS LIMITED
The Heliport, Lyncastle Road, Appleton,
Warrington, Cheshire, WA4 4SN
Area of Operation: Worldwide
Tel: 01925 860999   **Fax:** 01925 860066
Email: info@euroform.co.uk **Web:** www.euroform.co.uk

JOHN BRASH LTD
The Old Shipyard, Gainsborough, Lincolnshire, DN21 1NG
Area of Operation: UK & Ireland
Tel: 01427 613858   **Fax:** 01427 810218
Email: info@johnbrash.co.uk
Web: www.johnbrash.co.uk

MARLEY ETERNIT LTD
Station Road, Coleshill, Birmingham, West Midlands, B46 1HP
Area of Operation: UK (Excluding Ireland)
Tel: 01763 264686   **Fax:** 01763 262338
Email: cladding@marleyeternit.co.uk
Web: www.marleyeternit.co.uk **Material Type:** G) 2

NATURAL BUILDING TECHNOLOGIES
The Hangar, Worminghall Road,
Oakley, Buckinghamshire, HP18 9UL
Tel: 01844 338338   **Fax:** 01844 338525
Email: info@natural-building.co.uk
Web: www.natural-building.co.uk

**NORBUILD TIMBER FABRICATION &
FINE CARPENTRY LTD**
Marcassie Farm, Rafford, Forres, Moray, IV36 2RH
Area of Operation: UK & Ireland
Tel: 01309 676865   **Fax:** 01309 676865
Email: norbuild@marcassie.fsnet.co.uk

NORTHWOOD FORESTRY LTD
Goose Green Lane, Nr Ashington,
Pulborough, West Sussex, RH20 2LW
Area of Operation: South East England
Tel: 01798 813029   **Fax:** 01798 813139
Email: enquiries@northwoodforestry.co.uk
Web: www.northwoodforestry.co.uk
Other Info: ✎ ✋   **Material Type:** A) 2

PLASTIVAN LTD
Unit 4 Bonville Industrial Estate,
Bonville Road, Brislington, Bristol, BS4 5QU
Area of Operation: Worldwide
Tel: 0117 300 5625   **Fax:** 0117 971 5028
Email: sales@plastivan.co.uk
Web: www.plastivan.co.uk

SWISH BUILDING PRODUCTS LTD
Pioneer House, Mariner, Litchfield Road Industrial
Estate, Tamworth, Staffordshire, B79 7TF
Area of Operation: UK & Ireland
Tel: 01827 317200   **Fax:** 01827 317201
Email: info@swishbp.co.uk
Web: www.swishbp.co.uk   **Material Type:** D) 1

TAYLOR MAXWELL & COMPANY LIMITED
4 John Oliver Buildings, 53 Wood Street,
Barnet, Hertfordshire, EN5 4BS
Tel: 0208 440 0551   **Fax:** 0208 440 0552
Email: barnet@taylor.maxwell.co.uk
Web: www.taylor.maxwell.co.uk

VISION ASSOCIATES
Demita House, North Orbital Road,
Denham, Buckinghamshire, UB9 5EY
Tel: 01895 831600   **Fax:** 01895 835323
Email: info@visionassociates.co.uk
Web: www.visionassociates.co.uk

STONE CLADDING

KEY

PRODUCT TYPES: 1= Ashlar   2 = Cobble
3 = Dressed Stone   4 = Rubble

OTHER: ▽ Reclaimed ⊕ On-line shopping
✎ Bespoke ✋ Hand-made ECO Ecological

ADDSTONE CAST STONE
2 Millers Gate, Stone, Staffordshire, ST15 8ZF
Area of Operation: UK (Excluding Ireland)
Tel: 01785 818810   **Fax:** 01785 819958
Email: sales@addstone.co.uk
Web: www.addstone.co.uk ⊕   **Product Type:** 1, 3
Other Info: ✎ ✋   **Material Type:** E) 11, 13

JOHN BRASH LTD
The Old Shipyard, Gainsborough, Lincolnshire, DN21 1NG
Area of Operation: UK & Ireland
Tel: 01427 613858   **Fax:** 01427 810218
Email: info@johnbrash.co.uk
Web: www.johnbrash.co.uk

ALBION STONE PLC
27-33 Brighton Road, Redhill, Surrey, RH1 6PP
Area of Operation: UK (Excluding Ireland)
Tel: 01737 771772   **Fax:** 01737 771776
Email: sales@albionstone.co.uk
Web: www.albionstone.com ⊕

ALMURA BUILDING PRODUCTS LTD
Cantay House, St George's Place,
Cheltenham, Gloucestershire, GL50 3PN
Area of Operation: Europe
Tel: 01242 262900   **Fax:** 01242 221333
Email: philipmarsh@almura.co.uk
Web: www.almuracladdings.co.uk

ASPECTS OF STONE LTD
Unit 29, Broughton Grounds, Broughton,
Newport Pagnell, Buckinghamshire, MK16 0HZ
Area of Operation: UK (Excluding Ireland)
Tel: 01908 830061   **Fax:** 01908 830062
Email: sales@aspectsofstone.co.uk
Web: www.aspectsofstone.co.uk   **Product Type:** 1, 3

BINGLEY STONE
Cullingworth Mills, Cullingworth, West Yorkshire, BD13 5AB
Area of Operation: UK (Excluding Ireland)
Tel: 01535 273813   **Email:** info@bingleystone.co.uk
Web: www.bingleystone.co.uk   **Product Type:** 1, 2, 3, 4

BLACK MOUNTAIN QUARRIES LTD
Howton Court, Pontrilas, Herefordshire, HR2 0BG
Area of Operation: UK & Ireland
Tel: 01981 241541
Email: info@blackmountainquarries.com
Web: www.blackmountainquarries.com ⊕
Product Type: 2, 3, 4   **Other Info:** ECO ✋

BLANC DE BIERGES
Eastrea Road, Whittlesey, Cambridgeshire, PE7 2AG
Area of Operation: Worldwide
Tel: 01733 202566   **Fax:** 01733 205405
Email: info@blancdebierges.com
Web: www.blancdebierges.com

BRADSTONE STRUCTURAL
Aggregate Industries UK Ltd, North End,
Ashton Keynes, Swindon, Wiltshire, SN6 3QX
Area of Operation: UK (Excluding Ireland)
Tel: 01285 646884   **Fax:** 01285 646891
Email: bradstone.structural@aggregate.com
Web: www.bradstone.com
Product Type: 1   **Material Type:** E) 13

BRIDGE STREET STONE LTD
The Old Gas Works Yard, Knotts Lane,
Colne, Lancashire, BB8 8AA
Area of Operation: UK & Ireland
Tel: 01282 860571   **Fax:** 01282 867446
Email: sales@stonepaving.co.uk
Web: www.stonepaving.co.uk
Product Type: 1, 2, 3, 4

BRS YORK STONE
50 High Green Road, Altofts,
Normanton, Lancashire, WF6 2LQ
Area of Operation: UK (Excluding Ireland)
Tel: 01924 220356   **Fax:** 01924 220356
Email: john@york-stone.fsnet.co.uk
Web: www.yorkstonepaving.co.uk

CAMBRIDGE MASONRY LTD
Station Road, Longstanton,
Nr Cambridge, Cambridgeshire, CB4 5FB
Area of Operation: East England, Greater London,
Midlands & Mid Wales, South East England, South
West England and South Wales
Tel: 01954 261907   **Fax:** 01954 260847
Email: coling@cambridgemasonry.co.uk
Web: www.cambridgemasonry.co.uk
Product Type: 1, 3   **Material Type:** E) 5

CAWARDEN BRICK & TILE CO. LTD
Cawarden Springs Farm, Blithbury Road,
Rugeley, Staffordshire, WS15 3HL
Area of Operation: UK (Excluding Ireland)
Tel: 01889 574066   **Fax:** 01889 575695
Email: home-garden@cawardenreclaim.co.uk
Web: www.cawardenreclaim.co.uk
Product Type: 2

Weatherboard
Number one for wood style without woodcare

With its superb choice of factory-painted colours, Weatherboard is first choice
for creating spectacular timber-style cladding.

Perfect wherever wood simply wouldn't be practical.

Totally resistant to rot in even the most hostile conditions; quick and easy to install with no special skills or equipment;

fire resistant (Class 0); minimal maintenance; supplied factory-painted or ready to paint on site... the advantages are numerous.

And, as a host of award-winning projects prove, the possibilities are endless.

Contact Marley Eternit today for the full facts.

T 01763 264686 E cladding@marleyeternit.co.uk
www.marleyeternit.co.uk

an **Etex** GROUP ✧ company

CHINA SLATE LTD
Wingfield View, Coney Green, Clay Cross,
Chesterfield, Derbyshire, S45 9JW
Area of Operation: UK & Ireland
Tel: 01246 865222   **Fax:** 01246 865999
Email: sales@chinaslate.co.uk
Web: www.chinaslate.co.uk

D F FIXINGS
15 Aldham Gardens, Rayleigh, Essex, SS6 9TB
Area of Operation: UK (Excluding Ireland)
Tel: 07956 674673   **Fax:** 01268 655072

FARMINGTON NATURAL STONE
Northleach, Cheltenham, Gloucestershire, GL54 3NZ
Tel: 01451 860280   **Fax:** 01451 860115
Email: cotswold.stone@farmington.co.uk
Web: www.farmingtonnaturalstone.co.uk
Product Type: 2, 3

FRANCIS N. LOWE LTD.
The Marble Works, New Road, Middleton,
Matlock, Derbyshire, DE4 4NA
Area of Operation: Europe
Tel: 01629 822216   **Fax:** 01629 824348
Email: info@lowesmarble.com
Web: www.lowesmarble.com   **Product Type:** 1, 3

FYFESTONE
Aquithie Road, Kemnay, Aberdeen,
Aberdeenshire, AB51 5PD
Area of Operation: UK (Excluding Ireland)
Tel: 01467 651000   **Fax:** 01467 642342
Web: www.fyfestone.com   **Product Type:** 1, 3, 4

GWRHYD SPECIALIST STONE QUARRY
Gwrhyd Road, Rhiwfawr, Swansea, Neath, SA9 2SB
Area of Operation: UK & Ireland
Tel: 01639 830743   **Fax:** 01639 830930
Email: enquiries@specialiststone.com
Web: www.specialiststone.com
Product Type: 2, 3, 4   **Other Info:** ✍ ✋
Material Type: E) 4

HEART OF STONE LTD
Cotsbrook Farm Buildings, Higford,
Nr. Shifnal, Shropshire, TF11 9ES
Area of Operation: UK (Excluding Ireland)
Tel: 01952 730231
Email: heartofstone@btinternet.com
Web: www.heartofstone.co.uk
Product Type: 2, 3
Material Type: E) 1, 2, 3, 4, 5, 8, 9

INNOVATIVE BUILDING SOLUTIONS
Mill Green House, 48-50 Mill Green Road,
Mitcham, Surrey, CR4 4HY
Area of Operation: UK & Ireland
Tel: 0208 687 2260   **Fax:** 0208 687 2249
Email: ibs@charterhouseplc.co.uk

KIRK NATURAL STONE
Bridgend, Fyvie, Turriff, Aberdeenshire, AB53 8LL
Area of Operation: Worldwide
Tel: 01651 891891   **Fax:** 01651 891794
Email: info@kirknaturalstone.com
Web: www.kirknaturalstone.com
Product Type: 1, 2, 3, 4

MANCHESTER BRICK & PRECAST LTD
Haigh Avenue, Whitehill Industrial Estate,
Stockport, Cheshire, SK4 1NU
Tel: 0161 480 2621   **Fax:** 0161 480 0108
Email: sales@manbrick.co.uk
Web: www.manbrick.co.uk   **Product Type:** 3

MARBLE HART.COM
1 Edwin Street, Daybrook, Arnold, Nottingham,
Nottinghamshire, NG5 6AX
Area of Operation: Worldwide
Tel: 0115 920 3159   **Fax:** 0115 952 5752
Email: chris@cghart.com
Web: www.marblehart.com ⌐   **Product Type:** 3

MEADOWSTONE (DERBYSHIRE) LTD
West Way, Somercotes, Derbyshire, DE55 4QJ
Tel: 01773 540707   **Fax:** 01773 527261
Email: info@meadowstone.co.uk
Web: www.meadowstone.co.uk ⌐   **Product Type:** 1

NATIONAL STONE PRODUCTS
Unit 25, M1 Commerce Park, Markham Lane,
Duckmanton, Chesterfield, Derbyshire, S44 5HS
Area of Operation: UK (Excluding Ireland)
Tel: 01246 240881   **Fax:** 01246 240685
Email: bobhockley-nsp@btconnect.com
Product Type: 3

NICAN STONE LTD
Bank House, School Lane,
Bronington, Shropshire, SY13 3HN
Area of Operation: UK (Excluding Ireland)
Tel: 01948 780670   **Fax:** 01948 780679
Email: enquiries@nicanstone.com
Web: www.nicanstone.com

ORCHARD STONEMASONS
48 West Street, Axbridge, Somerset, BS26 2AD
Area of Operation: UK (Excluding Ireland)
Tel: 01934 732718   **Fax:** 01934 732718
Email: info@orchardstonemasons.co.uk
Web: www.orchardstonemasons.co.uk
Product Type: 1, 3, 4   **Other Info:** ▽ ✍ ✋

PADIPA LIMITED
Unit East 2, Sway Storage and Workshops,
Barrow's Lane, Sway, Lymington, Hampshire, SO41 6DD
Area of Operation: UK & Ireland
Tel: 01590 681710   **Fax:** 01425 616955
Email: enquiries@padipa.co.uk
Web: www.padipa.co.uk

PENNINE STONE LTD
Askern Road, Carcroft, Doncaster, DN6 8DH
Area of Operation: UK (Excluding Ireland)
Tel: 01302 729277   **Fax:** 01302 729288
Email: info@penninestone.co.uk
Web: www.penninestone.co.uk
Product Type: 1   **Material Type:** G) 1

PROCTER CASTSTONE &
CONCRETE PRODUCTS
Ash Lane, Garforth, Leeds, West Yorkshire, LS25 2QH
Area of Operation: UK (Excluding Ireland)
Tel: 01132 862586   **Fax:** 01132 867376
Email: websales@proctergarforth.co.uk
Web: www.caststoneuk.co.uk

RICHARD CLEGG DWS
5 Springfield Lane, Kirkburton,
Huddersfield, West Yorkshire, HD8 0NZ
Area of Operation: UK (Excluding Ireland)
Tel: 01484 608357
Email: richardclegg@customnet.co.uk
Web: www.richardclegg.co.uk   **Product Type:** 3

ROCK UNIQUE LTD
c/o Select Garden and Pet Centre,
Main Road, Sundridge, Kent, TN14 6ED
Area of Operation: Europe
Tel: 01959 565 608   **Fax:** 01959 569 312
Email: stone@rock-unique.com
Web: www.rock-unique.com
Product Type: 2   **Other Info:** ▽ ECO ✍ ✋
Material Type: E) 1, 2, 3, 4, 5, 8, 9, 10

SNOWDONIA SLATE & STONE
Glandwr Workshops, Glanypwll Road,
Blaenau Ffestiniog, Gwynedd, LL41 3PG
Tel: 01766 832525   **Fax:** 01766 832404
Email: richard@snowdoniaslate.co.uk
Web: www.snowdoniaslate.co.uk   **Product Type:** 3

SOUTHERN MASONRY LTD
37b Broadway East, West Wilts Trading Estate,
Westbury, Wiltshire, BA13 4AJ
Area of Operation: South East England, South West
England and South Wales
Tel: 07976 613421   **Fax:** 01749 345170
Email: charlie@stonefiresurrounds.co.uk
Web: www.southernmasonry.co.uk
Product Type: 1, 2, 3, 4   **Other Info:** ▽ ECO ✍ ✋

STANCLIFFE STONE
Grange Mill, Matlock, Derbyshire, DE4 4BW
Area of Operation: Worldwide
Tel: 01629 653000   **Fax:** 01629 650996
Email: sales@stancliffe.com
Web: www.stancliffe.com   **Product Type:** 1, 3, 4

STONE ESSENTIALS CO LTD
Mount Spring Works, Off Burnley Road East,
Rossendale, Lancashire, BB4 9LA
Area of Operation: UK (Excluding Ireland)
Tel: 01706 210605   **Fax:** 01706 228707
Email: ken.howe@btconnect.com
Web: www.stone-essentials.co.uk
Product Type: 1, 2, 3, 4   **Other Info:** ✍ ✋
Material Type: E) 1, 2, 3, 4, 5, 8

THE HOME OF STONE
Boot Barn, Newcastle, Monmouth,
Monmouthshire, NP25 5NU
Area of Operation: UK (Excluding Ireland)
Tel: 01600 750462   **Fax:** 01600 750462

THORVERTON STONE COMPANY LTD
Seychelles Farm, Upton Pyne, Exeter, Devon, EX5 5HY
Area of Operation: UK & Ireland
Tel: 01392 851 822   **Fax:** 01392 851833
Email: caststone@thorvertonstone.co.uk
Web: www.thorvertonstone.co.uk
Product Type: 3

TRADSTOCKS LTD
Dunaverig, Thornhill, Stirling, Stirlingshire, FK8 3QW
Area of Operation: Scotland
Tel: 01786 850400   **Fax:** 01786 850404
Email: info@tradstocks.co.uk
Web: www.tradstocks.co.uk
Product Type: 1, 2, 3, 4

VOBSTER CAST STONE CO LTD
Newbury Works, Coleford, Radstock, Somerset, BA3 5RX
Area of Operation: UK (Excluding Ireland)
Tel: 01373 812514   **Fax:** 01373 813384
Email: tombrewster@caststonemasonry.co.uk
Web: www.caststonemasonry.co.uk

WARMSWORTH STONE LTD
1-3 Sheffield Road, Warmsworth,
Doncaster, South Yorkshire, DN4 9QH
Area of Operation: UK & Ireland
Tel: 01302 858617   **Fax:** 01302 855844
Email: info@warmsworth-stone.co.uk
Web: www.warmsworth-stone.co.uk
Product Type: 1, 2, 3, 4   **Material Type:** E) 1, 2, 4, 5, 8

WELLS CATHEDRAL STONEMASONS
Brunel Stoneworks, Station Road,
Cheddar, Somerset, BS27 3AH
Area of Operation: Worldwide
Tel: 01934 743544   **Fax:** 01934 744536
Email: wcs@stone-mason.co.uk
Web: www.stone-mason.co.uk   **Product Type:** 1, 3

WOODKIRK STONE SALES LTD
Britannia Quarries, Rein Road, Morley,
Leeds, West Yorkshire, LS27 0SW
Area of Operation: Europe
Tel: 0113 253 0464   **Fax:** 0113 252 7520
Email: sales@woodkirkstone.co.uk
Web: www.woodkirkstone.co.uk
Product Type: 1, 2, 3   **Material Type:** E) 4, 5

BLOCKS

KEY

PRODUCT TYPES: 1 = Solid   2 = Dense
3 = Lightweight   4 = Super-lightweight
5 = Fairfaced   6 = Insulant Filled   7 = Glazed
8 = Foundation Blocks

OTHER: ▽ Reclaimed   ⌐ On-line shopping
✍ Bespoke   ✋ Hand-made   ECO Ecological

BLANC DE BIERGES
Eastrea Road, Whittlesey, Cambridgeshire, PE7 2AG
Area of Operation: Worldwide
Tel: 01733 202566   **Fax:** 01733 205405
Email: info@blancdebierges.com
Web: www.blancdebierges.com

BORDER CONCRETE PRODUCTS
Jedburgh Road, Kelso, Borders, TD5 8JG
Area of Operation: North East England, North West
England and North Wales, Scotland
Tel: 01573 224393   **Fax:** 01573 276360
Email: sales@borderconcrete.co.uk
Web: www.borderconcrete.co.uk   **Product Type:** 5

BRADSTONE STRUCTURAL
Aggregate Industries UK Ltd, North End,
Ashton Keynes, Swindon, Wiltshire, SN6 3QX
Area of Operation: UK (Excluding Ireland)
Tel: 01285 646884   **Fax:** 01285 646891
Email: bradstone.structural@aggregate.com
Web: www.bradstone.com
Product Type: 1   **Material Type:** E) 13

BRIDGE STREET STONE LTD
The Old Gas Works Yard, Knotts Lane,
Colne, Lancashire, BB8 8AA
Area of Operation: UK & Ireland
Tel: 01282 860571   **Fax:** 01282 867446
Email: sales@stonepaving.co.uk
Web: www.stonepaving.co.uk

BUILDMART.CO.UK LIMITED
Area of Operation: UK (Excluding Ireland)
Tel: 0870 874 1135
Email: enquiries@buildmart.co.uk
Web: www.buildmart.co.uk ⌐   **Product Type:** 8

CAMBRIDGE MASONRY LTD
Station Road, Longstanton,
Nr Cambridge, Cambridgeshire, CB4 5FB
Area of Operation: East England, Greater London,
Midlands & Mid Wales, South East England, South
West England and South Wales
Tel: 01954 261907   **Fax:** 01954 260847
Email: coling@cambridgemasonry.co.uk
Web: www.cambridgemasonry.co.uk
Product Type: 1   **Material Type:** E) 5

CAPITAL GROUP (M/CR) LIMITED
Victoria Mills, Highfield Road,
Little Hulton, Manchester, M38 9ST
Area of Operation: Worldwide
Tel: 0161 799 7555
Fax: 0161 799 7666
Email: leigh@choosecapital.co.uk
Web: www.choosecapital.co.uk ⌐
Product Type: 1, 2, 3, 5, 6, 8

H+H CELCON LIMITED
Celcon House, Ightham, Sevenoaks, Kent, TN15 9HZ
Area of Operation: UK (Excluding Ireland)
Tel: 01732 880520   **Fax:** 01732 880531
Email: marketing@celcon.co.uk
Web: www.celcon.co.uk   **Product Type:** 3, 4, 8

HANSON BUILDING PRODUCTS
Stewartby, Bedford, Bedfordshire, MK43 9LZ
Area of Operation: Worldwide
Tel: 08705 258258   **Fax:** 01234 762040
Email: info@hansonbp.com   **Web:** www.hanson.biz
Product Type: 1, 2, 3, 4, 5, 8

HISTON CONCRETE PRODUCTS LTD
Wisbech Road, Littleport, Cambridgeshire, CB6 1RA
Area of Operation: UK (Excluding Ireland)
Tel: 01353 861416
Fax: 01353 862165
Email: sales@histonconcrete.co.uk
Web: www.histonconcrete.co.uk

IBSTOCK BRICK LTD
Leicester Road, Ibstock, Leicester, Leicestershire, LE67 6HS
Area of Operation: UK & Ireland
Tel: 01530 261999   **Fax:** 01530 263478
Email: marketing@ibstock.co.uk
Web: www.ibstock.com   **Product Type:** 1, 7

INNOVATIVE BUILDING SOLUTIONS
Mill Green House, 48-50 Mill Green Road,
Mitcham, Surrey, CR4 4HY
Area of Operation: UK & Ireland
Tel: 0208 687 2260   **Fax:** 0208 687 2249
Email: ibs@charterhouseplc.co.uk
Product Type: 3   **Material Type:** G) 1

MARSHALLS
Birkby Grange, Birkby Hall Road, Birkby,
Huddersfield, West Yorkshire, HD2 27A
Area of Operation: UK (Excluding Ireland)
Tel: 01422 306400   **Web:** www.marshalls.co.uk

MASTERBLOCK
North End, Ashton Keynes, Wiltshire, SN6 3QX
Area of Operation: UK (Excluding Ireland)
Tel: 01285 646900   **Fax:** 01285 646949
Web: www.masterblock.co.uk
Product Type: 1, 2, 3, 5

NATURAL BUILDING TECHNOLOGIES
The Hangar, Worminghall Road,
Oakley, Buckinghamshire, HP18 9UL
Tel: 01844 338338   **Fax:** 01844 338525
Email: info@natural-building.co.uk
Web: www.natural-building.co.uk
Product Type: 1, 2, 3, 7

PENNINE STONE LTD
Askern Road, Carcroft, Doncaster, DN6 8DH
Tel: 01302 729277   **Fax:** 01302 729288
Email: info@penninestone.co.uk
Web: www.penninestone.co.uk
Product Type: 1   **Material Type:** G) 1

PLASMOR
P.O. Box 44, Womersley Road,
Knottingley, West Yorkshire, WF11 0DN
Area of Operation: UK (Excluding Ireland)
Tel: 01977 673221   **Fax:** 01977 607071
Email: knott@plasmor.co.uk
Web: www.plasmor.co.uk   **Product Type:** 2, 3, 4, 8

POLARLIGHT ACRYLIC BLOCK WINDOWS
Unit 4 Townspark Industrial Estate,
Athlone Road, Langford, Ireland
Tel: 00 353 43 45 794   **Fax:** 00 353 43 46 531
Email: info@polarlight.co.uk
Web: www.polarlight.co.uk   **Product Type:** 7

QUINN-LITE
Derrylin, Co Fermanagh, BT92 9AU
Area of Operation: Europe
Tel: 02867 748866   **Fax:** 02867 6774 8800
Email: info@quinn-lite.com
Web: www.quinn-lite.com   **Product Type:** 3, 4

SOUTHERN MASONRY LTD
37b Broadway East, West Wilts Trading Estate,
Westbury, Wiltshire, BA13 4AJ
Area of Operation: South East England, South West
England and South Wales
Tel: 07976 613421   **Fax:** 01749 345170
Email: charlie@stonefiresurrounds.co.uk
Web: www.southernmasonry.co.uk
Product Type: 2, 3, 4, 5

TARMAC LIMITED
Millfields Road, Ettingshall,
Wolverhampton, West Midlands, WV4 6JP
Area of Operation: Europe
Tel: 01902 353522   **Fax:** 01902 382922
Email: info@tarmac.co.uk
Web: www.tarmac.co.uk   **Material Type:** G) 1

TARMAC TOPBLOCK LTD
Millfields Road, Ettingshall,
Wolverhampton, West Midlands, WV4 6JP
Tel: 01902 382844   **Fax:** 01902 382922
Email: wendy.hinett@tarmac.co.uk
Web: www.topblock.co.uk   **Product Type:** 2, 3, 4, 8

THE MATCHING BRICK COMPANY
Lockes Yard, Hartcliffe Way, Bedminster, Bristol, BS3 5RJ
Tel: 0117 963 7000   **Fax:** 0117 966 4612
Email: matchingbrick@btconnect.com
Web: www.matchingbrick.co.uk   **Product Type:** 1

WOODKIRK STONE SALES LTD
Britannia Quarries, Rein Road,
Morley, Leeds, West Yorkshire, LS27 0SW
Area of Operation: Europe
Tel: 0113 253 0464   **Fax:** 0113 252 7520
Email: sales@woodkirkstone.co.uk
Web: www.woodkirkstone.co.uk
Product Type: 1   **Material Type:** E) 4, 5

SPONSORED BY: Homebuilding & Renovating Book of Great Value Self-Build Homes
Tel: 01527 834435 Web: www.homebuilding.co.uk/bookshop

SPONSORED BY: HOMEBUILDING & RENOVATING BOOK OF GREAT VALUE SELF-BUILD HOMES   www.homebuilding.co.uk/bookshop

Roof Details

Marley Eternit

Marley Eternit

Decorative features such as ornate chimney pots, weathervanes, finials and crested ridge tiles can add a great deal of character to a period-style roof.

Whilst the shape and form of a roof's design and the choice of covering are the two biggest factors in its appearance, finishing decorative touches and ornamentation can add a great deal of character and interest, especially on a period-style property. Victorian houses, particularly, benefit from roof detailing.

Decorative ridge tiles
Ridge tiles cover the apex of a pitched roof and help weatherproof the joint where the two roof planes meet. As well as the standard angled ridge tiles (inverted V-shaped) and half-round tiles (inverted U-shaped), ridge tiles are also available with decorative crests in a variety of patterns such as fleur-de-lys, hole crested, club crested and cockscomb crested.

Decorative ridge tiles were traditionally either handmade in clay, or cast in iron. More recently, ridge tiles are also made from concrete and uPVC, both of which are less expensive alternatives. The basic rule of thumb is that clay roofs should have decorative ridges of clay, in a similar shade and tone. Stone should have a plain ridge – ideally in stone but more commonly in concrete, whilst slate roofs can have a ridge in a contrasting colour, either terracotta, buff or matching dark grey, traditionally in clay, but more commonly today in reconstituted slate or concrete.

Some Victorian slate roofs had black or even white painted, cast iron decorative ridge tiles that were highly ornate. These are still available today, but due to their costs, are generally used only for renovation.

When ordering ridge tiles, make sure you take account of the roof pitch as this will dictate the angle of the tiles you require. With steep roof pitches, half-rounded ridges are better suited because they are not dependent on any particular pitch.

Finials
A finial is an ornamental feature that sits at the top of a gable or porch, creating a focal point that adds emphasis and definition. It is also said that the original purpose of the finial was to weigh down the most vulnerable end tiles on a roof. They are typical of Gothic architecture, but are also common on mediaeval, Tudor and Victorian houses.

RoofDragon.com

A common decorative finial is the gargoyle, thought in mediaeval times to ward off evil spirits. These styles are sometimes mimicked on properties in the UK today, although a finial can be any shape or ornament – such as a ball top, a peg, a scroll shape or a fleur-de-lys.

Traditionally finials were carved in stone or handmade from clay. Many clay tile manufacturers offer standard finial designs, some handmade, but today they are normally made using the slip cast method, where liquid clay is poured into a mould. There are also several specialist firms which will make a one-off handmade design to your specification. Alternatively, you can often find finials in reclamation yards. Finials can also be found in terracotta, uPVC and concrete, which can be used to imitate stone or clay. You will find that certain finials, such as spikes, are commonly made of metals such as iron, brass, copper or lead. A cheaper option is uPVC or GRP. Timber is a relatively popular choice, though timber finials need regular repainting.

Sandtoft Roof Tiles

TILES, SHINGLES AND SLATES

KEY

PRODUCT TYPES:

1 = Profiled Tiles including Pantiles

2 = Plain Tiles including Pegs   3 = Crease Tiles

4 = Interlocking Tiles   5 = Slates   6 = Shingles

SEE ALSO: BRICKS, BLOCKS, STONE AND CLADDING - Shakes and Shingles

OTHER: ▽ Reclaimed   🖱 On-line shopping
📐 Bespoke   🖐 Hand-made   ECO Ecological

ALDERSHAW HANDMADE CLAY TILES LTD
Pokehold Wood, Kent Street, Sedlescombe,
Nr Battle, East Sussex, TN33 0SD
Area of Operation: Europe
Tel: 01424 756777   **Fax:** 01424 756888
Email: tiles@aldershaw.co.uk
Web: www.aldershaw.co.uk   **Product Type:** 2, 3, 5

ASPECT ROOFING CO LTD
The Old Mill, East Harling, Norwich, Norfolk, NR16 2QW
Tel: 01953 717777   **Fax:** 01953 717164
Email: info@raretiles.co.uk
Web: www.raretiles.co.uk
Product Type: 1, 2, 3, 4, 5, 6

BANBURY BRICKS LTD
83a Yorke Street, Mansfield Woodhouse,
Nottinghamshire, NG19 9NH
Area of Operation: UK & Ireland
Tel: 0845 230 0941   **Fax:** 0845 230 0942
Email: enquires@banburybricks.co.uk
Web: www.banburybricks.co.uk

BICESTER ROOFING CO.LTD
Manor Farm, Weston on the Green,
Nr. Bicester, Oxfordshire, OX25 3QL
Area of Operation: South East England
Tel: 0870 264 6454   **Fax:** 0870 264 6455
Email: sales@bicesterroofing.co.uk
Web: www.bicesterroofing.co.uk

BINGLEY STONE
Cullingworth Mills, Cullingworth,
West Yorkshire, BD13 5AB
Area of Operation: UK (Excluding Ireland)
Tel: 01535 273813
Email: info@bingleystone.co.uk
Web: www.bingleystone.co.uk   **Product Type:** 5

BLACK MOUNTAIN QUARRIES LTD
Howton Court, Pontrilas, Herefordshire, HR2 0BG
Area of Operation: UK & Ireland   **Tel:** 01981 241541
Email: info@blackmountainquarries.com
Web: www.blackmountainquarries.com 🖱
Product Type: 5, 6   **Other Info:** ECO 🖐
Material Type: E) 3, 4, 5

BRADSTONE STRUCTURAL
Aggregate Industries UK Ltd, North End,
Ashton Keynes, Swindon, Wiltshire, SN6 3QX
Area of Operation: UK (Excluding Ireland)
Tel: 01285 646884   **Fax:** 01285 646891
Email: bradstone.structural@aggregate.com
Web: www.bradstone.com
Product Type: 5   **Material Type:** E) 13

BRETT LANDSCAPING LTD
Salt Lane, Cliffe, Rochester, Kent, ME3 7SZ
Area of Operation: Worldwide
Tel: 01634 222188   **Fax:** 01634 222186
Email: cliffeenquiries@brett.co.uk
Web: www.brett.co.uk/landscaping
Product Type: 2

BRIDGE STREET STONE LTD
The Old Gas Works Yard, Knotts Lane,
Colne, Lancashire, BB8 8AA
Area of Operation: UK & Ireland
Tel: 01282 860571   **Fax:** 01282 867446
Email: sales@stonepaving.co.uk
Web: www.stonepaving.co.uk   **Other Info:** ▽ 📐 🖐

CANADA WOOD UK
PO Box 1, Farnborough, Hampshire, GU14 6WE
Area of Operation: UK & Ireland
Tel: 01252 522545   **Fax:** 01252 522546
Email: office@canadawooduk.org
Web: www.canadawood.info
Product Type: 6   **Material Type:** A) 12

CEMBRIT BLUNN
6 Coleshill Street, Fazeley,
Tamworth, Staffordshire, B78 3XJ
Area of Operation: UK & Ireland
Tel: 01827 288827   **Fax:** 01827 288176
Email: parcher@cembritblunn.co.uk
Web: www.cembritblunn.co.uk   **Product Type:** 5

CEMEX ROOF TILES
Nicolson Way, Wellington Road,
Burton On Trent, Staffordshire, DE14 2AW
Area of Operation: UK & Ireland
Tel: 01283 517070   **Fax:** 01283 516290
Email: enquiries.russellrooftiles@cemex.co.uk
Web: www.russell-rooftiles.co.uk   **Product Type:** 2

CHESHIRE BRICK & SLATE
Brook House Farm, Salters Bridge,
Tarvin Sands, Tarvin, Cheshire, CH3 8NR
Area of Operation: UK (Excluding Ireland)
Tel: 01829 740883   **Fax:** 01829 740481
Email: enquiries@cheshirebrickandslate.co.uk
Web: www.cheshirebrickandslate.co.uk
Product Type: 1, 4, 5

CHESHIRE ROOFING SUPPLIES
Tarporley Road, Lower Whitley,
Warrington, Cheshire, WA4 4EZ
Area of Operation: North West England and North
Wales, Scotland
Tel: 01928 796100   **Fax:** 01928 796101
Email: info@clayrooftile.co.uk
Web: www.clayrooftile.co.uk   **Product Type:** 1, 2, 3, 4, 5

CHINA SLATE LTD
Wingfield View, Coney Green, Clay Cross,
Chesterfield, Derbyshire, S45 9JW
Area of Operation: UK & Ireland
Tel: 01246 865222   **Fax:** 01246 865999
Email: sales@chinaslate.co.uk
Web: www.chinaslate.co.uk   **Product Type:** 5

CREST BRICK, SLATE & TILE LTD
Howdenshire Way, Knedlington Road,
Howden, East Riding of Yorks, DN14 7HZ
Area of Operation: UK (Excluding Ireland)
Tel: 0870 241 1398   **Fax:** 01430 433000
Email: info@crest-bst.co.uk
Web: www.crest-bst.co.uk   **Product Type:** 1, 2, 4, 5

DELABOLE SLATE COMPANY
Pengelly, Delabole, Cornwall, PL33 9AZ
Area of Operation: UK & Ireland
Tel: 01840 212242   **Fax:** 01840 212948
Email: sales@delaboleslate.co.uk
Web: www.delaboleslate.co.uk   **Product Type:** 5

DENBY DALE CAST PRODUCTS LTD
230 Cumberworth Lane, Denby Dale,
Huddersfield, West Yorkshire, HD8 8PR
Area of Operation: UK & Ireland
Tel: 01484 863560   **Fax:** 01484 865597
Email: mail@denbydalecastproducts.co.uk
Web: www.denbydalecastproducts.co.uk
Product Type: 5

DREADNOUGHT WORKS
Dreadnought Road, Pensnett,
Brierley Hill, West Midlands, DY5 4TH
Area of Operation: Europe
Tel: 01384 77405   **Fax:** 01384 74553
Email: office@dreadnought.co.uk
Web: www.dreadnought-tiles.co.uk
Product Type: 2, 3   **Material Type:** F) 1, 3

FORTICRETE ROOFING PRODUCTS
Boss Avenue, Leighton Buzzard, Bedfordshire, LU7 4SD
Area of Operation: UK & Ireland
Tel: 01525 244900   **Fax:** 01525 850432
Email: roofing@forticrete.co.uk
Web: www.forticrete.co.uk   **Product Type:** 1, 4, 5

GREYS ARTSTONE LTD
Burdwell Works, New Mill Road, Brockholes,
Holmfirth, West Yorkshire, HD9 7AZ
Area of Operation: UK (Excluding Ireland)
Tel: 01484 666400
Fax: 01484 662709
Email: info@greysartstone.co.uk
Web: www.greysartstone.co.uk
Product Type: 5   **Material Type:** E) 12

GREYSLATE & STONE SUPPLIES
Unit 1 Cae Pawb Industrial Estate, Off Madog Street,
Port Madog, Nr. Blaenau Ffestiniog, Gwynedd, LL49 9EE
Tel: 01766 514700   **Fax:** 01766 515200
Email: greyslate@slateandstone.net
Web: www.slateandstone.net
Product Type: 5   **Material Type:** E) 3

IMERYS ROOFTILES
PO Box 88, Driffield, East Riding of Yorks, YO25 6XJ
Area of Operation: UK & Ireland
Tel: 0161 928 4572
Fax: 0161 929 8513
Email: enquiries.rooftiles@imerys.com
Web: www.imerys-rooftiles.com
Product Type: 1, 2, 4

INTERLOC BUILDING SOLUTIONS
Sybrig House, Ridge Way,
Dalgety Bay, Fife, KY11 9JN
Area of Operation: Europe
Tel: 0870 050 5925
Fax: 0870 050 5926
Email: info@interlocbuild.co.uk
Web: www.interlocbuild.co.uk
Product Type: 4, 6   **Material Type:** C) 2, 7, 9

JOHN BRASH LTD
The Old Shipyard, Gainsborough, Lincolnshire, DN21 1NG
Area of Operation: UK & Ireland
Tel: 01427 613858   **Fax:** 01427 810218
Email: info@johnbrash.co.uk
Web: www.johnbrash.co.uk
Product Type: 6   **Material Type:** A) 2, 8, 12

KEYMER TILES LTD
Nye Road, Burgess Hill, West Sussex, RH15 0LZ
Area of Operation: East England, Greater London,
Midlands & Mid Wales, South East England, South
West England and South Wales
Tel: 01444 232931   **Fax:** 01444 871852
Email: info@keymer.co.uk
Web: www.keymer.co.uk   **Product Type:** 2
Other Info: 📐 🖐   **Material Type:** F) 3

MARLEY ETERNIT LTD
Station Road, Coleshill,
Birmingham, West Midlands, B46 1HP
Area of Operation: UK (Excluding Ireland)
Tel: 01763 264686
Fax: 01763 262338
Email: roofingsales@marleyeternit.co.uk
Web: www.marleyeternit.co.uk
Product Type: 2, 4, 5

MATTHEW HEBDEN
54 Blacka Moor Road, Sheffield,
South Yorkshire, S17 3GJ
Area of Operation: UK (Excluding Ireland)
Tel: 0114 2368122
Fax: 0114 2368122
Email: sales@matthewhebden.co.uk
Web: www.matthewhebden.co.uk
Product Type: 6

METROTILE UK LTD
Unit 3 Sheldon Business Park,
Sheldon Corner, Chippenham, Wiltshire, SN14 0RQ
Area of Operation: UK & Ireland
Tel: 01249 658514
Fax: 01249 658453
Email: sales@metrotile.co.uk
Web: www.metrotile.co.uk   **Product Type:** 1, 2, 6

MIDLANDS SLATE & TILE
Units 9-12, Star Industrial Estate,
Chadwell St Mary, Essex, RM16 4LR
Area of Operation: UK & Ireland
Tel: 0871 4743185   **Fax:** 01375 846478
Email: mark@slate-tile-brick.co.uk
Web: www.slate-tile-brick.co.uk
Product Type: 1, 2, 3, 4, 5   **Material Type:** E) 3, 4

MIDLANDS SLATE & TILE
Area of Operation: UK & Ireland
Tel: 0871 4743185
Fax: 01375 846478
Email: mark@slate-tile-brick.co.uk
Web: www.slate-tile-brick.co.uk
Product Type: 1, 2, 3, 4, 5

Midlands Slate & Tile's range of natural roofing slate is sourced from quarries in China and Brazil. The combination of quality, availability and competitive pricing have made them the preferred choice for those architects and developers wishing to use natural slate.

NU-LOK ROOFING SYSTEMS.
Chelmsine Court, Bury Street,
Ruislip, Buckinghamshire, HA47TL
Tel: 01895 622689   **Fax:** 01895 631308
Email: nulok@internode.on.net
Web: www.nu-lok.com   **Product Type:** 2, 4, 5, 6

NUMBER 9 STUDIO UK
ARCHITECTURAL CERAMICS
Mole Cottage Industries, Mole Cottage,
Watertown, Chittlehamholt, Devon, EX37 9HF
Area of Operation: Worldwide
Tel: 01769 540471   **Fax:** 01769 540471
Email: arch.ceramics@moley.uk.com
Web: www.moley.uk.com

OCTAVEWARD LTD
Balle Street Mill, Balle Street, Darwen, Lancashire, BB3 2AZ
Area of Operation: Worldwide
Tel: 01254 773300   **Fax:** 01254 773950
Email: info@octaveward.com
Web: www.octaveward.com

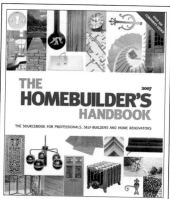

THE HOMEBUILDER'S HANDBOOK
THE SOURCEBOOK FOR PROFESSIONALS, SELF-BUILDERS AND HOME RENOVATORS

Don't forget to let us know about companies you think should be listed in the next edition
email:
customerservice@centaur.co.uk

ONDULINE BUILDING PRODUCTS LTD
Eardley House, 182-184 Campden Hill Road,
Kensington, London, W8 7AS
Area of Operation: UK & Ireland
Tel: 0207 727 0533
Fax: 0207 792 1390
Email: enquiries@onduline.net
Web: www.onduline.net

ROOFSURE
Metro House, 14-17 Metropolitan Business Park,
Preston New Road, Blackpool, Lancashire, FY3 9LT
Area of Operation: UK (Excluding Ireland)
Tel: 0800 597 2828   **Fax:** 01253 798193
Email: roofsureltd@btconnect.com
Web: www.roofsure.co.uk

RUBEROID BUILDING PRODUCTS
Appley Lane North, Appley Bridge,
Lancashire, WN6 9AB
Area of Operation: UK (Excluding Ireland)
Tel: 0800 028 5573
Fax: 01257 252514
Email: marketing@ruberoid.co.uk
Web: www.ruberoid.co.uk
Product Type: 2   **Material Type:** M) 2

SANDTOFT ROOF TILES LTD
Belton Road, Sandtoft, Doncaster, DN8 5SY
Area of Operation: UK & Ireland
Tel: 01427 871200   **Fax:** 01427 871222
Email: elaine.liversadge@sandtoft.co.uk
Web: www.sandtoft.co.uk
Product Type: 1, 2, 3, 4, 5
Material Type: E) 3, 12, 14

SEAC LTD
46 Chesterfield Road, Leicester, Leicestershire, LE5 5LP
Area of Operation: Worldwide
Tel: 0116 273 9501   **Fax:** 0116 273 8373
Email: enquiries@seac.uk.com
Web: www.seac.uk.com   **Product Type:** 5

SLATE WORLD LTD
Westmoreland Road, Kingsbury, Greater London, NW9 9RN
Area of Operation: UK & Ireland
Tel: 0208 204 3444   **Fax:** 0208 204 3311
Email: kingsbury@slateworld.com
Web: www.slateworld.com
Product Type: 5   **Material Type:** E) 3

SLATE WORLD LTD
Area of Operation: Europe
Tel: 0208 204 3444 / 014 8345 9115
Fax: 0208 204 3311 / 014 8345 9117
Email: kingsbury@slateworld.com
Web: www.slateworld.com
Product Type: E) 3

Suppliers of the most comprehensive range of QUARRY-DIRECT, non-slip and low maintenance natural slate flooring tiles in the UK.

SNOWDONIA SLATE & STONE
Glandwr Workshops, Glanypwll Road,
Blaenau Ffestiniog, Gwynedd, LL41 3PG
Area of Operation: UK (Excluding Ireland)
Tel: 01766 832525   **Fax:** 01766 832404
Email: richard@snowdoniaslate.co.uk
Web: www.snowdoniaslate.co.uk

BUILDING STRUCTURE & MATERIALS

SOUTH WEST RECLAMATION LTD
Wireworks Estate, Bristol Road,
Bridgwater, Somerset, TA6 4AP
Area of Operation: South West England and South Wales
Tel: 01278 444141   **Fax:** 01278 444114
Email: info@southwest-rec.co.uk
Web: www.southwest-rec.co.uk
Product Type: 1, 2, 3, 4, 5
Other Info: ▽   **Material Type:** E) 3

SSQ
301 Elveden Road, Park Royal,
Greater London, NW10 7SS
Area of Operation: Worldwide
Tel: 0208 961 7725   **Fax:** 0208 965 7013
Email: alain@ssq.co.uk   **Web:** www.ssq.co.uk
Product Type: 5   **Other Info:** ECO 🖱 🖐

STONE AND SLATE
Coney Green Farm, Lower Market Street,
Claycross, Chesterfield, Derbyshire, S45 9NE
Area of Operation: UK & Ireland
Tel: 01246 250088   **Fax:** 01246 250099
Email: sales@stoneandslate.ltd.uk
Web: www.stoneandslate.co.uk   **Product Type:** 5

SWALLOWS TILES (CRANLEIGH) LTD
Bookhurst Hill, Cranleigh, Guildford, Surrey, GU6 7DP
Area of Operation: UK (Excluding Ireland)
Tel: 01483 274100   **Fax:** 01483 267593
Email: info@swallowsrooftiles.co.uk
Web: www.swallowsrooftiles.co.uk

SWALLOWS TILES (CRANLEIGH) LTD

Area of Operation: UK
Tel: 01483 274100
Fax: 01483 267593
Email: info@swallowsrooftiles.co.uk
Web: www.swallowsrooftiles.co.uk

Swallow's Tiles provide unique hand made tiles
in a variety of antique colours, which give any
roof an appearance of maturity and quality.

TAYLOR MAXWELL & COMPANY LIMITED
4 John Oliver Buildings, 53 Wood Street,
Barnet, Hertfordshire, EN5 4BS
Area of Operation: UK (Excluding Ireland)
Tel: 0208 440 0551   **Fax:** 0208 440 0552
Email: barnet@taylor.maxwell.co.uk
Web: www.taylor.maxwell.co.uk
Product Type: 1, 2, 3, 4

THE LOFT SHOP
The Loft Shop, Eldon Way,
Littlehampton, West Sussex, BN17 7HE
Area of Operation: UK & Ireland
Tel: 0870 604 0404   **Fax:** 01903 738501
Email: enquiries@loftshop.co.uk
Web: www.loftshop.co.uk 🖱
Product Type: 6

THE NATURAL SLATE COMPANY LTD
161 Ballards Lane, Finchley, London, N3 1LJ
Area of Operation: Worldwide
Tel: 0845 177 5008
Fax: 0870 429 9891
Email: sales@theslatecompany.net
Web: www.theslatecompany.net
Product Type: 5
Other Info: ECO 🖐

TRITON CHEMICAL MANUFACTURING LTD
129 Felixstowe Road, Abbey Wood, London, SE2 9SG
Area of Operation: Worldwide
Tel: 0208 310 3929   **Fax:** 0208 312 0349
Email: neil@triton-chemicals.com
Web: www.triton-chemicals.com   **Product Type:** 6

TUDOR ROOF TILE CO LTD
Denge Marsh Road, Lydd, Kent, TN29 9JH
Area of Operation: Worldwide
Tel: 01797 320202   **Fax:** 01797 320700
Email: info@tudorrooftiles.co.uk
Web: www.tudorrooftiles.co.uk
Product Type: 2   **Other Info:** 🖐
Material Type: F) 1

WELSH SLATE
Business Design Centre, Unit 205,
52 Upper Street, London, N1 0QH
Area of Operation: Worldwide
Tel: 0207 354 0306   **Fax:** 0207 354 8485
Email: enquiries@welshslate.com
Web: www.welshslate.com
Product Type: 5   **Material Type:** E) 3

WIENERBERGER LTD
Wienerberger House, Brooks Drive, Cheadle Royal
Business Park, Cheadle, Cheshire, SK8 3SA
Area of Operation: UK & Ireland
Tel: 0161 491 8200   **Fax:** 0161 491 6213
Email: nicky.webb@wienerberger.com
Web: www.wienerberger.co.uk

WILLIAM BLYTHE
Monckton Manor, Chevet Lane, Notton,
Wakefield, West Yorkshire, WF4 2PD
Tel: 01652 632175   **Fax:** 01226 700350
Email: enquiries@williamblythe.co.uk
Web: www.williamblythe.co.uk

METAL ROOFING

KEY
SEE ALSO: ROOFING - Flat Roofing

OTHER: ▽ Reclaimed   🖱 On-line shopping
🖊 Bespoke   🖐 Hand-made   ECO Ecological

ALUMASC EXTERIOR BUILDING PRODUCTS
White House Works, Bold Road, Sutton,
St Helens, Merseyside, WA9 4JG
Area of Operation: UK & Ireland
Tel: 01744 648400   **Fax:** 01744 648401
Email: info@alumasc-exteriors.co.uk
Web: www.alumasc-exteriors.co.uk

CATNIC
Pontypandy Industrial Estate, Caerphilly, CF83 3GL
Area of Operation: Worldwide
Tel: 029 2033 7900   **Fax:** 029 2033 7900
Email: barry.jenkins@corusgroup.com
Web: www.catnic.com

CORUS CONSTRUCTION
Swinden Technology Centre, Moorgate,
Rotherham, South Yorkshire, S60 3AR
Area of Operation: Worldwide
Tel: 01724 405060
Email: corusconstruction@corusgroup.com
Web: www.corusconstruction.com

INTERLOC BUILDING SOLUTIONS
Sybrig House, Ridge Way, Dalgety Bay, Fife, KY11 9JN
Area of Operation: Europe
Tel: 0870 050 5925   **Fax:** 0870 050 5926
Email: info@interlocbuild.co.uk
Web: www.interlocbuild.co.uk

LONSDALE METAL COMPANY LTD
Unit 40, Millmead Industrial Centre,
Millmead Road, London, N17 9QU
Tel: 0208 801 4221   **Fax:** 0208 801 1287
Email: info@lonsdalemetal.co.uk
Web: www.patentglazing.co.uk

METROTILE UK LTD
Unit 3 Sheldon Business Park, Sheldon Corner,
Chippenham, Wiltshire, SN14 0RQ
Area of Operation: UK & Ireland
Tel: 01249 658514   **Fax:** 01249 658453
Email: sales@metrotile.co.uk
Web: www.metrotile.co.uk   **Material Type:** C) 2

ONDULINE BUILDING PRODUCTS LTD
Eardley House, 182-184 Campden Hill Road,
Kensington, London, W8 7AS
Area of Operation: UK & Ireland
Tel: 0207 727 0533   **Fax:** 0207 792 1390
Email: enquiries@onduline.net
Web: www.onduline.net

BEAMS AND TRUSSES

KEY
SEE ALSO: MERCHANTS - Timber Merchants

OTHER: ▽ Reclaimed   🖱 On-line shopping
🖊 Bespoke   🖐 Hand-made   ECO Ecological

AC ROOF TRUSSES LTD
Severn Farm Industrial Estate, Welshpool, Powys, SY21 7DF
Area of Operation: UK & Ireland
Tel: 01938 554881   **Fax:** 01938 556265
Email: info@acrooftrusses.co.uk
Web: www.acrooftrusses.co.uk 🖱   **Other Info:** 🖊

ALTHAM OAK & CARPENTRY LTD
Altham Corn Mill, Burnley Road, Altham,
Accrington, Lancashire, BB5 5UP
Area of Operation: UK & Ireland
Tel: 01282 771618   **Fax:** 01282 777932
Email: info@oak-beams.co.uk
Web: www.oak-beams.co.uk

ASPECT ROOFING CO LTD
The Old Mill, East Harling, Norwich, Norfolk, NR16 2QW
Area of Operation: UK (Excluding Ireland)
Tel: 01953 717777   **Fax:** 01953 717164
Email: info@raretiles.co.uk
Web: www.raretiles.co.uk

BALCAS TIMBER LTD
Laragh, Enniskillen, Co Fermanagh, BT94 2FQ
Area of Operation: UK & Ireland
Tel: 0286 632 3003   **Fax:** 0286 632 7924
Email: info@balcas.com   **Web:** www.balcas.com

CATNIC
Pontypandy Industrial Estate, Caerphilly, CF83 3GL
Area of Operation: Worldwide
Tel: 029 2033 7900   **Fax:** 029 2033 7900
Email: barry.jenkins@corusgroup.com
Web: www.catnic.com

COLIN BAKER
Timberyard, Crownhill, Halberton,
Tiverton, Devon, EX16 7AY
Area of Operation: Europe
Tel: 01884 820152
Email: colinbaker@colinbakeroak.co.uk
Web: www.colinbakeroak.co.uk
Material Type: A) 2

DAVID SMITH ST IVES LTD
Marley Road, St Ives, Huntingdon,
Cambridgeshire, PE27 3EX
Area of Operation: East England, Greater London,
Midlands & Mid Wales, South East England
Tel: 01480 309900   **Fax:** 01480 309949
Email: jeremyenglish@davidsmith.co.uk
Web: www.davidsmith.co.uk   **Other Info:** ECO 🖱

FFOREST TIMBER ENGINEERING LTD
Kestrel Way, Garngoch Industrial Estate,
Gorseinon, Swansea, SA4 9WN
Area of Operation: Midlands & Mid Wales, South
West England and South Wales
Tel: 01792 895620   **Fax:** 01792 893969
Email: info@fforest.co.uk   **Web:** www.fforest.co.uk

FLIGHT TIMBER PRODUCTS
Earls Colne Business Park, Earls Colne, Essex, CO6 2NS
Area of Operation: East England, Greater London,
South East England
Tel: 01787 222336   **Fax:** 01787 222359
Email: sales@flighttimber.com
Web: www.flighttimber.com

G&T EVANS
Dulas Mill, Mochdre Lane, Newtown, Powys, SY16 4JD
Area of Operation: UK & Ireland
Tel: 01686 622 100
Fax: 01686 622 220
Email: gtevans1@aol.com
Web: www.gtevans.co.uk

GREEN OAK STRUCTURES
20 Bushy Coombe Gardens,
Glastonbury, Somerset, BA6 8JT
Area of Operation: UK & Ireland
Tel: 01458 833420   **Fax:** 01458 833420
Email: timberframes@greenoakstructures.co.uk
Web: www.greenoakstructures.co.uk
Other Info: ECO 🖊   **Material Type:** A) 2

HENRY VENABLES TIMBER LTD
Tollgate Drive, Tollgate Industrial Estate,
Stafford, Staffordshire, ST16 3HS
Area of Operation: UK (Excluding Ireland)
Tel: 01785 270600   **Fax:** 01785 270626
Email: enquiries@henryvenables.co.uk
Web: www.henryvenables.co.uk

HONEYSUCKLE BOTTOM SAWMILL LTD
Honeysuckle Bottom, Green Dene,
East Horsley, Leatherhead, Surrey, KT24 5TD
Area of Operation: Greater London, South East England
Tel: 01483 282394
Fax: 01483 282394
Email: honeysucklemill@aol.com
Web: www.easisites.co.uk/honeysucklebottomsawmill

LAMINATED WOOD LIMITED
Grain Silo Complex, Abbey Road, Hempsted,
Gloucester, Gloucestershire, GL2 5HU
Area of Operation: UK & Ireland
Tel: 01452 418000   **Fax:** 01452 418333
Email: mail@lamwood.co.uk
Web: www.lamwood.co.uk   **Other Info:** ECO

MITEK INDUSTRIES LTD
Mitek House, Grazebrook Industrial Park,
Peartree Lane, Dudley, West Midlands, DY2 0XW
Area of Operation: UK & Ireland
Tel: 01384 451400
Fax: 01384 451415
Email: roy.troman@mitek.co.uk
Web: www.mitek.co.uk

NORBUILD TIMBER FABRICATION &
FINE CARPENTRY LTD
Marcassie Farm, Rafford, Forres, Moray, IV36 2RH
Area of Operation: UK & Ireland
Tel: 01309 676865   **Fax:** 01309 676865
Email: norbuild@marcassie.fsnet.co.uk

OAKCAST REPRODUCTION BEAMS
Unit 9 Roberts Road Industrial Park,
Roberts Road, Balby, Doncaster, South Yorkshire
Area of Operation: UK (Excluding Ireland)
Tel: 01302 320638   **Fax:** 01302 320638
Email: william@oakcast.com
Web: www.oakcast.com

ORIGINAL OAK
Ashlands, Burwash, East Sussex, TN19 7HS
Area of Operation: UK (Excluding Ireland)
Tel: 01435 882228   **Fax:** 01435 882228
Web: www.originaloak.co.uk   **Material Type:** A) 2

RADNOR TIMBER COMPANY
The Offices, Old Impton Farm,
Norton, Presteigne, Powys, LD8 2EN
Area of Operation: Europe
Tel: 01544 260727   **Fax:** 01544 262113
Email: sales@rtc.enta.net
Web: www.radnortimbercompany
Other Info: ▽ ECO 🖱 🖐   **Material Type:** A) 2

SCOTTS OF THRAPSTON LTD.
Bridge Street, Thrapston, Northamptonshire, NN14 4LR
Area of Operation: UK & Ireland
Tel: 01832 732366
Fax: 01832 733703
Email: julia@scottsofthrapston.co.uk
Web: www.scottsofthrapston.co.uk   **Other Info:** ✎

SIPBUILD LTD
Unit 2 Expressway Industrial Estate,
Turnall Road, Widnes, Merseyside, WA8 8RB
Area of Operation: UK & Ireland
Tel: 0870 850 2264   **Fax:** 0870 850 2265
Email: sales@sipbuildltd.com
Web: www.sipbuildltd.com

TELEBEAM LOFT CONVERSION AND FLOORING SYSTEM
Cromwell House, 31 Market Place,
Devizes, Wiltshire, SN10 1JG
Area of Operation: UK & Ireland
Tel: 01380 739000
Fax: 01380 722205
Email: info@telebeam.co.uk
Web: www.telebeam.co.uk

THE GREEN OAK CARPENTRY CO LTD
Langley Farm, Langley, Rake,
Liss, Hampshire, GU33 7JW
Area of Operation: UK & Ireland
Tel: 01730 892049   **Fax:** 01730 895225
Email: enquiries@greenoakcarpentry.co.uk
Web: www.greenoakcarpentry.co.uk
Other Info: ✎ ✋   **Material Type:** A) 2

TIMBER ROUTES
42 Armoury Square, Easton, Bristol, BS5 0PT
Area of Operation: UK & Ireland
Tel: 0117 952 2585
Email: diana@timber-routes.co.uk
Web: www.timber-routes.co.uk

TRADITIONAL OAK & TIMBER COMPANY
P O Stores , Haywards Heath Road,
North Chailey, Nr Lewes, East Sussex, BN8 4EY
Area of Operation: Worldwide
Tel: 01825 723648   **Fax:** 01825 722215
Email: info@tradoak.co.uk
Web: www.tradoak.com

SARKING

KEY
OTHER: ▽ Reclaimed   ✋ On-line shopping
✎ Bespoke   ✋ Hand-made   ECO Ecological

HUNTON FIBER UK LTD
Rockleigh Court, Rock Road, Finedon,
Northamptonshire, NN9 5EL
Area of Operation: UK & Ireland
Tel: 01933 682683
Fax: 01933 680296
Email: admin@huntonfiber.co.uk
Web: www.hunton.no
Other Info: ▽ ECO   **Material Type:** K) 8

SMARTPLY EUROPE
Hawley Manor, Hawley Road, Dartford, Kent, DA1 1PX
Area of Operation: Europe
Tel: 01322 424900
Fax: 01322 424920
Email: info@smartply.com
Web: www.smartply.com
Other Info: ECO   **Material Type:** B) 2, 9

XTRATHERM UK LIMITED
Park Road, Holmewood, Chesterfield,
Derbyshire, S42 5UY
Area of Operation: UK & Ireland
Tel: 0871 222 1033
Fax: 0871 222 1044
Email: kerry@xtratherm.com
Web: www.xtratherm.com

FLAT ROOFING SYSTEMS

KEY
SEE ALSO: ROOFING - Metal Roofing,
ROOFING - Green Roofing
OTHER: ▽ Reclaimed   ✋ On-line shopping
✎ Bespoke   ✋ Hand-made   ECO Ecological

ALUMASC EXTERIOR BUILDING PRODUCTS
White House Works, Bold Road, Sutton,
St Helens, Merseyside, WA9 4JG
Tel: 01744 648400   **Fax:** 01744 648401
Email: info@alumasc-exteriors.co.uk
Web: www.alumasc-exteriors.co.uk

BRETT MARTIN DAYLIGHT SYSTEMS
Sandford Close, Alderford's Green Industrial Estate,
Coventry, West Midlands, CV2 2QU
Area of Operation: Worldwide
Tel: 02476 602022   **Fax:** 02476 602744
Email: daylight@brettmartin.com
Web: www.daylightsystems.com
Other Info: ✎   **Material Type:** D) 1, 3, 5, 6

DIY ROOFING LTD
Hillcrest House, Featherbed Lane, Hunt End,
Redditch, Worcestershire, B97 5QL
Tel: 0800 783 4890   **Fax:** 01527 403483
Email: chris@diyroofing.co.uk
Web: www.diyroofing.co.uk

EVEREST LTD
Sopers Road, Cuffley, Hertfordshire, EN6 4SG
Area of Operation: UK & Ireland
Tel: 0800 010123   **Web:** www.everest.co.uk ✋

FIRESTONE BUILDING PRODUCTS
Meridian House, Road One, Winsford, Cheshire, CW7 3EN
Area of Operation: UK & Ireland
Tel: 01606 552026   **Fax:** 01606 592666
Email: info@fbpl.co.uk
Web: www.firestonebpe.com

GLAZING VISION
6 Barns Close, Brandon, Suffolk, IP27 0NY
Area of Operation: Worldwide
Tel: 01842 815581   **Fax:** 01842 815515
Email: sales@visiongroup.co.uk
Web: www.visiongroup.co.uk

INTERLOC BUILDING SOLUTIONS
Sybrig House, Ridge Way, Dalgety Bay, Fife, KY11 9JN
Area of Operation: Europe
Tel: 0870 050 5925   **Fax:** 0870 050 5926
Email: info@interlocbuild.co.uk
Web: www.interlocbuild.co.uk
Other Info: ECO   **Material Type:** K) 5, 11, 12

MARLEY ETERNIT LTD
Station Road, Coleshill, Birmingham,
West Midlands, B46 1HP
Area of Operation: UK (Excluding Ireland)
Tel: 01763 264686
Fax: 01763 262338
Email: profile@marleyeternit.co.uk
Web: www.marleyeternit.co.uk

MARLEY WATERPROOFING
Covert Road, Aylesham Industrial Estate,
Aylesham, Canterbury, Kent, CT3 3EQ
Area of Operation: UK (Excluding Ireland)
Tel: 01304 843300   **Fax:** 01304 843500
Email: info@marleywaterproofing.com
Web: www.marleywaterproofing.com   **Other Info:** ✋

MIDLAND BUTYL LTD
Windmill Farm, Biggin Lane,
Ashbourne, Derbyshire, DE6 3FN
Area of Operation: Worldwide
Tel: 01335 372133   **Fax:** 01335 372199
Email: sales@midland-butyl.co.uk
Web: www.midland-butyl.co.uk

OCTAVEWARD LIMITED
Balle Street, Darwen, Lancashire, BB3 2AZ
Area of Operation: UK (Excluding Ireland)
Tel: 01254 773300   **Fax:** 01254 773950
Email: info@octaveward.com
Web: www.octaveward.com

**PHOENIX WATERPROOFING
(A DIVISION OF CONTITECH UK LTD)**
Chestnut Field House, Chestnut Field,
Rugby, Warwickshire, CU21 2PA
Area of Operation: UK & Ireland
Tel: 01788 571482   **Fax:** 01788 542245
Email: tonyb@phoenix-gb.com
Web: www.phoenix-ag.com

PMS LTD
Barima House, Springhill Road,
Peebles, Borders, EH45 9ER
Area of Operation: Scotland
Tel: 01721 720917
Email: pmsflatroofing@tiscali.co.uk
Web: www.pmsflatroofing.co.uk

PROTEC SYSTEMS (UK) LTD
93 High Street, Worle,
Weston-Super-Mare, Somerset, BS22 6ET
Area of Operation: UK (Excluding Ireland)
Tel: 01934 524926   **Fax:** 01934 524903
Email: info@protecsystems.uk.net
Web: www.protecsystems.uk.net

RENOTHERM
New Street House, New Street,
Petworth, West Sussex, GU 28 0AS
Area of Operation: UK (Excluding Ireland)
Tel: 01798 343658   **Fax:** 01798 344093
Email: sales@renotherm.co.uk
Web: www.renotherm.co.uk   **Material Type:** D) 4

RIVINGTON ROOFING SERVICES
102 Tigfold Road, Farnworth,
Bolton, Lancashire, BL4 0PF
Area of Operation: North West England and North Wales
Tel: 01204 701630
Email: daveivill@ntlworld.com   **Other Info:** ECO

ROOF-TEK LTD
19 Lynx Crescent, Weston-Super-Mare,
Somerset, BS24 9DJ
Area of Operation: East England, Greater London,
Midlands & Mid Wales, South East England, South
West England and South Wales
Tel: 01934 642929   **Fax:** 01934 644290
Email: enquiries@rooftek.co.uk
Web: www.rooftek.co.uk

SIPBUILD LTD
Unit 2 Expressway Industrial Estate,
Turnall Road, Widnes, Merseyside, WA8 8RB
Area of Operation: UK & Ireland
Tel: 0870 850 2264   **Fax:** 0870 850 2265
Email: sales@sipbuildltd.com
Web: www.sipbuildltd.com

SMARTPLY EUROPE
Hawley Manor, Hawley Road, Dartford, Kent, DA1 1PX
Area of Operation: Europe
Tel: 01322 424900   **Fax:** 01322 424920
Email: info@smartply.com
Web: www.smartply.com
Other Info: ECO   **Material Type:** B) 2, 9

SPARTAN TILES
Slough Lane, Ardleigh, Essex, CO7 7RU
Area of Operation: UK & Ireland
Tel: 01206 230553   **Fax:** 01206 230516
Email: sales@spartantiles.com
Web: www.spartantiles.com   **Material Type:** G) 1, 5

SPRY PRODUCTS LTD
64 Nottingham Road, Long Eaton,
Nottingham, Nottinghamshire, NG10 2AU
Area of Operation: UK & Ireland
Tel: 0115 973 2914   **Fax:** 0115 972 5172
Email: jerspry@aol.com
Web: www.spryproducts.com
Other Info: ECO   **Material Type:** D) 1

**STRUCTURAL INSULATED PANEL
TECHNOLOGY LTD (SIPTEC)**
PO Box 429, Turvey, Bedfordshire, MK43 8DT
Area of Operation: Europe
Tel: 0870 743 9866   **Fax:** 0870 762 5612
Email: mail@sips.ws   **Web:** www.sips.ws
Material Type: H) 4, 6

SUNSQUARE LIMITED
5A Barton Road Trading Estate,
Bury St Edmunds, Suffolk, IP32 7BE
Area of Operation: UK & Ireland
Tel: 0845 226 3172   **Fax:** 0845 226 3173
Email: info@sunsquare.co.uk
Web: www.sunsquare.co.uk
Other Info: ECO ✎

TOPSEAL SYSTEMS LIMITED
Unit 1-5 Hookstone Chase,
Harrogate, North Yorkshire, HG2 7HP
Area of Operation: Europe
Tel: 01423 886495   **Fax:** 01423 889550
Email: sales@topseal.co.uk
Web: www.topseal.co.uk   **Material Type:** D) 5, 6

TRITON CHEMICAL MANUFACTURING LTD
129 Felixstowe Road, Abbey Wood, London, SE2 9SG
Area of Operation: Worldwide
Tel: 0208 310 3929   **Fax:** 0208 312 0349
Email: neil@triton-chemicals.com
Web: www.triton-chemicals.com

TWINFIX
201 Cavendish Place, Birchwood Park,
Birchwood, Warrington, Cheshire, WA3 6WU
Area of Operation: UK & Ireland
Tel: 01925 811311   **Fax:** 01925 852955
Email: enquiries@twinfix.co.uk
Web: www.twinfix.co.uk

FELTS, MEMBRANES AND WATERPROOFING

KEY
PRODUCT TYPES:
1= Waterproof   2 = Breathable
OTHER: ▽ Reclaimed   ✋ On-line shopping
✎ Bespoke   ✋ Hand-made   ECO Ecological

ALUMASC EXTERIOR BUILDING PRODUCTS
White House Works, Bold Road,
Sutton, St Helens, Merseyside, WA9 4JG
Area of Operation: UK & Ireland
Tel: 01744 648400   **Fax:** 01744 648401
Email: info@alumasc-exteriors.co.uk
Web: www.alumasc-exteriors.co.uk
Product Type: 1

BICESTER ROOFING CO. LTD
Manor Farm, Weston on the Green,
Nr. Bicester, Oxfordshire, OX25 3QL
Area of Operation: South East England
Tel: 0870 264 6454   **Fax:** 0870 264 6455
Email: sales@bicesterroofing.co.uk
Web: www.bicesterroofing.co.uk

DEGUSSA CONSTRUCTION CHEMICALS (UK)
Albany House, Swinton Hall Road,
Swinton, Manchester, M27 4DT
Area of Operation: Worldwide
Tel: 0161 794 7411   **Fax:** 0161 727 8547
Email: mbtfeb@basf.com
Web: www.degussa-cc.co.uk   **Product Type:** 1, 2

DIY ROOFING LTD
Hillcrest House, Featherbed Lane, Hunt End,
Redditch, Worcestershire, B97 5QL
Area of Operation: UK & Ireland
Tel: 0800 783 4890   **Fax:** 01527 403483
Email: chris@diyroofing.co.uk
Web: www.diyroofing.co.uk   **Product Type:** 1

BUILDING STRUCTURE & MATERIALS - **Roofing** - Felts, Membranes & Waterproofing; Soakers & Flashings; Decorative Trims; Soffits

SPONSORED BY: HOMEBUILDING & RENOVATING BOOK OF GREAT VALUE SELF-BUILD HOMES   www.homebuilding.co.uk/bookshop

ECOLOGICAL BUILDING SYSTEMS UK LTD
The Manse, High Street, Creaton,
Northamptonshire, NN6 8NA
Area of Operation: UK & Ireland
Tel: 05600 758025
Fax: 05600 758026
Email: ecologicalbuild@btconnect.com
Web: www.ecologicalbuildingsystems.co.uk
Product Type: 1, 2

FIRESTONE BUILDING PRODUCTS
Meridian House, Road One, Winsford, Cheshire, CW7 3EN
Area of Operation: UK & Ireland
Tel: 01606 552026   **Fax:** 01606 592666
Email: info@fbpl.co.uk
Web: www.firestonebpe.com
Product Type: 1   **Material Type:** M) 2

INDUSTRIAL TEXTILES & PLASTICS LTD
Stillington Road, Easingwold,
York, North Yorkshire, YO61 3FA
Area of Operation: Worldwide
Tel: 01347 825200
Email: info@itpltd.com
Web: www.itpltd.com
Product Type: 1, 2   **Other Info:** ECO

INTERLOC BUILDING SOLUTIONS
Sybrig House, Ridge Way, Dalgety Bay, Fife, KY11 9JN
Area of Operation: Europe
Tel: 0870 050 5925   **Fax:** 0870 050 5926
Email: info@interlocbuild.co.uk
Web: www.interlocbuild.co.uk
Product Type: 1   **Material Type:** G) 6

KLOBER LTD
Ingleberry Road, Shepshed,
Nr Loughborough, Leicestershire, LE12 9DE
Area of Operation: UK & Ireland
Tel: 01509 500660   **Fax:** 01509 600061
Email: info@klober.co.uk
Web: www.klober.co.uk   **Product Type:** 1, 2

MARLEY WATERPROOFING
Covert Road, Aylesham Industrial Estate,
Aylesham, Canterbury, Kent, CT3 3EQ
Area of Operation: UK (Excluding Ireland)
Tel: 01304 843300
Fax: 01304 843500
Email: info@marleywaterproofing.com
Web: www.marleywaterproofing.com
Product Type: 1, 2   **Other Info:** ✐

MIDLAND BUTYL LTD
Windmill Farm, Biggin Lane,
Ashbourne, Derbyshire, DE6 3FN
Area of Operation: Worldwide
Tel: 01335 372133   **Fax:** 01335 372199
Email: sales@midland-butyl.co.uk
Web: www.midland-butyl.co.uk   **Product Type:** 1

NOISE STOP SYSTEMS
Unit 2, Car House Farm, Poole Lane,
Nun Monkton, York, North Yorkshire, YO26 8EH
Area of Operation: UK & Ireland
Tel: 0845 130 6269   **Fax:** 01423 339153
Email: info@noisestopsystems.co.uk
Web: www.noisestopsystems.co.uk ✐
Product Type: 1, 2

**PHOENIX WATERPROOFING
(A DIVISION OF CONTITECH UK LTD)**
Chestnut Field House, Chestnut Field,
Rugby, Warwickshire, CU21 2PA
Area of Operation: UK & Ireland
Tel: 01788 571482
Fax: 01788 542245
Email: tonyb@phoenix-gb.com
Web: www.phoenix-ag.com   **Product Type:** 1

RENOTHERM
New Street House, New Street,
Petworth, West Sussex, GU 28 0AS
Area of Operation: UK (Excluding Ireland)
Tel: 01798 343658
Fax: 01798 344093
Email: sales@renotherm.co.uk
Web: www.renotherm.co.uk

ROOFBOND LTD
66-68 Ashfield Road, Bispham,
Blackpool, Lancashire, FY2 0DJ
Area of Operation: East England, Greater London,
Midlands & Mid Wales, North East England, North
West England and North Wales, South East England,
South West England and South Wales
Tel: 01253 500250   **Fax:** 01253 595545
Email: roofbond2000@btconnect.com
Web: www.roofbond.biz ✐
Product Type: 2

RUBEROID BUILDING PRODUCTS
Appley Lane North, Appley Bridge, Lancashire, WN6 9AB
Area of Operation: UK (Excluding Ireland)
Tel: 08000 285573   **Fax:** 01257 252514
Email: marketing@ruberoid.co.uk
Web: www.ruberoid.co.uk

SPRY PRODUCTS LTD
64 Nottingham Road, Long Eaton,
Nottingham, Nottinghamshire, NG10 2AU
Area of Operation: UK & Ireland
Tel: 0115 973 2914   **Fax:** 0115 972 5172
Email: jerspry@aol.com
Web: www.spryproducts.com   **Product Type:** 1
Other Info: ECO   **Material Type:** D) 1

TOPSEAL SYSTEMS LIMITED
Unit 1-5 Hookstone Chase,
Harrogate, North Yorkshire, HG2 7HP
Area of Operation: Europe
Tel: 01423 886495   **Fax:** 01423 889550
Email: sales@topseal.co.uk
Web: www.topseal.co.uk
Product Type: 1   **Material Type:** D) 6

TRITON CHEMICAL MANUFACTURING LTD
129 Felixstowe Road, Abbey Wood, London, SE2 9SG
Area of Operation: Worldwide
Tel: 0208 310 3929   **Fax:** 0208 312 0349
Email: neil@triton-chemicals.com
Web: www.triton-chemicals.com   **Product Type:** 1

VISQUEEN BUILDING PRODUCTS
Maerdy Industrial Estate, Rhymney,
Blaenau Gwent, NP22 5PY
Area of Operation: UK & Ireland
Tel: 01685 840672   **Fax:** 01685 842580
Email: enquiries@visqueenbuilding.co.uk
Web: www.visqueenbuilding.co.uk
Product Type: 1, 2

XTRATHERM UK LIMITED
Park Road, Holmewood,
Chesterfield, Derbyshire, S42 5UY
Area of Operation: UK & Ireland
Tel: 0871 222 1033   **Fax:** 0871 222 1044
Email: kerry@xtratherm.com
Web: www.xtratherm.com

SOAKERS AND FLASHINGS

KEY

OTHER: ▽ Reclaimed   ✐ On-line shopping
✐ Bespoke   ✋ Hand-made   ECO Ecological

BICESTER ROOFING CO.LTD
Manor Farm, Weston on the Green,
Nr. Bicester, Oxfordshire, OX25 3QL
Area of Operation: South East England
Tel: 0870 264 6454
Fax: 0870 264 6455
Email: sales@bicesterroofing.co.uk
Web: www.bicesterroofing.co.uk

DIY ROOFING LTD
Hillcrest House, Featherbed Lane, Hunt End,
Redditch, Worcestershire, B97 5QL
Area of Operation: UK & Ireland
Tel: 0800 783 4890
Fax: 01527 403483
Email: chris@diyroofing.co.uk
Web: www.diyroofing.co.uk

TOPSEAL SYSTEMS LIMITED
Unit 1-5 Hookstone Chase, Harrogate,
North Yorkshire, HG2 7HP
Area of Operation: Europe
Tel: 01423 886495
Fax: 01423 889550
Email: sales@topseal.co.uk
Web: www.topseal.co.uk

DECORATIVE TRIMS

KEY

PRODUCT TYPES: 1 = Finials   2 = Ridges
3 = Other

OTHER: ▽ Reclaimed   ✐ On-line shopping
✐ Bespoke   ✋ Hand-made   ECO Ecological

ALDERSHAW HANDMADE CLAY TILES LTD
Pokehold Wood, Kent Street, Sedlescombe,
Nr Battle, East Sussex, TN33 0SD
Area of Operation: Europe
Tel: 01424 756777   **Fax:** 01424 756888
Email: tiles@aldershaw.co.uk
Web: www.aldershaw.co.uk   **Product Type:** 1

ALLAN CALDER'S LTD
Leekbrook Way, Leekbrook Industrial Estate,
Leek, Staffordshire, ST13 7AP
Area of Operation: UK (Excluding Ireland)
Tel: 01538 387738   **Fax:** 01538 387738
Email: allancalder@btconnect.com

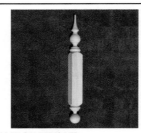

ALLAN CALDER'S LTD
Roof, Porch & Dorma Finials
Area of Operation: UK (Excluding Ireland)
Tel: 01538 387738
Fax: 01538 387738
Email: allancalder@btconnect.com
Other Info: ✐ ✋

Allan Calder's was established in 1994 doing
bespoke turning and copy lathe turning. We pride
ourselves in the quality of our products. We
provide a range of turned products for the
outdoor market. Such as a range of fence finials,
roof finials and finials for summer houses.

ASPECT ROOFING CO LTD
The Old Mill, East Harling, Norwich, Norfolk, NR16 2QW
Area of Operation: UK (Excluding Ireland)
Tel: 01953 717777   **Fax:** 01953 717164
Email: info@raretiles.co.uk
Web: www.raretiles.co.uk   **Product Type:** 1, 2

ENVIROMAT BY Q LAWNS
Corkway Drove, Hockwold, Thetford, Norfolk, IP26 4JR
Area of Operation: UK (Excluding Ireland)
Tel: 01842 828266   **Fax:** 01842 827911
Email: sales@qlawns.co.uk
Web: www.enviromat.co.uk ✐   **Product Type:** 3

GAP
Partnership Way, Shadsworth Business Park,
Blackburn, Lancashire, BB1 2QP
Area of Operation: Midlands & Mid Wales, North
East England, North West England and North Wales
Tel: 01254 682888   **Web:** www.gap.uk.com
Product Type: 1, 2, 3   **Material Type:** D) 1

**HANSON RED BANK MANUFACTURING
COMPANY LIMITED**
Measham, Swadlincote, Derbyshire, DE12 7EL
Area of Operation: UK & Ireland
Tel: 01530 270333   **Fax:** 01530 273667
Email: sales@redbankmfg.co.uk
Web: www.redbankmfg.co.uk
Product Type: 1, 2   **Other Info:** ECO ✐
Material Type: F) 3

**NORBUILD TIMBER FABRICATION &
FINE CARPENTRY LTD**
Marcassie Farm, Rafford, Forres, Moray, IV36 2RH
Area of Operation: UK & Ireland
Tel: 01309 676865   **Fax:** 01309 676865
Email: norbuild@marcassie.fsnet.co.uk

**NUMBER 9 STUDIO UK
ARCHITECTURAL CERAMICS**
Mole Cottage Industries, Mole Cottage,
Watertown, Chittlehamholt, Devon, EX37 9HF
Area of Operation: Worldwide
Tel: 01769 540471   **Fax:** 01769 540471
Email: arch.ceramics@moley.uk.com
Web: www.moley.uk.com

PLASTIVAN LTD
Unit 4 Bonville Industrial Estate,
Bonville Road, Brislington, Bristol, BS4 5QU
Area of Operation: Worldwide
Tel: 0117 300 5625   **Fax:** 0117 971 5028
Email: sales@plastivan.co.uk
Web: www.plastivan.co.uk
Product Type: 1

ROOFDRAGON.COM
Battlesbridge Antique Centre, Motling Road,
Battlesbridge, Essex, SS11 7RF
Area of Operation: UK & Ireland
Tel: 07717 055530
Email: colin@roofdragon.com
Web: www.roofdragon.com ✐
Product Type: 1, 2

THE EXPANDED METAL COMPANY LIMITED
PO Box 14, Longhill Industrial Estate (North),
Hartlepool, Durham, TS25 1PR
Area of Operation: Worldwide
Tel: 01429 867388   **Fax:** 01429 866795
Email: paulb@expamet.co.uk
Web: www.expandedmetalcompany.co.uk

TOPSEAL SYSTEMS LIMITED
Unit 1-5 Hookstone Chase,
Harrogate, North Yorkshire, HG2 7HP
Area of Operation: Europe
Tel: 01423 886495   **Fax:** 01423 889550
Email: sales@topseal.co.uk
Web: www.topseal.co.uk   **Product Type:** 1, 2

SOFFITS, FASCIAS AND BARGEBOARDS

KEY

OTHER: ▽ Reclaimed   ✐ On-line shopping
✐ Bespoke   ✋ Hand-made   ECO Ecological

ALLAN CALDER'S LTD
Leekbrook Way, Leekbrook Industrial Estate,
Leek, Staffordshire, ST13 7AP
Area of Operation: UK (Excluding Ireland)
Tel: 01538 387738   **Fax:** 01538 387738
Email: allancalder@btconnect.com
Other Info: ✐ ✋   **Material Type:** B) 5

ARP LTD
Unit 2 Vitruvius Way, Meridian Business Park,
Braunstone Park, Leicestershire, LE19 1WA
Area of Operation: UK & Ireland
Tel: 0116 289 4400   **Fax:** 0116 289 4433
Email: sales@arp-ltd.com
Web: www.arp-ltd.com

CATNIC
Pontypandy Industrial Estate, Caerphilly, CF83 3GL
Area of Operation: Worldwide
Tel: 029 2033 7900   **Fax:** 029 2033 7900
Email: barry.jenkins@corusgroup.com
Web: www.catnic.com

CLEARVIEW WINDOWS & DOORS
Unit 14, Sheddingdean Industrial Estate, Marchants
Way, Burgess Hill, West Sussex, RH15 8QY
Area of Operation: UK (Excluding Ireland)
Tel: 01444 250111   **Fax:** 01444 250678
Email: sales@clearviewsussex.co.uk
Web: www.clearviewsussex.co.uk

DRAIN CENTER
Branches Nationwide.
Area of Operation: UK & Ireland
Tel: 0870 1622 557   **Web:** www.draincenter.co.uk

EVERWHITE PLASTICS LTD
Everwhite House, Aberaman Park Industrial Estate,
Aberdare, Mid Glamorgan, CF44 6DA
Area of Operation: UK (Excluding Ireland)
Tel: 01685 882447   **Fax:** 01685 870887
Email: sales@everwhiteplastics.com
Web: www.everwhite.biz ⌂   **Material Type:** D) 1

EXTERIOR IMAGE LTD
5 Hursley Road, Chandlers Ford,
Eastleigh, Hampshire, SO53 2FW
Tel: 02380 271777   **Fax:** 02380 269091
Email: info@exteriorimage.co.uk
Web: www.exteriorimage.co.uk

GAP
Partnership Way, Shadsworth Business Park,
Blackburn, Lancashire, BB1 2QP
Area of Operation: Midlands & Mid Wales, North
East England, North West England and North Wales
Tel: 01254 682888
Web: www.gap.uk.com   **Material Type:** D) 1

NATIONAL PLASTICS
Bridge Street, Abercarn, Gwent, NP11 4SB
Area of Operation: UK & Ireland
Tel: 01495 244551   **Fax:** 01495 247990
Email: srholt@nationalplastics.co.uk
Web: www.nationalplastics.co.uk ⌂

NORTHANTS RAINWATER SYSTEMS
Unit 10 Chapel Farm, Hanslope Road,
Hartwell, Northamptonshire, NN7 2EU
Area of Operation: UK (Excluding Ireland)
Tel: 01604 877775   **Fax:** 01604 674447
Email: mail@northantsrainwater.co.uk
Web: www.northantsrainwater.co.uk

OCTAVEWARD LIMITED
Balle Street, Darwen, Lancashire, BB3 2AZ
Area of Operation: UK (Excluding Ireland)
Tel: 01254 773300   **Fax:** 01254 773950
Email: info@octaveward.com
Web: www.octaveward.com

PLASTIVAN LTD
Unit 4 Bonville Industrial Estate,
Bonville Road, Brislington, Bristol, BS4 5QU
Area of Operation: Worldwide
Tel: 0117 300 5625   **Fax:** 0117 971 5028
Email: sales@plastivan.co.uk
Web: www.plastivan.co.uk

SUPERIOR FASCIAS
Adelaide House, Portsmouth Road, Lowford,
Southampton, Hampshire, SO31 8EQ
Area of Operation: South East England, South West
England and South Wales
Tel: 0700 596 4603   **Fax:** 0700 596 4609
Email: info@superiorfascias.co.uk
Web: www.superiorfascias.co.uk

SWISH BUILDING PRODUCTS LTD
Pioneer House, Mariner, Litchfield Road Industrial
Estate, Tamworth, Staffordshire, B79 7TF
Area of Operation: UK & Ireland
Tel: 01827 317200   **Fax:** 01827 317201
Email: info@swishbp.co.uk
Web: www.swishbp.co.uk   **Material Type:** D) 1

SWISH BUILDING PRODUCTS LTD

Area of Operation: UK & Ireland
Tel: 01827 317200
Fax: 01827 317201
Email: info@swishbp.co.uk
Web: www.swishbp.co.uk

Quality PVC roofline, cladding and window trims,
in white or wood effect, that never need painting.
Available from Swish Approved Installers or
plastics stockists throughout the UK.

THE EXPANDED METAL COMPANY LIMITED
PO Box 14, Longhill Industrial Estate (North),
Hartlepool, Durham, TS25 1PR
Area of Operation: Worldwide
Tel: 01429 867388   **Fax:** 01429 866795
Email: paulb@expamet.co.uk
Web: www.expandedmetalcompany.co.uk

TLG GUTTERS
20 Crawley Road, Alvaston, Derby, Derbyshire, DE24 9FZ
Area of Operation: UK (Excluding Ireland)
Tel: 0800 298 4619   **Fax:** 01332 754133
Email: knopptony@hotmail.com
Web: www.tlg-gutter.co.uk

WARWICKSHIRE FASCIAS
Unit 8&9 Cattell Road, Cape Road Industrial Estate,
Warwick, Warwickshire, CV34 4JN
Area of Operation: UK & Ireland
Tel: 01926 496 830   **Fax:** 01926 491 630
Email: warwickshirefascias@hotmail.com
Web: www.warwickshirefascias.co.uk

EAVES CLOSERS

KEY
OTHER: ▽ Reclaimed   ⌂ On-line shopping
✎ Bespoke   ✋ Hand-made   ECO Ecological

CLEARVIEW WINDOWS & DOORS
Unit 14, Sheddingdean Industrial Estate,
Marchants Way, Burgess Hill, West Sussex, RH15 8QY
Area of Operation: UK (Excluding Ireland)
Tel: 01444 250111
Fax: 01444 250678
Email: sales@clearviewsussex.co.uk
Web: www.clearviewsussex.co.uk

KLOBER LTD
Ingleberry Road, Shepshed,
Nr Loughborough, Leicestershire, LE12 9DE
Area of Operation: UK & Ireland
Tel: 01509 500660
Fax: 01509 600061
Email: info@klober.co.uk
Web: www.klober.co.uk   **Other Info:** ✎

NATIONAL PLASTICS
Bridge Street, Abercarn, Gwent, NP11 4SB
Area of Operation: UK & Ireland
Tel: 01495 244551   **Fax:** 01495 247990
Email: srholt@nationalplastics.co.uk
Web: www.nationalplastics.co.uk ⌂
Material Type: D) 1

TOPSEAL SYSTEMS LIMITED
Unit 1-5 Hookstone Chase,
Harrogate, North Yorkshire, HG2 7HP
Area of Operation: Europe
Tel: 01423 886495   **Fax:** 01423 889550
Email: sales@topseal.co.uk
Web: www.topseal.co.uk

GRASS ROOFING

KEY
SEE ALSO: HORTICULTURE & WATER
GARDENING - Lawns & Turf
OTHER: ▽ Reclaimed   ⌂ On-line shopping
✎ Bespoke   ✋ Hand-made   ECO Ecological

ECOLOGICAL BUILDING SYSTEMS UK LTD
The Manse, High Street, Creaton,
Northamptonshire, NN6 8NA
Area of Operation: UK & Ireland
Tel: 05600 758025   **Fax:** 05600 758026
Email: ecologicalbuild@btconnect.com
Web: www.ecologicalbuildingsystems.co.uk

ENVIROMAT BY Q LAWNS
Corkway Drive, Hockwold, Thetford, Norfolk, IP26 4JR
Area of Operation: UK (Excluding Ireland)
Tel: 01842 828266   **Fax:** 01842 827911
Email: sales@qlawns.co.uk
Web: www.enviromat.co.uk ⌂

TRITON CHEMICAL MANUFACTURING LTD
129 Felixstowe Road, Abbey Wood, London, SE2 9SG
Area of Operation: Worldwide
Tel: 0208 310 3929   **Fax:** 0208 312 0349
Email: neil@triton-chemicals.com
Web: www.triton-chemicals.com

NOTES

Company Name ....
....
Address ....
....
....
email ....
Web ....

Company Name ....
....
Address ....
....
....
email ....
Web ....

Company Name ....
....
Address ....
....
....
email ....
Web ....

Company Name ....
....
Address ....
....
....
email ....
Web ....

Company Name ....
....
Address ....
....
....
email ....
Web ....

ADDING SPACE & VALUE

@ the click of a mouse!

WRECK TO HIGH SPEC

Access to hundreds of projects to get an inside look on how real people added space and value to their home. Provides detailed costs, plans and extensions plus amazing before and after images. Just click wreck to high spec.

LATEST NEWS

News that can make all the difference to the success of your improved home. Includes the top ten tips to achieve your dream home and the latest figures on the UK housing market. Just click on latest news.

THE GUIDE

Everything you need to know about moving or improving. By the time the cost of moving and stamp duty has been taken into account, it can turn out to be far more cost effective to improve rather than move. Our guide will help you to decide. Just click on latest news.

ALSO AVAILABLE AT
www.moveorimprove.co.uk

○ **Hot topics featured in the current magazine** - never miss out on the information that will make a difference to your project.

○ **Product & Service Directory** - all the contacts you will need to make your improvement project a success.

○ **Bookshop** - choose from our large selection of recommended reads.

SUBSCRIBE

Subscribe to *Move or Improve?* magazine
- Receive 2 free tickets to all Homebuilding & Renovating shows (worth £140)
- Further savings on all H&R products

www.moveorimprove.co.uk

REGISTER ONLINE NOW TO RECEIVE HOT NEWS AND UPDATES

Image courtesy of Architectural Doors & Windows (01236 780022)

SPONSORED BY ARCHITECTURAL DOORS & WINDOWS LIMITED
Tel: 01236 780022 Web: www.adwlimited.co.uk

Stained Glass

A revival of traditional crafts has led to an increase in the popularity of stained glass in new builds as well as renovation projects.

Whilst antique stained glass continues to attract a high demand in architectural salvage yards, new bespoke designed glass is also coming into its own. The spectrum of stained glass artists and restorers is increasing every day, meaning there is certainly someone out there whose talents are perfect for your project. Whether you choose original or new glass, a stained glass panel – if used well – will provide a valuable, eye-catching addition to your home.

Unique designs can be commissioned for door panels or windows, whether to frame a stunning view, or conceal a less pleasant one, and will ensure privacy without losing light. It is the way in which stained glass maximizes the effect of natural light, responding to its changes as the day and seasons progress, which makes it such a striking feature.

When thinking about commissioning stained glass for your home as part of a renovation, it is worth keeping in mind both the age of the house and its location, as well as whether it is terraced or detached. It has become popular for renovation projects to reflect the traditional style of the local vernacular. And where original glass can be found in either your home or any houses within your street, stained glass artists are generally happy to replicate designs. Synchronizing your new addition with your neighbours only serves to increase the striking effect it will have on your property.

In new builds and contemporary homes there is, perhaps, more freedom to create a modern piece of stained glass without detracting from the traditional architecture of the area. This is a great way to create a

valuable and eye-catching original feature to your home. Designs can easily be worked through in collaboration with a stained glass artist, allowing you to inject your own personality and tastes into the panel.

The first stage of production is a full size working drawing, which is then used as a template for the glass to be selected and cut. Each piece of glass is individually painted using glass paint, with the paint then fired into the surface by heating the glass in a furnace. When all of the glass has been painted it is assembled into panels by bending strips of lead around the pieces of glass and soldering the strips together where they meet.

Whilst prices for stained glass vary greatly according to the complexity of the design, small panels can often be produced for a minimal cost and can be used to great effect, thus are a fantastic investment when creating a unique feature for your home.

A stained glass panel can provide visual interest to an otherwise plain door or window. Examples ABOVE LEFT by Dooria, and ABOVE by JB Kind.

For a list of stained glass professionals, try the British Society of Master Glass Painters' website
www.bsmgp.org.uk

INTERNAL DOORS

KEY

PRODUCT TYPES: 1= Plain 2 = Panelled
3 = Glazed   4 = French   5 = Folding / Sliding
6 = Fire Doors   7 = Ledged / Braced
8 = Security   9 = Other

OTHER: ▽ Reclaimed ⌐ On-line shopping
⟋ Bespoke ⌙ Hand-made ECO Ecological

AACORN JOINERY AND DESIGN LTD.
2 Balaclava Place, South Street,
Bridport, Dorset, DT6 3PE
Area of Operation: Europe
Tel: 01308 456217   **Fax:** 01308 424511
Email: info@aacornjoinery.co.uk
Web: www.aacornjoinery.co.uk

ARBOR WINDOW SYSTEMS LIMITED
1240 Park Avenue, Aztec West, Bristol, BS32 4SH
Area of Operation: UK (Excluding Ireland)
Tel: 01454 270039   **Fax:** 01454 270049
Email: enquiries@arborwinsys.co.uk
Web: www.arborwinsys.co.uk

ARCHITECTURAL DOORS & WINDOWS LIMITED
3 Tollpark Road, Wardpark East,
Cumbernauld, Glasgow, G68 0LW
Area of Operation: UK
Tel: 01236 780022   **Fax:** 01236 780021
Email: info@adwlimited.co.uk
Web: www.adwlimited.co.uk

ASTON HOUSE JOINERY
Aston House, Tripontium Business Centre,
Newton Lane, Rugby, Warwickshire, CV23 0TB
Area of Operation: UK & Ireland
Tel: 01788 860032   **Fax:** 01788 860614
Email: enquiries@astonhousejoinery.co.uk
Web: www.astonhousejoinery.co.uk
Product Type: 1, 2, 3, 4, 5, 6, 7, 8
Other Info: ECO ⟋ ⌙   **Material Type:** A) 1, 2

BARHAM & SONS
58 Finchley Avenue, Mildenhall, Suffolk, IP28 7BG
Area of Operation: UK (Excluding Ireland)
Tel: 01638 711611   **Fax:** 01638 716688
Email: info@barhamwoodfloors.com
Web: www.barhamwoodfloors.com
Product Type: 1, 2, 3, 7

BARRON GLASS
Unit 11, Lansdown Industrial Estate,
Cheltenham, Gloucestershire, GL51 8PL
Area of Operation: UK & Ireland
Tel: 01242 22800   **Fax:** 01242 226555
Email: admin@barronglass.co.uk
Web: www.barronglass.co.uk   **Product Type:** 1, 2, 3

BECKER SLIDING PARTITIONS LTD
Wemco House, 477 Whippendell Road,
Herefordshire, WD18 7QY
Area of Operation: UK & Ireland
Tel: 01923 236906   **Fax:** 01923 230149
Email: sales@becker.uk.com
Web: www.becker.uk.com   **Product Type:** 5

BROADLEAF TIMBER
Llandeilo Road Industrial Estate,
Carms, Carmarthenshire, SA18 3JG
Tel: 01269 851910   **Fax:** 01269 851911
Email: sales@broadleaftimber.com
Web: www.broadleaftimber.com
Product Type: 2, 3, 4, 6, 7
Other Info: ⟋ ⌙   **Material Type:** A) 2

BROCKHOUSE MODERNFOLD LIMITED
Aztec House, 137 Molesey Avenue,
West Molesey, Surrey, KT8 2RY
Area of Operation: Worldwide
Tel: 0208 481 7288   **Fax:** 0208 481 7289
Email: neilohalleran@brockhouse.net
Web: www.brockhouse.net   **Product Type:** 3, 5

BUILDING & DESIGN SOLUTIONS GERMANY
Auf den Haien 14, 55471 Sargenroth
Area of Operation: UK (Excluding Ireland)
Tel: 0049 6761 970 871
Email: mail@buildingdesign-germany.eu
Web: www.buildingdesign-germany.eu

CENTURION
Westhill Business Park, Arnhall Business Park,
Westhill, Aberdeen, Aberdeenshire, AB32 6UF
Area of Operation: Scotland
Tel: 01224 744440
Fax: 01224 744819
Email: info@centurion-solutions.co.uk
Web: www.centurion-solutions.co.uk
Product Type: 6

CHAMBERLAIN & GROVES LTD - THE DOOR & SECURITY STORE
101 Boundary Road, Walthamstow, London, E17 8NQ
Area of Operation: UK (Excluding Ireland)
Tel: 0208 520 6776
Fax: 0208 520 2190
Email: ken@securedoors.co.uk
Web: www.securedoors.co.uk
Product Type: 1, 2, 3, 4, 6, 8, 9
Other Info: ECO ⟋ ⌙
Material Type: A) 1, 2

CHESHIRE DOOR COMPANY
Paradise Mill, Old Park Lane,
Macclesfield, Cheshire, SK11 6TJ
Area of Operation: UK & Ireland
Tel: 01625 421221
Fax: 01625 421422
Email: info@cheshiredoorcompany.co.uk
Web: www.cheshiredoorcompany.co.uk

CHIPPING NORTON GLASS LTD
Units 1 & 2, Station Yard Industrial Estate,
Chipping Norton, Oxfordshire, OX7 5HX
Area of Operation: Midlands & Mid Wales,
South West England and South Wales
Tel: 01608 643261   **Fax:** 01608 641768
Email: gill@cnglass.plus.com
Web: www.chippingnortonglass.co.uk
Product Type: 3, 4, 5, 6
Material Type: D) 1

CHROMA INTERNATIONAL GLASS LTD
Unit 200 Bridgwater Business Park,
Bridgwater, Somerset, TA6 4TB
Area of Operation: Europe
Tel: 01278 426226   **Fax:** 01278 450088
Email: info@chroma-glass.com
Web: www.chroma-glass.com
Product Type: 2, 9

CONSTRUCTION TECHNICAL SERVICES
Dunedin House, Alexandra Road,
Penzance, Cornwall, TR18 4LZ
Area of Operation: UK & Ireland
Tel: 01736 330303
Fax: 01736 360497
Email: ctecs@aol.com
Web: www.hometown.aol.co.uk/carpinjohn
Product Type: 5

COUNTY HARDWOODS
Creech Mill, Mill Lane, Creech Saint Michael,
Taunton, Somerset, TA3 5PX
Area of Operation: UK & Ireland
Tel: 01823 443760
Fax: 01823 443940
Email: sales@countyhardwoods.co.uk
Web: www.countyhardwoods.co.uk ⌐
Product Type: 7   **Material Type:** A) 2

COUNTY JOINERY (SOUTH EAST) LTD
Tetley House, Marley Lane Business Park,
Marley Lane, Battle, East Sussex, TN33 0RE
Area of Operation: Greater London,
South East England
Tel: 01424 871500   **Fax:** 01424 871550
Email: info@countyjoinery.co.uk
Web: www.countyjoinery.co.uk
Product Type: 1, 2, 3, 4, 5, 6, 7, 8, 9

CROXFORD'S JOINERY MANUFACTURERS & WOODTURNERS
Meltham Joinery, Works New Street, Meltham,
Holmfirth, West Yorkshire, HD9 5NT
Area of Operation: UK (Excluding Ireland)
Tel: 01484 850892   **Fax:** 01484 850969
Email: croxford1@btconnect.com
Web: www.croxfords.co.uk   **Product Type:** 1, 2, 3, 4, 5, 7

CUSTOM WOOD PRODUCTS
Cliffe Road, Easton on the Hill,
Stamford, Lincolnshire, PE9 3NP
Area of Operation: East England
Tel: 01780 755711   **Fax:** 01780 480834
Email: customwoodprods@aol.com
Web: www.cwpuk.com   **Other Info:** ECO ⟋ ⌙
Product Type: 1, 2, 3, 4, 5, 7, 8

DAVID SMITH ST IVES LTD
Marley Road, St Ives, Huntingdon,
Cambridgeshire, PE27 3EX
Area of Operation: East England, Greater London,
Midlands & Mid Wales, South East England
Tel: 01480 309900   **Fax:** 01480 309949
Email: jeremyenglish@davidsmith.co.uk
Web: www.davidsmith.co.uk   **Product Type:** 3, 6
Material Type: A) 1, 2, 3, 4, 5, 6, 7, 8, 9, 10, 14

DICTATOR DIRECT
Inga House, Northdown Business Park,
Ashford Road, Lenham, Kent, ME17 2DL
Area of Operation: Worldwide
Tel: 01622 854770   **Fax:** 01622 854771
Email: mail@dictatordirect.com
Web: www.dictatordirect.com

DIRECTDOORS.COM
Bay 5 Eastfield Industrial Estate,
Eastfield Drive, Penicuik, Lothian, EH26 8JA
Area of Operation: UK (Excluding Ireland)
Tel: 01968 671681   **Fax:** 01968 671684
Email: info@directdoors.com
Web: www.directdoors.com ⌐
Product Type: 1, 2, 3, 4, 5, 6, 7, 8

DISABILITY ACCESS COMPANY LTD
Access House, 16-18 Chapel Street,
Glossop, Derbyshire, Sk13 8AT
Tel: 01457 868547   **Fax:** 0871 733 5071
Email: sales@disabilityaccessco.com
Web: www.disabilityaccessco.com

DISTINCTIVE DOORS
14 & 15 Chambers Way, Newton Chambers Road,
Chapeltown, Sheffield, South Yorkshire, S35 2PH
Area of Operation: UK & Ireland
Tel: 0114 220 2250   **Fax:** 0114 220 2254
Email: enquiries@distinctivedoors.co.uk
Web: www.distinctivedoors.co.uk ⌐
Product Type: 2, 4, 6, 7   **Material Type:** A) 1, 2, 6

DISTINCTIVE DOORS
Area of Operation: UK & Ireland
Tel: 0114 220 2250   **Fax:** 0114 220 2254
Email: enquiries@distinctivedoors.co.uk
Web: www.distinctivedoors.co.uk
Product Type: 2, 4, 6, 7

Suppliers of High Class External & Internal Doors.
Exclusive Product Range Triple Glazed Doors.
Oak Internal Engineered Doors.
Hardwood Doors, Clear Pine Doors.

DOORIA UK LTD
20 - 22 Glenburn Road, East Kilbride, Lanarkshire, G74 5BA
Area of Operation: UK & Ireland
Tel: 01355 243918
Email: lars.lund@dooria.co.uk
Web: www.dooria.net
Product Type: 1, 2, 3, 4, 5, 6, 8, 9
Material Type: A) 1, 2, 3, 4, 9, 10, 15

DYNASTY DOORS
Unit 3, The Micro Centre,
Gillette Way, Reading, Berkshire, RG2 0LR
Area of Operation: South East England, South West
England and South Wales
Tel: 0118 987 4000   **Fax:** 0118 921 2999
Email: info@dynastydoors.co.uk
Web: www.dynastydoors.co.uk
Product Type: 1, 2, 3, 4, 6

ENGELS WINDOWS & DOORS LTD
1 Kingley Centre, Downs Road, West Stoke,
Chichester, West Sussex, PO18 9HJ
Area of Operation: UK (Excluding Ireland)
Tel: 01243 576633
Fax: 01243 576644
Email: admin@engels.co.uk
Web: www.engels.co.uk

EVEREST LTD
Sopers Road, Cuffley, Hertfordshire, EN6 4SG
Area of Operation: UK & Ireland
Tel: 0800 010123
Web: www.everest.co.uk ⌐   **Product Type:** 1, 3, 5

FAIRMITRE WINDOWS & JOINERY LTD
2A Cope Road, Banbury, Oxfordshire, OX16 2EH
Area of Operation: UK (Excluding Ireland)
Tel: 01295 268441
Fax: 01295 268468
Email: info@fairmitrewindows.co.uk
Web: www.fairmitrewindows.co.uk
Product Type: 2, 3, 4, 7

FINNISH WOOD PRODUCTS LTD
Tresparrett Farm Villa, Tresparrett,
Cornwall, PL32 9ST
Area of Operation: UK & Ireland
Tel: 01840 261415   **Fax:** 01840 261415
Email: sales@finnishwoodproducts.com
Web: www.finnishwoodproducts.com
Product Type: 1, 3, 5, 9

FITZROY JOINERY
Garden Close, Langage Industrial Estate,
Plympton, Plymouth, Devon, PL7 5EU
Area of Operation: UK & Ireland
Tel: 0870 428 9110   **Fax:** 0870 428 9111
Email: admin@fitzroy.co.uk
Web: www.fitzroyjoinery.co.uk ⌐
Product Type: 1, 2, 3, 4, 5, 6   **Other Info:** ECO ⟋
Material Type: A) 1, 2, 3, 4, 5, 6, 7, 8, 9, 10, 12, 14

FLETCHER JOINERY
261 Whessoe Road, Darlington, Durham, DL3 0YL
Area of Operation: North East England
Tel: 01325 357347
Fax: 01325 357347
Email: enquiries@fletcherjoinery.co.uk
Web: www.fletcherjoinery.co.uk
Product Type: 1, 2, 3, 4, 5, 6, 7, 8, 9

FLOORS AND DOORS DIRECT
Unit 7 Blaydon Trade Park, Toll Bridge Road,
Blaydob, Tyne & Wear, NE21 5TR
Area of Operation: North East England
Tel: 0191 414 5055   **Fax:** 0191 414 5066
Email: fddbleydon@aol.co.uk
Web: www.floorsanddoorsdirect.co.uk
Product Type: 1

FOLDING SLIDING DOORS LIMITED
FSD Works, Hopbine Avenue, West Bowling,
Bradford, West Yorkshire, BD5 8ER
Area of Operation: UK (Excluding Ireland)
Tel: 0845 644 6630   **Fax:** 0845 644 6631
Email: sales@foldingslidingdoors.com
Web: www.foldingslidingdoors.com ⌐
Product Type: 5

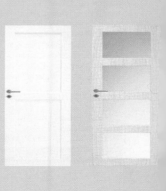

ARCHITECTURAL DOORS & WINDOWS LTD

Area of Operation: UK
Tel: 01236 780022
Fax: 01236 780021
Email: info@adwlimited.co.uk
Web: www.adwlimited.co.uk

For Timber Folding Doorsets, External Screens, External & Internal Doorsets, H Reversible, SideSwing and Tilt & Turn Windows, Balcony & Sliding Doorsets

ARCHITECTURAL DOORS & WINDOWS LTD

Area of Operation: UK
Tel: 01236 780022
Fax: 01236 780021
Email: info@adwlimited.co.uk
Web: www.adwlimited.co.uk

For Timber Folding Doorsets, External Screens, External & Internal Doorsets, H Reversible, SideSwing and Tilt & Turn Windows, Balcony & Sliding Doorsets

ARCHITECTURAL DOORS & WINDOWS LTD

Area of Operation: UK
Tel: 01236 780022
Fax: 01236 780021
Email: info@adwlimited.co.uk
Web: www.adwlimited.co.uk

For Timber Folding Doorsets, External Screens, External & Internal Doorsets, H Reversible, SideSwing and Tilt & Turn Windows, Balcony & Sliding Doorsets

ARCHITECTURAL DOORS & WINDOWS LTD

Area of Operation: UK
Tel: 01236 780022
Fax: 01236 780021
Email: info@adwlimited.co.uk
Web: www.adwlimited.co.uk

For Timber Folding Doorsets, External Screens, External & Internal Doorsets, H Reversible, SideSwing and Tilt & Turn Windows, Balcony & Sliding Doorsets

ARCHITECTURAL DOORS & WINDOWS LTD

Area of Operation: UK
Tel: 01236 780022
Fax: 01236 780021
Email: info@adwlimited.co.uk
Web: www.adwlimited.co.uk

For Timber Folding Doorsets, External Screens, External & Internal Doorsets, H Reversible, SideSwing and Tilt & Turn Windows, Balcony & Sliding Doorsets

ARCHITECTURAL DOORS & WINDOWS LTD

Area of Operation: UK
Tel: 01236 780022
Fax: 01236 780021
Email: info@adwlimited.co.uk
Web: www.adwlimited.co.uk

For Timber Folding Doorsets, External Screens, External & Internal Doorsets, H Reversible, SideSwing and Tilt & Turn Windows, Balcony & Sliding Doorsets

ARCHITECTURAL DOORS & WINDOWS LTD

Area of Operation: UK
Tel: 01236 780022
Fax: 01236 780021
Email: info@adwlimited.co.uk
Web: www.adwlimited.co.uk

For Timber Folding Doorsets, External Screens, External & Internal Doorsets, H Reversible, SideSwing and Tilt & Turn Windows, Balcony & Sliding Doorsets

ARCHITECTURAL DOORS & WINDOWS LTD

Area of Operation: UK
Tel: 01236 780022
Fax: 01236 780021
Email: info@adwlimited.co.uk
Web: www.adwlimited.co.uk

For Timber Folding Doorsets, External Screens, External & Internal Doorsets, H Reversible, SideSwing and Tilt & Turn Windows, Balcony & Sliding Doorsets

ARCHITECTURAL DOORS & WINDOWS LTD

Area of Operation: UK
Tel: 01236 780022
Fax: 01236 780021
Email: info@adwlimited.co.uk
Web: www.adwlimited.co.uk

For Timber Folding Doorsets, External Screens, External & Internal Doorsets, H Reversible, SideSwing and Tilt & Turn Windows, Balcony & Sliding Doorsets

ARCHITECTURAL DOORS & WINDOWS LTD

Area of Operation: UK
Tel: 01236 780022
Fax: 01236 780021
Email: info@adwlimited.co.uk
Web: www.adwlimited.co.uk

For Timber Folding Doorsets, External Screens, External & Internal Doorsets, H Reversible, SideSwing and Tilt & Turn Windows, Balcony & Sliding Doorsets

ARCHITECTURAL DOORS & WINDOWS LTD

Area of Operation: UK
Tel: 01236 780022
Fax: 01236 780021
Email: info@adwlimited.co.uk
Web: www.adwlimited.co.uk

For Timber Folding Doorsets, External Screens, External & Internal Doorsets, H Reversible, SideSwing and Tilt & Turn Windows, Balcony & Sliding Doorsets

ARCHITECTURAL DOORS & WINDOWS LTD

Area of Operation: UK
Tel: 01236 780022
Fax: 01236 780021
Email: info@adwlimited.co.uk
Web: www.adwlimited.co.uk

For Timber Folding Doorsets, External Screens, External & Internal Doorsets, H Reversible, SideSwing and Tilt & Turn Windows, Balcony & Sliding Doorsets

Architectural Doors & Windows
Scandinavian Performance & Quality

Architectural Doors & Windows supply a range of quality timber doorsets and windows to the self build market. with the emphas on high performance, quality and value for money, We have buil wealth of experience in supplying Doors and Windows to projec ranging from major construction contracts to self build projects.

Architectural Doors & Windows offer a comprehensive range of doorsets and windows in a variety of styles and finishes. As a result the range o products that we offer is one of the most diverse and of the highest quality available on the market.

Windows and doors are among the most exciting effects at your disposal when you build a new house, or restore an existing one. Windows and doors give life to your house and character to its façade. In the 'H' window modern functions are combined with flexible design to create solutions to fit your building.

For a choice of windows and doors to be successful, a condition must be that these products maintain the same high quality level, even after many years' use. The 'H' window guarantee this quality level - for years to come!

Swedoor doorsets deliver Individuality and a wide range of options. Whether you are building a new house, renovating an old one, or just redecorating, you will find a door suitable for you from our extensive range.

Our range covers everything from practical yet stylish interior and exterior doors to high performance doorsets

The ADW folding doorset system is a unique alternative to French or sliding patio doors, It is the only option which will allow your room and ga den to become one, blending the garden or patio area with the inside.

This product can be used in a number of applications to maximize the opening area between inside and outside, Whether that be a Sunroom, Conservatory, Balcony or pool the applications are endless.

When there are 3, 5 or 7 door leafs they can be folded back to one side in a concertina effect and then left fully open or alternatively just one do can be opened, if you desire. When there are 4 or 6 leafs the main leaf will be hinged to one side with the other leafs folding back in the opposi direction again offering a complete opening, Alternatively a 6 leaf door can open from the centre with 3 leafs folding back to each side.

The folding doorset system can be ordered with the doors opening into the property or outward as desired and you can also choose in which direction you wish the folding doors to open. To ensure the door opens effectively the maximum leaf size is 950mm X 2400mm however we car manufacture and will consider requests for sizes out with the standard parameters.

The product is produced with timber from sustainable sources and manufactured with a commitment to the environment.
In order to achieve various design looks we can manufacture with solid transoms & mullions, overlays bars or glazing bars within glass units to achieve a finer bar look, along with various glass, timber material and finish options we can offer a product suited to your design needs.

Matching sidelights and hinged doorsets are also available so that other items within the same location will not look out of place and will blend into the overall design requirements.

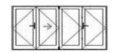

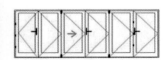
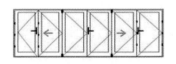

3 Tollpark Road, Wardpark East, Cumbernauld, G68 0LW
Tel: 01236 780022 Fax: 01236 780021 Email: info@adwlimited.co.uk www.adwlimited.co.

GARY BYNG AND SONS
Unit 17 Metal and Ores Industrial Estate, Hanbury Road,
Stoke Prior, Bromsgrove, Worcestershire, B60 4JZ
Area of Operation: UK & Ireland
Tel: 01527 876348   **Fax:** 01527 876339
Email: garybyng@byng.fsbusiness.co.uk
Web: www.gbands.co.uk
Product Type: 1, 2, 3, 4, 7, 9

HAYMANS TIMBER PRODUCTS
Haymans Farm, Hocker Lane, Over Alderley,
Macclesfield, Cheshire, SK10 4SD
Area of Operation: UK & Ireland
Tel: 01625 590098   **Fax:** 01625 586174
Email: haymanstimber@aol.com
Web: www.haymanstimber.co.uk
Product Type: 1, 2, 3, 4, 5, 6, 7, 8
Material Type: A) 2, 4, 6, 7

HOLME TREE LTD
Units 2 and 3 Machins Business Centre, 29 Wood
Street, Asby-de-la-Zouch, Leicestershire, LE65 1EL
Area of Operation: UK (Excluding Ireland)
Tel: 01530 564561   **Fax:** 01530 417986
Email: info@holmetree.co.uk
Web: www.holmetree.co.uk

IMAJ STEEL DOORS
704 Lea Bridge Road, London, E10 6AW
Area of Operation: Worldwide
Tel: 02030 223000   **Fax:** 02030 223001
Email: sales@imajsteeldoors.com
Web: www.imajsteeldoors.com

IN DOORS
Beechinwood Farm, Beechinwood Lane,
Platt, Nr. Sevenoaks, Kent, TN15 8QN
Area of Operation: UK (Excluding Ireland)
Tel: 01732 887445   **Fax:** 01732 887446
Email: info@indoorsltd.co.uk
Web: www.indoorsltd.co.uk
Product Type: 1, 2, 3, 4, 5, 7

INNERDOOR LTD
Royds Enterprise Park, Future Fields,
Bradford, West Yorkshire, BD6 3EW
Area of Operation: Worldwide
Tel: 0845 128 3958   **Fax:** 0845 128 3959
Email: info@innerdoor.co.uk
Web: www.innerdoor.co.uk
Product Type: 1, 2, 3, 4, 5, 6

INNERDOOR LTD
Area of Operation: Worldwide
Tel: 0845 128 3958
Fax: 0845 128 3959
Email: info@innerdoor.co.uk
Web: www.innerdoor.co.uk
Product Type: 1, 2, 3, 4, 5, 6
Other Info: ✎

Innerdoor supply a wide range of internal doors in period and contemporary styles. Doors are supplied made to measure and complete with door frame, hinges, locks, glass and handles. 1000's of door variations available.

INNERDOOR LTD
Area of Operation: Worldwide
Tel: 0845 128 3958
Fax: 0845 128 3959
Email: info@innerdoor.co.uk
Web: www.innerdoor.co.uk
Product Type: 1, 2, 3, 4, 5, 6
Other Info: ✎

Innerdoor supply a wide range of internal sliding doors in traditional and contemporary styles in glass or wood. If it is in the wall or on the wall sliding doors and screens you are looking to source, Innerdoor have the answer.

INPUT JOINERY LTD
The Fairground, Weyhill, Andover, Hampshire, SP11 0ST
Area of Operation: UK (Excluding Ireland)
Tel: 01264 771900   **Fax:** 01264 771901
Email: info@inputjoinery.co.uk
Web: www.inputjoinery.co.uk
Product Type: 2, 3, 4, 5, 7
Material Type: A) 1, 2, 5, 6

J L JOINERY
Cockerton View, Grange Lane, Preston, Lancashire, PR4 5JE
Area of Operation: UK (Excluding Ireland)
Tel: 01772 616123   **Fax:** 01772 619182
Email: mail@jljoinery.co.uk
Web: www.jljoinery.co.uk

JB KIND LTD
Shobnall Street, Burton-on-Trent, Staffordshire, DE14 2HP
Area of Operation: UK & Ireland
Tel: 01283 510210   **Fax:** 01283 511132
Email: info@jbkind.com   **Web:** www.jbkind.com
Product Type: 1, 2, 3, 4, 5, 6, 7, 9
Material Type: A) 2, 3, 4, 5, 6, 7, 8, 15

JB KIND LTD
Area of Operation: UK & Ireland
Tel: 01283 510210
Fax: 01283 511132
Email: info@jbkind.com
Web: www.jbkind.com

At JB Kind we take great care to ensure our doors are not only the most fashionable but that their specification and quality completely fulfil customer aspiration

JB KIND LTD
Area of Operation: UK & Ireland
Tel: 01283 510210
Fax: 01283 511132
Email: info@jbkind.com
Web: www.jbkind.com

JB Kind doors are both distinctive and individual, offered in a variety of styles that will accentuate any type of property

JELD-WEN
Watch House Lane, Doncaster, South Yorkshire, DN5 9LR
Area of Operation: UK & Ireland
Tel: 0870 126 0000   **Fax:** 01302 787383
Email: customer-services@jeld-wen.co.uk
Web: www.jeld-wen.co.uk
Product Type: 1, 2, 3

JOINERY-PLUS
Bentley Hall Barn, Alkmonton,
Ashbourne, Derbyshire, DE6 3DJ
Area of Operation: UK (Excluding Ireland)
Tel: 07931 386233
Fax: 01335 330922
Email: info@joinery-plus.co.uk
Web: www.joinery-plus.co.uk
Product Type: 1, 2, 3, 4, 6, 7, 8
Material Type: A) 1, 2, 3, 4, 5, 6, 7, 8, 9, 10, 11, 12, 13, 14

JONATHAN ELWELL
Bryn Teg Workshop & Tan y Bryn Cottage,
Tanrallt Road, Gwespyr, Flintshire, CH8 9JT
Area of Operation: UK (Excluding Ireland)
Tel: 01745 887766
Email: jonathanelwell@ukonline.co.uk
Web: www.jonathanelwell.co.uk

KERSHAWS DOORS LTD
Main Street, Wyke, Bradford,
West Yorkshire, BD12 8BN
Area of Operation: UK (Excluding Ireland)
Tel: 01274 604488
Fax: 0845 126 0275
Email: help@door-warehouse.co.uk
Web: www.doorwarehouse.co.uk
Product Type: 1, 2, 3, 4, 5, 6, 7, 9

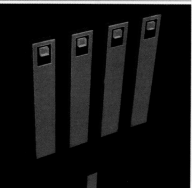

LAMWOOD LTD
Unit 1, Riverside Works, Station Road,
Cheddleton, Staffordshire, ST13 7EE
Area of Operation: UK & Ireland
Tel: 01538 361888   **Fax:** 01538 361912
Email: info@lamwoodltd.co.uk
Web: www.lamwoodltd.co.uk
Material Type: A) 2

LPD DOORS
Holme Well Road, Leeds, West Yorkshire, LS10 4SL
Area of Operation: UK & Ireland
Tel: 0845 658 5115
Email: sales@lpddoors.co.uk
Product Type: 1, 2, 3

MASONITE EUROPE
10 Carr Hill Drive, Calverly, Pudsey,
Leeds, West Yorkshire, LS28 5QA
Area of Operation: Europe
Tel: 0113 256 7063   **Fax:** 0113 256 9216
Email: masonite-europe@masonite.com
Web: www.masonite-europe.com
Product Type: 2, 3, 5, 6

MERLIN UK LIMITED
Unit 5 Fence Avenue, Macclesfield, Cheshire, SK10 1LT
Area of Operation: North West England and North Wales
Tel: 01625 424488
Fax: 0871 781 8967
Email: info@merlinuk.net
Web: www.merlindoors.co.uk
Product Type: 1, 2, 3, 4, 5, 6, 7, 9

MIDLANDS SLATE & TILE
Units 9-12, Star Industrial Estate,
Chadwell St Mary, Essex, RM16 4LR
Area of Operation: UK & Ireland
Tel: 0871 4743185   **Fax:** 01375 846478
Email: mark@slate-tile-brick.co.uk
Web: www.slate-tile-brick.co.uk
Product Type: 3, 7   **Material Type:** A) 2

NATIONAL DOOR COMPANY
Unit 55 Dinting Vale Business Park,
Dinting Vale, Glossop, Derbyshire, SK13 6JD
Area of Operation: UK (Excluding Ireland)
Tel: 01457 867079   **Fax:** 01457 868795
Email: sales@nationaldoor.co.uk
Web: www.nationaldoor.co.uk
Product Type: 1, 2, 3, 4, 5, 6, 7, 8, 9

NATIONAL PLASTICS
Bridge Street, Abercarn, Gwent, NP11 4SB
Area of Operation: UK & Ireland
Tel: 01495 244551   **Fax:** 01495 247990
Email: srholt@nationalplastics.co.uk
Web: www.nationalplastics.co.uk
Product Type: 1, 2, 3   **Material Type:** D) 1

NFP JOINERY
Milford Village Hall, Portsmouth Road,
Milford, Godalming, Surrey, GU8 5DS
Tel: 01483 414291   **Fax:** 01483 414831
Email: olly@nfpeurope.co.uk
Web: www.nfpeurope.co.uk
Product Type: 2, 3, 4, 8   **Material Type:** B) 13

NOISE STOP SYSTEMS
Unit 2, Car House Farm, Poole Lane,
Nun Monkton, York, North Yorkshire, YO26 8EH
Area of Operation: UK & Ireland
Tel: 0845 130 6269
Fax: 01423 339153
Email: info@noisestopsystems.co.uk
Web: www.noisestopsystems.co.uk
Product Type: 1, 2, 4, 5, 6, 8, 9

NORBUILD TIMBER FABRICATION & FINE CARPENTRY LTD
Marcassie Farm, Rafford, Forres, Moray, IV36 2RH
Area of Operation: UK & Ireland
Tel: 01309 676865   **Fax:** 01309 676865
Email: norbuild@marcassie.fsnet.co.uk
Product Type: 2, 3, 5, 9   **Other Info:** ECO
Material Type: A) 1, 2, 4, 6, 9, 11

NORTH YORKSHIRE TIMBER
Standard House, Thurston Road, Northallerton Business
Park, Northallerton, North Yorkshire, DL6 2NA
Area of Operation: UK (Excluding Ireland)
Tel: 01609 780777   **Fax:** 01609 777888
Email: sales@nytimber.co.uk
Web: www.nytimber.co.uk

NORTHWOOD FORESTRY LTD
Goose Green Lane, Nr Ashington,
Pulborough, West Sussex, RH20 2LW
Area of Operation: South East England
Tel: 01798 813029   **Fax:** 01798 813139
Email: enquiries@northwoodforestry.co.uk
Web: www.northwoodforestry.co.uk
Product Type: 7   **Material Type:** A) 2

OLDE WORLDE OAK JOINERY LTD
Unit 12, Longford Industrial Estate,
Longford Road, Cannock, Staffordshire, WS11 0DG
Area of Operation: Europe
Tel: 01543 469328
Fax: 01543 469328
Email: sales@oldeworldeoakjoinery.co.uk
Web: www.oldeworldeoakjoinery.co.uk
Product Type: 1, 2, 6, 7

ORIGINAL OAK
Ashlands, Burwash, East Sussex, TN19 7HS
Area of Operation: UK (Excluding Ireland)
Tel: 01435 882228   **Fax:** 01435 882228
Web: www.originaloak.co.uk

PELLFOLD PARTHOS LTD
1 The Quadrant, Howarth Road,
Maidenhead, Berkshire, SL6 1AP
Area of Operation: UK & Ireland
Tel: 01628 773353
Fax: 01628 773363
Email: sales@pellfoldparthos.co.uk
Web: www.designs4space.com
Product Type: 5

PENNY BRICKS & TIMBER LIMITED
The Old Timber Yard, York Road,
Wetherby, West Yorkshire, LS22 5EF
Area of Operation: UK (Excluding Ireland)
Tel: 01937 580580   **Fax:** 01937 580587
Email: pw@penny-bricks.co.uk
Web: www.penny-bricks.co.uk
Product Type: 1, 2, 3, 7

PERIOD OAK DOORS LTD
7 Saint Davids House, Brawdey Business Park,
Brawdey, Haverford West, Pembrokeshire, SA62 6NP
Area of Operation: UK & Ireland
Tel: 01437 720373   **Fax:** 01437 720406
Email: perioddoors@yahoo.com
Web: www.perioddoors.com
Product Type: 1, 2, 7

PREMDOR
Gemini House, Hargreaves Road, Groundwell
Industrial Estate, Swindon, Wiltshire, SN25 5AJ
Area of Operation: UK & Ireland
Tel: 0870 990 7998
Email: ukmarketing@premdor.com
Web: www.premdor.co.uk
Product Type: 1, 2, 3, 4, 5, 6, 7, 9

RADNOR TIMBER COMPANY
The Offices, Old Impton Farm,
Norton, Presteigne, Powys, LD8 2EN
Area of Operation: Europe
Tel: 01544 260727   **Fax:** 01544 262113
Email: sales@rtc.enta.net
Web: www.radnortimbercompany
Product Type: 1, 2, 3, 4, 6, 7, 9
Other Info: ECO   **Material Type:** A) 2

REYNAERS LTD
Kettles Wood Drive, Birmingham, West Midlands, B32 3DB
Area of Operation: UK (Excluding Ireland)
Tel: 0121 421 1999   **Fax:** 0121 421 9797
Email: reynaersltd@reynaers.com
Web: www.reynaers.com   **Product Type:** 5

Dooria® Milano 400
in wenge-stained oak.

New ideas, new lines

The Milano range consists of veneered oak doors with integrated bands of stainless steel. Choose lacquered or dark wenge-stained.

Milano 401	Milano 400	Milano 402	Milano 403
oak, lacquered	oak, wenge-stained	oak, wenge-stained	oak, lacquered

All Dooria doors are delivered as pre-finished door-sets, which can be installed in 20 minutes.

www.Dooria.net

DOORIA®

The doors that make the difference

RHONES JOINERY (WREXHAM) LTD
Mold Road Industrial Estate,
Gwersyllt, Wrexham, LL11 4AQ
Area of Operation: UK (Excluding Ireland)
Tel: 01978 262488 **Fax:** 01978 262488
Email: info@rhonesjoinery.co.uk
Web: www.rhonesjoinery.co.uk
Product Type: 2, 4, 7 **Material Type:** A) 2, 4, 5, 6, 12

ROBERT J TURNER & CO
Roe Green, Sandon, Buntingford, Hertfordshire, SG9 0QE
Area of Operation: East England, Greater London
Tel: 01763 288371 **Fax:** 01763 288440
Email: sales@robertjturner.co.uk
Web: www.robertjturner.co.uk **Other Info:** ✎ ☝
Product Type: 1, 2, 3, 4, 5, 6, 7, 8, 9

SABRINA OAK DOORS LTD
Alma Street, Mountfields,
Shrewsbury, Shropshire, SY3 8QL
Area of Operation: UK (Excluding Ireland)
Tel: 01743 357977 **Fax:** 01743 352233
Email: mail@oakdoors.co.uk
Web: www.oakdoors.co.uk
Product Type: 1, 2, 3, 4, 5, 7, 8, 9
Other Info: ✎ ☝ **Material Type:** A) 2

SAFEGUARD DOORS LIMITED
Units 6-9 Bridge Business Park, Bridge Street,
Wednesbury, West Midlands, WS10 0AW
Area of Operation: Worldwide
Tel: 0121 556 9138 **Fax:** 0121 556 7275
Email: sales@safeguarddoors.co.uk
Web: www.safeguarddoors.co.uk
Product Type: 1, 2, 3, 6, 9

SANDERSON'S FINE FURNITURE
Unit 5 & 6, The Village Workshop, Four Crosses
Business Park, Four Crosses, Powys, SY22 6ST
Area of Operation: UK (Excluding Ireland)
Tel: 01691 830075 **Fax:** 01691 830075
Email: sales@sandersonsfinefurniture.co.uk
Web: www.sandersonsfinefurniture.co.uk
Product Type: 1, 2, 3, 4, 7, 9 **Other Info:** ✎ ☝

SASH CRAFT
3 The Dairy, Priston Mill Farm, Bath, BA2 9EQ
Area of Operation: South West England and South Wales
Tel: 01225 424434 **Fax:** 01761 470 777
Email: info@sashcraftofbath.com
Web: www.sashcraftofbath.com
Product Type: 1, 2, 3, 4, 5, 7
Material Type: B) 8, 12

**SASH RESTORATION COMPANY
(HEREFORD) LTD**
Pigeon House Farm, Lower Breinton,
Hereford, Herefordshire, HR4 7PG
Area of Operation: UK & Ireland
Tel: 01432 359562 **Fax:** 01432 269749
Email: sales@sash-restoration.co.uk
Web: www.sash-restoration.co.uk
Product Type: 4

SCANDINAVIAN WINDOW SYSTEMS LTD
10 Eldon Street, Tuxford, Newark,
Nottinghamshire, NG22 0LH
Area of Operation: UK & Ireland
Tel: 01777 871847 **Fax:** 01777 872650
Email: enquiries@scandinavian-windows.co.uk
Web: www.scandinavian-windows.co.uk
Product Type: 1, 2, 3, 4, 5, 6, 9 **Other Info:** ECO
Material Type: A) 1, 2, 3, 4, 5, 6, 7, 8, 9, 10, 12, 14

SCOTTS OF THRAPSTON LTD.
Bridge Street, Thrapston, Northamptonshire, NN14 4LR
Area of Operation: UK & Ireland
Tel: 01832 732366 **Fax:** 01832 733703
Email: julia@scottsofthrapston.co.uk
Web: www.scottsofthrapston.co.uk
Product Type: 1, 2, 3, 5, 6, 8, 9 **Other Info:** ✎

SOLARLUX SYSTEMS LTD
Holmfield Lane, Wakefield, West Yorkshire, WF2 7AD
Area of Operation: Worldwide
Tel: 01924 204444 **Fax:** 01924 204455
Email: info@solarlux.co.uk
Web: www.solarlux.uk.com
Product Type: 5

SPECTUS SYSTEMS
Spectus Window Systems, Pinewood Court,
Tytherington Business Park, Macclesfield,
Cheshire, SK10 2XR
Area of Operation: UK & Ireland
Tel: 01625 420400 **Fax:** 01625 501418
Email: contact@spectus.co.uk
Web: www.spectus.co.uk

STANDARDS GROUP
Bentley Hall Barn, Alkmonton,
Ashbourne, Derbyshire, DE6 3DJ
Area of Operation: UK & Ireland
Tel: 01335 330263 **Fax:** 01335 330922
Email: uk@standardsgroup.com
Web: www.standardsgroup.com
Product Type: 1, 2, 3, 6, 9

STRATHEARN STONE AND TIMBER LTD
Glenearn, Bridge of Earn, Perth,
Perth and Kinross, PH2 9HL
Area of Operation: North East England, Scotland
Tel: 01738 813215 **Fax:** 01738 815946
Email: info@stoneandoak.com
Web: www.stoneandoak.com

STROUDS WOODWORKING COMPANY LTD.
Ashmansworthy, Woolsery, Bideford, Devon, EX39 5RE
Area of Operation: South West England and South Wales
Tel: 01409 241624 **Fax:** 01409 241769
Email: enquiries@stroudswoodworking.co.uk
Web: www.stroudswoodworking.co.uk
Product Type: 1, 2, 3, 4, 5, 6, 7, 8, 9
Other Info: ✎ ☝
Material Type: A) 2, 3, 4, 5, 6, 7, 8, 10

SUN PARADISE UK LTD
Phoenix Wharf, Eel Pie Island,
Twickenham, Middlesex, TW1 3DY
Area of Operation: UK & Ireland
Tel: 0870 240 7604 **Fax:** 0870 240 7614
Email: info@sunparadise.co.uk
Web: www.sunparadise.co.uk **Product Type:** 5

SUNFOLD LTD
Sunfold House, Wymondham Business Park,
Chestnut Drive, Wymondham, Norfolk, NR18 9SB
Area of Operation: Europe
Tel: 01953 423423
Fax: 01953 423430
Email: info@sunfold.com **Web:** www.sunfold.com
Product Type: 1, 3, 5
Other Info: ✎ **Material Type:** B) 1

THE DAVID BARLEY COMPANY
Unit D, Holmes Court, Horncastle, Lincolnshire, LN9 6AS
Area of Operation: UK & Ireland
Tel: 01507 523838 **Fax:** 01507 524465
Email: padraic@eclisse.co.uk
Web: www.eclisse.co.uk
Product Type: 2, 3, 4, 5, 6, 7, 8, 10

THE DISAPPEARING DOOR COMPANY
3 Southern House, Anthony's Way, Medway City
Estate, Strood, Rochester, Kent, ME2 4DN
Area of Operation: UK (Excluding Ireland)
Tel: 01634 729055
Fax: 01634 720866
Email: sales@disappearingdoors.co.uk
Web: www.disappearingdoors.co.uk
Product Type: 1, 3, 5, 9 **Material Type:** H) 2

THE NATIONAL DOOR COMPANY
Unit 55, Dinting Vale Business Park,
Dinting Vale, Glossop, Derbyshire, SK13 6JD
Area of Operation: UK (Excluding Ireland)
Tel: 01457 867079 **Fax:** 01457 868795
Email: sales@nationaldoor.co.uk
Web: www.nationaldoor.co.uk
Product Type: 1, 2, 3

THE REAL DOOR COMPANY
Unit 5, Cadwell Lane, Hitchen, Hertfordshire, SG4 0SA
Area of Operation: UK & Ireland
Tel: 01462 451230 **Fax:** 01462 440459
Email: sales@realdoor.co.uk
Web: www.realdoor.co.uk
Product Type: 1, 2, 6, 7 **Other Info:** ✎

THE ROUNDWOOD TIMBER COMPANY LTD
Roundwood, Newick Lane,
Mayfield, East Sussex, TN20 6RG
Area of Operation: UK & Ireland
Tel: 01435 867072 **Fax:** 01435 864708
Email: sales@roundwoodtimber.com
Web: www.roundwoodtimber.com

TODD DOORS LTD
112-116 Church Road, Northolt, Greater London, UB5 5AE
Area of Operation: UK (Excluding Ireland)
Tel: 0208 845 2493 **Fax:** 0208 845 7579
Email: info@todd-doors.co.uk
Web: www.todd-doors.co.uk **Other Info:** ECO
Product Type: 1, 2, 3, 4, 5, 6, 7, 8, 9
Material Type: A) 1, 2, 3, 4, 5, 6, 7

TOMPKINS LTD
High March Close, Long March Industrial Estate,
Daventry, Northamptonshire, NN11 4EZ
Area of Operation: UK (Excluding Ireland)
Tel: 01327 877187 **Fax:** 01327 310491
Email: info@tompkinswood.co.uk
Web: www.tompkinswood.co.uk
Product Type: 1, 2, 3, 4, 5, 6, 7
Other Info:
Material Type: A) 1, 2, 3, 4, 5, 6, 7, 8, 9, 10, 11, 12, 13, 14

TRADITIONAL OAK & TIMBER COMPANY
P O Stores , Haywards Heath Road,
North Chailey, Nr Lewes, East Sussex, BN8 4EY
Area of Operation: Worldwide
Tel: 01825 723648 **Fax:** 01825 722215
Email: info@tradoak.co.uk
Web: www.tradoak.com **Product Type:** 1, 2, 4, 7

TRANIK HOUSE DOORSTORE
63-91 Cobham Road, Ferndown Industrial Estate,
Wimborne, Dorset, BH21 7QA
Area of Operation: UK (Excluding Ireland)
Tel: 01202 872211 **Email:** sales@tranik.co.uk
Web: www.tranik.co.uk

UK HARDWOODS LTD T/A BEDFORD TIMBERS
Wade Mill, Molland, South Molton, Devon, EX36 3NL
Area of Operation: Europe
Tel: 01769 550526
Email: bedfordtimbers@talk21.com
Product Type: 7 **Material Type:** A) 2, 6, 8

VICAIMA LIMITED
Drakes Way Business Centre,
Marlowe Avenue, Greenbridge Industrial Estate,
Swindon, Wiltshire, SN3 3JF
Area of Operation: UK & Ireland
Tel: 01793 532333 **Fax:** 01793 530193
Email: info@vicaima.com
Web: www.vicaima.com **Product Type:** 1, 2, 3, 6
Material Type: A) 1, 2, 3, 4, 5, 6, 7

WOODHOUSE TIMBER
Unit 15 Quarry Farm Industrial Estate,
Staplecross Rd, Bodiam, East Sussex, TN32 5RA
Area of Operation: UK (Excluding Ireland)
Tel: 01580 831700 **Fax:** 01580 830054
Email: info@woodhousetimber.co.uk
Web: www.woodhousetimber.co.uk
Product Type: 2, 7, 9 **Other Info:**
Material Type: A) 2, 6

WOODLAND PRODUCTS DESIGN LTD
St.Peter's House, 6 Cambridge Road,
Kingston Upon Thames, Surrey, KT1 3JY
Area of Operation: UK (Excluding Ireland)
Tel: 0208 547 2171 **Fax:** 0208 547 1722
Email: enquiries@woodland-products.co.uk
Web: www.woodland-products.co.uk
Product Type: 4

EXTERNAL DOORS

KEY
PRODUCT TYPES: 1= Plain 2 = Panelled
3 = Glazed 4 = French 5 = Folding / Sliding
6 = Ledged / Braced 7 = Stable 8 = Other
SEE ALSO:
GARAGES AND OUTHOUSES - Garage Doors
OTHER: ▽ Reclaimed On-line shopping
Bespoke Hand-made ECO Ecological

AACORN JOINERY AND DESIGN LTD.
2 Balaclava Place, South Street, Bridport, Dorset, DT6 3PE
Tel: 01308 456217 **Fax:** 01308 424511
Email: info@aacornjoinery.co.uk
Web: www.aacornjoinery.co.uk

AMBASSADOOR WINDOWS & DOORS LTD
18 Bidwell Road, Rackheath Industrial Estate,
Rackheath, Norwich, Norfolk, NR13 6PT
Area of Operation: East England, Greater London, Midlands & Mid Wales
Tel: 01603 720332
Email: enquiries@ambassadoor.fsnet.co.uk
Web: www.ambassadoor.co.uk
Product Type: 1, 2, 3, 4, 5, 6 **Material Type:** A) 1

ANDERSEN WINDOWS / BLACK MILLWORK CO.
Andersen House, Dallow Street,
Burton on Trent, Staffordshire, DE14 2PQ
Tel: 01283 511122 **Fax:** 01283 510863
Email: info@blackmillwork.co.uk
Web: www.blackmillwork.co.uk
Product Type: 3, 4, 8 **Other Info:** ECO
Material Type: A) 2, 5, 15

ARBOR WINDOW SYSTEMS LIMITED
1240 Park Avenue, Aztec West, Bristol, BS32 4SH
Area of Operation: UK (Excluding Ireland)
Tel: 01454 270039 **Fax:** 01454 270049
Email: enquiries@arborwinsys.co.uk
Web: www.arborwinsys.co.uk

ARCHITECTURAL BRONZE CASEMENTS
Vale Garden Houses Ltd, Belton Park, Londonthorpe Road, Grantham, Lincolnshire, NG31 9SJ
Area of Operation: Worldwide
Tel: 01476 564433 **Fax:** 01476 578555
Email: enquiries@bronzecasements.com
Web: www.bronzecasements.com
Product Type: 4

ARCHITECTURAL DOORS & WINDOWS LIMITED
3 Tollpark Road, Wardpark East,
Cumbernauld, Glasgow, G68 0LW
Area of Operation: UK
Tel: 01236 780022 **Fax:** 01236 780021
Email: info@adwlimited.co.uk
Web: www.adwlimited.co.uk

ASTON HOUSE JOINERY
Aston House, Tripontium Business Centre,
Newton Lane, Rugby, Warwickshire, CV23 0TB
Area of Operation: UK & Ireland
Tel: 01788 860032 **Fax:** 01788 860614
Email: enquiries@astonhousejoinery.co.uk
Web: www.astonhousejoinery.co.uk
Product Type: 1, 2, 3, 4, 5, 6, 7
Other Info: ECO **Material Type:** A) 1, 2, 12

B & M WINDOW & KITCHEN CENTRE
2-6 Whitworth Drive,
Aycliffe Industrial Park, Durham, DL5 6SZ
Area of Operation: Worldwide
Tel: 01325 308888
Fax: 01325 316002
Email: sales@bandmhomeimprovements.com
Web: www.bandmhomeimprovements.com
Product Type: 1, 2, 3, 4, 5, 7

BUILDING STRUCTURE & MATERIALS

BARHAM & SONS
58 Finchley Avenue, Mildenhall, Suffolk, IP28 7BG
Area of Operation: UK (Excluding Ireland)
Tel: 01638 711611   **Fax:** 01638 716688
Email: info@barhamwoodfloors.com
Web: www.barhamwoodfloors.com
Product Type: 1, 2, 3, 6

BDG GROUP LTD
5 Wenlock Road, Lurgan, Craigavon, Co Armagh, BT66 8QR
Area of Operation: UK & Ireland
Tel: 02838 327741   **Fax:** 02838 324358
Email: wosb@bdg.co.uk   **Web:** www.bdg.co.uk
Product Type: 1, 2, 3, 4, 5   **Material Type:** C) 1

BETTER LIVING PRODUCTS UK LTD
14 Riverside Business Park, Stansted, Essex, CM24 8PL
Tel: 01279 812958   **Fax:** 01279 817771
Email: info@dispenser.co.uk
Web: www.dispenser.co.uk
Product Type: 1   **Material Type:** C) 4

BETTERDEAL WINDOWS & CONSERVATORIES
17 Ensign House, Admirals Way, London, E14 9JX
Area of Operation: East England, Greater London,
South East England
Tel: 01268 732599   **Email:** betterdealltd@aol.com
Web: www.betterdealwindows.co.uk
Product Type: 3, 4, 5, 7, 8

BIRCHDALE GLASS LTD
Unit L, Eskdale Road, Uxbridge, Greater London, UB8 2RT
Area of Operation: UK & Ireland
Tel: 01895 259111   **Fax:** 01895 810087
Email: info@birchdaleglass.com
Web: www.birchdaleglass.com
Product Type: 1, 2, 3, 4, 5, 7, 8

BIRTLEY BUILDING PRODUCTS LTD
Mary Avenue, Birtley, County Durham, DH3 1JF
Tel: 0191 410 6631   **Fax:** 0191 410 0650
Email: info@birtley-building.co.uk
Web: www.birtley-building.co.uk
Product Type: 3   **Material Type:** C) 2

BOWATER BUILDING PRODUCTS
Water Orton Lane, Minworth,
Sutton Coldfield, West Midlands, B76 9BW
Tel: 0121 749 3000   **Fax:** 0121 749 8210
Email: info@theprimeconnection.co.uk
Web: www.theprimeconnection.co.uk
Product Type: 1, 2, 3, 4, 5, 6, 7, 8
Material Type: D) 1, 6

BROADLEAF TIMBER
Llandeilo Road Industrial Estate,
Carms, Carmarthenshire, SA18 3JG
Area of Operation: UK & Ireland
Tel: 01269 851910   **Fax:** 01269 851911
Email: sales@broadleaftimber.com
Web: www.broadleaftimber.com
Product Type: 1, 2, 3, 4, 6, 7
Other Info: ✍ ✋   **Material Type:** A) 2

BROXWOOD LTD
Broxwood Ltd, Inveralmond Way,
Inveralmond Industrial Estate, Perth, PH1 3UQ
Area of Operation: Europe
Fax: 01738 444452
Email: sales@broxwood.com
Web: www.broxwood.com ✍
Product Type: 1, 2, 3, 4, 5, 6, 7

BWF - TWA SCHEME
55 Tufton Street, London, SW1P 3QL
Area of Operation: UK (Excluding Ireland)
Tel: 0870 458 6939   **Fax:** 0870 458 6949
Email: ruth.soundarajah@bwf.org.uk ✍
Web: http://www.bwf.org.uk/about_the_scheme_twa.cfm

CAREY & FOX LTD
51 Langthwaite Business Park, South Kirkby,
Pontefract, West Yorkshire, WF9 3NR
Area of Operation: UK & Ireland
Tel: 01977 608069   **Fax:** 01977 646791
Email: enquiries@careyandfox.co.uk
Web: www.careyandfox.co.uk
Product Type: 1, 2, 3, 4, 5, 6, 7, 8
Material Type: A) 2

CAWARDEN BRICK & TILE CO. LTD
Cawarden Springs Farm, Blithbury Road,
Rugeley, Staffordshire, WS15 3HL
Area of Operation: UK (Excluding Ireland)
Tel: 01889 574066   **Fax:** 01889 575695
Email: home-garden@cawardenreclaim.co.uk
Web: www.cawardenreclaim.co.uk

CENTURION
Westhill Business Park, Arnhall Business Park,
Westhill, Aberdeen, Aberdeenshire, AB32 6UF
Area of Operation: Scotland
Tel: 01224 744440   **Fax:** 01224 744819
Email: info@centurion-solutions.co.uk
Web: www.centurion-solutions.co.uk
Product Type: 5

**CHAMBERLAIN & GROVES LTD -
THE DOOR & SECURITY STORE**
101 Boundary Road, Walthamstow, London, E17 8NQ
Area of Operation: UK (Excluding Ireland)
Tel: 0208 520 6776   **Fax:** 0208 520 2190
Email: ken@securedoors.co.uk
Web: www.securedoors.co.uk
Product Type: 1, 2, 3, 4, 7, 8
Other Info: ECO ✍ ✋   **Material Type:** A) 1, 2

CHESHIRE DOOR COMPANY
Paradise Mill, Old Park Lane,
Macclesfield, Cheshire, SK11 6TJ
Area of Operation: UK & Ireland
Tel: 01625 421221   **Fax:** 01625 421422
Email: info@cheshiredoorcompany.co.uk
Web: www.cheshiredoorcompany.co.uk

CHIPPING NORTON GLASS LTD
Units 1 & 2, Station Yard Industrial Estate,
Chipping Norton, Oxfordshire, OX7 5HX
Area of Operation: Midlands & Mid Wales, South
West England and South Wales
Tel: 01608 643261   **Fax:** 01608 641768
Email: gill@cnglass.plus.com
Web: www.chippingnortonglass.co.uk
Product Type: 3, 4, 5, 7   **Material Type:** C) 1

CLASSIC PVC HOME IMPROVEMENTS
Unit 36 LEC Workshops, Trostre Road,
Llanelli, Carmarthenshire, SA15 2EA
Area of Operation: South West England and South Wales
Tel: 01554 777158   **Fax:** 01554 775086
Email: enquiries@classic.uk.com
Web: www.classic.uk.com
Product Type: 1, 2, 3, 4, 7   **Material Type:** D) 1, 6

CLEARVIEW WINDOWS & DOORS
Unit 14, Sheddingdean Industrial Estate, Marchants
Way, Burgess Hill, West Sussex, RH15 8QY
Area of Operation: UK (Excluding Ireland)
Tel: 01444 250111   **Fax:** 01444 250678
Email: sales@clearviewsussex.co.uk
Web: www.clearviewsussex.co.uk

CLEMENT STEEL WINDOWS
Clement House, Weydown Road,
Haslemere, Surrey, GU27 1HR
Area of Operation: Worldwide
Tel: 01428 643393   **Fax:** 01428 644436
Email: info@clementwg.co.uk
Web: www.clementsteelwindows.com
Product Type: 3, 4

CONSERVATORY & WINDOW WORLD LTD
Watling Road, Bishop Aukland, Durham, DL14 9AU
Area of Operation: North East England
Tel: 01388 458 088   **Fax:** 01388 458 518
Email: paldennis20@aol.com
Web: www.conservatoryandwindowworld.co.uk
Product Type: 2, 3, 4, 5, 7
Material Type: D) 1, 3, 6

CONSERVATORY OUTLET
Unit 8 Headway Business Park, Denby Dale Road,
Wakefield, West Yorkshire, WF2 7AZ
Area of Operation: North East England
Tel: 01924 881920
Web: www.conservatoryoutlet.co.uk
Product Type: 1, 2, 3, 4, 5, 7, 8
Material Type: D) 1

CONSTRUCTION TECHNICAL SERVICES
Dunedin House, Alexandra Road,
Penzance, Cornwall, TR18 4LZ
Area of Operation: UK & Ireland
Tel: 01736 330303
Fax: 01736 360497
Email: ctecs@aol.com
Web: www.hometown.aol.co.uk/carpinjohn
Product Type: 5, 8

COUNTY JOINERY (SOUTH EAST) LTD
Tetley House, Marley Lane Business Park,
Marley Lane, Battle, East Sussex, TN33 0RE
Area of Operation: Greater London, South East England
Tel: 01424 871500
Fax: 01424 871550
Email: info@countyjoinery.co.uk
Web: www.countyjoinery.co.uk
Product Type: 1, 2, 3, 4, 5, 6, 7, 8
Material Type: A) 2, 3, 4, 5, 6, 7, 8, 9, 10, 11, 12, 13, 14

CREATE JOINERY
The Wood Yard, Castell Ddu Road, Waun Gron,
Pontarddulais, Swansea, SA4 8DH
Area of Operation: Greater London, Midlands & Mid
Wales, North West England and North Wales, South
East England, South West England and South Wales
Tel: 01792 386677
Fax: 01792 386677
Email: mail@create-joinery.co.uk
Web: www.create-joinery.co.uk
Product Type: 1, 2, 3, 4, 5, 6, 7, 8

**CROXFORD'S JOINERY
MANUFACTURERS & WOODTURNERS**
Meltham Joinery, Works New Street, Meltham,
Holmfirth, West Yorkshire, HD9 5NT
Area of Operation: UK (Excluding Ireland)
Tel: 01484 850892
Fax: 01484 850969
Email: croxford1@btconnect.com
Web: www.croxfords.co.uk
Product Type: 1, 2, 3, 4, 5, 6, 7, 8

CUSTOM WOOD PRODUCTS
Cliffe Road, Easton on the Hill,
Stamford, Lincolnshire, PE9 3NP
Area of Operation: East England
Tel: 01780 755711 **Fax:** 01780 480834
Email: customwoodprods@aol.com
Web: www.cwpuk.com **Other Info:** ECO
Product Type: 1, 2, 3, 4, 5, 6, 7

DICTATOR DIRECT
Inga House, Northdown Business Park,
Ashford Road, Lenham, Kent, ME17 2DL
Area of Operation: Worldwide
Tel: 01622 854770 **Fax:** 01622 854771
Email: mail@dictatordirect.com
Web: www.dictatordirect.com

DIRECTDOORS.COM
Bay 5 Eastfield Industrial Estate,
Eastfield Drive, Penicuik, Lothian, EH26 8JA
Area of Operation: UK (Excluding Ireland)
Tel: 01968 671681 **Fax:** 01968 671684
Email: info@directdoors.com
Web: www.directdoors.com
Product Type: 1, 2, 3, 4, 5, 6, 7, 8

DISABILITY ACCESS COMPANY LTD
Access House, 16 - 18 Chapel Street,
Glossop, Derbyshire, SK13 8AT
Area of Operation: UK & Ireland
Tel: 01457 868547 **Fax:** 0871 733 5071
Email: sales@disabilityaccessco.com
Web: www.disabilityaccessco.com
Product Type: 1, 3, 5

DISTINCTIVE DOORS
14 & 15 Chambers Way, Newton Chambers Road,
Chapeltown, Sheffield, South Yorkshire, S35 2PH
Area of Operation: UK & Ireland
Tel: 0114 220 2250 **Fax:** 0114 220 2254
Email: enquiries@distinctivedoors.co.uk
Web: www.distinctivedoors.co.uk
Product Type: 2, 3, 4, 6, 7
Material Type: A) 1, 2, 6

DISTINCTIVE DOORS

Area of Operation: UK & Ireland
Tel: 0114 220 2250 **Fax:** 0114 220 2254
Email: enquiries@distinctivedoors.co.uk
Web: www.distinctivedoors.co.uk
Product Type: 2, 3, 4, 6, 7

Suppliers of High Class External & Internal Doors.
Exclusive Product Range Triple Glazed Doors.
Oak Internal Engineered Doors.
Hardwood Doors, Clear Pine Doors.

DIY SASH WINDOWS
2 - 6 Whitworth Drive, Aycliffe Industrial Park,
Newton Aycliffe, Durham, DL56SZ
Tel: 01325 308888 **Fax:** 01325 316002
Email: sales@diysashwindows.co.uk
Web: www.diysashwindows.co.uk
Product Type: 1, 2, 3, 4, 5, 7

DOORIA UK LTD
20 - 22 Glenburn Road, East Kilbride, Lanarkshire, G74 5BA
Area of Operation: UK & Ireland
Tel: 01355 243918
Email: lars.lund@dooria.co.uk
Web: www.dooria.net **Product Type:** 1, 2, 3, 4, 8
Material Type: A) 1, 2, 3, 4, 7, 9, 10, 15

DORLUXE LIMITED
30 Pinbush Road, Lowestoft, Suffolk, NR33 7NL
Area of Operation: UK & Ireland
Tel: 01502 567744
Fax: 01502 567743
Email: info@dorluxe.co.uk
Web: www.dorluxe.co.uk **Product Type:** 3, 7

DYNASTY DOORS
Unit 3, The Micro Centre, Gillette Way,
Reading, Berkshire, RG2 0LR
Area of Operation: South East England, South West
England and South Wales
Tel: 0118 987 4000
Fax: 0118 921 2999
Email: info@dynastydoors.co.uk
Web: www.dynastydoors.co.uk
Product Type: 1, 2, 3, 4, 7

EDEN HOUSE LIMITED
Elveden, Kennel Lane, Windlesham, Surrey, GU20 6AA
Area of Operation: Greater London, South East England
Tel: 01276 470192 **Fax:** 01276 489689
Email: info@internalshutters.co.uk
Web: www.edenhouse.biz
Product Type: 3, 4, 5

ENERGY SUPERSTORE
3 Wellington Park, Belfast, BT9 6DJ
Area of Operation: UK & Ireland
Tel: 02890 388391
Email: info@energysuperstore.co.uk
Web: www.energysuperstore.co.uk
Product Type: 1, 2, 3, 4, 5, 6, 7, 8

ENGELS WINDOWS & DOORS LTD
1 Kingley Centre, Downs Road, West Stoke,
Chichester, West Sussex, PO18 9HJ
Area of Operation: UK (Excluding Ireland)
Tel: 01243 576633
Fax: 01243 576644
Email: admin@engels.co.uk
Web: www.engels.co.uk

SUN PARADISE

Contemporary aluminium folding/sliding doors and roof systems

Duncan Foster Architect

Glazed folding sliding doors are secure, weathertight, thermally efficient and a delight to use, folding right back to bring in the outside world. Designed to compliment our contemporary roof and window systems, unique flexible conservatories can be created with the help of our enthusiastic, knowledgeable staff.

Exceptional quality, technical expertise and level of service from your first phone call to installation and handover are assured. Technical brochures and CAD files can be downloaded from our website or ask for our CD ROM.

office and showroom **sunparadise uk ltd** phoenix wharf eel pie island twickenham middlesex TW1 3DY
tel 0870 240 7604 **fax** 0870 240 7614 **email** info@sunparadise.co.uk **web** www.sunparadise.co.uk

ESOGRAT LTD
Caldervale Works, River Street, Brighouse,
Huddersfield, West Yorkshire, HD6 1JS
Area of Operation: UK & Ireland
Tel: 01484 716228
Fax: 01484 400107
Email: info@esograt.com **Web:** www.esograt.com
Product Type: 1, 2, 3, 4, 7, 8

EUROCELL PROFILES LTD
Fairbrook House, Clover Nook Road,
Alfreton, Derby, Derbyshire, DE55 4RF
Area of Operation: UK (Excluding Ireland)
Tel: 01773 842100
Fax: 01773 842298
Email: sales@eurocell.co.uk
Web: www.eurocell.co.uk
Product Type: 1, 3, 4, 5, 7, 8
Material Type: D) 1, 6

EVEREST LTD
Sopers Road, Cuffley, Hertfordshire, EN6 4SG
Area of Operation: UK & Ireland
Tel: 0800 010123 **Web:** www.everest.co.uk
Product Type: 1, 3, 5

FAIRMITRE WINDOWS & JOINERY LTD
2A Cope Road, Banbury, Oxfordshire, OX16 2EH
Area of Operation: UK (Excluding Ireland)
Tel: 01295 268441 **Fax:** 01295 268468
Email: info@fairmitrewindows.co.uk
Web: www.fairmitrewindows.co.uk
Product Type: 2, 3, 4, 5, 6, 7

FAIROAK TIMBER PRODUCTS LIMITED
Manor Farm, Chilmark, Salisbury, Wiltshire, FP3 5AG
Area of Operation: UK (Excluding Ireland)
Tel: 01722 716779
Fax: 01722 716761
Email: sales@fairoak.co.uk
Web: www.fairoakwindows.co.uk
Product Type: 1, 2, 3, 4, 7 **Material Type:** A) 2, 12

FINNISH WOOD PRODUCTS LTD
Tresparrett Farm Villa, Tresparrett, Cornwall, PL32 9ST
Area of Operation: UK & Ireland
Tel: 01840 261415 **Fax:** 01840 261415
Email: sales@finnishwoodproducts.com
Web: www.finnishwoodproducts.com
Product Type: 1, 3, 5, 7, 8

FITZROY JOINERY
Garden Close, Langage Industrial Estate,
Plympton, Plymouth, Devon, PL7 5EU
Area of Operation: UK & Ireland
Tel: 0870 428 9110 **Fax:** 0870 428 9111
Email: admin@fitzroy.co.uk
Web: www.fitzroyjoinery.co.uk
Product Type: 1, 2, 3, 4, 5, 7
Other Info: ECO
Material Type: A) 1, 2, 3, 4, 5, 6, 7, 8, 9, 10, 12, 14

FLETCHER JOINERY
261 Whessoe Road, Darlington, Durham, DL3 0YL
Area of Operation: North East England
Tel: 01325 357347
Fax: 01325 357347
Email: enquiries@fletcherjoinery.co.uk
Web: www.fletcherjoinery.co.uk
Product Type: 1, 2, 3, 4, 5, 6, 7, 8

FOLDING SLIDING DOORS LIMITED
FSD Works, Hopbine Avenue, West Bowling,
Bradford, West Yorkshire, BD5 8ER
Area of Operation: UK (Excluding Ireland)
Tel: 0845 644 6630 **Fax:** 0845 644 6631
Email: sales@foldingslidingdoors.com
Web: www.foldingslidingdoors.com
Product Type: 5

FRANKLIN LEEDS LLP
Carlton Works, Cemetery Road, Yeadon,
Leeds, West Yorkshire, LS19 7BD
Area of Operation: UK & Ireland
Tel: 0113 250 2991 **Fax:** 0113 250 0991
Email: david.franklin@franklinwindows.co.uk
Web: www.franklinwindows.co.uk
Product Type: 1, 2, 3, 4, 5, 7, 8

GAP
Partnership Way, Shadsworth Business Park,
Blackburn, Lancashire, BB1 2QP
Area of Operation: Midlands & Mid Wales, North
East England, North West England and North Wales
Tel: 01254 682888
Web: www.gap.uk.com
Product Type: 1, 2, 3, 7 **Material Type:** D) 1

GARY BYNG AND SONS
Unit 17 Metal and Ores Industrial Estate, Hanbury Road,
Stoke Prior, Bromsgrove, Worcestershire, B60 4JZ
Area of Operation: UK & Ireland
Tel: 01527 876348 **Fax:** 01527 876339
Email: garybyng@byng.fsbusiness.co.uk
Web: www.gbands.co.uk
Product Type: 1, 2, 3, 4, 6, 7, 8

GREEN BUILDING STORE
11 Huddersfield Road, Meltham,
Holmfirth, West Yorkshire, HD9 4NJ
Area of Operation: UK & Ireland
Tel: 01484 854898
Fax: 01484 854899
Email: info@greenbuildingstore.co.uk
Web: www.greenbuildingstore.co.uk
Product Type: 1, 2, 3, 4, 5, 7, 8
Other Info: ECO **Material Type:** B) 8

HAYMANS TIMBER PRODUCTS
Haymans Farm, Hocker Lane, Over Alderley,
Macclesfield, Cheshire, SK10 4SD
Area of Operation: UK & Ireland
Tel: 01625 590098 **Fax:** 01625 586174
Email: haymanstimber@aol.com
Web: www.haymanstimber.co.uk
Product Type: 1, 2, 3, 4, 5, 6, 7
Material Type: A) 2, 4, 6, 7

HIGHSEAL WINDOWS LIMITED
Moat Road, Scunthorpe, Lincolnshire, DN15 9GA
Area of Operation: East England, Greater London,
Midlands & Mid Wales, North East England, North West
England and North Wales, Scotland, South East England
Tel: 01724 276213
Fax: 01724 276214
Email: david.maybank@hwlgroup.co.uk
Web: www.hwlgroup.co.uk **Material Type:** D) 1
Product Type: 1, 2, 3, 4, 5, 6, 7

HM DOORS
620 Bradford Road, Batley, West Yorkshire, WF17 8HF
Area of Operation: UK & Ireland
Tel: 01924 440114 **Fax:** 01924 477761
Email: keithhutchinson@hmdoors.co.uk
Web: www.hmdoors.co.uk
Product Type: 1, 2, 3, 4, 8

HOLME TREE LTD
Units 2 and 3 Machins Business Centre, 29 Wood
Street, Asby-de-la-Zouch, Leicestershire, LE65 1EL
Area of Operation: UK (Excluding Ireland)
Tel: 01530 564561 **Fax:** 01530 417986
Email: info@holmetree.co.uk
Web: www.holmetree.co.uk

HOWARTH WINDOWS AND DOORS LTD
The Dock, New Holland, Lincolnshire, DN19 7RT
Area of Operation: UK & Ireland
Tel: 01469 530577 **Fax:** 01469 531559
Email: ktopliss@howarth-timber.co.uk
Web: www.howarth-timber.co.uk
Product Type: 1, 2, 3, 4 **Material Type:** B) 6, 8, 13

ID SYSTEMS
Sunflex House, Rhombus Business Park,
Diamond Road, Norwich, Norfolk, NR6 6NN
Area of Operation: UK & Ireland
Tel: 01603 408804 **Fax:** 01603 258648
Email: info@i-d-systems.co.uk
Web: www.i-d-systems.co.uk **Product Type:** 5

IDM DOORS LTD
Rock Wharf, Mill Parade, Newport, Gwent, NP20 2UL
Area of Operation: UK (Excluding Ireland)
Tel: 01633 843098 **Fax:** 01633 259079
Email: info@idmdoorsltd.co.uk
Web: www.idmdoorsltd.co.uk

IMAJ STEEL DOORS
704 Lea Bridge Road, London, E10 6AW
Area of Operation: Worldwide
Tel: 02030 223000 **Fax:** 02030 223001
Email: sales@imajsteeldoors.com
Web: www.imajsteeldoors.com **Material Type:** C) 2

IN DOORS
Beechinwood Farm, Beechinwood Lane,
Platt, Nr. Sevenoaks, Kent, TN15 8QN
Area of Operation: UK (Excluding Ireland)
Tel: 01732 887445 **Fax:** 01732 887446
Email: sales@indoorsltd.co.uk
Web: www.indoorsltd.co.uk
Product Type: 1, 2, 3, 4, 5, 6, 7

INPUT JOINERY LTD
The Fairground, Weyhill, Andover, Hampshire, SP11 0ST
Area of Operation: UK (Excluding Ireland)
Tel: 01264 771900 **Fax:** 01264 771901
Email: info@inputjoinery.co.uk
Web: www.inputjoinery.co.uk
Product Type: 2, 3, 4, 5, 6, 7
Material Type: A) 1, 2, 6

J L JOINERY
Cockerton View, Grange Lane, Preston, Lancashire, PR4 5JE
Area of Operation: UK (Excluding Ireland)
Tel: 01772 616123 **Fax:** 01772 619182
Email: mail@jljoinery.co.uk
Web: www.jljoinery.co.uk

JAMES BENTLEY
James Bentley Limited, 13 Tennyson Road,
Hinckley, Leicestershire, LE10 0TH
Area of Operation: UK (Excluding Ireland)
Tel: 0870 850 2057
Email: paul.smith@james-bentley.co.uk
Web: www.james-bentley.co.uk
Product Type: 1, 2, 3, 4, 5, 8 **Material Type:** D) 1

JB KIND LTD
Shobnall Street, Burton-on-Trent,
Staffordshire, DE14 2HP
Area of Operation: UK & Ireland
Tel: 01283 510210
Fax: 01283 511132
Email: info@jbkind.com
Web: www.jbkind.com
Product Type: 1, 2, 3, 4
Material Type: A) 1, 2

JELD-WEN
Watch House Lane, Doncaster, South Yorkshire, DN5 9LR
Area of Operation: UK & Ireland
Tel: 0870 126 0000 **Fax:** 01302 787383
Email: customer-services@jeld-wen.co.uk
Web: www.jeld-wen.co.uk
Product Type: 1, 2, 3, 5
Material Type: C) 18

JOHN FLEMING & CO LTD
Silverhill Place, Bridge of Don,
Aberdeen, Aberdeenshire, AB23 8EG
Area of Operation: Scotland
Tel: 0800 085 8728 **Fax:** 01224 825377
Email: info@johnfleming.co.uk
Web: www.johnfleming.co.uk

JOHN VINNIE LTD
Unit 4 Milnsbridge Business Centre, Colne Vale Road,
Milnsbridge, Huddersfield, West Yorkshire, HD3 4NY
Area of Operation: UK (Excluding Ireland)
Tel: 01484 647666 **Fax:** 01484 648666
Email: sales@jvjoinery.co.uk
Web: www.jvjoinery.co.uk
Product Type: 1, 2, 3, 4, 5, 6, 7, 8

JOINERY-PLUS
Bentley Hall Barn, Alkmonton,
Ashbourne, Derbyshire, DE6 3DJ
Area of Operation: UK (Excluding Ireland)
Tel: 07931 386233 **Fax:** 01335 330922
Email: info@joinery-plus.co.uk
Web: www.joinery-plus.co.uk
Product Type: 1, 2, 3, 4, 6, 7
Material Type: A) 1, 2, 3, 4, 5, 6, 7, 8, 9, 10, 11, 12, 13, 14

JONATHAN ELWELL
Bryn Teg Workshop & Tan y Bryn Cottage,
Tanrallt Road, Gwespyr, Flintshire, CH8 9JT
Area of Operation: UK (Excluding Ireland)
Tel: 01745 887766
Email: jonathanelwell@ukonline.co.uk
Web: www.jonathanelwell.co.uk

KERSHAWS DOORS LTD
Main Street, Wyke, Bradford, West Yorkshire, BD12 8BN
Area of Operation: UK (Excluding Ireland)
Tel: 01274 604488 **Fax:** 0845 126 0275
Email: help@door-warehouse.co.uk
Web: www.doorwarehouse.co.uk
Product Type: 1, 2, 3, 4, 5, 6, 7, 8

LAMWOOD LTD
Unit 1, Riverside Works, Station Road,
Cheddleton, Staffordshire, ST13 7EE
Area of Operation: UK & Ireland
Tel: 01538 361888 **Fax:** 01538 361912
Email: info@lamwoodltd.co.uk
Web: www.lamwoodltd.co.uk **Material Type:** A) 2

LATTICE PERIOD WINDOWS
Unit 85 Northwick Business Centre, Blockley,
Moreton in Marsh, Gloucestershire, Gl56 9RF
Area of Operation: UK & Ireland
Tel: 01386 701079 **Fax:** 01386 701114
Email: sales@latticewindows.net
Web: www.latticewindows.net
Product Type: 1, 2, 3, 4, 6
Other Info: **Material Type:** A) 2

BUILDING STRUCTURE & MATERIALS

LPD DOORS
Holme Well Road, Leeds, West Yorkshire, LS10 4SL
Area of Operation: UK & Ireland
Tel: 0845 658 5115   **Email:** sales@lpddoors.co.uk
Product Type: 3, 5

MANSE MASTERDOR LIMITED
Hambleton Grove, Knaresborough,
North Yorkshire, HG5 0DB
Area of Operation: UK (Excluding Ireland)
Tel: 01423 866868   **Fax:** 01423 866368
Email: info@masterdor.co.uk
Web: www.masterdor.co.uk
Product Type: 1, 2, 3, 4, 7, 8
Other Info: ✎   **Material Type:** B) 1

MARVIN ARCHITECTURAL
Canal House, Catherine Wheel Road, Brentford,
Middlesex, Greater London, TW8 8BD
Area of Operation: UK & Ireland
Tel: 0208 569 8222   **Fax:** 0208 560 6374
Email: sales@marvinuk.com
Web: www.marvin-architectural.com
Product Type: 1, 3, 4, 5, 7

MARVIN ARCHITECTURAL

Area of Operation: UK & Ireland
Tel: 0208 569 8222
Fax: 0208 560 6374
Email: sales@marvinUK.com
Web: www.marvin-architectural.com

Marvin's 4 Wide Sliding French Doors allow you
to flood your room with natural light and provide
easy accessibility to the outdoors. Available in
solid wood or composite aluminium clad/wood.

MARVIN ARCHITECTURAL

Area of Operation: UK & Ireland
Tel: 0208 569 8222
Fax: 0208 560 6374
Email: sales@marvinUK.com
Web: www.marvin-architectural.com

Marvin Windows and Doors are made for you.
With 11, 000 standard sizes and almost limitless
custom capabilities, they fit to your exact
specifications, style, size and lifestyle.

MERLIN UK LIMITED
Unit 5 Fence Avenue, Macclesfield, Cheshire, SK10 1LT
Area of Operation: North West England and North Wales
Tel: 01625 424488   **Fax:** 0871 781 8967
Email: info@merlinuk.net
Web: www.merlindoors.co.uk
Product Type: 1, 2, 3, 4, 5, 7, 8

MULTIWOOD HOME IMPROVEMENTS LTD
1298 Chester Road, Stretford, Manchester, M32 9AU
Area of Operation: Europe
Tel: 0161 866 9991   **Fax:** 0161 866 9992
Email: sales@multiwoodconservatories.co.uk
Web: www.multiwoodconservatories.co.uk
Product Type: 3, 4, 5

MUMFORD & WOOD LTD
Tower Business Park,
Kelvedon Road, Tiptree, Essex, CO5 0LX
Area of Operation: Worldwide
Tel: 01621 818155   **Fax:** 01621 818175
Email: sales@mumfordwood.com
Web: www.mumfordwood.com
Product Type: 1, 2, 4

NATIONAL DOOR COMPANY
Unit 55 Dinting Vale Business Park,
Dinting Vale, Glossop, Derbyshire, SK13 6JD
Area of Operation: UK (Excluding Ireland)
Tel: 01457 867079   **Fax:** 01457 868795
Email: sales@nationaldoor.co.uk
Web: www.nationaldoor.co.uk
Product Type: 1, 2, 3, 4, 6, 7, 8

NOISE STOP SYSTEMS
Unit 2, Car House Farm, Poole Lane,
Nun Monkton, York, North Yorkshire, Y026 8EH
Area of Operation: UK & Ireland
Tel: 0845 130 6269   **Fax:** 01423 339153
Email: info@noisestopsystems.co.uk
Web: www.noisestopsystems.co.uk ✎
Product Type: 1, 2, 4, 5, 7, 8

NORBUILD TIMBER FABRICATION &
FINE CARPENTRY LTD
Marcassie Farm, Rafford, Forres, Moray, IV36 2RH
Area of Operation: UK & Ireland
Tel: 01309 676865   **Fax:** 01309 676865
Email: norbuild@marcassie.fsnet.co.uk
Product Type: 2, 3, 8   **Other Info:** ECO ✎ ☞
Material Type: A) 1, 2, 6, 11

NORTH YORKSHIRE TIMBER
Standard House, Thurston Road, Northallerton Business
Park, Northallerton, North Yorkshire, DL6 2NA
Area of Operation: UK (Excluding Ireland)
Tel: 01609 780777   **Fax:** 01609 777888
Email: sales@nytimber.co.uk
Web: www.nytimber.co.uk

NORTHWOOD FORESTRY LTD
Goose Green Lane, Nr Ashington,
Pulborough, West Sussex, RH20 2LW
Area of Operation: South East England
Tel: 01798 813029
Fax: 01798 813139
Email: enquiries@northwoodforestry.co.uk
Web: www.northwoodforestry.co.uk
Product Type: 6

NORVIK PVCU WINDOW SYSTEMS LTD
Mitchells Industrial Park, Wombwell,
Barnsley, South Yorkshire, S35 7AE
Area of Operation: UK & Ireland
Tel: 01226 340182   **Fax:** 01226 340375
Email: nhibberd@norvik.co.uk
Web: www.norvik.co.uk
Product Type: 1, 2, 3, 4, 5, 7

OCTAVEWARD LIMITED
Balle Street, Darwen, Lancashire, BB3 2AZ
Area of Operation: UK (Excluding Ireland)
Tel: 01254 773300
Fax: 01254 773950
Email: info@octaveward.com
Web: www.octaveward.com   **Product Type:** 2, 6, 7

OLDE WORLDE OAK JOINERY LTD
Unit 12, Longford Industrial Estate,
Longford Road, Cannock, Staffordshire, WS11 0DG
Area of Operation: Europe
Tel: 01543 469328
Fax: 01543 469328
Email: sales@oldeworldeoakjoinery.co.uk
Web: www.oldeworldeoakjoinery.co.uk
Product Type: 1, 2, 6, 7

ORIGINAL OAK
Ashlands, Burwash, East Sussex, TN19 7HS
Area of Operation: UK (Excluding Ireland)
Tel: 01435 882228   **Fax:** 01435 882228
Web: www.originaloak.co.uk   **Material Type:** A) 2

OXFORD SASH WINDOW CO LTD.
Eynsham Park Estate Yard, Cuckoo Lane,
North Leigh, Oxfordshire, OX29 6PW
Area of Operation: Greater London, Midlands & Mid Wales,
South East England, South West England and South Wales
Tel: 01993 883536   **Fax:** 01993 883027
Email: oxsash@globalnet.co.uk
Web: www.sashwindow.co.uk **Product Type:** 1, 2, 3

PERIOD OAK DOORS LTD
7 Saint Davids House, Brawdey Business Park,
Brawdey, Haverford West, Pembrokeshire, SA62 6NP
Area of Operation: UK & Ireland
Tel: 01437 720373   **Fax:** 01437 720406
Email: perioddoors@yahoo.co.uk
Web: www.perioddoors.com
Product Type: 1, 2, 3, 6, 7

PERIOD OAK DOORS LTD.

Area of Operation: UK & Ireland
Tel: 01437 720373   **Fax:** 01437 720406
Email: perioddoors@yahoo.co.uk
Web: www.perioddoors.com
Product Type: 1, 2, 3, 6, 7

Quality bespoke doors [made to measure]
designed to recreate the cottage style of years
gone by, in both pine and beautiful oak, at
affordable prices.

PERMADOOR
Upton on Severn, Worcestershire, WR8 0RX
Area of Operation: UK (Excluding Ireland)
Tel: 01684 595200   **Fax:** 01684 594283
Email: info@permadoor.co.uk
Web: www.permadoor.co.uk
Product Type: 1, 3, 8   **Material Type:** D) 1, 3, 6

PORTICO GB LTD
Unit 9 Windmill Avenue, Woolpit Business Park,
Woolpit , Bury St Edmunds , Suffolk, IP30 9UP
Area of Operation: Greater London, South East England
Tel: 01359 244299   **Fax:** 01359 244232
Email: info@portico-gb.co.uk
Web: www.portico-newbuild.co.uk
Product Type: 4, 5

PREMDOR
Gemini House, Hargreaves Road, Groundwell
Industrial Estate, Swindon, Wiltshire, SN25 5AJ
Area of Operation: UK & Ireland
Tel: 0870 990 7998
Email: ukmarketing@premdor.com
Web: www.premdor.co.uk
Product Type: 1, 2, 3, 4, 6, 7, 8

RADNOR TIMBER COMPANY
The Offices, Old Impton Farm,
Norton, Presteigne, Powys, LD8 2EN
Area of Operation: Europe
Tel: 01544 260727   **Fax:** 01544 262113
Email: sales@rtc.enta.net
Web: www.radnortimbercompany
Product Type: 1, 2, 3, 4, 6, 7, 8
Other Info: ECO ✎ ☞   **Material Type:** A) 2

RATIONEL WINDOWS LTD
7 Avonbury Business Park, Howes Lane,
Bicester, Oxfordshire, OX26 2UA
Area of Operation: UK (Excluding Ireland)
Tel: 01869 248181   **Fax:** 01869 249693
Email: enquire@rationel.co.uk
Web: www.rationel.com
Product Type: 2, 3, 4, 5, 7   **Material Type:** B) 2, 13

REYNAERS LTD
Kettles Wood Drive,
Birmingham, West Midlands, B32 3DB
Area of Operation: UK (Excluding Ireland)
Tel: 0121 421 1999   **Fax:** 0121 421 9797
Email: reynaersltd@reynaers.com
Web: www.reynaers.com   **Product Type:** 5

RHONES JOINERY (WREXHAM) LTD
Mold Road Industrial Estate,
Gwersyllt, Wrexham, LL11 4AQ
Area of Operation: UK (Excluding Ireland)
Tel: 01978 262488   **Fax:** 01978 262488
Email: info@rhonesjoinery.co.uk
Web: www.rhonesjoinery.co.uk
Product Type: 2, 4, 6, 7

ROBERT J TURNER & CO
Roe Green, Sandon,
Buntingford, Hertfordshire, SG9 0QE
Area of Operation: East England, Greater London
Tel: 01763 288371   **Fax:** 01763 288440
Email: sales@robertjturner.co.uk
Web: www.robertjturner.co.uk
Product Type: 1, 2, 3, 4, 5, 6, 7, 8

RO-DOR LIMITED
Stevens Drove, Houghton,
Stockbridge, Hampshire, SO20 6LP
Area of Operation: UK & Ireland
Tel: 01794 388080   **Fax:** 01794 388090
Email: info@ro-dor.co.uk
Web: www.ro-dor.co.uk
Product Type: 8   **Other Info:** ✎ ☞

SABRINA OAK DOORS LTD
Alma Street, Mountfields,
Shrewsbury, Shropshire, SY3 8QL
Area of Operation: UK (Excluding Ireland)
Tel: 01743 357977   **Fax:** 01743 352233
Email: mail@oakdoors.co.uk
Web: www.oakdoors.co.uk
Product Type: 1, 2, 3, 4, 5, 6, 7
Other Info: ✎ ☞   **Material Type:** A) 2

SAFEGUARD DOORS LIMITED
Units 6-9 Bridge Business Park,
Bridge Street, Wednesbury,
West Midlands, WS10 0AW
Area of Operation: Worldwide
Tel: 0121 556 9138   **Fax:** 0121 556 7275
Email: sales@safeguarddoors.co.uk
Web: www.safeguarddoors.co.uk
Product Type: 1, 2, 3

SANDERSON'S FINE FURNITURE
Unit 5 & 6, The Village Workshop,
Four Crosses Business Park,
Four Crosses, Powys, SY22 6ST
Area of Operation: UK (Excluding Ireland)
Tel: 01691 830075   **Fax:** 01691 830075
Email: sales@sandersonsfinefurniture.co.uk
Web: www.sandersonsfinefurniture.co.uk
Product Type: 1, 2, 3, 4, 6, 7, 8
Other Info: ✏ ✋

SANDERSONS FINE FURNITURE

Area of Operation: UK
Tel: 01691 830075
Fax: 01691 830075
Email: sales@sandersonsfinefurniture.co.uk
Web: www.sandersonsfinefurniture.co.uk
Product Type: 1, 2, 3, 4, 6, 7, 8

Traditional manufacturers of quality bespoke oak
furniture & joinery. Skirting, architrave and
flooring. For further information visit our website.

SAPA BUILDING SYSTEMS LIMITED
Alexandra Way, Ashchurch,
Tewkesbury, Gloucestershire, GL20 8NB
Area of Operation: UK & Ireland
Tel: 01684 853500
Fax: 01684 851850
Email: nicola.abbey@sapagroup.com
Web: www.sapagroup.com/uk/buildingsystems
Product Type: 1, 2, 3, 4, 5
Other Info: ✏   **Material Type:** C) 1

SASH CRAFT
3 The Dairy, Priston Mill Farm, Bath, BA2 9EQ
Area of Operation: South West England and South Wales
Tel: 01225 424434   **Fax:** 01761 470 777
Email: info@sashcraftofbath.com
Web: www.sashcraftofbath.com
Product Type: 1, 2, 3, 4, 5, 6, 7
Material Type: B) 8, 12

**SASH RESTORATION COMPANY
(HEREFORD) LTD**
Pigeon House Farm, Lower Breinton,
Hereford, Herefordshire, HR4 7PG
Area of Operation: UK & Ireland
Tel: 01432 359562   **Fax:** 01432 269749
Email: sales@sash-restoration.co.uk
Web: www.sash-restoration.co.uk
Product Type: 4

SASH UK LTD
Ferrymoor Way, Park Springs, Grimethorpe,
Barnsley, South Yorkshire, S72 7BN
Area of Operation: Worldwide
Tel: 01226 715619   **Fax:** 01226 719968
Email: mailbox@sashuk.com
Web: www.sashuk.com
Product Type: 1, 3, 7, 8
Material Type: D) 1

SCANDINAVIAN WINDOW SYSTEMS LTD
10 Eldon Street, Tuxford, Newark,
Nottinghamshire, NG22 0LH
Area of Operation: UK & Ireland
Tel: 01777 871847   **Fax:** 01777 872650
Email: enquiries@scandinavian-windows.co.uk
Web: www.scandinavian-windows.co.uk
Product Type: 1, 2, 3, 4, 5, 7, 8
Material Type: B) 8, 13

SCANDINAVIAN WINDOW SYSTEMS LTD

Area of Operation: UK & Ireland
Tel: 01777 871847
Fax: 01777 872650
Email: enquiries@scandinavian-windows.co.uk
Web: www.scandinavian-windows.co.uk

SWS are market leading suppliers of large lift and
slide doors in all timber, aluminium clad timber
and thermally broken aluminium.
Sophisticated German gearing allows huge
panels to be created without compromising ease
of use or air and water tightness.

SCANDINAVIAN WINDOW SYSTEMS LTD

Area of Operation: UK & Ireland
Tel: 01777 871847
Fax: 01777 872650
Email: enquiries@scandinavian-windows.co.uk
Web: www.scandinavian-windows.co.uk

SWS are the UK's largest distributor of the
extensive range of folding sliding door systems
from Sunflex. Systems are available in laminated
timber (pine / Meranti / Oak), aluminium-clad
timber and all aluminium(thermal or non-
thermal). SWS take pride in our attention to detail
and customer service from design to delivery.

SCHUCO INTERNATIONAL KG
Whitehall Avenue, Kingston,
Milton Keynes, Buckinghamshire, MK10 0AL
Area of Operation: Worldwide
Tel: 01908 282111   **Fax:** 01908 282124
Email: shamman@schueco.com
Web: www.schueco.co.uk   **Material Type:** C) 1

SCOTTS OF THRAPSTON LTD.
Bridge Street, Thrapston, Northamptonshire, NN14 4LR
Tel: 01832 732366   **Fax:** 01832 733703
Email: julia@scottsofthrapston.co.uk
Web: www.scottsofthrapston.co.uk
Product Type: 1, 2, 3, 7, 8   **Other Info:** ✏

SHERBORNE LIMITED
135 Lynchford Road, Farnborough, Hampshire, GU14 6HD
Area of Operation: South East England
Tel: 01252 370917   **Fax:** 01252 515800
Email: peter.white@sherbornewindows.co.uk
Web: www.sherbornewindows.co.uk
Product Type: 2, 3, 4, 5, 6, 7, 8

SOLARLUX SYSTEMS LTD
Holmfield Lane, Wakefield, West Yorkshire, WF2 7AD
Area of Operation: Worldwide
Tel: 01924 204444   **Fax:** 01924 204455
Email: info@solarlux.co.uk
Web: www.solarlux.uk.com
Product Type: 5   **Other Info:** ✏

SPECTUS SYSTEMS
Spectus Window Systems, Pinewood Court,
Tytherington Business Park,
Macclesfield, Cheshire, SK10 2XR
Area of Operation: UK & Ireland
Tel: 01625 420400   **Fax:** 01625 501418
Email: contact@spectus.co.uk
Web: www.spectus.co.uk

SPS TIMBER WINDOWS
Units 2 and 3, 34 Eveline Road, Mitcham, Surrey, CR4 3LE
Area of Operation: Greater London
Tel: 0208 640 5035   **Fax:** 0208 685 1570
Email: info@spstimberwindows.co.uk
Web: www.spstimberwindows.co.uk ✄
Product Type: 2, 3, 4, 7, 8
Other Info: ✏   **Material Type:** A) 2

STEEL WINDOW SERVICE AND SUPPLIES LTD
30 Oxford Road, Finsbury Park, London, N4 3EY
Area of Operation: Greater London
Tel: 0207 272 2294   **Fax:** 0207 281 2309
Email: post@steelwindows.co.uk
Web: www.steelwindows.co.uk
Product Type: 1, 3, 4   **Material Type:** C) 2, 4

STEVENSWOOD CONSERVATORIES
21 Napier Square, Houstoun Road Industrial Estate,
Livingston, West Lothian, EH54 5DG
Area of Operation: Scotland
Tel: 01506 438111   **Fax:** 01506 438444
Email: info@stevenswood.co.uk
Web: www.stevenswood.co.uk
Product Type: 3, 4, 5

STRATHEARN STONE AND TIMBER LTD
Glenearn, Bridge of Earn, Perth, Perth and Kinross, PH2 9HL
Area of Operation: North East England, Scotland
Tel: 01738 813215   **Fax:** 01738 815946
Email: info@stoneandoak.com
Web: www.stoneandoak.com
Product Type: 3, 4, 7   **Other Info:** ✏ ✋

STROUDS WOODWORKING COMPANY LTD.
Ashmansworthy, Woolsery, Bideford, Devon, EX39 5RE
Area of Operation: South West England and South Wales
Tel: 01409 241624   **Fax:** 01409 241769
Email: enquiries@stroudswoodworking.co.uk
Web: www.stroudswoodworking.co.uk
Product Type: 1, 2, 3, 4, 5, 6, 7
Other Info: ECO ✏ ✋
Material Type: A) 1, 2, 7, 8, 10, 12

STROUDS WOODWORKING COMPANY LTD

Area of Operation: UK & Ireland, South West
England and South Wales
Tel: 01409 241 624
Fax: 01409 241 769
Email: enquiries@stroudswoodworking.co.uk
Web: www.stroudswoodworking.co.uk

We specialise in the production of high quality
bespoke joinery for the discerning self-builder
and home improver. Doors, windows, stairs,
architraves and skirtings.

SUN PARADISE UK LTD
Phoenix Wharf, Eel Pie Island,
Twickenham, Middlesex, TW1 3DY
Area of Operation: UK & Ireland
Tel: 0870 240 7604   **Fax:** 0870 240 7614
Email: info@sunparadise.co.uk
Web: www.sunparadise.co.uk   **Product Type:** 5

SUNFOLD LTD
Sunfold House, Wymondham Business Park,
Chestnut Drive, Wymondham, Norfolk, NR18 9SB
Area of Operation: Europe
Tel: 01953 423423
Fax: 01953 423430
Email: info@sunfold.com   **Web:** www.sunfold.com
Product Type: 3, 5   **Other Info:** ✏
Material Type: A) 1, 2, 15

THE CAMDEN GROUP
Unit 4-7, Steeple Industrial Estate,
Antrim, Co Antrim, BT41 1AB
Area of Operation: UK & Ireland
Tel: 028 9446 2419   **Fax:** 028 9442 8138
Email: info@camdengroup.co.uk
Web: www.camdengroup.co.uk
Product Type: 1, 2, 3, 4, 5, 7, 8

THE NATIONAL DOOR COMPANY
Unit 55, Dinting Vale Business Park,
Dinting Vale, Glossop, Derbyshire, SK13 6JD
Area of Operation: UK (Excluding Ireland)
Tel: 01457 867079   **Fax:** 01457 868795
Email: sales@nationaldoor.co.uk
Web: www.nationaldoor.co.uk

THE ORIGINAL BOX SASH WINDOW COMPANY
29/30 The Arches, Alma Road,
Windsor, Berkshire, SL4 1QZ
Area of Operation: UK (Excluding Ireland)
Tel: 01753 858196
Fax: 01753 857827
Email: info@boxsash.com   **Web:** www.boxsash.com

THE ROUNDWOOD TIMBER COMPANY LTD
Roundwood, Newick Lane,
Mayfield, East Sussex, TN20 6RG
Area of Operation: UK & Ireland
Tel: 01435 867072   **Fax:** 01435 864708
Email: sales@roundwoodtimber.com
Web: www.roundwoodtimber.com ✄

TODD DOORS LTD
112-116 Church Road, Northolt, Greater London, UB5 5AE
Area of Operation: UK (Excluding Ireland)
Tel: 0208 845 2493   **Fax:** 0208 845 7579
Email: info@todd-doors.co.uk
Web: www.todd-doors.co.uk
Product Type: 1, 2, 3, 4, 5, 6, 7, 8
Other Info: ECO ✏   **Material Type:** A) 1, 2, 3, 4, 5, 6, 7

TOMPKINS LTD
High March Close, Long March Industrial Estate,
Daventry, Northamptonshire, NN11 4EZ
Area of Operation: UK (Excluding Ireland)
Tel: 01327 877187
Fax: 01327 310491
Email: info@tompkinswood.co.uk
Web: www.tompkinswood.co.uk
Product Type: 1, 2, 3, 4, 5, 6, 7   **Other Info:** ✏ ✋
Material Type: A) 1, 2, 3, 4, 5, 6, 7, 8, 9, 10, 11, 12, 13, 14

TONY HOOPER
Unit 18 Camelot Court,
Bancombe Trading Estate, Somerton, TA11 6SB
Area of Operation: UK (Excluding Ireland)
Tel: 01458 274221   **Fax:** 01458 274690
Email: tonyhooper1@aol.com
Web: www.tonyhooper.co.uk

TOTAL GLASS LIMITED
Total Complex, Overbrook Lane,
Knowsley, Merseyside, L34 9FB
Area of Operation: Midlands & Mid Wales, North
East England, North West England and North Wales
Tel: 0151 549 2339   **Fax:** 0151 546 0022
Email: sales@totalglass.com
Web: www.totalglass.com   **Product Type:** 1, 3, 4, 7, 8

TRADE CONSERVATORIES 2 U LTD
36 Temple Way, Maldon, Essex, CM9 4PX
Area of Operation: UK (Excluding Ireland)
Tel: 0845 130 3871
Fax: 0845 130 3872
Email: sales@tradeconservatories2u.co.uk
Web: www.tradeconservatories2u.co.uk ✄
Product Type: 1, 3, 5, 8

BUILDING STRUCTURE & MATERIALS

TRADITIONAL OAK & TIMBER COMPANY
PO Stores , Haywards Heath Road,
North Chailey, Nr Lewes, East Sussex, BN8 4EY
Area of Operation: Worldwide
Tel: 01825 723648   **Fax:** 01825 722215
Email: info@tradoak.co.uk
Web: www.tradoak.com   **Product Type:** 1, 2, 4, 6, 7

TRANIK HOUSE DOORSTORE
63-91 Cobham Road, Ferndown Industrial Estate,
Wimborne, Dorset, BH21 7QA
Area of Operation: UK (Excluding Ireland)
Tel: 01202 872211   **Email:** sales@tranik.co.uk
Web: www.tranik.co.uk

TWC NATIONWIDE UK
Units 1&2, The Drill Hall, 262 Huddersfield Road,
Thongsbridge, Holmfirth, West Yorkshire, HD9 3JQ
Area of Operation: UK & Ireland
Tel: 0800 7832782   **Fax:** 01484 685210
Email: admin@twcthewindowcompany.net
Web: www.twcthewindowcompany.net
Product Type: 5, 7

URBAN FRONT LTD
Design Studio, 1 Little Hill, Heronsgate,
Rickmansworth, Hertfordshire, WD3 5BX
Area of Operation: UK & Ireland
Tel: 0870 609 1525   **Fax:** 0870 609 3564
Email: info@urbanfront.co.uk
Web: www.urbanfront.co.uk   **Material Type:** A) 2, 7, 12

WINDOWS 2 YOU LTD
Unt 5 Higher Tweed Mills, Dartington,
Totnes, Devon, TQ9 6JY
Area of Operation: UK & Ireland
Tel: 01803 840200   **Fax:** 01803 840169
Email: sales@windows2you.co.uk
Web: www.windows2you.co.uk
Product Type: 2, 3, 4, 5, 6, 7   **Material Type:** B) 8

WINDOWS OF DISTINCTION
133 Bitton Park Road, Teignmouth, Devon, TQ14 9DQ
Area of Operation: South West England and South Wales
Tel: 01626 879359   **Fax:** 01626 870483
Email: windowsofdistinction@tiscali.co.uk
Web: www.windowsofdistinction.co.uk
Product Type: 1, 2, 3, 4, 5, 7
Other Info: ✎   **Material Type:** D) 1

WOODLAND PRODUCTS DESIGN LTD
St.Peter's House, 6 Cambridge Road,
Kingston Upon Thames, Surrey, KT1 3JY
Area of Operation: UK (Excluding Ireland)
Tel: 0208 547 2171   **Fax:** 0208 547 1722
Email: enquiries@woodland-products.co.uk
Web: www.woodland-products.co.uk
Product Type: 4

WINDOWS

KEY
PRODUCT TYPES: 1= Sash 2 = Casement
3 = Bow / Bay   4 = Oriel   5 = Tilt and Turn
6 = Picture Windows

SEE ALSO: DOORS, WINDOWS AND
CONSERVATORIES - Glass and Glazing, DOORS,
WINDOWS AND CONSERVATORIES - Roof
Windows and Light Pipes, DOORS, WINDOWS
AND CONSERVATORIES - Stained Glass

OTHER: ▽ Reclaimed   On-line shopping
Bespoke   Hand-made   ECO Ecological

AACORN JOINERY AND DESIGN LTD.
2 Balaclava Place, South Street,
Bridport, Dorset, DT6 3PE
Area of Operation: Europe
Tel: 01308 456217 **Fax:** 01308 424511
Email: info@aacornjoinery.co.uk
Web: www.aacornjoinery.co.uk

ALUPLAST UK/PLUSPLAN
Leicester Road, Lutterworth,
Leicestershire, LE17 4HE
Area of Operation: UK & Ireland
Tel: 01455 556771 **Fax:** 01455 555323
Email: info@aluplastuk.com
Web: www.aluplastuk.com **Product Type:** 1, 2, 3, 5

AMBASSADOOR WINDOWS & DOORS LTD
18 Bidwell Road, Rackheath Industrial Estate,
Rackheath, Norwich, Norfolk, NR13 6PT
Area of Operation: East England, Greater London,
Midlands & Mid Wales
Tel: 01603 720332
Email: enquiries@ambassadoor.fsnet.co.uk
Web: www.ambassadoor.co.uk
Product Type: 1, 2, 3, 5, 6   **Material Type:** A) 1

ANDERSEN WINDOWS / BLACK MILLWORK CO.
Andersen House, Dallow Street,
Burton on Trent, Staffordshire, DE14 2PQ
Area of Operation: UK & Ireland
Tel: 01283 511122   **Fax:** 01283 510863
Email: info@blackmillwork.co.uk
Web: www.blackmillwork.co.uk
Product Type: 1, 2, 3, 4, 6
Other Info: ECO ✎   **Material Type:** A) 2, 5, 15

ANDERSEN WINDOWS/BLACK MILLWORK
Area of Operation: UK & Ireland
Tel: +44 (0) 1283 511 122
Fax: +44 (0) 1283 510 863
Email: info@blackmillwork.co.uk
Web: www.blackmillwork.co.uk

Andersen's new Woodwright™ made to measure
sliding sash window incorporates Fibrex® - a
revolutionary new material with the strength of
natural wood and the low maintenance qualities
of PVC-u.

ARBOR WINDOW SYSTEMS LIMITED
1240 Park Avenue, Aztec West, Bristol, BS32 4SH
Area of Operation: UK (Excluding Ireland)
Tel: 01454 270039
Fax: 01454 270049
Email: enquiries@arborwinsys.co.uk
Web: www.arborwinsys.co.uk

ARCHITECTURAL BRONZE CASEMENTS
Vale Garden Houses Ltd, Belton Park,
Londonthorpe Road, Grantham,
Lincolnshire, NG31 9SJ
Area of Operation: Worldwide
Tel: 01476 564433
Fax: 01476 578555
Email: enquiries@bronzecasements.com
Web: www.bronzecasements.com
Product Type: 2

ARCHITECTURAL DOORS & WINDOWS LIMITED
3 Tollpark Road, Wardpark East,
Cumbernauld, Glasgow, G68 0LW
Area of Operation: Scotland
Tel: 01236 780022   **Fax:** 01236 780021
Email: info@adwlimited.co.uk
Web: www.adwlimited.co.uk

ARDEN WINDOWS LIMITED
Arden House, Spark Brook Street,
Coventry, West Midlands, CV1 5ST
Area of Operation: UK (Excluding Ireland)
Tel: 08707 890160
Fax: 08707 890161
Email: sales@ardenwindows.net
Web: www.ardenwindows.net
Product Type: 1, 2   **Other Info:** ✎

ASTON HOUSE JOINERY
Aston House, Tripontium Business Centre,
Newton Lane, Rugby, Warwickshire, CV23 0TB
Area of Operation: UK & Ireland
Tel: 01788 860032   **Fax:** 01788 860614
Email: enquiries@astonhousejoinery.co.uk
Web: www.astonhousejoinery.co.uk
Product Type: 1, 2, 3, 4, 6
Other Info: ECO ✎   **Material Type:** A) 1, 2, 12

B & M WINDOW & KITCHEN CENTRE
2-6 Whitworth Drive,
Aycliffe Industrial Park, Durham, DL5 6SZ
Area of Operation: Worldwide
Tel: 01325 308888   **Fax:** 01325 316002
Email: sales@bandmhomeimprovements.com
Web: www.bandmhomeimprovements.com
Product Type: 1, 2, 3, 5

BDG GROUP LTD
5 Wenlock Road, Lurgan, Craigavon, Co Armagh, BT66 8QR
Area of Operation: UK & Ireland
Tel: 02838 327741   **Fax:** 02838 324358
Email: wosb@bdg.co.uk
Web: www.bdg.co.uk   **Product Type:** 1, 2, 3, 5

BETTERDEAL WINDOWS & CONSERVATORIES
17 Ensign House, Admirals Way, London, E14 9JX
Area of Operation: East England, Greater London,
South East England   **Tel:** 01268 732599
Email: betterdealltd@aol.com
Web: www.betterdealwindows.co.uk
Product Type: 1, 2, 3, 4, 5, 6

BIRCHDALE GLASS LTD
Unit L, Eskdale Road, Uxbridge, Greater London, UB8 2RT
Area of Operation: UK & Ireland
Tel: 01895 259111   **Fax:** 01895 810087
Email: info@birchdaleglass.com
Web: www.birchdaleglass.com
Product Type: 1, 2, 3, 4, 5, 6

BOWATER BUILDING PRODUCTS
Water Orton Lane, Minworth,
Sutton Coldfield, West Midlands, B76 9BW
Area of Operation: UK (Excluding Ireland)
Tel: 0121 749 3000   **Fax:** 0121 749 8210
Email: www.theprimeconnection.co.uk
Web: www.theprimeconnection.co.uk
Product Type: 1, 2, 3, 4, 5, 6   **Material Type:** D) 1

BOX SASH WILLY'S (JOINERY) LTD
33 Ormside Way, Holmethorpe Industrial Estate,
RedHill, Surrey, RH1 2LW
Area of Operation: UK (Excluding Ireland)
Tel: 01737 826700   **Fax:** 01737 826800
Email: sales@box-sash.co.uk
Web: www.box-sash.co.uk   **Product Type:** 1

BROXWOOD LTD
Broxwood Ltd, Inveralmond Way,
Inveralmond Industrial Estate, Perth, PH1 3UQ
Area of Operation: Europe
Fax: 01738 444452   **Email:** sales@broxwood.com
Web: www.broxwood.com
Product Type: 1, 2, 3, 4, 5, 6

Don't Forget! You can use the materials key at the beginning of the Handbook to get much more information from a company's listing.

BUILDING & DESIGN SOLUTIONS GERMANY
Auf den Haien 14, 55471 Sargenroth
Area of Operation: UK (Excluding Ireland)
Tel: 0049 6761 970 871
Email: mail@buildingdesign-germany.eu
Web: www.buildingdesign-germany.eu
Product Type: 5, 6 **Material Type:** A) 1, 2, 4

BUILDING & DESIGN SOLUTIONS GERMANY

Tel: 0049 6761 970 871
Email: mail@buildingdesign-germany.eu
Web: www.buildingdesign-germany.eu

High insulation windows at factory prices from Germany.
Also viewing and purchasing trips to quality suppliers of doors, stairs, kitchens, bedrooms, tiles, etc.
70 inspirational show houses to view.

BUILDMART.CO.UK LIMITED
Area of Operation: UK (Excluding Ireland)
Tel: 0870 874 1135
Email: enquiries@buildmart.co.uk
Web: www.buildmart.co.uk **Product Type:** 2, 10

BWF - TWA SCHEME
55 Tufton Street, London, SW1P 3QL
Area of Operation: UK (Excluding Ireland)
Tel: 0870 458 6939
Fax: 0870 458 6949
Email: ruth.soundarajah@bwf.org.uk
Web: www.bwf.org.uk/about_the_scheme_twa.cfm

CAREY & FOX LTD
51 Langthwaite Business Park, South Kirkby, Pontefract, West Yorkshire, WF9 3NR
Area of Operation: UK & Ireland
Tel: 01977 608069 **Fax:** 01977 646791
Email: enquiries@careyandfox.co.uk
Web: www.careyandfox.co.uk
Product Type: 1, 2, 3, 4, 5, 6 **Material Type:** A) 2

CASTAWAY CAST PRODUCTS AND WOODWARE
Brocklesby Station, Brocklesby Road, Ulceby, Lincolnshire, DN39 6ST
Tel: 01469 588995
Fax: 01469 588995
Email: castawaycastproducts@btinternet.com
Product Type: 1, 2, 4 **Other Info:**
Material Type: C) 1, 2, 4, 5, 11, 12

CHIPPING NORTON GLASS LTD
Units 1 & 2, Station Yard Industrial Estate, Chipping Norton, Oxfordshire, OX7 5HX
Area of Operation: Midlands & Mid Wales, South West England and South Wales
Tel: 01608 643261 **Fax:** 01608 641768
Email: gill@cnglass.plus.com
Web: www.chippingnortonglass.co.uk
Product Type: 1, 2, 3, 4, 5, 6 **Material Type:** C) 1

CLASSIC PVC HOME IMPROVEMENTS
Unit 36 LEC Workshops, Trostre Road, Llanelli, Carmarthenshire, SA15 2EA
Area of Operation: South West England and South Wales
Tel: 01554 777158
Fax: 01554 775086
Email: enquiries@classic.uk.com
Web: www.classic.uk.com
Product Type: 1, 2, 3, 4, 5, 6 **Material Type:** D) 1

CLEARVIEW WINDOWS & DOORS
Unit 14, Sheddingdean Industrial Estate, Marchants Way, Burgess Hill, West Sussex, RH15 8QY
Tel: 01444 250111 **Fax:** 01444 250678
Email: sales@clearviewsussex.co.uk
Web: www.clearviewsussex.co.uk

CLEMENT STEEL WINDOWS
Clement House, Weydown Road, Haslemere, Surrey, GU27 1HR
Area of Operation: Worldwide
Tel: 01428 643393 **Fax:** 01428 644436
Email: info@clementwg.co.uk
Web: www.clementsteelwindows.com
Product Type: 2, 3, 4, 6

CONSERVATORY & WINDOW WORLD LTD
Watling Road, Bishop Aukland, Durham, DL14 9AU
Area of Operation: North East England
Tel: 01388 458 088
Fax: 01388 458 518
Email: paldennis20@aol.com
Web: www.conservatoryandwindowworld.co.uk
Product Type: 1, 2, 3, 4, 5, 6

CONSERVATORY OUTLET
Unit 8 Headway Business Park, Denby Dale Road, Wakefield, West Yorkshire, WF2 7AZ
Area of Operation: North East England
Tel: 01924 881920
Web: www.conservatoryoutlet.co.uk
Product Type: 2, 3, 5 **Material Type:** D) 1

COUNTY JOINERY (SOUTH EAST) LTD
Tetley House, Marley Lane Business Park, Marley Lane, Battle, East Sussex, TN33 0RE
Area of Operation: Greater London, South East England
Tel: 01424 871500 **Fax:** 01424 871550
Email: info@countyjoinery.co.uk
Web: www.countyjoinery.co.uk

CREATE DESIGN SOLUTIONS LTD
The Wood Yard, Castell Ddu Road, Waun Gron, Pontarddulais, Swansea, SA4 8DH
Tel: 01792 386677 **Fax:** 01792 386677
Email: mail@createdesignsolutions.co.uk
Web: www.createdesignsolutions.co.uk
Product Type: 1, 2, 3, 5

CREATE JOINERY
The Wood Yard, Castell Ddu Road, Waun Gron, Pontarddulais, Swansea, SA4 8DH
Area of Operation: Greater London, Midlands & Mid Wales, North West England and North Wales, South East England, South West England and South Wales
Tel: 01792 386677 **Fax:** 01792 386677
Email: mail@create-joinery.co.uk
Web: www.create-joinery.co.uk
Product Type: 1, 2, 3, 5, 6

CROXFORD'S JOINERY MANUFACTURERS & WOODTURNERS
Meltham Joinery, Works New Street, Meltham, Holmfirth, West Yorkshire, HD9 5NT
Area of Operation: UK (Excluding Ireland)
Tel: 01484 850892 **Fax:** 01484 850969
Email: croxford1@btconnect.com
Web: www.croxfords.co.uk
Product Type: 1, 2, 3, 5, 6 **Material Type:** A) 1, 2

CUSTOM WOOD PRODUCTS
Cliffe Road, Easton on the Hill, Stamford, Lincolnshire, PE9 3NP
Area of Operation: East England
Tel: 01780 755711 **Fax:** 01780 480834
Email: customwoodprods@aol.com
Web: www.cwpuk.com
Product Type: 1, 2, 3, 4, 6
Other Info: ECO

DISTINCTIVE DOORS
14 & 15 Chambers Way, Newton Chambers Road, Chapeltown, Sheffield, South Yorkshire, S35 2PH
Area of Operation: UK & Ireland
Tel: 0114 220 2250 **Fax:** 0114 220 2254
Email: enquiries@distinctivedoors.co.uk
Web: www.distinctivedoors.co.uk
Product Type: 1, 2, 3

DIY SASH WINDOWS
2 - 6 Whitworth Drive, Aycliffe Industrial Park, Newton Aycliffe, Durham, DL56SZ
Area of Operation: UK & Ireland
Tel: 01325 308888 **Fax:** 01325 316002
Email: sales@diysashwindows.co.uk
Web: www.diysashwindows.co.uk
Product Type: 1, 2, 3, 5

DUPLUS DOMES LTD
370 Melton Road, Leicester, Leicestershire, LE4 7SL
Area of Operation: Worldwide
Tel: 0116 261 0710 **Fax:** 0116 261 0539
Email: sales@duplus.co.uk
Web: www.duplus.co.uk **Product Type:** 7

EDEN HOUSE LIMITED
Elveden, Kennel Lane, Windlesham, Surrey, GU20 6AA
Area of Operation: Greater London, South East England
Tel: 01276 470192 **Fax:** 01276 489689
Email: info@internalshutters.co.uk
Web: www.edenhouse.biz **Product Type:** 2, 6

EDGETECH UK
Unit 3C, Swallow Gate Business Park, Holbrook Lane, Coventry, West Midlands, CV6 4BL
Area of Operation: UK (Excluding Ireland)
Tel: 02476 705570 **Fax:** 02476 705510
Email: ukenquiries@edgetechig.com
Web: www.superspacer.co.uk
Product Type: 1, 2, 5, 6

ENERGY SUPERSTORE
3 Wellington Park, Belfast, BT9 6DJ
Area of Operation: UK & Ireland
Tel: 02890 388391
Email: info@energysuperstore.co.uk
Web: www.energysuperstore.co.uk
Product Type: 5, 6

ENGELS WINDOWS & DOORS LTD
1 Kingley Centre, Downs Road, West Stoke, Chichester, West Sussex, PO18 9HJ
Area of Operation: UK (Excluding Ireland)
Tel: 01243 576633 **Fax:** 01243 576644
Email: admin@engels.co.uk **Web:** www.engels.co.uk

ESOGRAT LTD
Caldervale Works, River Street, Brighouse, Huddersfield, West Yorkshire, HD6 1JS
Tel: 01484 716228 **Fax:** 01484 400107
Email: info@esograt.com **Web:** www.esograt.com
Product Type: 2, 3, 5, 6

EUROCELL PROFILES LTD
Fairbrook House, Clover Nook Road, Alfreton, Derby, Derbyshire, DE55 4RF
Tel: 01773 842100 **Fax:** 01773 842298
Email: sales@eurocell.co.uk
Web: www.eurocell.co.uk
Product Type: 2, 3, 5 **Material Type:** D) 1

EVEREST LTD
Sopers Road, Cuffley, Hertfordshire, EN6 4SG
Area of Operation: UK & Ireland
Tel: 0800 010123 **Web:** www.everest.co.uk

FAIRMITRE WINDOWS & JOINERY LTD
2A Cope Road, Banbury, Oxfordshire, OX16 2EH
Tel: 01295 268441 **Fax:** 01295 268468
Email: info@fairmitrewindows.co.uk
Web: www.fairmitrewindows.co.uk
Product Type: 1, 2, 3, 5, 6

FAIROAK TIMBER PRODUCTS LIMITED
Manor Farm, Chilmark, Salisbury, Wiltshire, FP3 5AG
Area of Operation: UK (Excluding Ireland)
Tel: 01722 716779 **Fax:** 01722 716761
Email: sales@fairoak.co.uk
Web: www.fairoakwindows.co.uk
Product Type: 2, 3, 4, 6 **Material Type:** A) 2, 12

FINNISH WOOD PRODUCTS LTD
Tresparrett Farm Villa, Tresparrett, Cornwall, PL32 9ST
Tel: 01840 261415 **Fax:** 01840 261415
Email: sales@finnishwoodproducts.com
Web: www.finnishwoodproducts.com
Product Type: 2, 5

FLETCHER JOINERY
261 Whessoe Road, Darlington, Durham, DL3 0YL
Area of Operation: North East England
Tel: 01325 357347 **Fax:** 01325 357347
Email: enquiries@fletcherjoinery.co.uk
Web: www.fletcherjoinery.co.uk
Product Type: 1, 2, 3, 4, 6

FRANKLIN LEEDS LLP
Carlton Works, Cemetery Road, Yeadon, Leeds, West Yorkshire, LS19 7BD
Area of Operation: UK & Ireland
Tel: 0113 250 2991 **Fax:** 0113 250 0991
Email: david.franklin@franklinwindows.co.uk
Web: www.franklinwindows.co.uk
Product Type: 1, 2, 3, 4, 5, 6

FRANKLIN LEEDS LLP

Area of Operation: UK & Ireland
Tel: 0113 2502991
Fax: 0113 2500991
Email: david.franklin@franklinwindows.co.uk
Web: www.franklinwindows.co.uk

Whichever style of conservatory you prefer, we can design and build the perfect addition to your home. As well as conservatories, we also supply and fit our wide variety of windows and doors.

G2K JOINERY LTD
Trench Farm, Tilley Green, Wem, Shropshire, SY4 5PJ
Area of Operation: UK (Excluding Ireland)
Tel: 01939 236640 **Fax:** 01939 236650
Email: graham@g2kjoinery.co.uk
Web: www.g2kjoinery.co.uk

GARY BYNG AND SONS
Unit 17 Metal and Ores Industrial Estate, Hanbury Road, Stoke Prior, Bromsgrove, Worcestershire, B60 4JZ
Area of Operation: UK & Ireland
Tel: 01527 876348 **Fax:** 01527 876339
Email: garybyng@byng.fsbusiness.co.uk
Web: www.gbands.co.uk **Product Type:** 1, 2, 3, 4, 6

GREEN BUILDING STORE
11 Huddersfield Road, Meltham, Holmfirth, West Yorkshire, HD9 4NJ
Tel: 01484 854898 **Fax:** 01484 854899
Email: info@greenbuildingstore.co.uk
Web: www.greenbuildingstore.co.uk
Product Type: 1, 2, 3, 4, 5, 6
Other Info: ECO **Material Type:** B) 8

HAYMANS TIMBER PRODUCTS
Haymans Farm, Hocker Lane, Over Alderley, Macclesfield, Cheshire, SK10 4SD
Area of Operation: UK & Ireland
Tel: 01625 590098 **Fax:** 01625 586174
Email: haymanstimber@aol.com
Web: www.haymanstimber.co.uk
Product Type: 1, 3

HIGHSEAL WINDOWS LIMITED
Moat Road, Scunthorpe, Lincolnshire, DN15 9GA
Area of Operation: East England, Greater London, Midlands & Mid Wales, North East England, North West England and North Wales, Scotland, South East England
Tel: 01724 276213 **Fax:** 01724 276214
Email: david.maybank@hwlgroup.co.uk
Web: www.hwlgroup.co.uk
Product Type: 1, 2, 3, 4, 5, 6

BUILDING STRUCTURE & MATERIALS - Doors, Windows & Conservatories - Windows
SPONSORED BY: ARCHITECTURAL DOORS & WINDOWS www.adwlimited.co.uk

BUILDING STRUCTURE & MATERIALS

HOLDSWORTH WINDOWS LTD
Darlingscote Road, Shipston-on-Stour,
Warwickshire, CV36 4PR
Area of Operation: UK & Ireland
Tel: 01608 661883   **Fax:** 01608 661008
Email: info@holdsworthwindows.co.uk
Web: www.holdsworthwindows.co.uk
Product Type: 2   **Material Type:** C) 2, 4

HOWARTH WINDOWS AND DOORS LTD
The Dock, New Holland, Lincolnshire, DN19 7RT
Area of Operation: UK & Ireland
Tel: 01469 530577   **Fax:** 01469 531559
Email: ktopliss@howarth-timber.co.uk
Web: www.howarth-timber.co.uk
Product Type: 1, 2, 3, 5   **Material Type:** B) 1, 8

INPUT JOINERY LTD
The Fairground, Weyhill, Andover, Hampshire, SP11 0ST
Area of Operation: UK (Excluding Ireland)
Tel: 01264 771900   **Fax:** 01264 771901
Email: info@inputjoinery.co.uk
Web: www.inputjoinery.co.uk
Product Type: 1, 2, 3, 4, 5   **Material Type:** A) 1, 2

J L JOINERY
Cockerton View, Grange Lane, Preston, Lancashire, PR4 5JE
Area of Operation: UK (Excluding Ireland)
Tel: 01772 616123   **Fax:** 01772 619182
Email: mail@jljoinery.co.uk   **Web:** www.jljoinery.co.uk

JAMES BENTLEY
James Bentley Limited, 13 Tennyson Road,
Hinckley, Leicestershire, LE10 0TH
Tel: 0870 850 2057
Email: paul.smith@james-bentley.co.uk
Web: www.james-bentley.co.uk
Product Type: 1, 2, 3, 4, 5, 6   **Material Type:** D) 1

**Don't forget to let us
know about companies
you think should be listed
in the next edition
email:
customerservice@centaur.co.uk**

JELD-WEN
Watch House Lane, Doncaster, South Yorkshire, DN5 9LR
Area of Operation: UK & Ireland
Tel: 0870 126 0000
Fax: 01302 787383
Email: customer-services@jeld-wen.co.uk
Web: www.jeld-wen.co.uk
Product Type: 1, 2, 3   **Material Type:** D) 1

JELD-WEN
Area of Operation: UK & Ireland
Tel: 0870 126 0000
Fax: 01302 787383
Email: customer-services@jeld-wen.co.uk
Web: www.jeld-wen.co.uk

Timber Windows

JELD-WEN offers a full range of timber windows, from traditional sliding sash windows to more contemporary designs. All softwood windows are PEFC Chain of Custody certified and are available factory glazed along with a wide choice of performance enhancing factory finishes.

JOHN FLEMING & CO LTD
Silverburn Place, Bridge of Don,
Aberdeen, Aberdeenshire, AB23 8EG
Area of Operation: Scotland
Tel: 0800 085 8728   **Fax:** 01224 825377
Email: info@johnfleming.co.uk
Web: www.johnfleming.co.uk

JOHN VINNIE LTD
Unit 4 Milnsbridge Business Centre, Colne Vale Road,
Milnsbridge, Huddersfield, West Yorkshire, HD3 4NY
Area of Operation: UK (Excluding Ireland)
Tel: 01484 647666
Fax: 01484 648666
Email: sales@jvjoinery.co.uk
Web: www.jvjoinery.co.uk
Product Type: 1, 2, 3, 4, 6

JOINERY-PLUS
Bentley Hall Barn, Alkmonton,
Ashbourne, Derbyshire, DE6 3DJ
Area of Operation: UK (Excluding Ireland)
Tel: 07931 386233   **Fax:** 01335 330922
Email: info@joinery-plus.co.uk
Web: www.joinery-plus.co.uk
Product Type: 1, 2, 3, 4, 5, 6
Material Type: A) 2

JONATHAN ELWELL
Bryn Teg Workshop & Tan y Bryn Cottage,
Tanrallt Road, Gwespyr, Flintshire, CH8 9JT
Area of Operation: UK (Excluding Ireland)
Tel: 01745 887766
Email: jonathanelwell@ukonline.co.uk
Web: www.jonathanelwell.co.uk

LAMWOOD LTD
Unit 1, Riverside Works, Station Road,
Cheddleton, Staffordshire, ST13 7EE
Tel: 01538 361888   **Fax:** 01538 361912
Email: info@lamwoodltd.co.uk
Web: www.lamwoodltd.co.uk
Material Type: A) 2

LATTICE PERIOD WINDOWS
Unit 85 Northwick Business Centre, Blockley,
Moreton in Marsh, Gloucestershire, Gl56 9RF
Area of Operation: UK & Ireland
Tel: 01386 701079
Fax: 01386 701114
Email: sales@latticewindows.net
Web: www.latticewindows.net
Product Type: 2, 3, 5
Material Type: A) 2

MARVIN ARCHITECTURAL
Canal House, Catherine Wheel Road, Brentford,
Middlesex, Greater London, TW8 8BD
Area of Operation: UK & Ireland
Tel: 0208 569 8222
Fax: 0208 560 6374
Email: sales@marvinUK.com
Web: www.marvin-architectural.com
Product Type: 1, 2, 3, 5, 6
Material Type: A) 2, 3, 15

MARVIN ARCHITECTURAL
Area of Operation: UK & Ireland
Tel: 0208 569 8222
Fax: 0208 560 6374
Email: sales@marvinUK.com
Web: www.marvin-architectural.com

By redefining a traditional favourite, Marvin have changed the way people look at windows. The Marvin Sliding Sash state-of-the-art window design is combined with the style and beauty of an earlier era.

MARVIN ARCHITECTURAL
Area of Operation: UK & Ireland
Tel: 0208 569 8222
Fax: 0208 560 6374
Email: sales@marvinUK.com
Web: www.marvin-architectural.com

A beautiful window only enhances the view. Choose from over 11,000 standard shapes and sizes and virtually unlimited custom capabilities. See the difference Marvin makes.

MARVIN ARCHITECTURAL
Area of Operation: UK & Ireland
Tel: 0208 569 8222
Fax: 0208 560 6374
Email: sales@marvinUK.com
Web: www.marvin-architectural.com

The Marvin clad colour range allows you to colour match with colour tones in stone or plaster finish facades. The special Marvin patented "Kynar" finish means the colour is baked onto the aluminium and not powder coated. Which ensures the colour will be the same in 20 years as the day it was installed.

MASTERFRAME WINDOWS LTD
4 Crittall Road, Witham, Essex, CM8 3DR
Area of Operation: UK (Excluding Ireland)
Tel: 01376 510410   **Fax:** 01376 510400
Email: sales@masterframe.co.uk
Web: www.masterframe.co.uk
Product Type: 1, 6
Other Info: ✐   **Material Type:** D) 1

MERLIN UK LIMITED
Unit 5 Fence Avenue, Macclesfield, Cheshire, SK10 1LT
Area of Operation: North West England and North Wales
Tel: 01625 424488
Fax: 0871 781 8967
Email: info@merlinuk.net
Web: www.merlindoors.co.uk
Product Type: 1, 2, 3, 5

MH JOINERY SERVICES
25b Camwall Road, Harrogate, North Yorkshire, HG1 4PT
Area of Operation: North East England
Tel: 01423 888856
Fax: 01423 888856
Email: info@mhjoineryservices.co.uk
Web: www.mhjoineryservices.co.uk
Product Type: 1 **Other Info:** ✏ 🖐

MIGHTON PRODUCTS LTD
PO Box 1, Saffron Walden, Essex, CB10 1QJ
Area of Operation: UK (Excluding Ireland)
Tel: 0800 0560471
Email: sales@mightonproducts.com
Web: www.mightonproducts.com 🖐
Product Type: 1, 5

MULTIWOOD HOME IMPROVEMENTS LTD
1298 Chester Road, Stretford, Manchester, M32 9AU
Area of Operation: Europe
Tel: 0161 866 9991 **Fax:** 0161 866 9992
Email: sales@multiwoodconservatories.co.uk
Web: www.multiwoodconservatories.co.uk
Product Type: 1, 2, 5

MUMFORD & WOOD LTD
Tower Business Park, Kelvedon Road,
Tiptree, Essex, CO5 0LX
Area of Operation: Worldwide
Tel: 01621 818155 **Fax:** 01621 818175
Email: sales@mumfordwood.com
Web: www.mumfordwood.com
Product Type: 1, 2, 3, 5

NORBUILD TIMBER FABRICATION & FINE CARPENTRY LTD
Marcassie Farm, Rafford, Forres, Moray, IV36 2RH
Area of Operation: UK & Ireland
Tel: 01309 676865
Fax: 01309 676865
Email: norbuild@marcassie.fsnet.co.uk
Product Type: 2, 6 **Other Info:** ECO ✏ 🖐
Material Type: A) 1, 2, 6

NORTH YORKSHIRE TIMBER
Standard House, Thurston Road, Northallerton Business Park, Northallerton, North Yorkshire, DL6 2NA
Area of Operation: UK (Excluding Ireland)
Tel: 01609 780777 **Fax:** 01609 777888
Email: sales@nytimber.co.uk
Web: www.nytimber.co.uk

NORVIK PVCU WINDOW SYSTEMS LTD
Mitchells Industrial Park, Wombwell,
Barnsley, South Yorkshire, S35 7AE
Area of Operation: UK & Ireland
Tel: 01226 340182 **Fax:** 01226 340375
Email: nhibberd@norvik.co.uk
Web: www.norvik.co.uk
Product Type: 2, 3, 5

NSB CASEMENTS LTD
Steele Road, Park Royal, London, NW10 7AR
Area of Operation: UK (Excluding Ireland)
Tel: 0208 961 3090
Fax: 0208 961 3050
Email: info@nsbcasements.co.uk
Product Type: 2

NULITE LTD
41 Hutton Close, Crowther Industrial Estate,
Washington, Tyne & Wear, NE38 0AH
Area of Operation: UK & Ireland
Tel: 0191 419 1111 **Fax:** 0191 419 1123
Email: sales@nulite-ltd.co.uk
Web: www.nulite-ltd.co.uk
Other Info: ✏ **Material Type:** C) 1, 2, 4

OCTAVEWARD LTD
Balle Street Mill, Balle Street,
Darwen, Lancashire, BB3 2AZ
Area of Operation: Worldwide
Tel: 01254 773300 **Fax:** 01254 773950
Email: info@octaveward.com
Web: www.octaveward.com
Product Type: 1, 2, 5, 6
Other Info: ECO ✏ **Material Type:** D) 6

OLD MANOR COTTAGES
Turnpike Lane, Ickleford, Hitchin, Hertfordshire, SG5 3UZ
Area of Operation: UK & Ireland
Tel: 01462 456033 **Fax:** 01462 456033
Email: oldmanorco@aol.com

ORIGINAL
3 Festival Units, The Showground,
Bridgwater, Somerset, TA6 6LS
Area of Operation: South West England and South Wales
Tel: 0870 011 0808 **Fax:** 0870 011 0606
Email: enquiries@obsc.co.uk **Web:** www.obsc.co.uk

OXFORD SASH WINDOW CO LTD.
Eynsham Park Estate Yard, Cuckoo Lane,
North Leigh, Oxfordshire, OX29 6PW
Area of Operation: Greater London, Midlands & Mid Wales, South East England, South West England and South Wales
Tel: 01993 883536 **Fax:** 01993 883027
Email: oxsash@globalnet.co.uk
Web: www.sashwindow.co.uk
Product Type: 1, 2, 3, 4, 5

PORTICO GB LTD
Unit 9 Windmill Avenue, Woolpit Business Park,
Woolpit, Bury St Edmunds, Suffolk, IP30 9UP
Area of Operation: Greater London, South East England
Tel: 01359 244299
Fax: 01359 244232
Email: info@portico-gb.co.uk
Web: www.portico-newbuild.co.uk
Product Type: 1, 2, 5

PREMDOR
Gemini House, Hargreaves Road, Groundwell
Industrial Estate, Swindon, Wiltshire, SN25 5AJ
Area of Operation: UK & Ireland
Tel: 0870 990 7998
Email: ukmarketing@premdor.com
Web: www.premdor.com
Product Type: 2, 3, 4, 6

PRITCHARDS
Unit 22 Brookend Lane, Kempsey,
Worcester, Worcestershire, WR5 3LF
Area of Operation: UK (Excluding Ireland)
Tel: 01905 828335 **Fax:** 01905 828357
Email: info@pritchards.tv **Web:** www.pritchards.tv

QUICKSLIDE LTD
Unit 15 Heaton Estate, Bradford Road,
Bailiff Bridge, Brighouse, West Yorkshire, HD6 4BW
Area of Operation: UK & Ireland
Tel: 0870 8504201 **Fax:** 0870 8504202
Email: sales@quickslide.co.uk
Web: www.quickslide.co.uk **Product Type:** 1

RADNOR TIMBER COMPANY
The Offices, Old Impton Farm,
Norton, Presteigne, Powys, LD8 2EN
Area of Operation: Europe
Tel: 01544 260727 **Fax:** 01544 262113
Email: sales@rtc.enta.net
Web: www.radnortimbercompany
Product Type: 1, 2, 3
Other Info: ECO ✏ 🖐 **Material Type:** A) 2

RATIONEL WINDOWS LTD
7 Avonbury Business Park, Howes Lane,
Bicester, Oxfordshire, OX26 2UA
Area of Operation: UK (Excluding Ireland)
Tel: 01869 248181 **Fax:** 01869 249693
Email: enquire@rationel.co.uk
Web: www.rationel.com
Product Type: 2, 3, 4, 6
Material Type: B) 2, 13

REDDISEALS
The Furlong, Berry Hill Industrial Estate,
Droitwich, Worcestershire, WR9 9BG
Area of Operation: UK & Ireland
Tel: 01905 791876 **Fax:** 01905 791877
Email: reddiseals@reddiseals.com
Web: www.reddiseals.com
Product Type: 1, 2

REDDISEALS DIRECT

Area of Operation: UK & Ireland
Tel: 01905 791876 **Fax:** 01905 791877
Email: Reddiseals@Reddiseals.com
Web: www.Reddiseals.com

We supply EVERYTHING you will ever need to renovate, repair and install your timber windows and doors. Sash windows being a speciality. New Catalogue Available.

REYNAERS LTD
Kettles Wood Drive, Birmingham, West Midlands, B32 3DB
Area of Operation: UK (Excluding Ireland)
Tel: 0121 421 1999 **Fax:** 0121 421 9797
Email: reynaersltd@reynaers.com
Web: www.reynaers.com **Product Type:** 2, 5

RHONES JOINERY (WREXHAM) LTD
Mold Road Industrial Estate,
Gwersyllt, Wrexham, LL11 4AQ
Area of Operation: UK (Excluding Ireland)
Tel: 01978 262488 **Fax:** 01978 262488
Email: info@rhonesjoinery.co.uk
Web: www.rhonesjoinery.co.uk
Product Type: 1, 2, 3 **Other Info:**

ROBERT J TURNER & CO
Roe Green, Sandon, Buntingford, Hertfordshire, SG9 0QE
Area of Operation: East England, Greater London
Tel: 01763 288371 **Fax:** 01763 288440
Email: sales@robertjturner.co.uk
Web: www.robertjturner.co.uk
Product Type: 1, 2, 3, 6

SAPA BUILDING SYSTEMS LIMITED
Alexandra Way, Ashchurch,
Tewkesbury, Gloucestershire, GL20 8NB
Area of Operation: UK & Ireland
Tel: 01684 853500 **Fax:** 01684 851850
Email: nicola.abbey@sapagroup.com
Web: www.sapagroup.com/uk/buildingsystems
Product Type: 1, 2, 3, 4, 5, 6
Other Info: **Material Type:** C) 1

SASH CRAFT
3 The Dairy, Priston Mill Farm, Bath, BA2 9EQ
Area of Operation: South West England and South Wales
Tel: 01225 424434 **Fax:** 01761 470 777
Email: info@sashcraftofbath.com
Web: www.sashcraftofbath.com
Product Type: 1, 2, 3, 4 **Material Type:** B) 8, 12

SASH RESTORATION COMPANY (HEREFORD) LTD
Pigeon House Farm, Lower Breinton,
Hereford, Herefordshire, HR4 7PG
Area of Operation: UK & Ireland
Tel: 01432 359562 **Fax:** 01432 269749
Email: sales@sash-restoration.co.uk
Web: www.sash-restoration.co.uk **Other Info:**
Product Type: 1, 3, 6 **Material Type:** A) 2

SASH UK LTD
Ferrymoor Way, Park Springs, Grimethorpe,
Barnsley, South Yorkshire, S72 7BN
Area of Operation: Worldwide
Tel: 01226 715619 **Fax:** 01226 719968
Email: mailbox@sashuk.com **Web:** www.sashuk.com
Product Type: 2, 3, 5, 6 **Material Type:** D) 1

SASHPRO
51a Norbury Road, Thornton Heath, Surrey, CR7 8JP
Area of Operation: UK & Ireland
Tel: 0845 603 6027 **Fax:** 0208 771 5956
Email: enquiries@sashpro.co.uk
Web: www.sashpro.co.uk **Product Type:** 1, 6

SCANDINAVIAN WINDOW SYSTEMS LTD
10 Eldon Street, Tuxford, Newark,
Nottinghamshire, NG22 0LH
Area of Operation: UK & Ireland
Tel: 01777 871847 **Fax:** 01777 872650
Email: enquiries@scandinavian-windows.co.uk
Web: www.scandinavian-windows.co.uk
Product Type: 2, 5, 6
Other Info: ECO **Material Type:** B) 1, 8, 13

SCANDINAVIAN WINDOW SYSTEMS

Area of Operation: UK & Ireland
Tel: 01777 871847 **Fax:** 01777 872650
Email: enquiries@scandinavian-windows.co.uk
Web: www.scandinavian-windows.co.uk
Product Type: 2, 5, 6, 9
Materials Type: B) 1, 8, 13

Suppliers of made to measure high performance windows, doors and sliding doors from Norway. Options include factory finished & factory glazed frames in all timber or aluminium and timber composite.Sunflex folding sliding doors also available in all timber, all aluminium or aluminium clad timber.

SCHUCO INTERNATIONAL KG
Whitehall Avenue, Kingston,
Milton Keynes, Buckinghamshire, MK10 0AL
Area of Operation: Worldwide
Tel: 01908 282111 **Fax:** 01908 282124
Email: shamman@schueco.com
Web: www.schueco.co.uk **Material Type:** C) 1

SHERBORNE LIMITED
135 Lynchford Road, Farnborough, Hampshire, GU14 6HD
Area of Operation: South East England
Tel: 01252 370917 **Fax:** 01252 515800
Email: peter.white@sherbornewindows.co.uk
Web: www.sherbornewindows.co.uk
Product Type: 2, 3, 4, 5, 6

SLIDING SASH WINDOWS LTD
The Workshop, Rope Walk,
Wotton-Under-Edge, Gloucestershire, GL12 7AA
Area of Operation: UK (Excluding Ireland)
Tel: 01453 844877 **Fax:** 01453 844877
Email: mark@slidingsashwindows.biz
Web: slidingsashwindows.com
Product Type: 1, 2, 3, 4, 6 **Material Type:** B) 8, 12

SPECTUS SYSTEMS
Spectus Window Systems,
Pinewood Court, Tytherington Business Park,
Macclesfield, Cheshire, SK10 2XR
Area of Operation: UK & Ireland
Tel: 01625 420400 **Fax:** 01625 501418
Email: contact@spectus.co.uk
Web: www.spectus.co.uk
Product Type: 1, 2, 3, 5 **Material Type:** D) 1

BUILDING STRUCTURE & MATERIALS *(vertical sidebar)*

SPS TIMBER WINDOWS
Units 2 and 3, 34 Eveline Road, Mitcham, Surrey, CR4 3LE
Area of Operation: Greater London
Tel: 0208 640 5035   **Fax:** 0208 685 1570
Email: info@spstimberwindows.co.uk
Web: www.spstimberwindows.co.uk ✎⊕
Product Type: 1, 2, 6
Other Info: ECO ✎ ✋   **Material Type:** B) 8

STEEL WINDOW SERVICE AND SUPPLIES LTD
30 Oxford Road, Finsbury Park, London, N4 3EY
Area of Operation: Greater London
Tel: 0207 272 2294   **Fax:** 0207 281 2309
Email: post@steelwindows.co.uk
Web: www.steelwindows.co.uk
Product Type: 2, 3, 6   **Material Type:** C) 2, 4

STEVENSWOOD CONSERVATORIES
21 Napier Square Houstoun Road Industrial Estate,
Livingston, West Lothian, EH54 5DG
Area of Operation: Scotland
Tel: 01506 438111   **Fax:** 01506 438444
Email: info@stevenswood.co.uk
Web: www.stevenswood.co.uk
Product Type: 2, 3, 5, 6

STORM WINDOWS LIMITED
Unit 7, James Scott Road, Off Park Lane,
Halesowen, West Midlands, B63 2QT
Area of Operation: UK (Excluding Ireland)
Tel: 0845 0611444   **Fax:** 01384 410307
Email: sandra.lamb@virgin.net
Web: www.stormwindows.co.uk
Product Type: 1, 2, 3   **Material Type:** J) 4

STROUDS WOODWORKING COMPANY LTD.
Ashmansworthy, Woolsery, Bideford, Devon, EX39 5RE
Area of Operation: South West England and South Wales
Tel: 01409 241624
 Fax: 01409 241769
Email: enquiries@stroudswoodworking.co.uk
Web: www.stroudswoodworking.co.uk
Product Type: 1, 2, 3, 4, 5, 6
Other Info: ECO ✎ ✋
Material Type: A) 1, 2, 8, 10, 12

SUNFOLD LTD
Sunfold House, Wymondham Business Park,
Chestnut Drive, Wymondham, Norfolk, NR18 9SB
Area of Operation: Europe
Tel: 01953 423423   **Fax:** 01953 423430
Email: info@sunfold.com   **Web:** www.sunfold.com
Product Type: 5   **Other Info:** ✎
Material Type: A) 1, 2, 15

THE CAMDEN GROUP
Unit 4-7, Steeple Industrial Estate, Antrim, BT41 1AB
Tel: 028 9446 2419   **Fax:** 028 9442 8138
Email: info@camdengroup.co.uk
Web: www.camdengroup.co.uk
Product Type: 1, 2, 3, 5, 6

THE ORIGINAL BOX SASH WINDOW COMPANY
29/30 The Arches, Alma Road, Windsor, Berkshire, SL4 1QZ
Area of Operation: UK (Excluding Ireland)
Tel: 01753 858196
Fax: 01753 857827
Email: info@boxsash.com   **Web:** www.boxsash.com
Product Type: 1   **Other Info:** ✎

TOMPKINS LTD
High March Close, Long March Industrial Estate,
Daventry, Northamptonshire, NN11 4EZ
Area of Operation: UK (Excluding Ireland)
Tel: 01327 877187   **Fax:** 01327 310491
Email: info@tompkinswood.co.uk
Web: www.tompkinswood.co.uk
Product Type: 1, 2, 3, 4, 5   **Other Info:** ✎ ✋
Material Type: A) 1, 2, 3, 4, 5, 6, 7, 8, 9, 10, 11, 12, 13, 14

TONY HOOPER
Unit 18 Camelot Court,
Bancombe Trading Estate, Somerton, TA11 6SB
Area of Operation: UK (Excluding Ireland)
Tel: 01458 274221
Fax: 01458 274690
Email: tonyhooper1@aol.com
Web: www.tonyhooper.co.uk

TOTAL GLASS LIMITED
Total Complex, Overbrook Lane,
Knowsley, Merseyside, L34 9FB
Area of Operation: Midlands & Mid Wales, North
East England, North West England and North Wales
Tel: 0151 549 2339   **Fax:** 0151 546 0022
Email: sales@totalglass.com
Web: www.totalglass.com **Product Type:** 1, 2, 3, 5, 6

TRADE CONSERVATORIES 2 U LTD
36 Temple Way, Maldon, Essex, CM9 4PX
Area of Operation: UK (Excluding Ireland)
Tel: 0845 130 3871   **Fax:** 0845 130 3872
Email: sales@tradeconservatories2u.co.uk
Web: www.tradeconservatories2u.co.uk ✎⊕
Product Type: 1, 2, 3, 4, 5, 6

TWC NATIONWIDE UK
Units 1 and 2, The Drill Hall, 262 Huddersfield Road,
Thongsbridge, Holmfirth, West Yorkshire, HD9 3JQ
Area of Operation: UK & Ireland
Tel: 0800 7832782   **Fax:** 01484 685210
Email: admin@twcthewindowcompany.net
Web: www.twcthewindowcompany.net
Product Type: 1, 2, 5   **Material Type:** D) 1

UNIVERSAL ARCHES LTD
103 Peasley Cross Lane, Peasley Cross,
St Helens, Merseyside, WA9 3AL
Area of Operation: UK & Ireland
Tel: 01744 612844   **Fax:** 01744 694250
Email: sales@universalarches.com
Web: www.universalarches.com
Other Info: ✎ ✋   **Material Type:** D) 1

VALE GARDEN HOUSES LTD
Londonthorpe Road, Grantham,
Lincolnshire, NG31 9SJ
Area of Operation: UK & Ireland
Tel: 01476 564433   **Fax:** 01476 578555
Email: ken@valegardenhouses.com
Web: www.bronzecasements.com
Product Type: 2   **Material Type:** C) 12

VELFAC
Kettering Parkway, Wellingborough Road,
Kettering, Northamptonshire, NN15 6XR
Area of Operation: UK (Excluding Ireland)
Tel: 01223 897100   **Fax:** 01223 897101
Email: ac@velfac.co.uk   **Web:** www.velfac.co.uk
Product Type: 2, 5, 6, 9   **Other Info:** ✎

VELUX WINDOWS
Woodside Way, Glenrothes East, Fife, KY7 4ND
Area of Operation: Worldwide
Tel: 0870 240 0617   **Fax:** 0870 380 9395
Email: service@velux.co.uk
Web: www.velux.co.uk ✎⊕   **Product Type:** 7

VENTROLLA LTD
11 Hornbeam Square South, Harrogate,
North Yorkshire, HG2 8NB
Area of Operation: UK & Ireland
Tel: 0800 378 278   **Fax:** 01423 859321
Email: info@ventrolla.co.uk
Web: www.ventrolla.co.uk   **Product Type:** 1, 2, 3

VENTROLLA LTD
Area of Operation: UK & Ireland
Tel: 0800 378 278   **Fax:** 01423 859321
Email: info@ventrolla.co.uk
Web: www.ventrolla.co.uk
Product Type: 1,2,3

The UK's market leader in the repair, renovation
and upgrade of original sliding sash windows.
Recognised for use in listed buildings and
properties within conservation areas.

VICTORIAN SLIDERS LTD
Unit B Greenfields Business Centre,
Kidwelly, Carmarthenshire, SA17 4PT
Tel: 0845 1700 810   **Fax:** 0845 1700 820
Email: info@victoriansliderssltd.co.uk
Web: www.victoriansliderssltd.co.uk   **Product Type:** 1

WAYNE RICKETTS STAINED GLASS
Units 9-11 The White Factory,
18 Netham Road, Redfield, Bristol, BS5 9PF
Tel: 0117 955 5390   **Fax:** 0117 955 5390
Email: wayne.ricketts@btconnect.com
Web: www.waynerickettsstainedglass.com
Other Info: ✎ ✋

WINDOWS 2 YOU LTD
Unt 5 Higher Tweed Mills,
Dartington, Totnes, Devon, TQ9 6JY
Tel: 01803 840200   **Fax:** 01803 840169
Email: sales@windows2you.co.uk
Web: www.windows2you.co.uk
Product Type: 1, 2, 3, 4, 5, 10   **Material Type:** B) 8

WINDOWS OF DISTINCTION
133 Bitton Park Road, Teignmouth, Devon, TQ14 9DQ
Area of Operation: South West England and South Wales
Tel: 01626 879359   **Fax:** 01626 870483
Email: windowsofdistinction@tiscali.co.uk
Web: www.windowsofdistinction.co.uk
Product Type: 1, 2, 3, 4, 5, 10
Other Info: ✎   **Material Type:** D) 1

WOODLAND PRODUCTS DESIGN LTD
St.Peter's House, 6 Cambridge Road,
Kingston Upon Thames, Surrey, KT1 3JY
Tel: 0208 547 2171   **Fax:** 0208 547 1722
Email: enquiries@woodland-products.co.uk
Web: www.woodland-products.co.uk
Product Type: 1, 2

GLASS & GLAZING

KEY

PRODUCT TYPES: 1= Standard
2 = Double Glazing   3 = Toughened
4 = Secondary Glazing   5 = Decorative
6 = Leaded Windows   7 = Other
SEE ALSO: DOORS, WINDOWS AND
CONSERVATORIES - Windows, DOORS,
WINDOWS AND CONSERVATORIES - Roof
Windows and Light Pipes, DOORS, WINDOWS
AND CONSERVATORIES - Stained Glass

OTHER: ▽ Reclaimed ⊕ On-line shopping
✎ Bespoke ✋ Hand-made ECO Ecological

ADDISON DESIGN SYSTEMS
Unit 23, 106A Bedford Road,
Wootton, Bedfordshire, MK43 9JB
Tel: 01234 767721
Fax: 01234 767781
Email: nejzer@addison-design.co.uk
Web: www.addison-design.co.uk

AMBASSADOOR WINDOWS & DOORS LTD
18 Bidwell Road, Rackheath Industrial Estate,
Rackheath, Norwich, Norfolk, NR13 6PT
Area of Operation: East England, Greater London,
Midlands & Mid Wales
Tel: 01603 720332
Email: enquiries@ambassadoor.fsnet.co.uk
Web: www.ambassadoor.co.uk
Product Type: 1, 2, 3, 5

APROPOS TECTONIC LTD
Greenside House, Richmond Street,
Ashton Under Lyne, Lancashire, OL6 7ES
Tel: 0870 777 0326   **Fax:** 0161 3428265
Email: enquiries@apropos-tectonic.com
Web: www.apropos-tectonic.com   **Product Type:** 2

B & M WINDOW & KITCHEN CENTRE
2-6 Whitworth Drive,
Aycliffe Industrial Park, Durham, DL5 6SZ
Area of Operation: Worldwide
Tel: 01325 308888   **Fax:** 01325 316002
Email: sales@bandmhomeimprovements.com
Web: www.bandmhomeimprovements.com ✎⊕
Product Type: 1, 2, 3, 4, 5, 6

BARRON GLASS
Unit 11, Lansdown Industrial Estate,
Cheltenham, Gloucestershire, GL51 8PL
Tel: 01242 22800   **Fax:** 01242 226555
Email: admin@barronglass.co.uk
Web: www.barronglass.co.uk
Product Type: 1, 2, 5, 8

BIRCHDALE GLASS LTD
Unit L, Eskdale Road, Uxbridge, Greater London, UB8 2RT
Area of Operation: UK & Ireland
Tel: 01895 259111   **Fax:** 01895 810087
Email: info@birchdaleglass.com
Web: www.birchdaleglass.com
Product Type: 1, 2, 3, 4, 5, 6, 7

CHAMBERLAIN & GROVES LTD -
THE DOOR & SECURITY STORE
101 Boundary Road, Walthamstow, London, E17 8NQ
Area of Operation: UK (Excluding Ireland)
Tel: 0208 520 6776   **Fax:** 0208 520 2190
Email: ken@securedoors.co.uk
Web: www.securedoors.co.uk
Product Type: 1, 2, 3, 5, 6, 7

CHARLES HENSHAW & SONS LTD
Russell Road, Edinburgh, Lothian, EH11 2LS
Area of Operation: UK (Excluding Ireland)
Tel: 0131 337 4204
Fax: 0131 346 2441
Email: admin@charles-henshaw.co.uk
Web: www.charles-henshaw.com

CHEAM LEADED LIGHTS LTD
8 Upper Mulgrave Road, Cheam Village, Surrey, SM2 9AZ
Area of Operation: South East England
Tel: 0208 643 7849 **Fax:** 0208 770 3878
Email: sales@cheamleadedlights.com
Web: www.cheamleadedlights.com
Product Type: 5, 6

CHIPPING NORTON GLASS LTD
Units 1 & 2, Station Yard Industrial Estate,
Chipping Norton, Oxfordshire, OX7 5HX
Area of Operation: Midlands & Mid Wales, South
West England and South Wales
Tel: 01608 643261
Fax: 01608 641768
Email: gill@cnglass.plus.com
Web: www.chippingnortonglass.co.uk
Product Type: 1, 2, 3, 4, 5, 6
Material Type: J) 1, 2, 4, 5, 6, 7, 8, 9, 10

CHROMA INTERNATIONAL GLASS LTD
Unit 200 Bridgwater Business Park,
Bridgwater, Somerset, TA6 4TB
Area of Operation: Europe
Tel: 01278 426226
Fax: 01278 450088
Email: info@chroma-glass.com
Web: www.chroma-glass.com
Product Type: 3, 5 **Other Info:** ✍

CLASSIC PVC HOME IMPROVEMENTS
Unit 36 LEC Workshops, Trostre Road,
Llanelli, Carmarthenshire, SA15 2EA
Area of Operation: South West England and South Wales
Tel: 01554 777158
Fax: 01554 775086
Email: enquiries@classic.uk.com
Web: www.classic.uk.com
Product Type: 1, 2, 3, 4, 5, 6, 7
Material Type: D) 1

DUPLUS DOMES LTD
370 Melton Road, Leicester, Leicestershire, LE4 7SL
Area of Operation: Worldwide
Tel: 0116 261 0710 **Fax:** 0116 261 0539
Email: sales@duplus.co.uk
Web: www.duplus.co.uk
Material Type: D) 3

DURABUILD GLAZED STRUCTURES LTD
Carlton Road, Coventry, West Midlands, CV6 7FL
Area of Operation: Worldwide
Tel: 02476 669169
Fax: 02476 669170
Email: enquiries@durabuild.co.uk
Web: www.durabuild.co.uk
Product Type: 2, 3, 5, 6, 7 **Other Info:** ECO ✍ ✋
Material Type: J) 2, 4, 5, 10

EDEN DECORATIVE GLASS LTD
Alder House, Aylburton Business Centre, Stockwell
Lane, Aylburton, Lydney, Gloucestershire, GL15 6ST
Area of Operation: UK (Excluding Ireland)
Tel: 0845 658 0230 **Fax:** 01594 840028
Email: info@edenglass.co.uk
Web: www.edenglass.co.uk **Product Type:** 5, 6, 7

EDGETECH UK
Unit 3C, Swallow Gate Business Park,
Holbrook Lane, Coventry, West Midlands, CV6 4BL
Area of Operation: UK (Excluding Ireland)
Tel: 02476 705570
Fax: 02476 705510
Email: ukenquiries@edgetechig.com
Web: www.superspacer.co.uk
Product Type: 1, 2, 4

ENERGY SUPERSTORE
3 Wellington Park, Belfast, BT9 6DJ
Area of Operation: UK & Ireland
Tel: 02890 388391 **Product Type:** 2, 3
Web: www.energysuperstore.co.uk

EVEREST LTD
Sopers Road, Cuffley, Hertfordshire, EN6 4SG
Area of Operation: UK & Ireland
Tel: 0800 010123 **Web:** www.everest.co.uk ✍ ✋

FITZROY JOINERY
Garden Close, Langage Industrial Estate,
Plympton, Plymouth, Devon, PL7 5EU
Area of Operation: UK & Ireland
Tel: 0870 428 9110 **Fax:** 0870 428 9111
Email: admin@fitzroy.co.uk
Web: www.fitzroyjoinery.co.uk ✍
Product Type: 1, 2, 3, 4, 5, 6 **Other Info:** ECO ✍
Material Type: J) 2, 4, 5, 6, 7, 8, 9, 10

FRANKLIN LEEDS LLP
Carlton Works, Cemetery Road, Yeadon,
Leeds, West Yorkshire, LS19 7BD
Area of Operation: UK & Ireland
Tel: 0113 250 2991
Fax: 0113 250 0991
Email: david.franklin@franklinwindows.co.uk
Web: www.franklinwindows.co.uk
Product Type: 1, 2, 3, 5, 6, 7

GLASS AND GLAZING FEDERATION
44-48 Borough High Street, London, SE1 1XB
Area of Operation: UK (Excluding Ireland)
Tel: 0845 257 7956 **Fax:** 0870 042 4266
Email: info@ggf.org.uk **Web:** www.ggf.org.uk ✍

GLASS DESIGN STUDIO LTD
27B Morelands Trading Estate, Bristol Road,
Gloucester, Gloucestershire, GL1 5RZ
Tel: 01452 413773 **Fax:** 01452 521717
Email: info@glassdesignstudio.co.uk
Web: www.glassdesignstudio.co.uk
Product Type: 5

GLAVERBEL (UK) LTD.
Chestnut Field, Regent Place,
Rugby, Warwickshire, CV21 2TL
Area of Operation: Europe
Tel: 01788 535353 **Fax:** 01788 560853
Email: gvb.uk@glaverbel.com
Web: www.myglaverbel.com
Material Type: J) 1, 2, 4, 5, 6, 7, 9, 10

GREEN BUILDING STORE
11 Huddersfield Road, Meltham,
Holmfirth, West Yorkshire, HD9 4NJ
Tel: 01484 854898 **Fax:** 01484 854899
Email: info@greenbuildingstore.co.uk
Web: www.greenbuildingstore.co.uk ✍
Product Type: 2, 3, 7 **Other Info:** ECO ✍
Material Type: J) 2, 4, 10

HARAN GLASS
Southpoint, 15 Lawmoor Road,
Dixon Blazes, City of Glasgow
Area of Operation: UK (Excluding Ireland)
Tel: 0141 418 4510 **Fax:** 0141 429 8655
Email: info@harans.co.uk
Web: www.haranglass.com ✍

HIGHSEAL WINDOWS LIMITED
Moat Road, Scunthorpe, Lincolnshire, DN15 9GA
Area of Operation: East England, Greater London,
Midlands & Mid Wales, North East England, North West
England and North Wales, Scotland, South East England
Tel: 01724 276213 **Fax:** 01724 276214
Email: david.maybank@hwlgroup.co.uk
Web: www.hwlgroup.co.uk
Product Type: 2, 3, 5, 6 **Material Type:** J) 2, 4, 5, 7, 10

HOLDSWORTH WINDOWS LTD
Darlingscote Road, Shipston-on-Stour,
Warwickshire, CV36 4PR
Area of Operation: UK & Ireland
Tel: 01608 661883 **Fax:** 01608 661008
Email: info@holdsworthwindows.co.uk
Web: www.holdsworthwindows.co.uk
Product Type: 6 **Other Info:** ✍
Material Type: C) 2, 4

HOT GLASS DESIGN
Unit 24 Crosby Yard Industrial Estate,
Bridgend, Mid Glamorgan, CF31 1JZ
Area of Operation: Europe
Tel: 01656 659884 **Fax:** 01656 659884
Email: info@hotglassdesign.co.uk
Web: www.hotglassdesign.co.uk
Product Type: 3, 5, 7 **Material Type:** J) 1, 2, 4, 5, 6

JAMES BENTLEY
James Bentley Limited, 13 Tennyson Road,
Hinckley, Leicestershire, LE10 0TH
Area of Operation: UK (Excluding Ireland)
Tel: 0870 850 2057
Email: paul.smith@james-bentley.co.uk
Web: www.james-bentley.co.uk **Product Type:** 2

LATTICE PERIOD WINDOWS
Unit 85 Northwick Business Centre, Blockley,
Moreton in Marsh, Gloucestershire, Gl56 9RF
Area of Operation: UK & Ireland
Tel: 01386 701079 **Fax:** 01386 701114
Email: sales@latticewindows.net
Web: www.latticewindows.co.uk
Product Type: 1, 2, 3, 4, 5, 6
Material Type: J) 1, 2, 3, 4, 5, 6, 7, 8, 9, 10

LEAD & LIGHT
35a Hartland Road, London, NW1 8DB
Area of Operation: Worldwide
Tel: 0207 485 0997 **Fax:** 0207 284 2660
Email: leadandlight@msn.com
Web: www.leadandlight.co.uk
Product Type: 3, 5, 6 **Other Info:** ✍ ✋

MH JOINERY SERVICES
25b Camwall Road, Harrogate, North Yorkshire, HG1 4PT
Area of Operation: North East England
Tel: 01423 888856 **Fax:** 01423 888856
Email: info@mhjoineryservices.co.uk
Web: www.mhjoineryservices.co.uk
Product Type: 1, 2, 3, 6

NORVIK PVCU WINDOW SYSTEMS LTD
Mitchells Industrial Park, Wombwell,
Barnsley, South Yorkshire, S35 7AE
Area of Operation: UK & Ireland
Tel: 01226 340182 **Fax:** 01226 340375
Email: nhibberd@norvik.co.uk
Web: www.norvik.co.uk **Product Type:** 2, 3, 8

NULITE LTD
41 Hutton Close, Crowther Industrial Estate,
Washington, Tyne & Wear, NE38 0AH
Area of Operation: UK & Ireland
Tel: 0191 419 1111 **Fax:** 0191 419 1123
Email: sales@nulite-ltd.co.uk
Web: www.nulite-ltd.co.uk
Product Type: 2, 3, 7
Other Info: ✍ **Material Type:** C) 1, 2, 4

OXFORD SASH WINDOW CO LTD.
Eynsham Park Estate Yard, Cuckoo Lane,
North Leigh, Oxfordshire, OX29 6PW
Area of Operation: Greater London, Midlands & Mid
Wales, South East England, South West England and
South Wales
Tel: 01993 883536 **Fax:** 01993 883027
Email: oxsash@globalnet.co.uk
Web: www.sashwindow.co.uk
Product Type: 1, 2, 3, 7

REDDISEALS
The Furlong, Berry Hill Industrial Estate,
Droitwich, Worcestershire, WR9 9BG
Area of Operation: UK & Ireland
Tel: 01905 791876 **Fax:** 01905 791877
Email: reddiseals@reddiseals.com
Web: www.reddiseals.com ✍

ROOFLIGHT ARCHITECTURAL LTD
Unit 17 South Nelson Rd, South Nelson Industrial
Estate, Cramlington, Northumberland, NE23 1WF
Area of Operation: UK (Excluding Ireland)
Tel: 01670 736124
Fax: 01670 738080
Email: sales@rooflight.co.uk
Web: www.rooflight.co.uk

SAINT-GOBAIN GLASS
Weeland Road, Eggborough,
East Riding of Yorks, DN14 0FD
Area of Operation: UK & Ireland
Tel: 01977 666196 **Fax:** 01977 666203
Email: glassinfo@saint-gobain-glass.com
Web: www.saint-gobain-glass.com
Product Type: 1, 2, 3, 5

SASH UK LTD
Ferrymoor Way, Park Springs, Grimethorpe,
Barnsley, South Yorkshire, S72 7BN
Area of Operation: Worldwide
Tel: 01226 715619 **Fax:** 01226 719968
Email: mailbox@sashuk.com
Web: www.sashuk.com
Product Type: 1, 2, 3, 5, 6 **Material Type:** D) 1

SCHUCO INTERNATIONAL KG
Whitehall Avenue, Kingston,
Milton Keynes, Buckinghamshire, MK10 0AL
Area of Operation: Worldwide
Tel: 01908 282111 **Fax:** 01908 282124
Email: shamman@schueco.com
Web: www.schueco.co.uk

SPS TIMBER WINDOWS
Units 2 and 3, 34 Eveline Road,
Mitcham, Surrey, CR4 3LE
Area of Operation: Greater London
Tel: 0208 640 5035 **Fax:** 0208 685 1570
Email: info@spstimberwindows.co.uk
Web: www.spstimberwindows.co.uk ✍
Product Type: 1, 2, 3, 5, 6 **Other Info:** ✍

STANDARDS GROUP
Bentley Hall Barn, Alkmonton,
Ashbourne, Derbyshire, DE6 3DJ
Area of Operation: UK & Ireland
Tel: 01335 330263 **Fax:** 01335 330922
Email: uk@standardsgroup.com
Web: www.standardsgroup.com
Product Type: 1, 3, 5, 6

STEVENSWOOD CONSERVATORIES
21 Napier Square Houstoun Road Industrial Estate,
Livingston, West Lothian, EH54 5DG
Area of Operation: Scotland
Tel: 01506 438111 **Fax:** 01506 438444
Email: info@stevenswood.co.uk
Web: www.stevenswood.co.uk
Product Type: 1, 2, 3, 4, 5, 6

STORM WINDOWS LIMITED
Unit 7, James Scott Road, Off Park Lane,
Halesowen, West Midlands, B63 2QT
Area of Operation: UK (Excluding Ireland)
Tel: 0845 0611444 **Fax:** 01384 410307
Email: sandra.lamb@virgin.net
Web: www.stormwindows.co.uk **Product Type:** 4

STUART OWEN NORTON GLASS AND SIGN LTD
Unit 6, Hill Court, Dunne Road,
Blaydon, Tyne & Wear, NE21 5NH
Area of Operation: Worldwide
Tel: 0191 4140123 **Fax:** 0191 4140157
Email: brilliant.cutter@btinternet.com
Web: www.glass-and-sign.com
Product Type: 1, 2, 3, 5, 6
Other Info: ✍ ✋ **Material Type:** J) 4, 5, 6

SUNRISE STAINED GLASS
58-60 Middle Street, Southsea,
Portsmouth, Hampshire, PO5 4BP
Area of Operation: UK (Excluding Ireland)
Tel: 02392 750512 **Fax:** 02392 875488
Email: sunrise@stained-windows.co.uk
Web: www.stained-windows.co.uk
Product Type: 5, 6

SUNSQUARE LIMITED
5A Barton Road Trading Estate,
Bury St Edmunds, Suffolk, IP32 7BE
Area of Operation: UK & Ireland
Tel: 0845 226 3172 **Fax:** 0845 226 3173
Email: info@sunsquare.co.uk
Web: www.sunsquare.co.uk
Product Type: 1, 2, 3 **Other Info:** ECO ✍

THE CAMDEN GROUP
Unit 4-7, Steeple Industrial Estate, Antrim, BT41 1AB
Area of Operation: UK & Ireland
Tel: 028 9446 2419
Fax: 028 9442 8138
Email: info@camdengroup.co.uk
Web: www.camdengroup.co.uk
Product Type: 2, 3, 5, 7

Let the
sun shine in...

- Energy free natural lighting

- No heat loss in winter or solar gain in the summer

- No limit to the length of SunPipe or number of bends that can be used

- No structural alterations necessary in most cases

- Virtually burglar proof and vandal-resistant

- Self-cleaning and condense free top dome

THE STAINED GLASS STUDIO
Unit 5, Brewery Arts, Brewery Court,
Cirencester, Gloucestershire, GL7 1JH
Area of Operation: Worldwide
Tel: 01285 644430
Email: daniella@stainedglassbreweryarts.co.uk
Web: www.stainedglassbrewery arts.co.uk
Product Type: 5

THE STAINED GLASS WORKS
188 Archway Road, London, N6 5BB
Area of Operation: Greater London
Tel: 0208 348 0220
Fax: 0208 348 0220
Email: user@bennis.fsworld.co.uk
Web: www.thestainedglassworks.co.uk
Product Type: 5

TOTAL GLASS LIMITED
Total Complex, Overbrook Lane,
Knowsley, Merseyside, L34 9FB
Area of Operation: Midlands & Mid Wales, North
East England, North West England and North Wales
Tel: 0151 549 2339
Fax: 0151 546 0022
Email: sales@totalglass.com
Web: www.totalglass.com
Product Type: 1, 2, 3, 5, 6, 7

TRADE CONSERVATORIES 2 U LTD
36 Temple Way, Maldon, Essex, CM9 4PX
Area of Operation: UK (Excluding Ireland)
Tel: 0845 130 3871
Fax: 0845 130 3872
Email: sales@tradeconservatories2u.co.uk
Web: www.tradeconservatories2u.co.uk
Product Type: 1, 2, 3, 4, 5, 6, 7

TWINFIX
201 Cavendish Place, Birchwood Park,
Birchwood, Warrington, Cheshire, WA3 6WU
Area of Operation: UK & Ireland
Tel: 01925 811311
Fax: 01925 852955
Email: enquiries@twinfix.co.uk
Web: www.twinfix.co.uk

UAP
Bank House, 16-18 Bank Street,
Walshaw, Bury, Lancashire, BL8 3AZ
Area of Operation: UK & Ireland
Tel: 0161 763 5290   **Fax:** 0161 763 6726
Email: uap@btconnect.com
Web: www.universal-imports.com
Product Type: 5

ULTRAFRAME UK
Salthill Road, Clitheroe, Lancashire, BB7 1PE
Area of Operation: UK & Ireland
Tel: 01200 443311
Fax: 0870 414 1020
Email: sales@ultraframe.com
Web: www.ultraframe-conservatories.co.uk
Product Type: 1, 3, 7
Material Type: D) 1, 3

WAYNE RICKETTS STAINED GLASS
Units 9-11 The White Factory,
18 Netham Road, Redfield, Bristol, BS5 9PF
Area of Operation: Worldwide
Tel: 0117 955 5390
Fax: 0117 955 5390
Email: wayne.ricketts@btconnect.com
Web: www.waynerickettsstainedglass.com
Product Type: 5
Other Info:

WINDSOR GLASS & GLAZING CO LTD
Invest House, Bruce Road, Swansea West Industrial
Park, Fforestfach, Swansea, SA5 4HS
Area of Operation: Midlands & Mid Wales, North
West England and North Wales, South West England
and South Wales
Tel: 01792 589761   **Fax:** 01792 585063
Email: sales@windsor-glass.co.uk
Web: www.windsor-glass.co.uk
Product Type: 2, 3, 5, 6, 7   **Other Info:**
Material Type: J) 1, 2, 4, 5, 6, 7, 8, 9, 10

ROOF WINDOWS AND LIGHT PIPES

KEY

OTHER: ▽ Reclaimed   🛒 On-line shopping
✏ Bespoke   ✋ Hand-made   ECO Ecological

ABOVE IT ALL
56 Hardman Avenue, Rawtenstall,
Rossendale, Lancashire, BB4 6BB
Area of Operation: North West England and North Wales
Tel: 0800 505 3344   **Email:** info@above-it-all.co.uk
Web: www.above-it-all.co.uk

ANDERSEN WINDOWS / BLACK MILLWORK CO.
Andersen House, Dallow Street,
Burton on Trent, Staffordshire, DE14 2PQ
Area of Operation: UK & Ireland
Tel: 01283 511122   **Fax:** 01283 510863
Email: info@blackmillwork.co.uk
Web: www.blackmillwork.co.uk

APROPOS TECTONIC LTD
Greenside House, Richmond Street,
Ashton Under Lyne, Lancashire, OL6 7ES
Area of Operation: UK & Ireland
Tel: 0870 777 0326   **Fax:** 0161 3428265
Email: enquiries@apropos-tectonic.com
Web: www.apropos-tectonic.com

AUTOMATED CONTROL SERVICES LTD
Unit 16, Hightown Industrial Estate,
Crow Arch Lane, Ringwood, Hampshire, BH24 1ND
Area of Operation: UK (Excluding Ireland)
Tel: 01425 461008   **Fax:** 01425 461009
Email: sales@automatedcontrolservices.co.uk
Web: www.automatedcontrolservices.co.uk

BRETT MARTIN DAYLIGHT SYSTEMS
Sandford Close, Alderford's Green Industrial Estate,
Coventry, West Midlands, CV2 2QU
Area of Operation: Worldwide
Tel: 02476 602022   **Fax:** 02476 602744
Email: daylight@brettmartin.com
Web: www.daylightsystems.com

BROXWOOD LTD
Broxwood Ltd, Inveralmond Way,
Inveralmond Industrial Estate, Perth, PH1 3UQ
Area of Operation: Europe
Fax: 01738 444452   **Email:** sales@broxwood.com
Web: www.broxwood.com

CLEMENT STEEL WINDOWS
Clement House, Weydown Road,
Haslemere, Surrey, GU27 1HR
Area of Operation: Worldwide
Tel: 01428 643393   **Fax:** 01428 644436
Email: info@clementwg.co.uk
Web: www.clementsteelwindows.com

DURABUILD GLAZED STRUCTURES LTD
Carlton Road, Coventry, West Midlands, CV6 7FL
Area of Operation: UK & Ireland
Tel: 02476 669169   **Fax:** 02476 669170
Email: enquiries@durabuild.co.uk
Web: www.durabuild.co.uk

E. RICHARDS
PO Box 1115, Winscombe, Somerset, BS25 1WA
Area of Operation: UK & Ireland
Tel: 0845 330 8859   **Fax:** 0845 330 7260
Email: info@e-richards.co.uk
Web: www.e-richards.co.uk

FAKRO GB LTD
Astron Business Park, Hearthcote Lane,
Swadlincote, Derbyshire, DE11 9DW
Area of Operation: UK & Ireland
Tel: 01283 554755   **Fax:** 01283 224545
Email: sales@fakrogb.com
Web: www.fakro.co.uk
Other Info: ECO   **Material Type:** B) 2

GLAZING VISION
6 Barns Close, Brandon, Suffolk, IP27 0NY
Area of Operation: Worldwide
Tel: 01842 815581   **Fax:** 01842 815515
Email: sales@visiongroup.co.uk
Web: www.visiongroup.co.uk

JOULESAVE EMES LTD
27 Water Lane, South Witham,
Grantham, Lincolnshire, NG33 5PH
Area of Operation: UK & Ireland
Tel: 01572 768362   **Fax:** 01572 767146
Email: sales@joulesave.co.uk
Web: www.joulesave.co.uk

KEYLITE ROOF WINDOWS
Derryloran Industrial Estate, Sandholes Road,
Cookstown, Co Tyrone, BT80 9LU
Area of Operation: UK & Ireland
Tel: 028 8675 8921
Fax: 028 8675 8923
Email: info@keylite.co.uk   **Web:** www.keylite.co.uk

MONODRAUGHT SUNPIPE LIMITED
Halifax House, Cressex Business Park,
High Wycombe, Buckinghamshire, HP12 3SE
Area of Operation: UK (Excluding Ireland)
Tel: 01494 897700
Fax: 01494 532465
Email: info@monodraught.com
Web: www.sunpipe.co.uk

NULITE LTD
41 Hutton Close, Crowther Industrial Estate,
Washington, Tyne & Wear, NE38 0AH
Area of Operation: UK & Ireland
Tel: 0191 419 1111   **Fax:** 0191 419 1123
Email: sales@nulite-ltd.co.uk
Web: www.nulite-ltd.co.uk

ROOFLIGHT ARCHITECTURAL LTD
Unit 17 South Nelson Road, South Nelson Industrial
Estate, Cramlington, Northumberland, NE23 1WF
Area of Operation: UK (Excluding Ireland)
Tel: 01670 736124
Fax: 01670 738080
Email: sales@rooflight.co.uk
Web: www.rooflight.co.uk
Other Info: ECO   **Material Type:** C) 1, 4

RPL SOLATUBE IN SCOTLAND
4 Blythbank Cottages, West Linton, Lothian, EH46 7DF
Area of Operation: Scotland
Tel: 0845 601 5785   **Fax:** 01721 752624
Email: info@solabright.co.uk
Web: www.solatubescotland.co.uk

SOLA SKYLIGHTS UK LTD
10 George Reynolds Industrial Estate,
Shildon, Durham, DL4 2RB
Area of Operation: UK & Ireland
Tel: 01388 778445   **Fax:** 01388 778216
Email: jean@solaskylights.com
Web: www.solaskylights.com   **Other Info:** ECO
Material Type: C) 1, 3, 8, 9, 10, 15, 17

SOLALIGHTING
17 High Street, Olney, Buckinghamshire, MK46 4EB
Area of Operation: UK & Ireland
Tel: 01234 241466   **Fax:** 01234 241766
Email: sales@solalighting.co.uk
Web: www.solalighting.com

SUNSQUARE LIMITED
5A Barton Road Trading Estate,
Bury St Edmunds, Suffolk, IP32 7BE
Area of Operation: UK & Ireland
Tel: 0845 226 3172   **Fax:** 0845 226 3173
Email: info@sunsquare.co.uk
Web: www.sunsquare.co.uk   **Other Info:** ECO

THE GREEN SHOP
Cheltenham Road, Bisley,
Nr Stroud, Gloucestershire, GL6 7BX
Area of Operation: UK & Ireland
Tel: 01452 770629   **Fax:** 01452 770104
Email: paint@greenshop.co.uk
Web: www.greenshop.co.uk

THE LIGHTPIPE CO. LTD
7 Mill Road, Cranfield, Bedfordshire, MK43 0JG
Area of Operation: UK (Excluding Ireland)
Tel: 08702 416680
Email: sales@lightpipe.org.uk
Web: www.lightpipe.org.uk

THE LOFT SHOP
The Loft Shop, Eldon Way,
Littlehampton, West Sussex, BN17 7HE
Area of Operation: UK & Ireland
Tel: 0870 604 0404   **Fax:** 01903 738501
Email: enquiries@loftshop.co.uk
Web: www.loftshop.co.uk

THE ROOFLIGHT COMPANY
Unit 8, Wychwood Business Centre,
Shipton Under Wychwood, Oxfordshire, OX7 6XU
Area of Operation: UK (Excluding Ireland)
Tel: 01993 830613   **Fax:** 01993 831066
Email: info@therooflightcompany.co.uk
Web: www.therooflightcompany.co.uk

TUBZZZ.COM
Area of Operation: UK & Ireland
Tel: 0207 078 7477   **Email:** marianne@tubzzz.com
Web: www.tubzzz.com

TUSCAN FOUNDRY PRODUCTS
Units C1-C3, Oakendene Industrial Estate,
Bolney Road, Cowfold, West Sussex, RH13 8AZ
Area of Operation: Worldwide
Tel: 01403 860040   **Fax:** 0845 345 0215
Email: enquiries@tuscanfoundry.co.uk
Web: www.tuscanfoundry.com

TUSCAN FOUNDRY PRODUCTS

Area of Operation: Worldwide
Tel: 01403 860040
Fax: 0845 345 0215
Email: enquiries@tuscanfoundry.co.uk
Web: www.tuscanfoundry.com

Tuscan Foundry exclusively manufacture Lumen
Conservation Rooflights as well as a wide range
of other cast metal products including Radiators,
Gutters and Pipes. Free Expert advice available.

WESSEX BUILDING PRODUCTS (MULTITEX)
Dolphin Industrial Estate, Southampton Road,
Salisbury, Wiltshire, SP1 2NB
Area of Operation: UK & Ireland
Tel: 01722 332139   **Fax:** 01722 338458
Email: sales@wessexbuildingproducts.co.uk
Web: www.wessexbuildingproducts.co.uk
Material Type: D) 6

CURTAINS, BLINDS, SHUTTERS AND ACCESSORIES

KEY

OTHER: ▽ Reclaimed ⌂ On-line shopping
✎ Bespoke ✋ Hand-made ECO Ecological

A W PROTECTION FILMS
P.O Box 62, Hedge End,
Southampton, Hampshire, SO30 3ZJ
Tel: 02380 477550
Fax: 02380 477886
Email: sales@andywrap.co.uk
Web: www.maskingfilm.co.uk **Other Info:** ✎

AMBASSADOOR WINDOWS & DOORS LTD
18 Bidwell Road, Rackheath Industrial Estate,
Rackheath, Norwich, Norfolk, NR13 6PT
Area of Operation: East England, Greater London,
Midlands & Mid Wales
Tel: 01603 720332
Email: enquiries@ambassadoor.fsnet.co.uk
Web: www.ambassadoor.co.uk **Material Type:** A) 1

AMDEGA CONSERVATORIES
Woodside, Church Lane, Bursledon,
Southampton, Hampshire, SO31 8AB
Area of Operation: Worldwide **Tel:** 0800 591523
Web: www.amdega-conservatories.co.uk

APOLLO BLINDS
The Courtyard, Matthewsgreen Farm,
Matthewsgreen Road , Wokingham,
Berkshire, RG41 1JX
Area of Operation: South East England
Tel: 0118 977 0220 **Fax:** 0118 979 6009
Email: apolloblinds@onetel.com
Web: www.apolloblindsreading.co.uk

ARC-COMP
Friedrichstr. 3, 12205 Berlin-Lichterfelde, Germany
Area of Operation: Europe
Tel: +49 (0)308 430 9956
Fax: +49 (0)308 430 9957
Email: jvs@arc-comp.com
Web: www.arc-com.com **Material Type:** C) 1

ARC-COMP (IRISH BRANCH)
Whitefield Cottage, Lugduff, Tinahely,
Co. Wicklow, Republic of Ireland
Area of Operation: Europe
Tel: +353 (0)868 729 945
Fax: +353 (0)402 28900
Email: jvs@arc-comp.com
Web: www.arc-comp.com **Material Type:** C) 1

AVOLON BLINDS
Unit 52 Armagh Business Centre,
Loughgall Road, Armagh, Co Armagh, BT61 7NJ
Area of Operation: Ireland Only
Tel: 02837 527874 **Fax:** 02837 527468
Email: info @avolonblinds.co.uk
Web: www.avolonblinds.com

B ROURKE & CO LTD
Vulcan Works, Accrington Road,
Burnley, Lancashire, BB11 5QD
Area of Operation: Worldwide
Tel: 01282 422841 **Fax:** 01282 458901
Email: info@rourkes.co.uk
Web: www.rourkes.co.uk
Material Type: C) 5, 11, 14

BALMORAL BLINDS
Beresford Close, Frimley Green,
Camberley, Surrey, GU16 6LB
Area of Operation: Greater London, South East England
Tel: 01252 674172
Fax: 0870 132 7683
Email: sales@balmoralblinds.co.uk
Web: www.balmoralblinds.co.uk

BLINDS BY ELEGANCE
8 Daish Way, Dodnor Industrial Estate,
Newport, Isle of Wight, PO30 5XB
Area of Operation: UK (Excluding Ireland)
Tel: 01983 533900 **Fax:** 01983 533900
Email: enquiries@blindsbyelegance.co.uk
Web: www.blindsbyelegance.co.uk ⌂

BLINDS.CO.UK
17-19 Gt. Eastern Street, London, EC2A 3EJ
Area of Operation: UK (Excluding Ireland)
Tel: 0800 0567446 **Fax:** 020 73778787
Email: sales@blinds.co.uk
Web: www.blinds.co.uk ⌂

BLINDSHAPERS LTD
86, Park Street, Congleton, Cheshire, CW12 1EG
Area of Operation: Worldwide
Tel: 01260 297976 **Fax:** 01260 297515
Email: info@blindshapers.com
Web: www.blindshapers.com

BRITISH BLIND AND SHUTTER ASSOCIATION
42 Heath Street, Tamworth, Staffordshire, B79 7JH
Area of Operation: UK & Ireland
Tel: 01827 52337 **Fax:** 01827 310827
Email: info@bbsa.org.uk **Web:** www.bbsa.org.uk

CHESHIRE SUNBLIND COMPANY
116 Chester Road, Northwich, Cheshire, CW8 1JH
Area of Operation: North West England and North Wales
Tel: 01606 74318 **Fax:** 01606 871004
Email: info@cheshiresunblind.co.uk
Web: www.cheshiresunblind.co.uk

COLORFLAIR BLINDS
86 High Street, Lee on the Solent, Hampshire, PO13 9DA
Area of Operation: South East England
Tel: 02392 552265 **Fax:** 02392 552265
Email: windowblinds@blinds-at-colorflair.co.uk
Web: www.blinds-at-colorflair.co.uk

CONSERVATORY BLINDS LTD
8-10 Ruxley Lane, Ewell, Epsom, Surrey, KT19 0JD
Area of Operation: England & Wales
Tel: 0800 071 8888
Fax: 0208 394 0022
Email: info@conservatoryblinds.co.uk
Web: www.conservatoryblinds.co.uk

COOLSCAPES LTD - PHOTO ROLLER BLINDS
114a Top Lane, Whitley, Melksham, Wiltshire, SN12 8QU
Area of Operation: Worldwide
Tel: 01225 702938
Email: info@coolscapes.co.uk
Web: www.photorollerblinds.co.uk

CUSTOM MADE SHUTTERS
Avalon, Swan Lane, Marlpit Hill,
Eadenbridge, Kent, TN8 6BA
Area of Operation: UK & Ireland
Tel: 01732 863554
Email: info@custommadeshutters.co.uk
Web: www.custommadeshutters.co.uk

D & S BLINDS & CURTAINS
21 Delamere Street, Ashton Under Lyne,
Lancashire, OL6 7LZ
Area of Operation: North West England and North Wales
Tel: 0161 339 5755 **Fax:** 0161 339 5755
Email: sales@kcblinds.co.uk
Web: www.kcblinds.co.uk

ELERO UK LIMITED
Unit 4, Foundry Lane, Halebank,
Widnes, Cheshire, WA8 8TZ
Area of Operation: UK & Ireland
Tel: 0870 240 4219 **Fax:** 0870 240 4086
Email: sales@elerouk.co.uk
Web: www.elerouk.co.uk

ELITE BLINDS UK
39 Whalley New Road, Blackburn, Lancashire, BB1 6JY
Area of Operation: UK (Excluding Ireland)
Tel: 01254 674263
Fax: 01254 261935
Email: sales@eliteblindsuk.co.uk
Web: www.eliteblindsuk.com **Other Info:** ✎ ✋

FABER BLINDS UK LTD
Kilvey Road, Brackmills, Northampton, NN4 7BQ
Area of Operation: UK & Ireland
Tel: 01604 766 251
Fax: 01604 768 802
Email: faberblinds-uk@faber.dk
Web: www.faberblinds.co.uk **Other Info:** ✎

FINISHING TOUCH
The Barn at Hudsons Cottage, 251 Lower Shelton
Road, Upper Shelton, Bedford, Bedfordshire, MK43 0LS
Area of Operation: Worldwide
Tel: 01234 764098
Fax: 01234 764098
Email: finishingtouchinteriors@fsmail.net
Web: www.finishingtouchinteriors.co.uk ⌂

FLAMINGO BLINDS & FABRICS
12 Chaseville Parade, Chaseville Park Road,
Winchmore Hill, London, N21 1PG
Area of Operation: East England, Greater London,
Midlands & Mid Wales, South East England
Tel: 0870 777 1665
Fax: 0208 245 8323
Email: admin@flamingoblinds.co.uk
Web: www.flamingoblinds.co.uk ⌂

FLYDOR LIMITED
Priory Works, Newton Street,
Newton St. Faith, Norwich, Norfolk, NR10 3AD
Area of Operation: UK & Ireland
Tel: 01603 892 080 **Fax:** 01603 897 280
Email: sales@flydor.co.uk **Web:** www.flydor.co.uk

GEMINI BLINDS & AWNINGS (GLOUCESTER) LTD
Unit 16, St James Trading Estate, 280 Barton Street,
Gloucester, Gloucestershire, GL1 4JJ
Area of Operation: Midlands & Mid Wales
Tel: 01452 546814
Fax: 01452 546814
Email: derek@gemini-blindsawnings.co.uk
Web: www.gemini-blindsawnings.co.uk ⌂

GRANT MERCER
PO Box 246, Banstead, Surrey, SM7 3LE
Area of Operation: Europe
Tel: 01737 357957 **Fax:** 01737 373003
Email: grantmercer@shuttersuk.com
Web: www.shuttersuk.com

HUMBERSIDE SUNBLINDS LTD
Marlin House, Kings Road,
Immingham, Lincolnshire, DN40 1AW
Area of Operation: UK (Excluding Ireland)
Tel: 01469 574490 **Fax:** 01469 578164
Email: humbersideblinds@aol.com
Web: www.humbersidesunblinds.co.uk

INNER SPACE DESIGNS
6 Norfolk Road, Newport, NP19 7SL
Area of Operation: South West England and South Wales
Tel: 01633 782505 **Fax:** 01633 782506
Email: info@innerspacedesigns.co.uk
Web: www.innerspacedesigns.co.uk
Other Info: ✎ ✋

INTELLI-BLINDS
Roman House, Wood Street,
Macclesfield, Cheshire, SK11 6JQ
Area of Operation: UK (Excluding Ireland)
Tel: 01625 669779 **Web:** www.intelli-blinds.com ⌂

JIM LAWRENCE LTD
Scotland Hall Farm, Stoke by Nayland,
Colchester, Essex, CO6 4QG
Area of Operation: UK (Excluding Ireland)
Tel: 01206 263459 **Fax:** 01206 262166
Email: sales@jim-lawrence.co.uk
Web: www.jim-lawrence.co.uk ⌂

KARENS BLINDS
38 Kenilworth Drive, Oadby,
Leicester, Leicestershire, LE2 5LG
Area of Operation: Midlands & Mid Wales
Tel: 0116 271 7090 **Fax:** 0116 271 4086
Email: karen@karensblinds.co.uk
Web: www.karensblinds.co.uk

KESTREL SHUTTERS
9 East Race Street, Stowe, Pennsylvania, 19464, USA
Area of Operation: Worldwide
Tel: +1 610 326 6679 **Fax:** +1 610 326 6779
Email: sales@diyshutters.com
Web: www.diyshutters.com ⌂

LEVOLUX LTD
1 Forward Drive, Harrow, Middlesex,
Greater London, HA3 8NT
Area of Operation: Worldwide
Tel: 0208 863 9111 **Fax:** 0208 863 8760
Email: info@levolux.com
Web: www.levolux.com

LONDON BLIND COMPANY LTD
205A Long Lane , Bexleyheath, Kent, DA7 5AF
Area of Operation: UK (Excluding Ireland)
Tel: 0208 303 7964 **Fax:** 0208 301 3586
Email: gino@londonblinds.co.uk
Web: www.londonblinds.co.uk

LUTRON EA LTD
Lutron House, 6 Sovereign Close,
Wapping, Greater London, E1W 3JF
Area of Operation: Worldwide
Tel: 0207 702 0657 **Fax:** 0207 480 6899
Email: lutronlondon@lutron.com
Web: www.lutron.com/europe

MEL-TEC LTD
1 Boundary Road, Buckingham Road Industrial
Estate, Brackley, Northamptonshire, NN13 7ES
Area of Operation: UK & Ireland
Tel: 01280 705323 **Fax:** 01280 702258
Email: sales@meltec.co.uk
Web: www.meltec.co.uk
Other Info: ✎ **Material Type:** C) 1

MERRICK & DAY
Redbourne Hall, Redbourne,
Gainsborough, Lincolnshire, DN21 4JG
Tel: 0870 757 0980 **Fax:** 0870 757 0985
Email: sales@merrick-day.com
Web: www.merrick-day.com

NATIONAL PLASTICS
Bridge Street, Abercarn, Gwent, NP11 4SB
Area of Operation: UK & Ireland
Tel: 01495 244551 **Fax:** 01495 247990
Email: srholt@nationalplastics.co.uk
Web: www.nationalplastics.co.uk ⌂

NIGEL TYAS HANDCRAFTED IRONWORK
Bullhouse Mill, Lee Lane, Millhouse Green,
Penistone, Sheffield, South Yorkshire, S36 6BE
Area of Operation: Worldwide
Tel: 01226 766618
Email: sales@nigeltyas.co.uk
Web: www.nigeltyas.co.uk **Material Type:** C) 2, 4, 5, 6

PEELS OF LONDON
PO Box 160, Richmond, Surrey, TW10 7XL
Area of Operation: Worldwide
Tel: 0208 948 0689 **Fax:** 0208 948 0689
Email: info@e-peels.co.uk **Web:** www.e-peels.co.uk

PLANTATION SHUTTERS
131 Putney Bridge Road, London, SW15 2PA
Area of Operation: UK & Ireland
Tel: 0208 871 9222 / 9333 **Fax:** 0208 871 0041
Email: sales@plantation-shutters.co.uk
Web: www.plantation-shutters.co.uk

PURLFROST WINDOW FILM
PO Box 53306, London, NW10 5ZS
Area of Operation: UK (Excluding Ireland)
Tel: 0208 968 4798 **Fax:** 0871 733 4587
Email: emmanuel@purlfrost.com
Web: www.purlfrost.com

RUFFLETTE
Sharston Road, Manchester , M22 4TH
Area of Operation: UK & Ireland
Tel: 0161 998 1811
Fax: 0161 945 9468
Email: customer-care@rufflette.com
Web: www.rufflette.com ⌂

SBI LTD
85c Beckenham Lane, Shortlands, Bromley, Kent, BR2 0DN
Area of Operation: South East England
Tel: 0800 0742 721 **Fax:** 01634 670354
Email: mail@sbiukltd.co.uk
Web: www.sbiukltd.co.uk
Other Info: ✎ **Material Type:** A) 15

SHAFTESBURYS//SHUTTERS
44 Victoria Road, Victoria Business Park,
Burgess Hill, West Sussex, RH15 9LR
Area of Operation: UK (Excluding Ireland)
Tel: 0845 166 4103
Email: info@shaftesburyshutters.co.uk
Web: www.shaftesburys.co.uk ⤴

SHUTTER FRONTIER LTD
2 Rosemary Farmhouse, Rosemary Lane,
Flimwell, Wadhurst, East Sussex, TN5 7PT
Area of Operation: Worldwide
Tel: 01580 878 137
Fax: 01580 878 137
Email: jane@shutterfrontier.co.uk
Web: www.shutterfrontier.co.uk

SHUTTERCRAFT
Newdown Farm, Micheldever,
Winchester, Hampshire, SO21 3BT
Area of Operation: UK & Ireland
Tel: 01962 794530
Fax: 01962 794531
Email: leebartlett@shuttercraft.co.uk
Web: www.shuttercraft.co.uk **Other Info:** ✎ ✋

SHUTTERLY FABULOUS
18a Clermont Road, Brighton, East Sussex, BN1 6SG
Area of Operation: Greater London, Scotland, South
East England, South West England and South Wales
Tel: 0845 644 2873
Fax: 0845 280 1760
Email: hello@shutterlyfabulous.com
Web: www.shutterlyfabulous.com

SIMPLY SHUTTERS LTD
Unit 2A Station Way, Brandon, Suffolk, IP27 0BH
Area of Operation: Europe
Tel: 01842 814260 **Fax:** 01842 814460
Email: sales@simplyshutters.co.uk
Web: www.simplyshutters.co.uk **Material Type:** D)1

SUN SHADE SYSTEMS
Unit 3a Tyne Dock East Side, Port of Tyne,
South Shields, Tyne & Wear, NE33 5SQ
Area of Operation: UK & Ireland
Tel: 0845 838 1655 **Fax:** 0845 838 1677
Email: sales@sunshadesystems.com
Web: www.sunshadesystems.com ⤴

SUNSCREEN BLINDS
372 London Road , Hadleigh, Benfleet, Essex, SS7 2DA
Area of Operation: South East England
Tel: 01702 551444 **Fax:** 01702 554058
Email: sales@sunscreenblinds.com

SUPABLIND
Unit 7 BGW Business Park,
84 Sherwood Road, Bromsgrove,
Worcestershire, B60 3DR
Area of Operation: Midlands & Mid Wales
Tel: 01527 831940
Fax: 01527 575266
Email: enquries@supablind.co.uk
Web: www.supablind.co.uk

SURFACEMATERIALDESIGN
17 Skiffington Close, London, SW2 3UL
Area of Operation: Worldwide
Tel: 0208 671 3383
Email: info@surfacematerialdesign.co.uk
Web: www.surfacematerialdesign.co.uk ⤴

THE BLIND SPOT
23 Castlehill Street, New Elgin,
Elgin, Moray, IV30 6HB
Area of Operation: Scotland
Tel: 01343 549939
Fax: 01343 555223
Email: blindspotinelgin@aol.com

THE BRADLEY COLLECTION
Lion Barn, Maitland Road,
Needham Market, Suffolk, IP6 8NS
Area of Operation: Worldwide
Tel: 01449 722724
Fax: 0845 118 7228
Email: claus.fortmann@bradleycollection.co.uk
Web: www.bradleycollection.co.uk

**THE CALIFORNIA SHUTTER AND
BLIND COMPANY LTD**
18a Clermont Road, Brighton,
East Sussex, BN1 6SG
Area of Operation: UK & Ireland
Tel: 0845 123 5661 **Fax:** 0845 280 1760
Email: hello@thecaliforniacompany.co.uk
Web: www.thecaliforniacompany.co.uk ⤴
Other Info: ✎

UC BLINDS
1150 Stratford Road, Hall Green,
Birmingham, West Midlands, B28 8AF
Area of Operation: UK (Excluding Ireland)
Tel: 0800 026 9394 **Fax:** 0121 777 3143
Email: ben@ucblinds.co.uk
Web: www.ucblinds.co.uk

VELUX WINDOWS
Woodside Way, Glenrothes East,
Fife, KY7 4ND
Area of Operation: Worldwide
Tel: 0870 240 0617 **Fax:** 0870 380 9395
Email: service@velux.co.uk
Web: www.velux.co.uk ⤴

WINDOWSCREENS UK
P.O.Box 181, Upminster, Essex, RM14 1GX
Area of Operation: UK & Ireland
Tel: 01708 222273 **Fax:** 01708 641898
Email: info@flyscreensuk.co.uk
Web: www.flyscreensUK.co.uk

WM SHUTTERS LTD
Unit 4 Springhill Trading Estate,
Aston Street, Shifnal, Telford, Shropshire, TF11 8DR
Area of Operation: UK & Ireland
Tel: 01952 272269 **Fax:** 01952 272331
Email: sales@wmshutters.com
Web: www.wmshutters.com

WWW.OPENNSHUT.CO.UK
Forum House, Stirling Road,
Chichester, West Sussex, PO19 7DN
Area of Operation: UK (Excluding Ireland)
Tel: 01243 774 888
Email: shutters@opennshut.co.uk
Web: www.opennshut.co.uk ⤴

CONSERVATORIES

KEY

PRODUCT TYPES: 1= Victorian
2 = Edwardian / Georgian   3 = Lean-to
4 = P-Shaped   5 = L-Shaped
6 = Double Height   7 = Contemporary

OTHER: ▽ Reclaimed ⤴ On-line shopping
✎ Bespoke ✋ Hand-made   ECO Ecological

ALUPLAST UK/PLUSPLAN
Leicester Road, Lutterworth, Leicestershire, LE17 4HE
Area of Operation: UK & Ireland
Tel: 01455 556771 **Fax:** 01455 555323
Email: info@aluplastuk.com
Web: www.aluplastuk.com
Product Type: 1, 2, 3, 4, 5, 6 **Material Type:** D) 1

AMDEGA CONSERVATORIES
Woodside, Church Lane, Bursledon,
Southampton, Hampshire, SO31 8AB
Area of Operation: Worldwide
Tel: 0800 591523
Web: www.amdega-conservatories.co.uk

ANDERSEN WINDOWS / BLACK MILLWORK CO.
Andersen House, Dallow Street,
Burton on Trent, Staffordshire, DE14 2PQ
Area of Operation: UK & Ireland
Tel: 01283 511122
Fax: 01283 510863
Email: info@blackmillwork.co.uk
Web: www.blackmillwork.co.uk
Product Type: 1, 2, 7
Other Info: ECO **Material Type:** A) 2, 5, 15

APROPOS TECTONIC LTD
Greenside House, Richmond Street,
Ashton Under Lyne, Lancashire, OL6 7ES
Area of Operation: UK & Ireland
Tel: 0870 777 0326
Fax: 0161 3428265
Email: enquiries@apropos-tectonic.com
Web: www.apropos-tectonic.com
Other Info: ✎ **Material Type:** C) 1

ARC-COMP
Friedrichstr. 3, 12205 Berlin-Lichterfelde, Germany
Area of Operation: Europe
Tel: +49 (0)308 430 9956
Fax: +49 (0)308 430 9957
Email: jvs@arc-comp.com
Web: www.arc-com.com
Product Type: 3 **Material Type:** C) 1

ARC-COMP (IRISH BRANCH)
Whitefield Cottage, Lugduff, Tinahely,
Co. Wicklow, Republic of Ireland
Area of Operation: Europe
Tel: +353 (0)868 729 945
Fax: +353 (0)402 28900
Email: jvs@arc-comp.com
Web: www.arc-comp.com
Product Type: 3 **Material Type:** C) 1

ASTON HOUSE JOINERY
Aston House, Tripontium Business Centre,
Newton Lane, Rugby, Warwickshire, CV23 0TB
Area of Operation: UK & Ireland
Tel: 01788 860032
Fax: 01788 860614
Email: enquiries@astonhousejoinery.co.uk
Web: www.astonhousejoinery.co.uk
Product Type: 1, 2, 3, 4, 5, 6, 7
Other Info: ECO ✎ ✋ **Material Type:** A) 1, 2, 12

AURORA CONSERVATORIES
The Old Station, Naburn, York, North Yorkshire, YO19 4RW
Area of Operation: UK (Excluding Ireland)
Tel: 01904 631234 **Fax:** 01904 610318
Email: louise@auroraconservatories.co.uk
Web: www.auroraconservatories.co.uk
Product Type: 1, 2, 3, 4, 5, 6
Other Info: ✎ ✋ **Material Type:** J) 4, 10

B & M WINDOW & KITCHEN CENTRE
2-6 Whitworth Drive, Aycliffe Industrial Park,
Durham, DL5 6SZ
Area of Operation: Worldwide
Tel: 01325 308888 **Fax:** 01325 316002
Email: sales@bandmhomeimprovements.com
Web: www.bandmhomeimprovements.com ⤴
Product Type: 1, 2, 3, 4, 5, 6

BALTIC CONSERVATORIES LTD
Unit 8, Bickland Business Park,
Falmouth, Cornwall, TR11 4RY
Area of Operation: UK (Excluding Ireland)
Tel: 01736 332200 **Fax:** 01326 371587
Email: enquiries@balticconservatories.co.uk
Web: www.balticconservatories.co.uk
Product Type: 1, 2, 3, 4, 5, 6 **Other Info:** ✎

BARTHOLOMEW
Rakers Yard, Rake Road, Milland,
West Sussex, GU30 7JS
Area of Operation: Europe
Tel: 01428 742800
Fax: 01428 743801
Email: denise@bartholomew-conservatories.co.uk
Web: www.bartholomew-conservatories.co.uk
Product Type: 4, 7 **Other Info:** ECO ✎
Material Type: A) 2, 10

BDG GROUP LTD
5 Wenlock Road, Lurgan,
Craigavon, Co Armagh, BT66 8QR
Area of Operation: UK & Ireland
Tel: 02838 327741 **Fax:** 02838 324358
Email: wosb@bdg.co.uk
Web: www.bdg.co.uk
Product Type: 1, 2, 3, 5, 6, 7
Material Type: C) 1

BETTERDEAL WINDOWS & CONSERVATORIES
17 Ensign House, Admirals Way, London, E14 9JX
Area of Operation: East England, Greater London,
South East England
Tel: 01268 732599
Email: betterdealltd@aol.com
Web: www.betterdealwindows.co.uk
Product Type: 1, 2, 3, 5, 6, 7

BIRCHDALE GLASS LTD
Unit L, Eskdale Road, Uxbridge, Greater London, UB8 2RT
Area of Operation: UK & Ireland
Tel: 01895 259111 **Fax:** 01895 810087
Email: info@birchdaleglass.com
Web: www.birchdaleglass.com

BRECKENRIDGE CONSERVATORIES
Unit 10 Papyrus Road, Werrington,
Peterborough, Cambridgeshire, PE4 5BH
Area of Operation: East England
Tel: 01733 575750 **Fax:** 01733 292875
Email: sales@breckenridgeconservatories.co.uk
Web: www.breckenridgeconservatories.co.uk
Material Type: D) 1

CAREY & FOX LTD
51 Langthwaite Business Park, South Kirkby,
Pontefract, West Yorkshire, WF9 3NR
Area of Operation: UK & Ireland
Tel: 01977 608069 **Fax:** 01977 646791
Email: enquiries@careyandfox.co.uk
Web: www.careyandfox.co.uk
Product Type: 1, 2, 3, 4, 5, 6 **Material Type:** A) 2

**CARPENTER OAK LTD &
RODERICK JAMES ARCHITECT LTD**
The Framing Yard, East Cornworthy,
Totnes, Devon, TQ9 7HF
Area of Operation: Worldwide
Tel: 01803 732900 **Fax:** 01803 732901
Email: enquiries@carpenteroak.com
Web: www.carpenteroak.com
Material Type: A) 2, 8

CHARTERHOUSE CONSERVATORIES
Park Street, Gosport, Hampshire, PO12 4UH
Area of Operation: South East England
Tel: 02392 504006 **Fax:** 02392 513765
Email: info@charterhouse.nu
Web: www.charterhouse.nu

CHIPPING NORTON GLASS LTD
Units 1 & 2, Station Yard Industrial Estate,
Chipping Norton, Oxfordshire, OX7 5HX
Area of Operation: Midlands & Mid Wales, South
West England and South Wales
Tel: 01608 643261 **Fax:** 01608 641768
Email: gill@cnglass.plus.com
Web: www.chippingnortonglass.co.uk
Product Type: 1, 2, 3, 4, 5, 6, 7
Material Type: C) 1

CLASSIC PVC HOME IMPROVEMENTS
Unit 36 LEC Workshops, Trostre Road,
Llanelli, Carmarthenshire, SA15 2EA
Area of Operation: South West England and South Wales
Tel: 01554 777158 **Fax:** 01554 775086
Email: enquiries@classic.uk.com
Web: www.classic.uk.com
Product Type: 1, 2, 3, 4, 5, 6 **Material Type:** D) 1

CLEARVIEW WINDOWS & DOORS
Unit 14, Sheddingdean Industrial Estate, Marchants
Way, Burgess Hill, West Sussex, RH15 8QY
Area of Operation: UK (Excluding Ireland)
Tel: 01444 250111 **Fax:** 01444 250678
Email: sales@clearviewsussex.co.uk
Web: www.clearviewsussex.co.uk

CONSERVATORIES 2 YOU
Andover Garden Centre, Salisbury Road,
Andover, Hampshire, SP11 7DN
Area of Operation: UK (Excluding Ireland)
Tel: 01264 710888
Email: info@conservatories2you.co.uk
Web: www.conservatories2you.co.uk
Product Type: 1, 2, 3, 4, 5, 6

CONSERVATORY & WINDOW WORLD LTD
Watling Road, Bishop Aukland, Durham, DL14 9AU
Area of Operation: North East England
Tel: 01388 458 088   **Fax:** 01388 458 518
Email: paldennis20@aol.com
Web: www.conservatoryandwindowworld.co.uk
Product Type: 1, 2, 3, 4, 5, 6
Material Type: D) 1, 3, 6

CONSERVATORY OUTLET
Unit 8 Headway Business Park, Denby Dale Road,
Wakefield, West Yorkshire, WF2 7AZ
Area of Operation: North East England
Tel: 01924 881920
Web: www.conservatoryoutlet.co.uk
Product Type: 1, 2, 3, 4, 5, 6, 7
Other Info: ✎   **Material Type:** D) 1

CUSTOM WOOD PRODUCTS
Cliffe Road, Easton on the Hill,
Stamford, Lincolnshire, PE9 3NP
Area of Operation: East England
Tel: 01780 755711   **Fax:** 01780 480834
Email: customwoodprods@aol.com
Web: www.cwpuk.com
Product Type: 1, 2, 3, 4, 5, 6 **Other Info:** ECO ✎ ✆

DAVID SALISBURY CONSERVATORIES
Bennett Rd, Isleport Business Park,
Highbridge, Somerset, TA9 4PW
Area of Operation: UK (Excluding Ireland)
Tel: 01278 764444   **Fax:** 01278 764422
Email: sales@davidsalisbury.com
Web: www.dscons.com
Product Type: 1, 2, 3, 4, 5, 6
Other Info: ✎   **Material Type:** A) 15

DESIGN IN WOOD
73 Nannymar Road, Darfield, South Yorkshire, S73 9AW
Area of Operation: UK (Excluding Ireland)
Tel: 01226 750527   **Fax:** 01226 341790

DIRECT CONSERVATORIES 4 U
Suite 27, Silk House, Park Green, Macclesfield, SK11 7QJ
Area of Operation: UK & Ireland
Tel: 0800 279 3928
Fax: 0845 058 6002
Email: info@directconservatories4u.co.uk
Web: www.directconservatories4u.co.uk ✆
Product Type: 1, 2, 3, 4, 5, 6, 7
Material Type: D) 1

DIY SASH WINDOWS
2 - 6 Whitworth Drive, Aycliffe Industrial Park,
Newton Aycliffe, Durham, DL56SZ
Area of Operation: UK & Ireland
Tel: 01325 308888   **Fax:** 01325 316002
Email: sales@diysashwindows.co.uk
Web: www.diysashwindows.co.uk
Product Type: 1, 2, 3, 4, 5, 6, 7

DIY2GO.COM
diy2go Ltd, Aquila, Woodgates Close,
North Ferriby, East Riding of Yorks, HU14 3JS
Area of Operation: Worldwide
Tel: 0845 094 2271   **Fax:** 01482 633334
Email: support@diy2go.com
Web: www.diy2go.com ✆
Product Type: 1, 2, 3, 5, 6, 7
Material Type: D) 1

DURABUILD GLAZED STRUCTURES LTD
Carlton Road, Coventry, West Midlands, CV6 7FL
Area of Operation: Worldwide
Tel: 02476 669169   **Fax:** 02476 669170
Email: enquiries@durabuild.co.uk
Web: www.durabuild.co.uk
Product Type: 1, 2, 3, 4, 5, 6
Other Info: ECO ✎ ✆   **Material Type:** A) 12, 15

ENGELS WINDOWS & DOORS LTD
1 Kingley Centre, Downs Road, West Stoke,
Chichester, West Sussex, PO18 9HJ
Area of Operation: UK (Excluding Ireland)
Tel: 01243 576633   **Fax:** 01243 576644
Email: admin@engels.co.uk
Web: www.engels.co.uk

ESOGRAT LTD
Caldervale Works, River Street, Brighouse,
Huddersfield, West Yorkshire, HD6 1JS
Area of Operation: UK & Ireland
Tel: 01484 716228   **Fax:** 01484 400107
Email: info@esograt.com
Web: www.esograt.com
Product Type: 1, 2, 3, 4, 5, 6

EUROCELL PROFILES LTD
Fairbrook House, Clover Nook Road,
Alfreton, Derby, Derbyshire, DE55 4RF
Area of Operation: UK (Excluding Ireland)
Tel: 01773 842100   **Fax:** 01773 842298
Email: sales@eurocell.co.uk
Web: www.eurocell.co.uk
Product Type: 1, 2, 3, 4, 5, 6
Material Type: D) 1, 3

EVEREST LTD
Sopers Road, Cuffley, Hertfordshire, EN6 4SG
Area of Operation: UK & Ireland
Tel: 0800 010123
Web: www.everest.co.uk ✆
Product Type: 1, 2, 3, 4, 5, 6

FAIRMITRE WINDOWS & JOINERY LTD
2A Cope Road, Banbury, Oxfordshire, OX16 2EH
Area of Operation: UK (Excluding Ireland)
Tel: 01295 268441
Fax: 01295 268468
Email: info@fairmitrewindows.co.uk
Web: www.fairmitrewindows.co.uk
Product Type: 1, 2, 3, 4, 5, 6, 7

FLETCHER JOINERY
261 Whessoe Road, Darlington, Durham, DL3 0YL
Area of Operation: North East England
Tel: 01325 357347   **Fax:** 01325 357347
Email: enquiries@fletcherjoinery.co.uk
Web: www.fletcherjoinery.co.uk
Product Type: 1, 2, 3, 4, 5, 6
Other Info: ✎ ✆   **Material Type:** A) 2

FRANKLIN LEEDS LLP
Carlton Works, Cemetery Road, Yeadon,
Leeds, West Yorkshire, LS19 7BD
Area of Operation: UK & Ireland
Tel: 0113 250 2991   **Fax:** 0113 250 0991
Email: david.franklin@franklinwindows.co.uk
Web: www.franklinwindows.co.uk
Product Type: 1, 2, 3, 4, 5, 6, 7

FRANKLIN LEEDS LLP
Area of Operation: UK & Ireland
Tel: 0113 2502991
Fax: 0113 2500991
Email: david.franklin@franklinwindows.co.uk
Web: www.franklinwindows.co.uk

Whichever style of conservatory you prefer, we
can design and build the perfect addition to your
home. As well as conservatories, we also supply
and fit our wide variety of windows and doors.

FROST CONSERVATORIES AND
GARDEN BUILDINGS LTD
The Old Forge, Tempsford, Sandy,
Bedfordshire, SG19 2AG
Area of Operation: UK (Excluding Ireland)
Tel: 01767 640808   **Fax:** 01767 640561
Email: sales@frostconservatories.co.uk
Web: www.frostconservatories.co.uk

G MIDDLETON LTD
Cross Croft Industrial Estate, Appleby, Cumbria, CA16 6HX
Area of Operation: Europe
Tel: 01768 352067
Fax: 01768 353228
Email: info@graham-middleton.co.uk
Web: www.graham-middleton.co.uk ✆
Material Type: A) 2

G2K JOINERY LTD
Trench Farm, Tilley Green, Wem, Shropshire, SY4 5PJ
Area of Operation: UK (Excluding Ireland)
Tel: 01939 236640   **Fax:** 01939 236650
Email: graham@g2kjoinery.co.uk
Web: www.g2kjoinery.co.uk

GREEN BUILDING STORE
11 Huddersfield Road, Meltham,
Holmfirth, West Yorkshire, HD9 4NJ
Area of Operation: UK & Ireland
Tel: 01484 854898
Fax: 01484 854899
Email: info@greenbuildingstore.co.uk
Web: www.greenbuildingstore.co.uk ✆
Product Type: 1, 2, 3, 5, 6
Other Info: ECO ✎   **Material Type:** B) 8

HIGHSEAL WINDOWS LIMITED
Moat Road, Scunthorpe, Lincolnshire, DN15 9GA
Area of Operation: East England, Greater London,
Midlands & Mid Wales, North East England, North
West England and North Wales, Scotland,
South East England
Tel: 01724 276213   **Fax:** 01724 276214
Email: david.maybank@hwlgroup.co.uk
Web: www.hwlgroup.co.uk
Product Type: 1, 2, 3, 5, 6, 7
Other Info: ✎ ✆   **Material Type:** D) 1, 3

INPUT JOINERY LTD
The Fairground, Weyhill, Andover, Hampshire, SP11 0ST
Area of Operation: UK (Excluding Ireland)
Tel: 01264 771900   **Fax:** 01264 771901
Email: info@inputjoinery.co.uk
Web: www.inputjoinery.co.uk
Product Type: 1, 2, 3, 5, 6, 7, 8

JAMES BENTLEY
James Bentley Limited, 13 Tennyson Road,
Hinckley, Leicestershire, LE10 0TH
Area of Operation: UK (Excluding Ireland)
Tel: 0870 850 2057
Email: paul.smith@james-bentley.co.uk
Web: www.james-bentley.co.uk
Product Type: 1, 2, 3, 5, 6, 7, 8

KIRK NATURAL STONE
Bridgend, Fyvie, Turriff, Aberdeenshire, AB53 8LL
Area of Operation: Worldwide
Tel: 01651 891891   **Fax:** 01651 891794
Email: info@kirknaturalstone.com
Web: www.kirknaturalstone.com
Product Type: 1, 2, 3, 4

LAMWOOD LTD
Unit 1, Riverside Works, Station Road,
Cheddleton, Staffordshire, ST13 7EE
Area of Operation: UK & Ireland
Tel: 01538 361888   **Fax:** 01538 361912
Email: info@lamwoodltd.co.uk
Web: www.lamwoodltd.co.uk   **Material Type:** A) 2

LATTICE PERIOD WINDOWS
Unit 85 Northwick Business Centre, Blockley,
Moreton in Marsh, Gloucestershire, Gl56 9RF
Area of Operation: UK & Ireland
Tel: 01386 701079   **Fax:** 01386 701114
Email: sales@latticewindows.net
Web: www.latticewindows.net
Product Type: 1, 2, 3, 4, 6   **Material Type:** A) 2

LLOYD CHRISTIE
Greystones, Sudbrook Lane, Petersham, TW10 7AT
Area of Operation: Worldwide
Tel: 020 8332 6766   **Fax:** 020 8332 2229
Email: info@lloydchristie.com
Web: www.lloydchristie.com **Other Info:** ✎

MERLIN UK LIMITED
Unit 5 Fence Avenue, Macclesfield, Cheshire, SK10 1LT
Area of Operation: North West England and North Wales
Tel: 01625 424488   **Fax:** 0871 781 8967
Email: info@merlinuk.net
Web: www.merlindoors.co.uk
Product Type: 1, 2, 3, 4, 5, 6, 7

MULTIWOOD HOME IMPROVEMENTS LTD
1298 Chester Road, Stretford, Manchester, M32 9AU
Area of Operation: Europe
Tel: 0161 866 9991   **Fax:** 0161 866 9992
Email: sales@multiwoodconservatories.co.uk
Web: www.multiwoodconservatories.co.uk

NORVIK PVCU WINDOW SYSTEMS LTD
Mitchells Industrial Park, Wombwell,
Barnsley, South Yorkshire, S35 7AE
Area of Operation: UK & Ireland
Tel: 01226 340182   **Fax:** 01226 340375
Email: nhibberd@norvik.co.uk
Web: www.norvik.co.uk
Product Type: 1, 2, 3, 5, 6, 7

OLDE WORLDE OAK JOINERY LTD
Unit 12, Longford Industrial Estate, Longford Road,
Cannock, Staffordshire, WS11 0DG
Area of Operation: Europe
Tel: 01543 469328   **Fax:** 01543 469328
Email: sales@oldeworldeoakjoinery.co.uk
Web: www.oldeworldeoakjoinery.co.uk

OPTIMUM CONSERVATORY KITS LTD
2A Halliwell Mill, Raglan Street,
Bolton, Greater Manchester, BL1 8AG
Area of Operation: UK (Excluding Ireland)
Tel: 01204 555920   **Fax:** 01204 385111
Email: sales@optimum.co.uk
Web: www.optimumconservatorykits.com
Product Type: 1, 2, 3, 4, 5, 6 **Material Type:** D) 1

PORTICO GB LTD
Unit 9 Windmill Avenue, Woolpit Business Park,
Woolpit , Bury St Edmunds , Suffolk, IP30 9UP
Area of Operation: Greater London, South East England
Tel: 01359 244299   **Fax:** 01359 244232
Email: info@portico-gb.co.uk
Web: www.portico-newbuild.co.uk

PRITCHARDS
Unit 22 Brookend Lane, Kempsey,
Worcester, Worcestershire, WR5 3LF
Area of Operation: UK (Excluding Ireland)
Tel: 01905 828335   **Fax:** 01905 828357
Email: info@pritchards.tv **Web:** www.pritchards.tv

RADNOR TIMBER COMPANY
The Offices, Old Impton Farm, Norton,
Presteigne, Powys, LD8 2EN
Area of Operation: Europe
Tel: 01544 260727   **Fax:** 01544 262113
Email: sales@rtc.enta.net
Web: www.radnortimbercompany
Other Info: ECO ✎ ✆   **Material Type:** A) 2

RHONES JOINERY (WREXHAM) LTD
Mold Road Industrial Estate,
Gwersyllt, Wrexham, LL11 4AQ
Area of Operation: UK (Excluding Ireland)
Tel: 01978 262488   **Fax:** 01978 262488
Email: info@rhonesjoinery.co.uk
Web: www.rhonesjoinery.co.uk **Other Info:** ✎ ✆

ROOFLIGHT ARCHITECTURAL LTD
Unit 17 South Nelson Rd, South Nelson Industrial
Estate, Cramlington, Northumberland, NE23 1WF
Area of Operation: UK (Excluding Ireland)
Tel: 01670 736124   **Fax:** 01670 738080
Email: sales@rooflight.co.uk
Web: www.rooflight.co.uk
Product Type: 1, 2, 3, 5, 6, 7
Other Info: ✎   **Material Type:** C) 1

SPONSORED BY: ARCHITECTURAL DOORS & WINDOWS www.adwlimited.co.uk

ROUNDWOOD CONSTRUCTION LTD
The Packhouse, Cryals Farm,
Cryals Road, Matfield, Kent, TN12 7HN
Area of Operation: Europe
Tel: 0800 328 3847 **Fax:** 01892 725416
Email: mary@roundwoodconstruction.com
Web: www.roundwoodconstruction.com

SAPA BUILDING SYSTEMS LIMITED
Alexandra Way, Ashchurch,
Tewkesbury, Gloucestershire, GL20 8NB
Area of Operation: UK & Ireland
Tel: 01684 853500 **Fax:** 01684 851850
Email: nicola.abbey@sapagroup.com
Web: www.sapagroup.com/uk/buildingsystems
Product Type: 1, 2, 3, 4, 5, 6
Other Info: ✍ ✋ **Material Type:** C) 1A

SASH CRAFT
3 The Dairy, Priston Mill Farm, Bath, BA2 9EQ
Area of Operation: South West England and South Wales
Tel: 01225 424434 **Fax:** 01761 470 777
Email: info@sashcraftofbath.com
Web: www.sashcraftofbath.com
Product Type: 1, 2, 3, 4, 5, 6

SASH UK LTD
Ferrymoor Way, Park Springs, Grimethorpe,
Barnsley, South Yorkshire, S72 7BN
Area of Operation: Worldwide
Tel: 01226 715619 **Fax:** 01226 719968
Email: mailbox@sashuk.com
Web: www.sashuk.com
Product Type: 1, 2, 3, 4, 5, 6 **Material Type:** D) 1

SCHUCO INTERNATIONAL KG
Whitehall Avenue, Kingston,
Milton Keynes, Buckinghamshire, MK10 0AL
Area of Operation: Worldwide
Tel: 01908 282111 **Fax:** 01908 282124
Email: shamman@schueco.com
Web: www.schueco.co.uk

SHERBORNE LIMITED
135 Lynchford Road,
Farnborough, Hampshire, GU14 6HD
Area of Operation: South East England
Tel: 01252 370917 **Fax:** 01252 515800
Email: peter.white@sherbornewindows.co.uk
Web: www.sherbornewindows.co.uk
Product Type: 1, 2, 3, 5, 6, 7

SPECTUS SYSTEMS
Spectus Window Systems, Pinewood Court,
Tytherington Business Park,
Macclesfield, Cheshire, SK10 2XR
Tel: 01625 420400 **Fax:** 01625 501418
Email: contact@spectus.co.uk
Web: www.spectus.co.uk **Material Type:** D) 1

STEVENSWOOD CONSERVATORIES
21 Napier Square Houstoun Road Industrial Estate,
Livingston, West Lothian, EH54 5DG
Area of Operation: Scotland
Tel: 01506 438111 **Fax:** 01506 438444
Email: info@stevenswood.co.uk
Web: www.stevenswood.co.uk
Product Type: 1, 2, 3, 4, 5, 6, 7
Material Type: D) 1, 3

STUDLEY CONSERVATORIES
Shawbank House, Shawbank Road, Lakeside,
Redditch, Warwickshire, B98 8YN
Area of Operation: Greater London, Midlands & Mid
Wales, South East England, South West England and
South Wales
Tel: 01527 527415 **Fax:** 01527 857341
Email: sales@studleyconservatoryvillage.co.uk
Web: www.studleyconservatoryvillage.co.uk

SUN PARADISE UK LTD
Phoenix Wharf, Eel Pie Island,
Twickenham, Middlesex, TW1 3DY
Area of Operation: UK & Ireland
Tel: 0870 240 7604 **Fax:** 0870 240 7614
Email: info@sunparadise.co.uk
Web: www.sunparadise.co.uk
Product Type: 3, 4, 5, 6 **Material Type:** C) 1

SUNFOLD LTD
Sunfold House, Wymondham Business Park,
Chestnut Drive, Wymondham, Norfolk, NR18 9SB
Area of Operation: Europe
Tel: 01953 423423 **Fax:** 01953 423430
Email: info@sunfold.com **Web:** www.sunfold.com
Other Info: ✍ **Material Type:** A) 1

THE CAMDEN GROUP
Unit 4-7, Steeple Industrial Estate, Antrim, BT41 1AB
Area of Operation: UK & Ireland
Tel: 028 9446 2419 **Fax:** 028 9442 8138
Email: info@camdengroup.co.uk
Web: www.camdengroup.co.uk
Product Type: 1, 2, 5, 6, 7

THE GREEN OAK CARPENTRY CO LTD
Langley Farm, Langley, Rake, Liss, Hampshire, GU33 7JW
Area of Operation: UK & Ireland
Tel: 01730 892049
Fax: 01730 895225
Email: enquiries@greenoakcarpentry.co.uk
Web: www.greenoakcarpentry.co.uk
Material Type: A) 2

**THE INCREDIBILY SENSIBLE
GREENHOUSE COMPANY**
Trifford, Plasters Green, Winford,
North Somerset, BS40 8BH
Area of Operation: Europe
Tel: 01761 463102 **Fax:** 01761 463154
Email: enquiries@isgreenhouses.co.uk
Web: www.isgreenhouses.co.uk **Product Type:** 3

THE PATIO ROOM COMPANY
52 Castlemaine Avenue, South Croydon, Surrey, CR2 7HR
Tel: 0208 406 3001 **Fax:** 0208 686 4928
Email: helpdesk@patioroom.co.uk
Web: www.patioroom.co.uk **Other Info:** ✍

TOTAL GLASS LIMITED
Total Complex, Overbrook Lane,
Knowsley, Merseyside, L34 9FB
Area of Operation: Midlands & Mid Wales, North
East England, North West England and North Wales
Tel: 0151 549 2339 **Fax:** 0151 546 0022
Email: sales@totalglass.com
Web: www.totalglass.com
Product Type: 1, 2, 3, 4, 5, 6, 7

TRADE CONSERVATORIES 2 U LTD
36 Temple Way, Maldon, Essex, CM9 4PX
Area of Operation: UK (Excluding Ireland)
Tel: 0845 130 3871 **Fax:** 0845 130 3872
Email: sales@tradeconservatories2u.co.uk
Web: www.tradeconservatories2u.co.uk ✍
Product Type: 2, 3, 5, 6, 7

TRADE CONSERVATORIES 2 U LTD

Area of Operation: UK (Excluding Ireland)
Tel: 0845 130 3871
Fax: 0845 130 3872
Email: sales@tradeconservatories2u.co.uk
Web: www.tradeconservatories2u.co.uk
Product Type: 2, 3, 4, 5, 6

Specialist supplier of high quality PVCu
Conservatories, Windows and Doors for self build
at trade prices with free delivery to UK mainland.

TRADITIONAL CONSERVATORIES LTD
St Andrews Works, Weston Lane, Tyseley,
Birmingham, West Midlands, B11 3RP
Area of Operation: Midlands & Mid Wales
Tel: 0121 706 0102 **Fax:** 0121 708 1585
Email: sales@traditionalconservatories.com
Web: www.traditionalconservatories.co.uk
Product Type: 1, 2, 3, 4, 5, 6, 7

TWC NATIONWIDE UK
Units 1 and 2, The Drill Hall, 262 Huddersfield Road,
Thongsbridge, Holmfirth, West Yorkshire, HD9 3JQ
Area of Operation: UK & Ireland
Tel: 0800 7832782 **Fax:** 01484 685210
Email: admin@twcthewindowcompany.net
Web: www.twcthewindowcompany.net
Product Type: 1, 2, 3, 5 **Material Type:** D) 1

ULTRAFRAME UK
Salthill Road, Clitheroe, Lancashire, BB7 1PE
Tel: 01200 443311 **Fax:** 0870 414 1020
Email: sales@ultraframe.com
Web: www.ultraframe-conservatories.co.uk
Product Type: 1, 2, 3, 4, 5, 6, 7
Material Type: D) 1, 3

WICKES
Wickes House, 120-138 Station Road, Harrow,
Middlesex, Greater London, HA1 2QB
Area of Operation: UK (Excluding Ireland)
Tel: 0870 608 9001 **Fax:** 0208 863 6225
Web: www.wickes.co.uk

WINDOWS 2 YOU LTD
Unt 5 Higher Tweed Mills,
Dartington, Totnes, Devon, TQ9 6JY
Area of Operation: UK & Ireland
Tel: 01803 840200 **Fax:** 01803 840169
Email: sales@windows2you.co.uk
Web: www.windows2you.co.uk
Product Type: 1, 2, 3, 5, 6, 7
Material Type: B) 8

WINDOWS OF DISTINCTION
133 Bitton Park Road, Teignmouth, Devon, TQ14 9DQ
Area of Operation: South West England and South Wales
Tel: 01626 879359 **Fax:** 01626 870483
Email: windowsofdistinction@tiscali.co.uk
Web: www.windowsofdistinction.co.uk
Product Type: 1, 2, 3, 5, 6, 7 **Other Info:** ✍
Material Type: D) 1

STAINED GLASS

KEY

SEE ALSO: DOORS, WINDOWS AND
CONSERVATORIES - Glass and Glazing

OTHER: ▽ Reclaimed ✍ On-line shopping
✍ Bespoke ✋ Hand-made ECO Ecological

ANDERSEN WINDOWS / BLACK MILLWORK CO.
Andersen House, Dallow Street,
Burton on Trent, Staffordshire, DE14 2PQ
Area of Operation: UK & Ireland
Tel: 01283 511122 **Fax:** 01283 510863
Email: info@blackmillwork.co.uk
Web: www.blackmillwork.co.uk

ARTIZAN.UK.NET
29 Fore Street, Bradninch, Exeter, Devon, EX5 4NN
Area of Operation: South West England and South Wales
Tel: 01392 882165 **Email:** info@artizan.uk.net
Web: www.artizan.uk.net

BARRON GLASS
Unit 11, Lansdown Industrial Estate,
Cheltenham, Gloucestershire, GL51 8PL
Area of Operation: UK & Ireland
Tel: 01242 22800 **Fax:** 01242 226555
Email: admin@barronglass.co.uk
Web: www.barronglass.co.uk

BIRCHDALE GLASS LTD
Unit L, Eskdale Road, Uxbridge, Greater London, UB8 2RT
Area of Operation: UK & Ireland
Tel: 01895 259111 **Fax:** 01895 810087
Email: info@birchdaleglass.com
Web: www.birchdaleglass.com

BOURNEMOUTH STAINED GLASS
790 Wimborne Road, Moordown,
Bournemouth, Dorset, BH9 2DX
Area of Operation: UK & Ireland
Tel: 01202 514734 **Fax:** 01202 250239
Email: shop@stainedglass.co.uk
Web: www.stainedglass.co.uk

CHEAM LEADED LIGHTS LTD
8 Upper Mulgrave Road,
Cheam Village, Surrey, SM2 9AZ
Area of Operation: South East England
Tel: 0208 643 7849 **Fax:** 0208 770 3878
Email: sales@cheamleadedlights.com
Web: www.cheamleadedlights.com

CHIPPING NORTON GLASS LTD
Units 1 & 2, Station Yard Industrial Estate,
Chipping Norton, Oxfordshire, OX7 5HX
Area of Operation: Midlands & Mid Wales, South
West England and South Wales
Tel: 01608 643261 **Fax:** 01608 641768
Email: gill@cnglass.plus.com
Web: www.chippingnortonglass.co.uk

EDEN DECORATIVE GLASS LTD
Alder House, Aylburton Business Centre, Stockwell
Lane, Aylburton, Lydney, Gloucestershire, GL15 6ST
Tel: 0845 6580230 **Fax:** 01594 840028
Email: info@edenglass.co.uk
Web: www.edenglass.co.uk

FRANKLIN LEEDS LLP
Carlton Works, Cemetery Road, Yeadon,
Leeds, West Yorkshire, LS19 7BD
Area of Operation: UK & Ireland
Tel: 0113 250 2991 **Fax:** 0113 250 0991
Email: david.franklin@franklinwindows.co.uk
Web: www.franklinwindows.co.uk

GLASS & LIGHTING STUDIO
56 The Tything, Worcester, Worcestershire, WR1 1JT
Area of Operation: UK & Ireland
Tel: 01905 26285 **Fax:** 01905 26285
Email: Studio@glass-lighting.co.uk
Web: www.glass-lighting.co.uk

SPONSORED BY: ARCHITECTURAL DOORS & WINDOWS www.adwlimited.co.uk

BUILDING STRUCTURE & MATERIALS

GLASS DESIGN STUDIO LTD
27B Morelands Trading Estate, Bristol Road,
Gloucester, Gloucestershire, GL1 5RZ
Tel: 01452 413773
Fax: 01452 521717
Email: info@glassdesignstudio.co.uk
Web: www.glassdesignstudio.co.uk

HOLDSWORTH WINDOWS LTD
Darlingscote Road, Shipston-on-Stour,
Warwickshire, CV36 4PR
Area of Operation: UK & Ireland
Tel: 01608 661883 **Fax:** 01608 661008
Email: info@holdsworthwindows.co.uk
Web: www.holdsworthwindows.co.uk

IT'S A BLAST!
27a Westfield Road, Bishops Stortford,
Hertfordshire, CM23 2RE
Area of Operation: UK (Excluding Ireland)
Tel: 01279 656133
Email: carole@itsablast.co.uk
Web: www.itsablast.co.uk

LEAD & LIGHT
35a Hartland Road, London, NW1 8DB
Area of Operation: Worldwide
Tel: 0207 485 0997 **Fax:** 0207 284 2660
Email: leadandlight@msn.com
Web: www.leadandlight.co.uk

SIMPLY STAINED
7 Farm Mews, Farm Road,
Brighton & Hove, East Sussex, BN3 1GH
Area of Operation: UK (Excluding Ireland)
Tel: 01273 220030
Email: david@simply-stained.co.uk
Web: www.simply-stained.co.uk

STUART OWEN NORTON GLASS AND SIGN LTD
Unit 6, Hill Court, Dunne Road,
Blaydon, Tyne & Wear, NE21 5NH
Area of Operation: Worldwide
Tel: 0191 4140123 **Fax:** 0191 4140157
Email: brilliant.cutter@btinternet.com
Web: www.glass-and-sign.com

SUNRISE STAINED GLASS
58-60 Middle Street, Southsea,
Portsmouth, Hampshire , PO5 4BP
Area of Operation: UK (Excluding Ireland)
Tel: 02392 750512
Fax: 02392 875488
Email: sunrise@stained-windows.co.uk
Web: www.stained-windows.co.uk

THE CAMDEN GROUP
Unit 4-7, Steeple Industrial Estate, Antrim, BT41 1AB
Area of Operation: UK & Ireland
Tel: 028 9446 2419 **Fax:** 028 9442 8138
Email: info@camdengroup.co.uk
Web: www.camdengroup.co.uk

THE STAINED GLASS STUDIO
Unit 5, Brewery Arts, Brewery Court,
Cirencester, Gloucestershire, GL7 1JH
Area of Operation: Worldwide
Tel: 01285 644430
Email: daniella@stainedglassbrewery arts.co.uk
Web: www.stainedglassbreweryarts.co.uk

THE STAINED GLASS WORKS
188 Archway Road, London, N6 5BB
Area of Operation: Greater London
Tel: 0208 348 0220
Fax: 0208 348 0220
Email: user@bennis.fsworld.co.uk
Web: www.thestainedglassworks.co.uk

TOTAL GLASS LIMITED
Total Complex, Overbrook Lane,
Knowsley, Merseyside, L34 9FB
Area of Operation: Midlands & Mid Wales, North
East England, North West England and North Wales
Tel: 0151 549 2339
Fax: 0151 546 0022
Email: sales@totalglass.com
Web: www.totalglass.com

WAYNE RICKETTS STAINED GLASS
Units 9-11 The White Factory,
18 Netham Road, Redfield, Bristol, BS5 9PF
Area of Operation: Worldwide
Tel: 0117 955 5390 **Fax:** 0117 955 5390
Email: wayne.ricketts@btconnect.com
Web: www.waynerickettsstainedglass.com

LINTELS AND CILLS

KEY

PRODUCT TYPES: 1= Sleeper Lintels
2 = Cavity Closing Lintels   3 = Cills

OTHER: ▽ Reclaimed 🛒 On-line shopping
✎ Bespoke ✋ Hand-made ECO Ecological

**A D CALVERT ARCHITECTURAL
STONE SUPPLIES LTD**
Smithy Lane, Grove Square,
Leyburn, North Yorkshire, DL8 5DZ
Area of Operation: UK & Ireland
Tel: 01969 622515 **Fax:** 01969 624345
Email: stone@calverts.co.uk
Web: www.calverts.co.uk

ACE STONE BUILDING PRODUCTS
98/99 Reddal Hill Road, Cradley Heath,
West Midlands, B64 5JT
Area of Operation: UK & Ireland
Tel: 01384 638076 **Fax:** 01384 566179
Email: info@acenu-look.co.uk
Web: www.acenu-look.co.uk **Product Type:** 3

ADDSTONE CAST STONE
2 Millers Gate, Stone, Staffordshire, ST15 8ZF
Area of Operation: UK (Excluding Ireland)
Tel: 01785 818810 **Fax:** 01785 819958
Email: sales@addstone.co.uk
Web: www.addstone.co.uk 🛒
Product Type: 2, 3   **Other Info:** ✎ ✋
Material Type: E) 11, 13

ARUNDEL STONE LTD
62 Aldwick Road, Bognor Regis, West Sussex, PO21 2PE
Area of Operation: Greater London, South East England
Tel: 01243 829151 **Fax:** 01243 860341
Email: sales@arundelstone.co.uk
Web: www.arundelstone.co.uk

ASPECTS OF STONE LTD
Unit 29, Broughton Grounds, Broughton,
Newport Pagnell, Buckinghamshire, MK16 0HZ
Area of Operation: UK (Excluding Ireland)
Tel: 01908 830061 **Fax:** 01908 830062
Email: sales@aspectsofstone.co.uk
Web: www.aspectsofstone.co.uk

BIRTLEY BUILDING PRODUCTS LTD
Mary Avenue, Birtley, County Durham, DH3 1JF
Area of Operation: UK & Ireland
Tel: 0191 410 6631
Fax: 0191 410 0650
Email: info@birtley-building.co.uk
Web: www.birtley-building.co.uk
Product Type: 2   **Material Type:** C) 4

BLACK MOUNTAIN QUARRIES LTD
Howton Court, Pontrilas, Herefordshire, HR2 0BG
Area of Operation: UK & Ireland
Tel: 01981 241541
Email: info@blackmountainquarries.com
Web: www.blackmountainquarries.com 🛒

BORDER CONCRETE PRODUCTS
Jedburgh Road, Kelso, Borders, TD5 8JG
Area of Operation: North East England, North West
England and North Wales, Scotland
Tel: 01573 224393
Fax: 01573 276360
Email: sales@borderconcrete.co.uk
Web: www.borderconcrete.co.uk
Product Type: 3

BULMER BRICK CUTTING SERVICES
The Brickfields, Hedingham Road,
Bulmer, Sudbury, Suffolk, CO10 7EF
Area of Operation: UK & Ireland
Tel: 01787 269132 **Fax:** 01787 269044
Email: info@brickcutters.com
Web: www.brickcutters.com **Other Info:** ✎

CATNIC
Pontypandy Industrial Estate, Caerphilly, CF83 3GL
Area of Operation: Worldwide
Tel: 029 2033 7900 **Fax:** 029 2033 7900
Email: barry.jenkins@corusgroup.com
Web: www.catnic.com

CAWARDEN BRICK & TILE CO. LTD
Cawarden Springs Farm, Blithbury Road,
Rugeley, Staffordshire, WS13 3HL
Area of Operation: UK (Excluding Ireland)
Tel: 01889 574066 **Fax:** 01889 575695
Email: home-garden@cawardenreclaim.com
Web: www.cawardenreclaim.com
Product Type: 1, 3

EXCEL BUILDING SOLUTIONS
Maerdy Industrial Estate, Gwent, NP22 5PY
Area of Operation: Worldwide
Tel: 01685 845200 **Fax:** 01685 844106
Email: sales@excelfibre.com
Web: www.excelfibre.com

FLIGHT TIMBER PRODUCTS
Earls Colne Business Park, Earls Colne, Essex, CO6 2NS
Area of Operation: East England, Greater London,
South East England
Tel: 01787 222336 **Fax:** 01787 222359
Email: sales@flighttimber.com
Web: www.flighttimber.com

GREYSLATE & STONE SUPPLIES
Unit 1 Cae Pawb Industrial Estate, Off Madog Street,
Port Madog, Nr. Blaenau Ffestiniog, Gwynedd, LL49 9EE
Area of Operation: UK & Ireland
Tel: 01766 514700 **Fax:** 01766 515200
Email: greyslate@slateandstone.net
Web: www.slateandstone.net **Product Type:** 3

GWRHYD SPECIALIST STONE QUARRY
Gwrhyd Road, Rhiwfawr, Swansea, Neath, SA9 2SB
Area of Operation: UK & Ireland
Tel: 01639 830743 **Fax:** 01639 830930
Email: enquiries@specialiststone.com
Web: www.specialiststone.com
Product Type: 1, 3
Other Info: ✎ ✋   **Material Type:** E) 4

I G LTD (STEEL LINTELS)
Avondale Road, Cumbran, Gwent, Torfaen, NP44 1XY
Area of Operation: UK & Ireland
Tel: 01633 486486 **Fax:** 01633 486492
Email: info@igltd.co.uk
Web: www.igltd.co.uk **Product Type:** 1, 2

KEYSTONE LINTELS LIMITED
Ballyreagh Industrial Estate, Sandholes Road,
Cookstown, Co Tyrone, BT80 9DG
Area of Operation: UK & Ireland
Tel: 028 8676 2184 **Fax:** 028 8676 1011
Email: info@keystonelintels.co.uk
Web: www.keystonelintels.co.uk
Product Type: 1, 2

LAMINATED WOOD LIMITED
Grain Silo Complex, Abbey Road, Hempsted,
Gloucester, Gloucestershire, GL2 5HU
Area of Operation: UK & Ireland
Tel: 01452 418000 **Fax:** 01452 418333
Email: mail@lamwood.co.uk
Web: www.lamwood.co.uk

MANCHESTER BRICK & PRECAST LTD
Haigh Avenue, Whitehill Industrial Estate,
Stockport, Cheshire, SK4 1NU
Area of Operation: UK & Ireland
Tel: 0161 480 2621 **Fax:** 0161 480 0108
Email: sales@manbrick.co.uk
Web: www.manbrick.co.uk
Product Type: 2, 3

PENNINE STONE LTD
Askern Road, Carcroft, Doncaster, DN6 8DH
Area of Operation: UK (Excluding Ireland)
Tel: 01302 729277 **Fax:** 01302 729288
Email: info@penninestone.co.uk
Web: www.penninestone.co.uk
Product Type: 3   **Material Type:** G) 1

RADNOR TIMBER COMPANY
The Offices, Old Impton Farm,
Norton, Presteigne, Powys, LD8 2EN
Area of Operation: Europe
Tel: 01544 260727 **Fax:** 01544 262113
Email: sales@rtc.enta.net
Web: www.radnortimbercompany
Product Type: 1, 2, 3
Other Info: ECO ✎ ✋   **Material Type:** A) 2

SNOWDONIA SLATE & STONE
Glandwr Workshops, Glanypwll Road,
Blaenau Ffestiniog, Gwynedd, LL41 3PG
Tel: 01766 832525 **Fax:** 01766 832404
Email: richard@snowdoniaslate.co.uk
Web: www.snowdoniaslate.co.uk **Product Type:** 1, 3

THE GREEN OAK CARPENTRY CO LTD
Langley Farm, Langley, Rake, Liss, Hampshire, GU33 7JW
Area of Operation: UK & Ireland
Tel: 01730 892049 **Fax:** 01730 895225
Email: enquiries@greenoakcarpentry.co.uk
Web: www.greenoakcarpentry.co.uk **Product Type:** 3

TRADITIONAL OAK & TIMBER COMPANY
P O Stores, Haywards Heath Road,
North Chailey, Nr Lewes, East Sussex, BN8 4EY
Area of Operation: Worldwide
Tel: 01825 723648 **Fax:** 01825 722215
Email: info@tradoak.co.uk **Web:** www.tradoak.com

WARWICKSHIRE FASCIAS
Unit 8&9 Cattell Road, Cape Road Industrial Estate,
Warwick, Warwickshire, CV34 4JN
Tel: 01926 496 830 **Fax:** 01926 491 630
Email: warwickshirefascias@hotmail.com

WINDOWS 2 YOU LTD
Unt 5 Higher Tweed Mills,
Dartington, Totnes, Devon, TQ9 6JY
Area of Operation: UK & Ireland
Tel: 01803 840200 **Fax:** 01803 840169
Email: sales@windows2you.co.uk
Web: www.windows2you.co.uk
Product Type: 1, 2, 3, 5, 6, 7, 8 **Material Type:** B) 8

WINDOWS OF DISTINCTION
133 Bitton Park Road, Teignmouth, Devon, TQ14 9DQ
Area of Operation: South West England and South Wales
Tel: 01626 879359 **Fax:** 01626 870483
Email: windowsofdistinction@tiscali.co.uk
Web: www.windowsofdistinction.co.uk
Product Type: 1, 2, 3, 5, 6, 7
Other Info: ✎   **Material Type:** D) 1

DOOR FURNITURE &
ARCHITECTURAL
IRONMONGERY

KEY

PRODUCT TYPES: 1= Door Handles and Knobs
2 = Door Closers and Locks   3 = Letter Boxes
4 = Finger Plates   5 = Other

OTHER: ▽ Reclaimed 🛒 On-line shopping
✎ Bespoke ✋ Hand-made ECO Ecological

A & H BRASS
201-203 Edgware Road, London, W2 1ES
Area of Operation: Worldwide
Tel: 0207 402 1854 **Fax:** 0207 402 0110
Email: ahbrass@btinternet.com
Web: www.aandhbrass.co.uk 🛒
Product Type: 1, 2, 3, 4, 5
Material Type: C) 3, 11, 12, 13, 14

A C LEIGH
61-67 Benedicts Street, Norwich, Norfolk, NR2 4PD
Tel: 01603 216500 **Fax:** 01603 760707
Email: marketing@acleigh.co.uk
Web: www.acleigh-handles.co.uk
Product Type: 1, 2, 3, 4, 5

ACORN IRONMONGERY LTD
Unit C The Factory, Dippenhall,
Farnham, Surrey, GU10 5DW
Area of Operation: Europe
Tel: 01252 820858 **Fax:** 01252 820878
Email: suzanne@handles4doors.co.uk
Web: www.handles4doors.co.uk
Product Type: 1, 2, 3, 4, 5

ALCESTER LOCKS LTD
Unit 12, 34 Tything Road, Alcester, Warwickshire, B49 6ES
Area of Operation: Midlands & Mid Wales
Tel: 01527 401011 **Fax:** 01527 457056
Email: sales@alcesterlocks.co.uk
Web: www.alcesterlocks.co.uk **Product Type:** 2

ANY OLD IRON
PO Box 198, Ashford, Kent, TN26 3SE
Area of Operation: Worldwide
Tel: 01622 685336 **Fax:** 01622 672335
Email: anyoldiron@aol.com
Web: www.anyoldiron.co.uk
Product Type: 1, 2, 3, 4

APPART
72-73 Warren Street, London, W1T 5PE
Area of Operation: Worldwide
Tel: 0870 7521054 **Fax:** 0207 255 9356
Email: info@appart.co.uk
Web: www.appart.co.uk **Product Type:** 1, 2, 3, 4, 5

ARCHITECTURAL COMPONENTS LTD
4-8 Exhibition Road, South Kensington, London, SW7 2HF
Area of Operation: Worldwide
Tel: 0207 581 2401 **Fax:** 0207 589 4928
Email: sales@knobs.co.uk
Web: www.doorhandles.co.uk
Product Type: 1, 2, 3, 4, 5

ARCHITECTURAL IRONMONGERY LTD
28 Kyrle Street, Ross-on-Wye, Herefordshire, HR9 7DB
Area of Operation: Worldwide
Tel: 01989 567946 **Fax:** 01989 567946
Email: info@arciron.co.uk
Web: www.arciron.com
Product Type: 1, 2, 3, 4, 5

ASHFIELD TRADITIONAL
119 High Street, Needham Market,
Ipswich, Suffolk, IP6 8DQ
Area of Operation: Europe
Tel: 01449 723601 **Fax:** 01449 723602
Email: mail@limelightgb.com
Web: www.limelightgb.com
Product Type: 1, 2, 3

B ROURKE & CO LTD
Vulcan Works, Accrington Road,
Burnley, Lancashire, BB11 5QD
Area of Operation: Worldwide
Tel: 01282 422841 **Fax:** 01282 458901
Email: info@rourkes.co.uk
Web: www.rourkes.co.uk
Product Type: 1, 2, 3, 4, 5

BASTA PARSONS
Alma St, Wolverhampton, West Midlands, WV10 0EY
Area of Operation: UK & Ireland
Tel: 01902 877770 **Fax:** 01902 877771
Email: sjohnson@bastaparsonsgb.com
Web: www.bastaparsons.com
Product Type: 1, 2

BENNETTS (IRONGATE) LIMITED
11-13 Jubilee Parkway, Stores Road,
Derby, Derbyshire, DE21 4BJ
Area of Operation: UK (Excluding Ireland)
Tel: 01332 346521 **Fax:** 01332 293453
Email: mark.rowland@bennettsirongate.co.uk
Web: www.bennettsirongate.co.uk
Product Type: 1, 2, 3, 4, 5

BOYALLS ARCHITECTURAL IRONMONGERS
187 High Street, Hampton Hill,
Greater London, TW12 1NL
Area of Operation: UK (Excluding Ireland)
Tel: 0208 941 0880 **Fax:** 0208 941 3718
Email: sales@boyalls.com
Web: www.boyalls.com

BRAMAH SECURITY EQUIPMENT LTD
31 Oldbury Place, London, W1U 5PT
Area of Operation: Worldwide
Tel: 020 7486 1739 **Fax:** 0207 935 2779
Email: lock.sales@bramah.co.uk
Web: www.bramah.co.uk **Product Type:** 2

BRASS ART
Unit L1, Lockside, Anchor Brook Industrial Estate,
Aldridge, Walsall, West Midlands, WS9 8EG
Area of Operation: UK (Excluding Ireland)
Tel: 01922 740512 **Fax:** 01922 740510
Email: sales@brassart.co.uk
Web: www.brassart.co.uk **Product Type:** 1, 2, 4

BRASS FOUNDRY CASTINGS
PO Box 151, Westerham, Kent, TN16 1YF
Area of Operation: Worldwide
Tel: 01959 563863 **Fax:** 01959 561262
Email: info@brasscastings.co.uk
Web: www.brasscastings.co.uk
Product Type: 1, 3, 4, 5

BROADLEAF TIMBER
Llandeilo Road Industrial Estate,
Carms, Carmarthenshire, SA18 3JG
Area of Operation: UK & Ireland
Tel: 01269 851910 **Fax:** 01269 851911
Email: sales@broadleaftimber.com
Web: www.broadleaftimber.com
Product Type: 1, 2

BROUGHTONS OF LEICESTER
The Old Cinema, 69 Cropston Road,
Anstey, Leicester, Leicestershire, LE7 7BP
Area of Operation: Worldwide
Tel: 0116 235 2555 **Fax:** 0116 234 1188
Email: sale@broughtons.com
Web: www.broughtons.com

BROXWOOD LTD
Broxwood Ltd, Inveralmond Way,
Inveralmond Industrial Estate, Perth, PH1 3UQ
Area of Operation: Europe
Fax: 01738 444452
Email: sales@broxwood.com
Web: www.broxwood.com **Product Type:** 1, 2

BUILDMART.CO.UK LIMITED
Area of Operation: UK (Excluding Ireland)
Tel: 0870 874 1135
Email: enquiries@buildmart.co.uk
Web: www.buildmart.co.uk
Product Type: 1

C & R ARCHITECTURAL HARDWARE LTD
Unit 6, Scotshawbrook Industrial Estate, Branch
Road, Lower Darwen, Darwen, Lancashire, BB30PR
Area of Operation: UK & Ireland
Tel: 01254278757 **Fax:** 01254 278767
Email: info@theaishop.com
Web: www.theaishop.com

CARLISLE BRASS
Park House Road, Carlisle, Cumbria, CA3 0JU
Area of Operation: UK & Ireland
Tel: 01228 511770 **Fax:** 01228 815306
Email: enquiries@carlislebrass.com
Web: www.carlislebrass.com
Product Type: 1, 2, 3, 4, 5

CASTAWAY CAST PRODUCTS AND WOODWARE
Brocklesby Station, Brocklesby Road,
Ulceby, Lincolnshire, DN39 6ST
Area of Operation: Worldwide
Tel: 01469 588995 **Fax:** 01469 588995
Email: castawaycastproducts@btinternet.com
Product Type: 1, 3, 4
Other Info: ✎ ✍ **Material Type:** C) 1, 5, 6, 11, 12

CHAMBERLAIN & GROVES LTD -
THE DOOR & SECURITY STORE
101 Boundary Road, Walthamstow, London, E17 8NQ
Area of Operation: UK (Excluding Ireland)
Tel: 0208 520 6776 **Fax:** 0208 520 2190
Email: ken@securedoors.co.uk
Web: www.securedoors.co.uk
Product Type: 1

CHARLES MASON LTD
Unit 11A Brook Street Mill, Off Goodall Street,
Macclesfield, Cheshire, SK11 7AW
Area of Operation: Worldwide
Tel: 0800 085 3616 **Fax:** 01625 668789
Email: info@charles-mason.com
Web: www.charles-mason.com
Product Type: 1, 2, 3, 4, 5

CIFIAL UK LTD
7 Faraday Court, Park Farm Industrial Estate,
Wellingborough, Northamptonshire, NN8 6XY
Area of Operation: UK & Ireland
Tel: 01933 402008 **Fax:** 01933 402063
Email: sales@cifial.co.uk **Web:** www.cifial.co.uk

CIFIAL UK
Area of Operation: UK & Ireland
Tel: 01933 402008 **Fax:** 01933 402063
Email: sales@cifial.co.uk
Web: www.cifial.co.uk
Materials Type: C) 1

Add a touch of glamour to your home with luxury
door furniture from Cifial. Their new designer
collection, EuroDesign, comprises of 6 stylish
handle options.

CLAYTON MUNROE LIMITED
15 - 20 Burke Road, Totnes Industrial Estate,
Totnes, Devon, TQ9 5XL
Area of Operation: Worldwide
Tel: 01803 865700 **Fax:** 01803 840720
Email: mail@claytonmunroe.com
Web: www.claytonmunroe.com
Product Type: 1, 3, 4

COBALT BLACKSMITHS
The Forge, English Farm, English Lane,
Nuffield, Oxfordshire, RG9 5TH
Tel: 01491 641990
Fax: 01491 640909
Email: enquiries@cobalt-blacksmiths.co.uk
Web: www.cobalt-blacksmiths.co.uk
Product Type: 1, 2

CORE AND ORE LTD
16 Portland Street, Clifton, Bristol, BS8 4JH
Area of Operation: UK (Excluding Ireland)
Tel: 01179 042408 **Fax:** 01179 094010
Email: sales@coreandore.com
Web: www.coreandore.com
Product Type: 1

COUNTY HARDWOODS
Creech Mill, Mill Lane, Creech Saint Michael,
Taunton, Somerset, TA3 5PX
Area of Operation: UK & Ireland
Tel: 01823 443760
Fax: 01823 443940
Email: sales@countyhardwoods.co.uk
Web: www.countyhardwoods.co.uk

D & E ARCHITECTURAL HARDWARE LTD
17 Royce Road, Carr Road Industrial Estate,
Fengate, Peterborough, Cambridgeshire, PE1 5YB
Area of Operation: UK & Ireland
Tel: 01733 896123 **Fax:** 01733 894466
Email: wan@DandE.co.uk
Web: www.DandE.co.uk
Product Type: 1, 2, 3, 4, 5

DANICO BRASS LTD
31-35 Winchester Road,
Swiss Cottage, London, NW3 3NR
Area of Operation: Worldwide
Tel: 0207 483 4477 **Fax:** 0207 722 7992
Email: sales@danico.co.uk
Product Type: 1, 2, 3, 4, 5 **Other Info:** ✎ ✍

DARTINGTON STEEL DESIGN
Webbers Yard, Dartington Industrial Estate,
Totnes, Devon, TQ9 6JY
Area of Operation: Worldwide
Tel: 01803 868671 **Fax:** 01803 868665
Email: sales@dartington.com
Web: www.dartington.com
Product Type: 1, 3, 4 **Other Info:** ✍

DAVID K COOPER
ARCHITECTURAL IRONMONGERY
Unit 27 Maybrook Industrial Estate, Maybrook Road,
Walsall Wood, Walsall, West Midlands, WS8 7DG
Area of Operation: UK & Ireland
Tel: 01543 454479 **Fax:** 01543 453707
Email: sales@dkcooper.co.uk
Web: www.dkcooper.co.uk
Product Type: 1, 2, 3, 4, 5

DESA UK LTD
11 Beech House, Padgate Business Park,
Green Lane, Warrington, Cheshire, WA1 4JN
Area of Operation: UK (Excluding Ireland)
Tel: 01925 828854 **Fax:** 01925 284124
Email: info@desauk.co.uk
Web: www.desauk.co.uk **Product Type:** 5

DICTATOR DIRECT
Inga House, Northdown Business Park,
Ashford Road, Lenham, Kent, ME17 2DL
Area of Operation: Worldwide
Tel: 01622 854770 **Fax:** 01622 854771
Email: mail@dictatordirect.com
Web: www.dictatordirect.com **Product Type:** 2

DIRECTDOORS.COM
Bay 5 Eastfield Industrial Estate,
Eastfield Drive, Penicuik, Lothian, EH26 8JA
Area of Operation: UK (Excluding Ireland)
Tel: 01968 671681 **Fax:** 01968 671684
Email: info@directdoors.com
Web: www.directdoors.com
Product Type: 1, 2, 3, 4, 5

DISTINCTIVE DOORS
14 & 15 Chambers Way, Newton Chambers Road,
Chapeltown, Sheffield, South Yorkshire, S35 2PH
Area of Operation: UK & Ireland
Tel: 0114 220 2250
Fax: 0114 220 2254
Email: enquiries@distinctivedoors.co.uk
Web: www.distinctivedoors.co.uk
Product Type: 1, 2, 3, 4, 5   **Material Type:** A) 2, 3

E.W. FITTON & CO
6 Top Schwabe Street, Rhodes,
Middleton, Manchester, M24 4TQ
Area of Operation: Europe
Tel: 0161 643 1296   **Fax:** 0161 643 1296
Email: ernest.fitton@tiscali.co.uk
Web: www.fit-onfixseal.com

EVERGREEN DOOR
Unit 1, Oakwell Park Industrial Estate,
Birstall, West Yorkshire, WF17 9LU
Area of Operation: Worldwide
Tel: 01924 423171
Fax: 01924 423175
Email: sales@evergreendoor.co.uk
Web: www.evergreendoor.co.uk   **Product Type:** 5

EXPRESS HANDLES LTD
Unit 118 Golborne Enterprise Park, Kid Glove Road,
Golborne, Warrington, Cheshire, WA3 3GR
Area of Operation: UK (Excluding Ireland)
Tel: 01942 728677   **Fax:** 01942 727547
Email: marina.express@btconnect.com
Product Type: 1

FORGERIES
The Loft, 108 Brassey Road,
Winchester, Hampshire, SO22 6SA
Area of Operation: UK (Excluding Ireland)
Tel: 01962 842822   **Fax:** 01962 842822
Email: penny@forgeriesonline.co.uk
Web: www.forgeriesonline.co.uk   **Product Type:** 1, 2

HARBRINE LTD
27-31 Payne Road, London, E3 2SP
Area of Operation: Worldwide
Tel: 0208 980 8000   **Fax:** 0208 980 6050
Email: info@harbrine.co.uk
Web: www.harbrine.co.uk   **Product Type:** 1, 2

HAYMANS TIMBER PRODUCTS
Haymans Farm, Hocker Lane, Over Alderley,
Macclesfield, Cheshire, SK10 4SD
Area of Operation: UK & Ireland
Tel: 01625 590098
Fax: 01625 586174
Email: haymanstimber@aol.com
Web: www.haymanstimber.co.uk

HERITAGE HANDLES
17-19 Old Woking Road, West Byfleet, Surrey, KT14 6LW
Area of Operation: UK & Ireland
Tel: 01932 344434   **Fax:** 01932 340559
Email: sales@heritagehandles.co.uk
Web: www.heritagehandles.co.uk
Product Type: 1, 2, 3, 4, 5

HOLDEN + PARTNERS
26 High Street, Wimbledon,
Greater London, SW19 5BY
Area of Operation: Worldwide
Tel: 0208 946 5502   **Fax:** 0208 879 0310
Email: arch@holdenpartners.co.uk
Web: www.holdenpartners.co.uk
Product Type: 1, 3, 5

HOUSE OF BRASS
122 North Sherwood Street, Nottingham,
Nottinghamshire, NG1 4EF
Area of Operation: Worldwide
Tel: 0115 947 5430
Fax: 0115 947 5430
Email: sales@houseofbrass.co.uk
Web: www.houseofbrass.co.uk
Product Type: 1, 2, 3, 4, 5

IN DOORS
Beechinwood Farm, Beechinwood Lane,
Platt, Nr. Sevenoaks, Kent, TN15 8QN
Tel: 01732 887445   **Fax:** 01732 887446
Email: info@indoorsltd.co.uk
Web: www.indoorsltd.co.uk   **Product Type:** 1, 3

INSPIRATION 360 LTD -
TRADING AS WWW.DOORCHIC.CO.UK
4 Sandbeds Court, Sandbeds Trading Estate,
Ossett, West Yorkshire, WF5 9ND
Tel: 01924 230265   **Fax:** 01924 230266
Email: sales@doorchic.co.uk
Web: www.doorchic.co.uk
Product Type: 1, 2, 3, 4, 5
Material Type: C) 1, 2, 3, 5, 9, 11, 12, 13, 14, 16

INTERIOR ASSOCIATES
3 Highfield Road, Windsor, Berkshire, SL4 4DN
Area of Operation: UK & Ireland
Tel: 01753 865339   **Fax:** 01753 865339
Email: sales@interiorassociates.fsnet.co.uk
Web: www.interiorassociates.co.uk
Product Type: 5

IRONMONGERY DIRECT
Unit 2-3 Eldon Way Trading Estate,
Eldon Way, Hockley, Essex, SS5 4AD
Area of Operation: Worldwide
Tel: 01702 562770   **Fax:** 01702 562799
Email: sales@ironmongerydirect.com
Web: www.ironmongerydirect.com
Product Type: 1, 2, 3, 4

ISAAC LORD LTD
West End Court, Suffield Road,
High Wycombe, Buckinghamshire, HP11 2JY
Area of Operation: East England, Greater London,
North East England, South East England, South West
England and South Wales
Tel: 01494 462121   **Fax:** 01494 461376
Email: info@isaaclord.co.uk
Web: www.isaaclord.co.uk

ITFITZ
11-12 Woodlands Farm, Spring Lane,
Cookham Dean, Berkshire, SL6 9PN
Area of Operation: UK (Excluding Ireland)
Tel: 01628 890432   **Fax:** 0870 133 7955
Email: sales@itfitz.co.uk
Web: www.itfitz.co.uk
Product Type: 1, 2, 3, 4, 5

JAMES BENTLEY
13 Tennyson Road, Hinckley, Leicestershire, LE10 0TH
Area of Operation: UK (Excluding Ireland)
Tel: 0870 850 2057
Email: paul.smith@james-bentley.co.uk
Web: www.james-bentley.co.uk   **Product Type:** 1

JAMES GIBBONS FORMAT LTD
Vulcan Road, Bilston, Wolverhampton,
West Midlands, WV14 7JG
Area of Operation: Worldwide
Tel: 01902 405500   **Fax:** 01902 385915
Email: info@jgf.co.uk
Web: www.jgf.co.uk   **Product Type:** 1, 2, 3, 4

JIM LAWRENCE LTD
Scotland Hall Farm, Stoke by Nayland,
Colchester, Essex, CO6 4QG
Area of Operation: UK (Excluding Ireland)
Tel: 01206 263459
Fax: 01206 262166
Email: sales@jim-lawrence.co.uk
Web: www.jim-lawrence.co.uk
Product Type: 1, 2, 3, 4, 5

JOHN ARMISTEAD RESTORATIONS
Malham Cottage, Bellingdon,
Nr.Chesham, Buckinghamshire, HP5 2UR
Area of Operation: Worldwide
Tel: 01494 758209
Fax: 01494 758209
Email: j.armistead@ntlworld.com
Web: www.john-armistead-restorations.co.uk

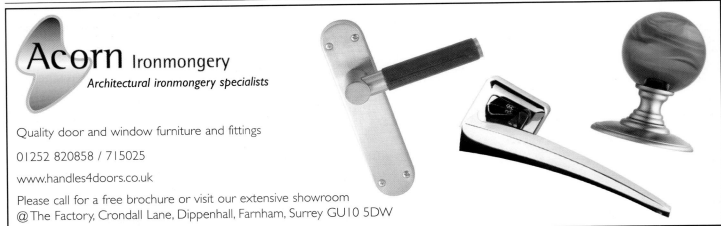

JOHN PLANCK LTD
Southern House, Anthonys Way,
Medway City Estate, Rochester, Kent, ME2 4DN
Area of Operation: UK (Excluding Ireland)
Tel: 01634 720077   **Fax:** 01634 720111
Email: john@johnplanck.co.uk
Web: www.johnplanck.co.uk
Product Type: 1, 2, 3, 4, 5

KASPAR SWANKEY
405, Goldhawk Road,
Hammersmith, West London, W6 0SA
Area of Operation: Worldwide
Tel: 020 8746 3586   **Fax:** 020 8746 3586
Email: kaspar@swankeypankey.com
Web: www.swankeypankey.com   **Product Type:** 1, 5

KERSHAWS DOORS LTD
Main Street, Wyke, Bradford,
West Yorkshire, BD12 8BN
Area of Operation: UK (Excluding Ireland)
Tel: 01274 604488
Fax: 0845 126 0275
Email: help@door-warehouse.co.uk
Web: www.door-warehouse.co.uk
Product Type: 1, 2, 3, 4

LEOHARDWARE.COM
Unit.3, Scotshawbrook Industrial Estate,
Branch Road, Lower Darwen,
Darwen, Lancashire, BB3 0PR
Area of Operation: UK & Ireland
Tel: 01254 278757
Fax: 01254 278767
Email: info@leohardware.com
Web: www.leohardware.com
Product Type: 1, 2, 3, 4, 5
Material Type: A) 4, 7, 15

LEVOLUX LTD
1 Forward Drive, Harrow, Middlesex,
Greater London, HA3 8NT
Area of Operation: Worldwide
Tel: 0208 863 9111   **Fax:** 0208 863 8760
Email: info@levolux.com
Web: www.levolux.com   **Product Type:** 5

LOCKS & HANDLES
8 Exhibition Road,
South Kensington, London, SW7 2HF
Area of Operation: Worldwide
Tel: 0207 584 6800   **Fax:** 0207 589 4928
Email: sales@knobs.co.uk
Web: www.doorhandles.co.uk

**MACO DOOR AND WINDOW
HARDWARE (UK) LTD**
Castle Road, Eurolink Business Centre,
Sittingbourne, Kent, ME10 8LY
Area of Operation: Europe
Tel: 01795 433900
Fax: 01795 433902
Email: enquiry@macouk.net
Web: www.macouk.net
Product Type: 1, 2, 5   **Material Type:** D) 1

MBL
55 High Street, Biggleswade, Bedfordshire, SG18 0JH
Area of Operation: UK (Excluding Ireland)
Tel: 01767 318695
Fax: 01767 318834
Email: info@mblai.co.uk   **Web:** www.mblai.co.uk
Product Type: 1, 2, 3, 4, 5

MERLIN UK LIMITED
Unit 5 Fence Avenue, Macclesfield, Cheshire, SK10 1LT
Area of Operation: North West England and North Wales
Tel: 01625 424498   **Fax:** 0871 781 8967
Email: info@merlinuk.net
Web: www.merlindoors.co.uk
Product Type: 1, 2, 3, 4, 5

MIGHTON PRODUCTS LTD
PO Box 1, Saffron Walden, Essex, CB10 1QJ
Area of Operation: UK (Excluding Ireland)
Tel: 0800 0560471
Email: sales@mightonproducts.com
Web: www.mightonproducts.com

MIKE WYE & ASSOCIATES
Buckland Filleigh Sawmills,
Buckland Filleigh, Beaworthy, Devon, EX21 5RN
Area of Operation: Worldwide
Tel: 01409 281644
Fax: 01409 281669
Email: sales@mikewye.co.uk
Web: www.mikewye.co.uk

MODERN DOOR CLOSERS LTD
Lloyds Bank Chambers, High Street,
Littlehampton, West Sussex, BN17 5AG
Area of Operation: Worldwide
Tel: 01903 724003   **Fax:** 01903 739806
Email: moderndoorclosers@btconnect.com
Web: www.moderndoorclosers.co.uk
Product Type: 2

NORVIK PVCU WINDOW SYSTEMS LTD
Mitchells Industrial Park, Wombwell,
Barnsley, South Yorkshire, S35 7AE
Area of Operation: UK & Ireland
Tel: 01226 340182   **Fax:** 01226 340375
Email: nhibberd@norvik.co.uk
Web: www.norvik.co.uk

OLD HOUSE STORE LTD
Hampstead Farm, Binfield Heath,
Henley on Thames, Oxfordshire, RG9 4LG
Area of Operation: Worldwide
Tel: 0118 969 7711   **Fax:** 0118 969 8822
Email: info@oldhousestore.co.uk
Web: www.oldhousestore.co.uk
Product Type: 1

OLD HOUSE STORE LTD

Area of Operation: Worldwide
Tel: 0118 969 7711
Fax: 0118 969 8822
Email: info@oldhousestore.co.uk
Web: www.oldhousestore.co.uk
Material Type: C) 2, 6, 17
Other Info:

Traditional door and window furniture, ironmongery and brassware - many handcrafted and forged by in-house blacksmiths. Commissioned works also undertaken. Delivery throughout UK and worldwide mail order.

ORIGINAL
3 Festival Units, The Showground,
Bridgwater, Somerset, TA6 6LS
Area of Operation: South West England and South Wales
Tel: 0870 0110808
Fax: 0870 011 0606
Email: enquiries@obsc.co.uk
Web: www.obsc.co.uk

PENNY BRICKS & TIMBER LIMITED
The Old Timber Yard, York Road,
Wetherby, West Yorkshire, LS22 5EF
Area of Operation: UK & Ireland
Tel: 01937 580580   **Fax:** 01937 580587
Email: pw@penny-bricks.co.uk
Web: www.penny-bricks.co.uk   **Product Type:** 1

**RAVEN SEALS LTD
(C/O DISTRIBUTOR, ROYDE & TUCKER LTD)**
Bilton Road, Cadwell Lane,
Hitchin, Hertfordshire, SG4 0SB
Area of Operation: Europe
Tel: 01462 444444   **Fax:** 01462 444433
Email: info@ravenseals.com
Web: www.ravenseals.co.uk   **Product Type:** 5

REDDISEALS
The Furlong, Berry Hill Industrial Estate,
Droitwich, Worcestershire, WR9 9BG
Area of Operation: UK & Ireland
Tel: 01905 791876
Fax: 01905 791877
Email: reddiseals@reddiseals.com
Web: www.reddiseals.com   **Product Type:** 2, 5

ROTO FRANK LTD
Swift Point, Rugby, Warwickshire, CV21 1QH
Area of Operation: Worldwide
Tel: 01788 558600   **Fax:** 01788 558605
Email: uksales@roto-frank.co.uk
Web: www.roto-frank.co.uk   **Product Type:** 1, 2, 5

RYELUND LTD
Sawmill Lane, Helmsley,
North Yorkshire, YO62 5DQ
Area of Operation: Worldwide
Tel: 01439 772802   **Fax:** 01439 771002
Email: info@ryelund.co.uk
Web: www.ryelund.co.uk

SAMUEL HEATH
Leopold Street, Birmingham,
West Midlands, B12 0UJ
Area of Operation: Worldwide
Tel: 0121 772 2303   **Fax:** 0121 772 3334
Email: info@samuel-heath.com
Web: www.samuel-heath.com

STANDARDS GROUP
Bentley Hall Barn, Alkmonton,
Ashbourne, Derbyshire, DE6 3DJ
Area of Operation: UK & Ireland
Tel: 01335 330263   **Fax:** 01335 330922
Email: uk@standardsgroup.com
Web: www.standardsgroup.com   **Product Type:** 1

STRATHEARN STONE AND TIMBER LTD
Glenearn, Bridge of Earn,
Perth, Perth and Kinross, PH2 9HL
Area of Operation: North East England, Scotland
Tel: 01738 813215   **Fax:** 01738 815946
Email: info@stoneandoak.com
Web: www.stoneandoak.com
Product Type: 1, 5
Other Info: **Material Type:** C) 5

THE ANTIQUE DOOR KNOCKER COMPANY
Jasmine Cottage, Prees Green,
Nr Whitchurch, Shropshire, SY13 2BL
Area of Operation: Worldwide
Tel: 01948 840666
Email: sales@antiquedoorknockers.co.uk
Web: www.antiquedoorknockers.co.uk

THE BRADLEY COLLECTION
Lion Barn, Maitland Road,
Needham Market, Suffolk, IP6 8NS
Area of Operation: Worldwide
Tel: 01449 722724   **Fax:** 0845 118 7228
Email: claus.fortmann@bradleycollection.co.uk
Web: www.bradleycollection.co.uk
Product Type: 1

THE CAMDEN GROUP
Unit 4-7, Steeple Industrial Estate, Antrim, BT41 1AB
Area of Operation: UK & Ireland
Tel: 028 9446 2419   **Fax:** 028 9442 8138
Email: info@camdengroup.co.uk
Web: www.camdengroup.co.uk
Product Type: 1, 2, 3

THE DAVID BARLEY COMPANY
Unit D, Holmes Court, Horncastle, Lincolnshire, LN9 6AS
Area of Operation: UK & Ireland
Tel: 01507 523838   **Fax:** 01507 524465
Email: padraic@eclisse.co.uk
Web: www.eclisse.co.uk   **Product Type:** 1, 2

THE EXPANDED METAL COMPANY LIMITED
PO Box 14, Longhill Industrial Estate (North),
Hartlepool, Durham, TS25 1PR
Area of Operation: Worldwide
Tel: 01429 867388   **Fax:** 01429 866795
Email: paulb@expamet.com
Web: www.expandedmetalcompany.co.uk

THE JACKLOC COMPANY LTD
Ulverscroft Lodge, Priory Lane,
Ulverscroft, Leicestershire, LE67 9PB
Area of Operation: Europe
Tel: 01530 249034   **Fax:** 01530 245710
Email: sales@jackloc.com
Web: www.jackloc.com   **Product Type:** 2

THE NATIONAL DOOR COMPANY
Unit 55, Dinting Vale Business Park,
Dinting Vale, Glossop, Derbyshire, SK13 6JD
Area of Operation: UK (Excluding Ireland)
Tel: 01457 867079   **Fax:** 01457 868795
Email: sales@nationaldoor.co.uk
Web: www.nationaldoor.co.uk

TITON
International House, Peartree Road,
Stanway, Colchester, Essex, CO3 0JL
Area of Operation: Worldwide
Tel: 01206 713800   **Fax:** 01206 543126
Email: sales@titon.co.uk   **Web:** www.titon.co.uk

TRAPEX
26 Pindar Road, Hoddesdon, Hertfordshire, EN11 0DE
Area of Operation: Worldwide
Tel: 01992 462150   **Fax:** 01992 446736
Email: info@trapex.com
Web: www.trapex.com   **Product Type:** 1, 2, 3, 4, 5

UAP
Bank House, 16-18 Bank Street,
Walshaw, Bury, Lancashire, BL8 3AZ
Tel: 0161 763 5290   **Fax:** 0161 763 6726
Email: uap@btconnect.com
Web: www.universal-imports.com   **Product Type:** 1

URBAN FRONT LTD
Design Studio, 1 Little Hill, Heronsgate,
Rickmansworth, Hertfordshire, WD3 5BX
Area of Operation: UK & Ireland
Tel: 0870 609 1525   **Fax:** 0870 609 3564
Email: info@urbanfront.co.uk
Web: www.urbanfront.co.uk   **Product Type:** 1, 2

WAGNER (GB) LTD
VBH House, Bailey Drive, Gillingham Business Park,
Gillingham, Kent, ME8 0WG
Area of Operation: Worldwide
Tel: 01634 263263   **Fax:** 01634 263504
Email: sales@wagnergb.com
Web: www.wagnergb.com   **Product Type:** 2

WMC ANTIQUES
141 Baldocks Lane, Melton Mowbray,
Leicester, Leicestershire, LE13 1EP
Area of Operation: Worldwide
Tel: 01664 851488
Email: willcoo1@ntlworld.com
Web: www.wmcantiques.co.uk
Product Type: 1, 2, 3, 4, 5

ZERO SEAL SYSTEMS LTD
Unit 6, Ladford Covert, Seighford,
Stafford, Staffordshire, ST18 9QG
Area of Operation: Europe
Tel: 01785 282910   **Fax:** 01785 282498
Email: sales@zeroplus.co.uk
Web: www.zeroplus.co.uk   **Product Type:** 5

FRENCH PROPERTY BOOKS

How to Renovate a House in France:

Whether you are buying an old house, worrying about damp stone walls, struggling to understand lime render, shopping for partition walling, hunting for builders, doing your own plumbing, trying to get planning permission… in short, if you are involved in any way with a renovation project in France, this book will be essential reading.

How to Create a Jardin Paysan:

This is a book about creating a traditional, rural French-style garden which will have a timeless charm. It's about organic gardens, creating natural habitats for birds and insects, and making the garden a seamless link between your house and the natural world of the French countryside on the other side of your garden fence.

For current offers visit:
www.homebuilding.co.uk/bookshop

Image courtesy of Kingspan Insulation Ltd (0870 850 8555)

SPONSORED BY KINGSPAN INSULATION LTD
Tel 0870 850 8555 Web www.insulation.kingspan.com

BUILDING STRUCTURE & MATERIALS

BUILDING STRUCTURE & MATERIALS - Insulation & Proofing Materials
SPONSORED BY: KINGSPAN INSULATION LTD www.insulation.kingspan.com

Acoustic Insulation

It's not surprising that most new homebuyers rate a quiet house right up there at the top of their wish-lists – and self-builders and renovators are no different. Thankfully there are a range of techniques that can transform the way sound travels, in both new and old homes.

Noisy homes came with the change in construction methods after Edwardian times. During this period, the timber used in construction was virgin growth, solid pine, with the floors planks an inch thick. Ceilings and walls were built from thick, heavy materials such as timber laths.

These materials were slowly but surely replaced by lightweight options such as chipboard and plasterboard. Other housing fashions, such as lighter windows, lightweight curtains and thinner (or no) carpets, made matters worse. More recent trends such as hard floor surfaces and downlighters – which require spaces to be made in the ceiling – have further compounded the problem.

Masonry vs. Timber Frame

One might assume that heavy materials are good, and lightweight materials bad. But this is only partially right. Clearly, mass is good for sound insulation, but it is not the only way of

achieving good sound insulation. A well-sealed lightweight structure can be less noisy than a structure with larger mass that is full of holes for fittings such as downlighters.

However, the fashion for fitting downlighters shows no sign of abating, and punching holes in ceilings is a sure way to reduce soundproofing. Whether this matters in an individual home is questionable: downlighters are often used in the living room or kitchen below a bedroom, so when one is occupied the other is empty. Also, acoustic downlights are becoming increasingly available on the market, providing a simple solution to this common problem.

Soundproofing floors

The simplest and cheapest floor to build in a new home is a timber-joisted floor. A chipboard or timber floor above, with plasterboard below, provides very poor sound insulation levels.

A decent alternative is a precast masonry floor

system. It substantially boosts airborne sound reduction between floors by around 15 decibels. But bear in mind that there is a cost penalty for switching from timber or I-beam joists.

If you are working with an existing structure options are more limited, but the techniques involved are no different to new build. If you are lifting floors, you can easily add acoustic insulation into the void. Alternatively, adding an extra layer of plasterboard from the underside will improve matters considerably.

Layout – points to consider

- Plan the layout of all rooms to help reduce noise problems in the home.
- Placing bathrooms next to one another is not only good plumbing practice, it can also reduce the impact of plumbing and bathing sounds in the surrounding bedrooms.
- Built-in wardrobes in bedrooms can also stop noise penetrating through bedroom walls.
- Large galleries and stairwells may look great, but they can also act as sound transmitters.

LEFT: Making holes in the ceiling for downlighters is a sure way to reduce the effectiveness of soundproofing, although you could consider acoustically rated downlighters to combat this.
BELOW: Heavy drapes and thick carpets will considerably dampen the noise characteristics of a house.

BUILDING STRUCTURE & MATERIALS - Insulation & Proofing Materials - Thermal Insulation
SPONSORED BY: KINGSPAN INSULATION LTD   www.insulation.kingspan.com

BUILDING STRUCTURE & MATERIALS

THERMAL INSULATION

KEY

PRODUCT TYPES: 1= Wall Cavity
2 = Floor   3 = Roof   4 = Internal Wall
5 = External Wall   6 = Pipe

OTHER: ▽ Reclaimed   ᵍ On-line shopping
✑ Bespoke   ✋ Hand-made   ECO Ecological

A PROCTOR GROUP LTD
The Haugh, Blairgowrie, Perth and Kinross, PH10 7ER
Area of Operation: Worldwide
Tel: 01250 872261   **Fax:** 01250 872727
Email: lynsay.johnston@proctorgroup.com
Web: www.proctorgroup.com   **Product Type:** 1, 3, 4

ACTIS
Unit 1 Cornbrash Park, Bumpers Way, Bumpers Farm
Industrial Estate, Chippenham, Wiltshire, SN14 6RA
Area of Operation: Europe
Tel: 01249 446123   **Fax:** 01249 446345
Email: solutions@actis-isolation.com
Web: www.insulation-actis.com
Product Type: 2, 3, 4, 5

APOLLO INSULATION LIMITED
PO Box 200, Horley, Surrey, RH6 7FU
Area of Operation: Worldwide
Tel: 01293 776974   **Fax:** 01293 776975
Email: info@apollo-energy.com
Web: www.apollo-energy.com
Product Type: 1, 2, 3, 4, 5, 6

ARMACELL (UK) LTD
Mars Street, Oldham, Lancashire, OL9 6LY
Area of Operation: Worldwide
Tel: 0161 287 7100   **Fax:** 0161 633 2685
Email: info.uk@armacell.com
Web: www.armacell.com   **Product Type:** 6

BECO PRODUCTS LTD
Beco House, 6 Exmoor Avenue,
Scunthorpe, Lincolnshire, DN15 8NJ
Area of Operation: UK & Ireland
Tel: 01724 747576   **Fax:** 01724 747579
Email: www.becowallform.co.uk
Web: www.becowallform.co.uk   **Product Type:** 4, 5
Material Type: G) 1, K) 11

BMD INSULATION
Urquhart House, Basingstoke Close,
Freshbrook, Swindon, Wiltshire, SN5 8RB
Area of Operation: UK (Excluding Ireland)
Tel: 01793 326026
Email: info@bmdinsulation.com
Web: www.bmdinsulation.com
Product Type: 1, 2, 3, 4, 5

**BRITISH URETHANE FOAM
CONTRACTORS ASSOCIATION**
PO Box 12, Haslemere, Surrey, GU27 3AH
Area of Operation: UK (Excluding Ireland)
Tel: 01428 654011   **Fax:** 01428 651401
Email: info@bufca.co.uk   **Web:** www.bufca.co.uk
Material Type: K) 5

CELOTEX LIMITED
Lady Lane Industrial Estate,
Hadleigh, Ipswich, Suffolk, IP7 6BA
Area of Operation: UK & Ireland
Tel: 01473 822093   **Fax:** 01473 820880
Email: dbirch@celotex.co.uk   **Web:** www.celotex.co.uk
Product Type: 1, 2, 3, 4, 5   **Material Type:** K) 14

CHILTERN DYNAMICS
Chiltern House , Stocking Lane, Hughenden Valley,
High Wycombe, Buckinghamshire, HP14 4ND
Area of Operation: UK & Ireland
Tel: 01494 569800   **Fax:** 01494 564895
Email: cd@chilterndynamics.com
Web: www.chilternfire.co.uk
Product Type: 1, 2, 3, 4, 5, 6

CICO CHIMNEY LININGS LTD
The Street, Westleton, Saxmundham, Suffolk, IP17 3AG
Area of Operation: UK (Excluding Ireland)
Tel: 01728 648608   **Fax:** 01728 648428
Email: cico@chimney-problems.co.uk
Web: www.chimney-problems.co.uk   **Product Type:** 3

CONSTRUCTION RESOURCES
16 Great Guildford Street, London, SE1 0HS
Area of Operation: UK (Excluding Ireland)
Tel: 0207 450 2211   **Fax:** 0207 450 2212
Email: info@constructionresources.com
Web: www.constructionresources.com
Product Type: 1, 2, 3, 4, 5

DACATIE BUILDING SOLUTIONS
Quantum House, Salmon Fields,
Royton, Oldham, Lancashire, OL2 6JG
Area of Operation: UK & Ireland
Tel: 0161 627 4222   **Fax:** 0161 627 4333
Email: info@dacatie.co.uk
Web: www.dacatie.co.uk   **Product Type:** 1

DOW CONSTRUCTION PRODUCTS
2 Heathrow Boulevard, 284 Bath Road,
West Drayton, Middlesex, UB7 0DQ
Area of Operation: Worldwide
Tel: 0208 917 5050   **Fax:** 0208 917 5413
Email: styrofoam-uk@dow.com
Web: www.styrofoameurope.com
Product Type: 1, 2, 3, 4, 6

DRAUGHT PROOFING ADVISORY ASSOCIATION
PO Box 12, Haslemere, Surrey, GU27 3AH
Area of Operation: UK (Excluding Ireland)
Tel: 01428 654011   **Fax:** 01428 651401
Email: dpaaassociation@aol.com
Web: www.dpaa-association.org.uk

ECO POLYURETHANE SYSTEMS LTD
Unit 10, Amber Close, Amington,
Tamworth, Staffordshire, B77 4RP
Area of Operation: UK (Excluding Ireland)
Tel: 01827 313951
Email: info@eps-systemsltd.com
Web: www.eps-systems.com   **Product Type:** 1, 3, 5

ECOLOGICAL BUILDING SYSTEMS UK LTD
The Manse, High Street, Creaton,
Northamptonshire, NN6 8NA
Tel: 05600 758025   **Fax:** 05600 758026
Email: ecologicalbuild@btconnect.com
Web: www.ecologicalbuildingsystems.co.uk
Product Type: 2, 3, 4

ECOSHOP
Unit 1, Glen of the Downs Garden Centre,
Kilmacanogue, Co Wicklow, Republic of Ireland
Area of Operation: Ireland Only
Tel: +353 01 488 0400   **Fax:** +353 01 201 6480
Email: info@ecoshop.ie   **Web:** www.ecoshop.ie ᵍ
Product Type: 1, 2, 3, 4, 5

EDULAN UK LTD
Unit M, Northstage, Broadway,
Salford, Greater Manchester, M50 2UW
Area of Operation: Worldwide
Tel: 0161 876 8040   **Fax:** 0161 876 8041
Email: peter@polyurethane.uk.com
Web: www.edulan.com
Product Type: 1, 3, 5   **Material Type:** K) 5, 14

ELLIOTTS INSULATION AND DRYLINING
Unit 8 Goodwood Road, Boyatt Wood Industrial
Estate, Eastleigh, Hampshire, SO50 4NT
Area of Operation: South East England, South West
England and South Wales
Tel: 02380 623960   **Fax:** 02380 623965
Email: insulation@elliott-brothers.co.uk
Web: www.elliotts.uk.com
Product Type: 1, 2, 3, 4, 5

ENCON INSULATION
Brunswick House, 1 Deighton Close,
Wetherby, West Yorkshire, LS22 7GZ
Area of Operation: UK (Excluding Ireland)
Tel: 01937 524200   **Fax:** 01937 524280
Email: info@encon.co.uk   **Web:** www.encon.co.uk
Product Type: 1, 3, 5

EPS INSULATION LTD
Unit 10 Amber Close, Amington Industrial Estate,
Tamworth, Staffordshire, B79 8BH
Area of Operation: UK (Excluding Ireland)
Tel: 01827 313951
Fax: 01827 54683
Email: info@eps-systemsltd.com
Web: www.eps-systemsltd.com
Product Type: 2, 3, 4, 5

EUROFORM PRODUCTS LIMITED
The Heliport, Lyncastle Road,
Appleton, Warrington, Cheshire, WA4 4SN
Area of Operation: Worldwide
Tel: 01925 860999   **Fax:** 01925 860066
Email: info@euroform.co.uk
Web: www.euroform.co.uk   **Product Type:** 1, 2, 3

EXCEL BUILDING SOLUTIONS
Maerdy Industrial Estate, Gwent, NP22 5PY
Area of Operation: Worldwide
Tel: 01685 845200
Fax: 01685 844106
Email: sales@excelfibre.com
Web: www.excelfibre.com
Product Type: 1, 2, 3, 4, 5
Other Info: ▽ ECO   **Material Type:** K) 3

FILLCRETE LTD
Maple House, 5 Over Minnis,
New Ash Green, Longfield, Kent, DA3 8JA
Area of Operation: UK (Excluding Ireland)
Tel: 01474 872444   **Fax:** 01474 872426
Email: timfolkes@fillcrete.com
Web: www.fillcrete.com   **Product Type:** 3, 4, 5

FOAMSEAL LTD
New Street House, New Street,
Petworth, West Sussex, GU28 0AS
Area of Operation: Worldwide
Tel: 01798 345400   **Fax:** 01798 345410
Email: info@foamseal.co.uk
Web: www.foamseal.co.uk
Product Type: 1, 2, 3, 4, 5, 6   **Material Type:** K) 5

GREEN BUILDING STORE
11 Huddersfield Road, Meltham,
Holmfirth, West Yorkshire, HD9 4NJ
Area of Operation: UK & Ireland
Tel: 01484 854898
Fax: 01484 854899
Email: info@greenbuildingstore.co.uk
Web: www.greenbuildingstore.co.uk ᵍ
Product Type: 2, 3, 4   **Other Info:** ECO

H+H CELCON LIMITED
Celcon House, Ightham, Sevenoaks, Kent, TN15 9HZ
Area of Operation: UK (Excluding Ireland)
Tel: 01732 880520   **Fax:** 01732 880531
Email: marketing@celcon.co.uk
Web: www.celcon.co.uk   **Product Type:** 1, 4, 5

HERAKLITH
Broadway House, 21, Broadway,
Maidenhead, Berkshire, SL6 1NJ
Area of Operation: UK & Ireland
Tel: 01628 784330   **Fax:** 01628 633080
Email: muirwork@btinternet.com
Product Type: 4, 5   **Other Info:** ECO
Material Type: K) 8, 10

HUNTON FIBER UK LTD
Rockleigh Court, Rock Road,
Finedon, Northamptonshire, NN9 5EL
Area of Operation: UK & Ireland
Tel: 01933 682683   **Fax:** 01933 680296
Email: admin@huntonfiber.co.uk
Web: www.hunton.no
Product Type: 1, 3   **Other Info:** ▽ ECO

**INSULATED RENDER &
CLADDING ASSOCIATION**
PO Box 12, Haslemere, Surrey, GU27 3AH
Area of Operation: UK (Excluding Ireland)
Tel: 01428 654011   **Fax:** 01428 651401
Email: incaassociation@aol.com
Web: www.inca-ltd.org.uk
Product Type: 5   **Material Type:** K) 4, 5, 8, 11, 12, 14

INSULATEUK.COM
Unit 7, The South West Centre, Troutbeck Road,
Sheffield, South Yorkshire, S7 2QU
Area of Operation: UK (Excluding Ireland)
Tel: 0114 250 6181   **Fax:** 0114 258 3705
Email: maggie@insulateuk.com
Web: www.insulateuk.com ᵍ
Product Type: 2, 3, 4, 6

KINGSPAN INSULATION LTD
Pembridge, Nr Leominster, Herefordshire, HR6 9LA
Area of Operation: Worldwide
Tel: 0870 850 8555
Fax: 0870 850 8666
Email: info.uk@insulation.kingspan.com
Web: www.insulation.kingspan.com
Product Type: 1, 2, 3, 4, 5, 6
Other Info: ECO   **Material Type:** K) 5, 14

KNAUF DIY
PO BOX 732, Maidstone, Kent, ME15 6ST
Area of Operation: UK & Ireland
Tel: 0845 601 1763   **Fax:** 0845 601 1762
Email: knaufdiy@knauf.co.uk
Web: www.teachmediy.co.uk
Product Type: 1, 2, 3, 4, 5, 6

LAFARGE GYVLON LTD
221 Europa Boulevard, Westbrook,
Warrington, Cheshire, WA5 7TN
Area of Operation: UK (Excluding Ireland)
Tel: 01925 428780   **Fax:** 01925 428788
Email: sales@gyvlon-floors.co.uk
Web: www.gyvlon-floors.co.uk   **Product Type:** 2

MH JOINERY SERVICES
25b Camwall Road, Harrogate, North Yorkshire, HG1 4PT
Area of Operation: North East England
Tel: 01423 888856   **Fax:** 01423 888856
Email: info@mhjoineryservices.co.uk
Web: www.mhjoineryservices.co.uk

MIKE WYE & ASSOCIATES
Buckland Filleigh Sawmills, Buckland Filleigh,
Beaworthy, Devon, EX21 5RN
Area of Operation: Worldwide
Tel: 01409 281644   **Fax:** 01409 281669
Email: sales@mikewye.co.uk
Web: www.mikewye.co.uk
Other Info: ECO   **Material Type:** K) 9

MIRATEX LIMITED
Unit 10, Park Hall Farm, Brookhouse Road,
Cheadle, Staffordshire, ST10 2NJ
Area of Operation: UK & Ireland
Tel: 01538 750923
Fax: 01538 752078
Email: info@miratex.co.uk
Web: www.miratex.co.uk   **Product Type:** 5

MOULD GROWTH CONSULTANTS LTD
McMillan House, Cheam Common Road,
Worcester Park, Surrey, KT4 8RH
Area of Operation: UK & Ireland
Tel: 0208 337 0731   **Fax:** 0208 337 3739
Email: info@mgcltd.co.uk
Web: www.mgcltd.co.uk
Product Type: 2, 3, 4   **Material Type:** M) 2

NATURAL BUILDING TECHNOLOGIES
The Hangar, Worminghall Road,
Oakley, Buckinghamshire, HP18 9UL
Area of Operation: UK & Ireland
Tel: 01844 338338
Fax: 01844 338525
Email: info@natural-building.co.uk
Web: www.natural-building.co.uk
Product Type: 1, 2, 3, 4, 5
Other Info: ECO   **Material Type:** K) 3, 8, 9

NOISE STOP SYSTEMS
Unit 2, Car House Farm, Poole Lane,
Nun Monkton, York, North Yorkshire, YO26 8EH
Area of Operation: UK & Ireland
Tel: 0845 130 6269   **Fax:** 01423 339153
Email: info@noisestopsystems.co.uk
Web: www.noisestopsystems.co.uk ᵍ
Product Type: 1, 2, 3, 4, 5

Wiped Out?

Don't panic!
Kingspan Kooltherm® *Simply Superior* has got it covered!

Are you running out of patience trying to comply with the new Building Regulations: Approved Documents L1A, L1B, L2A and L2B? Are you losing your temper with SAP and SBEM?

Relax! Kingspan Insulation can get you out of a tight spot!

The **Kool**therm® K-range of rigid phenolic insulation products can provide you with the thinnest overall constructions for any given U-value when compared with other common insulation materials. This will allow you to comply with the demands of the new Approved Documents without radical changes to the way in which you build.

Wall U-values of 0.27 W/m²·K hold no fear for **Kool**therm® K8 Cavity Board, K5 External Wall Board, K12 Framing Board, K15 Rainscreen Board or K17 Insulated Dry-lining Board. Likewise, **Kool**therm® K7 Pitched Roof Board and K18 Insulated Dry-lining Board can solve pitched roof U-values of 0.16 W/m²·K and below with ease. As for floors and soffits, U-values of 0.22 W/m²·K are a piece of cake for **Kool**therm® K3 Floorboard and K10 Soffit Board.

So bring on the Kooltherm® **K-range and let it take the heat off and keep the heat in!**

Further information on the new Building Regulations is available from Kingspan Insulation on:

Tel: +44 (0) 870 733 8333 (UK)
email: literature.uk@insulation.kingspan.com

Tel: +353 (0) 42 97 95038 (Ireland)
email: literature.ie@insulation.kingspan.com

www.insulation.kingspan.com

Kingspan®
Kingspan Insulation Ltd
Pembridge, Leominster, Herefordshire HR6 9LA, UK
Castleblayney, County Monaghan, Ireland

KINGSPAN INSULATION LIMITED

Area of Operation: Worldwide
Tel: 0870 850 8555
Fax: 0870 850 8666
Email: info.uk@insulation.kingspan.com
Web: www.insulation.kingspan.com

Kingspan Kooltherm® K3 Floorboard

Suspended and solid floor insulation solution. Literature contains design considerations, technical data, sitework details, thermal performance and U-value tables.

KINGSPAN INSULATION LIMITED

Area of Operation: Worldwide
Tel: 0870 850 8555
Fax: 0870 850 8666
Email: info.uk@insulation.kingspan.com
Web: www.insulation.kingspan.com

Kingspan Kooltherm® K7 Pitched Roof Board

Pitched roof insulation solution. Literature contains design considerations, technical data, sitework details, thermal performance and U-value tables.

KINGSPAN INSULATION LIMITED

Area of Operation: Worldwide
Tel: 0870 850 8555
Fax: 0870 850 8666
Email: info.uk@insulation.kingspan.com
Web: www.insulation.kingspan.com

Kingspan Kooltherm® K8 Cavity Board

Partial fill cavity wall insulation solution. Literature contains design considerations, technical data, sitework details, thermal performance and U-value tables.

KINGSPAN INSULATION LIMITED

Area of Operation: Worldwide
Tel: 0870 850 8555
Fax: 0870 850 8666
Email: info.uk@insulation.kingspan.com
Web: www.insulation.kingspan.com

Kingspan Kooltherm® K12 Framing Board

Timber and steel framing insulation solution. Literature contains design considerations, technical data, sitework details, thermal performance and U-value tables.

KINGSPAN INSULATION LIMITED

Area of Operation: Worldwide
Tel: 0870 850 8555
Fax: 0870 850 8666
Email: info.uk@insulation.kingspan.com
Web: www.insulation.kingspan.com

Kingspan Kooltherm® K17 Insulated Dry-lining Board / Kingspan Kooltherm® K18 Insulated Dry-lining Board

Insulated plasterboard dry-lining solutions for plaster-dab or mechanical fixing. Literature contains design considerations, technical data, sitework details, thermal performance and U-value tables.

KINGSPAN INSULATION LIMITED

Area of Operation: Worldwide
Tel: 0870 850 8555
Fax: 0870 850 8666
Email: info.uk@insulation.kingspan.com
Web: www.insulation.kingspan.com

Kingspan Thermafloor TF73

Insulated chipboard laminate solution for floating and suspended floors. Literature contains design considerations, technical data, sitework details, thermal performance and U-value tables.

KINGSPAN INSULATION LIMITED

Area of Operation: Worldwide
Tel: 0870 850 8555
Fax: 0870 850 8666
Email: info.uk@insulation.kingspan.com
Web: www.insulation.kingspan.com

Kingspan Thermaroof™ TR31

Structural 6mm plywood composite insulation solution for use beneath partially bonded built-up felt on flat roofs. Literature contains design considerations, technical data, sitework details, thermal performance and U-value tables.

KINGSPAN INSULATION LIMITED

Area of Operation: Worldwide
Tel: 0870 850 8555
Fax: 0870 850 8666
Email: info.uk@insulation.kingspan.com
Web: www.insulation.kingspan.com

Kingspan nilvent®

Premium performance next-generation breathable membrane which is completely waterproof and airtight. Literature contains design considerations, product and technical data and sitework details.

KINGSPAN INSULATION LIMITED

Area of Operation: Worldwide
Tel: 0870 850 8555
Fax: 0870 850 8666
Email: info.uk@insulation.kingspan.com
Web: www.insulation.kingspan.com

Life Cycle Assessment

First insulation manufacturer to commission and openly publish BRE certified Life Cycle Assessment. Paper shows manufacturing impact on the environment.

KINGSPAN INSULATION LIMITED

Area of Operation: Worldwide
Tel: 0870 850 8555
Fax: 0870 850 8666
Email: info.uk@insulation.kingspan.com
Web: www.insulation.kingspan.com

Building Regulations / Standards

Literature detailing insulation solutions for walls, roofs and floors in accordance with the Building Regulations: Approved Documents L1A/B and L2A/B in England and Wales and the Building Standards in Scotland.

KINGSPAN INSULATION LIMITED

Area of Operation: Worldwide
Tel: 0870 850 8555
Fax: 0870 850 8666
Email: info.uk@insulation.kingspan.com
Web: www.insulation.kingspan.com

Kingspan Insulation Quick Guide

Comprehensive information on premium and high performance insulation solutions for pitched and flat roofs, walls and floors.

KINGSPAN INSULATION LIMITED

Area of Operation: Worldwide
Tel: 0870 850 8555
Fax: 0870 850 8666
Email: info.uk@insulation.kingspan.com
Web: www.insulation.kingspan.com

Sustainability Appraisal

The first study of its kind within the UK's construction product industry looking at every aspect of Kingspan Insulation's Pembridge production facility in Herefordshire. The detailed findings have been published in full in a report called "Sustainability Appraisal".

Nature's Best Comfort & Protection...
Natural Insulation

LOW ENERGY
LOW ALLERGY

Protect Your Family, Your Home & Your Environment...Naturally

OLD HOUSE STORE LTD
Hampstead Farm, Binfield Heath,
Henley on Thames, Oxfordshire, RG9 4LG
Tel: 0118 969 7711   **Fax:** 0118 969 8822
Email: info@oldhousestore.co.uk
Web: www.oldhousestore.co.uk
Product Type: 1, 2, 3, 4
Other Info: ECO   **Material Type:** K) 3, 9

PERMAROCK PRODUCTS LTD
Jubilee Drive, Loughborough, Leicestershire, LE11 5TW
Area of Operation: UK & Ireland
Tel: 01509 262924   **Fax:** 01509 230063
Email: permarock@permarock.com
Web: www.permarock.com   **Product Type:** 5

POLARWALL LIMITED
Unit 3 Old Mill Industrial Estate,
Stoke Canon, Exeter, Devon, EX5 4RJ
Area of Operation: Europe
Tel: 01392 841777   **Fax:** 01392 841936
Email: info@polarwall.co.uk
Web: www.polarwall.co.uk

QUAD-LOCK (ENGLAND) LTD
Unit B3.1, Maws Centre, Jackfield,
Telford, Shropshire, TF8 7LS
Area of Operation: UK (Excluding Ireland)
Tel: 0870 443 1901   **Fax:** 0870 443 1902
Email: info@quadlock.co.uk
Web: www.quadlock.co.uk   **Product Type:** 4, 5

RAVEN SEALS LTD
(C/O DISTRIBUTOR, ROYDE & TUCKER LTD)
Bilton Road, Cadwell Lane,
Hitchin, Hertfordshire, SG4 0SB
Area of Operation: Europe
Tel: 01462 444444   **Fax:** 01462 444433
Email: info@ravenseals.com
Web: www.ravenseals.co.uk

RENOTHERM
New Street House, New Street,
Petworth, West Sussex, GU28 0AS
Tel: 01798 343658   **Fax:** 01798 344093
Email: sales@renotherm.co.uk
Web: www.renotherm.co.uk
Product Type: 1, 2, 3   **Material Type:** K) 5, 14

ROOFING INSULATION SERVICES
Hilldale House, 9 Hilldale Avenue,
Blackley, Manchester, M9 6PQ
Area of Operation: UK (Excluding Ireland)
Tel: 0800 731 8314
Email: info@roofinginsulationservices.co.uk
Web: www.roofinginsulationservices.co.uk
Product Type: 2, 3, 4

ROOFSURE
Metro House, 14-17 Metropolitan Business Park,
Preston New Road, Blackpool, Lancashire, FY3 9LT
Tel: 0800 597 2828   **Fax:** 01253 798193
Email: roofsureltd@btconnect.com
Web: www.roofsure.co.uk

SECOND NATURE UK LTD
Soulands Gate, Soulby, Dacre,
Penrith, Cumbria, CA11 0JF
Area of Operation: Worldwide
Tel: 01768 486285   **Fax:** 01768 486825
Email: info@secondnatureuk.com
Web: www.secondnatureuk.com
Product Type: 2, 3, 4
Other Info: ECO   **Material Type:** K) 9

SECONDS & CO
Industrial Estate, Presteigne, Powys, LD8 2UF
Area of Operation: UK (Excluding Ireland)
Tel: 01544 260501   **Fax:** 01544 260525
Email: info@secondsandco.co.uk
Web: www.secondsandco.co.uk
Product Type: 1, 2, 3, 4

SIPBUILD LTD
Unit 2 Expressway Industrial Estate,
Turnall Road, Widnes, Merseyside, WA8 8RB
Tel: 0870 850 2264   **Fax:** 0870 850 2265
Email: sales@sipbuildltd.com
Web: www.sipbuildltd.com   **Product Type:** 2, 4

SIP'S INDUSTRIES
Crossway, Donibristle Industrial Estate,
Dalgety Bay, Fife, KY11 9JE
Area of Operation: UK & Ireland
Tel: 01383 823995   **Fax:** 01383 823518
Email: info@sipsindustries.com
Web: www.sipsindustries.com

SONAE (UK) LTD
Moss Lane, Knowsley Industrial Park,
Knowsley, Liverpool, Merseyside, L33 7XQ
Area of Operation: UK & Ireland
Tel: 0151 545 4000   **Fax:** 0151 545 4090
Email: sonaeuklink@sonae.co.uk
Web: www.sonaeuk.com
Product Type: 2   **Material Type:** D) 2

SPRAYSEAL CONTRACTS LTD
Bollin House, Blakeley Lane,
Mobberley, Cheshire, WA16 7LX
Area of Operation: East England, Greater London,
Midlands & Mid Wales, North East England, North
West England and North Wales, South East England,
South West England and South Wales
Tel: 01565 872303   **Fax:** 01565 872599
Email: info@sprayseal.co.uk
Web: www.sprayseal.co.uk
Product Type: 3

SPRINGVALE EPS LTD
Dinting Vale Business Park,
Dinting Vale, Glossop, Derbyshire, SK13 6LG
Area of Operation: UK & Ireland
Tel: 01457 863211   **Fax:** 01457 869269
Email: salesg@springvale.com
Web: www.springvale.com
Product Type: 1, 2, 3, 5   **Material Type:** K) 11

STOPG-P LTD
PO Box 2389, Cardiff, CF23 5WJ
Area of Operation: Worldwide
Tel: 02920 213736   **Fax:** 02920 213736
Email: info@stopg-p.com
Web: www.stopg-p.com   **Product Type:** 2

STRUCTURAL INSULATED PANEL
TECHNOLOGY LTD (SIPTEC)
PO Box 429, Turvey, Bedfordshire, MK43 8DT
Area of Operation: Europe
Tel: 0870 743 9866
Fax: 0870 762 5612
Email: mail@sips.ws   **Web:** www.sips.ws
Product Type: 2, 3, 4, 5   **Material Type:** H) 4, 6

THE GREEN SHOP
Cheltenham Road, Bisley, Nr Stroud,
Gloucestershire, GL6 7BX
Area of Operation: UK & Ireland
Tel: 01452 770629   **Fax:** 01452 770104
Email: paint@greenshop.co.uk
Web: www.greenshop.co.uk
Product Type: 1, 2, 3, 4
Other Info: ▽ ECO   **Material Type:** K) 3, 9

THERMILATE EUROPE
The Media Centre, 7 Northumberland Street,
Huddersfield, West Yorkshire, HD1 1RL
Area of Operation: Worldwide
Tel: 0870 744 1759   **Fax:** 0870 744 1760
Email: info@thermilate.com
Web: www.thermilate.com
Product Type: 2, 3, 4, 5, 6

THERMOBRICK
20 Underwood Drive, Stoney Stanton,
Leicester, Leicestershire, LE9 4TA
Area of Operation: UK & Ireland
Tel: 01455 272860
Fax: 01455 271324
Email: info@rutlandtimber.co.uk
Web: www.rutlandtimber.co.uk   **Product Type:** 5

TY-MAWR LIME LTD
Ty-Mawr, Llangasty, Brecon, Powys, LD3 7PJ
Area of Operation: UK & Ireland
Tel: 01874 658000
Email: joyce.gervis@lime.org.uk
Web: www.lime.org.uk
Product Type: 1, 2, 3, 4, 5   **Material Type:** H) 8

WEBER BUILDING SOLUTIONS
Dickens House, Enterprise Way, Maulden Road,
Flitwick, Bedford, Bedfordshire, MK45 5BY
Tel: 0870 333 0070   **Fax:** 01525 718988
Email: info@weberbuildingsolutions.co.uk
Web: www.weberbuildingsolutions.co.uk
Product Type: 5

WEBSTERS INSULATION LTD
Crow Tree Farm, Crow Tree Bank, Thorne Levels,
Doncaster, South Yorkshire, DN8 5TF
Area of Operation: UK (Excluding Ireland)
Tel: 01405 812682   **Fax:** 01405 817201
Email: info@webstersinsulation.com
Web: www.webstersinsulation.com
Product Type: 1, 2, 3, 4, 5

WEBSTERS INSULATION
Area of Operation: UK (Excluding Ireland)
Tel: 01405 812682
Fax: 01405 817201
Email: info@webstersinsulation.com
Web: www.webstersinsulation.com
Product Type: 1, 2, 3, 4, 5

Leading installers of Polyurethane Sprayed Foam Insulation
the only method approved by Websters for insulating and
weatherproofing old/new buildings. Adheres to almost all
surfaces. Exceptional alternative to dry lining. Provides a
continuous membrane of unrivalled properties.

WETHERBY BUILDING SYSTEMS LIMITED
1 Kidglove Road, Golborne Enterprise Park,
Golborne, Greater Manchester, WA3 3GS
Area of Operation: UK & Ireland
Tel: 01942 717100   **Fax:** 01942 717101
Email: info@wbs-ltd.co.uk
Web: www.wbs-ltd.co.uk   **Product Type:** 4, 5

XTRATHERM UK LIMITED
Park Road, Holmewood,
Chesterfield, Derbyshire, S42 5UY
Tel: 0871 222 1033   **Fax:** 0871 222 1044
Email: kerry@xtratherm.com
Web: www.xtratherm.com
Product Type: 1, 2, 3, 4   **Material Type:** K) 14

YEOVIL PLUMBING SUPPLIES
Unit 1 Bartlett Park, Linx Trading Estate,
Yeovil, Somerset, BA20 2PJ
Area of Operation: UK (Excluding Ireland)
Tel: 01935 474780   **Fax:** 01935 432405

ACOUSTIC INSULATION

KEY

PRODUCT TYPES: 1= Door and Window
2 = Wall   3 = Floor

OTHER: ▽ Reclaimed   On-line shopping
Bespoke   Hand-made   ECO Ecological

A PROCTOR GROUP LTD
The Haugh, Blairgowrie, Perth and Kinross, PH10 7ER
Area of Operation: Worldwide
Tel: 01250 872261   **Fax:** 01250 872727
Email: lynsay.johnston@proctorgroup.com
Web: www.proctorgroup.com
Product Type: 2, 3

ACOUSTIC GRG PRODUCTS LTD
Lower Wall Road, West Hythe, Kent, CT21 4NN
Area of Operation: Europe
Tel: 01303 230962
Fax: 01303 230961
Email: moule@rpgeurope.com
Web: www.rpgeurope.com

ACTIS
Unit 1 Cornbrash Park, Bumpers Way, Bumpers Farm
Industrial Estate, Chippenham, Wiltshire, SN14 6RA
Area of Operation: Europe
Tel: 01249 446123
Fax: 01249 446345
Email: solutions@actis-isolation.com
Web: www.insulation-actis.com
Product Type: 2, 3

AUDIO AGENCY EUROPE
PO Box 4601, Kiln Farm, Milton Keynes,
Buckinghamshire, MK19 7ZN
Area of Operation: Europe
Tel: 01908 510123   **Fax:** 01908 511123
Email: info@audioagencyeurope.com
Web: www.audioagencyeurope.com
Product Type: 2

BECO PRODUCTS LTD
Beco House, 6 Exmoor Avenue,
Scunthorpe, Lincolnshire, DN15 8NJ
Area of Operation: UK & Ireland
Tel: 01724 747576   **Fax:** 01724 747579
Email: info@becowallform.co.uk
Web: www.becowallform.co.uk   **Product Type:** 2
Material Type: G) 1, K) 11   **Other Info:** ✎

BMD INSULATION
Urquhart House, Basingstoke Close,
Freshbrook, Swindon, Wiltshire, SN5 8RB
Area of Operation: UK (Excluding Ireland)
Tel: 01793 326026
Email: info@bmdinsulation.com
Web: www.bmdinsulation.com   **Product Type:** 1, 2

BRITISH URETHANE FOAM
CONTRACTORS ASSOCIATION
PO Box 12, Haslemere, Surrey, GU27 3AH
Area of Operation: UK (Excluding Ireland)
Tel: 01428 654011   **Fax:** 01428 651401
Email: info@bufca.co.uk
Web: www.bufca.co.uk   **Material Type:** K) 5

CHILTERN DYNAMICS
Chiltern House, Stocking Lane, Hughenden Valley,
High Wycombe, Buckinghamshire, HP14 4ND
Area of Operation: UK & Ireland
Tel: 01494 569800
Fax: 01494 564895
Email: cd@chilterndynamics.co.uk
Web: www.chilternfire.co.uk   **Product Type:** 1, 2, 3

CONSTRUCTION RESOURCES
16 Great Guildford Street, London, SE1 0HS
Area of Operation: UK (Excluding Ireland)
Tel: 0207 450 2211
Fax: 0207 450 2212
Email: info@constructionresources.com
Web: www.constructionresources.com
Product Type: 2, 3

CUSTOM AUDIO DESIGNS LTD
Unit 2 Amey Industrial Estate,
Petersfield, Hampshire, GU32 3LN
Area of Operation: UK & Ireland
Tel: 0870 747 5511   **Fax:** 0870 747 9878
Email: sales@customaudiodesigns.co.uk
Web: www.customaudiodesigns.co.uk
Product Type: 1, 2, 3
Other Info: ECO   **Material Type:** K) 2, 4, 10

DRAUGHT PROOFING ADVISORY ASSOCIATION
PO Box 12, Haslemere, Surrey, GU27 3AH
Area of Operation: UK (Excluding Ireland)
Tel: 01428 654011
Fax: 01428 651401
Email: dpaaassociation@aol.com
Web: www.dpaa-association.org.uk
Product Type: 1

ECOLOGICAL BUILDING SYSTEMS UK LTD
The Manse, High Street, Creaton,
Northamptonshire, NN6 8NA
Area of Operation: UK & Ireland
Tel: 05600 758025   **Fax:** 05600 758026
Email: ecologicalbuild@btconnect.com
Web: www.ecologicalbuildingsystems.co.uk
Product Type: 2, 3

EDULAN UK LTD
Unit M, Northstage, Broadway,
Salford, Greater Manchester, M50 2UW
Area of Operation: Worldwide
Tel: 0161 876 8040   **Fax:** 0161 876 8041
Email: peter@polyurethane.uk.com
Web: www.edulan.com
Product Type: 2, 3   **Material Type:** K) 5

ELLIOTTS INSULATION AND DRYLINING
Unit 8 Goodwood Road, Boyatt Wood Industrial
Estate, Eastleigh, Hampshire, SO50 4NT
Area of Operation: South East England,
South West England and South Wales
Tel: 02380 623960   **Fax:** 02380 623965
Email: insulation@elliott-brothers.co.uk
Web: www.elliotts.uk.com   **Product Type:** 2, 3

EUROFORM PRODUCTS LIMITED
The Heliport, Lyncastle Road, Appleton,
Warrington, Cheshire, WA4 4SN
Area of Operation: Worldwide
Tel: 01925 860999   **Fax:** 01925 860066
Email: info@euroform.co.uk
Web: www.euroform.co.uk   **Product Type:** 3

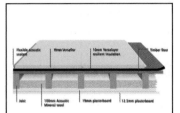

EUROFORM PRODUCTS LTD
Area of Operation: Worldwide
Tel: 01925 860999
Fax: 01925 860066
Email: info@euroform.co.uk
Web: www.euroform.co.uk
Product Type: 3

**Versalayer Acoustic Floor Systems for Efficient
Sound Insulation of Buildings**
The Versalayer™ range of soundproofing is
designed to Absorb and damp acoustic vibrations
through floors and Walls. Complies with
Approved Doc 'E' latest requirements

EXCEL BUILDING SOLUTIONS
Maerdy Industrial Estate, Gwent, NP22 5PY
Area of Operation: Worldwide
Tel: 01685 845200   **Fax:** 01685 844106
Email: sales@excelfibre.com
Web: www.excelfibre.com
Product Type: 2, 3
Other Info: ▽ ECO   **Material Type:** K) 3

FOAMSEAL LTD
New Street House, New Street,
Petworth, West Sussex, GU28 0AS
Area of Operation: Worldwide
Tel: 01798 345400   **Fax:** 01798 345410
Email: info@foamseal.co.uk
Web: www.foamseal.co.uk
Product Type: 1, 2, 3   **Material Type:** K) 5

GREEN GLUE UK LTD
Lower Wall Road, West Hythe, Kent, CT21 4NN
Area of Operation: Europe
Tel: 01303 230962   **Fax:** 01303 230961
Email: moule@rpgeurope.com
Web: www.rpgeurope.com   **Product Type:** 2, 3

H+H CELCON LIMITED
Celcon House, Ightham, Sevenoaks, Kent, TN15 9HZ
Area of Operation: UK (Excluding Ireland)
Tel: 01732 880520   **Fax:** 01732 880531
Email: marketing@celcon.co.uk
Web: www.celcon.co.uk   **Product Type:** 2

HERAKLITH
Broadway House, 21 Broadway,
Maidenhead, Berkshire, SL6 1NJ
Area of Operation: UK & Ireland
Tel: 01628 784330   **Fax:** 01628 633080
Email: muirwork@btinternet.com
Product Type: 2   **Other Info:** ECO

HUNTON FIBER UK LTD
Rockleigh Court, Rock Road,
Finedon, Northamptonshire, NN9 5EL
Area of Operation: UK & Ireland
Tel: 01933 682683   **Fax:** 01933 680296
Email: admin@huntonfiber.co.uk
Web: www.hunton.no
Product Type: 2   **Other Info:** ▽ ECO

INSTACOUSTIC LIMITED
Insta House, Ivanhoe Road, Hogwood Business Park,
Finchampstead, Wokingham, Berkshire, RG40 4PZ
Area of Operation: UK & Ireland
Tel: 0118 932 8811   **Fax:** 0118 973 9547
Email: instacoustic@instagroup.co.uk
Web: www.instagroup.co.uk   **Product Type:** 2, 3

**INSULATED RENDER &
CLADDING ASSOCIATION**
PO Box 12, Haslemere, Surrey, GU27 3AH
Area of Operation: UK (Excluding Ireland)
Tel: 01428 654011   **Fax:** 01428 651401
Email: incaassociation@aol.com
Web: www.inca-ltd.org.uk
Product Type: 2   **Material Type:** K) 4, 5, 8, 11, 12, 14

KNAUF DIY
PO Box 732, Maidstone, Kent, Kent, ME15 6ST
Area of Operation: UK & Ireland
Tel: 0845 601 1763   **Fax:** 0845 6011762
Email: knaufdiy@knauf.co.uk
Web: www.teachmediy.co.uk   **Product Type:** 2, 3

LAFARGE GYVLON LTD
221 Europa Boulevard, Westbrook,
Warrington, Cheshire, WA5 7TN
Area of Operation: UK & Ireland
Tel: 01925 428780   **Fax:** 01925 428788
Email: sales@gyvlon-floors.co.uk
Web: www.gyvlon-floors.co.uk
Product Type: 3

LORIENT POLYPRODUCTS LTD
Endeavour House, Fairfax Road, Heathfield Industrial
Estate, Newton Abbot, Devon, TQ12 6UD
Area of Operation: Worldwide
Tel: 01626 834252   **Fax:** 01626 833166
Email: mktg@lorientuk.com
Web: www.lorientgroup.com   **Product Type:** 1

MINELCO SPECIALITIES LIMITED
Raynesway, Derby, Derbyshire, DE21 7BE
Area of Operation: Worldwide
Tel: 01332 545224   **Fax:** 01332 677590
Email: minelco.specialities@minelco.com
Web: www.minelco.com   **Product Type:** 2, 3

MOULD GROWTH CONSULTANTS LTD
McMillan House, Cheam Common Road,
Worcester Park, Surrey, KT4 8RH
Area of Operation: UK & Ireland
Tel: 0208 337 0731   **Fax:** 0208 337 3739
Email: info@mgcltd.co.uk
Web: www.mgcltd.co.uk
Product Type: 2, 3   **Material Type:** M) 2

NATURAL BUILDING TECHNOLOGIES
The Hangar, Worminghall Road,
Oakley, Buckinghamshire, HP18 9UL
Area of Operation: UK & Ireland
Tel: 01844 338338   **Fax:** 01844 338525
Email: info@natural-building.co.uk
Web: www.natural-building.co.uk
Other Info: ECO   **Material Type:** K) 3, 8, 9

NOISE STOP SYSTEMS
Unit 2, Car House Farm, Poole Lane,
Nun Monkton, York, North Yorkshire, YO26 8EH
Area of Operation: UK & Ireland
Tel: 0845 130 6269   **Fax:** 01423 339153
Email: info@noisestopsystems.co.uk
Web: www.noisestopsystems.co.uk ⏱
Product Type: 1, 2, 3

OSCAR ACOUSTICS
Michaels Lane, Ash, Kent, TN15 7HT
Area of Operation: UK (Excluding Ireland)
Tel: 01474 873122   **Fax:** 01474 879554
Email: mail@oscar-acoustics.co.uk
Web: www.oscar-acoustics.co.uk
Product Type: 2, 3
Other Info: ▽ ECO   **Material Type:** K) 3

POLARWALL LIMITED
Unit 3 Old Mill Industrial Estate,
Stoke Canon, Exeter, Devon, EX5 4RJ
Area of Operation: Europe
Tel: 01392 841777   **Fax:** 01392 841936
Email: info@polarwall.co.uk
Web: www.polarwall.co.uk

QUAD-LOCK (ENGLAND) LTD
Unit B3.1, Maws Centre, Jackfield,
Telford, Shropshire, TF8 7LS
Area of Operation: UK (Excluding Ireland)
Tel: 0870 443 1901   **Fax:** 0870 443 1902
Email: info@quadlock.co.uk
Web: www.quadlock.co.uk   **Product Type:** 2

**RAVEN SEALS LTD
(C/O DISTRIBUTOR, ROYDE & TUCKER LTD)**
Bilton Road, Cadwell Lane,
Hitchin, Hertfordshire, SG4 0SB
Area of Operation: Europe
Tel: 01462 444444   **Fax:** 01462 444433
Email: info@ravenseals.com
Web: www.ravenseals.co.uk   **Product Type:** 1

SECOND NATURE UK LTD
Soulands Gate, Soulby, Dacre, Penrith, Cumbria, CA11 0JF
Area of Operation: Worldwide
Tel: 01768 486285   **Fax:** 01768 486825
Email: info@secondnatureuk.com
Web: www.secondnatureuk.com
Product Type: 2, 3

SONAE (UK) LTD
Moss Lane, Knowsley Industrial Park,
Knowsley, Liverpool, Merseyside, L33 7XQ
Area of Operation: UK & Ireland
Tel: 0151 545 4000
Fax: 0151 545 4090
Email: sonaeuklink@sonae.co.uk
Web: www.sonaeuk.com
Product Type: 2   **Material Type:** H) 1, 2, 5, 6, 7

SOUND REDUCTION SYSTEMS LTD
Adam Street, Off Lever Street,
Bolton, Greater Manchester, BL3 2AP
Area of Operation: Worldwide
Tel: 01204 380074
Fax: 01204 380957
Email: info@soundreduction.co.uk
Web: www.soundreduction.co.uk
Product Type: 2, 3

SOUND SERVICE (OXFORD) LTD
55 West End, Witney, Oxfordshire, OX28 1NJ
Area of Operation: UK & Ireland
Tel: 01993 704981
Fax: 01993 779569
Email: soundservice@btconnect.com
Web: www.soundservice.co.uk
Product Type: 2, 3   **Material Type:** K) 1, 2, 10

**STRUCTURAL INSULATED PANEL
TECHNOLOGY LTD (SIPTEC)**
PO Box 429, Turvey, Bedfordshire, MK43 8DT
Area of Operation: Europe
Tel: 0870 743 9866
Fax: 0870 762 5612
Email: mail@sips.ws   **Web:** www.sips.ws
Product Type: 2, 3   **Material Type:** H) 4, 6

THE EXPANDED METAL COMPANY LIMITED
PO Box 14, Longhill Industrial Estate (North),
Hartlepool, Durham, TS25 1PR
Area of Operation: Worldwide
Tel: 01429 867388   **Fax:** 01429 866795
Email: paulb@expamet.co.uk
Web: www.expandedmetalcompany.co.uk

WEBSTERS INSULATION LTD
Crow Tree Farm, Crow Tree Bank, Thorne Levels,
Doncaster, South Yorkshire, DN8 5TF
Area of Operation: UK (Excluding Ireland)
Tel: 01405 812682   **Fax:** 01405 817201
Email: info@webstersinsulation.com
Web: www.webstersinsulation.com
Product Type: 2, 3

WINTUN
Wintun Works, Millerston,
Paisley, Renfrewshire, PA1 2XR
Area of Operation: UK & Ireland
Tel: 0141 889 5969   **Fax:** 0141 887 8907
Email: mail@wintun.co.uk
Web: www.wintun.co.uk   **Product Type:** 1

XETAL CONSULTANTS LIMITED
Unit 28 Cryant Business Park,
Crynant, Neath, Swansea, SA10 8PA
Area of Operation: Worldwide
Tel: 01639 751056   **Fax:** 01639 751058
Email: jdickson@xetal.co.uk
Web: www.xetal.co.uk   **Product Type:** 2, 3
Material Type: K) 2, 3, 4, 7, 8, 9

FIRE PROOFING

KEY
PRODUCT TYPES: 1= Barriers and Stops
2 = Boards and Sheets   3 = Coatings
4 = Membranes   5 = Sealants
SEE ALSO: SMART HOMES AND SECURITY -
Fire Protection

OTHER: ▽ Reclaimed   ⏱ On-line shopping
✎ Bespoke   ✋ Hand-made   ECO Ecological

BMD INSULATION
Urquhart House, Basingstoke Close,
Freshbrook, Swindon, Wiltshire, SN5 8RB
Area of Operation: UK (Excluding Ireland)
Tel: 01793 326026
Email: info@bmdinsulation.com
Web: www.bmdinsulation.com
Product Type: 1, 2, 3, 4

CAVITY TRAYS LTD
New Administration Centre,
Boundary Avenue, Yeovil, Somerset, BA22 8HU
Area of Operation: Worldwide
Tel: 01935 474769   **Fax:** 01935 428223
Email: enquiries@cavitytrays.co.uk
Web: www.cavitytrays.com ⏱
Product Type: 1

CHILTERN DYNAMICS
Chiltern House, Stocking Lane, Hughenden Valley,
High Wycombe, Buckinghamshire, HP14 4ND
Area of Operation: UK & Ireland
Tel: 01494 569800
Fax: 01494 564895
Email: cd@chilterndynamics.co.uk
Web: www.chilternfire.co.uk
Product Type: 1, 2, 3, 4, 5

DACATIE BUILDING SOLUTIONS
Quantum House, Salmon Fields,
Royton, Oldham, Lancashire, OL2 6JG
Area of Operation: UK & Ireland
Tel: 0161 627 4222
Fax: 0161 627 4333
Email: info@dacatie.co.uk
Web: www.dacatie.co.uk   **Product Type:** 1

ELLIOTTS INSULATION AND DRYLINING
Unit 8 Goodwood Road, Boyatt Wood Industrial
Estate, Eastleigh, Hampshire, SO50 4NT
Area of Operation: South East England, South West
England and South Wales
Tel: 02380 623960
Fax: 02380 623965
Email: insulation@elliott-brothers.co.uk
Web: www.elliotts.uk.com   **Product Type:** 1, 2, 5

EUROFORM PRODUCTS LIMITED
The Heliport, Lyncastle Road, Appleton,
Warrington, Cheshire, WA4 4SN
Area of Operation: Worldwide
Tel: 01925 860999
Fax: 01925 860066
Email: info@euroform.co.uk
Web: www.euroform.co.uk   **Product Type:** 2

H+H CELCON LIMITED
Celcon House, Ightham, Sevenoaks, Kent, TN15 9HZ
Area of Operation: UK (Excluding Ireland)
Tel: 01732 880520
Fax: 01732 880531
Email: marketing@celcon.co.uk
Web: www.celcon.co.uk   **Product Type:** 1

KNAUF DIY
PO Box 732, Maidstone, Kent, ME15 6ST
Area of Operation: Worldwide
Tel: 0845 6011763
Fax: 0845 6011762
Email: knaufdiy@knauf.co.uk
Web: www.teachmediy.co.uk   **Product Type:** 2

LORIENT POLYPRODUCTS LTD
Endeavour House, Fairfax Road, Heathfield Industrial
Estate, Newton Abbot, Devon, TQ12 6UD
Area of Operation: Worldwide
Tel: 01626 834252   **Fax:** 01626 833166
Email: mktg@lorientuk.com
Web: www.lorientgroup.com   **Product Type:** 1, 5

RAVEN SEALS LTD
(C/O DISTRIBUTOR, ROYDE & TUCKER LTD)
Bilton Road, Cadwell Lane, Hitchin, Hertfordshire, SG4 0SB
Area of Operation: Europe
Tel: 01462 444444   **Fax:** 01462 444433
Email: info@ravenseals.com
Web: www.ravenseals.co.uk
Product Type: 1

WINTUN
Wintun Works, Millerston, Paisley, Renfrewshire, PA1 2XR
Area of Operation: UK & Ireland
Tel: 0141 889 5969   **Fax:** 0141 887 8907
Email: mail@wintun.co.uk
Web: www.wintun.co.uk
Product Type: 5

DAMP PROOFING

KEY

PRODUCT TYPES: 1= Cavity Closers
2 = Boards and Sheets   3 = Backing Boards
4 = Other

SEE ALSO: SUBSTRUCTURE AND
FOUNDATIONS - Basements

OTHER: ▽ Reclaimed   🛒 On-line shopping
✏ Bespoke   ✋ Hand-made   ECO Ecological

A PROCTOR GROUP LTD
The Haugh, Blairgowrie, Perth and Kinross, PH10 7ER
Area of Operation: Worldwide
Tel: 01250 872261
Fax: 01250 872727
Email: lynsay.johnston@proctorgroup.com
Web: www.proctorgroup.com   **Product Type:** 2, 3

ABTECH (UK) LTD
Sheiling House, Invincible Road,
Farnborough, Hampshire, GU14 7QU
Area of Operation: UK (Excluding Ireland)
Tel: 0800 085 1431   **Fax:** 01252 378665
Email: sales@abtechbasements.co.uk
Web: www.abtechbasements.co.uk

APOLLO INSULATION LIMITED
PO Box 200, Horley, Surrey, RH6 7FU
Area of Operation: Worldwide
Tel: 01293 776974   **Fax:** 01293 776975
Email: info@apollo-energy.com
Web: www.apollo-energy.com   **Product Type:** 2

AQUAPANEL
PO Box 732, Maidstone, Kent, ME15 6ST
Area of Operation: UK (Excluding Ireland)
Tel: 0800 169 6545   **Fax:** 0845 601 1762
Email: knaufdiy@knauf.co.uk
Web: www.teachmediy.co.uk   **Product Type:** 3

AQUATECNIC
211 Heathhall Industrial Estate, Dumfries,
Dumfries & Galloway, DG1 3PH
Area of Operation: UK & Ireland
Tel: 0845 226 8283   **Fax:** 0845 226 8293
Email: info@aquatecnic.net
Web: www.aquatecnic.net 🛒   **Product Type:** 2, 4

ARDEX UK LIMITED
Homefield Road, Haverhill, Suffolk, CB9 8QP
Area of Operation: UK (Excluding Ireland)
Tel: 01440 714939   **Fax:** 01440 716660
Email: info@ardex.co.uk
Web: www.ardex.co.uk   **Product Type:** 4

BIOCRAFT LTD
25B Chapel Hill, Reading, Berkshire, RG31 5BT
Area of Operation: East England, Greater London, South
East England, South West England and South Wales
Tel: 01189 451144   **Email:** info@biocraft.co.uk
Web: www.biocraft.co.uk

BMD INSULATION
Urquhart House, Basingstoke Close,
Freshbrook, Swindon, Wiltshire, SN5 8RB
Area of Operation: UK (Excluding Ireland)
Tel: 01793 326026
Email: info@bmdinsulation.com
Web: www.bmdinsulation.com
Product Type: 1, 2, 4

CAVITY TRAYS LTD
New Administration Centre,
Boundary Avenue, Yeovil, Somerset, BA22 8HU
Area of Operation: Worldwide
Tel: 01935 474769   **Fax:** 01935 428223
Email: enquiries@cavitytrays.co.uk
Web: www.cavitytrays.com 🛒
Product Type: 1

DACATIE BUILDING SOLUTIONS
Quantum House, Salmon Fields,
Royton, Oldham, Lancashire, OL2 6JG
Area of Operation: UK & Ireland
Tel: 0161 627 4222   **Fax:** 0161 627 4333
Email: info@dacatie.co.uk
Web: www.dacatie.co.uk   **Product Type:** 1

DELTA MEMBRANE SYSTEMS LTD
Bassett Business Centre, Hurricane Way,
North Weald, Epping, Essex, CM16 6AA
Area of Operation: UK & Ireland
Tel: 01992 523 811   **Fax:** 01992 524046
Email: info@deltamembranes.com
Web: www.deltamembranes.com
Product Type: 2, 3

DIY ROOFING LTD
Hillcrest House, Featherbed Lane,
Hunt End, Redditch, Worcestershire, B97 5QL
Area of Operation: UK & Ireland
Tel: 0800 783 4890   **Fax:** 01527 403483
Email: chris@diyroofing.co.uk
Web: www.diyroofing.co.uk
Product Type: 2

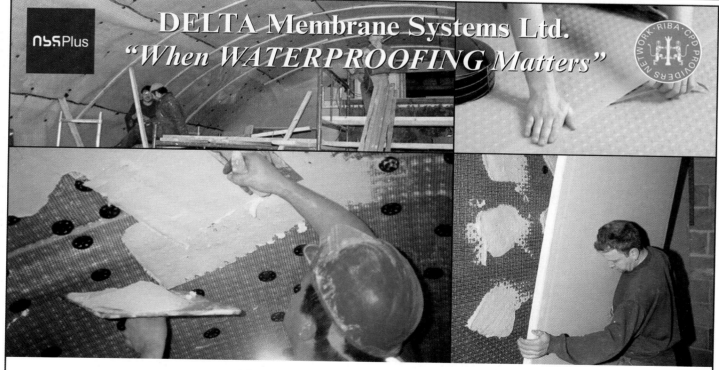

SPONSORED BY: KINGSPAN INSULATION LTD www.insulation.kingspan.com

ECOLOGICAL BUILDING SYSTEMS UK LTD
The Manse, High Street, Creaton,
Northamptonshire, NN6 8NA
Area of Operation: UK & Ireland
Tel: 05600 758025
 Fax: 05600 758026
Email: ecologicalbuild@btconnect.com
Web: www.ecologicalbuildingsystems.co.uk
Product Type: 4

FOAMSEAL LTD
New Street House, New Street,
Petworth, West Sussex, GU28 0AS
Area of Operation: Worldwide
Tel: 01798 345400
Fax: 01798 345410
Email: info@foamseal.co.uk
Web: www.foamseal.co.uk

GUARDIAN PRESERVATION SERVICES LLP
12 Woods Orchard Road, Gloucester,
Gloucestershire, GL4 0BU
Area of Operation: UK (Excluding Ireland)
Tel: 01452 530030
Fax: 01452 530031
Email: info@guardianpreservation.co.uk
Web: www.guardianpreservation.co.uk

HIGHTEX-COATINGS LTD
Unit 14 Chapel Farm, Hanslope Road,
Hartwell, Northamptonshire, NN7 2EU
Area of Operation: UK (Excluding Ireland)
Tel: 01604 861250   **Fax:** 01604 871116
Email: bob@hightexcoatings.co.uk
Web: www.hightexcoatings.co.uk
Product Type: 4

INDOOR CLIMATE SOLUTIONS
6 Charlesworth Avenue, Monkspath,
Solihull, West Midlands, B90 4SE
Area of Operation: Midlands & Mid Wales
Tel: 0121 733 2525
Email: info@ics-aircon.com
Web: www.ics-aircon.com   **Product Type:** 4

KILTOX CONTRACTS LIMITED
Unit 6 Chiltonian Industrial Estate,
203 Manor Lane, Lee, London, SE12 0TX
Area of Operation: Worldwide
Tel: 0845 166 2040   **Fax:** 0845 166 2050
Email: info@kiltox.co.uk
Web: www.kiltox.co.uk

MUNTERS LTD
Blackstone Road, Huntingdon,
Cambridgeshire, PE29 6EE
Area of Operation: UK & Ireland
Tel: 01480 442327   **Fax:** 01480 458333
Web: www.munters.co.uk
Product Type: 4

NEVER PAINT AGAIN INTERNATIONAL
NPA International, 2nd Floor,
145-157 St John's Street, London, EC1V 4PY
Area of Operation: Worldwide
Tel: 0800 970 4928
Email: info@neverpaintagain.co.uk
Web: www.neverpaintagain.co.uk
Product Type: 4

PHOENIX WATERPROOFING
(A DIVISION OF CONTITECH UK LTD)
Chestnut Field House, Chestnut Field,
Rugby, Warwickshire, CU21 2PA
Area of Operation: UK & Ireland
Tel: 01788 571482
Fax: 01788 542245
Email: tonyb@phoenix-gb.com
Web: www.phoenix-ag.com
Product Type: 4

RUBEROID BUILDING PRODUCTS
Appley Lane North, Appley Bridge, Lancashire, WN6 9AB
Area of Operation: UK (Excluding Ireland)
Tel: 08000 285573
Fax: 01257 252514
Email: marketing@ruberoid.co.uk
Web: www.ruberoid.co.uk   **Product Type:** 4

SAFEGUARD EUROPE LTD
Redkiln Close, Redkiln Way,
Horsham, West Sussex, RH13 5QL
Area of Operation: Worldwide
Tel: 01403 210204
Fax: 01403 217529
Email: info@safeguardeurope.com
Web: www.safeguardeurope.com
Product Type: 4

SAFEGUARD
MAKING BUILDINGS DRY

SAFEGUARD
Area of Operation: Worldwide
Tel: 01403 210204
Fax: 01403 217529
Email: info@safeguardeurope.com
Web: www.safeguardeurope.com
Product Type: 4

Safeguard supply a wide range of damp-proofing
products including the easy-to-use Dryzone
damp-proofing cream (pictured).

SPRY PRODUCTS LTD
64 Nottingham Road, Long Eaton,
Nottingham, Nottinghamshire, NG10 2AU
Area of Operation: UK & Ireland
Tel: 0115 973 2914
Fax: 0115 972 5172
Email: jerspry@aol.com
Web: www.spryproducts.com
Product Type: 2, 4   **Other Info:** ECO

TIMBERWISE (UK) LTD
1 Drake Mews, Gadbrook Park,
Northwich, Cheshire, CW9 7XF
Area of Operation: UK (Excluding Ireland)
Tel: 0800 991100
Email: hq@timberwise.co.uk
Web: www.timberwise.co.uk
Product Type: 4

TRITON CHEMICAL MANUFACTURING LTD
129 Felixstowe Road,
Abbey Wood, London, SE2 9SG
Area of Operation: Worldwide
Tel: 0208 310 3929
Fax: 0208 312 0349
Email: neil@triton-chemicals.com
Web: www.triton-chemicals.com
Product Type: 2, 4

VISQUEEN BUILDING PRODUCTS
Maerdy Industrial Estate, Rhymney,
Blaenau Gwent, NP22 5PY
Area of Operation: UK & Ireland
Tel: 01685 840672
Fax: 01685 842580
Email: enquiries@visqueenbuilding.co.uk
Web: www.visqueenbuilding.co.uk
Product Type: 1, 2, 4
Other Info: ▽ ECO

WISE PROPERTY CARE
8 Muriel Street, Barrhead, Glasgow, G78 1QB
Area of Operation: Scotland
Tel: 0141 876 0300
Fax: 0141 876 0301
Email: les@wisepropertycare.com
Web: www.wisepropertycare.com

NOTES

Company Name ....

Address ....

email ....

Web ....

Company Name ....

Address ....

email ....

Web ....

Company Name ....

Address ....

email ....

Web ....

Company Name ....

Address ....

email ....

Web ....

Company Name ....

Address ....

email ....

Web ....

Company Name ....

Address ....

email ....

Web ....

Company Name ....

Address ....

email ....

Web ....

Company Name ....

Address ....

email ....

Web ....

Image courtesy of Balmoral Tanks (01224 859100)

Off-Mains Drainage

It may not be the part of the project that the self-builder looks forward to the most, but off-mains drainage is something that should be tackled early on. Depending on the location of the plot, there could be a few options, and it's worth considering them all before making your choice.

Details of drainage provision is now required at planning permission stage for any new dwelling. Before giving consent, the planners will liaise with Building Control to ensure the provision meets the requirements of the Building Regulations Part H, and also with its environmental health department. The planners will also consult the relevant environment regulator responsible for protecting national water resources. If your proposal is accepted, the environment regulator will issue a 'consent to discharge'. The agencies responsible for this are:

England & Wales: The Environment Agency
www.environment-agency.gov.uk
Scotland: Scottish Environment Protection Agency (SEPA) – www.sepa.org.uk
Northern Ireland: Department of Environment www.doeni.gov.uk
Republic of Ireland: Environmental Protection Agency (EPA) – www.epa.ie

Reed beds (ABOVE) are a natural off mains drainage system.

Septic tanks

Septic tanks are the most popular solution to dealing with sewage away from the mains. Untreated waste water flows from the house into the tank, where the solids separate from the liquids. Some solids, such as soap scum or fat, float to the top of the tank forming a scum layer, while heavier solids, such as human wastes, settle to the bottom of the tank as sludge. So septic tanks need to be pumped out, at least annually.

Because around 70% of pollutants remain in the effluent, there are very strict rules controlling where a septic tank can be installed. They are not allowed near watercourses, aquifers, wells or boreholes, as they could contaminate drinking water. Ground must have the right porosity for the soakaways to work effectively. Septic tanks require a large area for the drainage field, and should be located as far away from the main dwelling as possible. The minimum distance is 15m.

Reed beds

A reed bed is a more ecologically sound, low-maintenance option. It is a natural way to create an environment that encourages aerobic bacterial activity, which can be harnessed to help purify the liquid effluent from household sewage. A reed bed filter can be useful for dealing with the produce of a septic tank, or packaged sewage treatment plant, when sufficient purity cannot be achieved to satisfy the environment regulators.

Other advantages to reed beds are that they are relatively easy to install, aesthetically pleasing and perhaps more importantly, satisfy new building regulations.

Packaged sewage treatment plants

Where you cannot use a septic tank, a packaged sewage treatment plant is an option. These operate in much the same way as septic tanks, except that conditions are controlled to allow aerobic bacterial activity to thrive. As no chemicals should be flushed into the system, effluent draining off the tank can feed into a ditch, watercourse or drainage field, subject to consent from the environment regulator.

Conversion units: If there is an existing septic tank or cesspool in good condition, it is possible to install a conversion unit that will turn the tank into a mini sewage treatment plant. This is usually cheaper than installing a complete new system and can improve the quality of effluent, getting rid of the smell and preventing pollution.

Cesspools: Where there is no option to drain-off effluent on the site, or where infrequent or seasonal use prevents the successful functioning of a packaged sewage treatment plant, the only option is to store all solid and liquid waste in a sealed tank buried in the ground. A cess tank must be frequently emptied.

PIPES AND PUMPS

KEY

PRODUCT TYPES: 1= Below Ground Pipes
2 = Pumps   3 = Other

SEE ALSO: MERCHANTS, TOOLS AND
EQUIPMENT - Plumbers Merchants,
PLUMBING - Plumbing, Pipes and Fittings

OTHER: ▽ Reclaimed   🖱 On-line shopping
🖐 Bespoke   🤚 Hand-made   ECO Ecological

ALLERTON DRAINAGE
Woodbridge Road, Sleaford, Lincolnshire, NG34 7EW
Area of Operation: UK (Excluding Ireland)
Tel: 01529 305757
Fax: 01529 414232
Email: sales@allertonuk.com
Web: www.allertonuk.com 🖱   **Product Type:** 2

ALTON PUMPS
Redwood Lane, Medstead, Alton, Hampshire, GU34 5PE
Area of Operation: Worldwide
Tel: 01420 561661   **Fax:** 01420 561661
Email: sales@altonpumps.com
Web: www.altonpumps.com   **Product Type:** 2

AQUATEK
Unit 1 Brookfield Farm Industrial Estate,
Gravel Pit Lane, Prestbury, Cheltenham,
Gloucestershire, GL52 3NQ
Area of Operation: UK (Excluding Ireland)
Tel: 01242 227700
Fax: 01242 227744
Email: sales@aquatekltd.co.uk
Web: www.aquatekltd.co.uk   **Product Type:** 1, 2

CONDER PRODUCTS LTD
2 Whitehouse Way, South West Industrial Estate,
Peterlee, Durham, SR8 2HZ
Area of Operation: Worldwide
Tel: 0870 264 0004   **Fax:** 0870 264 0005
Email: sales@conderproducts.com
Web: www.conderproducts.com   **Product Type:** 2

DRAIN CENTER
Branches Nationwide
Area of Operation: UK & Ireland
Tel: 0870 1622 557
Web: www.draincenter.co.uk

DRAINSTORE.COM
Units 1 & 2, Heanor Gate Road, Heanor Gate
Industrial Estate, Heanor, Derbyshire, DE75 7RJ
Area of Operation: Europe
Tel: 01773 767611   **Fax:** 01773 767613
Email: adrian@drainstore.com
Web: www.drainstore.com 🖱
Product Type: 1, 2   **Material Type:** D) 1

DYNO-GROUP (DYNO-ROD & DYNO-SECURE)
Head Office, Sutherland House,
Maple Road, Surbiton, Surrey, KT6 4BJ
Area of Operation: UK & Ireland
Tel: 0800 000 999
Fax: 0208 541 1150
Email: postmaster@dyno.com
Web: www.dyno.com   **Product Type:** 1, 3

E. RICHARDS
PO Box 1115, Winscombe, Somerset, BS25 1WA
Area of Operation: UK & Ireland
Tel: 0845 330 8859   **Fax:** 0845 330 7260
Email: info@e-richards.co.uk
Web: www.e-richards.co.uk 🖱   **Product Type:** 1

EDINCARE
Unit 10 Avebury Court, Mark Road,
Hemel Hempstead, Hertfordshire, HP2 7TA
Area of Operation: UK (Excluding Ireland)
Tel: 01442 211554   **Fax:** 01442 211553
Email: info@edincare.com
Web: www.edincare.com   **Product Type:** 2

ENVIRONMENTAL CONSTRUCTION SOLUTIONS LIMITED
Head Office, 21 Kielder Road, South Wellfield,
Whitley Bay, Tyne & Wear, NE25 9QW
Area of Operation: Worldwide
Tel: 08456 123332   **Fax:** 08456 123334
Email: enquiries@ecs-sales.co.uk
Web: www.ecs-sales.co.uk   **Product Type:** 2

EUROPEAN PIPE SUPPLIERS LTD
Unit B, Vale of Neath Suppliers Park,
Resolven, Neath, SA11 5SR
Area of Operation: Europe
Tel: 01639 711000   **Fax:** 01639 711777
Email: sales@epsonline.co.uk
Web: www.epsonline.co.uk
Product Type: 2   **Material Type:** C) 5

GEBERIT LTD
New Hythe Business Park,
New Hythe Lane, Aylesford, Kent, ME20 7PJ
Area of Operation: UK & Ireland
Tel: 01622 717 811   **Fax:** 01622 716 920
Web: www.geberit.co.uk   **Product Type:** 1, 3

GREEN BUILDING STORE
11 Huddersfield Road, Meltham,
Holmfirth, West Yorkshire, HD9 4NJ
Area of Operation: UK & Ireland
Tel: 01484 854898   **Fax:** 01484 854899
Email: info@greenbuildingstore.co.uk
Web: www.greenbuildingstore.co.uk 🖱
Product Type: 3   **Other Info:** ECO
Material Type: C) 4, 7

GRUNDFOS PUMPS LTD
Grovebury Road, Leighton Buzzard,
Bedfordshire, LU7 4TL
Area of Operation: Worldwide
Tel: 01525 850000   **Fax:** 01525 850011
Email: uk_sales@grundfos.com
Web: www.grundfos.co.uk   **Product Type:** 2, 3

GRUNDFOS PUMPS LTD
Area of Operation: Worldwide
Tel: 01525 850000
Fax: 01525 850011
Email: uk_sales@grundfos.com
Web: www.grundfos.com
Product Type: 2, 3

Grundfos Pump plan – 2 heads are better than 1.
The Pump plan provides independent pumping for
heating and hot water in a compact, integrated unit.
Pump plan is compatible with all types of domestic
controls and modern boilers (which incorporate high
efficiency heat exchangers) and includes a unique
wiring centre.

GRUNDFOS PUMPS LTD
Area of Operation: Worldwide
Tel: 01525 850000
Fax: 01525 850011
Email: uk_sales@grundfos.com
Web: www.grundfos.com
Product Type: 2, 3

The new Grundfos Alpha+ - One pump fits all.
The latest innovation to emerge from the Grundfos
pumps design team is the Alpha+, the domestic
circulator with added value. The new Grundfos Alpha+
features both automatic and fixed speed operation,
which means that the Alpha+ is suitable for all domestic
heating systems.

GRUNDFOS
Area of Operation: Worldwide
Tel: 01525 775402   **Fax:** 01525 775236
Email: uk_sales@grundfos.com
Web: www.grundfos.co.uk
Product Type: 2, 3

The MQ is a complete, whole house domestic booster
pump suitable for pumping potable water, rain water or
other clean, thin, non-aggressive liquids containing no
solid particles or fibres. This makes it ideal for use in
private homes, summer houses and weekend cottages.

GRUNDFOS
Area of Operation: Worldwide
Tel: 01525 775402   **Fax:** 01525 775236
Email: uk_sales@grundfos.com
Web: www.grundfos.co.uk
Product Type: 2, 3

The Grundfos Unilift KP/AP is a portable drainage
pump designed for the removal of wastewater from
washing machines, swimming pools and ponds
among many other general transfer duties. These
Grundfos Pumps are ideal for use in flooded areas,
for example: cellars.

HARGREAVES FOUNDRY LTD
Water Lane, South Parade,
Halifax, West Yorkshire, HX3 9HG
Area of Operation: UK & Ireland
Tel: 01422 330607   **Fax:** 01422 320349
Email: info@hargreavesfoundry.co.uk
Web: www.hargreavesfoundry.co.uk
Product Type: 1

HUNTER PLASTICS
Nathan Way, London, SE28 0AE
Area of Operation: Worldwide
Tel: 0208 855 9851   **Fax:** 0208 317 7764
Email: john.morris@hunterplastics.co.uk
Web: www.hunterplastics.co.uk   **Product Type:** 1

HUTCHINSON DRAINAGE LTD
White Wall Nook, Wark, Hexham,
Northumberland, NE48 3PX
Area of Operation: UK (Excluding Ireland)
Tel: 01434 220508   **Fax:** 01875 321150
Email: enquiries@hutchinson-drainage.co.uk
Web: www.hutchinson-drainage.co.uk
Product Type: 2

INTERFLOW UK
Leighton, Shrewsbury, Shropshire, SY5 6SQ
Area of Operation: UK & Ireland
Tel: 01952 510050   **Fax:** 01952 510967
Email: villiers@interflow.co.uk
Web: www.interflow.co.uk   **Product Type:** 1

KLARGESTER ENVIRONMENTAL
College Road North, Aston Clinton,
Aylesbury, Buckinghamshire, HP22 5EW
Area of Operation: Worldwide
Tel: 01296 633000   **Fax:** 01296 633001
Email: uksales@klargester.co.uk
Web: www.klargester.com   **Product Type:** 2

KS PROFILES LTD
Broad March, Long March Industrial Estate,
Daventry, Northamptonshire, NN11 4HE
Area of Operation: UK & Ireland
Tel: 01327 316960   **Fax:** 01327 876412
Email: sales@ksprofiles.com
Web: www.ksprofiles.com   **Product Type:** 1, 2

MARLEY PLUMBING & DRAINAGE
Lenham, Maidstone, Kent, ME17 2DE
Area of Operation: Europe
Tel: 01622 858888   **Fax:** 01622 858725
Email: marketing@marleyext.com
Web: www.marley.co.uk
Product Type: 1, 3   **Material Type:** D) 1

PUMPMASTER UK LIMITED
Manor House Offices, Malvern Road, Lower Wick,
Worcester, Worcestershire, WR2 4BS
Area of Operation: UK (Excluding Ireland)
Tel: 01905 420170   **Fax:** 01905 749419
Email: pumpsales@pumpmaster.co.uk
Web: www.pumpmaster.co.uk   **Product Type:** 2

RAINHARVESTING SYSTEMS LTD
Unit S2 Inchbrook Trading Estate, Bath Road,
Woodchester, Stroud, Gloucestershire, GL5 5EY
Area of Operation: UK & Ireland
Tel: 0845 2235430   **Fax:** 01453 839260
Email: sales@rainharvesting.co.uk
Web: www.rainharvesting.co.uk   **Product Type:** 2, 3

ROCKBOURNE ENVIRONMENTAL
6 Silver Business Park, Airfield Way,
Christchurch, Dorset, BH23 3TA
Area of Operation: UK & Ireland
Tel: 01202 480980   **Fax:** 01202 490590
Email: info@rockbourne.net
Web: www.rockbourne.net   **Product Type:** 2

SAINT-GOBAIN PIPELINES
Lows Lane, Stanton-by-Dale,
Ilkeston, Derbyshire, DE7 4QU
Area of Operation: UK & Ireland
Tel: 0115 930 5000   **Fax:** 0115 932 9513
Email: mike.rawlings@saint-gobain.com
Web: www.saint-gobain-pipelines.co.uk 🖱
Product Type: 1   **Material Type:** C) 5

SANIFLO LTD
Howard House, The Runway,
South Ruislip, Middlesex, HA4 6SE
Area of Operation: UK (Excluding Ireland)
Tel: 0208 842 4040   **Fax:** 0208 842 1671
Email: andrews@saniflo.co.uk
Web: www.saniflo.co.uk   **Product Type:** 2

UPONOR HOUSING SOLUTIONS LTD
Snapethorpe House, Rugby Road,
Lutterworth, Leicestershire, LE17 4HN
Area of Operation: UK & Ireland
Tel: 01455 550355   **Fax:** 01455 550366
Email: hsenquiries@uponor.co.uk
Web: www.uponorhousingsolutions.co.uk
Product Type: 1

WAVIN PLASTICS LTD (OSMA)
Parsonage Way, Chippenham,
Wiltshire, SN15 5PN
Area of Operation: UK (Excluding Ireland)
Tel: 01249 766600   **Fax:** 01249 443286
Email: info@wavin.co.uk
Web: www.wavin.co.uk
Product Type: 1, 3   **Material Type:** D) 1

GROUNDWATER MANAGEMENT

KEY

PRODUCT TYPES:
1 = Culverts   2 = Gullies and Gratings
3 = Land Drains   4 = Soakaways
5 = Surface Water Drainage

OTHER: ▽ Reclaimed   On-line shopping
Bespoke   Hand-made   ECO Ecological

ACO BUILDING DRAINAGE
ACO Business Park, Hitchin Road,
Shefford, Bedfordshire, SG17 5TE
Area of Operation: UK & Ireland
Tel: 01462 816666
Fax: 01462 851490
Email: buildingdrainage@aco.co.uk
Web: www.acobuildingdrainage.co.uk

AQUATEK
Unit 1 Brookfield Farm Industrial Estate, Gravel Pit Lane,
Prestbury, Cheltenham, Gloucestershire, GL52 3NQ
Area of Operation: UK (Excluding Ireland)
Tel: 01242 227700   **Fax:** 01242 227744
Email: sales@aquatekltd.co.uk
Web: www.aquatekltd.co.uk
Product Type: 1, 3, 4, 5

DRAIN CENTER
Branches Nationwide
Area of Operation: UK & Ireland
Tel: 0870 1622 557
Web: www.draincenter.co.uk

DRAINSTORE.COM
Units 1 & 2 , Heanor Gate Road, Heanor Gate
Industrial Estate, Heanor, Derbyshire, DE75 7RJ
Area of Operation: Europe
Tel: 01773 767611
Fax: 01773 767613
Email: adrian@drainstore.com
Web: www.drainstore.com
Product Type: 4   **Material Type:** D) 1

ENVIRONMENTAL CONSTRUCTION SOLUTIONS LIMITED
Head Office, 21 Kielder Road, South Wellfield,
Whitley Bay, Tyne & Wear, NE25 9QW
Area of Operation: Worldwide
Tel: 08456 123332
Fax: 08456 123334
Email: enquiries@ecs-sales.co.uk
Web: www.ecs-sales.co.uk   **Product Type:** 4, 5

GRAMM ENVIRONMENTAL LIMITED
17-19 Hight Street, Ditchling,
Hassocks, West Sussex, BN6 8SY
Area of Operation: Worldwide
Tel: 01273 844899   **Fax:** 01273 846397
Email: info@grammenvironmental.com
Web: www.grammenvironmental.com
Product Type: 4, 5

HIBERNIA RAINHARVESTING
Unit 530 Storehire, Stanstead Distribution Centre,
Start Hill, Bishops Stortford, Hertfordshire, CM22 7DG
Area of Operation: UK & Ireland
Tel: 02890 249954   **Fax:** 02890 249964
Email: rain@hiberniaeth.com
Web: www.hiberniaeth.com   **Product Type:** 5

KLARGESTER ENVIRONMENTAL
College Road North, Aston Clinton,
Aylesbury, Buckinghamshire, HP22 5EW
Area of Operation: Worldwide
Tel: 01296 633000   **Fax:** 01296 633001
Email: uksales@klargester.co.uk
Web: www.klargester.com   **Product Type:** 5

MAYFIELD (MANUFACTURING) LTD
Wenden House, New End, Hemingby,
Horncastle, Lincolnshire, LN9 5QQ
Area of Operation: Worldwide
Tel: 01507 578630   **Fax:** 01507 578609
Email: john@aludrain.co.uk
Web: www.aludrain.co.uk   **Product Type:** 2

RIVERSIDE WATER TECHNOLOGIES
Pipe House Wharf, Morfa Road, Swansea, SA1 1TD
Area of Operation: UK & Ireland
Tel: 01792 655968   **Fax:** 01792 644461
Email: sales@riverside-water.co.uk
Web: www.riverside-water.co.uk

ROCKBOURNE ENVIRONMENTAL
6 Silver Business Park, Airfield Way,
Christchurch, Dorset, BH23 3TA
Area of Operation: UK & Ireland
Tel: 01202 480980   **Fax:** 01202 490590
Email: info@rockbourne.net
Web: www.rockbourne.net   **Product Type:** 1, 3, 4, 5

SEVENOAKS ENVIRONMENTAL CONSULTANCY LTD
19 Gimble Way, Pembury,
Tunbridge Wells, Kent, TN2 4BX
Area of Operation: East England, Greater London,
Midlands & Mid Wales, North East England, North
West England and North Wales, South East England,
South West England and South Wales
Tel: 01892 822999   **Fax:** 01892 822992
Email: enquires@sevenoaksenvironmental.co.uk
Web: www.sevenoaksenvironmental.co.uk

SPRY PRODUCTS LTD
64 Nottingham Road, Long Eaton,
Nottingham, Nottinghamshire, NG10 2AU
Area of Operation: UK & Ireland
Tel: 0115 973 2914   **Fax:** 0115 972 5172
Email: jerspry@aol.com
Web: www.spryproducts.com
Product Type: 3, 5   **Other Info:**
Material Type: D) 1

TERRAIN AERATION SERVICES
Aeration House, 20 Mill Fields, Haughley,
Stowmarket, Suffolk, IP14 3PU
Area of Operation: Europe
Tel: 01449 673783   **Fax:** 01449 614564
Email: terrainaeration@aol.com
Web: www.terrainaeration.co.uk
Product Type: 3

WATLING HOPE (INSTALLATIONS) LTD
1 Goldicote Business Park, Banbury Road,
Stratford Upon Avon, Warwickshire, CV37 7NB
Area of Operation: UK & Ireland
Tel: 01789 740757
Fax: 01789 740 404
Email: enquiries@watling-hope.co.uk
Web: www.watling-hope.co.uk
Product Type: 3, 4, 5

WAVIN PLASTICS LTD (OSMA)
Parsonage Way, Chippenham, Wiltshire, SN15 5PN
Area of Operation: UK (Excluding Ireland)
Tel: 01249 766 600   **Fax:** 01249 443 286
Email: info@wavin.co.uk   **Web:** www.wavin.co.uk
Product Type: 1, 2, 3, 4, 5   **Material Type:** D) 1

RAINWATER MANAGEMENT

KEY

PRODUCT TYPES: 1 = Rainwater Goods
2 = Rainwater Storage   3 = Water Recycling

SEE ALSO: PLUMBING - Plumbing, Pipes and Fittings

OTHER: ▽ Reclaimed   On-line shopping
Bespoke   Hand-made   ECO Ecological

ACO BUILDING DRAINAGE
ACO Business Park, Hitchin Road,
Shefford, Bedfordshire, SG17 5TE
Area of Operation: UK & Ireland
Tel: 01462 816666   **Fax:** 01462 851490
Email: buildingdrainage@aco.co.uk
Web: www.acobuildingdrainage.co.uk

ACORN ENVIRONMENTAL SYSTEMS LIMITED
Somerset Bridge, Bridgwater, Somerset, TA6 6LL
Area of Operation: Europe
Tel: 01278 439325   **Fax:** 01278 439324
Email: info@acornsystems.com
Web: www.acornsystems.com   **Product Type:** 3

ALMURA BUILDING PRODUCTS LTD
Cantay House, St George's Place,
Cheltenham, Gloucestershire, GL50 3PN
Area of Operation: Europe
Tel: 01242 262900   **Fax:** 01242 221333
Email: philipmarsh@almura.co.uk
Web: www.almuracladdings.co.uk
Product Type: 1   **Material Type:** C) 1

ALUMASC EXTERIOR BUILDING PRODUCTS
White House Works, Bold Road, Sutton,
St Helens, Merseyside, WA9 4JG
Area of Operation: UK & Ireland
Tel: 01744 648400   **Fax:** 01744 648401
Email: info@alumasc-exteriors.co.uk
Web: www.alumasc-exteriors.co.uk
Product Type: 1

ALUMINIUM ROOFLINE PRODUCTS
Unit 2 Vitruvius Way, Meridian Business Park,
Braunstone, Leicester, Leicestershire, LE19 1WA
Area of Operation: UK (Excluding Ireland)
Tel: 0116 289 4400
Email: jim.muddimer@arp-ltd.com
Web: www.arp-ltd.com   **Product Type:** 1

AQUATEK
Unit 1 Brookfield Farm Industrial Estate, Gravel Pit Lane,
Prestbury, Cheltenham, Gloucestershire, GL52 3NQ
Area of Operation: UK (Excluding Ireland)
Tel: 01242 227700   **Fax:** 01242 227744
Email: sales@aquatekltd.co.uk
Web: www.aquatekltd.co.uk   **Product Type:** 2, 3

ARP LTD
Unit 2 Vitruvius Way, Meridian Business Park,
Braunstone Park, Leicestershire, LE19 1WA
Area of Operation: UK & Ireland
Tel: 0116 289 4400   **Fax:** 0116 289 4433
Email: sales@arp-ltd.com
Web: www.arp-ltd.com   **Product Type:** 1

BALMORAL TANKS
Balmoral Park, Loirston, Aberdeenshire, AB12 3GY
Area of Operation: Worldwide
Tel: 01224 859100   **Fax:** 01224 859123
Email: tanks@balmoral.co.uk
Web: www.balmoraltanks.com   **Product Type:** 2

BALMORAL TANKS
Area of Operation: Worldwide
Tel: 01224 859100
Fax: 01244 859123
Email: tanks@balmoral.co.uk
Web: www.balmoraltanks.com
Product Type: 1, 3, 5
Balmoral Tanks provides the homebuilding and
renovating markets with cost effective,
innovative wastewater treatment plant.

CASTAWAY CAST PRODUCTS AND WOODWARE
Brocklesby Station, Brocklesby Road,
Ulceby, Lincolnshire, DN39 6ST
Area of Operation: Worldwide
Tel: 01469 588995   **Fax:** 01469 588995
Email: castawaycastproducts@btinternet.com
Product Type: 1   **Other Info:**
Material Type: C) 1, 5, 8, 12

CAVALOK BUILDING PRODUCTS LIMITED
Northway Lane, Newtown Industrial Estate,
Tewkesbury, Gloucestershire, GL20 8JG
Area of Operation: UK & Ireland
Tel: 08701 203003   **Fax:** 08701 213003
Email: info@cavalok.com
Web: www.cavalok.com   **Product Type:** 1

CLARENDON BRICK
Studio 2, Jennymount Court, Belfast, BT15 3HN
Area of Operation: Ireland Only
Tel: 028 9075 1751   **Fax:** 028 9075 1155
Email: info@clarendonbrick.com
Web: www.clarendonbrick.com
Product Type: 1   **Other Info:**

COBURG GUTTER GRID
Little Gunnerby, Hatcliffe, Grimsby,
Lincolnshire, DN37 0SP
Area of Operation: UK & Ireland
Tel: 01472 371406   **Fax:** 01469 560435
Email: sue@guttergrid.com
Web: www.guttergrid.com   **Product Type:** 1

CONDER PRODUCTS LTD
2 Whitehouse Way, South West Industrial Estate,
Peterlee, Durham, SR8 2HZ
Area of Operation: Worldwide
Tel: 0870 264 0004   **Fax:** 0870 264 0005
Email: sales@conderproducts.com
Web: www.conderproducts.com   **Product Type:** 2, 3

COPPAGUTTA
8 Bottings Industrial Estate, Hilltons Road,
Botley, Southampton, Hampshire , SO30 2DY
Area of Operation: UK & Ireland
Tel: 01489 797774   **Fax:** 01489 796700
Email: coppagutta@good-directions.co.uk
Web: www.coppagutta.com
Product Type: 1   **Material Type:** C) 7

CRESS WATER LTD
18 Forcefield Road, Cullompton, Devon, EX15 1QB
Area of Operation: Europe
Tel: 01884 839000
Fax: 01884 839909
Email: info@cresswater.co.uk
Web: www.cresswater.co.uk
Product Type: 3
Other Info: ECO

DIY ROOFING LTD
Hillcrest House, Featherbed Lane, Hunt End,
Redditch, Worcestershire, B97 5QL
Tel: 0800 783 4890   **Fax:** 01527 403483
Email: chris@diyroofing.co.uk
Web: www.diyroofing.co.uk   **Product Type:** 1

DRAIN CENTER
Branches Nationwide
Area of Operation: UK & Ireland
Tel: 0870 1622 557   **Web:** www.draincenter.co.uk

DRAINSMART
5 Hursley Road, Chandlers Ford,
Eastleigh, Hampshire, SO53 2FW
Area of Operation: UK & Ireland
Tel: 02380 269091   **Fax:** 02380 269091
Email: info@drainsmart.co.uk
Web: www.drainsmart.co.uk.
Product Type: 1   **Other Info:** ✎

E. RICHARDS
PO Box 1115, Winscombe, Somerset, BS25 1WA
Area of Operation: UK & Ireland
Tel: 0845 330 8859   **Fax:** 0845 330 7260
Email: info@e-richards.co.uk
Web: www.e-richards.co.uk ⌂   **Product Type:** 1

ECOSHOP
Unit 1, Glen of the Downs Garden Centre,
Kilmacanogue, Co Wicklow, Republic of Ireland
Area of Operation: Ireland Only
Tel: +353 01 488 0400   **Fax:** +353 01 201 6480
Email: info@ecoshop.ie   **Web:** www.ecoshop.ie ⌂

**ENVIRONMENTAL CONSTRUCTION
SOLUTIONS LIMITED**
Head Office, 21 Kielder Road, South Wellfield,
Whitley Bay, Tyne & Wear, NE25 9QW
Area of Operation: Worldwide
Tel: 08456 123332   **Fax:** 08456 123334
Email: enquiries@ecs-sales.co.uk
Web: www.ecs-sales.co.uk   **Product Type:** 2, 3

EUROPEAN PIPE SUPPLIERS LTD
Unit B , Vale of Neath Suppliers Park,
Resolven, Neath, SA11 5SR
Tel: 01639 711000   **Fax:** 01639 711777
Email: sales@epsonline.co.uk
Web: www.epsonline.co.uk
Product Type: 1   **Material Type:** C) 1, 2, 3, 4, 5, 6, 7

EXTERIOR IMAGE LTD
5 Hursley Road, Chandlers Ford,
Eastleigh, Hampshire, SO53 2FW
Tel: 02380 271777   **Fax:** 02380 269091
Email: info@exteriorimage.co.uk
Web: www.exteriorimage.co.uk   **Product Type:** 1

FREEWATER UK LTD
6 Lime Tree Close, Lincoln, Lincolnshire, LN6 0RT
Area of Operation: UK & Ireland
Tel: 01522 720862   **Fax:** 01522 720862
Email: info@freewateruk.co.uk
Web: www.freewateruk.co.uk   **Product Type:** 2, 3

GAP
Partnership Way, Shadsworth Business Park,
Blackburn, Lancashire, BB1 2QP
Area of Operation: Midlands & Mid Wales, North
East England, North West England and North Wales
Tel: 01254 682888   **Web:** www.gap.uk.com
Product Type: 1   **Material Type:** D) 1

GRAMM ENVIRONMENTAL LIMITED
17-19 Hight Street, Ditchling,
Hassocks, West Sussex, BN6 8SY
Tel: 01273 844899   **Fax:** 01273 846397
Email: info@grammenvironmental.com
Web: www.grammenvironmental.com

GREENFINGERS.COM
10 Lindsay Square, Deans Industrial Estate,
Livingston, Lothian, EH54 8RL
Tel: 0845 345 0728
Email: customer.services@greenfingers.com
Web: www.greenfingers.com ⌂   **Product Type:** 2

HARGREAVES FOUNDRY LTD
Water Lane, South Parade,
Halifax, West Yorkshire, HX3 9HG
Area of Operation: UK & Ireland
Tel: 01422 330607   **Fax:** 01422 320349
Email: info@hargreavesfoundry.co.uk
Web: www.hargreavesfoundry.co.uk
Product Type: 1

**HARRISON THOMPSON & CO. LTD.
(YEOMAN RAINGUARD)**
Yeoman House, Whitehall Estate, Whitehall Road,
Leeds, West Yorkshire, LS12 5JB
Area of Operation: UK & Ireland
Tel: 0113 279 5854   **Fax:** 0113 231 0406
Email: info@rainguard.co.uk
Web: www.rainguard.co.uk   **Product Type:** 1

HIBERNIA RAINHARVESTING
Unit 530 Storehire, Stansted Distribution Centre,
Start Hill, Bishops Stortford, Hertfordshire, CM22 7DG
Area of Operation: UK & Ireland
Tel: 02890 249954   **Fax:** 02890 249964
Email: rain@hiberniaeth.com
Web: www.hiberniaeth.com   **Product Type:** 1, 2, 3

HIGHSEAL WINDOWS LIMITED
Moat Road, Scunthorpe, Lincolnshire, DN15 9GA
Area of Operation: East England, Greater London,
Midlands & Mid Wales, North East England, North West
England and North Wales, Scotland, South East England
Tel: 01724 276213
Fax: 01724 276214
Email: david.maybank@hwlgroup.co.uk
Web: www.hwlgroup.co.uk   **Product Type:** 1

HUNTER PLASTICS
Nathan Way, London, SE28 0AE
Area of Operation: Worldwide
Tel: 0208 855 9851   **Fax:** 0208 317 7764
Email: john.morris@hunterplastics.co.uk
Web: www.hunterplastics.co.uk
Product Type: 1

HYDRO INTERNATIONAL
Clevedon Hall Estate, Victoria Road, Clevedon, BS21 7RD
Area of Operation: UK & Ireland
Tel: 01275 878371   **Fax:** 01275 874979
Email: enquiries@hydro-international.co.uk
Web: www.hydro-international.biz
Product Type: 1, 2   **Other Info:** ✎

JONES NASH ECO HOMES
12 Lee Street, Louth, Lincolnshire, LN11 9HJ
Area of Operation: UK (Excluding Ireland)
Tel: 01507 609637   **Fax:** 01507 609637
Email: sd@jones-nash.co.uk
Web: www.eco-houses.co.uk   **Product Type:** 2, 3

KLARGESTER ENVIRONMENTAL
College Road North, Aston Clinton,
Aylesbury, Buckinghamshire, HP22 5EW
Area of Operation: Worldwide
Tel: 01296 633000   **Fax:** 01296 633001
Email: uksales@klargester.co.uk
Web: www.klargester.com   **Product Type:** 2, 3

LINDAB LTD
Shenstone Trading Estate, Bromsgrove Road,
Halesowen, West Midlands, B63 3XB
Area of Operation: UK & Ireland
Tel: 0121 585 2780 **Fax:** 0121 585 2782
Email: jonathan.fennell@lindab.co.uk
Web: www.lindab.co.uk **Product Type:** 1

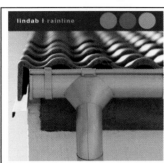

LINDAB
Area of Operation: UK & Ireland
Tel: 0121 585 2780
Fax: 0121 585 2782
Email: jonathan.fennell@lindab.co.uk
Web: www.lindab.co.uk
Product Type: 1

Lindab Rainline is a truly complete rain drainage system. With gutters in four dimensions, down pipes in five dimensions and an extensive range of components, this system offers solutions for any type of building, large or small, classic or contemporary.

MARLEY PLUMBING & DRAINAGE
Lenham, Maidstone, Kent, ME17 2DE
Area of Operation: Europe
Tel: 01622 858888 **Fax:** 01622 858725
Email: marketing@marleyext.com
Web: www.marley.co.uk
Product Type: 1 **Material Type:** C) 1

MAYFIELD (MANUFACTURING) LTD
Wenden House, New End, Hemingby,
Horncastle, Lincolnshire, LN9 5QQ
Area of Operation: Worldwide
Tel: 01507 578630 **Fax:** 01507 578609
Email: john@aludrain.co.uk
Web: www.aludrain.co.uk **Product Type:** 1

NATIONAL PLASTICS
Bridge Street, Abercarn, Gwent, NP11 4SB
Area of Operation: UK & Ireland
Tel: 01495 244551 **Fax:** 01495 247990
Email: srholt@nationalplastics.co.uk
Web: www.nationalplastics.co.uk
Product Type: 1

NORTHANTS RAINWATER SYSTEMS
Unit 10 Chapel Farm, Hanslope Road,
Hartwell, Northamptonshire, NN7 2EU
Area of Operation: UK (Excluding Ireland)
Tel: 01604 877775
Fax: 01604 674447
Email: mail@northantsrainwater.co.uk
Web: www.northantsrainwater.co.uk
Product Type: 1

RAINHARVESTING SYSTEMS LTD
Unit S2 Inchbrook Trading Estate, Bath Road,
Woodchester, Stroud, Gloucestershire, GL5 5EY
Area of Operation: UK & Ireland
Tel: 0845 2235430 **Fax:** 01453 839260
Email: sales@rainharvesting.co.uk
Web: www.rainharvesting.co.uk
Product Type: 1, 2, 3

RIVERSIDE WATER TECHNOLOGIES
Pipe House Wharf, Morfa Road, Swansea, SA1 1TD
Area of Operation: UK & Ireland
Tel: 01792 655968
Fax: 01792 644461
Email: sales@riverside-water.co.uk
Web: www.riverside-water.co.uk

ROCKBOURNE ENVIRONMENTAL
6 Silver Business Park, Airfield Way,
Christchurch, Dorset, BH23 3TA
Area of Operation: UK & Ireland
Tel: 01202 480980 **Fax:** 01202 490590
Email: info@rockbourne.net
Web: www.rockbourne.net **Product Type:** 2, 3

SAINT-GOBAIN PIPELINES
Lows Lane, Stanton-by-Dale,
Ilkeston, Derbyshire, DE7 4QU
Area of Operation: UK & Ireland
Tel: 0115 930 5000
Fax: 0115 932 9513
Email: mike.rawlings@saint-gobain.com
Web: www.saint-gobain-pipelines.co.uk
Product Type: 1 **Material Type:** C) 5

SURAFLOW
Horsebridge Mill, Kings Somborne,
Stockbridge, Hampshire, SO20 6PX
Area of Operation: UK & Ireland
Tel: 01794 389589 **Fax:** 01794 389597
Email: enquiries@suraflow.co.uk
Web: www.suraflow.co.uk
Product Type: 1 **Material Type:** C) 1

TITAN POLLUTION CONTROL
West Portway Industrial Estate,
Andover, Hampshire, SP10 3LF
Area of Operation: UK (Excluding Ireland)
Tel: 01264 353222 **Fax:** 01264 366446
Email: info@titanpc.co.uk
Web: www.titanpc.co.uk **Product Type:** 2, 3

TLG GUTTERS
20 Crawley Road, Alvaston, Derby, Derbyshire, DE24 9FZ
Area of Operation: UK (Excluding Ireland)
Tel: 0800 298 4619
Fax: 01332 754133
Email: knopptony@hotmail.com
Web: www.tlg-gutter.co.uk **Product Type:** 1

TUSCAN FOUNDRY PRODUCTS
Units C1-C3, Oakendene Industrial Estate,
Bolney Road, Cowfold, West Sussex, RH13 8AZ
Area of Operation: Worldwide
Tel: 01403 860040 **Fax:** 0845 345 0215
Email: enquiries@tuscanfoundry.co.uk
Web: www.tuscanfoundry.com
Product Type: 1

WARWICKSHIRE FASCIAS
Unit 8&9 Cattell Road, Cape Road Industrial Estate,
Warwick, Warwickshire, CV34 4JN
Area of Operation: UK & Ireland
Tel: 01926 496 830 **Fax:** 01926 491 630
Email: warwickshirefascias@hotmail.com
Web: www.warwickshirefascias.co.uk
Product Type: 1

WATER SUPPORT SERVICES
18a High West Street, Dorchester, Dorset, DT1 1UW
Area of Operation: East England, Midlands & Mid Wales, South East England, South West England and South Wales
Tel: 01935 382490 **Fax:** 01935 412371
Email: info@water-support.co.uk
Web: www.water-support.co.uk
Product Type: 2, 3

WATERBANK LTD
Lasyard House, Underhill Street,
Bridgnorth, Shropshire, WV16 4BB
Area of Operation: UK (Excluding Ireland)
Tel: 01746 769604 **Fax:** 01746 769217
Email: enquiries@waterbank.co.uk
Web: www.waterbank.co.uk **Product Type:** 2, 3

WAVIN PLASTICS LTD (OSMA)
Parsonage Way, Chippenham, Wiltshire, SN15 5PN
Area of Operation: UK (Excluding Ireland)
Tel: 01249 766 600 **Fax:** 01249 443 286
Email: info@wavin.co.uk
Web: www.wavin.co.uk
Product Type: 1, 2, 3 **Material Type:** D) 1

SEWAGE MANAGEMENT

KEY

PRODUCT TYPES: 1= Treatment Systems
2 = Cess Pools   3 = Septic Tanks
4 = Reed Beds   5 = Access Fittings
6 = Pumping Equipment   7 = Other

OTHER: ▽ Reclaimed   🖱 On-line shopping
✏ Bespoke   ✋ Hand-made   ECO Ecological

ACORN ENVIRONMENTAL SYSTEMS LIMITED
Somerset Bridge, Bridgwater, Somerset, TA6 6LL
Area of Operation: Europe
Tel: 01278 439325
Fax: 01278 439324
Email: info@acornsystems.com
Web: www.acornsystems.com
Product Type: 1, 2, 3, 6

ALLERTON CONSTRUCTION LTD
Woodbridge Road, Sleaford, Lincolnshire, NG34 7EW
Area of Operation: UK (Excluding Ireland)
Tel: 01529 305757
Fax: 01529 414232
Email: sales@allertonuk.com
Web: www.allertonuk.com
Product Type: 1, 6

ALLERTON DRAINAGE
Woodbridge Road, Sleaford, Lincolnshire, NG34 7EW
Area of Operation: UK (Excluding Ireland)
Tel: 01529 305757
Fax: 01529 414232
Email: sales@alltertonuk.com
Web: www.allertonuk.com 🖱
Product Type: 1

ALTON PUMPS
Redwood Lane, Medstead,
Alton, Hampshire, GU34 5PE
Area of Operation: Worldwide
Tel: 01420 561661   **Fax:** 01420 561661
Email: sales@altonpumps.com
Web: www.altonpumps.com   **Product Type:** 6

AQUATEK
Unit 1 Brookfield Farm Industrial Estate, Gravel Pit Lane,
Prestbury, Cheltenham, Gloucestershire, GL52 3NQ
Area of Operation: UK (Excluding Ireland)
Tel: 01242 227700   **Fax:** 01242 227744
Email: sales@aquatekltd.co.uk
Web: www.aquatekltd.co.uk
Product Type: 1, 3, 6

ATB ENVIRONMENTAL (UK) LTD.
Unit 6, Markham Vale Environmental Centre,
Markham Lane, Markham Vale,
Chesterfield, Derbyshire, S44 5HY
Area of Operation: UK (Excluding Ireland)
Tel: 01246 825870   **Fax:** 01246 827563
Email: a.law@aquamax.net
Web: www.aquamax.net
Product Type: 1

> ## Don't Forget!
>
> You can use the materials key at the beginning of this Handbook to get much more information from a company's listing.

BALMORAL TANKS
Balmoral Park, Loirston, Aberdeenshire, AB12 3GY
Area of Operation: Worldwide
Tel: 01224 859100   **Fax:** 01224 859123
Email: tanks@balmoral.co.uk
Web: www.balmoraltanks.com   **Product Type:** 1, 3, 5

BALMORAL TANKS
Area of Operation: Worldwide
Tel: 01224 859100
Fax: 01244 859123
Email: tanks@balmoral.co.uk
Web: www.balmoraltanks.com
Product Type: 1, 3, 5

Balmoral Tanks provides the homebuilding and renovating markets with cost effective, innovative, water, wastewater and fuel storage solutions.

BIO BUBBLE LTD
Emsworth Yacht Harbour, Thorney Road,
Emsworth, Hampshire, PO10 8BW
Tel: 01243 370100   **Fax:** 01243 370090
Email: sales@bio-bubble.com
Web: www.bio-bubble.com
Product Type: 1   **Other Info:** ECO ✏ ✋

BIOCLERE TECHNOLOGY LTD
The Oaks, Moons Hill, Frensham, Surrey, GU10 3AW
Area of Operation: Worldwide
Tel: 01252 792688   **Fax:** 01252 794068
Email: adrian@bioclere.co.uk
Web: www.bioclere.co.uk   **Product Type:** 1

BIODIGESTER
27 Brightstowe Road,
Burnham On Sea, Somerset, TA8 2HW
Area of Operation: UK (Excluding Ireland)
Tel: 01278 786104   **Fax:** 01278 793380
Email: sales@biodigester.co.uk
Web: www.biodigester.co.uk
Product Type: 1, 3

CLEANWATER SOUTH WEST LTD
Foxfield, Welcombe, Bideford, Devon, EX39 6HF
Area of Operation: South East England, South West England and South Wales
Tel: 01288 331561
Email: sales@cleanwatersw.co.uk
Web: www.cleanwatersw.co.uk
Product Type: 1, 2, 3, 4, 6, 7

CONDER PRODUCTS LTD
2 Whitehouse Way, South West Industrial Estate,
Peterlee, Durham, SR8 2HZ
Area of Operation: Worldwide
Tel: 0870 264 0004
Fax: 0870 264 0005
Email: sales@conderproducts.com
Web: www.conderproducts.com
Product Type: 1, 2, 3, 6

CRESS WATER LTD
18 Forcefield Road, Cullompton, Devon, EX15 1QB
Area of Operation: Europe
Tel: 01884 839000   **Fax:** 01884 839909
Email: info@cresswater.co.uk
Web: www.cresswater.co.uk
Product Type: 1, 3, 4, 6   **Other Info:** ECO

DRAIN CENTER
Branches Nationwide
Area of Operation: UK & Ireland
Tel: 0870 1622 557
Web: www.draincenter.co.uk

DRAINSTORE.COM
Units 1 & 2, Heanor Gate Road, Heanor Gate
Industrial Estate, Heanor, Derbyshire, DE75 7RJ
Area of Operation: Europe
Tel: 01773 767611 **Fax:** 01773 767613
Email: adrian@drainstore.com
Web: www.drainstore.com
Product Type: 1, 3, 6

DYNO-GROUP (DYNO-ROD & DYNO-SECURE)
Head Office, Sutherland House,
Maple Road, Surbiton, Surrey, KT6 4BJ
Area of Operation: UK & Ireland
Tel: 0800 000 999
Fax: 0208 541 1150
Email: postmaster@dyno.com
Web: www.dyno.com **Product Type:** 3, 5, 7

EDINCARE
Unit 10 Avebury Court, Mark Road,
Hemel Hempstead, Hertfordshire, HP2 7TA
Area of Operation: UK (Excluding Ireland)
Tel: 01442 211554
Fax: 01442 211553
Email: info@edincare.com
Web: www.edincare.com
Product Type: 1, 6, 7

ENVIRONMENTAL CONSTRUCTION SOLUTIONS LIMITED
Head Office, 21 Kielder Road, South Wellfield,
Whitley Bay, Tyne & Wear, NE25 9QW
Area of Operation: Worldwide
Tel: 08456 123332 **Fax:** 08456 123334
Email: enquiries@ecs-sales.co.uk
Web: www.ecs-sales.co.uk
Product Type: 1, 2, 3, 6, 7

ENVIRONMENTAL CONSTRUCTION SOLUTIONS LIMITED
Area of Operation: Worldwide
Tel: 08456 123 332
Fax: 08456 123 334
Email: enquiries@ecs-sales.co.uk
Web: www.ecs-sales.co.uk

Specializing in the design & supply of surface & waste water (inc petroleum) products, our dedicated team of environmental specialists are able to offer independant, quality advice to ensure that the products we offer, are those that best suit your requirements.

GRAMM ENVIRONMENTAL LIMITED
17-19 Hight Street, Ditchling,
Hassocks, West Sussex, BN6 8SY
Area of Operation: Worldwide
Tel: 01273 844899 **Fax:** 01273 846397
Email: info@grammenvironmental.com
Web: www.grammenvironmental.com
Product Type: 2, 3

GREEN ROCK
3 Elmhurst Road, Harwich, Essex, CO12 3SA
Area of Operation: UK (Excluding Ireland)
Tel: 01255 554055 **Fax:** 01255 554055
Web: www.greenrock.fi

Please mention The Homebuilder's Handbook when you call

GRUNDFOS PUMPS LTD
Grovebury Road, Leighton Buzzard,
Bedfordshire, LU7 4TL
Area of Operation: Worldwide
Tel: 01525 850000 **Fax:** 01525 850011
Email: uk_sales@grundfos.com
Web: www.grundfos.co.uk

GRUNDFOS
Area of Operation: Worldwide
Tel: 01525 850000
Fax: 01525 850011
Email: uk_sales@grundfos.com
Web: www.grundfos.co.uk

For sewage and wastewater removal, these compact, easy to install Grundfos Products are ideal for many refurbishment situations – from attics to basements, where toilet bathroom, kitchens and laundry facilities are required.

GRUNDFOS PUMPS LTD
Area of Operation: Worldwide
Tel: 01525 850000
Fax: 01525 850011
Email: uk_sales@grundfos.com
Web: www.grundfos.com
Product Type: 2, 3

Grundfos Pump plan – 2 heads are better than 1.
The Pump plan provides independent pumping for heating and hot water in a compact, integrated unit. Pump plan is compatible with all types of domestic controls and modern boilers (which incorporate high efficiency heat exchangers) and includes a unique wiring centre.

HUNTER PLASTICS
Nathan Way , London, SE28 0AE
Area of Operation: Worldwide
Tel: 0208 855 9851 **Fax:** 0208 317 7764
Email: john.morris@hunterplastics.co.uk
Web: www.hunterplastics.co.uk **Product Type:** 5

HUTCHINSON DRAINAGE LTD
White Wall Nook, Wark, Hexham,
Northumberland, NE48 3PX
Tel: 01434 220508 **Fax:** 01875 321150
Email: enquiries@hutchinson-drainage.co.uk
Web: www.hutchinson-drainage.co.uk
Product Type: 1, 3, 4, 6

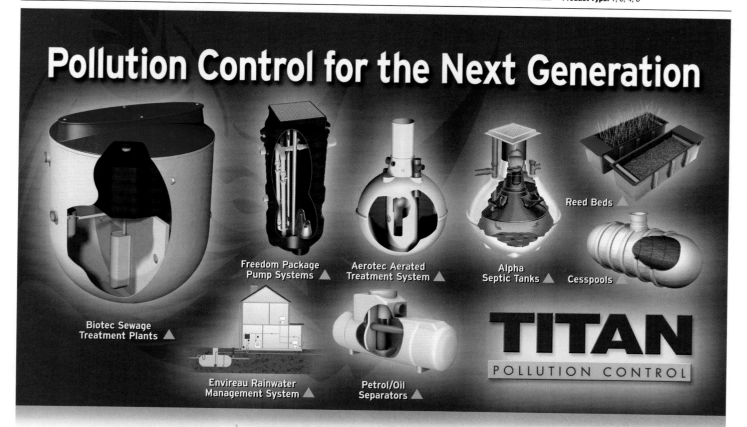

To recommend a company for inclusion in the next edition of The Homebuilder's Handbook, email

customerservice@centaur.co.uk

KLARGESTER ENVIRONMENTAL
College Road North, Aston Clinton,
Aylesbury, Buckinghamshire, HP22 5EW
Area of Operation: Worldwide
Tel: 01296 633000 **Fax:** 01296 633001
Email: uksales@klargester.co.uk
Web: www.klargester.com
Product Type: 1, 2, 3, 4, 6, 7

RIVERSIDE WATER TECHNOLOGIES
Pipe House Wharf, Morfa Road,
Swansea, SA1 1TD
Area of Operation: UK & Ireland
Tel: 01792 655968 **Fax:** 01792 644461
Email: sales@riverside-water.co.uk
Web: www.riverside-water.co.uk
Product Type: 1

ROCKBOURNE ENVIRONMENTAL
6 Silver Business Park, Airfield Way,
Christchurch, Dorset, BH23 3TA
Area of Operation: UK & Ireland
Tel: 01202 480980 **Fax:** 01202 490590
Email: info@rockbourne.net
Web: www.rockbourne.net
Product Type: 1, 2, 3, 4, 6

SERIOUS WASTE MANAGEMENT LTD
58-60 Wetmore Road, Burton-upon-Trent,
Staffordshire, DE14 1SN
Area of Operation: UK (Excluding Ireland)
Tel: 01283 562382 **Fax:** 01283 562312
Email: info@weareserious.co.uk
Web: www.weareserious.co.uk
Product Type: 1, 2, 3, 6, 7

TITAN POLLUTION CONTROL
West Portway Industrial Estate,
Andover, Hampshire , SP10 3LF
Area of Operation: UK (Excluding Ireland)
Tel: 01264 353222 **Fax:** 01264 366446
Email: info@titanpc.co.uk
Web: www.titanpc.co.uk
Product Type: 1, 2, 3, 4, 6, 7

WATLING HOPE (INSTALLATIONS) LTD
1 Goldicote Business Park, Banbury Road,
Stratford Upon Avon, Warwickshire, CV37 7NB
Area of Operation: UK & Ireland
Tel: 01789 740757 **Fax:** 01789 740 404
Email: enquiries@watling-hope.co.uk
Web: www.watling-hope.co.uk
Product Type: 1, 3, 5, 6

WAVIN PLASTICS LTD (OSMA)
Parsonage Way, Chippenham, Wiltshire, SN15 5PN
Area of Operation: UK (Excluding Ireland)
Tel: 01249 766 600 **Fax:** 01249 443 286
Email: info@wavin.co.uk
Web: www.wavin.co.uk
Product Type: 5, 7   **Material Type:** D) 1

WPL LTD
Units 1 & 2 Aston Road,
Waterlooville, Hampshire, PO7 7UX
Area of Operation: Europe
Tel: 0845 450 4818 **Fax:** 02392 242624
Email: domestic@wpl.co.uk
Web: www.wpl.co.uk **Product Type:** 1

FIXING, ADHESIVES AND TREATMENTS

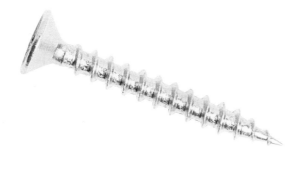

Hinges

Hinges come in all shapes and sizes, so it's important that you choose one that is right for the job. Factors such as the material and finish of the hinge are crucial, as is the weight of the door or gate you are planning to hang.

All door hinges consist of two wings held together with a pin called a pivot pin. Some can be used in either right or left-handed openings but others are made `handed' - one way or the other.

The most common types of door hinges are butt hinges and they are usually recessed in a mortise, making them flush-fitting and placing the pivot pin central to the space between door and jamb. There are many variations on the standard door's butt hinges, but some of the most popular are:

- rising butt hinges, which have a self-closing effect and can help clear some small floor obstacles

- security hinges, which are more difficult to break free with a jimmy

- parliament hinges, where the knuckle projects thus allowing the door to swing back flush with the frame and wall

Before buying hinges, you need to know the weight of the door/s you will be hanging. You can refer to published tables of sizes to find out which ones you need. One such source can be found at Robert Bernard & Son Ltd – www.bernards.co.uk/hinges_faq.htm.

Obviously you should select a hinge that is suitable to the door to be hanged. This depends on the weight and size of the door. For internal doors in the home a pair of hinges will normally be sufficient, but for heavy doors of more than, say 20kg, it's best to opt for three. The extra hinge helps prevent warping.

TOP TIPS TO SOLVE SOME COMMON PROBLEMS

Problem 1: Squeaky hinges

Noise usually occurs because of friction caused by a rusty hinge pin or hinges fitted out of alignment. Use a hammer and small nail to drive the hinge pin part of the way out. Next, place the tip of a screwdriver under the head of the pin and lever the pin fully out. Use wire wool, an abrasive washing-up pad or fine abrasive paper to removed dirt and rust from the hinge pin and leaves.

Problem 2: Door closes by itself

Increase friction in the hinges. Remove one hinge pin from the door (as above). Place hinge pin across the jaws of a vice or a pair of metal strips and tap the hinge pin halfway along its length with a hammer. You're aiming to put a very slight bend in it. Refit the hinge pin with a hammer.

Problem 3: Screws coming loose

Remove and replace the screws. If the hinge screw threads are stripped, you must replace them with longer ones. However, this often means using screws with a larger diameter, and you must be sure that the heads of the replacement screws sit into the countersinks in the hinges. If they don't, the hinges can become `screw bound' and won't close properly without distorting, pulling loose again or making the door bind in the frame. You can sometimes improve matters by using a metal countersink bit and drill to increase the amount of countersink on the hinge leaves. If necessary, refit the hinges by remaking the screwholes (see Problem 2).

ADHESIVES

KEY

PRODUCT TYPES: 1 = Carpet 2 = Ceramics
3 = Concrete 4 = Cork 5 = Rubber
6 = Timber 7 = Linoleum 8 = Plastics
9 = Other

OTHER: ▽ Reclaimed On-line shopping
Bespoke Hand-made ECO Ecological

ACE FIXINGS
Woodside Industrial Estate,
Woodside Road, Ballymena, BT42 4HX
Area of Operation: UK & Ireland
Tel: 02825 649323 **Fax:** 02825 659334
Email: mark.robinson@acefixings.com
Web: www.acefixings.com
Product Type: 6

ARDEX UK LIMITED
Homefield Road, Haverhill, Suffolk, CB9 8QP
Area of Operation: UK (Excluding Ireland)
Tel: 01440 714939 **Fax:** 01440 716660
Email: info@ardex.co.uk
Web: www.ardex.co.uk
Product Type: 1, 2, 4, 5, 7

BATHROOM CITY
Seeleys Road, Tyseley Industrial Estate,
Birmingham, West Midlands, B11 2LQ
Area of Operation: UK & Ireland
Tel: 0121 753 0700
Fax: 0121 753 1110
Email: sales@bathroomcity.com
Web: www.bathroomcity.com
Product Type: 2

BUILDING ADHESIVES LTD
Longton Road, Trentham,
Stoke on Trent, Staffordshire, ST4 8JB
Area of Operation: Worldwide
Tel: 01782 591100 **Fax:** 01782 591101
Email: info@building-adhesives.com
Web: www.building-adhesives.com

DEGUSSA CONSTRUCTION CHEMICALS (UK)
Albany House, Swinton Hall Road,
Swinton, Manchester, M27 4DT
Tel: 0161 794 7411 **Fax:** 0161 727 8547
Email: mbtfeb@basf.com
Web: www.degussa-cc.co.uk **Product Type:** 2, 3, 6

FIBERTECH
11 James Terrace, Malahide, Dublin, Ireland
Area of Operation: UK & Ireland
Tel: +353 1 8168450 **Fax:** +353 1 8168455
Email: info@fibertech.ie **Web:** www.fibertech.ie

GEOCEL LIMITED
Western Wood Way, Langage Science Park,
Plympton, Plymouth, Devon, PL7 5BG
Tel: 01752 334350 **Fax:** 01752 202065
Email: info@geocel.co.uk
Web: www.geocel.co.uk **Product Type:** 2, 5, 6, 8, 9

HAFIXS INDUSTRIAL PRODUCTS
Park Royal House, 23 Park Royal Road,
London, Greater London, NW10 7JH
Area of Operation: Europe
Tel: 0208 969 3034 **Fax:** 0208 964 4580
Email: sales@hafixs.co.uk
Web: www.hafixs.co.uk
Product Type: 1, 2, 3, 4, 5, 6, 7, 8, 9

HENKEL CONSUMER ADHESIVES
Apollo Court, 2 Bishop Square Business Park,
Hatfield, Hertfordshire, AL10 9EY
Area of Operation: Worldwide
Tel: 01707 635000 **Fax:** 01707 289029
Web: www.henkel.co.uk **Product Type:** 3, 9

MAPEI UK LTD
Mapei House, Steel Park Road,
Halesowen, West Midlands, B62 8HD
Area of Operation: UK & Ireland
Tel: 0121 508 6970 **Fax:** 0121 508 6960
Email: info@mapei.co.uk
Web: www.mapei.co.uk **Other Info:** ECO
Product Type: 1, 2, 3, 4, 5, 6, 7, 8, 9

MASKING FILM COMPANY
P.O.Box 62, Hedge End,
Southampton, Hampshire, SO30 3ZJ
Area of Operation: Worldwide
Tel: 02380 477550
Fax: 02380 477886
Email: mckphil@lowtackfilm.co.uk
Web: www.lowtackfilm.co.uk
Product Type: 1

RESIN BONDED LTD
Unit 7 Ashdown Court, Vernon Road,
Uckfield, East Sussex, TN22 5DX
Area of Operation: UK & Ireland
Tel: 01825 766186 **Fax:** 01825 766186
Email: info@resinbonded.co.uk
Web: www.resinbonded.co.uk
Product Type: 3

S.L. HARDWOODS
390 Sydenham Road, Croydon, Surrey, CR0 2EA
Area of Operation: UK (Excluding Ireland)
Tel: 0208 683 0292
Fax: 0208 683 0404
Email: info@slhardwoods.co.uk
Web: www.slhardwoods.co.uk **Product Type:** 9

TOPSEAL SYSTEMS LIMITED
Unit 1-5 Hookstone Chase,
Harrogate, North Yorkshire, HG2 7HP
Area of Operation: Europe
Tel: 01423 886495 **Fax:** 01423 889550
Email: sales@topseal.co.uk
Web: www.topseal.co.uk **Product Type:** 8, 9

UNIFIX LTD
St Georges House, Grove Lane, Smethwick,
Birmingham, West Midlands, B66 2QT
Area of Operation: Europe
Tel: 0800 096 1110 **Fax:** 0800 096 1115
Email: sales@unifix.com
Web: www.unifix-online.co.uk
Product Type: 6, 8, 9

WEBER BUILDING SOLUTIONS
Dickens House, Enterprise Way, Maulden Road,
Flitwick, Bedford, Bedfordshire, MK45 5BY
Area of Operation: Worldwide
Tel: 0870 333 0070 **Fax:** 01525 718988
Email: info@weberbuildingsolutions.co.uk
Web: www.weberbuildingsolutions.co.uk
Product Type: 2, 9

TREATMENTS, PRESERVATIONS & STAINS

KEY

PRODUCT TYPES: 1= Dry Rot 2 = Wet Rot
3 = Pre-paint Repair 4 = Woodworm
5 = Coloured Stains 6 = Rust Proofing
7 = Other

OTHER: ▽ Reclaimed On-line shopping
Bespoke Hand-made ECO Ecological

AQUAFIRE SYSTEMS
5 Engine Road, Loanhead, EH20 9RF
Area of Operation: UK & Ireland
Tel: 0131 4404450 **Fax:** 0131 4404780
Email: sales@aquafire.co.uk
Web: www.aquafire.co.uk **Product Type:** 5, 7

RAPID REPAIR
POWERFUL PERMANENT PATCH

PRODUCT INFORMATION

The FiberTech Patch provides a quick, easy and effective solution to all your maintenance and repair problems. There is no sealing, mixing or brushing needed, simply peel off the backing paper and press it firmly on to the damaged surface. The Patch will bond to almost any clean dry surface such as wood, metal, fibreglass, concrete, glass and most plastics.

The Patch is soft and pliable and will mould to virtually any shape. It cures on exposure to UV light (daylight) and the typical cure times range from 10 minutes to one hour depending on the intensity of the UV exposure.

Once the product has hardened, it provides a permanent repair as it is heat resistant, tough, and waterproof and can be drilled, sanded and painted if required.

PERMANENT BUILDING MAINTENANCE REPAIRS

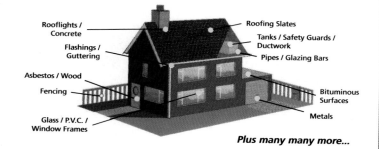

Rooflights / Concrete
Roofing Slates
Flashings / Guttering
Tanks / Safety Guards / Ductwork
Pipes / Glazing Bars
Asbestos / Wood
Fencing
Bituminous Surfaces
Metals
Glass / P.V.C. / Window Frames

Plus many many more...

**See our special offers and buy online at
www.fibertechDIY.com or give us a call on 01236755404**

Tel: 01236755404 | Fax: 01236763409 | Email: mail@fibertech.ie

BUILDING STRUCTURE & MATERIALS

ARCH TIMBER PROTECTION
Wheldon Road, Castleford, West Yorkshire, WF10 2JT
Area of Operation: Worldwide
Tel: 01977 714000   **Fax:** 01977 714001
Email: advice@archchemicals.com
Web: www.archtp.com   **Product Type:** 5, 7

BEHLEN LTD
15 Huss's Lane, Main Street,
Long Eaton, Nottinghamshire, NG10 1GS
Area of Operation: Europe
Tel: 0871 910 0900   **Fax:** 0871 271 0451
Email: enquiries@behlen.co.uk
Web: www.behlen.co.uk   **Product Type:** 3, 5, 7

ECO SOLUTIONS LIMITED
Summerleaze House, Church Road,
Winscombe, Somerset, BS25 1BH
Area of Operation: UK (Excluding Ireland)
Tel: 01934 844484   **Fax:** 01934 844119
Email: info@ecosolutions.co.uk
Web: www.strip-paint.com   **Product Type:** 7

GEOCEL LIMITED
Western Wood Way, Langage Science Park,
Plympton, Plymouth, Devon, PL7 5BG
Area of Operation: UK & Ireland
Tel: 01752 334350   **Fax:** 01752 202065
Email: info@geocel.co.uk   **Web:** www.geocel.co.uk
Product Type: 7   **Other Info:** ECO

GREEN BUILDING STORE
11 Huddersfield Road, Meltham,
Holmfirth, West Yorkshire, HD9 4NJ
Area of Operation: UK & Ireland
Tel: 01484 854898   **Fax:** 01484 854899
Email: info@greenbuildingstore.co.uk
Web: www.greenbuildingstore.co.uk
Product Type: 3, 4, 5, 7
Other Info: ECO

GUARDIAN PRESERVATION SERVICES LLP
12 Woods Orchard Road, Gloucester,
Gloucestershire, GL4 0BU
Area of Operation: UK (Excluding Ireland)
Tel: 01452 530030   **Fax:** 01452 530031
Email: info@guardianpreservation.co.uk
Web: www.guardianpreservation.co.uk
Product Type: 1, 2, 4, 7

INDOOR CLIMATE SOLUTIONS
6 Charlesworth Avenue, Monkspath, Solihull,
West Midlands, B90 4SE
Area of Operation: Midlands & Mid Wales
Tel: 0121 733 2525
Email: info@ics-aircon.com
Web: www.ics-aircon.com   **Product Type:** 1, 2, 4

MOULD GROWTH CONSULTANTS LTD
McMillan House, Cheam Common Road, Worcester
Park, Surrey, KT4 8RH
Area of Operation: UK & Ireland
Tel: 0208 337 0731   **Fax:** 0208 337 3739
Email: info@mgcltd.co.uk
Web: www.mgcltd.co.uk   **Product Type:** 3, 5, 7

NUTSHELL NATURAL PAINTS
PO Box 72, South Brent, Devon, TQ10 9YR
Area of Operation: Worldwide
Tel: 0870 033 1140   **Fax:** 01752 692200
Email: info@nutshellpaints.com
Web: www.nutshellpaints.com   **Product Type:** 5

OSMO UK LTD
Unit 24 Anglo Business Park, Smeaton Close,
Aylesbury, Buckinghamshire, HP19 8UP
Area of Operation: UK & Ireland
Tel: 01296 481220   **Fax:** 01296 424090
Email: info@osmouk.com
Web: www.osmouk.com   **Product Type:** 5

REPAIR CARE INTERNATIONAL LIMITED
Unit E, Sawtry Business Park, Glatton Road,
Sawtry, Huntingdon, Cambridgeshire, PE28 5GQ
Area of Operation: UK & Ireland
Tel: 01487 830311   **Fax:** 01487 832876
Email: salesuk@repair-care.com
Web: www.repair-care.com   **Product Type:** 2, 3

ROOF-TEK LTD
19 Lynx Crescent, Weston-Super-Mare,
Somerset, BS24 9DJ
Area of Operation: East England, Greater London,
Midlands & Mid Wales, South East England, South
West England and South Wales
Tel: 01934 642929   **Fax:** 01934 644290
Email: enquiries@rooftek.co.uk
Web: www.rooftek.co.uk

RUSTINS LTD
Waterloo Road, London, NW2 7TX
Tel: 0208 450 4666   **Fax:** 0208 452 2008
Email: rustins@rustins.co.uk
Web: www.rustins.co.uk

SAFEGUARD EUROPE LTD
Redkiln Close, Redkiln Way,
Horsham, West Sussex, RH13 5QL
Area of Operation: Worldwide
Tel: 01403 210204
 Fax: 01403 217529
Email: info@safeguardeurope.com
Web: www.safeguardeurope.com
Product Type: 1, 2, 4

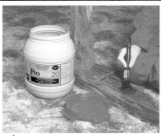

SAFEGUARD
Area of Operation: Worldwide
Tel: 01403 210204
Fax: 01403 217529
Email: info@safeguardeurope.com
Web: www.safeguardeurope.com
Product Type: 1, 2, 4

Safeguard's ProBor range of timber treatments
are specifically designed to treat woodworm,
dry rot and wet rot in refurbishment projects.

SAFEGUARD
Area of Operation: Worldwide
Tel: 01403 210204
Fax: 01403 217529
Email: info@safeguardeurope.com
Web: www.safeguardeurope.com

Protect expensive wooden flooring from damp &
contaminated floor-slabs with Oldroyd Xs
membrane – available from Safeguard.

SAFEGUARD
Area of Operation: Worldwide
Tel: 01403 210204
Fax: 01403 217529
Email: info@safeguardeurope.com
Web: www.safeguardeurope.com
Product Type: 2, 3, 4

Safeguard supply a choice of systems for
waterproofing new-build and existing basements.
CAD drawings can be downloaded from the
company's website.

WD-40 COMPANY LTD
PO Box 440, Kiln Farm, Milton Keynes, MK11 3LF
Area of Operation: Worldwide
Tel: 01908 555400   **Fax:** 01908 266900
Email: info@wd40.co.uk
Web: www.wd40.co.uk
Product Type: 6, 7

WINN & COALES (DENSO) LTD
Denso House, Chapel Road, London, SE27 0TR
Area of Operation: Worldwide
Tel: 0208 670 7511   **Fax:** 0208 761 2456
Email: mail@denso.net
Web: www.denso.net   **Product Type:** 7

WISE PROPERTY CARE
8 Muriel Street, Barrhead, Glasgow, G78 1QB
Area of Operation: Scotland
Tel: 0141 876 0300
Fax: 0141 876 0301
Email: les@wisepropertycare.com
Web: www.wisepropertycare.com
Product Type: 1, 2

FIXINGS

KEY

PRODUCT TYPES: 1= Mechanical Fixings
2 = Threaded Fixings

SEE ALSO: MERCHANTS - Builders Merchants,
FIXINGS, ADHESIVES AND TREATMENTS - Wall
Ties

OTHER: ▽ Reclaimed   On-line shopping
Bespoke   Hand-made   ECO Ecological

ACE FIXINGS
Woodside Industrial Estate,
Woodside Road, Ballymena, BT42 4HX
Area of Operation: UK & Ireland
Tel: 02825 649323
Fax: 02825 659334
Email: mark.robinson@acefixings.com
Web: www.acefixings.com
Product Type: 1

ANCON BUILDING PRODUCTS
President Way, President Park,
Sheffield, South Yorkshire, S4 7UR
Area of Operation: Worldwide
Tel: 0114 238 1238   **Fax:** 0114 276 8543
Email: info@ancon.co.uk
Web: www.ancon.co.uk   **Product Type:** 1, 2

BATHROOM CITY
Seeleys Road, Tyseley Industrial Estate,
Birmingham, West Midlands, B11 2LQ
Area of Operation: UK & Ireland
Tel: 0121 753 0700   **Fax:** 0121 753 1110
Email: sales@bathroomcity.com
Web: www.bathroomcity.com   **Product Type:** 1

BLIND BOLT COMPANY
Tollgate Industrial Estate, Stafford,
Staffordshire, ST16 3HS
Area of Operation: Worldwide
Tel: 01785 270629
Fax: 01785 270626
Email: sales@blindbolt.eu
Web: www.blindbolt.eu
Product Type: 1

BPB ARTEX LTD
Pasture Lane, Ruddington, Nottingham,
Nottinghamshire, NG11 6AE
Area of Operation: UK (Excluding Ireland)
Tel: 0115 984 5679   **Fax:** 0115 940 5240
Email: info@bpb.com
Web: www.bpbartex.co.uk

BPC BUILDING PRODUCTS LTD.
Flanshaw Way, Wakefield, West Yorkshire, WF2 9LP
Area of Operation: UK & Ireland
Tel: 01924 364794
Fax: 01924 373846
Email: gareth@bpcfixings.com
Web: www.bpcfixings.com
Product Type: 1

E.W. FITTON & CO
6 Top Schwabe Street, Rhodes,
Middleton, Manchester, M24 4TQ
Area of Operation: Europe
Tel: 0161 643 1296   **Fax:** 0161 643 1296
Email: ernest.fitton@tiscali.co.uk
Web: www.fit-onfixseal.com
Product Type: 1

HENKEL CONSUMER ADHESIVES
Apollo Court, 2 Bishop Square Business Park,
Hatfield, Hertfordshire, AL10 9EY
Area of Operation: Worldwide
Tel: 01707 635000   **Fax:** 01707 289029
Web: www.henkel.co.uk
Product Type: 1

LEOFIXINGS.COM
Unit 6, Scotshawbrook Industrial Estate, Branch
Road, Lower Darwen, Darwen, Lancashire, BB3 0PR
Area of Operation: UK & Ireland
Tel: 01254 278757   **Fax:** 01254 278767
Email: info@leofixings.com
Web: www.leofixings.com
Product Type: 1, 2

ORAC (UK) LIMITED
Unit 5, Hewitts Estate, Elmbridge Road,
Cranleigh, Surrey, GU6 8LW
Area of Operation: Worldwide
Tel: 01483 271211   **Fax:** 01483 278317
Email: stewart@oracdecor.com
Web: www.oracdecor.com

POWERPLACE LTD
The Firs, Newton, Frodsham, Cheshire, WA6 6TE
Area of Operation: UK & Ireland
Tel: 01928 787127
Fax: 01928 788448
Email: powerplace@fsbdial.com
Web: www.powerplaceltd.com
Product Type: 1, 2

RAPIERSTAR LTD
Star Business Park, Buxton Road, Bosley,
Macclesfield, Cheshire, SK11 0PS
Area of Operation: Europe
Tel: 0870 300 3312
Fax: 0870 300 3314
Email: enquiries@rapierstar.com
Web: www.rapierstar.com
Product Type: 1, 2

RAPIERSTAR LTD
Area of Operation: Europe
Tel: 0870 300 3312
Fax: 0870 300 3314
Email: enquiries@rapierstar.com
Web: www.rapierstar.com
Product Type: 1, 2

Rapierstar offer a complete range of superior performance fixings, including Universal Woodscrews, Direct Frame Fixings and Decking Screws, saving time and money on your project.

SEAC LTD
46 Chesterfield Road, Leicester, Leicestershire, LE5 5LP
Area of Operation: Worldwide
Tel: 0116 273 9501   **Fax:** 0116 273 8373
Email: enquiries@seac.uk.com
Web: www.seac.uk.com   **Product Type:** 1, 2

T I MIDWOOD & CO LIMITED
Green Lane, Wardle, Nantwich, Cheshire, CW5 6BJ
Area of Operation: Europe
Tel: 01829 261111   **Fax:** 01829 261102
Email: simon@timcouk.com
Web: www.timcouk.com   **Product Type:** 2

THIN JOINT TECHNOLOGY LTD
3 Albright Road, Speke Approaches Industrial Estate, Liverpool, Merseyside, WA8 8FY
Area of Operation: UK & Ireland
Tel: 0151 422 8000   **Fax:** 0151 422 8001
Email: sales@thinjoint.com
Web: www.thinjoint.com   **Product Type:** 1, 2

TITE-FIX LTD
PO Box 115, Castleford, West Yorkshire, WF10 4WR
Area of Operation: Worldwide
Tel: 0870 043 4571   **Fax:** 0870 043 4572
Email: michaelwilkinson@tite-fix.co.uk
Web: www.tite-fix.co.uk   **Product Type:** 1, 2

UNIFIX LTD
St Georges House, Grove Lane, Smethwick, Birmingham, West Midlands, B66 2QT
Area of Operation: Europe
Tel: 0800 096 1110   **Fax:** 0800 096 1115
Email: sales@unifix.com
Web: www.unifix-online.co.uk
Product Type: 1, 2

WETHERBY BUILDING SYSTEMS LIMITED
1 Kidglove Road, Golborne Enterprise Park, Golborne, Greater Manchester, WA3 3GS
Area of Operation: UK & Ireland
Tel: 01942 717100
Fax: 01942 717101
Email: info@wbs-ltd.co.uk
Web: www.wbs-ltd.co.uk   **Product Type:** 2

PLEASE MENTION

THE HOMEBUILDER'S HANDBOOK 2007

WHEN YOU CALL

WALL TIES

KEY
PRODUCT TYPES: 1= Brick-to-Block Ties
2 = Brick-to-Timber Ties   3 = Brick-to-Steel Ties   4 = Wall Starter Systems

OTHER: ▽ Reclaimed   On-line shopping
Bespoke   Hand-made   ECO Ecological

ACE FIXINGS
Woodside Industrial Estate, Woodside Road, Ballymena, BT42 4HX
Tel: 02825 649323   **Fax:** 02825 659334
Email: mark.robinson@acefixings.com
Web: www.acefixings.com
Product Type: 1, 2, 3, 4

ANCON BUILDING PRODUCTS
President Way, President Park, Sheffield, South Yorkshire, S4 7UR
Area of Operation: Worldwide
Tel: 0114 238 1238   **Fax:** 0114 276 8543
Email: info@ancon.co.uk
Web: www.ancon.co.uk   **Product Type:** 1, 2, 3, 4

BPC BUILDING PRODUCTS LTD.
Flanshaw Way, Wakefield, West Yorkshire, WF2 9LP
Tel: 01924 364794   **Fax:** 01924 373846
Email: gareth@bpcfixings.com
Web: www.bpcfixings.com   **Product Type:** 1, 2

CATNIC
Pontypandy Industrial Estate, Caerphilly, CF83 3GL
Area of Operation: Worldwide
Tel: 029 2033 7900   **Fax:** 029 2033 7900
Email: barry.jenkins@corusgroup.com
Web: www.catnic.com

HELICAL SYSTEMS LTD
The Old Police Station, 195 Main Road, Biggin Hill, Westerham, Kent, TN16 3JU
Tel: 01959 541148   **Fax:** 01959 540841
Email: janecannon@helicalsystems.co.uk
Web: www.helicalsystems.co.uk
Product Type: 1, 2, 4

LEOWALLTIES.COM
Unit 6, Scotshawbrook Industrial Estate, Branch Road, Lower Darwen, Darwen, Lancashire, BB3 0PR
Area of Operation: UK & Ireland
Tel: 01254 278757   **Fax:** 01254 278767
Email: info@leowallties.com
Web: www.leowallties.com

POWERPLACE LTD
The Firs, Newton, Frodsham, Cheshire, WA6 6TE
Area of Operation: UK & Ireland
Tel: 01928 787127   **Fax:** 01928 788448
Email: powerplace@fsbdial.co.uk
Web: www.powerplaceltd.com
Product Type: 1, 2, 3, 4

SAFEGUARD EUROPE LTD
Redkiln Close, Redkiln Way, Horsham, West Sussex, RH13 5QL
Area of Operation: Worldwide
Tel: 01403 210204   **Fax:** 01403 217529
Email: info@safeguardeurope.com
Web: www.safeguardeurope.com   **Product Type:** 2

THIN JOINT TECHNOLOGY LTD
3 Albright Road, Speke Approaches Industrial Estate, Liverpool, Merseyside, WA8 8FY
Tel: 0151 422 8000   **Fax:** 0151 422 8001
Email: sales@thinjoint.com
Web: www.thinjoint.com   **Product Type:** 1, 2

TRITON CHEMICAL MANUFACTURING LTD
129 Felixstowe Road, Abbey Wood, London, SE2 9SG
Area of Operation: Worldwide
Tel: 0208 310 3929   **Fax:** 0208 312 0349
Email: neil@triton-chemicals.com
Web: www.triton-chemicals.com

NOTES

Company Name ....
....
Address ....
....
....
email ....
Web ....

Company Name ....
....
Address ....
....
....
email ....
Web ....

Company Name ....
....
Address ....
....
....
email ....
Web ....

Company Name ....
....
Address ....
....
....
email ....
Web ....

Company Name ....
....
Address ....
....
....
email ....
Web ....

Company Name ....
....
Address ....
....
....
email ....
Web ....

Company Name ....
....
Address ....
....
....
email ....
Web ....

Company Name ....
....
Address ....
....
....
email ....
Web ....

Company Name ....
....
Address ....
....
....
email ....
Web ....

Company Name ....
....
Address ....
....
....
email ....
Web ....

HOMEBUILDING & RENOVATING ARCHIVE CD-ROM

Britain's Best Selling Self-Build Magazine

HOMEBUILDING & RENOVATING

12 ISSUES OF HOMEBUILDING & RENOVATING ON 2 CDS!

- All pages and pictures appear exactly as they do in the magazine.
- Easy to navigate and fully searchable.
- All supplier information and contacts are linked to email and web addresses.
- Clickable contents page.

To order visit our online shop at:
www.homebuilding.co.uk, or call 01527 834435

Unit 2 Sugar Brook Court
Aston Road
Bromsgrove
Worcestershire
B60 3EX

Tel: 01527 834435
Fax: 01527 837810
Email: customerservice@centaur.co.uk
Website: www.homebuilding.co.uk

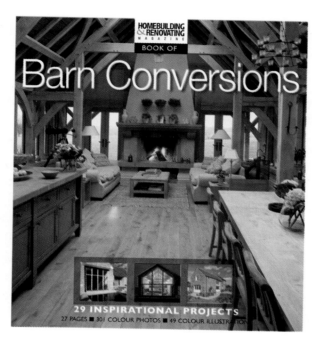

SPONSORED BY: Homebuilding & Renovating Book of Barn Conversions
Tel: 01527 834435 Web: www.homebuilding.co.uk/bookshop

Lime Mortars and Renders

"Green" builders are re-discovering the benefits of lime as the main setting agent in mortars, renders and concrete.

Lime Putty

Lime putty is made by adding water to quicklime - enough to make a thick creamy paste - and is the basis for all lime renders, plasters, mortars and washes. It is best to buy this ready-made from one of the specialist suppliers, as the procedure can be dangerous. Do not be tempted to make do with the 'bagged' hydrated lime commonly available in builders' merchants. It is a poor substitute and will not perform well in pure lime applications.

The use of pure lime products is labour intensive, needs planning well in advance and is not conducive to the quick-build, fast-track approach of the modern construction industry. On the other hand, it will be used and appreciated by those lovingly restoring old buildings in an authentic way, and by ecologically minded builders looking for a low-energy, 'soft' finish which will breathe and move with the building itself.

Hydraulic Lime

Hydraulic lime is produced using certain limestones containing impurities of silica and alumina. It has the practical advantage of a quick initial chemical set (like cement) on the outer surface, followed by a much slower process of carbonation (like lime). It is, therefore, easier to integrate its use with the demands of modern construction practice.

However, this convenience comes at an environmental cost. Hydraulic lime needs extreme firing temperatures of about 1,200°C and it absorbs only around half of the CO_2 given off in the production process.

Premixed Mortars and Renders

The performance of hydraulic lime mortars and renders is very dependant on using accurately gauged mixes, so many lime suppliers will also supply pre-bagged lime/sand mixes. For larger sites, ready-mixed, dry hydraulic lime mortars can be delivered to site using tankers and bulk

silos for storage. Equally welcome is the introduction of recycled aggregates, including attractive examples which use ground-coloured recycled glass.

Why Use Lime?

• Lime mortars and renders are less brittle and as such are not prone to cracking – generally no movement joints are required.

• Bricks and blocks set in lime mortar can be easily cleaned up for re-use.

• Lower firing temperature uses less fuel.

• Much of the CO2 emitted during the firing process is absorbed by the lime as it sets

Courses

A number of companies run lime courses and workshops - see the Exhibitions, Courses & Events Diary (starting on page 451) for examples taking place in 2007.

Clad in a combination of natural lime render, reinforced with horsehair, this house is highly ecological.

CONCRETE

KEY

PRODUCT TYPES: 1= Concrete Ready Mix
2 = Bagged Concrete   3 = Mini Loads
4 = Cement and Concrete Mixers

OTHER: ▽ Reclaimed   ⌐🖐 On-line shopping
✏ Bespoke   ✋ Hand-made   ECO Ecological

ACE MINIMIX
Millfields Road, Ettingshall, Wolverhampton,
West Midlands, WV4 6JP
Area of Operation: UK (Excluding Ireland)
Tel: 0121 5855559   **Fax:** 0121 585 5557
Email: info@tarmac.co.uk
Web: www.tarmac.co.uk   **Product Type:** 1, 3, 4

ARDEX UK LIMITED
Homefield Road, Haverhill, Suffolk, CB9 8QP
Area of Operation: UK (Excluding Ireland)
Tel: 01440 714939   **Fax:** 01440 716660
Email: info@ardex.co.uk
Web: www.ardex.co.uk   **Product Type:** 1, 2, 4

BORDER CONCRETE PRODUCTS
Jedburgh Road, Kelso, Borders, TD5 8JG
Area of Operation: North East England, North West
England and North Wales, Scotland
Tel: 01573 224393   **Fax:** 01573 276360
Email: sales@borderconcrete.co.uk
Web: www.borderconcrete.co.uk
Other Info: ✏ ✋

BRITISH CEMENT ASSOCIATION
The Concrete Centre, Riverside House,
4 Meadows Business Park, Station Approach,
Blackwater, Camberley, Surrey, GU17 9AB
Area of Operation: UK (Excluding Ireland)
Tel: 01276 608700   **Fax:** 01276 608701
Email: enquiries@concretecentre.com
Web: www.concretecentre.com

CASTLE CEMENT LIMITED
Park Square, 3160 Solihull Parkway, Birmingham
Business Park, Birmingham, West Midlands, B37 7YN
Area of Operation: UK (Excluding Ireland)
Tel: 0845 600 1616   **Fax:** 0121 606 1436
Email: customer.services@castlecement.co.uk
Web: www.castlecement.co.uk   **Product Type:** 2

CEMEX READYMIX
Cemex House, Rugby, Warwickshire, CV21 2DT
Area of Operation: Worldwide
Tel: 0800 667 827
Fax: 01788 564404
Email: info.readymix@cemex.co.uk
Web: www.cemex.co.uk ⌐🖐
Product Type: 1, 3

CJ O'SHEA & CO LTD
Unit 1 Granard Business Centre, Burns Lane, Mill Hill,
London, NW7 2DZ
Area of Operation: East England, Greater London, South
East England, South West England and South Wales
Tel: 0208 959 3600
Fax: 0208 959 0184
Email: admin@oshea.co.uk   **Web:** www.oshea.co.uk

H+H CELCON LIMITED
Celcon House, Ightham, Sevenoaks, Kent, TN15 9HZ
Area of Operation: UK (Excluding Ireland)
Tel: 01732 880520   **Fax:** 01732 880531
Email: marketing@celcon.co.uk
Web: www.celcon.co.uk

HANSON BUILDING PRODUCTS
Stewartby, Bedford, Bedfordshire, MK43 9LZ
Area of Operation: Worldwide
Tel: 08705 258258
Fax: 01234 762040
Email: info@hansonbp.com
Web: www.hanson.biz
Product Type: 1, 2, 4

NATURAL CEMENT DISTRIBUTION LTD
15 Fountain Parade, Mapplewell,
Barnsley, South Yorkshire, S75 6FW
Area of Operation: Worldwide
Tel: 01226 381133
Fax: 01226 381177
Email: phil@naturalcement.co.uk
Web: www.naturalcement.co.uk

STONE2YOURHOME
Area of Operation: UK (Excluding Ireland)
Tel: 0871 8732369
Email: info@stone2yourhome.co.uk
Web: www.stone2yourhome.co.uk ⌐🖐
Product Type: 2

TARMAC LIMITED
Millfields Road, Ettingshall,
olverhampton, West Midlands, WV4 6JP
Area of Operation: Europe
Tel: 01902 353522
Fax: 01902 382922
Email: info@tarmac.co.uk
Web: www.tarmac.co.uk

AGGREGATES

KEY

OTHER: ▽ Reclaimed   ⌐🖐 On-line shopping
✏ Bespoke   ✋ Hand-made   ECO Ecological

ACE MINIMIX
Millfields Road, Ettingshall,
Wolverhampton, West Midlands, WV4 6JP
Area of Operation: UK (Excluding Ireland)
Tel: 0121 585 5559   **Fax:** 0121 585 5557
Email: info@tarmac.co.uk   **Web:** www.tarmac.co.uk

BARDON AGGREGATES
Hulland Ward, Ashbourne, Derbyshire, DE6 3ET
Area of Operation: Worldwide
Tel: 0845 600 0860
Fax: 01335 372485
Web: www.bardon-aggregates.com

BRETT AGGREGATES LIMITED
Brett House, Bysing Wood Road,
Faversham, Kent, ME13 7UD
Area of Operation: South East England
Tel: 0800 028 5980   **Fax:** 0800 028 5979
Web: www.brett.co.uk

BRETT LANDSCAPING LTD
Salt Lane, Cliffe, Rochester, Kent, ME3 7SZ
Area of Operation: Worldwide
Tel: 01634 222188
Fax: 01634 222186
Email: cliffeenquiries@brett.co.uk
Web: www.brett.co.uk/landscaping

CEMEX UK MATERIALS LTD
Cemex House, Evreux Way,
Rugby, Warwickshire, CV21 2DT
Area of Operation: UK (Excluding Ireland)
Tel: 01788 542111
Fax: 01788 514747
Email: webmanager.hbm@cemex.com
Web: www.cemex.co.uk

HANSON BUILDING PRODUCTS
Stewartby, Bedford, Bedfordshire, MK43 9LZ
Area of Operation: Worldwide
Tel: 08705 258258
Fax: 01234 762040
Email: info@hansonbp.com
Web: www.hanson.biz

J & A PLASTERING
34 Moore Crescent, Netley Abbey,
Southampton, Hampshire, SA31 1PZ
Area of Operation: South East England
Tel: 02380 560762
Email: crosbykriss@aol.com

KIRK NATURAL STONE
Bridgend, Fyvie, Turriff, Aberdeenshire, AB53 8LL
Area of Operation: Worldwide
Tel: 01651 891891   **Fax:** 01651 891794
Email: info@kirknaturalstone.com
Web: www.kirknaturalstone.com

LAFARGE CEMENT
Manor Court, Chilton, Oxfordshire, OX11 0RN
Area of Operation: UK & Ireland
Tel: 01235 448400   **Fax:** 01235 448600
Email: info@lafargecement.co.uk
Web: www.lafargecement.co.uk

LIMEBASE PRODUCTS LTD
Walronds Park, Isle Brewers,
Taunton, Somerset, TA3 6QP
Area of Operation: UK & Ireland
Tel: 01460 281921   **Fax:** 01460 281100
Email: info@limebase.co.uk
Web: www.limebase.co.uk

MIRATEX LIMITED
Unit 10, Park Hall Farm, Brookhouse Road,
Cheadle, Staffordshire, ST10 2NJ
Area of Operation: UK & Ireland
Tel: 01538 750923   **Fax:** 01538 752078
Email: info@miratex.co.uk
Web: www.miratex.co.uk

RIVAR SAND & GRAVEL LTD
Pinchington Lane, Newbury, Berkshire, RG19 8SR
Area of Operation: South East England
Tel: 01635 523524   **Fax:** 01635 521621
Email: sales@rivarsandandgravel.co.uk
Web: www.rivarsandandgravel.co.uk
Other Info: ✏

ROSE OF JERICHO
Horchester Farm, Holywell, Dorchester, Dorset, DT2 0LL
Area of Operation: UK (Excluding Ireland)
Tel: 01935 83676   **Fax:** 01935 83903
Email: info@rose-of-jericho.demon.co.uk
Web: www.rose-of-jericho.demon.co.uk

SCOTTISH LIME CENTRE TRUST
Charleston Workshop, Rocks Road, Charlestown, Nr
Dunfermline, Fife, KY11 3EN
Area of Operation: Scotland
Tel: 01383 872722   **Fax:** 01383 872744
Email: info@scotlime.org   **Web:** www.scotlime.org

STONE2YOURHOME
Area of Operation: UK (Excluding Ireland)
Tel: 0871 8732369
Email: info@stone2yourhome.co.uk
Web: www.stone2yourhome.co.uk ⌐🖐

TARMAC LIMITED
Millfields Road, Ettingshall, Wolverhampton, West
Midlands, WV4 6JP
Area of Operation: Europe
Tel: 01902 353522   **Fax:** 01902 382922
Email: info@tarmac.co.uk
Web: www.tarmac.co.uk

THE CORNISH LIME COMPANY LTD.
Brims Park, Old Callywith Road,
Bodmin, Cornwall, PL31 2DZ
Area of Operation: UK (Excluding Ireland)
Tel: 01208 79779   **Fax:** 01208 73744
Email: sales@cornishlime.co.uk
Web: www.cornishlime.co.uk ⌐🖐

TRADITIONAL LIME CO
The Salvage Yard, Rath, Shillelagh Road, Tullow,
Co.Carlow, Ireland
Area of Operation: Ireland Only
Tel: 00353 599 151 750   **Fax:** 00353 599 152 113
Email: admin@traditionallime.com
Web: www.traditionallime.com

TY-MAWR LIME LTD
Ty-Mawr, Llangasty, Brecon, Powys, LD3 7PJ
Area of Operation: UK & Ireland
Tel: 01874 658000
Email: joyce.gervis@lime.org.uk
Web: www.lime.org.uk ⌐🖐
Other Info: ▽ ECO ✏ ✋

SAND

KEY

OTHER: ▽ Reclaimed   ⌐🖐 On-line shopping
✏ Bespoke   ✋ Hand-made   ECO Ecological

ACE MINIMIX
Millfields Road, Ettingshall,
Wolverhampton, West Midlands, WV4 6JP
Area of Operation: UK (Excluding Ireland)
Tel: 0121 5855559   **Fax:** 0121 585 5557
Email: info@tarmac.co.uk
Web: www.tarmac.co.uk

J & A PLASTERING
34 Moore Crescent, Netley Abbey,
Southampton, Hampshire , SA31 1PZ
Area of Operation: South East England
Tel: 02380 560762
Email: crosbykriss@aol.com

LIMEBASE PRODUCTS LTD
Walronds Park, Isle Brewers,
Taunton, Somerset, TA3 6QP
Area of Operation: UK & Ireland
Tel: 01460 281921   **Fax:** 01460 281100
Email: info@limebase.co.uk
Web: www.limebase.co.uk

RIVAR SAND & GRAVEL LTD
Pinchington Lane, Newbury, Berkshire, RG19 8SR
Area of Operation: South East England
Tel: 01635 523524
Fax: 01635 521621
Email: sales@rivarsandandgravel.co.uk
Web: www.rivarsandandgravel.co.uk

ROSE OF JERICHO
Horchester Farm, Holywell,
Dorchester, Dorset, DT2 0LL
Area of Operation: UK (Excluding Ireland)
Tel: 01935 83676
Fax: 01935 83903
Email: info@rose-of-jericho.demon.co.uk
Web: www.rose-of-jericho.demon.co.uk

SCOTTISH LIME CENTRE TRUST
Charleston Workshop, Rocks Road,
Charlestown, Nr Dunfermline, Fife, KY11 3EN
Area of Operation: Scotland
Tel: 01383 872722   **Fax:** 01383 872744
Email: info@scotlime.org
Web: www.scotlime.org

STONE2YOURHOME
Area of Operation: UK (Excluding Ireland)
Tel: 0871 8732369
Email: info@stone2yourhome.co.uk
Web: www.stone2yourhome.co.uk ⌐🖐

TARMAC LIMITED
Millfields Road, Ettingshall, Wolverhampton,
West Midlands, WV4 6JP
Area of Operation: Europe
Tel: 01902 353522   **Fax:** 01902 382922
Email: info@tarmac.co.uk
Web: www.tarmac.co.uk

THE CORNISH LIME COMPANY LTD.
Brims Park, Old Callywith Road,
Bodmin, Cornwall, PL31 2DZ
Area of Operation: UK (Excluding Ireland)
Tel: 01208 79779   **Fax:** 01208 73744
Email: sales@cornishlime.co.uk
Web: www.cornishlime.co.uk ⌐🖐

TRADITIONAL LIME CO
The Salvage Yard, Rath, Shillelagh Road,
Tullow, Co.Carlow, Ireland
Area of Operation: Ireland Only
Tel: 00353 599 151 750   **Fax:** 00353 599 152 113
Email: admin@traditionallime.com
Web: www.traditionallime.com

BUILDING STRUCTURE & MATERIALS *(vertical sidebar)*

TY-MAWR LIME LTD
Ty-Mawr, Llangasty, Brecon, Powys, LD3 7PJ
Area of Operation: UK & Ireland
Tel: 01874 658000 **Email:** joyce.gervis@lime.org.uk
Web: www.lime.org.uk ⊕ **Other Info:** ▽ ECO

LIMES

KEY
PRODUCT TYPES: 1= Bagged Limes
2 = Lime Putty   3 = Hydrated Lime
4 = Unhydrated Lime   5 = Lime Cement Mixes
6 = Pre-mixed Lime Renders, Lime Paints and
Washes

OTHER: ▽ Reclaimed ⊕ On-line shopping
✐ Bespoke 🖐 Hand-made   ECO Ecological

ANGLIA LIME COMPANY
Fishers Farm, Belchamp Walter,
Sudbury, Suffolk, CO10 7AP
Area of Operation: East England, Greater London
Tel: 01787 313974 **Fax:** 01787 313944
Email: info@anglialime.com
Web: www.anglialime.com **Product Type:** 2, 6

ARTIKA ORNAMENTAL PLASTERERS
6 The Retreat, Foxcote, Radstock, Somerset, BA3 5YF
Area of Operation: Worldwide
Tel: 01761 433740
Email: mark@artika.f9.co.uk
Web: www.bathbusinessfinder.co.uk/artika/index.php
Product Type: 2

BACK TO EARTH
Jubilee House, Cheriton Fitzpaine,
Crediton, Devon, EX17 4JH
Area of Operation: South West England and South Wales
Tel: 01363 866999 **Fax:** 01363 866998
Email: chris@backtoearth.co.uk
Web: www.backtoearth.co.uk **Product Type:** 4, 6

BUXTON LIME INDUSTRIES
Tunstead House, Buxton, Derbyshire, SK17 8TG
Area of Operation: UK (Excluding Ireland)
Tel: 01298 768444
Fax: 01298 72195
Email: buxton.sales@buxtonlime.co.uk
Web: www.buxtonline.co.uk **Product Type:** 3, 4

CASTLE CEMENT LIMITED
Park Square, 3160 Solihull Parkway ,
Birmingham Business Park, Birmingham,
West Midlands, B37 7YN
Area of Operation: UK (Excluding Ireland)
Tel: 0845 600 1616 **Fax:** 0121 606 1436
Email: customer.services@castlecement.co.uk
Web: www.castlecement.co.uk
Product Type: 1, 2, 3, 5

CHALK DOWN LIME
The Yard, Gate Farm, Northiam Road, Staplecross,
Nr Robertsbridge, East Sussex, TN32 5RP
Area of Operation: South East England
Tel: 01580 830092 **Fax:** 01580 830096
Email: chalkdownlime@aol.com
Web: www.chalkdownlime.co.uk
Product Type: 1, 2, 6

HYDRAULIC LIMES
The Lime Loft, Priestlands Lane, Sherborne, Dorset, DT9 4HL
Area of Operation: Worldwide
Tel: 01935 815290 **Fax:** 01935 815290
Email: info@hydrauliclimes.co.uk
Web: www.hydrauliclimes.co.uk
Product Type: 1, 2, 3, 4, 6 **Other Info:** ECO

J & A PLASTERING
34 Moore Crescent, Netley Abbey,
Southampton, Hampshire, SA31 1PZ
Area of Operation: South East England
Tel: 02380 560762 **Email:** crosbykriss@aol.com
Product Type: 2, 3, 4, 5

J&J SHARPE
Furzedon, Merton, Okehampton, Devon, EX20 3DS
Area of Operation: UK (Excluding Ireland)
Tel: 01805 603587 **Fax:** 01805 603587
Email: mail@jjsharpe.co.uk
Web: www.jjsharpe.co.uk **Product Type:** 2, 6

LIME TECHNOLOGY LIMITED
Unit 126, Milton Park, Abingdon,
Oxfordshire, OX14 4SA
Area of Operation: Worldwide
Tel: 0845 603 1143 **Fax:** 0845 634 1560
Email: info@limetechnology.co.uk
Web: www.limetechnology.co.uk
Product Type: 1, 3, 6

LIME TECHNOLOGY LIMITED
Area of Operation: Worldwide
Tel: 0845 603 1143
Fax: 0845 634 1560
Email: info@limetechnology.co.uk
Web: www.limetechnology.co.uk
Product Type: 1, 5
Other Info: ECO

Limetec hydraulic lime-based mortars, plasters
and renders. Suitable for conservation and new
build. Mortars in three mix proportions, sprayable
plasters and renders — basecoat, internal finish,
bonding, roughcast - in 25kg bags.

LIMEBASE PRODUCTS LTD
Walronds Park, Isle Brewers,
Taunton, Somerset, TA3 6QP
Area of Operation: UK & Ireland
Tel: 01460 281921 **Fax:** 01460 281100
Email: info@limebase.co.uk
Web: www.limebase.co.uk **Product Type:** 1, 2, 6

M CARRINGTON
20 High Street, Somersham,
Huntingdon, Cambridgeshire, PE28 3JA
Area of Operation: UK (Excluding Ireland)
Tel: 01487 840305 **Fax:** 01487 840305
Email: malcolm@mcarrington.com
Web: www.mcarrington.com
Product Type: 1, 2, 3, 4, 5, 6

MIKE WYE & ASSOCIATES
Buckland Filleigh Sawmills, Buckland Filleigh,
Beaworthy, Devon, EX21 5RN
Area of Operation: Worldwide
Tel: 01409 281644 **Fax:** 01409 281669
Email: sales@mikewye.co.uk
Web: www.mikewye.co.uk
Product Type: 2, 6 **Other Info:** ECO

NATURAL BUILDING TECHNOLOGIES
The Hangar, Worminghall Road,
Oakley, Buckinghamshire, HP18 9UL
Area of Operation: UK & Ireland
Tel: 01844 338338
Fax: 01844 338525
Email: info@natural-building.co.uk
Web: www.natural-building.co.uk
Product Type: 5 **Other Info:** ECO

OLD HOUSE STORE LTD
Hampstead Farm, Binfield Heath,
Henley on Thames, Oxfordshire, RG9 4LG
Area of Operation: Worldwide
Tel: 0118 969 7711 **Fax:** 0118 969 8822
Email: info@oldhousestore.co.uk
Web: www.oldhousestore.co.uk ⊕
Product Type: 1, 2, 6 **Other Info:** ECO

ROSE OF JERICHO
Horchester Farm, Holywell, Dorchester, Dorset, DT2 0LL
Area of Operation: UK (Excluding Ireland)
Tel: 01935 83676 **Fax:** 01935 83903
Email: info@rose-of-jericho.demon.co.uk
Web: www.rose-of-jericho.demon.co.uk
Product Type: 2, 6

SCOTTISH LIME CENTRE TRUST
Charleston Workshop, Rocks Road,
Charlestown, Nr Dunfermline, Fife, KY11 3EN
Area of Operation: Scotland
Tel: 01383 872722 **Fax:** 01383 872744
Email: info@scotlime.org
Web: www.scotlime.org
Product Type: 1, 2, 4, 6

TARMAC LIMITED
Millfields Road, Ettingshall, Wolverhampton, WV4 6JP
Area of Operation: Europe
Tel: 01902 353522 **Fax:** 01902 382922
Email: info@tarmac.co.uk
Web: www.tarmac.co.uk

THE CORNISH LIME COMPANY LTD.
Brims Park, Old Callywith Road,
Bodmin, Cornwall, PL31 2DZ
Area of Operation: UK (Excluding Ireland)
Tel: 01208 79779 **Fax:** 01208 73744
Email: sales@cornishlime.co.uk
Web: www.cornishlime.co.uk ⊕
Product Type: 1, 2, 3, 4, 5, 6 **Other Info:** ECO

TRADITIONAL LIME CO
The Salvage Yard, Rath, Shillelagh Road,
Tullow, Co.Carlow, Ireland
Area of Operation: Ireland Only
Tel: 00353 599 151 750 **Fax:** 00353 599 152 113
Email: admin@traditionallime.com
Web: www.traditionallime.com
Product Type: 2, 3, 4, 6

TY-MAWR LIME LTD
Ty-Mawr, Llangasty, Brecon, Powys, LD3 7PJ
Area of Operation: UK & Ireland
Tel: 01874 658000
Email: joyce.gervis@lime.org.uk
Web: www.lime.org.uk ⊕ **Product Type:** 1, 2, 6

MORTARS

KEY
PRODUCT TYPES:
1= Cement Mortar   2 = Mortar Additives
3 = Quick-setting Mortars
4 = Specialist Mortars

OTHER: ▽ Reclaimed ⊕ On-line shopping
✐ Bespoke 🖐 Hand-made   ECO Ecological

ANGLIA LIME COMPANY
Fishers Farm, Belchamp Walter,
Sudbury, Suffolk, CO10 7AP
Area of Operation: East England, Greater London
Tel: 01787 313974 **Fax:** 01787 313944
Email: info@anglialime.com
Web: www.anglialime.com **Product Type:** 4

ARDEX UK LIMITED
Homefield Road, Haverhill, Suffolk, CB9 8QP
Area of Operation: UK (Excluding Ireland)
Tel: 01440 714939
Fax: 01440 716660
Email: info@ardex.co.uk **Web:** www.ardex.co.uk
Product Type: 1, 2, 3, 4

ARTIKA ORNAMENTAL PLASTERERS
6 The Retreat, Foxcote, Radstock, Somerset, BA3 5YF
Area of Operation: Worldwide
Tel: 01761 433740
Email: mark@artika.f9.co.uk
www.bathbusinessfinder.co.uk/artika/index.php
Product Type: 4

BUXTON LIME INDUSTRIES
Tunstead House, Buxton, Derbyshire, SK17 8TG
Area of Operation: UK (Excluding Ireland)
Tel: 01298 768444 **Fax:** 01298 72195
Email: buxton.sales@buxtonlime.co.uk
Web: www.buxtonline.co.uk **Product Type:** 1

CASTLE CEMENT LIMITED
Park Square, 3160 Solihull Parkway, Birmingham
Business Park, Birmingham, West Midlands, B37 7YN
Area of Operation: UK (Excluding Ireland)
Tel: 0845 600 1616 **Fax:** 0121 606 1436
Email: customer.services@castlecement.co.uk
Web: www.castlecement.co.uk **Product Type:** 1

CEMEX READYMIX
Cemex House, Rugby, Warwickshire, CV21 2DT
Area of Operation: Worldwide
Tel: 0800 667827 **Fax:** 01788 564404
Email: info.readymix@cemex.co.uk
Web: www.cemex.co.uk ⊕ **Product Type:** 1, 2, 3, 4

CHALK DOWN LIME
The Yard, Gate Farm, Northiam Road, Staplecross,
Nr Robertsbridge, East Sussex, TN32 5RP
Area of Operation: South East England
Tel: 01580 830092 **Fax:** 01580 830096
Email: chalkdownlime@aol.com
Web: www.chalkdownlime.co.uk **Product Type:** 4

EASIPOINT MARKETING LIMITED
Restoration House, Drumhead Road,
Chorley North Industrial Estate,
Chorley, Lancashire, PR6 7DE
Area of Operation: UK & Ireland
Tel: 01257 224900 **Fax:** 01257 224901
Email: enquiries@easipoint.co.uk
Web: www.easipoint.co.uk **Product Type:** 4

HANSON BUILDING PRODUCTS
Stewartby, Bedford, Bedfordshire, MK43 9LZ
Area of Operation: Worldwide
Tel: 08705 258258 **Fax:** 01234 762040
Email: info@hansonbp.com
Web: www.hanson.biz **Product Type:** 1, 2, 3, 4

HYDRAULIC LIMES
The Lime Loft, Priestlands Lane,
Sherborne, Dorset, DT9 4HL
Area of Operation: Worldwide
Tel: 01935 815290 **Fax:** 01935 815290
Email: info@hydrauliclimes.co.uk
Web: www.hydrauliclimes.co.uk
Product Type: 4 **Other Info:** ECO

J & A PLASTERING
34 Moore Crescent, Netley Abbey,
Southampton, Hampshire, SA31 1PZ
Area of Operation: South East England
Tel: 02380 560762 **Email:** crosbykriss@aol.com
Product Type: 1

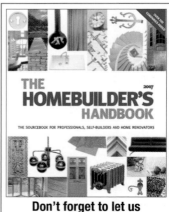

LIME TECHNOLOGY LIMITED
Unit 126, Milton Park, Abingdon,
Oxfordshire, OX14 4SA
Area of Operation: Worldwide
Tel: 0845 603 1143   **Fax:** 0845 634 1560
Email: info@limetechnology.co.uk
Web: www.limetechnology.co.uk   **Product Type:** 4

LIME TECHNOLOGY LIMITED

Area of Operation: Worldwide
Tel: 0845 603 1143
Fax: 0845 634 1560
Email: info@limetechnology.co.uk
Web: www.limetechnology.co.uk
Product Type: 4
Other Info: ECO

Limetec high performance hydraulic lime mortars suitable for conservation and new build. Mortars available in three dry pre-mixed proportions, supplied in silos for larger projects or 25kg bags.

LIMEBASE PRODUCTS LTD
Walronds Park, Isle Brewers, Taunton, Somerset, TA3 6QP
Area of Operation: UK & Ireland
Tel: 01460 281921   **Fax:** 01460 281100
Email: info@limebase.co.uk
Web: www.limebase.co.uk
Product Type: 4

MIRATEX LIMITED
Unit 10, Park Hall Farm, Brookhouse Road,
Cheadle, Staffordshire, ST10 2NJ
Area of Operation: UK & Ireland
Tel: 01538 750923   **Fax:** 01538 752078
Email: info@miratex.co.uk
Web: www.miratex.co.uk   **Product Type:** 4

NATURAL CEMENT DISTRIBUTION LTD
15 Fountain Parade, Mapplewell,
Barnsley, South Yorkshire, S75 6FW
Tel: 01226 381133   **Fax:** 01226 381177
Email: phil@naturalcement.co.uk
Web: www.naturalcement.co.uk
Product Type: 1, 3, 4   **Other Info:** ECO

OLD HOUSE STORE LTD
Hampstead Farm, Binfield Heath,
Henley on Thames, Oxfordshire, RG9 4LG
Area of Operation: Worldwide
Tel: 0118 969 7711
Fax: 0118 969 8822
Email: info@oldhousestore.co.uk
Web: www.oldhousestore.co.uk
Product Type: 4   **Other Info:** ECO

ROSE OF JERICHO
Horchester Farm, Holywell,
Dorchester, Dorset, DT2 0LL
Area of Operation: UK (Excluding Ireland)
Tel: 01935 83676
Fax: 01935 83903
Email: info@rose-of-jericho.demon.co.uk
Web: www.rose-of-jericho.demon.co.uk
Product Type: 2, 4

SCOTTISH LIME CENTRE TRUST
Charleston Workshop, Rocks Road,
Charlestown, Nr Dunfermline, Fife, KY11 3EN
Area of Operation: Scotland
Tel: 01383 872722
Fax: 01383 872744
Email: info@scotlime.org
Web: www.scotlime.org   **Product Type:** 4

STONE2YOURHOME
Area of Operation: UK (Excluding Ireland)
Tel: 0871 8732369
Email: info@stone2yourhome.co.uk
Web: www.stone2yourhome.co.uk

TARMAC LIMITED
Millfields Road, Ettingshall, Wolverhampton, WV4 6JP
Area of Operation: Europe
Tel: 01902 353522   **Fax:** 01902 382922
Email: info@tarmac.co.uk
Web: www.tarmac.co.uk

THE CORNISH LIME COMPANY LTD.
Brims Park, Old Callywith Road,
Bodmin, Cornwall, PL31 2DZ
Area of Operation: UK (Excluding Ireland)
Tel: 01208 79779   **Fax:** 01208 73744
Email: sales@cornishlime.co.uk
Web: www.cornishlime.co.uk
Product Type: 2, 3, 4

THERMASTEX COATINGS
Rivington House, 82 Great Eastern Street,
London, EC2A 3JF
Area of Operation: UK (Excluding Ireland)
Tel: 0207 749 7297
Email: thermastex@london.com
Web: www.thermastex.com
Product Type: 4

THIN JOINT TECHNOLOGY LTD
3 Albright Road, Speke Approaches Industrial Estate,
Liverpool, Merseyside, WA8 8FY
Area of Operation: UK & Ireland
Tel: 0151 422 8000   **Fax:** 0151 422 8001
Email: sales@thinjoint.com
Web: www.thinjoint.com
Product Type: 4

TRADITIONAL LIME CO
The Salvage Yard, Rath, Shillelagh Road,
Tullow, Co.Carlow, Ireland
Area of Operation: Ireland Only
Tel: 00353 599 151 750
Fax: 00353 599 152 113
Email: admin@traditionallime.com
Web: www.traditionallime.com   **Product Type:** 3, 4

TY-MAWR LIME LTD
Ty-Mawr, Llangasty, Brecon, Powys, LD3 7PJ
Area of Operation: UK & Ireland
Tel: 01874 658000
Email: joyce.gervis@lime.org.uk
Web: www.lime.org.uk   **Product Type:** 4

WEBER BUILDING SOLUTIONS
Dickens House, Enterprise Way, Maulden Road,
Flitwick, Bedford, Bedfordshire, MK45 5BY
Tel: 0870 333 0070   **Fax:** 01525 718988
Email: info@weberbuildingsolutions.co.uk
Web: www.weberbuildingsolutions.co.uk
Product Type: 4

To recommend a company for inclusion in the next edition of The Homebuilder's Handbook, email

customerservice@centaur.co.uk

NOTES

Company Name ....
....
Address ....
....
....
email ....
Web ....

Company Name ....
....
Address ....
....
....
email ....
Web ....

Company Name ....
....
Address ....
....
....
email ....
Web ....

Company Name ....
....
Address ....
....
....
email ....
Web ....

Company Name ....
....
Address ....
....
....
email ....
Web ....

Company Name ....
....
Address ....
....
....
email ....
Web ....

Company Name ....
....
Address ....
....
....
email ....
Web ....

Company Name ....
....
Address ....
....
....
email ....
Web ....

WWW.PLOTFINDER.NET

Area of Operation: UK
Tel: 01527 834436 **Fax:** 01527 837810
Email: customerservice@centaur.co.uk
Web: www.plotfinder.net

Plotfinder is an online database which holds details of around 6,000 building plots and properties in need of renovation or conversion currently for sale throughout the UK.

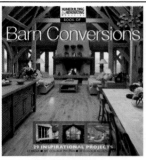

BOOK OF BARN CONVERSIONS

Area of Operation: UK & Ireland
Tel: 01527 834435 **Fax:** 01527 837810
Email: customerservice@centaur.co.uk
Web: www.homebuilding.co.uk/bookshop

Containing 29 inspirational case studies, ranging from rustic to contemporary, this book is a must for anyone contemplating a barn conversion or restoration, whatever their budget. Each project is fully costed with contact details for suppliers.

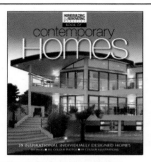

BOOK OF CONTEMPORARY HOMES

Area of Operation: UK & Ireland
Tel: 01527 834435 **Fax:** 01527 837810
Email: customerservice@centaur.co.uk
Web: www.homebuilding.co.uk/bookshop

39 individually designed, contemporary-styled homes, from urban homes to country houses. Each case study includes its floorplan and layout, inspirational pictures, costs for the build and a list of useful contacts.

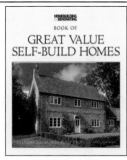

BOOK OF GREAT VALUE SELF-BUILD HOMES

Area of Operation: UK & Ireland
Tel: 01527 834435 **Fax:** 01527 837810
Email: customerservice@centaur.co.uk
Web: www.homebuilding.co.uk/bookshop

Twenty-four homes built for between £32,000 and £150,000. The features show how it is possible to use floor space without sacrificing unique features, and how to achieve maximum style without spending a fortune.

HOMEBUILDING & RENOVATING MAGAZINE

Area of Operation: UK & Ireland
Tel: 01527 834435 **Fax:** 01527 837810
Email: customerservice@centaur.co.uk
Web: www.homebuilding.co.uk

Homebuilding & Renovating, Britain's best selling self-build magazine is an essential read for anyone extending, renovating, converting or building their own home, providing practical advice and inspirational ideas.

BOOK OF HOUSE PLANS

Area of Operation: UK and Ireland
Tel: 01527 834435 **Fax:** 01527 837810
Email: customerservice@centaur.co.uk
Web: www.homebuilding.co.uk/bookshop

The first colour book of UK House Plans is finally here, packed full with colour illustrations throughout. All beautifully drawn and with ,more plans than ever before.

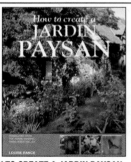

HOW TO CREATE A JARDIN PAYSAN

Area of Operation: UK & France
Tel: 01527 834435 **Fax:** 01527 837810
Email: customerservice@centaur.co.uk
Web: www.renovationfrance.net

How to create a traditional, rural French-style garden which will have a timeless charm. With plant lists, tips and techniques going back generations, this book shows you how to create an authentic, natural garden.

MOVE OR IMPROVE? MAGAZINE

Area of Operation: UK & Ireland
Tel: 01527 834435 **Fax:** 01527 837810
Email: customerservice@centaur.co.uk
Web: www.moveorimprove.co.uk

Move or Improve? magazine is the Bible for people adding adding space and value to their homes. Includes design guides, practical advice and inspiration on extensions, loft and basement conversions and improving your current home.

PERIOD LIVING MAGAZINE

Area of Operation: UK and Ireland
Tel: 01527 834435 **Fax:** 01527 837810
Email: customerservice@centaur.co.uk
Web: www.periodliving.co.uk

Period Living, Britain's best selling period homes magazine brings you pages of inspirational readers' homes with a wide range of stylish, decorative ideas for your period property.

WWW.PROPERTYFINDERFRANCE.NET

Area of Operation: UK & France
Tel: 01527 834435 **Fax:** 01527 837810
Email: customerservice@centaur.co.uk
Web: www.propertyfinderfrance.net

Looking for a property in France? This fully searchable website contains details of over 50,000 available properties throughout France, To get a 7-day free trial visit:
www.propertyfinderfrance.net.

HOW TO RENOVATE A HOUSE IN FRANCE

Area of Operation: UK & France
Tel: 01527 834435 **Fax:** 01527 837810
Email: customerservice@centaur.co.uk
Web: www.renovationfrance.net

An essential guide to help you turn an old rural property in France into a beautiful home. *How to Renovate* covers the whole process, from assessing and buying a property, through all jobs, large and small, required to get it into shape.

WWW.SITEFINDERIRELAND.COM

Area of Operation: Ireland
Tel: 01527 834435 **Fax:** 01527 837810
Email: customerservice@centaur.co.uk
Web: www.sitefinderireland.com

Whether you are looking for a building site, a property that needs renovating or a building to convert www.sitefinderireland.com can make your search easier; it holds around 2,000 listings currently for sale throughout Ireland.

Image courtesy of Independent Builders' Merchants (02380 226852)

SPONSORED BY INDEPENDENT BUILDERS' MERCHANTS
Tel 02380 226852. Web www.cbagroup.co.uk/homebuild

INDEPENDENT BUILDERS' MERCHANTS
helping homebuilders locally

MERCHANTS, TOOLS & EQUIPMENT

Merchants

Building materials – everything from the cement and blocks that form your house's shell, to the flooring, kitchen and lights that make it a living space – account for around half of a self-builder's expenditure. So it's critical, if you're building on a modest budget, to know how to negotiate the best deals possible.

Buying from builders' merchants

There are scores of established national and regional builders' merchants. Although they have a reputation of being intimidating, builders' merchants are pretty courteous to today's self-builders, who form a vital constituency of merchant's customer base. Become familiar with one local outlet and establish a relationship with the staff – you should be able to wield a greater leverage on discount terms.

Specialist merchants

While the main merchants offer a broad range of supplies covering all sectors, if it's something like an unusual-sized shower trap you're after, a specialist merchant is what you need. The Homebuilding & Renovating website directory is an excellent resource – www.homebuilding.co.uk/directory. Local directories are also useful.

The Internet

The advantage of buying online is that you can find almost anything you want from the comfort of your armchair, taking your time to look closely at materials, technical specifications and sizes. Prices are clearly displayed, so you know that everyone is paying the same, and delivery is usually fast and often free. You will receive email confirmation of your order, while a VAT invoice should arrive later in the post.

Many of the major merchants will not allow you to purchase huge quantities, but for the 'softer' materials – electrics, switches, radiators, showers etc – the internet provides a host of one-stop sites and smaller outlets.

It is perhaps the second-hand market for which the internet is most renowned, with both general auction and building-related sites giving varied levels of success for the self-builder. You can find some great bargains, particularly for salvaged and over-ordered goods. But be wary of the increased intrusion of commercial retailers selling their wares at not-very-bargain prices.

Top tips

Mark Brinkley – author of the Housebuilder's Bible – gives an insider's guide to some essential bartering techniques.

- Open accounts at all your local builders' merchants. While you're at it, give them copies of your plans and ask for a quote to supply the materials. It lets them know that you will be a substantial customer, if only for a brief period.

- Use specialists. Don't forget to also open accounts at tool hire shops and other useful outlets such as plumbers' merchants or electrical wholesalers. The best deals for items such as electrical goods and plumbing fittings rarely come from the general merchants.

- Buying on account has two clear advantages. Firstly, you get credit, and secondly, you get a monthly statement, which makes it easier to collate paperwork and reclaim VAT.

- Use the prices you have obtained for your materials to haggle. Speak to the manager or one of the reps about the prices – and if the competition is cheaper, tell them.

- Note that the main DIY stores work on a cash upfront basis. They don't operate accounts and rarely deliver. So they tend not to be very useful for heavy-side building materials, but their prices are usually keen for finishing items such as tiles, flooring and paint. Don't be fooled by half-price kitchen offers. They are always half-price, so negotiate.

- For the best discounts go where the merchants have the least work to do. For example, one load delivered in one trip, direct from the manufacturer, will get a much better discount than windows and doors sent out in dribs and drabs. Prepare your orders so that they can be delivered in as few trips as possible.

Image by B&Q

BUILDERS MERCHANTS

KEY

OTHER: ▽ Reclaimed   On-line shopping

Bespoke   Hand-made   ECO Ecological

ASHMEAD BUILDING SUPPLIES LIMITED
Portview Road, Avonmouth, Bristol, BS11 9LD
Area of Operation: South West England and South Wales
Tel: 0117 982 8281   **Fax:** 0117 982 0135
Email: avon@ashmead.co.uk
Web: www.ashmead.co.uk

B & Q PLC
Portswood House, 1 Hampshire Corporate Park,
Chandlers Ford, Eastleigh, Hampshire, SO5 3YX
Area of Operation: UK & Ireland
Tel: 02380 256256   **Fax:** 02380 256020
Email: claire.riches@b-and-q.co.uk
Web: www.diy.com

BRADFORDS BUILDING SUPPLIES
96 Hendford Hill, Yeovil, Somerset, BA20 2QT
Area of Operation: South West England and South Wales
Tel: 01935 845245   **Fax:** 01935 845242
Email: marketing@bradfords.co.uk
Web: www.bradfords.co.uk

BRAITH HERITAGE SUPPLIES
Herd House Farm, Halifax Road,
Briercliffe, Burnley, Lancashire, BB10 3QZ
Area of Operation: UK & Ireland
Tel: 01282 431155   **Fax:** 01282 431155
Email: office@heritage-supplies.com
Web: www.heritage-supplies.com

BUILD CENTER
Outlets Nationwide
Area of Operation: UK (Excluding Ireland)
Tel: 0800 529529   **Web:** www.build-center.co.uk

BUILDBASE LTD
Gemini One, 5520 John Smith Drive, Oxford Business
Park South, Cowley, Oxford, Oxfordshire, OX4 2LL
Area of Operation: UK (Excluding Ireland)
Tel: 0800 107 2255   **Fax:** 01865 747594
Email: info@buildbase.co.uk
Web: www.buildbase.co.uk

BUILDERS MERCHANTS FEDERATION
15 Soho Square, London, W1D 3HL
Area of Operation: UK (Excluding Ireland)
Tel: 0207 439 1753   **Fax:** 0207 734 2766
Email: info@bmf.org.uk
Web: www.bmf.org.uk

BUILDMART.CO.UK LIMITED
Area of Operation: UK (Excluding Ireland)
Tel: 0870 874 1135
Email: enquiries@buildmart.co.uk
Web: www.buildmart.co.uk

BUILDSTORE
Unit 1 Kingsthorne Park, Houstoun Industrial Estate,
Livingston, Lothian, EH54 5DB
Area of Operation: UK (Excluding Ireland)
Tel: 0870 870 9991   **Fax:** 0870 870 9992
Email: enquiries@buildstore.co.uk
Web: www.buildstore.co.uk

CONSTRUCTION RESOURCES
16 Great Guildford Street, London, SE1 0HS
Area of Operation: UK (Excluding Ireland)
Tel: 0207 450 2211   **Fax:** 0207 450 2212
Email: info@constructionresources.com
Web: www.constructionresources.com

COVERS TIMBER AND BUILDERS MERCHANTS
Sussex House, Quarry Lane,
Chichester, West Sussex, PO19 8PE
Area of Operation: South East England
Tel: 01243 785141   **Fax:** 01243 531151
Email: enquiries@covers.biz   **Web:** www.covers.biz

DIRECT BUILDERS MERCHANTS LTD
Unit Y Newington Industrial Estate, London Road,
Newington, Sittingbourne, Kent, ME9 7NU
Area of Operation: South East England
Tel: 0800 288 9790   **Fax:** 0800 288 9791
Email: info@directbuildersmerchants.co.uk
Web: www.directbuildersmerchants.co.uk

DISCOVERY CONTRACTORS LTD
Discovery House, Joseph Wilson Industrial Estate,
Whitstable, Kent, CT5 3PS
Area of Operation: UK (Excluding Ireland)
Tel: 01227 275559   **Fax:** 01227 275918
Email: info@dcontracts.com
Web: www.dcontracts.com

ECOMERCHANT
Head Hill Road, Goodnestone, Faversham, Kent, ME13 9BU
Area of Operation: UK (Excluding Ireland)
Tel: 01795 530130   **Email:** info@ecomerchant.co.uk
Web: www.ecomerchant.co.uk

ELLIOTT BROTHERS LTD
Millbank Wharf, Northam,
Southampton, Hampshire, SO14 5AG
Area of Operation: South East England, South West
England and South Wales
Tel: 02380 226852   **Fax:** 02380 638780
Email: laurenh@elliott-brothers.co.uk
Web: www.elliotts.uk.com

FIRST STOP BUILDERS MERCHANTS
PO Box 60, Queens Drive, Kilmarnock, Ayrshire, KA1 3XA
Area of Operation: Scotland
Tel: 01563 534818   **Fax:** 01563 537848
Email: admin@firststopbm.co.uk
Web: www.firststopbm.co.uk

G&T EVANS
Dulas Mill, Mochdre Lane, Newtown, Powys, SY16 4JD
Area of Operation: UK & Ireland
Tel: 01686 622 100   **Fax:** 01686 622 220
Email: gtevans1@aol.com
Web: www.gtevans.co.uk

GIBBS AND DANDY PLC
226 Dallow Road, Luton, Bedfordshire, LU1 1YB
Area of Operation: South East England
Tel: 01582 798798
Fax: 01582 798799
Email: luton@gibbsanddandy.com
Web: www.gibbsanddandy.com

GRANT & STONE LTD
Head Office, Unit 1, Blenheim Road, Cressex,
High Wycombe, Buckinghamshire, HP12 3RS
Area of Operation: UK (Excluding Ireland)
Tel: 01494 441191
Fax: 01494 536543
Email: info@grantandstone.co.uk
Web: www.grantandstone.co.uk

GREYSLATE & STONE SUPPLIES
Unit 1 Cae Pawb Industrial Estate, Off Madog Street,
Port Madog, Nr. Blaenau Ffestiniog, Gwynedd, LL49 9EE
Area of Operation: UK & Ireland
Tel: 01766 514700
Fax: 01766 515200
Email: greyslate@slateandstone.net
Web: www.slateandstone.net

HEPWORTH PLUMBING PRODUCTS
Edlington Lane, Edlington, Doncaster,
South Yorkshire, DN12 1BY
Area of Operation: Worldwide
Tel: 01709 856300   **Fax:** 01709 856301
Email: info@hepworth.co.uk
Web: www.hepworth.co.uk

JACKSON BUILDING CENTRES
Pelham House, Canwick Road,
Lincoln, Lincolnshire, LN5 8HG
Area of Operation: UK (Excluding Ireland)
Tel: 01522 511115   **Fax:** 01522 559156
Web: www.jacksonbc.co.uk

JAMES BURRELL LTD
Head Office, Deptford Road,
Gateshead, Tyne & Wear, NE8 2BR
Area of Operation: North East England
Tel: 0191 477 2249   **Fax:** 0191 477 4816
Email: jamesburrell@compuserve.com
Web: www.jamesburrell.com

JEWSON
Merchant House, Binley Business Park,
Coventry, Warwickshire, CV3 2TT
Area of Operation: UK & Ireland
Tel: 02476 438400
Email: jason.wenham@jewson.co.uk
Web: www.jewson.co.uk

LEGEND INDUSTRIES LTD
Wembley Point, One Harrow Road,
Wembley, Greater London, HA9 6DE
Area of Operation: UK & Ireland
Tel: 0208 903 3344
Fax: 0208 900 2120
Email: sales@theproductzone.com
Web: www.theproductzone.com

MACKENZIE DEAN LTD
Satinstown Farm Business Centre, Burwash Road,
Broad Oak, Heathfield, East Sussex, TN21 8RU
Area of Operation: UK & Ireland
Tel: 01435 862244   **Fax:** 01435 867781
Email: info@mackenziedean.co.uk
Web: www.mackenziedean.co.uk

MERRITT & FRYERS LTD
Firth Street Works, Skipton, North Yorkshire, BD23 2PX
Area of Operation: North East England, North West
England and North Wales
Tel: 01756 792485   **Fax:** 01756 700391
Email: info@merrittandfryers.co.uk
Web: www.merrittandfryers.co.uk

N & C BUILDING PRODUCTS LTD
41-51 Freshwater Road, Chadwell Heath,
Romford, Essex, RM8 1SP
Tel: 0208 586 4600   **Fax:** 0208 586 4646
Email: info@nichollsandclarke.com
Web: www.ncdirect.co.uk

OLD HOUSE STORE LTD
Hampstead Farm, Binfield Heath,
Henley on Thames, Oxfordshire, RG9 4LG
Area of Operation: Worldwide
Tel: 0118 969 7711   **Fax:** 0118 969 8822
Email: info@oldhousestore.co.uk
Web: www.oldhousestore.co.uk

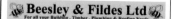

BEESLEY & FILDES LTD

"Established since 1820, an independent family run business with branches throughout the North West of England, offering a complete package of building products, timber, roofing, plumbing and bathrooms. We provide a prompt delivery service and a comprehensive sales support."

Head Office
Beesley & Fildes Ltd
Wilson Road
Huyton
Liverpool
L36 6AF
Tel: 0151 480 8304 Fax: 0151 481 0248
Email: jstanton@beesleyandfildes.co.uk
Web: www.beesleyandfildes.co.uk

BRADFORDS BUILDING SUPPLIES

Bradfords has been supplying building materials for over 200 years and is one of the UK's largest independent builders merchants with 26 branches throughout the South West, Herefordshire and Worcestershire. We have developed a renowned specialist expertise in home-build, having been the principal supplier to thousands of projects during the last decade.

Bradfords Building Supplies
96 Hendford Hill,
Yeovil,
Somerset,
BA20 2QR
Tel: 01935 845245
Fax: 01935 845242
Web: www.bradfords.co.uk

COVERS LTD

Covers is one of the largest privately owned timber and builders merchants on the south coast, with a total of ten depots situated in East and West Sussex, Hampshire and the Channel Islands. Covers stock a complete range of timber and building materials for the construction and allied trades, with comprehensive flooring, bathroom, and kitchen showrooms.

For more information, or to order a catalogue contact Covers on 01243 785141.

Covers Ltd
Sussex House,
Quarry Lane,
Chichester,
West Sussex
PO19 2PE
Tel: 01243 785141
Fax: 01243 531151
Web: www.dcover.co.uk

ELLIOTT BROTHERS LIMITED

Elliotts are Hampshire's leading independent Builders Merchant ideally located for self builders across Hampshire and Dorset. Established in 1842 and still family run with 10 branches across the county. To join our Self Build Club contact Lauren Haines on 023 8038 5305.

Elliott Brothers Limited
Head Office
Millbank Wharf
Northam
Southampton   SO14 5AG
Web: www.elliotts.uk.com

GIBBS & DANDY PLC

Gibbs & Dandy has everything for the home builder: building materials, timber, plumbing and heating supplies, sanitaryware, electrical fittings, paint and glass. Branches branches in Luton, Bedford, St Ives (Cambs), St Neots, Northampton, Slough, Maidenhead, Henley, Brackley and Kettering.

Gibbs and Dandy plc
PO Box 17
226 Dallow Road
Luton
LU1 1JG
Tel: 01582 798798 Fax: 01582 798799
Email: mail@gibbsanddandy.com
Web: www.gibbsanddandy.com

JOHN A. STEPHENS LTD.

JOHN A STEPHENS

"For over 35 years John A Stephens has provided a consistently high quality service to the building and construction industry from its five acre site in central Nottingham and is regarded as one of the largest and most comprehensively stocked depots in the region."

John A Stephens
Castle Meadow Road,
Nottingham
NG2 1AG
Tel: 0115 9412861
Web: www.johnastephens.co.uk

RAWLE GAMMON & BAKER

Rawle Gammon & Baker started in 1850 in Barnstaple, Devon as timber importers with premises beside the river and has gone from strength to strength over the generations, expanding gradually to sell the whole range of building materials. Still family owned, the Company now has ten branches, with branch number eleven due to open in Tiverton, Devon in 2006. RGB covers Devon, East Cornwall and West Somerset, with its own sawmills at Chapelton, North Devon. Under the Managing Directorship of Giles Isaac, RGB is proud to offer a wide range of building materials at competitive prices and our helpful and knowledgeable staff is very well placed to aid all builders in achieving their goals and avoiding pitfalls.

RGB Holdings Ltd,
Gammon House,
Riverside Road,
Barnstaple,
Devon,
EX31 1QN
Tel: 01271 313000
Fax: 01271 329982
E-mail: rgb@rgbltd.co.uk

RIDGEONS

"With 18 trading branches based in East Anglia, the Ridgeon Group is the largest family owned independent timber and builders merchant in the United Kingdom".

For your nearest contact visit www.ridgeons.co.uk

HOWARTH TIMBER & BUILDING SUPPLIES

With 25 branches nationwide and over 165 years of experience good advice comes as standard at Howarth Timber & Building Supplies. As part of the UK's largest privately owned timber group, Howarth Timber & Building Supplies offer a vast range of timber and building products and a knowledgeable and personal service to help you with your project.

For more information please visit www.howarth-timber.co.uk
or contact us on 0113 240 7198.

Howarth Timber & Building Supplies
Head Office
Prince Edward Works, Pontefract Lane
Leeds, LS9 0RA
Tel: 0113 240 7198
Fax: 0113 248 8474
Email: info@howarth-timber.co.uk
Website: www.howarth-timber.co.uk

ROBERT PRICE BUILDERS' MERCHANTS

Robert Price Builders' Merchants have over 40 years experience helping self-builders in South Wales build their dream homes. Self Build guide available.

Margaret Roy
Marketing Manager
Park Road
Abergavenny
NP7 5PF
01873 858585
01873 856854
07966 117952

TIPPERS

Midlands based Builders Merchant offering a full range of building materials including bricks, blocks, timber & joinery, landscaping materials, plumbing & heating and kitchens & bathrooms.

Tippers Building Materials
Europa Way
Lichfield
Staffs
WS14 9TZ
01543 440000
01543 440070
E-mail: info@tippersbm.co.uk

MERCHANTS, TOOLS & EQUIPMENT

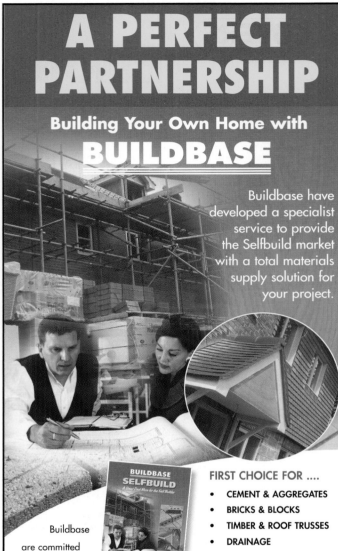
ROBERT PRICE BUILDERS' MERCHANTS
Park Road, Abergavenny, Monmouthshire, NP7 5PF
Area of Operation: South West England and South Wales
Tel: 01873 858585
Fax: 01873 856854
Email: info@robert-price.co.uk
Web: www.robert-price.co.uk

SCREWFIX DIRECT LTD
Trade House, Houndstone Business Park, Mead Avenue, Yeovil, Somerset, BA22 8RT
Area of Operation: UK (Excluding Ireland)
Tel: 0800 096 6226   **Fax:** 01935 401665
Email: online@screwfix.com
Web: www.screwfix.com

TIPPERS BUILDING MATERIALS
Europa Way, Brittania Business Park, Lichfield, Staffordshire, WS14 9TZ
Area of Operation: Midlands & Mid Wales
Tel: 01543 440000   **Fax:** 01543 414185
Email: info@tippersbm.co.uk
Web: www.tippersbm.co.uk

TRAVIS PERKINS PLC
Head Office, Lodge Way House, Lodge Way, Harlestone Road, Northampton, Northamptonshire, NN5 7UG
Area of Operation: UK (Excluding Ireland)
Tel: 01604 752424   **Fax:** 01604 591180
Email: nicola.mcgonagle@travisperkins.co.uk
Web: www.travisperkins.co.uk

UK BUILDING MATERIALS.COM
5 Belmont Drive, Belmont Drive, Taunton, Somerset, TA1 4QB
Area of Operation: South West England and South Wales
Tel: 01823 333364
Fax: 01823 338532
Email: sales@ukbuildingmaterials.com
Web: www.ukbuildingmaterials.com

VALUE DIY LIMITED
Unit 4, Phillips House, Chapel Lane, Emley, West Yorkshire, HD8 9ST
Area of Operation: UK (Excluding Ireland)
Tel: 0845 644 2306   **Fax:** 01924 844606
Email: sales@valuediy.co.uk
Web: www.valuediy.co.uk

PLUMBERS MERCHANTS

KEY
OTHER: ▽ Reclaimed   🛒 On-line shopping
🖋 Bespoke   🖐 Hand-made   ECO Ecological

ANDERSON FLOORWARMING LIMITED
IPPEC Scottish System House, Unit 119, Atlas Express Industrial Estate, 1 Rutherglen Road, Glasgow, G73 1SX
Area of Operation: Scotland
Tel: 0141 647 6716
Fax: 0141 647 6751
Email: mail@andersonfloorwarming.co.uk
Web: www.ippec.co.uk

ANDY PLUMB
Hathern House, Hathern Ware Industrial Estate, Rempstone Road, Loughborough, Leicestershire, LE12 5EH
Area of Operation: Worldwide
Tel: 0871 425 1672
Fax: 01509 843912
Email: sales@andyplumb.co.uk
Web: www.andyplumb.co.uk

B & Q PLC
Portswood House, 1 Hampshire Corporate Park, Chandlers Ford, Eastleigh, Hampshire, SO5 3YX
Area of Operation: UK & Ireland
Tel: 02380 256256
Fax: 02380 256020
Email: claire.riches@b-and-q.co.uk
Web: www.diy.com

BATHROOM STUDIOS
139 Old Road, Clacton-On-Sea, Essex, CO15 3AX
Area of Operation: South East England
Tel: 01255 434435
Email: sales@bathroomstudios.co.uk
Web: www.bathroomstudios.co.uk

BUILDBASE LTD
Gemini One, 5520 John Smith Drive, Oxford Business Park South, Cowley, Oxford, Oxfordshire, OX4 2LL
Area of Operation: UK (Excluding Ireland)
Tel: 0800 107 2255   **Fax:** 01865 747594
Email: info@buildbase.co.uk
Web: www.buildbase.co.uk

BUILDMART.CO.UK LIMITED
Area of Operation: UK (Excluding Ireland)
Tel: 0870 874 1135
Email: enquiries@buildmart.co.uk
Web: www.buildmart.co.uk

DISCOUNTED HEATING
57 Faringdon Road, Plymouth, Devon, PL4 9ER
Area of Operation: UK (Excluding Ireland)
Tel: 0870 042 8884
Fax: 0870 330 5815
Email: marc@discountedheating.co.uk
Web: www.discountedheating.co.uk

GIBBS AND DANDY PLC
226 Dallow Road, Luton, Bedfordshire, LU1 1YB
Area of Operation: South East England
Tel: 01582 798798   **Fax:** 01582 798799
Email: luton@gibbsanddandy.com
Web: www.gibbsanddandy.com

GRAHAM
4 Binley Street, Kirkstall Road, Leeds, West Yorkshire, LS3 1LU
Area of Operation: UK (Excluding Ireland)
Tel: 0113 242 7760   **Fax:** 0113 243 0302
Email: customer.services@graham-group.co.uk
Web: www.graham-group.co.uk

HEAT AND PLUMB
Area of Operation: UK & Ireland
Tel: 0845 226 2222   **Fax:** 01208 816354
Email: sales@heatandplumb.com
Web: www.heatandplumb.com

HEPWORTH PLUMBING PRODUCTS
Edlington Lane, Edlington, Doncaster, South Yorkshire, DN12 1BY
Area of Operation: Worldwide
Tel: 01709 856300   **Fax:** 01709 856301
Email: info@hepworth.co.uk
Web: www.hepworth.co.uk

JEWSON
Merchant House, Binley Business Park, Coventry, Warwickshire, CV3 2TT
Area of Operation: UK & Ireland
Tel: 02476 438400   **Web:** www.jewson.co.uk
Email: jason.wenham@jewson.co.uk

LEGEND INDUSTRIES LTD
Wembley Point, One Harrow Road, Wembley, Greater London, HA9 6DE
Tel: 0208 903 3344   **Fax:** 0208 900 2120
Email: sales@theproductzone.com
Web: www.theproductzone.com

MISCELLANEA DISCONTINUED BATHROOMWARE
Churt Place Nurseries, Tilford Road, Churt, Farnham, Surrey, GU10 2LN
Area of Operation: Worldwide
Tel: 01428 608164
Fax: 01428 608165
Email: email@brokenbog.com
Web: www.brokenbog.com

PLUMB CENTER
Wolfeley Center, Harrison Way, Spa Park, Leamington Spa, Warwickshire, CV31 3HH
Area of Operation: UK (Excluding Ireland)
Tel: 0870 1622557
Email: customerservices@wolseley.co.uk
Web: www.plumbcenter.co.uk

PLUMB CENTER
Branches Nationwide
Area of Operation: UK (Excluding Ireland)
Tel: 0870 1622 557
Web: www.plumbcenter.co.uk

PUMP WORLD LTD
Unit 11, Woodside Road, South Marston Business
Park, Swindon, Wiltshire, SN3 4WA
Area of Operation: UK & Ireland
Tel: 01793 820142
Fax: 01793 823800
Email: enquiries@pumpworld.co.uk
Web: www.pumpworld.co.uk

**RICHMONDS PLUMBING &
HEATING MERCHANTS LTD**
15-25 Carnoustie Place, Scotland Street, Glasgow, G5 8PA
Area of Operation: Scotland
Tel: 0141 429 7441
Fax: 0141 420 1406
Email: sales@richmonds-phm.co.uk
Web: www.richmonds-phm.co.uk

THE KITCHEN SINK COMPANY
Unit 10, Evans Place, South Bersted Industrial Estate,
Bognor Regis, West Sussex, PO22 9RY
Area of Operation: UK & Ireland
Tel: 01243 841332
Fax: 01243 837294
Email: colin@kitchensinkco.com
Web: www.kitchensinkco.com

TIPPERS BUILDING MATERIALS
Europa Way , Brittania Business Park,
Lichfield, Staffordshire, WS14 9TZ
Area of Operation: Midlands & Mid Wales
Tel: 01543 440000
Fax: 01543 414185
Email: info@tippersbm.co.uk
Web: www.tippersbm.co.uk

ROOFING MERCHANTS

KEY
OTHER: ▽ Reclaimed   On-line shopping
   Bespoke   Hand-made   ECO Ecological

BUILD CENTER
Outlets Nationwide
Area of Operation: UK (Excluding Ireland)
Tel: 0800 529529
Web: www.build-center.co.uk

BUILDMART.CO.UK LIMITED
Area of Operation: UK (Excluding Ireland)
Tel: 0870 874 1135
Email: enquiries@buildmart.co.uk
Web: www.buildmart.co.uk

ELLIOTT BROTHERS LTD
Millbank Wharf, Northam,
Southampton, Hampshire, SO14 5AG
Area of Operation: South East England, South West
England and South Wales
Tel: 02380 226852**Fax:** 02380 638780
Email: laurenh@elliott-brothers.co.uk
Web: www.elliotts.uk.com

GREYSLATE & STONE SUPPLIES
Unit 1 Cae Pawb Industrial Estate, Off Madog Street,
Port Madog, Nr. Blaenau Ffestiniog, Gwynedd, LL49 9EE
Area of Operation: UK & Ireland
Tel: 01766 514700   **Fax:** 01766 515200
Email: greyslate@slateandstone.net
Web: www.slateandstone.net

JEWSON
Merchant House, Binley Business Park,
Coventry, Warwickshire, CV3 2TT
Area of Operation: UK & Ireland
Tel: 02476 438400
Email: jason.wenham@jewson.co.uk
Web: www.jewson.co.uk

**ROBERT PRICE TIMBER AND
ROOFING MERCHANTS**
The Wood Yard, Forest Road,
Taffs Well, Cardiff, CF15 7YE
Area of Operation: South West England and South Wales
Tel: 02920 811681   **Fax:** 02920 813605
Email: sales@robert-price.co.uk
Web: www.robert-price.co.uk

SIG ROOFING SUPPLIES GROUP
Unit 3 Clare Hall, Parsons Green, St Ives Business
Park, St Ives, Cambridge, Cambridgeshire, PE27 4WY
Area of Operation: UK (Excluding Ireland)
Tel: 01480 466777   **Fax:** 01480 499715
Email: danielwaters@sigroofing.co.uk
Web: www.sigplc.co.uk

TIMBER MERCHANTS

KEY
OTHER: ▽ Reclaimed   On-line shopping
   Bespoke   Hand-made   ECO Ecological

**ASSOCIATION OF SCOTTISH
HARDWOOD SAWMILLERS**
Area of Operation: Scotland
Web: www.ashs.co.uk

B & Q PLC
Portswood House, 1 Hampshire Corporate Park,
Chandlers Ford, Eastleigh, Hampshire, SO5 3YX
Area of Operation: UK & Ireland
Tel: 02380 256256   **Fax:** 02380 256020
Email: claire.riches@b-and-q.co.uk
Web: www.diy.com

BOARD CENTRAL
Chiltern Business Centre, Couching Street,
Watlington, Oxfordshire, OX49 5PX
Area of Operation: Greater London, South East England
Tel: 0845 458 8016
Fax: 01844 354112
Email: howardmorrice@hotmail.com

BSW TIMBER
Cargo, Carlisle, Cumbria, CA6 4BA
Area of Operation: UK (Excluding Ireland)
Tel: 01228 673366   **Fax:** 01228 673353
Email: marketing@bsw.co.uk   **Web:** www.bsw.co.uk

BUILD CENTER
Outlets Nationwide
Area of Operation: UK (Excluding Ireland)
Tel: 0800 529529   **Web:** www.build-center.co.uk

COVERS TIMBER AND BUILDERS MERCHANTS
Sussex House, Quarry Lane, Chichester,
West Sussex, PO19 8PE
Area of Operation: South East England
Tel: 01243 785141   **Fax:** 01243 531151
Email: enquiries@covers.biz   **Web:** www.covers.biz

DEVON HARDWOODS LTD
Dotton, Colaton Raleigh, Sidmouth, Devon, EX10 0JH
Area of Operation: South West England and South Wales
Tel: 01395 568991
Fax: 01395 567881
Email: sales@devonhardwoods.ltd.uk

ECOHOMES LTD
First Floor, 52 Briggate, Brighouse,
West Yorkshire, HD6 1ES
Area of Operation: UK & Ireland
Tel: 01484 402040   **Fax:** 01484 400101
Email: sales@ecohomes.ltd.uk
Web: www.ecohomes.ltd.uk

ELLIOTT BROTHERS LTD
Millbank Wharf, Northam,
Southampton, Hampshire, SO14 5AG
Area of Operation: South East England, South West
England and South Wales
Tel: 02380 226852
Fax: 02380 638780
Email: laurenh@elliott-brothers.co.uk
Web: www.elliotts.uk.com

G&T EVANS
Dulas Mill, Mochdre Lane, Newtown, Powys, SY16 4JD
Area of Operation: UK & Ireland
Tel: 01686 622 100   **Fax:** 01686 622 220
Email: gtevans1@aol.com
Web: www.gtevans.co.uk

GIBBS AND DANDY PLC
226 Dallow Road, Luton, Bedfordshire, LU1 1YB
Area of Operation: South East England
Tel: 01582 798798
Fax: 01582 798799
Email: luton@gibbsanddandy.com
Web: www.gibbsanddandy.com

HONEYSUCKLE BOTTOM SAWMILL LTD
Honeysuckle Bottom, Green Dene,
East Horsley, Leatherhead, Surrey, KT24 5TD
Area of Operation: Greater London, South East England
Tel: 01483 282394
Fax: 01483 282394
Email: honeysucklemill@aol.com
Web: www.easisites.co.uk/honeysucklebottomsawmill

JEWSON
Merchant House, Binley Business Park,
Coventry, Warwickshire, CV3 2TT
Area of Operation: UK & Ireland
Tel: 02476 438400
Email: jason.wenham@jewson.co.uk
Web: www.jewson.co.uk

JOHN BODDY TIMBER LTD
Riverside Sawmills, Boroughbridge,
North Yorkshire, YO51 9LJ
Area of Operation: UK (Excluding Ireland)
Tel: 01423 322370
Fax: 01423 324334
Email: info@john-boddy-timber.ltd.uk
Web: www.john-boddy-timber.ltd.uk

LANARKSHIRE HARDWOODS
Girdwoodend Farm, Auchengray,
Carnwath, Lanark, Lanarkshire, ML11 8LL
Area of Operation: Scotland
Tel: 01501 785460
Email: patrickbaxter@girdwoodend.wanadoo.co.uk
Web: www.lanarkshirehardwoods.co.uk

MCKAY FLOORING LTD
8 Harmony Square, Govan, City of Glasgow, G51 3LW
Area of Operation: UK & Ireland
Tel: 0141 440 1586   **Fax:** 0141 425 1020
Email: enquiries@mckayflooring.co.uk
Web: www.mckayflooring.co.uk

N.P. TIMBER CO. LTD
Welham Lane, Great Bowden,
Market Harborough, Leicestershire, LE16 7HS
Area of Operation: Worldwide
Tel: 01858 468064   **Fax:** 01858 469408
Email: sales@nptimber.co.uk
Web: www.nptimber.co.uk

NORTH YORKSHIRE TIMBER
Standard House, Thurston Road, Northallerton Business
Park, Northallerton, North Yorkshire, DL6 2NA
Area of Operation: UK (Excluding Ireland)
Tel: 01609 780777   **Fax:** 01609 777888
Email: sales@nytimber.co.uk
Web: www.nytimber.co.uk

NORTHWOOD FORESTRY LTD
Goose Green Lane, Nr Ashington,
Pulborough, West Sussex, RH20 2LW
Area of Operation: South East England
Tel: 01798 813029
Fax: 01798 813139
Email: enquiries@northwoodforestry.co.uk
Web: www.northwoodforestry.co.uk

MERCHANTS, TOOLS & EQUIPMENT *(side tab)*

PANEL AGENCY LIMITED
Maple House, 5 Over Minnis,
New Ash Green, Longfield, Kent, DA3 8JA
Area of Operation: UK & Ireland
Tel: 01474 872578
Fax: 01474 872426
Email: sales@panelagency.com
Web: www.panelagency.com

PINE SUPPLIES
Lower Tongs Farm, Longshaw Ford Road,
Smithills, Bolton, Lancashire, BL1 7PP
Area of Operation: UK (Excluding Ireland)
Tel: 01204 841416
Fax: 01204 845814
Email: pine-info@telinco.co.uk
Web: www.pine-supplies.co.uk

**ROBERT PRICE TIMBER AND
ROOFING MERCHANTS**
The Wood Yard, Forest Road,
Taffs Well, Cardiff, CF15 7YE
Area of Operation: South West England and South Wales
Tel: 02920 811681
Fax: 02920 813605
Email: sales@robert-price.co.uk
Web: www.robert-price.co.uk

SCOTTISH WOOD
Inzievar Woods, Oakley,
Dunfermline, Fife, KY12 8HB
Area of Operation: Scotland
Tel: 01383 851328
Fax: 01383 851339
Email: enquiries@scottishwood.co.uk
Web: www.scottishwood.co.uk

T.BREWER & CO
Timber Mill Way, Gauden Road,
Clapham, London, SW4 6LY
Area of Operation: Greater London, South East England
Tel: 0207 720 9494
Fax: 0207 622 0426
Email: clapham@tbrewer.co.uk
Web: www.tbrewer.co.uk

THE CARPENTRY INSIDER - AIRCOMDIRECT
1 Castleton Crescent, Skegness,
Lincolnshire, PE25 2TJ
Area of Operation: Worldwide
Tel: 01754 767163
Email: aircom8@hotmail.com
Web: www.easycarpentry.com ⌐⌐

THE ROUNDWOOD TIMBER COMPANY LTD
Roundwood, Newick Lane, Mayfield,
East Sussex, TN20 6RG
Area of Operation: UK & Ireland
Tel: 01435 867072
Fax: 01435 864708
Email: sales@roundwoodtimber.com
Web: www.roundwoodtimber.com ⌐⌐

THE SPA & WARWICK TIMBER CO LTD
Harriott Drive, Heathcote Industrial Estate,
Warwick, Warwickshire, CV34 6TJ
Area of Operation: Midlands & Mid Wales
Tel: 01926 883876
Fax: 01926 450831
Email: spa.warwick@btconnect.com
Web: www.sawhardwood.co.uk

THOROGOOD TIMBER PLC
Colchester Road, Ardleigh,
Colchester, Essex, CO7 7PQ
Area of Operation: East England
Tel: 01206 233100
Fax: 01206 233115
Email: barry@thorogood.co.uk
Web: www.thorogood.co.uk

TREESPANNER TIMBER
East Cottage, Dry Hill Farm, Moons Lane,
Dormansland, Surrey, RH7 6PD
Area of Operation: South East England
Tel: 01342 871529
Email: treespanner@tiscali.co.uk
Web: www.treespanner.co.uk

VINCENT TIMBER LTD
8 Montgomery Street, Sparkbrook,
Birmingham, West Midlands, B11 1DU
Area of Operation: UK & Ireland
Tel: 0121 772 5511
Fax: 0121 766 6002
Email: enquires@vincenttimber.co.uk
Web: www.vincenttimber.co.uk

ARCHITECTURAL ANTIQUES & SALVAGE YARDS

KEY

PRODUCT TYPES: 1= Bathroom and
Accessories   2 = Chimney Pieces, Fireplaces
and Grates   3 = Church Salvage
4 = Doors and Door Furniture   5 = Garden
6 = Furniture and Mirrors   7 = Kitchen and
Accessories   8 = Lighting   9 = Staircases
10 = Statuary   11 = Windows and Window
Furniture   12 = Architectural Metalwork
13 = Architectural Stone and Terracotta
14 = Architectural Woodwork and Panelling
15 = Bricks   16 = Flagstones and Floor Tiles
17 = Roof Slates and Tiles   18 = Stone
19 = Timber   20 = Other

OTHER: ▽ Reclaimed   ⌐⌐ On-line shopping
✎ Bespoke   ✋ Hand-made   ECO Ecological

ACE RECLAMATION
Pineview, Barrack Road, West Parley,
Ferndown, Dorset, BH22 8UB
Area of Operation: Worldwide
Tel: 01202 579222
Fax: 01202 582043
Email: info@acereclamation.com
Web: www.acereclamation.com
Product Type: 1, 2, 4, 5, 10, 13, 14, 15, 16, 17, 18, 19

ANDY THORNTON LTD
Ainleys Industrial Estate, Elland,
West Yorkshire, HX5 9JP
Area of Operation: Worldwide
Tel: 01422 375595   **Fax:** 01422 377455
Email: marketing@ataa.co.uk
Web: www.andythornton.com

ANTIQUE BUILDINGS LTD
Dunsfold, Godalming, Surrey, GU8 4NP
Area of Operation: UK & Ireland
Tel: 01483 200477
Email: info@antiquebuildings.com
Web: www.antiquebuildings.com
Product Type: 14, 15, 16, 19

ARCHITECTURAL ANTIQUES
351 King Street, Hammersmith, London, W6 9NH
Area of Operation: UK (Excluding Ireland)
Tel: 0208 741 7883   **Fax:** 0208 741 1109
Email: info@aa-fireplaces.co.uk
Web: www.aa-fireplaces.co.uk
Product Type: 1, 2, 6, 8

ARCSAL.COM
PO Box 3333, Shepton Mallet, Somerset, BA4 6XN
Area of Operation: Worldwide
Tel: 07966 416 745   **Fax:** 01749 330076
Email: info@arcsal.com   **Web:** www.arcsal.com ⌐⌐

ATC (MONMOUTHSHIRE) LTD
Unit 2, Mayhill Industrial Estate,
Monmouth, Monmouthshire, NP25 3LX
Area of Operation: Worldwide
Tel: 01600 713036
Fax: 01600 715512
Email: info@floorsanddecking.com
Web: www.floorsanddecking.com ⌐⌐
Product Type: 14

BCA MATERIAUX ANCIENS S.A.
Route de Craon, L'Hotellerie-de-Flee,
Maine et Loire, France, 49500
Area of Operation: Worldwide
Tel: +33 233 947 400
Fax: +33 233 944 656
Email: enquiries@bca-materiauxanciens.com
Web: www.bca-antiquematerials.com

BINGLEY ANTIQUES
Springfield Farm Estate, Haworth,
West Yorkshire, BD21 5PT
Area of Operation: UK (Excluding Ireland)
Tel: 01535 646666   **Fax:** 01535 648527
Email: john@bingleyantiques.com
Web: www.bingleyantiques.com ⌐⌐
Product Type: 2, 3, 4, 5, 6, 9, 11, 12, 13, 14, 18

BUILDMART.CO.UK LIMITED
Area of Operation: UK (Excluding Ireland)
Tel: 0870 874 1135
Email: enquiries@buildmart.co.uk
Web: www.buildmart.co.uk ⌐⌐
Product Type: 2, 4, 7, 8, 11, 15, 16, 17

CAWARDEN BRICK & TILE CO. LTD
Cawarden Springs Farm, Blithbury Road,
Rugeley, Staffordshire, WS15 3HL
Area of Operation: UK (Excluding Ireland)
Tel: 01889 574066   **Fax:** 01889 575695
Email: home-garden@cawardenreclaim.co.uk
Web: www.cawardenreclaim.co.uk

CHESHIRE BRICK & SLATE
Brook House Farm, Salters Bridge,
Tarvin Sands, Tarvin, Cheshire, CH3 8NR
Area of Operation: UK (Excluding Ireland)
Tel: 01829 740883   **Fax:** 01829 740481
Email: enquiries@cheshirebrickandslate.co.uk
Web: www.cheshirebrickandslate.co.uk

CONSERVATION BUILDING PRODUCTS
Forge Works, Forge Lane,
Cradley Heath, West Midlands, B64 5AL
Area of Operation: Midlands & Mid Wales
Tel: 01384 569551   **Fax:** 01384 410625
Email: sales@conservationbuildingproducts.co.uk
Web: www.conservationbuildingproducts.co.uk
Product Type: 1, 2, 3, 4, 5, 6, 7, 8, 9, 10, 11, 12, 13, 14, 15, 16, 17, 18, 19, 20

COX'S ARCHITECTURAL SALVAGE YARD LTD.
10 Fosseway Business Park,
Moreton in Marsh, Gloucestershire, GL56 9NQ
Area of Operation: UK & Ireland
Tel: 01608 652505   **Fax:** 01608 652881
Email: info@coxsarchitectural.co.uk
Web: www.coxsarchitectural.co.uk ⌐⌐

COX'S ARCHITECTURAL SALVAGE YARD LTD

Area of Operation: UK & Ireland
Tel: 01608 652505   **Fax:** 01608 652881
Email: info@coxsarchitecural.co.uk
Web: www.coxsarchitectural.co.uk
Product Type: 1, 2, 3, 4, 5, 6, 8, 9, 11, 13, 14, 16, 18, 19, 20

Cox's Architectural Salvage Yard Ltd. (CASY) has been
trading in Moreton in Marsh since 1992. With 12,500 sq.
ft. of covered warehouse and 1/2 acre of outside yard,
CASY offers one of the largest and most varied stocks of
reclaimed building materials and architectural antiques in
the country.

**CRONINS RECLAMATION &
SOLID WOOD FLOORING**
Preston Farm Court, Lower Road,
Little Bookham, Surrey, KT23 4EF
Area of Operation: Worldwide
Tel: 0208 614 4370   **Fax:** 01932 241918
Email: dfc1@supanet.com
Web: www.croninsreclamation.co.uk
Product Type: 1, 2, 4, 5, 6, 11, 14, 15, 16, 17, 19, 20

DISMANTLE AND DEAL DIRECT
108, London Road, Aston Clinton,
Buckinghamshire, HP22 5HS
Area of Operation: Worldwide
Tel: 01296 632 300
Email: info@ddd-uk.com   **Web:** www.ddd-uk.com

DRUMMONDS ARCHITECTURAL ANTIQUES LTD
Kirkpatrick Buildings, 25 London Road (A3),
Hindhead, Surrey, GU36 6AB
Area of Operation: Worldwide
Tel: 01428 609444   **Fax:** 01428 609445
Email: davidcox@drummonds-arch.co.uk
Web: www.drummonds-arch.co.uk

GOWER RECLAMATION
Unit 17 Crofty Industrial Estate,
Crofty, Gower, Swansea, SA4 3RS
Area of Operation: Worldwide
Tel: 01792 851111
Email: sales@gowerreclamation.com
Web: www.gowerreclamation.com

GREYSLATE & STONE SUPPLIES
Unit 1 Cae Pawb Industrial Estate,
Off Madog Street, Port Madog,
Nr. Blaenau Ffestiniog, Gwynedd, LL49 9EE
Area of Operation: UK & Ireland
Tel: 01766 514700   **Fax:** 01766 515200
Email: greyslate@slateandstone.net
Web: www.slateandstone.net

H W POULTER & SON
279 Fulham Road, Chelsea, London, SW10 9PZ
Area of Operation: Worldwide
Tel: 0207 352 7268
Fax: 0207 351 0984
Email: hwpoulterandson@btconnect.com
Web: www.hwpoulterandson.co.uk
Product Type: 2

HOLYROOD ARCHITECTURAL SALVAGE
Holyrood Business Park, 146 Duddingston Road
West, Edinborough, Lothian, EH16 4AP
Area of Operation: UK & Ireland
Tel: 0131 661 9305
Fax: 0131 656 9404
Email: holyroodsalvage@btconnect.com
Web: www.holyroodarchitecturalsalvage.com ⌐⌐
Product Type: 1, 2, 3, 4, 5, 6, 10, 20

INSITU MANCHESTER
Talbot Mill, 44 Ellesmere Street,
Hulme, Manchester, M15 4JY
Area of Operation: UK (Excluding Ireland)
Tel: 0161 839 5525
Fax: 0161 839 2010
Email: info@insitumanchester.com
Web: www.insitumanchester.com

LASSCO
Brunswick House, 30 Wandsworth Road,
Vauxhall, London, SW8 2LG
Area of Operation: Worldwide
Tel: 0207 394 2100
Fax: 0207 501 7797
Email: brunswick@lassco.co.uk
Web: www.lassco.co.uk
Product Type: 1, 2, 4, 5, 6, 7, 8, 9, 10, 11, 12, 14

LAWSONS
Gorst Lane, Off New Lane, Burscough,
Ormskirk, Lancashire, L40 0RS
Area of Operation: Worldwide
Tel: 01704 893998
Fax: 01704 892526
Email: info@traditionaltimber.co.uk
Web: www.traditionaltimber.co.uk

MINCHINHAMPTON ARCHITECTURAL SALVAGE CO
Cirencester Road, Aston Downs,
Chalford, Stroud, Gloucestershire, GL6 8PE
Area of Operation: Worldwide
Tel: 01285 760886 **Fax:** 01285 760838
Email: masco@catbrain.com
Web: www.catbrain.com

NOTTINGHAM RECLAIMS
St Albans Works, 181 Hartley Road,
Nottinghamshire, NG7 3DW
Tel: 0115 9790666   **Fax:** 0115 9791607
Email: nottm.aar@ntlworld.com
Web: www.naar.co.uk
Product Type: 1, 2, 4, 5, 6, 7, 11, 13, 14, 16, 17, 19, 20

OAKBEAMS.COM
Hunterswood Farm, Alfold Road,
Dunsfold, Godalming, Surrey, GU8 4NP
Area of Operation: Worldwide
Tel: 01483 200477 **Email:** info@oakbeams.com
Web: www.oakbeams.com
Product Type: 14, 15, 16, 17, 19

PRIORS RECLAMATION LTD
Unit 65 Ditton Priors Industrial Estate,
Station Road, Ditton Priors, Bridgnorth,
Shropshire, WV16 6SS
Area of Operation: Worldwide
Tel: 01746 712450   **Fax:** 01746 712450
Email: vicki@priorsrec.co.uk
Web: www.priorsrec.co.uk   **Product Type:** 4, 19

RANSFORDS
Drayton Way, Drayton Fields Industrial Estate,
Daventry, Northamptonshire, NN11 8XW
Area of Operation: Worldwide
Tel: 01327 705310   **Fax:** 01327 706831
Email: sales@ransfords.com
Web: www.ransfords.com /
www.stoneflooringandpaving.com

ROBERT MILLS ARCHITECTURAL ANTIQUES
Narroways Road, Eastville, Bristol, BS2 9XB
Area of Operation: Worldwide
Tel: 0117 955 6542   **Fax:** 0117 955 8146
Email: info@rmills.co.uk **Web:** www.rmills.co.uk
Product Type: 2, 3, 4, 6, 8, 9, 11, 13, 20

SOUTH WEST RECLAMATION LTD
Wireworks Estate, Bristol Road,
Bridgwater, Somerset, TA6 4AP
Area of Operation: South West England and South Wales
Tel: 01278 444141   **Fax:** 01278 444114
Email: info@southwest-rec.co.uk
Web: www.southwest-rec.co.uk
Product Type: 1, 2, 3, 4, 5, 9, 10, 11, 18

STRIP IT LTD
109 Pope Street, Birmingham, West Midlands, B1 3AG
Area of Operation: Midlands & Mid Wales
Tel: 0121 243 4000
Email: sales@stripit.biz **Web:** www.stripit.biz
Product Type: 2, 3, 4, 6, 11, 14

THE CAST IRON RECLAMATION COMPANY
The Courtyard, Preston Farm Court,
Bookham, Surrey, KT23 4EF
Area of Operation: Worldwide
Tel: 0208 977 5977   **Fax:** 01372 459991
Email: enquiries@perfect-irony.com
Web: www.perfect-irony.com
Product Type: 1, 2, 3, 7, 12, 16, 20

THE HOUSE HOSPITAL
14a Winders Road, Battersea, London, SW11 3HE
Area of Operation: UK (Excluding Ireland)
Tel: 0207 223 3179
Email: info@thehousehospital.com
Web: www.thehousehospital.com
Product Type: 2, 4, 6, 7, 12, 20

THE KITCHEN SINK COMPANY
Unit 10, Evans Place, South Bersted Industrial Estate,
Bognor Regis, West Sussex, PO22 9RY
Area of Operation: UK & Ireland
Tel: 01243 841332
Fax: 01243 837294
Email: colin@kitchensinkco.com
Web: www.kitchensinkco.com
Product Type: 7

VIKING RECLAMATION LTD
Cow House Lane, Armthorpe,
Doncaster, South Yorkshire, DN3 3EE
Area of Operation: UK (Excluding Ireland)
Tel: 01302 835449   **Fax:** 01302 835449
Email: info@reclaimed.co.uk
Web: www.reclaimed.co.uk
Product Type: 1, 2, 3, 4, 5, 6, 9, 10, 13, 14, 15, 16, 17, 18, 19, 20

WALCOT RECLAMATION
108 Walcot Street, Bath, Somerset, BA1 5BG
Area of Operation: Worldwide
Tel: 01225 444404
Fax: 01225 448163
Email: rick@walcot.com
Web: www.walcot.com
Product Type: 1, 2, 3, 4, 5, 6, 9, 10, 12, 13, 15, 16, 17, 18, 19

WOODSIDE RECLAMATION
Woodside, Scremerston, Berwick upon Tweed,
Northumberland, TD15 2SY
Area of Operation: Worldwide
Tel: 01289 331211
Email: info@redbaths.co.uk
Web: www.redbaths.co.uk
Product Type: 1, 2, 3, 4, 6, 9, 11, 12, 13, 14, 15, 16, 17, 18, 19, 20

WYE VALLEY RECLAMATION LTD
Fordshill Road, Rotherwas,
Hereford, Herefordshire, HR2 6NS
Area of Operation: UK (Excluding Ireland)
Tel: 01432 353606
Fax: 01432 340020
Email: enquiries@valley-reclamation.co.uk
Web: www.wye-valley-reclamation.co.uk

NOTES

Company Name ....
Address
....
....
email ....
Web ....

Company Name ....
Address
....
....
email ....
Web ....

Company Name ....
....
Address
....
....
email ....
Web ....

Company Name ....
....
Address
....
....
email ....
Web ....

Company Name ....
....
Address
....
....
email ....
Web ....

Company Name ....
....
Address
....
....
email ....
Web ....

Company Name ....
....
Address
....
....
email ....
Web ....

Company Name ....
....
Address
....
....
email ....
Web ....

Company Name ....
....
Address
....
....
email ....
Web ....

Company Name ....
....
Address
....
....
email ....
Web ....

MERCHANTS, TOOLS & EQUIPMENT

INSPIRATION & WISDOM FOR YOUR PROJECT

BARN CONVERSIONS

A brand new selection of barn conversions in one of our most successful books packed with 29 inspirational projects. An essential read for anyone considering, about to start or in the middle of converting their barn. The appetite for barns with both traditional and contemporary finishes continues unabated.

CONTEMPORARY HOMES

The new edition of *Homebuilding & Renovating's* best selling book — it's bigger, better and completely re-designed, featuring 351 colour pictures, contact details of designers, builders and key suppliers of equipment and services. Enjoy reading about 29 of the most innovative houses to be built in the UK in the past five years. This book is both coffee table and practical, explaining how the houses were conceived and built.

HOUSEPLANS

The first colour book of UK houseplans is finally here, packed with 334 full colour illustrations. All beautifully drawn and with more plans than ever before, it offers superb value for money and is backed by the UK's biggest selling self-build magazine, *Homebuilding and Renovating*. This book also features an introduction to self-building.

ORDER YOUR COPY TODAY!
VISIT: WWW.HOMEBUILDING.CO.UK/BOOKSHOP
CALL: 01527 834 435

CENTAUR SPECIAL
INTEREST MEDIA

Image courtesy of Screwfix Direct Ltd (0800 096 6226)

MERCHANTS TOOLS & EQUIPMENT

SPONSORED BY SCREWFIX DIRECT LTD
Tel 0800 096 6226   Web www.screwfix.com

Decorating Tools

A good paint job depends on using the right tools as much as selecting the right paint. With the proper equipment, even the most inexperienced DIYer can achieve a professional-quality finish.

Paintbrushes

There are two main sorts of paintbrush: natural bristle brushes and synthetic bristle brushes. At one time, natural brushes made of animal hair were considered the best. But today the nylon varieties can be equally as good, and are actually the only option for certain applications such as water-based latex paints, as water makes natural bristles limp.

As a rule you should always buy the best brushes you can afford. Quality brushes will perform well and will last for many years if they are looked after and cleaned thoroughly after each job.

Good brushes can be easily distinguished from bad ones. If you spread the bristles and inspect the tips, the more split ends it has, the better its paint-spreading capabilities. Also, when tapped against a hard surface, a good brush may lose a few bristles, but a bad one will lose many. Long, tapered bristles are also something to look out for. As a general rule, the bristle length should be about one-and-a-half times as long as the width of the brush, except in wall brushes. Bristle length gives you flexibility to paint into corners and around the trim. Finally, choose smooth, well-shaped handles of wood or plastic that fit in your hand comfortably.

Paint rollers & pads

Paint rollers are great for large flat surface areas like walls and ceilings, as they speed up a simple paint job massively when compared to using a paintbrush.

The type of roller you should buy is largely determined by the kind of paint you'll be using, but most items are clearly labelled as to their purpose. All rollers are fibre or foam covered cylinders, which soak up paint from a paint tray and then release it when rolled over a surface, giving a more even coat over a large surface than a paintbrush would allow.

The alternative to rollers are foam pads, which often have a chamber behind the pad that provides a constant supply of paint for an even quicker and more even finish.

Of course, rollers and pads are great for covering large surfaces, but on small or intricate areas, such as window frames and coving, a paintbrush remains the optimum tool.

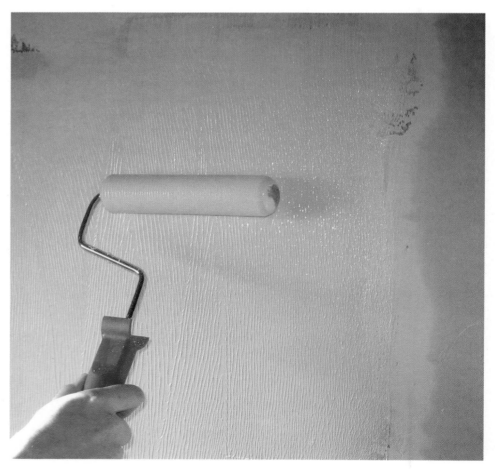

TOOLS & EQUIPMENT

KEY

SEE ALSO: TOOLS AND EQUIPMENT - Hire Companies

OTHER: ▽ Reclaimed ⌐ On-line shopping
✐ Bespoke ✋ Hand-made ECO Ecological

ACE FIXINGS
Woodside Industrial Estate,
Woodside Road, Ballymena, BT42 4HX
Area of Operation: UK & Ireland
Tel: 02825 649323
Fax: 02825 659334
Email: mark.robinson@acefixings.com
Web: www.acefixings.com ⌐

ASHTEAD TECHNOLOGY RENTALS
Campus Five, Letchworth Business Park,
Letchworth, Hertfordshire, SG6 2JF
Area of Operation: UK & Ireland
Tel: 0845 270 2707
Fax: 0845 270 2708
Email: rentals@ashtead-technology.co.uk
Web: www.ashtead-technology.co.uk

AXMINSTER POWER TOOL CENTRE LTD
Unit 10, Weycroft Avenue, Axminster, Devon, EX13 5PH
Area of Operation: Worldwide
Tel: 0800 371822
Fax: 01297 35242
Email: email@axminster.co.uk
Web: www.axminster.co.uk ⌐

B & Q PLC
Portswood House, 1 Hampshire Corporate Park,
Chandlers Ford, Eastleigh, Hampshire, SO5 3YX
Area of Operation: UK & Ireland
Tel: 02380 256256
Fax: 02380 256020
Email: claire.riches@b-and-q.co.uk
Web: www.diy.com ⌐

BENCHROVER
54 Egham Crescent, Sutton, Surrey, SM3 9AW
Area of Operation: UK (Excluding Ireland)
Tel: 0208 644 3322
Fax: 0208 644 3322
Email: ian@benchrover.fsnet.co.uk

BLISTER
PO Box 38, Hove, East Sussex, BN3 4RW
Area of Operation: Worldwide
Tel: 01273 727706
Email: sam@am-techplatinum.com
Web: www.am-techplatinum.com

BOARDMATE TOOLS
3a The Maltings, Station Road, Sawbridgeworth,
Hertfordshire, CM21 9JX
Area of Operation: Worldwide
Tel: 01279 722282
Fax: 01279 722286
Email: info@boardmate.com
Web: www.boardmate.com

BRAITH HERITAGE SUPPLIES
Herd House Farm, Halifax Road,
Briercliffe, Burnley, Lancashire, BB10 3QZ
Area of Operation: UK & Ireland
Tel: 01282 431155
Fax: 01282 431155
Email: office@heritage-supplies.com
Web: www.heritage-supplies.com ⌐

BURDENS INDUSTRIAL SUPPLIES
Earl Russell Way, Lawrence Hill, Bristol, BS5 0WT
Area of Operation: UK (Excluding Ireland)
Tel: 0845 604 3060
Fax: 0845 609 2525
Email: orders@bis-supply.co.uk
Web: www.bis-supply.co.uk ⌐

BURDENS INDUSTRIAL SUPPLIES
Area of Operation: UK (Excluding Ireland)
Tel: 0845 6043060
Fax: 0845 6092525
Email: orders@bis-supply.co.uk
Web: www.bis-supply.co.uk

BiS supply safety clothing and equipment, repair & refurbishment, tools from a knife to a mixer, everything you need to equip your site.
Order online.

CARL KAMMERLING INTERNATIONAL LTD
Glanydon, Pwllheli, Gwynedd, LL53 5LH
Area of Operation: Worldwide
Tel: 01758 701070 **Fax:** 01758 704777
Email: sales@ck-tools.com **Web:** www.ck-tools.com

CRAFT SUPPLIES LTD
Unit 6, Bradwell Head Road,
Bradwell, Derbyshire, S33 9NT
Tel: 01433 622550 **Fax:** 01433 622552
Email: sales@craft-supplies.co.uk
Web: www.craft-supplies.co.uk ⌐

CROMWELL GROUP HOLDINGS
65 Chartwell Drive, Wigston,
Leicester, Leicestershire, LE18 1AT
Area of Operation: UK (Excluding Ireland)
Tel: 0116 288 8000 **Fax:** 0116 288 8222
Email: sales@cromwell.co.uk
Web: www.cromwell.co.uk ⌐

DEESIGN PARTNERSHIP LTD
Unit 1C Quarry Crescent, Pennygillam Industrial
Estate, Launceston, Cornwall, PL15 7PF
Area of Operation: Worldwide
Tel: 01566 777140 **Fax:** 01566 777706
Email: info@mucktruck.com
Web: www.mucktruck.com

DUMPERLAND
No. 1 Venn Place, Joiners Square, Hanley,
Stoke-on-Trent, Staffordshire, ST1 3HP
Area of Operation: Worldwide
Tel: 07812 217647 **Fax:** 01782 744401
Email: info@dumperland.com
Web: www.dumperland.com

EARLEX LTD
Opus Park, Moorfield Road, Guildford, Surrey, GU1 1RU
Area of Operation: Worldwide
Tel: 01483 454666 **Fax:** 01483 454548
Email: enquiries@earlex.co.uk
Web: www.earlex.co.uk

ELLIOTT BROTHERS LTD
Millbank Wharf, Northam,
Southampton, Hampshire, SO14 5AG
Area of Operation: South East England, South West
England and South Wales
Tel: 02380 226852 **Fax:** 02380 638780
Email: laurenh@elliott-brothers.co.uk
Web: www.elliotts.uk.com

ELLIOTTS TOOL WAREHOUSE
Unit 10 Winchester Trade Park, Easton Lane,
Winchester, Hampshire, SO23 7FA
Area of Operation: UK (Excluding Ireland)
Tel: 01962 827610 **Fax:** 01962 827611
Email: tools@elliott-brothers.co.uk
Web: www.elliotts4tools.com ⌐

EXPRESS TOOLS LTD
7 Cooper Dean Drive, Bournemouth, Dorset, BH8 9LN
Area of Operation: UK & Ireland
Tel: 01202 395481 **Fax:** 01202 395481
Email: sales@expresstools.co.uk
Web: www.expresstools.co.uk ⌐

FEIN POWER TOOLS
4 Badby Park, Heartlands Business Park,
Daventry, Northamptonshire, NN11 8YT
Area of Operation: UK (Excluding Ireland)
Tel: 01327 308730 **Fax:** 01327 308739
Email: sales@fein-uk.co.uk **Web:** www.fein.com

FEIN POWER TOOLS
Area of Operation: UK (Excluding Ireland)
Tel: 01327 308730
Fax: 01327 308739
Email: sales@fein-uk.co.uk
Web: www.fein.com
The FEIN MultiMaster, a power tool designed for all renovation and repair tasks. The unique oscillating action of the MultiMaster allows different accessories to be fitted for sawing in timber or sheet metal, sanding on all surfaces, removing stained or damaged grout from tiled surfaces and much more.

FGM CLAYMORE
Waterloo Industrial Estate, Waterloo Road,
Bidford on Avon, Warwickshire, B50 4JH
Area of Operation: UK (Excluding Ireland)
Tel: 01789 490177 **Fax:** 01789 490170
Email: sales@fgmclaymore.co.uk
Web: www.fgmclaymore.co.uk

G GIBSON & CO LTD
Gibson House, Barrowby Lane, Garforth,
Leeds, West Yorkshire, LS25 1NG
Area of Operation: Worldwide
Tel: 0113 286 9245 **Fax:** 0113 286 6859
Email: sales@g-gibson.com
Web: www.g-gibson.com ⌐

GE SENSING
Shannon Industrial Estate,
Shannon, Co Clare, Dublin, Ireland
Area of Operation: Worldwide
Tel: +353 61 470 200 **Fax:** +353 61 471 359
Email: protimeter@ge.com
Web: www.gesensing.com ⌐

GIBBS AND DANDY PLC
226 Dallow Road, Luton, Bedfordshire, LU1 1YB
Area of Operation: South East England
Tel: 01582 798798 **Fax:** 01582 798799
Email: luton@gibbsanddandy.com
Web: www.gibbsanddandy.com

HARNSER SYSTEMS LIMITED
Saville House, 65 Bells Road, Gorleston,
Great Yarmouth, Norwich, Norfolk, NR31 6AG
Area of Operation: UK & Ireland
Tel: 0870 896 6000 **Fax:** 0870 896 6010
Email: sales@eazilift.com **Web:** www.eazilift.com

HC SLINGSBY PLC
Otley Road, Baildon, Shipley, West Yorkshire, BD17 7LW
Area of Operation: Worldwide
Tel: 01274 535030
Fax: 01274 535033
Email: sales@slingsby.com
Web: www.slingsby.com ⌐

HIPPOWASTE
Titchfield House, Pegham Industrial Park,
Laveys Lane, Fareham, Hampshire, PO15 6SD
Area of Operation: UK (Excluding Ireland)
Tel: 0870 880 2430 **Fax:** 01329 849538
Email: info@hippowaste.co.uk
Web: www.hippowaste.co.uk

HSS HIRE SHOPS
25 Willow Lane, Mitcham, Surrey, CR4 4TS
Area of Operation: Worldwide
Tel: 0845 728 2828 **Fax:** 0208 687 5005
Email: hire@hss.com **Web:** www.hss.com ⌐

ICF-IT LIMITED
Unit 26, Malmesbury Road, Kingsditch Trading
Estate, Cheltenham, Gloucestershire, GL51 9PL
Area of Operation: UK & Ireland
Tel: 0870 169 6869 **Fax:** 0870 169 6869
Email: info@icf-it.com

IRWIN INDUSTRIAL TOOLS
Parkway Works, Kettlebridge Road,
Sheffield, South Yorkshire, S9 3BL
Area of Operation: Worldwide
Tel: 0114 244 9066 **Fax:** 0114 256 1788
Email: uksales@irwin.co.uk **Web:** www.irwin.co.uk

JB TOOL HIRE
Comet Way, Hermitage Industrial Estate,
Coalville, Leicester, Leicestershire, LE67 3FS
Area of Operation: UK (Excluding Ireland)
Tel: 01530 510240 **Fax:** 01530 278470
Email: postmaster@jbtoolhire.co.uk
Web: www.Jbtoolhire.co.uk

JEWSON
Merchant House, Binley Business Park,
Coventry, Warwickshire, CV3 2TT
Area of Operation: UK & Ireland
Tel: 02476 438400
Email: jason.wenham@jewson.co.uk
Web: www.jewson.co.uk

KUBOTA (UK) LTD
Dormer Road, Thame, Oxon, Oxfordshire, OX9 3UN
Area of Operation: UK & Ireland
Tel: 01844 214500 **Fax:** 01844 216685
Email: richardh@kubota.co.uk
Web: www.kubota.co.uk

LADDERM8 LTD
Unit 4 Ohio Grove, Hot Lane Industrial Estate,
Burslem, Stoke-On-Trent, Staffordshire, ST6 2BL
Area of Operation: Worldwide
Tel: 01782 769494 **Fax:** 01782 869255
Email: sales@ladderm8.com
Web: www.ladderm8.com

LG HARRIS & CO. LTD
Head Office, Stoke Prior,
Bromsgrove, Worcestershire, B60 4AE
Area of Operation: Worldwide
Tel: 01527 575441 **Fax:** 01527 570522
Email: sales@lgharris.co.uk
Web: www.lgharris.co.uk

LITETEC LTD
Technologies House, 507 Ashingdon Road,
Rochford, Essex, SS4 3HE
Area of Operation: Europe
Tel: 01702 540187 **Fax:** 01702 541049
Email: info@litetec.co.uk
Web: www.litetec.co.uk

LOADMASTER ENGINEERING LTD
Area of Operation: Worldwide
Tel: 0870 386 7377 **Fax:** 0870 729 5623
Email: sales@loadrunner.co.uk
Web: www.loadrunner.co.uk

MACHINE MART LTD
211 Lower Parliament Street,
Nottingham, Nottinghamshire, NG1 1GN
Area of Operation: Worldwide
Tel: 0845 450 1855
Email: sales@machinemart.co.uk
Web: www.machinemart.co.uk ⌐

MERCHANTS, TOOLS & EQUIPMENT

SCREWFIX DIRECT LIMITED

Trade House, Mead Avenue,
Houndstone Business Park,
Yeovil, Somerset
BA22 8RT
Tel: 0500 41 41 41

www.screwfix.com
Email: online@screwfix.com

18V COMBI DRILL

Rugged Drill with ergonomic design for continual use. Features 13mm keyless jacobs 500 series chuck and run-out brake. Spirit bubble and magnetic tray.

1/2" ROUTER

For easy and precise cutting and shaping of different materials such as wood, MDF and plastic. Micro-depth adjustable.

TILE CUTTER

Tile Cutter with a convenient table size. Table is tiltable for various applications.

FORGE STEEL® JIG

For kitchen, bedroom and bathroom fitters. Cuts 500, 600, 650 and 700mm width worktops. 4 nylon aligning pegs included. Made of 13mm Tufnol, guaranteed never to warp.

CONSUMER UNIT

12-way flexible split load with varying configuration of up to 9 ways. Protected by RCD. Comes with 100A DP main switch and 80A. 30mA RCD.

SCREWDRIVER BIT SET

10 Piece Set. Make sure you have the right bit when you need it.

SITE® BOX LEVEL

Milled surfaces with professional, heavy-duty ribbed frame and high accuracy vials. Integral magnets ensure practical, easy use in all environments.

ROOF INSULATION

Clean, easy installation Airtec Double insulation. Suitable for multiple applications, including cavity walls and stud walls. Also suitable for pitched roofs, attics and under floorboards.

EXPANDING FOAM

PU fixing foam with fast application rate, non-stick safety valve and a longer shelf life. Heat-resistant.

BUILDERS TURBOGOLD® CASE

Everything you need in a Single Thread Woodscrew - top quality, durability and terrific driving - it's shaped to drive fast! The professional builder's perfect choice!

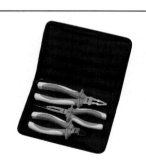

VDE COMBI PLIERS SET

High quality professional pliers set, manufactured to exacting standards, with features designed for comfort during prolonged use. For live line working.

MERCHANTS, TOOLS & EQUIPMENT

MAKITA (UK) LTD
Michigan Drive, Tongwell, Milton Keynes,
Buckinghamshire, MK15 8JD
Area of Operation: Worldwide
Tel: 01908 211678   **Fax:** 01908 211887
Email: leads@makitauk.com
Web: www.makitauk.com

MARSHALL TOOLS LTD
Bay 128, Shannon Industrial Estate, Co. Clare, Ireland
Area of Operation: Worldwide
Tel: +353 86 912 7534
Email: noel@brickytool.com
Web: www.bricky.com

METABO (UK) LTD
25 Majestic Road, Nursling Industrial Estate,
Southampton, Hampshire, SO16 0YT
Area of Operation: UK & Ireland
Tel: 02380 732000   **Fax:** 02380 747500
Email: madams@metabo.co.uk
Web: www.metabo.co.uk

MIKE WYE & ASSOCIATES
Buckland Filleigh Sawmills, Buckland Filleigh,
Beaworthy, Devon, EX21 5RN
Area of Operation: Worldwide
Tel: 01409 281644   **Fax:** 01409 281669
Email: sales@mikewye.co.uk
Web: www.mikewye.co.uk

MUCK TRUCK SALES
Catalpa, Ham Street, Baltonsborough,
Near Glastonbury, Somerset, BA6 8QQ
Area of Operation: UK & Ireland
Tel: 0845 134 2119   **Fax:** 0845 134 2120
Email: info@paulhelpsmucktrucksales.co.uk
Web: www.paulhelpsmucktrucksales.co.uk

OLD HOUSE STORE LTD
Hampstead Farm, Binfield Heath,
Henley on Thames, Oxfordshire, RG9 4LG
Area of Operation: Worldwide
Tel: 0118 969 7711   **Fax:** 0118 969 8822
Email: info@oldhousestore.co.uk
Web: www.oldhousestore.co.uk

PLASPLUGS LTD
Wetmore Road, Burton on Trent, Staffordshire, DE14 1SD
Area of Operation: Worldwide
Tel: 01283 530303   **Fax:** 01283 531246
Email: asmith@plasplugs.com
Web: www.plasplugs.com

POWER TEK
20 Market Street, Watford, Hertfordshire, WD1 7AD
Area of Operation: Worldwide
Tel: 01923 250295   **Fax:** 01923 818219
Email: info@diytools.com
Web: www.diytools.com

POWERMECH
Battersea Road, Heaton Mersey Industrial Estate,
Stockport, Cheshire, SK4 3EA
Area of Operation: UK (Excluding Ireland)
Tel: 0161 432 1999

RIGHT LINES LTD
Waverley House, Waverley Road,
Huddersfield, West Yorkshire, HD1 5NA
Area of Operation: UK (Excluding Ireland)
Tel: 01484 544111
Fax: 01484 549111
Email: enquiries@rightlines.ltd.uk
Web: www.rightlines.ltd.uk

ROLLINS & SONS LTD
Rollins House, 1 Parkway, Harlow, Essex, CM19 5QF
Area of Operation: Worldwide
Tel: 01279 401570   **Fax:** 01279 401580
Email: sales@rollins.co.uk
Web: www.rollins.co.uk

SCAFFOLDING SUPPLIES LTD
15 Wybers Way, Grimsby, Lincolnshire, DN37 9QR
Area of Operation: UK (Excluding Ireland)
Tel: 01472 501011   **Fax:** 01472 501022
Email: scaffolding@hotmail.com
Web: www.scaffoldingsupplies.com

SCAFFOLDING SUPPLIES LTD

Area of Operation: UK (Excluding Ireland)
Tel: 01472 501011
Mobile: 0771 232 2636
Fax: 01472 501022
Email: scaffolding@hotmail.com
Web: www.scaffoldingsupplies.com

New & Used Scaffolding For Sale
• Free design • Guaranteed Buy-Back •
Nationwide Delivery •

SCREWFIX DIRECT LTD
Trade House, Houndstone Business Park, Mead
Avenue, Yeovil, Somerset, BA22 8RT
Area of Operation: UK (Excluding Ireland)
Tel: 0800 096 6226   **Fax:** 01935 401665
Email: online@screwfix.com
Web: www.screwfix.com

SHOPSMITH
The Mill, Millers Dale, Buxton, Derbyshire, SK17 8SN
Area of Operation: UK & Ireland
Tel: 01433 622550   **Fax:** 01433 622552
Email: sales@craft-supplies.co.uk
Web: www.craft-supplies.co.uk

SOUTHERN PLANT AND TOOL HIRE
Centenary Business Park, Station Road,
Henley on Thames, Oxfordshire, RG9 1DS
Area of Operation: UK (Excluding Ireland)
Tel: 01491 576063   **Fax:** 01491 410596
Email: southernplant@supanet.com
Web: www.southernplant.co.uk

STONE2YOURHOME
Area of Operation: UK (Excluding Ireland)
Tel: 0871 8732369
Email: info@stone2yourhome.co.uk
Web: www.stone2yourhome.co.uk

STRIPPERS PAINT REMOVERS
PO Box 6, Sudbury, Suffolk, CO10 6TW
Area of Operation: UK & Ireland
Tel: 01787 371524   **Fax:** 01787 313944
Email: enquiries@stripperspaintremovers.com
Web: www.stripperspaintremovers.com

SURESET UK LTD
Unit 32, Deverill Road Trading Estate,
Sutton Veny, Warminster, Wiltshire, BA12 7BZ
Area of Operation: Europe
Tel: 01985 841180   **Fax:** 01985 841260
Email: mail@sureset.co.uk   **Web:** www.sureset.co.uk

SURVEY SUPPLIES DIRECT
34-44 Mersey View, Waterloo,
Liverpool, Merseyside, L22 6QB
Area of Operation: UK (Excluding Ireland)
Tel: 0845 241 4700   **Fax:** 01519 316734
Email: sales@surveysuppliesdirect.com
Web: www.surveysuppliesdirect.com

TARPAFLEX LTD
The Granary, Northlew, Okehampton, Devon, EX20 3BR
Area of Operation: UK & Ireland
Tel: 08701 657292   **Fax:** 08701 657290
Email: bob@tarpaflex.co.uk
Web: www.tarpaflex.co.uk

THE CORNISH LIME COMPANY LTD.
Brims Park, Old Callywith Road,
Bodmin, Cornwall, PL31 2DZ
Area of Operation: UK (Excluding Ireland)
Tel: 01208 79779   **Fax:** 01208 73744
Email: sales@cornishlime.co.uk
Web: www.cornishlime.co.uk

TILEASY LTD
Unit 10a, Railway Triangle, Walton Road,
Portsmouth, Hampshire, PO6 1TN
Area of Operation: UK & Ireland
Tel: 02392 220077   **Fax:** 02392 220088
Email: enquiries@craftceramics.com
Web: www.craftceramics.com

TOOLBANK
Long Reach, Galleons Boulevard, Crossways
Business Park, Dartford, Kent, DA2 6QE
Area of Operation: UK & Ireland
Tel: 01322 321460   **Fax:** 01322 321461
Email: phunt@toolbank.com
Web: www.toolbank.com

TOOLMAN
Area of Operation: Worldwide
Email: info@toolman.co.uk
Web: www.toolman.co.uk

TOOLSHOP DIRECT
Clough Road, Hull, East Riding of Yorks, HU6 7PE
Area of Operation: UK & Ireland
Tel: 01482 499955
Fax: 01482 440887
Email: sales@toolshopdirect.co.uk
Web: www.toolshopdirect.co.uk

TOOLSTATION
Express Park, Bridgwater, Somerset, TA6 4RN
Area of Operation: UK (Excluding Ireland)
Tel: 0808 100 7211
Fax: 0808 100 7210
Email: info@toolstation.com
Web: www.toolstation.com

TRADE COUNTER DIRECT LTD
Loribon House, Aspen Way, Yalberton Industrial
Estate, Paignton, Devon, TQ4 7QR
Area of Operation: Europe
Tel: 01803 666630
Fax: 01803 540157
Email: sales@tradecounterdirect.com
Web: www.tradecounterdirect.com

TURPTECH TOOLS (UK)
3a The Maltings, Station Road,
Sawbridgeworth, Hertfordshire, CM21 9JX
Area of Operation: Worldwide
Tel: 01279 722282
Fax: 01279 722286
Email: info@turptech.co.uk
Web: www.turptech.co.uk

VISA TOOLS
Gibson House, Barrowby Lane,
Garforth, Leeds, West Yorkshire, LS15 1NG
Area of Operation: Worldwide
Tel: 0113 286 9245
Fax: 0113 286 6859
Email: gc@g-gibson.com
Web: www.g-gibson.com

WD-40 COMPANY LTD
PO Box 440, Kiln Farm, Milton Keynes, MK11 3LF
Area of Operation: Worldwide
Tel: 01908 555400
Fax: 01908 266900
Email: info@wd40.co.uk
Web: www.wd40.co.uk

WHOTZ HOT
8 South Way, Southwell Business Park,
Portland, Dorset, DT5 2NL
Area of Operation: Worldwide
Tel: 01305 823888
Fax: 01305 823888
Email: whotzhot@whotzhot.fsnet.co.uk
Web: www.whotzhot.info

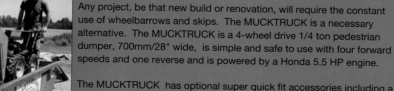

HIRE COMPANIES

KEY

SEE ALSO: TOOLS AND EQUIPMENT - Tools and Equipment

OTHER: ▽ Reclaimed On-line shopping Bespoke Hand-made ECO Ecological

ALEXANDRA TOOL HIRE
5-6 Huxley Parade, Gt Cambridge Road, London, N18 1HY
Area of Operation: Greater London
Tel: 0208 807 5577   **Fax:** 0208 967 7324
Email: bobrist@aol.com   **Web:** www.hiretools.com

ASHTEAD TECHNOLOGY RENTALS
Campus Five, Letchworth Business Park,
Letchworth, Hertfordshire, SG6 2JF
Tel: 0845 270 2707
Fax: 0845 270 2708
Email: rentals@ashtead-technology.co.uk
Web: www.ashtead-technology.co.uk

CJ O'SHEA & CO LTD
Unit 1 Granard Business Centre,
Burns Lane, Mill Hill, London, NW7 2DZ
Area of Operation: East England, Greater London, South East England, South West England and South Wales
Tel: 0208 959 3600   **Fax:** 0208 959 0184
Email: admin@oshea.co.uk
Web: www.oshea.co.uk

CLEAN MACHINE
2 St Peter's Place, Wallingford, Oxfordshire, OX10 0BG
Area of Operation: Europe
Tel: 01491 825600   **Fax:** 01491 825400
Email: ian.monk@machinesthatclean.com
Web: www.machinesthatclean.com

COMPACT HOISTS
Unit 8B, Blackbrook Business Park,
Narrowboat Way, Dudley, West Midlands, DY2 0XQ
Area of Operation: Midlands & Mid Wales
Tel: 01384 240400   **Fax:** 01384 240300
Email: compactft@aol.com
Web: www.thecompactgroup.co.uk

COUNTY GROUNDWORK SERVICES
6 Middlemarsh Street, Poundbury,
Dorchester, Dorset, DT1 3GD
Area of Operation: South West England and South Wales
Tel: 01305 261976
Email: info@countygroundworkservices.co.uk
Web: www.countygroundworkservices.co.uk

FRAME WISE
Presteigne Industrial Estate,
Presteigne, Powys, LD8 2UF
Area of Operation: UK (Excluding Ireland)
Tel: 01544 260125   **Fax:** 01544 260707
Email: framewise@framewiseltd.co.uk
Web: www.framewiseltd.co.uk

HEWDEN
Trafford House, Chester Road,
Stretford, Manchester, M32 0RL
Area of Operation: UK (Excluding Ireland)
Tel: 0845 60 70 111   **Fax:** 0247 666 6988
Email: jeff.schofield@hewden.co.uk
Web: www.hewden.co.uk

HIRE CENTER
Trowel House, Kettering Parkway,
Kettering, Northamptonshire, NN15 6XR
Tel: 0800 529 529
Email: centerline@centers.co.uk
Web: www.hirecenter.co.uk

> **Please mention The Homebuilder's Handbook when you call**

HSS HIRE SHOPS
25 Willow Lane, Mitcham, Surrey, CR4 4TS
Area of Operation: Worldwide
Tel: 0845 728 2828   **Fax:** 0208 687 5005
Email: hire@hss.com   **Web:** www.hss.com

ICF-IT LIMITED
Unit 26, Malmesbury Road,
Kingsditch Trading Estate,
Cheltenham, Gloucestershire, GL51 9PL
Area of Operation: UK & Ireland
Tel: 0870 169 6869   **Fax:** 0870 169 6869
Email: info@icf-it.com

JEWSON
Merchant House, Binley Business Park,
Coventry, Warwickshire, CV3 2TT
Area of Operation: UK & Ireland
Tel: 02476 438400   **Web:** www.jewson.co.uk
Email: jason.wenham@jewson.co.uk

OUTSOURCE SITE SERVICES
UK Control Centre, Bradford Street,
Shifnal, Shropshire, TF11 8AU
Area of Operation: UK & Ireland
Tel: 0870 701 9963   **Fax:** 0870 701 9964
Email: roger@out-source.biz
Web: www.out-source.biz

SOUTHERN PLANT AND TOOL HIRE
Centenary Business Park, Station Road,
Henley on Thames, Oxfordshire, RG9 1DS
Area of Operation: UK (Excluding Ireland)
Tel: 01491 576063   **Fax:** 01491 410596
Email: southernplant@supanet.com
Web: www.southernplant.co.uk

TOPSKIPS.COM
Baxall Business Centre, Adswood Road,
Stockport, Cheshire, SK3 8LF
Area of Operation: UK & Ireland
Tel: 0800 019 24 10   **Fax:** 0161 4806456
Email: mark.attwood@topskips.com
Web: www.topskips.com

Image courtesy of Handyheat (0800 881 8097)

HEATING, PLUMBING & ELECTRICAL

SPONSORED BY HANDYHEAT
Tel 0800 881 8097 Web www.handyheat.co.uk

HANDYHEAT ®
FLOOR HEATING SYSTEMS

Underfloor Heating

Image by Nu-Heat

Top tips
5 reasons to get underfloor heating

- Energy efficiency – water systems can save around 15% on fuel bills by using lower water temperatures
- It eliminates the need for radiators, giving freedom for furniture layouts
- Safety – unlike radiators, there are no sharp or very hot surfaces
- It's better for allergy sufferers – there are fewer draughts to disturb particles
- UFH generates a subtle background heat which is very comfortable

Underfloor heating (UFH) is rapidly becoming an essential feature in new-built homes. Not only does it provide good energy efficiency, it's also comfortable and discreet. So, is UFH for everyone, and what are the best systems on the market?

One of UFH's best selling points is its more efficient use of energy. It uses a layering effect of warm air emitted from the floor upwards so, unlike radiators, there is no need to heat the floor or lower parts of the room. This means UFH can be set at lower average room temperatures – around two degrees below that of conventional central heating.

The reduction in convection also reduces the heat loss through air changes, giving an average saving of 10-15% of energy consumption compared to conventional radiator systems.

Types of system – electric vs. warm water

Electric

In most instances, electric UFH involves a cable/ribbon being inserted into the floor/structure. Slightly cheaper and easier to install than warm water systems, it can be operated independently of the existing heating system. The electric cabling is so thin that it has little effect on finished floor levels. Although it is more expensive to run than its counterpart, electric UFH can be controlled in areas such as kitchens and bathrooms to only come on at certain times of the day.

Warm water

Flowing through pipes in much the same way as a radiator system, warm water UFH systems tend to be the preferred choice, as they can provide heating for the whole house. It is slightly more expensive and time-consuming to install than electric UFH, but cheaper to use in the long run. Warm water

manufacturers are also latching on to the popularity of the extension/remodelling market and bringing out specially tailored ranges that can function more independently.

How to compare prices

Comparing quotes is actually quite difficult because companies offer slightly different systems, using varying components. Don't simply go for the cheapest – ensure that you check like-for-like and know exactly what you are getting for your money.

UFH prices will vary depending on a number of factors. The main considerations will be installation and commissioning, the quantity and type of insulation, the quantity and type of pipe and the level of sophistication of the controls.

Bear in mind that package prices from the main UFH system suppliers will include some element for designing your individual system. Although you can buy the component parts for a DIY system from plumbers and builders merchants, this will not include design costs. If you are keen to take the DIY approach, the services of an experienced engineer/designer are essential. It's also worth remembering that the bigger package companies are likely to provide manufacturer's warranties.

What type of floor covering can I have?

Contrary to popular conception, UFH will work with almost any floor covering, although there are some issues to consider. Several users have reported problems with the warping of solid plank and timber floors, but perhaps the most controversial covering is carpet. It certainly can be used with UFH, but the carpet used should have a low tog value. The thinner the carpet, with a high quality underlay, the better UFH will perform. As a rule, UFH works best with flooring options like stone, slate and ceramic tiles.

UNDERFLOOR HEATING

KEY

PRODUCT TYPES: 1 = Electric 2 = Warm Water

SEE ALSO: HEATING - Heating Controls & Valves

ENERGY SOURCES: ★ Gas ○ Oil
☐ Coal ● Wood ✪ Multi-Fuel
✿ Electric ◆ Gel

OTHER: ▽ Reclaimed ✌ On-line shopping
✐ Bespoke ✋ Hand-made ECO Ecological

ADVANCED HEATING TECHNOLOGIES LTD
26 Stanley Avenue, Minster, Sheerness, Kent, ME12 2EY
Area of Operation: Worldwide
Tel: 07813 937360
Fax: 01795 87723
Email: wilson.mark@tinyworld.co.uk
Web: www.aht-heating.com **Product Type:** 1

ADVANCED HEATING TECHNOLOGIES LTD

Area of Operation: Worldwide
Tel: 07813 937360
Fax: 01795 877232
Email: wilson.mark@tinyworld.co.uk
Web: www.aht-heating.com
Product Type: 1

An innovative under floor system, new to the UK market, now makes installation almost as easy as laying a carpet.

ANDERSON FLOORWARMING LIMITED
IPPEC Scottish System House,
Unit 119, Atlas Express Industrial Estate, 1 Rutherglen Road, Glasgow, G73 1SX
Area of Operation: Scotland
Tel: 0141 647 6716 **Fax:** 0141 647 6751
Email: mail@andersonfloorwarming.co.uk
Web: www.ippec.co.uk ✌ **Product Type:** 2

APPLIED HEATING SERVICES LTD
9 Rosse Close, Parsons Industrial Estate,
Washington, Tyne & Wear, NE38 1ET
Area of Operation: North East England
Tel: 0191 417 7604
Fax: 0191 417 1549
Email: georgecossey1@btconnect.com
Web: www.appliedheat.co.uk
Product Type: 1, 2 **Other Info:** ECO ✐

ASTRA CEILING FANS & LIGHTING
Unit 6, Lowercroft Industrial Estate,
Bury, Lancashire, BL8 3PA
Area of Operation: Europe
Tel: 0161 7973222 **Fax:** 0161 7973444
Email: support@astra247.com
Web: www.astra247.com ✌ **Product Type:** 1

ATB AIR CONDITIONING AND HEATING
67 Melloway Road, Rushden,
Northamptonshire, NN10 6XX
Area of Operation: East England, Greater London, Midlands & Mid Wales, South East England
Tel: 0870 260 1650 **Fax:** 01933 411731
Email: enquiries@atbairconditioning.co.uk
Web: www.atbairconditioning.co.uk
Product Type: 2

BEGETUBE UK LTD
8 Carsegate Road South, Inverness, Highlands, IV3 8LL
Area of Operation: UK & Ireland
Tel: 01463 246600 **Fax:** 01463 246624
Email: rory@begetube.co.uk
Web: www.begetube-uk.co.uk ✌ **Product Type:** 2

BESPOKE UNDERFLOOR HEATING
Unit 28, Rotheram Close, Norwood Industrial Estate, Sheffield, South Yorkshire, S21 2 JU
Area of Operation: UK (Excluding Ireland)
Tel: 0114 248 3396
Fax: 0114 248 6146
Email: bespoke_ufh@btopenworld.com
Web: www.bespokeunderfloorheating.co.uk ✌
Product Type: 1

BORDERS UNDERFLOOR HEATING
26 Coopersknowe Crescent,
Galashiels, Borders, TD1 2DS
Area of Operation: UK & Ireland
Tel: 01896 668667
Fax: 01896 668678
Email: underfloor@btinternet.com
Web: www.bordersunderfloor.co.uk
Product Type: 2 ★ ○ ☐ ● ✪ ✿

CHELMER HEATING SERVICES LTD
Unit 12A, Baddow Park, West Hanningfield Road,
Chelmsford, Essex, CM2 7SY
Area of Operation: UK (Excluding Ireland)
Tel: 01245 471111
Fax: 01245 471117
Email: sales@chelmerheating.co.uk
Web: www.chelmerheating.co.uk
Product Type: 2 ★ ○ ● ✪ **Other Info:** ✐

COMFOOT FLOORING
Walnut Tree, Redgrave Road,
South Lopham, Diss, Norfolk, IP22 2HN
Area of Operation: Europe
Tel: 01379 688516 **Fax:** 01379 688517
Email: sales@comfoot.com
Web: www.comfoot.com ✌
Product Type: 1

COMFORT ZONE SYSTEMS LTD
Suite 5 Caxton House, 143 South Coast Road,
Peacehaven, East Sussex, BN10 8NN
Area of Operation: Europe
Tel: 01273 580888 **Fax:** 01273 580848
Email: clive@czsystems.co.uk
Web: www.czsystems.co.uk **Product Type:** 2

COMFYAIR LTD
Albion Works, Royd Ings Avenue,
Keighley, West Yorkshire, BD21 4BZ
Area of Operation: UK & Ireland
Tel: 01535 611333 **Fax:** 01535 611334
Email: david@comfyair.co.uk
Web: www.comfyair.co.uk **Product Type:** 1

CONSERVATION ENGINEERING LTD
The Street, Troston, Bury St Edmunds, Suffolk, IP31 1EW
Area of Operation: UK & Ireland
Tel: 01359 269360
Email: anne@conservation-engineering.co.uk
Web: www.conservation-engineering.co.uk
Product Type: 2

CONSTRUCTION RESOURCES
16 Great Guildford Street, London, SE1 0HS
Area of Operation: UK (Excluding Ireland)
Tel: 0207 450 2211 **Fax:** 0207 450 2212
Email: info@constructionresources.com
Web: www.constructionresources.com
Product Type: 2

CONTINENTAL UNDERFLOOR HEATING
Continental House, Kings Hill, Bude, Cornwall, EX23 0LU
Area of Operation: Europe
Tel: 0845 108 1204 **Fax:** 0845 108 1205
Email: info@continental-ufh.co.uk
Web: www.continental-ufh.co.uk ✌
Product Type: 1, 2 **Other Info:** ECO ✐

COSY ROOMS (COSY-HEATING.CO.UK)
17 Chiltern Way, North Hykeham,
Lincoln, Lincolnshire, LN6 9SY
Area of Operation: UK (Excluding Ireland)
Tel: 01522 696002 **Fax:** 01522 696002
Email: keith@cosy-rooms.com
Web: www.cosy-heating.co.uk ✌ **Product Type:** 1

DANFOSS RANDALL LTD
Ampthill Road, Bedford, Bedfordshire, MK42 9ER
Area of Operation: UK & Ireland
Tel: 0845 121 7400 **Fax:** 0845 121 7515
Email: danfossrandall@danfoss.com
Web: www.danfoss-randall.co.uk
Product Type: 1, 2

DEVI ELECTROHEAT LTD
Brickfields Business Park, Woolpit,
Bury St. Edmunds, Suffolk, IP30 9QS
Area of Operation: UK & Ireland
Tel: 0845 4349488
Fax: 0845 4349489
Email: projects@devi.co.uk
Web: www.devi.co.uk **Product Type:** 1

DIMPLEX
Millbrook House, Grange Drive, Hedge End,
Southampton, Hampshire, SO30 2DF
Area of Operation: UK & Ireland
Tel: 0845 600 5111
Fax: 01489 773050
Email: customer.services@glendimplex.com
Web: www.dimplex.co.uk **Product Type:** 1

DISCOUNT FLOOR HEATING
Studio 24, Torfaen Business Centre, Gilchrist Thomas Industrial Estate, Blaenavon, Torfaen, NP4 9RL
Area of Operation: UK (Excluding Ireland)
Tel: 0845 658 1511
Fax: 0871 661 3557
Email: sales@discountfloorheating.co.uk
Web: www.discountfloorheating.co.uk ✌
Product Type: 1

EBECO UNDERFLOOR HEATING
Unit N, Kingsfield Business Centre,
Philanthropic Road, Redhill, Surrey, RH1 4DP
Area of Operation: Europe
Tel: 01737 761767
Fax: 01737 507907
Email: uksales@ebeco.com
Web: www.ebeco.com **Product Type:** 1

EBECO UNDERFLOOR HEATING

Area of Operation: Europe
Tel: 01737 761767
Fax: 01737 507907
Email: uksales@ebeco.com
Web: www.ebeco.com
Product Type: 1

Ebeco's comprehensive range of electric underfloor heating cables, foils, thermostats and accessories combines luxurious heat with simple installation, reliability, durability, zero maintenance and competitive prices.

HEATING, PLUMBING & ELECTRICAL

Electric Under Floor Heating

Suitable for all floor types, especially tiles, wood and stone
Suitable for all rooms ● Ideal for both new builds and renovations
LIFETIME guarantee ● Supply only or fully installed service available

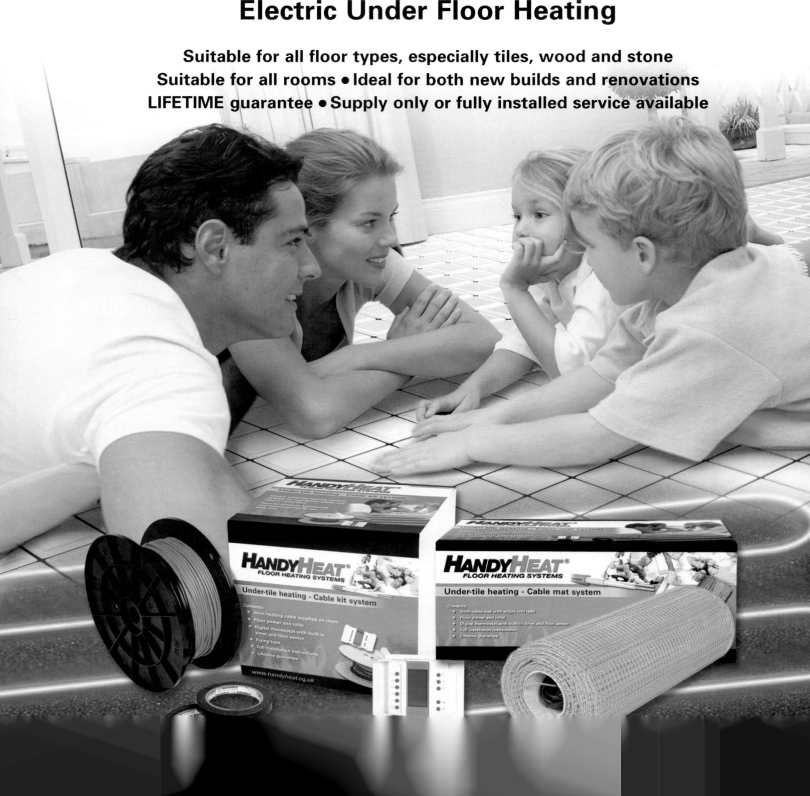

ECO HOMETEC UK LTD
Unit 11E, Carcroft Enterprise Park, Carcroft,
Doncaster, South Yorkshire, DN6 8DD
Area of Operation: Europe
Tel: 01302 722266   **Fax:** 01302 728634
Email: Stephen@eco-hometec.co.uk
Web: www.eco-hometec.co.uk
Product Type: 2

ECO SYSTEMS IRELAND LTD
40 Glensheck Road, Ballycastle,
Co. Antrim, BT54 6PH
Area of Operation: UK & Ireland
Tel: 02820 768708   **Fax:** 02820 769781
Email: info@ecosystemsireland.com
Web: www.ecosystemsireland.com
Product Type: 1

ELEKTRA (UK) LTD
19 Manning Road, Felixstowe, Suffolk, IP11 2AY
Area of Operation: UK & Ireland
Tel: 0845 226 8142   **Fax:** 0845 225 8143
Email: info@elektra-uk.com
Web: www.elektra-uk.com
Product Type: 1

ENERFOIL MAGNUM LTD
Kenmore Road, Comrie Bridge, Kenmore,
Aberfeldy, Perthshire, PH15 2LS
Area of Operation: Europe
Tel: 01887 822999   **Fax:** 01887 822954
Email: sales@enerfoil.com
Web: www.enerfoil.com   **Product Type:** 1

ENERGY MASTER
Keltic Business Park,
Unit 1 Clieveragh Industrial Estate, Listowel, Ireland
Area of Operation: Ireland Only
Tel: 00353 (0)68 23864   **Fax:** 00353 (0)68 24533
Email: info@energymaster.ie
Web: www.energymaster.ie   **Product Type:** 2

ENERGY SUPERSTORE
3 Wellington Park, Belfast, BT9 6DJ
Area of Operation: UK & Ireland
Tel: 02890 388391
Email: info@energysuperstore.co.uk
Web: www.energysuperstore.co.uk   **Product Type:** 2

ENERGY TECHNIQUE PLC
47 Central Avenue, West Molesey, Surrey, KT8 2QZ
Tel: 0208 783 0033   **Fax:** 0208 783 0140
Email: rob@etenv.co.uk
Web: www.diffusion-group.co.uk

EU SOLUTIONS
Maghull Business Centre, 1 Liverpool Road North,
Maghull, Liverpool, L31 2HB
Area of Operation: UK & Ireland
Tel: 0870 160 1660   **Fax:** 0151 526 8849
Email: ths@blueyonder.co.uk
Web: www.totalhomesolutions.co.uk
Product Type: 1, 2

EURO BATHROOMS
102 Annareagh Road, Richhill, Co Armagh, BT61 9JY
Area of Operation: Ireland Only
Tel: 02838 879996   **Fax:** 02838 879996
Product Type: 2

EVEN-HEAT
Unit 2A Wildmere Road Industrial Estate,
Banbury, Oxfordshire, OX16 3JU
Area of Operation: UK (Excluding Ireland)
Tel: 01295 277881   **Fax:** 01295 277556
Email: enquiries@even-heat.co.uk
Web: www.even-heat.co.uk   **Product Type:** 1, 2

FLEXEL INTERNATIONAL LTD
Queensway Industrial Estate,
Glenrothes, Fife, KY7 5QF
Area of Operation: Worldwide
Tel: 01592 757313   **Fax:** 01592 754535
Email: sales@flexel.co.uk
Web: www.flexel.co.uk   **Product Type:** 1

FLEXEL INTERNATIONAL LTD
Area of Operation: Worldwide
Tel: 01592 757313
Fax: 01592 754535
Email: sales@flexel.co.uk
Web: www.flexel.co.uk
Product Type: 1

EcofilmSet electric Underfloor Heating elements offers a balanced heat distribution with the lowest possible temperature leading to a high user comfort levels and improved economy.

FLEXELEC UK (FORMERLY JIMI-HEAT)
Unit 11 Kings Park Industrial Estate, Primrose Hill,
Kings Langley, Hertfordshire, WD4 8ST
Area of Operation: Worldwide
Tel: 01923 274477
Fax: 01923 270264
Email: sales@omerin.co.uk
Web: www.flexelec.com   **Product Type:** 1

FLOOR HEATING SYSTEMS LTD
Fairway Court, Hucknall, Nottinghamshire, NG15 7TA
Area of Operation: Europe
Tel: 01159 632314   **Fax:** 01159 632317
Email: sales@handyheat.co.uk
Web: www.handyheat.co.uk /
www.floorheatingsystems.co.uk   **Product Type:** 1

HANDYHEAT - FLOOR HEATING SYSTEMS
Area of Operation: Europe
Tel: 01159 632314
Fax: 01159 632317
Email: sales@handyheat.co.uk
Web: www.handyheat.co.uk
www.floorheatingsystems.co.uk
Product Type: 1

Handyheat - suppliers & installers of all types of electric underfloor heating systems plus insulation boards & mirror demisters. Suitable for new homes, extensions, conservatories & renovations

FLOORHEATECH LTD
Bowen House, Bredgar Road, Gillingham, Kent, ME8 6PL
Area of Operation: UK & Ireland
Tel: 0800 814 4328   **Fax:** 0870 131 6520
Email: tracey@floorheatech.co.uk
Web: www.floorheatech.co.uk
Product Type: 1, 2

FLOORS-2-GO
140 Stores Nationwide
Area of Operation: UK & Ireland
Tel: 08000 830 330   **Email:** info@floors2go.co.uk
Web: www.floors2go.co.uk

HEATING, PLUMBING & ELECTRICAL

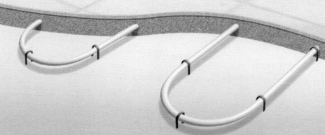
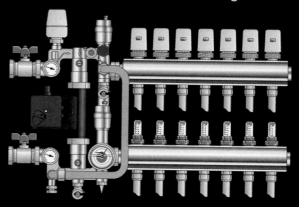

HEATING, PLUMBING & ELECTRICAL

FLOORWARMING (UK) LTD
Warwick Mill, Warwick Bridge,
Carlisle, Cumbria, CA4 8RR
Area of Operation: UK (Excluding Ireland)
Tel: 01228 631300   **Fax:** 01228 631333
Email: michael@floorwarming.co.uk
Web: www.floorwarming.co.uk
Product Type: 1, 2

FLORAD
Radiant House, The Crosspath,
Radlett, Hertfordshire, WD7 8HR
Area of Operation: Europe
Tel: 01923 850823   **Fax:** 01923 850823
Email: info@florad.co.uk
Web: www.florad.co.uk   **Product Type:** 2

GREENSHOP SOLAR LTD
Hullbrook Garage, Bisley,
Stroud, Gloucestershire, GL6 7BX
Area of Operation: UK (Excluding Ireland)
Tel: 01452 772030   **Fax:** 01452 770115
Email: eddie@greenshop.co.uk
Web: www.greenshop-solar.co.uk
Product Type: 2 ● ✪   **Other Info:** ECO

HEATSAFE CABLE SYSTEMS LIMITED
Mere's Edge, Chester Road,
Helsby, Frodsham, Cheshire, WA6 0DJ
Area of Operation: Worldwide
Tel: 01928 726451
Fax: 01928 727846
Email: michael.dicker@heat-trace.com
Web: www.heatsafe.com   **Product Type:** 1

HEPWORTH PLUMBING PRODUCTS
Edlington Lane, Edlington, Doncaster,
South Yorkshire, DN12 1BY
Area of Operation: Worldwide
Tel: 01709 856300   **Fax:** 01709 856301
Email: info@hepworth.co.uk
Web: www.hepworth.co.uk
Product Type: 2   **Other Info:** ✑

HILTON CROFT LTD
Southern Counties House, 27-43 Ilfield Road,
Crawley, West Sussex, RH11 7AT
Tel: 01293 452657   **Fax:** 01293 426561
Email: info@hilton-croft.co.uk
Web: www.hilton-croft.co.uk   **Product Type:** 1, 2

INVISIBLE HEATING SYSTEMS
IHS Design Centre, Morefield Industrial Estate,
Ullapool, Highlands, IV26 2SR
Area of Operation: UK & Ireland
Tel: 01854 613161   **Fax:** 01854 613160
Email: design@invisibleheating.co.uk
Web: www.invisibleheating.com   **Product Type:** 1, 2

IPPEC SYSTEMS LTD
66 Rea Street South, Birmingham, B5 6LB
Area of Operation: UK & Ireland
Tel: 0121 622 4333   **Fax:** 0121 622 5768
Email: info@ippec.co.uk
Web: www.ippec.co.uk ✍   **Product Type:** 1, 2

JOHN GUEST SPEEDFIT LTD
Horton Road, West Drayton, Middlesex, UB7 8JL
Tel: 01895 449233   **Fax:** 01895 420321
Email: info@johnguest.co.uk
Web: www.speedfit.co.uk   **Product Type:** 2

KV RADIATORS
6 Postle Close, Kilsby, Rugby, Warwickshire, CV23 8YG
Area of Operation: UK & Ireland
Tel: 01788 823286
Fax: 01788 823002
Email: solutions@kvradiators.com
Web: www.kvradiators.com   **Product Type:** 1, 2

LAFARGE GYVLON LTD
221 Europa Boulevard, Westbrook,
Warrington, Cheshire, WA5 7TN
Tel: 01925 428780   **Fax:** 01925 428788
Email: sales@gyvlon-floors.co.uk
Web: www.gyvlon-floors.co.uk   **Product Type:** 1, 2

LEEMICK LTD
79 Windermere Drive, Rainham, Kent, ME8 9DX
Area of Operation: UK (Excluding Ireland)
Tel: 01634 351666   **Fax:** 01634 351666
Email: sales@leemick.co.uk
Web: www.leemick.co.uk
Product Type: 1, 2 ★ ○ □ ● ✪ ✿ ♦

MYSON
Eastern Avenue, Team Valley, Gateshead, NE11 0PG
Area of Operation: Worldwide
Tel: 0845 402 3434
Email: sales@myson.co.uk
Web: www.myson.co.uk   **Product Type:** 1, 2

NEOHEAT
Smallmead Gate, Pingemead Business Centre,
Reading, Berkshire, RG30 3UR
Area of Operation: Worldwide
Tel: 0845 108 0361   **Fax:** 0845 108 1295
Email: info@neoheat.com
Web: www.neoheat.com   **Product Type:** 1 ✿

NU-HEAT UK LIMITED
Heathpark House, Devonshire Road, Heathpark
Industrial Estate, Honiton, Devon, EX14 1SD
Area of Operation: UK & Ireland
Tel: 0800 731 1976   **Fax:** 01404 549771
Email: ufh@nu-heat.co.uk   **Web:** www.nu-heat.co.uk ✍
Product Type: 2

HEATING, PLUMBING & ELECTRICAL

FLOORWARMING UK

Floorwarming UK leads the way in quality underfloor heating systems nationwide.

Providing comfort, space and style to any home or office, our individually-tailored systems are designed to complement today's busy life style - while maintaining traditional standards of workmanship and service.

Comprehensive design including full heat loss calculations which guarantee room temperatures. Our nationwide teams of engineers provide an unrivalled level of knowledge and expertise. With superior after-care to ensure you get the very best from your Floorwarming UK system.

- Nationwide service
- 10 year system guarantee
- 50 year pipe guarantee
- Technical support 24/7

- DESIGN
- SUPPLY
- INSTALL

For full details about Floorwarming UK's range of services and products, or a Personal Quotation including bespoke design, system specifications and all relevant components, contact us on: **t: 0870 8506660** or alternatively email us at: **info@floorwarming.co.uk**

NATIONWIDE UNDERFLOOR HEATING & RENEWABLE ENERGY SPECIALIST

YOU STAND ON OUR REPUTATION

THE UNDERFLO HEATIN MANUFACTURERS' ASSO

PARAGON SYSTEMS (SCOTLAND) LIMITED
The Office, Corbie Cottage, Maryculter,
Aberdeen, Aberdeenshire, AB12 5FT
Area of Operation: Scotland
Tel: 01224 735536 **Fax:** 01224 735537
Email: info@paragon-systems.co.uk
Web: www.paragon-systems.co.uk
Product Type: 2 ★ ○ ✿

PARKSIDE TILES
49-51 Highmeres Road, Thurmeston,
Leicester, Leicestershire, LE4 9LZ
Area of Operation: UK (Excluding Ireland)
Tel: 0116 276 2532 **Fax:** 0116 246 0649
Email: info@parksidetiles.co.uk
Web: www.parksidetiles.co.uk **Product Type:** 1

PEDARSON HEATING
Elektrek House, 19 Manning Road,
Felixstowe, Suffolk, IP11 2AY
Area of Operation: UK & Ireland
Tel: 01394 270777 **Fax:** 01394 670189
Email: info@pedarson.com
Web: www.pedarsonheating.co.uk
Product Type: 1

PETERSONS NATURAL FLOORINGS
Unit 10/11 Woodlands Park Industrial Estate,
Short Thorn Road, Stratton Strawless,
Norwich, Norfolk, NR10 5NU
Area of Operation: UK & Ireland
Tel: 01603 755511 **Fax:** 01603 755019
Email: office@petersons-natural-floorings.co.uk
Web: www.petersons-natural-floorings.co.uk

R&D MARKETING (DEMISTA) LTD
Land House, Anyards Road, Cobham, Surrey, KT11 2LW
Area of Operation: Worldwide
Tel: 01932 866600
Fax: 01932 866688
Email: rd@demista.co.uk
Web: www.demista.co.uk **Product Type:** 1

COSYFLOOR™

Area of Operation: Worldwide
Tel: 01932 866600
Fax: 01932 866688
Email: rd@demista.co.uk
Web: www.demista.co.uk
Product Type: 2

Transform cold but beautiful surfaces into inviting warm floors with **Cosyfloor™** underfloor heating systems. DIY or professional installation.

RADIANT HEATING SOLUTIONS LTD
Mill Farm, Hougham, Grantham,
Lincolnshire, NG32 2HZ
Tel: 01400 250572 **Fax:** 01400 251264
Email: sales@heating-solutions.biz
Web: www.heating-solutions.biz **Product Type:** 1, 2

RAYOTEC LTD
Unit 3, Brooklands Close,
Sunbury on Thames, Surrey, TW16 7DX
Area of Operation: UK & Ireland
Tel: 01932 784848 **Fax:** 01932 784849
Email: info@rayotec.com
Web: www.rayotec.com **Product Type:** 1, 2

REID UNDERFLOOR HEATING (SCOTLAND) LTD
8 Hillside Grove, Barrhead,
Glasgow, Renfrewshire, G78 1HB
Area of Operation: East England, Midlands & Mid Wales, North East England, North West England and North Wales, Scotland
Tel: 0141 880 4443 **Fax:** 0141 880 4442
Email: sales@ruhs.co.uk
Web: www.ruhs.co.uk **Product Type:** 2

ROBBENS SYSTEMS - UNDERFLOOR HEATING
69 Castleham Road, St Leonards On Sea,
East Sussex, TN38 9NU
Area of Operation: UK & Ireland
Tel: 01424 851111 **Fax:** 01424 851135
Email: robbens@underfloorheating.co.uk
Web: www.underfloorheating.co.uk
Product Type: 1, 2 **Other Info:** ✎

RUH(S) LTD
8 Hillside Grove, Barrhead, Glasgow, G78 1HB
Area of Operation: UK (Excluding Ireland)
Tel: 0141 880 4443 **Fax:** 0141 880 4442
Email: office@ruhs.co.uk
Web: www.ruhs.co.uk **Product Type:** 2

SCANDINAVIAN UNDERFLOOR HEATING CO. LTD.
314 Croydon Road, Beckenham, Kent, BR3 4HR
Area of Operation: UK & Ireland
Tel: 0208 663 6171
Fax: 0208 650 3556
Email: info@heatingunderfloor.co.uk
Web: www.heatingunderfloor.co.uk
Product Type: 2

SHIRES TECHNICAL SERVICES
57-63 Lea Road, Northampton,
Northamptonshire, NN1 4PE
Area of Operation: UK (Excluding Ireland)
Tel: 01604 472525 **Fax:** 01604 473837
Email: enquiries@shireservices.com
Web: www.shireservices.com **Product Type:** 2

SOLAR TWIN
2nd Floor, 50 Watergate Street,
Chester, Cheshire, CH1 2LA
Area of Operation: UK & Ireland
Tel: 01244 403407 **Fax:** 01244 403654
Email: hi@solartwin.com
Web: www.solartwin.com **Product Type:** 2

SPEEDHEAT UK
Iona House, Stratford Road, Wicken,
Milton Keynes, Buckinghamshire, MK19 6DF
Area of Operation: UK & Ireland
Tel: 0800 783 5831
Fax: 01908 562205
Email: info@speedheat.co.uk
Web: www.speedheat.co.uk **Product Type:** 1

STEP WARMFLOOR UK LTD
Fir Bank, 400 Tottington Road,
Bury, Lancashire, BL8 1TU
Area of Operation: Worldwide
Tel: 0161 764 8848
Fax: 0161 763 4078
Email: info@stepwarmfloor.co.uk
Web: www.stepwarmfloor.co.uk **Product Type:** 1

SUPAWARM UNDERFLOOR HEATING
Rose Brae, Toll Bar, Distington,
Cumbria, CA14 4PD
Area of Operation: UK & Ireland
Tel: 01946 832984 **Fax:** 01946 833588
Email: alanc348@aol.com
Web: www.supawarmunderfloorheating.co.uk
Product Type: 2

THERMALFLOOR SYSTEMS LTD
Ruthvenfield Grove, Perth,
Perth and Kinross, PH1 3FN
Area of Operation: UK & Ireland
Tel: 08450 620400 **Fax:** 08450 620401
Email: sales@thermalfloor-heating.co.uk
Web: www.thermalfloor-heating.co.uk
Product Type: 2

HEATING, PLUMBING & ELECTRICAL

Continental™
Underfloor Heating

What system do you want?

There is so much choice between warm-water and electrical underfloor heating, with different types of pipe and cable, simple and complex controls, joist systems, screed systems, different types of heat source, and systems for single rooms or whole houses

That's why we've made it simple, with water and electrical systems for projects large and small

And why time and time again we are the first choice for plumbers, architects, and people like you

"Continental gave us a lot of advice before, during and after installation ... we liked the fact they didn't try to sell us things we didn't need. We were helped to make the system fit our requirements"
Why I chose... feature, **Homebuilding & Renovating Magazine**

A quick call to our team will make you wonder why others make it so complicated, and you can rest assured that everything we supply is tried and tested, comes complete with robust guarantees, gets delivered on time, and has been designed to meet or exceed the toughest UK and European standards

underfloor heating made simple™

0845 108 1204   info@continental-ufh.co.uk • www.continental-ufh.co.uk

THERMO-FLOOR (GB) LTD
Unit 1 Babsham Farm, Chichester Road,
Bognor Regis, West Sussex, PO21 5EL
Area of Operation: UK (Excluding Ireland)
Tel: 01243 822058   **Fax:** 01243 860379
Email: sales@thermo-floor.co.uk
Web: www.thermo-floor.co.uk
Product Type: 1, 2 ★ ○ □ ● ✪ ✿
Other Info: ECO

TLC ELECTRICAL WHOLESALERS
TLC Building, Off Fleming Way,
Crawley, West Sussex, RH10 9JY
Area of Operation: Worldwide
Tel: 01293 565630   **Fax:** 01293 425234
Email: sales@tlc-direct.co.uk
Web: www.tlc-direct.co.uk ✍
Product Type: 1, 2

TOG SYSTEMS
Unit 2a Wildmere Road Industrial Estate,
Banbury, Oxfordshire, OX16 3JU
Area of Operation: UK & Ireland
Tel: 01295 277600   **Fax:** 01295 279402
Email: enquiries@togsystems.co.uk
Web: www.togsystems.co.uk ✍
Product Type: 1, 2

TRIANCO HEATING PRODUCTS LIMITED
Thorncliffe, Chapeltown, Sheffield,
South Yorkshire, S35 2PH
Area of Operation: UK & Ireland
Tel: 0114 257 2300
Fax: 0114 257 1419
Email: info@trianco.co.uk
Web: www.trianco.co.uk
Product Type: 1

UFH DESIGN LTD
83 Northwick Road, Worcester,
Worcestershire, WR3 7EA
Area of Operation: UK (Excluding Ireland)
Tel: 01905 756755   **Fax:** 0870 7062275
Email: info@ufh-design.co.uk
Web: www.ufh-design.co.uk

UNDERFLOOR DIRECT LTD
Unit 1 Lisburn Enterprise Centre,
Ballinderry Road, Lisburn, Co Antrim, BT28 2BP
Area of Operation: UK & Ireland
Tel: 02892 634068
Fax: 02892 669667
Email: info@keeheating.co.uk
Web: www.keeheating.co.uk/
www.underfloordirect.co.uk
Product Type: 2   **Other Info:** ✍

UNDERFLOOR HEATING SERVICES
Bakers Cottage, Pitt Hill Lane,
Moorlynch, Somerset, TA7 9BT
Area of Operation: UK (Excluding Ireland)
Tel: 07808 328135
Fax: 01278 427272
Web: www.underfloorheatingservices-sw.co.uk

UNDERFLOOR HEATING SYSTEMS LTD
Unit 1, 79 Friar Street,
Worcester, Worcestershire, WR1 2NT
Area of Operation: Europe
Tel: 01905 616928
Fax: 01905 611240
Email: info@underfloorheatingsystems.co.uk
Web: www.underfloorheatingsystems.co.uk ✍
Product Type: 2

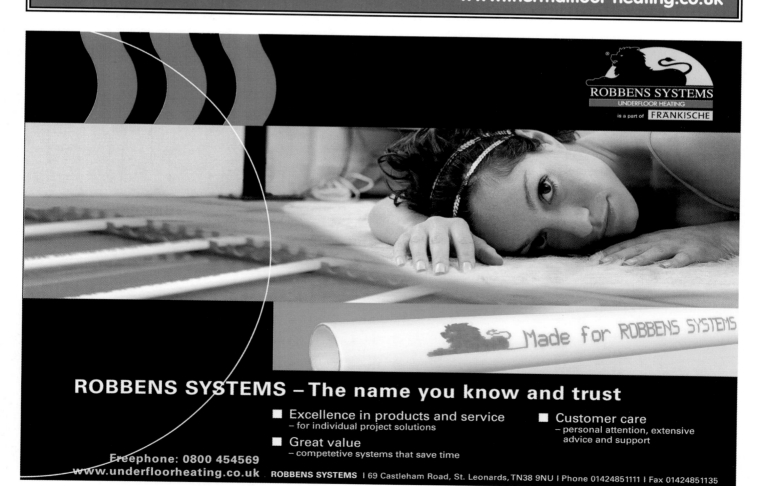
HEATING, PLUMBING & ELECTRICAL

UNDERFLOOR HEATING UK
Norris House, Elton Park Business Centre,
Hadleigh Road, Ipswich, Suffolk, IP2 0HU
Area of Operation: Europe
Tel: 01473 280 444 **Fax:** 01473 231 850
Email: sales@cjelectrical.co.uk
Web: www.cjelectrical.co.uk **Product Type: 1**

UPONOR HOUSING SOLUTIONS LTD
Snapethorpe House, Rugby Road,
Lutterworth, Leicestershire, LE17 4HN
Tel: 01455 550355 **Fax:** 01455 550366
Email: hsenquiries@uponor.co.uk
Web: www.uponorhousingsolutions.co.uk

VELTA-THE UNDERFLOOR HEATING COMPANY
Unit 1B Denby Dale Industrial Park, Wakefield Road,
Denby Dale, Huddersfield, West Yorkshire, HD8 8QH
Area of Operation: Worldwide
Tel: 01484 860811 **Fax:** 01484 865775
Email: info@velta-uk.com
Web: www.u-h-c.co.uk **Product Type: 2**

VIESSMANN LTD
Hortonwood 30, Telford, Shropshire, TF1 7YP
Area of Operation: UK & Ireland
Tel: 01952 675000 **Fax:** 01952 675040
Email: info@viessmann.co.uk
Web: www.viessmann.co.uk **Product Type: 2 ★ ○**

VYSAL UNDERFLOOR HEATING SYSTEMS
Unit 3 Lovett Farm, Little Somerford, Wiltshire, SN15 5BP
Area of Operation: Worldwide
Tel: 01666 822059 **Fax:** 01666 822422
Email: sales@floor-heating.co.uk
Web: www.floor-heating.co.uk **Product Type: 1**

WARM TILES LTD
18 Ernleigh Road, Ipswich, Suffolk, IP4 5LU
Area of Operation: UK & Ireland
Tel: 01473 725743 **Fax:** 01473 725743
Email: barry@warmtiles.co.uk
Web: www.warmtiles.co.uk **Product Type: 1**

WARMAFLOOR GB LTD
Concorde House, Concorde Way,
Segensworth North, Fareham, Hampshire, PO15 5RL
Area of Operation: UK (Excluding Ireland)
Tel: 01489 581787
Fax: 01489 576444
Email: sales@warmafloor.co.uk
Web: www.warmafloor.co.uk **Product Type: 1, 2**

WARMALUX MANUFACTURING
PO Box 1333, Huddersfield, West Yorkshire, HD1 9WB
Area of Operation: UK & Ireland
Tel: 01422 374801 **Fax:** 01422 370681
Email: sales@warmalux.co.uk
Web: www.warmalux.co.uk **Product Type: 1**

WARMFLOOR SOLUTIONS LTD
Business and Innovation Centre, Wearfield,
Sunderland, Tyne & Wear, SR5 2TA
Area of Operation: UK (Excluding Ireland)
Tel: 0845 060 3377
Fax: 0845 006 6526
Email: lisa.rose@warmfloor-solutions.com
Web: www.warmfloor-solutions.com
Product Type: 1, 2

WARMFLOORS LTD
Unit 1 Aire Street, Cross Hills, Keighley,
West Yorkshire, BD20 7RT
Area of Operation: UK & Ireland
Tel: 0800 043 3195
Fax: 01535 631196
Email: sales@warmfloorsonline.com
Web: www.warmfloorsonline.com
Product Type: 1

WARMUP PLC
702 Tudor Estate, Abbey Road, London, NW10 7UW
Area of Operation: UK (Excluding Ireland)
Tel: 0845 345 2288
Fax: 0845 345 2299
Email: uk@warmup.com
Web: www.warmup.com **Product Type: 1**

WARMUP PLC
Area of Operation: Europe
Tel: 0845 345 2288
Fax: 0845 345 2299
Email: uk@warmup.com
Web: www.warmup.com
Product Type: 1

Feel the warmth in any room from £200. Easy installation and economical to run. Unique Lifetime and SafetyNet Guarantees. Unparalleled 24/7 support. Call for a free DVD.

WAVIN PLASTICS LTD (OSMA)
Parsonage Way, Chippenham,
Wiltshire, SN15 5PN
Area of Operation: UK (Excluding Ireland)
Tel: 01249 766 600
Fax: 01249 443 286
Email: info@wavin.co.uk
Web: www.wavin.co.uk
Product Type: 1, 2

XETAL CONSULTANTS LIMITED
Unit 28 Crynant Business Park,
Crynant, Neath, Swansea, SA10 8PA
Area of Operation: Worldwide
Tel: 01639 751056
Fax: 01639 751058
Email: jdickson@xetal.co.uk
Web: www.xetal.co.uk
Product Type: 1 ✿

YEOVIL PLUMBING SUPPLIES
Unit 1, Bartlett Park, Linx Trading Estate,
Yeovil, Somerset, BA20 2PJ
Area of Operation: UK (Excluding Ireland)
Tel: 01935 474780
Fax: 01935 432405

HEATING, PLUMBING & ELECTRICAL

STOVES

KEY

PRODUCT TYPES: 1= Antique
2 = Contemporary   3 = Glass Fronted
4 = Open Fronted   5 = Integral Boilers
6 = Low Canopy   7 = High Canopy
8 = Flat Top   9 = Top Loading
10 = Double Sided

ENERGY SOURCES: ★ Gas   ○ Oil
□ Coal   ● Wood   ✪ Multi-Fuel
✿ Electric   ◆ Gel

OTHER: ▽ Reclaimed   ✍ On-line shopping
✍ Bespoke   ✋ Hand-made   ECO Ecological

ACANTHA LIFESTYLE LTD
32-34 Park Royal Road, Park Royal, London, NW10 7LN
Area of Operation: Worldwide
Tel: 0208 453 1537   **Fax:** 0208 453 1538
Email: sales@acanthalifestyle.com
Web: www.acanthalifestyle.co.uk

ACR HEAT PRODUCTS LTD
Weston Lane, Tyseley, Birmingham, B11 3RP
Area of Operation: UK (Excluding Ireland)
Tel: 0870 780 4549
Email: enquiries@acrheatproducts.co.uk

WANDERS by ACR HEAT PRODUCTS LTD

Area of Operation: UK (Excluding Ireland)
Tel: 0870 780 4549
Email: enquiries@acrheatproducts.co.uk
Web: www.acrheatproducts.co.uk

A stunning and individual range of gas & multifuel home heating solutions. For further information and a brochure please contact us today.

AGA-RAYBURN
Station Road, Ketley, Telford, Shropshire, TF1 5AQ
Area of Operation: Worldwide
Tel: 01952 642000
Fax: 01952 243138
Email: jkingsbury-webber@aga-web.co.uk
Web: www.aga-web.co.uk

ANGLIA FIREPLACES & DESIGN LTD
Anglia House, Kendal Court, Cambridge Road, Impington, Cambridgeshire, CB4 9YS
Area of Operation: UK & Ireland
Tel: 01223 234713
Fax: 01223 235116
Email: info@fireplaces.co.uk
Web: www.fireplaces.co.uk
Product Type: 2, 3, 5, 6, 7, 8, 10 ★ □ ● ✪

ARADA LIMITED (FORMERLY AARROW FIRES)
The Fireworks, Bridport, Dorset, DT6 3BE
Area of Operation: UK (Excluding Ireland)
Tel: 01308 427234
Fax: 01308 423441
Email: info@arada.uk.com
Web: www.arada.uk.com

AUSTROFLAMM
Falcon Road, Sowton Industrial Estate, Exeter, Devon, EX2 7LF
Area of Operation: UK & Ireland
Tel: 01392 474056   **Fax:** 01392 219932
Email: info@stovax.com   **Web:** www.stovax.com
Product Type: 2, 3 ★ ✪

BAXI FIRES DIVISION
Brookes House, Coventry Road, Warwick, Warwickshire, CV34 4LL
Area of Operation: UK (Excluding Ireland)
Tel: 0121 373 8111   **Fax:** 0121 373 8181
Email: sales@valor.co.uk   **Web:** www.valor.co.uk
Product Type: 1, 2, 3, 6, 7, 8

BAXI HEATING UK
Brooks House, Coventry Road, Warwick, Warwickshire, CV34 4LL
Area of Operation: UK & Ireland
Tel: 08706 060780   **Fax:** 01926 410006
Web: www.baxi.co.uk

BD BROOKS FIREPLACES
109 Halifax Road, Ripponden, Halifax, West Yorkshire, HX6 4DA
Area of Operation: UK (Excluding Ireland)
Tel: 01422 822220   **Fax:** 01422 822220
Email: sales@bdbrooksfireplaces.com
Web: www.bdbrooksfireplaces.com
Product Type: 3, 4, 6, 7, 8, 10

BROSELEY FIRES
Knights Way, Battlefield Enterprise Park, Shrewsbury, Shropshire, SY1 3AB
Area of Operation: UK & Ireland
Tel: 01743 461444
Fax: 01743 461446
Email: sales@broseleyfires.com
Web: www.broseleyfires.com
Product Type: 3, 4, 5, 6, 8

BURLEY APPLIANCES LIMITED
Lands End Way, Oakham, Rutland, Leicestershire, LE15 6RB
Area of Operation: Worldwide
Tel: 01572 756956
Fax: 01572 724390
Email: info@burley.co.uk
Web: www.burley.co.uk

CHARNWOOD STOVES & FIRES
Bishops Way, Newport, Isle of Wight, PO30 5WS
Area of Operation: Worldwide
Tel: 01983 537780   **Fax:** 01983 537788
Email: charnwood@ajwells.co.uk
Web: www.charnwood.com ✍
Product Type: 1, 2, 3, 5, 6, 7, 8 ★ □ ● ✪ ✿
Other Info: ECO ✋

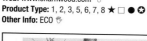

CHARNWOOD STOVES

Area of Operation: Worldwide
Tel: 01983 537780   **Fax:** 01983 537788
Email: charnwood@ajwells.co.uk
Web: www.charnwood.com
Product Type: 1, 2, 3, 5, 6, 7, 8

Britain's original designers and manufacturers of clean-burn multi-fuel, wood burning, Gas and Electric stoves, fires & boilers. Various models, choice of colours and accessories to suit every situation.

CLEARVIEW STOVES
More Works, Squilver Hill, Bishops Castle, Shropshire, SY9 5HH
Area of Operation: Worldwide
Tel: 01588 650401   **Fax:** 01588 650493
Email: mail@clearviewstoves.com
Web: www.clearviewstoves.com
Product Type: 5, 6, 7, 8 □ ● ✪

CONSTRUCTION RESOURCES
16 Great Guildford Street, London, SE1 0HS
Area of Operation: UK (Excluding Ireland)
Tel: 0207 450 2211   **Fax:** 0207 450 2212
Email: info@constructionresources.com
Web: www.constructionresources.com
Product Type: 2, 3, 5

CONTINENTAL FIRES LIMITED
Unit 1, Laundry Bank, Church Stretton, Shropshire, SY6 6PH
Area of Operation: UK & Ireland
Tel: 01694 724199   **Fax:** 01694 720100
Email: sales@continentalfires.com
Web: www.continentalfires.com
Product Type: 1, 2, 3, 4, 10 ★ ○ □ ● ✪ ✿

COSY ROOMS (COSY-HEATING.CO.UK)
17 Chiltern Way, North Hykeham, Lincoln, Lincolnshire, LN6 9SY
Area of Operation: UK (Excluding Ireland)
Tel: 01522 696002   **Fax:** 01522 696002
Email: keith@cosy-rooms.com
Web: www.cosy-heating.co.uk ✍
Product Type: 3, 4

COUNTRY STYLE COOKERS
Unit 8 Oakleys Yard, Gatehouse Road, Rotherwas Industrial Estate, Hereford, Herefordshire, HR2 6RQ
Area of Operation: UK & Ireland
Tel: 01432 342351   **Fax:** 01432 371331
Email: sales@countrystyle-cookers.com
Web: www.countrystyle-cookers.com
Product Type: 1 ★ ○ □ ● ✪   **Other Info:** ▽

DIMPLEX
Millbrook House, Grange Drive, Hedge End, Southampton, Hampshire, SO30 2DF
Area of Operation: UK & Ireland
Tel: 0845 600 5111   **Fax:** 01489 773050
Email: customer.services@glendimplex.com
Web: www.dimplex.co.uk

DOVRE
Falcon Road, Sowton Industrial Estate, Exeter, Devon, EX2 7LF
Area of Operation: UK & Ireland
Tel: 01392 474057   **Fax:** 01392 219932
Email: enquiries@dovre.co.uk
Web: www.dovre.co.uk
Product Type: 1, 2, 3, 4, 5, 6, 7, 8, 9, 10 ★ ● ✪

DOWLING STOVES
Unit 3, Bladnoch Bridge Estate, Newton Stewart, Dumfries & Galloway, DG8 9AB
Area of Operation: UK & Ireland
Tel: 01988 402 666
Fax: 01988 402 666
Email: enquiries@dowlingstoves.co.uk
Web: www.dowlingstoves.co.uk
Product Type: 2, 3, 4, 5, 6, 7, 8, 10 □ ● ✪

DUNSLEY HEAT LTD
Bridge Mills, Huddersfield Road, Holmfirth, Huddersfield, West Yorkshire, HD9 3TW
Area of Operation: UK & Ireland
Tel: 01484 682635
Fax: 01484 688428
Email: sales@dunsleyheat.co.uk
Web: www.dunsleyheat.co.uk
Product Type: 3, 5, 6, 8, 10 □ ● ✪

ECO SYSTEMS IRELAND LTD
40 Glenshesk Road, Ballycastle, Co Antrim, BT54 6PH
Area of Operation: UK & Ireland
Tel: 02820 768708   **Fax:** 02820 769781
Email: info@ecosystemsireland.com
Web: www.ecosystemsireland.com
Product Type: 2, 3, 5

CLEARVIEW STOVES

EMSWORTH FIREPLACES LIMITED
Unit 3, Station Approach, Emsworth, Hampshire, PO10 7PW
Area of Operation: Worldwide
Tel: 01243 373300   **Fax:** 01243 371023
Email: sales@emsworth.co.uk
Web: www.emsworth.co.uk ✍   **Product Type:** 2, 3

ENCOMPASS FURNITURE & ACCESSORIES
The Pool Room, Stansted House, Stansted Park, Rowlands Castle, Hampshire, PO9 6DX
Area of Operation: Worldwide
Tel: 02392 410045   **Fax:** 02392 412145
Email: info@encompassco.com
Web: www.encompassco.com   **Product Type:** 2

ESSE
Ouzledale Foundry, Long Ing, Barnoldswick, Lancashire, BB18 6BN
Area of Operation: Worldwide
Tel: 01282 813235   **Fax:** 01282 816876
Email: enquiries@ouzledale.co.uk
Web: www.esse.com
Product Type: 3, 5   **Other Info:** ✋

EUROFLAMES LIMITED
70 Churchill Square, Kings Hill, West Malling, Kent, ME19 4YU
Area of Operation: UK & Ireland
Tel: 01732 897919
Email: karolina.barnes@euroflames.com
Web: www.euroflames.com ✍
Product Type: 2, 3, 5 ● ✪

EUROFLAMES LTD

Area of Operation: UK & Ireland
Tel: 01732 897919
Email: karolina.barnes@euroflames.com
Web: www.euroflames.com

A woodburning stove for modern living. EuroFlames offers wide range of high quality woodburning and multifuel stoves to suit any self-build or renovation project.

FIREBELLY WOODSTOVES
Unit 9, Lee Bridge Industrial Estate, Lee Bridge Road, Halifax, West Yorkshire, HX3 5HE
Area of Operation: UK & Ireland
Tel: 0161 408 1710
Email: mail@firebellystoves.com
Web: www.firebellystoves.com ✍   **Product Type:** 2

FIREPLACE & TIMBER PRODUCTS
Unit 2 Holyrood Drive, Skippingdale Industrial Estate, Scunthorpe, Lincolnshire, DN15 8NN
Area of Operation: UK & Ireland
Tel: 01724 852888   **Fax:** 01724 277255
Email: ftprodcts@yahoo.com
Web: www.fireplaceandtimberproducts.co.uk
Product Type: 3, 4, 6, 8

FIREPLACE CONSULTANTS LTD
The Studio, The Old Rothschild Arms, Buckland Road, Buckland, Aylesbury, Buckinghamshire, HP22 5LP
Area of Operation: Greater London, Midlands & Mid Wales, South East England
Tel: 01296 632287   **Fax:** 01296 632287
Email: info@fireplaceconsultants.com
Web: www.fireplaceconsultants.com
Product Type: 2, 3, 4, 6, 7, 8, 9, 10

CLEARVIEW STOVES
The leading manufacturer of clean burning stoves

Clearly the heart of the home

CLEARVIEW STOVES SHOWROOM
Dinham House, Ludlow, Shropshire SY8 1EH   Tel: 01584 878100   Brochure Line: 01588 650123
www.clearviewstoves.com

All the warmth and character of a genuine cast iron stove...

Heritage

...with none of the old world disadvantages!

Manufactured from premium grade cast iron, the Heritage is the classic fireplace, allowing you to relax and enjoy the character of a real fire with the doors open, or safely ticking away with the doors closed enabling you the best of both worlds. Available in two sizes the Heritage is the perfect stove for creating a stunning inglenook setting, whether burning wood or solid fuel.

For further information and a brochure please contact us today on:

Tel: 0870 780 4548

E-mail: enquiries@acrheatproducts.co.uk   www.acrheatproducts.co.uk
ACR Heat Products, Weston Works, Weston Lane, Tyseley Birmingham B11 3RP.

ACR HEAT PRODUCTS LTD

Full details of the 10 year warranty are available from either your local stockists or from ACR Heat Products.

The art of cast iron

Whether you prefer to burn solid fuel, wood, gas, oil or even electricity we have a cast iron stove in our range to enhance your home and lifestyle. Our flueless gas stove doesn't even require a chimney or flue system, allowing you to enjoy the pleasures of a cast iron stove in a wider range of settings. Available in a range of traditional and luxurious enamel finishes all our stoves are designed and manufactured to offer a lifetime of cosy warmth in your home.

For further information and brochures on the full range of premium quality cast iron Franco Belge stoves contact us today:

Tel: 0870 780 4546

E-mail: enquiries@franco-belge.co.uk
Web site: www.franco-belge.co.uk

FRANCO BELGE

FIREPLACE DESIGN CONSULTANCY
Stansley Wood Farm, Dapple Heath,
Rugeley, Staffordshire, WS15 3PH
Area of Operation: UK & Ireland
Tel: 01889 500500   **Fax:** 01889 500500
Email: info@inglenooks.co.uk
Web: www.inglenooks.co.uk

FLAMEWAVE FIRES - DK UK LTD
PO Box 611, Folkestone, Kent, CT18 7WY
Area of Operation: UK (Excluding Ireland)
Tel: 0845 257 5028   **Fax:** 0845 257 5038
Email: info@flamewavefires.co.uk
Web: www.flamewavefires.co.uk

FRANCO BELGE
Unit 1 Weston Works, Weston Lane, Tyseley,
Birmingham, West Midlands, B11 3RP
Area of Operation: UK (Excluding Ireland)
Tel: 0121 706 8266
Fax: 0121 706 9182
Email: vicky@franco-belge.co.uk
Web: www.franco-belge.co.uk
Product Type: 1, 3, 4, 5 ★ ○ □ ● ✪

GAZCO LTD
Osprey Road, Sowton Industrial Estate,
Exeter, Devon, EX2 7JG
Area of Operation: Europe
Tel: 01392 261999   **Fax:** 01392 444148
Email: info@gazco.com   **Web:** www.gazco.com
Product Type: 2, 3, 4, 8 ★ ❆

GRENADIER FIRELIGHTERS LIMITED
Unit 3C, Barrowmore Enterprise Estate,
Great Barrow, Chester, Cheshire, CH3 7JS
Area of Operation: Worldwide
Tel: 01829 741649   **Fax:** 01829 741659
Email: enquiries@grenadier.co.uk
Web: www.grenadier.co.uk ⌐⌐   **Product Type:** 4

HEATLINE
16-19 The Manton Centre, Manton Lane,
Bedford, Bedfordshire, MK41 7PX
Area of Operation: Worldwide
Tel: 0870 777 8323   **Fax:** 0870 777 8320
Email: info@heatline.co.uk
Web: www.heatline.co.uk   **Product Type:** 1, 2, 3, 4, 5

HETA UK
The Street, Hatfield Peverel,
Chelmsford, Essex, CN3 2DY
Area of Operation: UK (Excluding Ireland)
Tel: 01245 381247   **Fax:** 01245 381606
Email: hetauk@woodstoves.co.uk
Web: www.woodstoves.co.uk
Product Type: 1, 2, 3, 6, 7, 8, 9, 10

HUNTER STOVES LTD
Unit 6, Old Mill Industrial Estate,
Stoke Canon, Exeter, Devon, EX5 4RJ
Area of Operation: UK (Excluding Ireland)
Tel: 01392 841744   **Fax:** 01392 841382
Email: info@hunterstoves.co.uk
Web: www.hunterstoves.co.uk

JOTUL (UK) LTD
1 The IO Centre, Nash Road, Park Farm North,
Redditch, Worcestershire, B98 7AS
Area of Operation: UK & Ireland
Tel: 01527 506010   **Fax:** 01527 528181
Email: sales@jotuluk.com   **Web:** www.jotul.com
Product Type: 1, 2, 3, 4, 7, 10 ★ ● ✪

KINGSWORTHY FOUNDRY CO LTD
London Road, Kingsworthy,
Winchester, Hampshire, SO23 7QG
Area of Operation: UK & Ireland
Tel: 01962 883776   **Fax:** 01962 882925
Email: kwf@fsbdial.co.uk
Web: www.kingsworthyfoundry.co.uk
Product Type: 3, 5, 6, 7, 8, 10 □ ● ✪ ❆

LEL FIREPLACES
Tre-Ifan Farmhouse, Caergeiliog,
Holyhead, Anglesey, LL65 3HP
Area of Operation: UK & Ireland
Tel: 01407 742240   **Fax:** 01407 742262
Email: sales@lel-fireplaces.com
Web: www.lel-fireplaces.com ⌐⌐
Product Type: 1, 2, 3, 4, 5, 6, 7, 8, 10 ★ ○ □ ● ✪ ❆

LIVINGSTYLE.CO.UK
Bridge Street, Shotton, Flintshire, CH5 1DU
Area of Operation: UK (Excluding Ireland)
Tel: 0800 2989190
Email: info@livingstyle.co.uk
Web: www.livingstyle.co.uk ⌐⌐
Product Type: 2, 3, 4, 5, 6, 7, 8, 9, 10

MARK RIPLEY FORGE & FIREPLACES
Robertsbridge, Bridge Bungalow, East Sussex, TN32 5NY
Tel: 01580 880324   **Fax:** 01580 881927
Email: info@ripleyfireplaces.co.uk
Web: www.ripleyfireplaces.co.uk
Product Type: 2, 3, 4, 6, 7, 8, 9, 10

NATIONAL FIREPLACE ASSOCIATION
6th Floor, McLaren Building, 35 Dale End,
Birmingham, West Midlands, B4 7LN
Area of Operation: UK & Ireland
Tel: 0121 200 1310   **Fax:** 0121 200 1306
Email: enquiries@nfa.org.uk
Web: www.nfa.org.uk ⌐⌐

OLDE ENGLANDE REPRODUCTIONS
Fireplace Works, Normacot Road, Longton, Stoke-
on-Trent, Staffordshire, ST3 1PN
Area of Operation: UK (Excluding Ireland)
Tel: 01782 319350
Fax: 01782 593479
Email: sales@oerfireplaces.com
Web: www.oerfireplaces.com
Product Type: 1, 2, 3, 4, 6, 8, 9

OPIES' THE STOVE SHOP
The Stove Shop, The Street, Hatfield Peverel,
Chelmsford, Essex, CM3 2DY
Area of Operation: East England, Greater London,
South East England
Tel: 01245 380471
Email: enquiries@opie-woodstoves.co.uk
Web: www.opie-woodstoves.co.uk
Product Type: 1, 2, 3, 6, 7, 10 ● ❋

PERCY DOUGHTY & CO
Imperial Point, Express Trading Estate, Stonehill
Road, Farnworth, Bolton, Lancashire, BL4 7TN
Area of Operation: Midlands & Mid Wales, North
West England and North Wales
Tel: 01204 868550   **Fax:** 01204 868551
Email: sales@percydoughty.com
Web: www.percydoughty.co.uk
Product Type: 2, 3, 4, 5, 6, 7, 8, 9, 10

R W KNIGHT & SON LTD
Castle Farm, Marshfield,
Chippenham, Wiltshire, SN14 8HU
Area of Operation: Midlands & Mid Wales, South
East England, South West England and South Wales
Tel: 01225 891469   **Fax:** 01225 892369
Email: enquiries@knight-stoves.co.uk
Web: www.knight-stoves.co.uk
Product Type: 2, 3, 4, 5, 6, 7, 8, 9, 10 ★ ○ □ ● ✪ ❆
Other Info: ECO

RUDLOE STONEWORKS LTD
Leafield Stoneyard, Potley Lane,
Corsham, Wiltshire, SN13 9RS
Area of Operation: UK & Ireland
Tel: 01225 816400
Fax: 01225 811343
Email: paul@rudloe-stone.com
Web: www.rudloe-stone.com
Product Type: 2, 3, 4, 6, 8, 9, 10

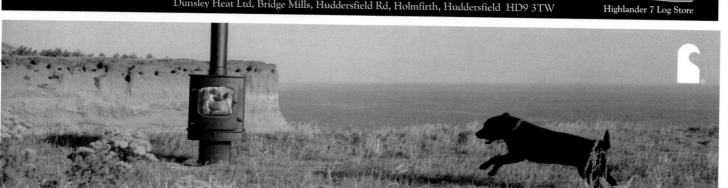
HEATING, PLUMBING & ELECTRICAL

STOVAX LIMITED
Falcon Road, Sowton Industrial Estate,
Exeter, Devon, EX2 7LF
Area of Operation: UK & Ireland
Tel: 01392 474011 **Fax:** 01392 219932
Email: info@stovax.com
Web: www.stovax.com
Product Type: 1, 2, 3, 4, 5, 6, 7, 8 ★ ○ □ ● ✪ ❄

STOVES ON LINE LTD
Capton, Dartmouth, Devon, TQ6 0JE
Area of Operation: UK (Excluding Ireland)
Tel: 0845 226 5754
Fax: 0870 220 0920
Email: info@stovesonline.com
Web: www.stovesonline.co.uk
Product Type: 1, 3 ★ ●

THE CERAMIC STOVE CO.
4 Earl Street, Oxford, Oxfordshire, OX2 0JA
Area of Operation: Worldwide
Tel: 01865 245077
Fax: 01865 245077
Email: info@ceramicstove.com
Web: www.ceramicstove.com
Product Type: 1, 2, 3, 10 ★ ●
Other Info: ▽ ECO ✐ ✋

THE CERAMIC STOVE COMPANY
Area of Operation: Worldwide
Tel: 01865 245077
Fax: 01865 245077
Email: info@ceramicstove.com
Web: www.ceramicstove.com
Product Type: 1, 2, 3, 10

We continue to offer a diverse selection of woodfired, heat-retaining stoves from manufacturers who value style and the environment in equal measure.

THE FIREPLACE GALLERY (UK) LTD
Clarence Road, Worksop, Nottinghamshire, S80 1QA
Area of Operation: UK & Ireland
Tel: 01909 500802 **Fax:** 01909 500810
Email: fireplacegallery@btinternet.com
Web: www.fireplacegallery.co.uk
Product Type: 2, 3, 4

THE FIREPLACE MARKETING COMPANY LIMITED
Haseley Manor, Birmingham Road,
Warwick, Warwickshire, CV35 7LS
Area of Operation: Worldwide
Tel: 02476 247246 **Fax:** 02476 247266
Email: info@fireplace.co.uk
Web: www.fireplace.co.uk ✐
Product Type: ★ ○ □ ● ✪ ✐ ✋ ◆

THE JRG GROUP
3 Crompton Way, North Newmoor Industrial Estate,
Irvine, Ayrshire, KA11 4HU
Area of Operation: Europe
Tel: 0871 200 8080 **Fax:** 01294 211 222
Email: chris@jrgfiresurrounds.com
Web: www.jrggroup.com **Product Type:** 3 ❄

THE ORGANIC ENERGY COMPANY
Severn Road, Welshpool, Powys, SY21 7AZ
Area of Operation: UK (Excluding Ireland)
Tel: 0845 458 4076 **Fax:** 01938 559222
Email: hbenq@organicenergy.co.uk
Web: www.organicenergy.co.uk **Other Info:** ECO

THEALE FIREPLACES RDG LTD
Milehouse Farm , Bath Road,
Theale, Berkshire, RG7 5HJ
Area of Operation: UK (Excluding Ireland)
Tel: 0118 930 2232 **Fax:** 0118 932 3344
Email: mail@theale-fireplaces.co.uk
Web: www.theale-fireplaces.co.uk

THORSTOVES
Canada Hill, East Ogwell,
Newton Abbot, Devon, TQ12 6AF
Area of Operation: UK (Excluding Ireland)
Tel: 01626 363 507
Email: info@antique-stoves.com
Web: www.antique-stoves.com
Product Type: 1 **Other Info:** ▽

TOWN AND COUNTRY FIRES
1 Enterprise Way, Thornton Road Industrial Estate,
Pickering, North Yorkshire, YO18 7NA
Area of Operation: Europe
Tel: 01751 474803 **Fax:** 01751 475205
Email: sales@townandcountryfires.co.uk
Web: www.townandcountryfires.co.uk

VERINE
52 Broton Drive, Halstead, Essex, CO9 1HB
Area of Operation: UK & Ireland
Tel: 01787 472551 **Fax:** 01787 476589
Email: sales@verine.co.uk
Web: www.verine.co.uk
Product Type: 3, 8 ★

VERINE AND PORTWAY
52 Broton Drive Industrial Estate,
Halstead, Essex, CO9 1HB
Area of Operation: Europe
Tel: 01787 472551 **Fax:** 01787 476589
Email: sales@portwayfires.com
Web: www.portwayfires.com

VILLAGER STOVES
Millwey Industrial Estate, Axminster, Devon, EX13 5HU
Area of Operation: UK & Ireland
Tel: 0870 160 2202
Fax: 01297 35900
Email: stoves@villager.co.uk
Web: www.villager.co.uk
Product Type: 2, 5, 6, 7, 8, 10 ★ ● ✪ ❄

VILLAGER STOVES
Area of Operation: UK & Ireland
Tel: 0870 160 2202 **Fax:** 01297 35900
Email: stoves@villager.co.uk
Web: www.villager.co.uk
Product Type: 2, 5, 6, 7, 8, 10

Quality........
Over 40 model options of British made wood burning, multi-fuel, gas fired and electric stoves. ....assured

WATERFORD STANLEY
Unit B8, Whitwood Enterprise Park, Speedwell Road,
Castleford, West Yorkshire, WF10 5PX
Area of Operation: UK & Ireland
Tel: 01977 603427 **Fax:** 01977 603692
Email: gbsales@waterfordstanley.com
Web: www.waterfordstanley.com **Product Type:** 5

WOODWARM STOVES
The Workshop, Wheatcroft Farm,
Cullompton, Devon, EX15 1RA
Area of Operation: Europe
Tel: 01884 35806 **Fax:** 01884 35505
Email: sales@woodwarmstoves.co.uk
Web: www.woodwarmstoves.co.uk
Product Type: 2, 3, 5, 6, 7, 8, 10 ○ □ ● ✪
Other Info: ✋

YEOMAN STOVES
Falcon Road, Sowton Industrial Estate,
Exeter, Devon, EX2 7LF
Area of Operation: UK (Excluding Ireland)
Tel: 01392 474060
Fax: 01392 219932
Email: yeoman@stovax.co.uk
Web: www.yeoman-stoves.co.uk

BOILERS

KEY
PRODUCT TYPES: 1= Standard / System
2 = Condensing   3 = Dual Output Condensing
4 = Combination   5 = Kitchen Ranges with
Boilers   6 = Other

ENERGY SOURCES: ★ Gas   ○ Oil
□ Coal   ● Wood   ✪ Multi-Fuel
❄ Electric   ◆ Gel

OTHER: ▽ Reclaimed   ✐ On-line shopping
✎ Bespoke   ✋ Hand-made   ECO Ecological

ACV UK LTD
St Davids Business Park, Dalgety Bay, Fife, KY11 9PF
Area of Operation: UK & Ireland
Tel: 01383 820100 **Fax:** 01383 820180
Email: information@acv-uk.com
Web: www.acv-uk.com
Product Type: 1, 2, 3, 4, 6 ★ ○ ❄

AEL
4 Berkeley Court, Manor Park,
Runcorn, Cheshire, WA7 1TQ
Area of Operation: UK & Ireland
Tel: 01928 579068
Fax: 01928 579523
Email: sales@aelheating.com
Web: www.aelheating.com
Product Type: 2, 6 ★ ○ □ ●

AGA-RAYBURN
Station Road, Ketley, Telford, Shropshire, TF1 5AQ
Area of Operation: Worldwide
Tel: 01952 642000
ax: 01952 243138
Email: jkingsbury-webber@aga-web.co.uk
Web: www.aga-web.co.uk

ALPHA BOILERS
Nepicar House, London Road,
Wrotham Heath, Kent, TN15 7RS
Area of Operation: UK (Excluding Ireland)
Tel: 01732 783000
Fax: 01732 783080
Email: info@alphatherm.co.uk
Web: www.alpha-boilers.com
Product Type: 1, 2, 4

APPLIED HEATING SERVICES LTD
9 Rosse Close, Parsons Industrial Estate,
Washington, Tyne & Wear, NE38 1ET
Area of Operation: North East England
Tel: 0191 4177604
Fax: 0191 4171549
Email: georgecossey1@btconnect.com
Web: www.appliedheat.co.uk
Product Type: 1, 2, 3, 4 ★ ○

ARCHIE KIDD (THERMAL) LTD
Poulshot, Devizes, Wiltshire, SN10 1RT
Area of Operation: UK & Ireland
Tel: 01380 828123 **Fax:** 01380 828186

BAXI HEATING UK
Brooks House, Coventry Road,
Warwick, Warwickshire, CV34 4LL
Area of Operation: UK & Ireland
Tel: 08706 060780 **Fax:** 01926 410006
Web: www.baxi.co.uk **Product Type:** 1, 4

BLAZES FIREPLACE CENTRES
23 Standish Street, Burnley, Lancashire, BB11 1AP
Area of Operation: UK (Excluding Ireland)
Tel: 01282 831176 **Fax:** 01282 424141
Email: info@blazes.co.uk
Web: www.blazes.co.uk **Product Type:** 2, 4

BORDERS UNDERFLOOR HEATING
26 Coopersknowe Crescent, Galashiels, Borders, TD1 2DS
Area of Operation: UK & Ireland
Tel: 01896 668667 **Fax:** 01896 668678
Email: underfloor@btinternet.com
Web: www.bordersunderfloor.co.uk
Product Type: 1, 2, 4, 6 ○

BTU HEATING
38 Weyside Road, Guildford, Surrey, GU1 1JB
Area of Operation: South East England
Tel: 01483 590600 **Fax:** 01483 590601
Email: enquiries@btu-heating.com
Web: www.btu-group.com
Product Type: 1, 2, 3, 4 ★○ ✪ ❄
Other Info: ECO ✎

CHARNWOOD STOVES & FIRES
Bishops Way, Newport, Isle of Wight, PO30 5WS
Area of Operation: Worldwide
Tel: 01983 537780 **Fax:** 01983 537788
Email: charnwood@ajwells.co.uk
Web: www.charnwood.com ✎
Product Type: 1 □●✪ **Other Info:** ECO ✎

CHARNWOOD STOVES

Area of Operation: Worldwide
Tel: 01983 537780 **Fax:** 01983 537788
Email: charnwood@ajwells.co.uk
Web: www.charnwood.com
Product Type: 1

Britain's original designers and manufacturers of clean-burn multi-fuel and wood burning fires & boilers. Ultra efficient and eco-friendly. Various models, choice of colours and accessories to suit every situation.

CLEARVIEW STOVES
More Works, Squilver Hill,
Bishops Castle, Shropshire, SY9 5HH
Area of Operation: Worldwide
Tel: 01588 650401 **Fax:** 01588 650493
Email: mail@clearviewstoves.com
Web: www.clearviewstoves.com
Product Type: 1 □●✪

COPPERJOB LTD
PO Box 110, Plymouth, Devon, PL7 2ZS
Area of Operation: UK & Ireland
Email: info@copperjob.com
Web: www.centralheatingrepair.co.uk ✎
Product Type: 1, 2, 4

DUNSLEY HEAT LTD
Bridge Mills, Huddersfield Road, Holmfirth,
Huddersfield, West Yorkshire, HD9 3TW
Area of Operation: UK & Ireland
Tel: 01484 682635 **Fax:** 01484 688428
Email: sales@dunsleyheat.co.uk
Web: www.dunsleyheat.co.uk
Product Type: 5 ○

ECO HOMETEC UK LTD
Unit 11E, Carcroft Enterprise Park, Carcroft,
Doncaster, South Yorkshire, DN6 8DD
Area of Operation: Europe
Tel: 01302 722266 **Fax:** 01302 728634
Email: Stephen@eco-hometec.co.uk
Web: www.eco-hometec.co.uk
Product Type: 2, 3, 4, 6

ENERGY MASTER
Keltic Business Park, Unit 1 Clieveragh Industrial
Estate, Listowel, Ireland
Area of Operation: Ireland Only
Tel: 00353 (0)68 23864 **Fax:** 00353 (0)68 24533
Email: info@energymaster.ie
Web: www.energymaster.ie **Product Type:** 2, 3, 4, 6

EURO BATHROOMS
102 Annareagh Road, Richhill, Co Armagh, BT61 9JY
Area of Operation: Ireland Only
Tel: 028 3887 9996 **Fax:** 028 3887 9996
Product Type: 1, 2, 3

FERROLI UK
Lichfield Road, Branston Industrial Estate,
Burton Upon Trent, Staffordshire, DE14 3HD
Area of Operation: UK (Excluding Ireland)
Tel: 08707 282882 **Fax:** 08707 282883
Email: sales@ferroli.co.uk
Web: www.ferroli.co.uk
Product Type: 1, 2, 3, 4, 6 ★

GAH HEATING PRODUCTS
Building 846, Bentwaters Parks, Rendlesham,
Woodbridge, Suffolk, IP12 2TW
Area of Operation: UK (Excluding Ireland)
Tel: 01394 421160 **Fax:** 01394 421170
Email: dcooper@gah.co.uk
Web: www.gah.co.uk
Product Type: 2 ○ ❄

GEMINOX UK
Blenheim House, 1 Blenheim Road,
Epsom, Surrey, KT19 9AP
Area of Operation: UK & Ireland
Tel: 01372 722277 **Fax:** 01372 744477
Email: sales@geminox-uk.com
Web: www.geminox-uk.com
Product Type: 2, 3, 4 ★○ ✪

GLEDHILL WATER STORAGE LIMITED
Sycamore Estate, Squires Gate,
Blackpool, Lancashire, FY4 3RL
Area of Operation: UK (Excluding Ireland)
Tel: 01253 474444 **Fax:** 01253 474445
Email: sales@gledhill.net
Web: www.gledhill.net **Product Type:** 2

GOTO PLUMBING
Area of Operation: UK & Ireland
Email: sales@gotoplumbing.co.uk
Web: www.gotoplumbing.co.uk ✎

GRANT ENGINEERING LTD
Crinkle, Birr, Co. Offaly, Ireland
Area of Operation: Ireland Only
Tel: 00 353 05791 20089
Fax: 00 353 05791 21060
Email: info@grantengineering.ie
Web: www.grantengineering.ie
Product Type: 1, 2, 4, 6 ○

GRANT UK
Hopton House, Hopton Industrial Estate,
Devizes, Wiltshire, SN10 2EU
Area of Operation: UK (Excluding Ireland)
Tel: 0870 777 5553 **Fax:** 0870 777 5559
Email: sales@grantuk.com
Web: www.grantuk.com
Product Type: 1, 2, 4 ○

HALSTEAD BOILERS LIMITED
20/22n First Avenue, Bluebridge Industrial Estate,
Halstead, Essex, CO9 2EX
Area of Operation: UK & Ireland
Tel: 01787 272800 **Fax:** 01787 474588
Email: sales@halsteadboilers.co.uk
Web: www.halsteadboilers.co.uk
Product Type: 1, 2, 4

HEATLINE
16-19 The Manton Centre,
Manton Lane, Bedford, Bedfordshire, MK41 7PX
Area of Operation: Worldwide
Tel: 0870 777 8323 **Fax:** 0870 777 8320
Email: info@heatline.co.uk
Web: www.heatline.co.uk **Product Type:** 1, 2, 3, 4

HRM BOILERS LTD
Haverscroft Industrial Estate,
Attleborough, Norfolk, NR17 1YE
Area of Operation: UK (Excluding Ireland)
Tel: 01953 455400 **Fax:** 01953 454483
Email: info@hrmboilers.co.uk
Web: www.hrmboilers.co.uk **Product Type:** 1, 4 ○

JOHNSON & STARLEY
Rhosili Road, Brackmills, Northampton,
Northamptonshire, NN4 7LZ
Area of Operation: UK & Ireland
Tel: 01604 762881 **Fax:** 01604 767408
Email: marketing@johnsonandstarleyltd.co.uk
Web: www.johnsonandstarley.co.uk
Product Type: 4

JONES NASH ECO HOMES
12 Lee Street, Louth, Lincolnshire, LN11 9HJ
Area of Operation: UK (Excluding Ireland)
Tel: 01507 609637 **Fax:** 01507 609637
Email: sd@jones-nash.co.uk
Web: www.eco-houses.co.uk

KESTON BOILERS
34 West Common Road, Hayes, Bromley, Kent, BR2 7BX
Area of Operation: UK & Ireland
Tel: 020 8462 0262 **Fax:** 020 8462 4459
Email: info@keston.co.uk
Web: www.keston.co.uk
Product Type: 2, 3, 4 ★ **Other Info:** ✎

KILTOX CONTRACTS LIMITED
Unit 6 Chiltonian Industrial Estate,
203 Manor Lane, Lee, London, SE12 0TX
Area of Operation: Worldwide
Tel: 0845 166 2040 **Fax:** 0845 166 2050
Email: info@kiltox.co.uk **Web:** www.kiltox.co.uk ✎
Product Type: 6 ❄ **Other Info:** ECO

LIONHEART HEATING SERVICES
PO Box 741, Harworth Park,
Doncaster, South Yorkshire, DN11 8WY
Area of Operation: UK (Excluding Ireland)
Tel: 01302 755200 **Fax:** 01302 750155
Email: enquiries@lionheartheating.co.uk
Web: www.lionheartheating.co.uk ✎

MALVERN BOILERS LTD
Spring Lane North, Malvern, Worcestershire, WR14 1BW
Area of Operation: UK (Excluding Ireland)
Tel: 01684 893777 **Fax:** 01684 893776
Email: nickyn@malvernboilers.co.uk
Web: www.malvernboilers.co.uk
Product Type: 1, 2, 4

MHS RADIATORS & BOILERS
3 Juniper West, Fenton Way, Southfields Business
Park, Basildon, Essex, SS15 6TD
Area of Operation: UK & Ireland
Tel: 01268 546700 **Fax:** 01268 888250
Email: sales@modular-heating-group.co.uk
Web: www.mhsradiators.com
Product Type: 1, 2, 3, 4 ★○ ❄

OSO HOTWATER (UK) LTD
E15 Marquis Court, Team Valley Trading Estate,
Gateshead, Tyne & Wear, NE11 0RU
Area of Operation: UK (Excluding Ireland)
Tel: 0191 482 0100 **Fax:** 0191 491 3655
Email: sales.uk@oso-hotwater.com
Web: www.oso-hotwater.com **Product Type:** 1, 2, 3, 4

PERCY DOUGHTY & CO
Imperial Point, Express Trading Estate, Stonehill
Road, Farnworth, Bolton, Lancashire, BL4 9TN
Area of Operation: Midlands & Mid Wales, North
West England and North Wales
Tel: 01204 868550 **Fax:** 01204 868551
Email: sales@percydoughty.com
Web: www.percydoughty.co.uk **Product Type:** 6

PHIL GREEN & SON
Unit 7, Maylite Trading Estate, Berrow Green Road,
Martley, Worcester, Worcestershire, WR6 6PQ
Area of Operation: UK (Excluding Ireland)
Tel: 01885 488936 **Fax:** 01885 488936
Email: info@philgreenandson.co.uk
Web: www.philgreenandson.co.uk
Product Type: 5 ★○ □

POWERGEN
Newstead Court, Sherwood Park, Little Oak Drive,
Annesley, Nottinghamshire, NG15 0DR
Area of Operation: UK (Excluding Ireland)
Tel: 0800 068 6515
Email: whispergen@powergen.co.uk
Web: www.powergen.co.uk **Product Type:** 1, 4 ★

R W KNIGHT & SON LTD
Castle Farm, Marshfield,
Chippenham, Wiltshire, SN14 8HU
Area of Operation: Midlands & Mid Wales, South
East England, South West England and South Wales
Tel: 01225 891469 **Fax:** 01225 892369
Email: enquiries@knight-stoves.co.uk
Web: www.knight-stoves.co.uk
Product Type: 5 ★○ □●✪

RAVENHEAT MANUFACTURING LTD
Chartists Way, Morley, Leeds, West Yorkshire, LS27 9ET
Area of Operation: Europe
Tel: 0113 252 7007 **Fax:** 0113 238 0229
Email: sales@ravenheat.co.uk
Web: www.ravenheat.co.uk **Product Type:** 2, 4 ★

SCALGON
115 Park Lane, Reading, Berkshire, RG31 4DR
Area of Operation: UK (Excluding Ireland)
Tel: 0118 9424981
Email: postmaster@scalgon.co.uk
Web: www.scalgon.co.uk **Product Type:** 2, 3, 4, 6

STREBEL LTD
1F Albany Park Industrial Estate,
Frimley Road, Camberley, Surrey, GU16 7PB
Area of Operation: UK & Ireland
Tel: 01276 685422 **Fax:** 01276 685405
Email: info@strebel.co.uk **Web:** www.strebel.co.uk
Product Type: 1, 2, 3, 4 ★○ ●✪

THE ORGANIC ENERGY COMPANY
Severn Road, Welshpool, Powys, SY21 7AZ
Area of Operation: UK (Excluding Ireland)
Tel: 0845 458 4076 **Fax:** 01938 559222
Email: hbenq@organicenergy.co.uk
Web: www.organicenergy.co.uk **Other Info:** ECO

TRIANCO HEATING PRODUCTS LIMITED
Thorncliffe, Chapeltown, Sheffield,
South Yorkshire, S35 2PH
Area of Operation: UK & Ireland
Tel: 0114 257 2300 **Fax:** 0114 257 1419
Email: info@trianco.co.uk **Web:** www.trianco.co.uk
Product Type: 1, 2, 4, 5 ★○ ❄

VIESSMANN LTD
Hortonwood 30, Telford, Shropshire, TF1 7YP
Area of Operation: UK & Ireland
Tel: 01952 675000 **Fax:** 01952 675040
Email: info@viessmann.co.uk
Web: www.viessmann.co.uk
Product Type: 1, 2, 3, 4 ★○ **Other Info:** ECO

VOKERA LTD
Borderlake House, Unit 7 Riverside Industrial Estate,
London Colney, Hertfordshire, AL2 1HG
Area of Operation: UK & Ireland
Tel: 0870 333 0220 **Fax:** 01727 744004
Email: enquiries@vokera.co.uk
Web: www.vokera.co.uk
Product Type: 1, 2, 4 ★

HEATING, PLUMBING & ELECTRICAL

setting the standards

Twin Coil Cylinders Now Available

The Ultimate Mains Pressure System for your House

Dualstream systems increase flow rates at mains pressure to both hot and cold supplies within the house, delivering a truly outstanding performance. They have been designed to work on poor mains supplies in towns or rural locations with flow rates as low as 9 litre. With most house designs now incorporating more than one bathroom or ensuite Dualstream Systems are the ideal choice for multi bathroom dwellings.

When buying or building your new home consider the importance of mains pressure and flow rates and the design of a system that can meet your demands. Then call GAH hating Products a company that offers a range of products at affordable prices to suit all house types.

Full design service and technical support available.

GAH (HEATING PRODUCTS) LIMITED
Building 846 • Bentwaters Parks • Rendlesham • Woodbridge • Suffolk • IP12 2TW
Tel: 01394 421160 • Fax: 01394 421170
Email: dcooper@gah.co.uk • www.gah.co.uk

The boiler that fits where space is tight.

X-ternal from HRM is designed for homes where space is at a premium, in the public or private sector, new or refurb projects.

X-ternal is a 12/20kW oil fired boiler, in conventional or condensing format, mounted on an external wall.

X-ternal uses the tried and tested heat exchanger technology of HRM's Wallstar, thru-the-wall boiler.

X-ternal excludes kerosene odours from the home: can be serviced routinely without entering the home: is quiet and unobtrusive: has a rustproof and stylish fibreglass casing.

X-ternal is available from merchants nationwide.

HRM Boilers Limited
Haverscroft Industrial Estate, Attleborough, Norfolk NR17 1YE
Tel: 01953 455400
email: info@hrmboilers.co.uk
www.hrmboilers.co.uk

WATERFORD STANLEY
Unit B8, Whitwood Enterprise Park, Speedwell Road,
Castleford, West Yorkshire, WF10 5PX
Area of Operation: UK & Ireland
Tel: 01977 603427   **Fax:** 01977 603692
Email: gbsales@waterfordstanley.com
Web: www.waterfordstanley.com   **Product Type:** 5

WORCESTER BOSCH GROUP
Cotswold Way, Warndon, Worcester, WR4 9SW
Area of Operation: UK & Ireland
Tel: 01905 754624   **Fax:** 01905 754619
Email: general.worcester@uk.bosch.com
Web: www.worcester-bosch.co.uk
Product Type: 1, 2, 4, 5

RADIATORS & CONVECTORS

KEY

SEE ALSO: HEATING - Convectors,
BATHROOMS - Heated Towel Rails
PRODUCT TYPES: 1= Column   2 = Panel
3 = Skirting   4 = Trench   5 = Low Surface
Temperature   6 = Radiator Covers   7 = Other

ENERGY SOURCES: ★ Gas   ○ Oil
□ Coal   ● Wood   ✪ Multi-Fuel
✳ Electric   ◆ Gel

OTHER: ▽ Reclaimed   ✍ On-line shopping
✐ Bespoke   ✋ Hand-made   ECO Ecological

ACOVA RADIATORS (UK) LTD
B15 Armstrong Mall, Southwood Business Park,
Farnborough, Hampshire , GU14 0NR
Area of Operation: UK & Ireland
Tel: 01252 531207   **Fax:** 01252 531201
Email: pam.hay@zehnder.co.uk
Web: www.acova.co.uk
Product Type: 1, 2, 7   **Material Type:** C) 1, 2, 11

AEL
4 Berkeley Court, Manor Park,
Runcorn, Cheshire, WA7 1TQ
Area of Operation: UK & Ireland
Tel: 01928 579068   **Fax:** 01928 579523
Email: sales@aelheating.com
Web: www.aelheating.com
Product Type: 1, 2, 3, 5, 6, 7   **Material Type:** C) 1, 2, 5

AESTUS
Unit 5 Strawberry Lane Industrial Estate,
Strawberry Lane, Willenhall,
West Midlands, WV13 3RS
Area of Operation: UK & Ireland
Tel: 0870 403 0115   **Fax:** 0870 403 0116
Email: melissa@publicityengineers.com
Product Type: 1, 2, 6

AGA-RAYBURN
Station Road , Ketley, Telford, Shropshire, TF1 5AQ
Area of Operation: Worldwide
Tel: 01952 642000   **Fax:** 01952 243138
Email: jkingsbury-webber@aga-web.co.uk
Web: www.aga-web.co.uk

ARC-COMP
Friedrichstr. 3, 12205 Berlin-Lichterfelde, Germany
Area of Operation: Europe
Tel: +49 (0)308 430 9956   **Fax:** +49 (0)308 430 9957
Email: jvs@arc-comp.com   **Web:** www.arc-com.com
Product Type: 2 ✳   **Material Type:** J) 5, 6

ARC-COMP (IRISH BRANCH)
Whitefield Cottage, Lugduff, Tinahely,
Co. Wicklow, Republic of Ireland
Area of Operation: Europe
Tel: +353 (0)868 729 945   **Fax:** +353 (0)402 28900
Email: jvs@arc-comp.com   **Web:** www.arc-comp.com
Product Type: 2 ✳   **Material Type:** J) 5, 6

AUTRON PRODUCTS LTD
Unit 17 Second Avenue, Bluebridge Industrial Estate,
Halstead, Essex, C09 2SU
Area of Operation: UK & Ireland
Tel: 01787 473964   **Fax:** 01787 474061
Email: sales@autron.co.uk   **Web:** www.autron.co.uk
Product Type: 1, 4, 5, 6, 7

BENTON RALPH INTERIORS
Ground Floor, Block A, Commercial Square,
Leigh Street, High Wycombe,
Buckinghamshire, HP11 2RH
Area of Operation: UK & Ireland
Tel: 01494 440144   **Fax:** 01494 440144
Product Type: 6

BISQUE LIMITED
23 Queen Square, Bath, Somerset, BA1 2HX
Area of Operation: Worldwide
Tel: 01225 478500   **Fax:** 01225 478581
Email: marketing@bisque.co.uk
Web: www.bisque.co.uk
Product Type: 1, 5, 7   **Material Type:** C) 2, 3, 7, 14

BLAZES FIREPLACE CENTRES
23 Standish Street, Burnley, Lancashire, BB11 1AP
Area of Operation: UK (Excluding Ireland)
Tel: 01282 831176   **Fax:** 01282 424141
Email: info@blazes.co.uk   **Web:** www.blazes.co.uk

BRASS GRILLES UK
Unit 174, 78 Marylebone High Street,
London, W1U 5AP
Area of Operation: UK (Excluding Ireland)
Tel: 07905 292101 / 01923 451600
Fax: 01923 451600
Email: sales@brass-grilles.co.uk
Web: www.brass-grilles.co.uk ✍   **Product Type:** 6

CHATSWORTH HEATING PRODUCTS LTD
Unit B Watchmoor Point, Camberley, Surrey, GU15 3EX
Area of Operation: UK (Excluding Ireland)
Tel: 01276 605880
Fax: 01276 605881
Email: enquiries@chatsworth-heating.co.uk
Web: www.chatsworth-heating.co.uk
Product Type: 2

CLASSIC WARMTH DIRECT LTD
Unit 8, Brunel Workshops, Ashburton Industrial
Estate, Ross-on-Wye, Herefordshire, HR9 7DX
Area of Operation: UK & Ireland
Tel: 01989 565555   **Fax:** 01989 561058
Email: patbur@tiscali.co.uk   **Product Type:** 2

CLYDE ENERGY SOLUTIONS LTD
Unit 10, Lion Park Avenue, Chessington, Surrey, KT9 1ST
Area of Operation: UK & Ireland
Tel: 020 8391 2020   **Fax:** 020 8397 4598
Email: info@clyde-nrg.com
Web: www.clyde-nrg.com ✍   **Product Type:** 1

CONTOUR CASINGS LTD
4 Horton Court, Hortonwood 50,
Telford, Shropshire, TF1 7GY
Area of Operation: UK & Ireland
Tel: 01952 676 940   **Fax:** 01952 677 043
Email: sales@contourcasings.co.uk
Web: www.contourcasings.co.uk   **Product Type:** 5, 6

CORNER FRIDGE COMPANY
Unit 6 Harworth Enterprise Park,
Brunel Industrial Estate, Harworth, Doncaster,
South Yorkshire, DN11 8SG
Area of Operation: UK & Ireland
Tel: 01302 759308   **Fax:** 01302 751203
Email: info@cornerfridge.com
Web: www.cornerfridge.com   **Product Type:** 2

COSY ROOMS (DESIGNER-WARMTH.CO.UK)
17 Chiltern Way, North Hykeham,
Lincoln, Lincolnshire, LN6 9SY
Area of Operation: UK (Excluding Ireland)
Tel: 01522 696002
Fax: 01522 696002
Email: keith@cosy-rooms.com
Web: www.designer-warmth.co.uk ✍

COSY ROOMS LTD
Area of Operation: UK (Excluding Ireland)
Tel: 01522 696002
Fax: 01522 696002
Email: keith@cosy-rooms.com
Web: www.designer-warmth.co.uk ✍
Product Type: 1, 3, 5, 7

Cosy rooms Ltd. is a family run company providing a
friendly efficient service to supply designer radiators,
towel warmers, heated towel rails, heaters and
bathroom items on-line at discount prices.

COVERAD LIMITED
Oakfeild Barn, The Brows, Farnham Road,
Liss, Hampshire , GU33 6JG
Area of Operation: UK & Ireland
Tel: 01730 893393   **Fax:** 01730 893696
Web: www.coverad.co.uk   **Product Type:** 6

DEEP BLUE SHOWROOM
299-313 Lewisham High Street, Lewisham, London,
Greater London, SE13 6NW
Area of Operation: UK (Excluding Ireland)
Tel: 0208 690 3401   **Fax:** 0208 690 1408

DESIGNER RADIATORS
Regent Street, Colne, Lancashire, BB8 8LD
Area of Operation: UK & Ireland
Tel: 01282 862509   **Fax:** 01282 871192
Email: sales@boundarybathrooms.co.uk
Web: www.designer-radiators.com ✍
Product Type: 1, 2, 3, 4, 5, 6, 7

DIMPLEX
Millbrook House, Grange Drive, Hedge End,
Southampton, Hampshire, SO30 2DF
Area of Operation: UK & Ireland
Tel: 0845 600 5111
Fax: 01489 773050
Email: customer.services@glendimplex.com
Web: www.dimplex.co.uk
Product Type: 1, 2 ✳

E. RICHARDS
PO Box 1115, Winscombe, Somerset, BS25 1WA
Area of Operation: UK & Ireland
Tel: 0845 330 8859   **Fax:** 0845 330 7260
Email: info@e-richards.co.uk
Web: www.e-richards.co.uk ✍

ECOLEC
Sharrocks Street, Wolverhampton, West Midlands, WV1 3RP
Area of Operation: UK & Ireland
Tel: 01902 457575   **Fax:** 01902 457797
Email: sales@ecolec.co.uk
Web: www.ecolec.co.uk ✍   **Product Type:** 1, 2, 3, 5, 7

ENERFOIL MAGNUM LTD
Kenmore Road, Comrie Bridge, Kenmore,
Aberfeldy, Perthshire, PH15 2LS
Area of Operation: Europe
Tel: 01887 822999   **Fax:** 01887 822954
Email: sales@enerfoil.com
Web: www.enerfoil.com ✍

ENERGY MASTER
Keltic Business Park, Unit 1 Clieveragh Industrial
Estate, Listowel, Ireland
Area of Operation: Ireland Only
Tel: 00353 (0)68 23864   **Fax:** 00353 (0)68 24533
Email: info@energymaster.ie   **Web:** www.energymaster.ie
Product Type: 2, 5

ENERGY TECHNIQUE PLC
47 Central Avenue, West Molesey, Surrey, KT8 2QZ
Area of Operation: UK (Excluding Ireland)
Tel: 0208 783 0033   **Fax:** 0208 783 0140
Email: rob@etenv.co.uk
Web: www.diffusion-group.co.uk

ESKIMO DESIGN LTD.
51-53 Llull, Barcelona, 08005
Area of Operation: Worldwide
Tel: 020 7117 0110   **Email:** ed@eskimodesign.co.uk
Web: www.eskimodesign.co.uk
Product Type: 1, 2, 3, 5, 6, 7 ✪ ✳ **Other Info:** ✐
Material Type: C) 1, 2, 3, 7, 11, 14, 15, 16

EURO BATHROOMS
102 Annareagh Road, Richhill, Co Armagh, BT61 9JY
Area of Operation: Ireland Only
Tel: 028 3887 9996   **Fax:** 028 3887 9996
Product Type: 1, 2

FEATURE RADIATORS
Bingley Railway Station, Wellington Street,
Bingley, West Yorkshire, BD16 2NB
Area of Operation: UK (Excluding Ireland)
Tel: 01274 567789   **Fax:** 01274 561183
Email: contactus@featureradiators.com
Web: www.featureradiators.com
Product Type: 1, 2, 3, 4, 5, 7

FERROLI UK
Lichfield Road, Branston Industrial Estate,
Burton Upon Trent, Staffordshire, DE14 3HD
Tel: 08707 282 882   **Fax:** 08707 282 883
Email: sales@ferroli.co.uk
Web: www.ferroli.co.uk   **Product Type:** 5, 7

GEA/ SAS AIRCON LTD
Office 9, Cowdray Centre House, Cowdray Centre,
Cowdray Avenue, Colchester, Essex, CO11 QB
Area of Operation: Europe
Tel: 01206 578 833   **Fax:** 01206 6574061
Email: chris@sasaircon.co.uk
Web: www.gea-acqua.com   **Product Type:** 7

GOTO PLUMBING
Area of Operation: UK & Ireland
Email: sales@gotoplumbing.co.uk
Web: www.gotoplumbing.co.uk ✍

HEATLINE
16-19 The Manton Centre, Manton Lane,
Bedford, Bedfordshire, MK41 7PX
Area of Operation: Worldwide
Tel: 0870 777 8323   **Fax:** 0870 777 8320
Email: info@heatline.co.uk
Web: www.heatline.co.uk   **Product Type:** 1, 2, 4

HEATPROFILE LTD
Horizon House, 4 Wey Court,
Mary Road, Guildford, Surrey, GU1 4QU
Area of Operation: Europe
Tel: 01483 537000   **Fax:** 01483 537500
Email: sales@heatprofile.co.uk
Web: www.heatprofile.co.uk   **Product Type:** 3, 4

HUDSON REED
Rylands Street, Burnley, Lancashire, BB10 1RG
Area of Operation: Worldwide
Tel: 01282 418000   **Fax:** 01282 428915
Email: info@ultra-group.co.uk
Web: www.hudsonreed.info
Product Type: 1, 7   **Material Type:** C) 2, 3, 11, 14

JAGA HEATING PRODUCTS
Jaga House, Orchard Business Park,
Bromyard Road, Ledbury, Herefordshire, HR8 1LG
Area of Operation: UK & Ireland
Tel: 01531 631533   **Fax:** 01531 631534
Email: jaga@jaga.co.uk
Product Type: 1, 2, 4, 5, 7 ✪
Web: www.theradiatorfactory.com

JALI LTD
Albion Works, Church Lane, Barham, Kent, CT4 6QS
Area of Operation: UK (Excluding Ireland)
Tel: 01227 833333   **Fax:** 01227 831950
Email: sales@jali.co.uk   **Web:** www.jali.co.uk ✍
Product Type: 6   **Material Type:** H) 2

Full Central Heating without Radiators or underfloor heating?

Are you looking for a full central heating system that provides all round radiant warmth without radiators or underfloor heating?

Then *HeatProfile* Skirting Heating Systems are the answer!

Skirting heating

Skirting panels laid flat under full height glazing

HeatProfile skirting heating is a radiant full central heating system that eliminates the need for radiators and skirting boards.

- **All round radiant warmth - no cold spots or wasted energy**
- **More space - More elegant rooms - More comfort**
- **Choice of water (our own PushFit) or electric systems**
- **Significant fuel bill savings - responds quickly to temperature demand - individual room control**
- **A healthier environment - clean - low allergen - less dust particles and dust mites in the air**
- **Complete freedom of choice with furniture placement**
- **Easy installation - easily accessible - maintenance free**

The *HeatProfile* radiant full central skirting heating systems are ideal for self-build and refurbishment projects. They are easy to install and have more added value benefits compared to other heating systems!

Skirting heating with heated threshold under doors

Follows any angle

These are just some of the added value benefits that *HeatProfile* Skirting Heating Systems offers. To find out the many more advantages that there are, please call on **01483 537000** or visit our Website

www.heatprofile.co.uk

HeatProfile Ltd, Horizon House, 4 Wey Court, Mary Road, Guildford, GU1 4QU.
Tel: 01483 537000   Fax: 01483 537500
Email: sales@heatprofile.co.uk

JIS EUROPE (SUSSEX RANGE)
Warehouse 2, Nash Lane, Scaynes Hill,
Haywards Heath, West Sussex, RH17 7NJ
Area of Operation: Europe
Tel: 01444 831200   **Fax:** 01444 831900
Email: info@jiseurope.co.uk
Web: www.sussexrange.co.uk
Product Type: 1, 7

JOULESAVE EMES LTD
27 Water Lane, South Witham,
Grantham, Lincolnshire, NG33 5PH
Area of Operation: UK & Ireland
Tel: 01572 768362   **Fax:** 01572 767146
Email: sales@joulesave.co.uk
Web: www.joulesave.co.uk
Product Type: 6, 7

KALIREL UK
32 Riverside Way, Brandon, Suffolk, IP27 0AN
Area of Operation: UK & Ireland
Tel: 01842 814489   **Fax:** 01842 814489
Email: contactuk@kalirel.com
Web: www.calo-confort.co.uk

KEELING HEATING PRODUCTS
Cranbourne Road, Gosport, Hampshire, PO12 1RJ
Area of Operation: UK & Ireland
Tel: 02392 796633   **Fax:** 02392 425028
Email: sales@keeling.co.uk
Web: www.keeling.co.uk
Product Type: 7

KERMI (UK) LTD
7 Brunel Road, Corby, Northamptonshire, NN17 4JW
Area of Operation: UK & Ireland
Tel: 01536 400004   **Fax:** 01536 446614
Email: cradcliff@kermi.co.uk
Web: www.kermi.co.uk
Product Type: 1, 2

KV RADIATORS
6 Postle Close, Kilsby, Rugby, Warwickshire, CV23 8YG
Area of Operation: UK & Ireland
Tel: 01788 823286   **Fax:** 01788 823002
Email: solutions@kvradiators.com
Web: www.kvradiators.com   **Product Type:** 1, 4, 5, 7

LIONHEART HEATING SERVICES
PO Box 741, Harworth Park,
Doncaster, South Yorkshire, DN11 8WY
Area of Operation: UK (Excluding Ireland)
Tel: 01302 755200   **Fax:** 01302 750155
Email: enquiries@lionheartheating.co.uk
Web: www.lionheartheating.co.uk

LOBLITE ELECTRIC LTD
Third Avenue, Team Valley Trading Estate,
Gateshead, Tyne & Wear, NE11 0QQ
Area of Operation: Europe
Tel: 0191 487 8103   **Fax:** 0191 491 5541
Email: sales@heatec-rads.com
Web: www.heatec-rads.com   **Product Type:** 1, 2, 7
Other Info: ✳ ✐   **Material Type:** C) 1, 2, 5, 14

M & O BATHROOM CENTRE
174-176 Goswell Road, Clarkenwell, London, EC1V 7DT
Area of Operation: East England, Greater London,
South East England
Tel: 0207 608 0111   **Fax:** 0207 490 3083
Email: mando@lineone.net

MARBLE HEATING CO LTD
139 Kennington Park Road, London, SE11 4JJ
Area of Operation: Worldwide
Tel: 0845 230 0877
Fax: 0845 230 0878
Email: sales@marbleheating.co.uk
Web: www.marbleheating.co.uk
Product Type: 1, 2, 7

MFT (UK) LTD.
P.O. Box 382, Grimsby, Lincolnshire, DN37 9SW
Area of Operation: UK & Ireland
Tel: 01472 886155
Fax: 01472 590887
Email: meinertzinuk@tiscali.co.uk
Web: www.meinertz.com
Product Type: 1, 2, 3, 4, 7

MFT (UK) LTD
Area of Operation: UK & Ireland
Tel: 01472 886155   **Fax:** 01472 590887
Email: meinertzinuk@tiscali.co.uk
Web: www.meinertz.com
Product Type: 1, 2, 3, 4, 7

The MFT range of stylish finned tube radiators, convectors and convection grilles reflect their Scandinavian origins, both in their appearance and efficiency.

MHS RADIATORS & BOILERS
3 Juniper West, Fenton Way, Southfields Business
Park, Basildon, Essex, SS15 6TD
Area of Operation: UK & Ireland
Tel: 01268 546700   **Fax:** 01268 888250
Email: sales@modular-heating-group.co.uk
Web: www.mhsradiators.com
Product Type: 1, 2, 7   **Material Type:** C) 1, 5, 6

MYSON
Eastern Avenue, Team Valley, Gateshead, NE11 0PG
Area of Operation: Worldwide
Tel: 0845 402 3434
Email: sales@myson.co.uk
Web: www.myson.co.uk   **Product Type:** 1, 2, 5, 7

PITACS LTD
7 Grovebury Road, Leighton Buzzard,
Bedfordshire, LU7 4SR
Area of Operation: Worldwide
Tel: 01525 379 505   **Fax:** 01525 379 170
Email: info@pitacs.com   **Web:** www.pitacs.com

QUINN RADIATORS
Spinning Jenny Way, Leigh, Lancashire, WN7 4PE
Area of Operation: Europe
Tel: 01942 671105
Fax: 01942 261801
Email: marketing@quinn-radiators.co.uk
Web: www.quinn-radiators.co.uk
Product Type: 1, 2, 5, 6

RADIANT RADIATORS LTD
7 Allandale Road, Stoneygate,
Leicester, Leicestershire, LE2 2DA
Area of Operation: UK (Excluding Ireland)
Tel: 0116 270 5777   **Fax:** 0116 274 5777
Email: sales@radiant-radiators.co.uk
Web: www.radiant-radiators.co.uk
Product Type: 1, 2, 4, 7

RADIATING ELEGANCE
32 Main Street, Orton-on-the-Hill,
Warwickshire, CV9 3NN
Area of Operation: UK (Excluding Ireland)
Tel: 08000 280 921
Email: info@radiatingelegance.co.uk
Web: www.radiatingelegance.co.uk
Product Type: 6

RADIATING STYLE
Unit 15 Thompon Road, Hounslow,
Middlesex, Greater London, TW3 3UH
Area of Operation: UK (Excluding Ireland)
Tel: 0870 072 3428   **Fax:** 0208 577 9222
Email: sales@radiatingstyle.com
Web: www.radiatingstyle.com   **Product Type:** 1, 2

RADIATORSHOWROOM.COM

326 London Road, Hilsea,
Portsmouth, Hampshire, PO2 9JT
Area of Operation: UK (Excluding Ireland)
Tel: 08450 580 540 **Fax:** 08451 274 125
Email: sales@radiatorshowroom.com
Web: www.radiatorshowroom.com
Product Type: 1, 2, 3, 7

RETTIG (UK) LIMITED

Rettig Park, Drum Lane, Birtley, Durham, DH2 1AB
Area of Operation: UK (Excluding Ireland)
Tel: 0845 070 1090 **Fax:** 0845 070 1080
Email: kevin.gunn@purmo.co.uk
Web: www.purmo.com
Product Type: 2, 5, 7

RICHARD BURBIDGE LTD

Whittington Road, Oswestry, Shropshire, SY11 1HZ
Area of Operation: UK & Ireland
Tel: 01691 655131 **Fax:** 01691 659091
Email: info@richardburbidge.co.uk
Web: www.richardburbidge.co.uk
Product Type: 6

SIMPLY RADIATORS

Sandycroft House, 20 Station Road,
Woburn Sands, Buckinghamshire, MK17 8RW
Area of Operation: UK & Ireland
Tel: 0870 991 3648
Fax: 0870 432 5213
Email: tony.trott@simplyradiators.co.uk
Web: www.simplyradiators.co.uk
Product Type: 1, 2, 3, 4, 5, 6, 7

STREBEL LTD

1F Albany Park Industrial Estate,
Frimley Road, Camberley, Surrey, GU16 7PB
Area of Operation: UK & Ireland
Tel: 01276 685422 **Fax:** 01276 685405
Email: info@strebel.co.uk
Web: www.strebel.co.uk
Product Type: 1, 2, 3, 4, 5 ★ ○ ● ✪

TASKWORTHY

The Old Brickyard, Pontrilas, Herefordshire, HR2 0DJ
Area of Operation: UK (Excluding Ireland)
Tel: 01981 242900 **Fax:** 01981 242901
Email: peter@taskworthy.co.uk
Web: www.taskworthy.co.uk
Product Type: 6 **Other Info:** ✍ ✋

THE OLD RADIATOR COMPANY

The Old Garage, Smarden Road,
Pluckley, Kent, TN27 0RF
Area of Operation: Worldwide
Tel: 01233 813 355
Email: andy@theoldradiatorcompany.co.uk
Web: www.theoldradiatorcompany.co.uk
Product Type: 1, 4, 7

THE RADIATOR COMPANY LTD

TRC House, Units 13/14 Charlwoods Road,
East Grinstead, West Sussex, RH19 2HU
Area of Operation: Worldwide
Tel: 08707 302250 **Fax:** 08707 302260
Email: sales@theradiatorcompany.co.uk
Web: www.theradiatorcompany.co.uk ✍
Product Type: 1, 2, 3, 4, 5, 7

TOWEL RAILS 2 GO LTD

Unit 4 Paper Mill End, Great Barr,
Birmingham, West Midlands, B44 8NH
Area of Operation: UK & Ireland
Tel: 0870 240 1601 **Fax:** 0870 240 1602
Email: sales@towelrails2go.com
Web: www.towelrails2go.com ✍
Product Type: 1, 2, 7

TUBES RADIATORS UK

241 Kings Road, London, SW3 5ES
Area of Operation: Europe
Tel: 0207 351 1988 **Fax:** 0207 351 3507
Email: salesdept@tubesradiatori.com
Web: www.tubesradiatori.com
Product Type: 1 ★ ✪ ✿
Material Type: C) 2, 14

TUBISM

27 Cauldwell Road, Linton,
Swadlincote, Derbyshire, DE12 6RX
Area of Operation: UK (Excluding Ireland)
Tel: 01283 761477 **Fax:** 01283 763852
Email: warm@tubism.co.uk
Web: www.tubism.co.uk
Product Type: 7
Other Info: ✍ ✋ **Material Type:** C) 3

TUSCAN FOUNDRY PRODUCTS

Units C1-C3, Oakendene Industrial Estate,
Bolney Road, Cowfold, West Sussex, RH13 8AZ
Area of Operation: Worldwide
Tel: 01403 860040
Fax: 0845 345 0215
Email: enquiries@tuscanfoundry.co.uk
Web: www.tuscanfoundry.com ✍

UNICO SYSTEM INTERNATIONAL LIMITED

Unit 3, Ynyshir Industrial Estate, Llanwonno Road,
Porth, Rhondda Cynon Taff, CF39 0HU
Area of Operation: Worldwide
Tel: 01443 684828 **Fax:** 01443 684838
Email: scott@unicosystem.com
Web: www.unicosystem.co.uk
Product Type: 4

VIESSMANN LTD

Hortonwood 30, Telford, Shropshire, TF1 7YP
Area of Operation: UK & Ireland
Tel: 01952 675000 **Fax:** 01952 675040
Email: info@viessmann.co.uk
Web: www.viessmann.co.uk **Product Type:** 2

VOGUE UK

Units 6-10, Strawberry Lane Industrial Estate,
Strawberry Lane, Willenhall, West Midlands, WV13 3RS
Area of Operation: UK & Ireland
Tel: 0870 403 0101 **Fax:** 0870 403 0102
Email: sales@vogue-uk.com
Web: www.vogue-uk.com

WALNEY RADIATORS

The Keys, Latchford Mews,
Wheathampstead, Hertfordshire, AL4 8BB
Area of Operation: Worldwide
Tel: 0870 733 0011
Fax: 0870 733 0016
Email: sara.hale@walneyuk.com
Web: www.walneyuk.com
Product Type: 1, 2, 3, 4, 5, 7
Material Type: C) 1, 2, 5, 11, 13, 14, 16

WARMROOMS

24 Corncroft Lane, St Leonards Park,
Gloucester, Gloucestershire, GL4 6XU
Area of Operation: UK (Excluding Ireland)
Tel: 01452 304460
Fax: 01452 304460
Email: sales@warmrooms.co.uk
Web: www.warmrooms.co.uk ✍
Product Type: 1, 2, 3, 4, 5, 6, 7 ★ ✪ ✿

WINTHER BROWNE

75 Bilton Way, Enfield, London, EN3 7ER
Area of Operation: UK (Excluding Ireland)
Tel: 0208 3449050
Fax: 0845 612 1894
Email: sales@wintherbrowne.co.uk
Web: www.wintherbrowne.co.uk
Product Type: 6
Material Type: B) 2

ZEHNDER LTD

B15 Armstrong Mall, Southwood Business Park,
Farnborough, Hampshire, GU14 0NR
Area of Operation: UK & Ireland
Tel: 01252 515151
Fax: 01252 522528
Email: sales@zehnder.co.uk
Web: www.zehnder.co.uk
Product Type: 1, 2, 3, 4, 5, 7
Other Info: ✍
Material Type: C) 2

HEATING, PLUMBING & ELECTRICAL

FIRES & FIREPLACES

KEY

PRODUCT TYPES: 1= Contemporary
2 = Edwardian   3 = Georgian   4 = Victorian
5 = Art Deco   6 = Art Nouveau
7 = Arts & Crafts   8 = Classical   9 = Other

ENERGY SOURCES: ★ Gas   ○ Oil
□ Coal   ● Wood   ✪ Multi-Fuel
✿ Electric   ◆ Gel

OTHER: ▽ Reclaimed   🖰 On-line shopping
✍ Bespoke   ✋ Hand-made   ECO Ecological

ACANTHA LIFESTYLE LTD
32-34 Park Royal Road, Park Royal, London, NW10 7LN
Area of Operation: Worldwide
Tel: 0208 453 1537   **Fax:** 0208 453 1538
Email: sales@acanthalifesyle.com
Web: www.acanthalifestyle.co.uk
Product Type: 1, 2, 3, 4, 5, 6, 7, 8
Material Type: E) 1, 2, 5, 8

ACR HEAT PRODUCTS LTD
Weston Lane, Tyseley, Birmingham, B11 3RP
Area of Operation: UK (Excluding Ireland)
Tel: 0870 780 4549
Email: enquiries@acrheatproducts.co.uk
Web: www.acrheatproducts.co.uk

AGA-RAYBURN
Station Road , Ketley, Telford, Shropshire, TF1 5AQ
Area of Operation: Worldwide
Tel: 01952 642000   **Fax:** 01952 243 138
Email: jkingsbury-webber@aga-web.co.uk
Web: www.aga-web.co.uk

ANGLIA FIREPLACES & DESIGN LTD
Anglia House, Kendal Court, Cambridge Road,
Impington, Cambridgeshire, CB4 9YS
Area of Operation: UK & Ireland
Tel: 01223 234713   **Fax:** 01223 235116
Email: info@fireplaces.co.uk
Web: www.fireplaces.co.uk
Product Type: 1, 8 ★ □ ● ✪

ARCHITECTURAL HERITAGE
Taddington Manor, Taddington, Nr Cutsdean,
Cheltenham, Gloucestershire, GL54 5RY
Area of Operation: Worldwide
Tel: 01386 584414   **Fax:** 01386 584236
Email: puddy@architectural-heritage.co.uk
Web: www.architectural-heritage.co.uk

ARCHITECTURAL TREASURES
The Old Garage, Smarden Road, Pluckley, Kent, TN27 0RF
Area of Operation: Worldwide
Tel: 01233 840004   **Fax:** 01233 840055
Email: info@architecturaltreasures.co.uk
Web: www.architecturaltreasures.co.uk
Product Type: 1, 2, 3, 4, 5, 6, 7, 8

ARO MARBLE
18 Minerva Road, London, NW10 6HJ
Area of Operation: UK (Excluding Ireland)
Tel: 020 8965 1144   **Fax:** 020 8965 1818
Email: info@aromarble.com **Web:** www.aromarble.com

AUSTROFLAMM
Falcon Road, Sowton Industrial Estate,
Exeter, Devon, EX2 7LF
Area of Operation: UK & Ireland
Tel: 01392 474056   **Fax:** 01392 219932
Email: info@stovax.com **Web:** www.stovax.com
Product Type: 1 ★ ✪   **Material Type:** C) 2

B&D
Unit 2 Park Mews, Kilburn Lane, London, W10 4BQ
Area of Operation: UK (Excluding Ireland)
Tel: 0208 964 5355   **Fax:** 0208 892 2590
Email: cathy@bddesign.freeserve.co.uk
Web: www.bd-designs.co.uk   **Product Type:** 1

BAXI FIRES DIVISION
Brookes House, Coventry Road,
Warwick, Warwickshire, CV34 4LL
Area of Operation: UK (Excluding Ireland)
Tel: 0121 373 8111   **Fax:** 0121 373 8181
Email: sales@valor.co.uk   **Web:** www.valor.co.uk
Product Type: 1, 2, 3, 4, 5, 6, 8

BAXI HEATING UK
Brooks House, Coventry Road, Warwick,
Warwickshire, CV34 4LL
Area of Operation: UK & Ireland
Tel: 08706 060780   **Fax:** 01926 410006
Web: www.baxi.co.uk

BD BROOKS FIREPLACES
109 Halifax Road, Ripponden,
Halifax, West Yorkshire, HX6 4DA
Tel: 01422 822220   **Fax:** 01422 822220
Email: sales@bdbrooksfireplaces.com
Web: www.bdbrooksfireplaces.com
Product Type: 1, 2, 3, 4, 5, 6, 7, 8

BE MODERN GROUP LTD
Western Approach, South Shields,
Tyne & Wear, NE33 5QZ
Area of Operation: UK & Ireland
Tel: 0191 455 3571   **Fax:** 0191 456 5556
Web: www.bemodern.co.uk
Product Type: 1, 6, 8, 9 ★ ✿
Material Type: C) 2, 3, 4, 5, 11, 12, 14

BLAZES FIREPLACE CENTRES
23 Standish Street, Burnley, Lancashire, BB11 1AP
Area of Operation: UK (Excluding Ireland)
Tel: 01282 831176   **Fax:** 01282 424141
Email: info@blazes.co.uk
Web: www.blazes.co.uk

BRILLIANT FIRES
Thwaites Close, Shadsworth Business Park,
Blackburn, Lancashire, BB1 2QQ
Area of Operation: UK & Ireland
Tel: 01254 682384   **Fax:** 01254 672 647
Email: info@brilliantfires.co.uk
Web: www.brilliantfires.co.uk
Product Type: 1, 2, 3, 4, 5, 8, 9 ★ ✿
Material Type: C) 1, 2, 3, 11, 14, 16

BROSELEY FIRES
Knights Way, Battlefield Enterprise Park,
Shrewsbury, Shropshire, SY1 3AB
Area of Operation: UK & Ireland
Tel: 01743 461444   **Fax:** 01743 461446
Email: sales@broseleyfires.com
Web: www.broseleyfires.com

BURLEY APPLIANCES LIMITED
Lands End Way, Oakham,
Rutland, Leicestershire, LE15 6RB
Area of Operation: Worldwide
Tel: 01572 756956   **Fax:** 01572 724390
Email: info@burley.co.uk
Web: www.burley.co.uk   **Product Type:** 1, 8

CHARLTON & JENRICK LTD
Units G1 & G2, Halesfield 5,
Telford, Shropshire, TF7 4QJ
Area of Operation: UK & Ireland
Tel: 01952 278020   **Fax:** 01952 278043
Email: info@charltonandjenrick.co.uk
Web: www.charltonandjenrick.co.uk
Product Type: 1, 8, 9 ★ ✿

CHARNWOOD STOVES & FIRES
Bishops Way, Newport, Isle of Wight, PO30 5WS
Area of Operation: Worldwide
Tel: 01983 537780   **Fax:** 01983 537788
Email: charnwood@ajwells.co.uk
Web: www.charnwood.com 🖰
Product Type: 1, 8 ★ □ ● ✪ ✿
Other Info: ECO ✍   **Material Type:** C) 2, 5

CHARNWOOD STOVES
Area of Operation: Worldwide
Tel: 01983 537780   **Fax:** 01983 537788
Email: charnwood@ajwells.co.uk
Web: www.charnwood.com
Product Type: 1, 8

Britain's original designers and manufacturers of
clean-burn multi-fuel and wood burning fires &
boilers. Ultra efficient and eco-friendly. Various
models, choice of colours and accessories to suit
every situation.

CHISWELL FIREPLACES LTD
Fireplace Showroom, 192 Watford Road,
Chiswell Green, St Albans, Hertfordshire, AL2 3EB
Area of Operation: South East England
Tel: 01727 859512
Email: sales@chiswellfireplaces.com
Web: www.chiswellfireplaces.com
Product Type: 1, 2, 3, 4, 5, 6, 7, 8, 9 ★ □ ● ✿
Material Type: C) 2, 3, 5, 11, 13, 14

CICO CHIMNEY LININGS LTD
The Street, Westleton,
Saxmundham, Suffolk, IP17 3AG
Area of Operation: UK (Excluding Ireland)
Tel: 01728 648608
Fax: 01728 648428
Email: cico@chimney-problems.co.uk
Web: www.chimney-problems.co.uk

CLARKES ANTIQUE FIREPLACES
Old Forge, 32 Fore Street,
Buckfastleigh, Devon, TQ11 0AA
Area of Operation: UK (Excluding Ireland)
Tel: 01364 643060

CONTINENTAL FIRES LIMITED
Unit 1 Laundry Bank,
Church Stretton, Shropshire, SY6 6PH
Area of Operation: UK & Ireland
Tel: 01694 724199
Fax: 01694 720100
Email: sales@continentalfires.com
Web: www.continentalfires.com

CONTINENTAL FIRES LTD
Area of Operation: UK & Ireland
Tel: 01694 724199
Fax: 01694 720100
Email: sales@continentalfires.com
Web: www.continentalfires.com
Product Type: 1, 2, 3, 4, 10

Continental Fires are responsible for the distribution
of the Barbas and Bellfires brands through a Dealer
network covering Britain and Ireland

COOLANDWARM.COM
Trigger Comfort, t/a cool and warm,
23 Walnut Tree Close, Guildford, Surrey, GU1 4UL
Area of Operation: Europe
Tel: 01483 30 66 50
Email: info@coolandwarm.com
Web: www.coolandwarm.com 🖰

COSY ROOMS (COSY-HEATING.CO.UK)
17 Chiltern Way, North Hykeham,
Lincoln, Lincolnshire, LN6 9SY
Area of Operation: UK (Excluding Ireland)
Tel: 01522 696002   **Fax:** 01522 696002
Email: keith@cosy-rooms.com
Web: www.cosy-heating.co.uk 🖰
Product Type: 1, 9

CVO FIRE LTD
4 Beaumont Square, Durham Way South, Aycliffe
Industrial Park, Newtom Aycliffe, Durham, DL5 6SW
Area of Operation: UK & Ireland
Tel: 01325 327221   **Fax:** 01325 327292
Email: officeadmin@cvo.co.uk   **Web:** www.cvo.co.uk

DILIGENCE
Dart Mills, Old Totnes Road,
Buckfastleigh, Devon, TQ11 0NF
Area of Operation: UK & Ireland
Tel: 01364 644 790   **Fax:** 01364 644 791
Email: info@diligenceinternational.com
Web: www.diligenceinternational.com
Product Type: 1 ★ □ ●   **Other Info:** ✍

Town and Country Fires (Pickering)
Top Quality British Stoves

Manufacturers of multi-fuel stoves, gas stoves and gas fires.
25 years of experience.

We have a full range of traditional and modern heating appliances
please phone for details or visit our website.

Tel: 01751 474803 Fax: 01751 475205

1 Enterprise Way, Thornton Road Industrial Estate, Pickering, North Yorkshire YO18 7NA
Email: sales@townandcountryfires.co.uk Website: www.townandcountryfires.co.uk

DIMPLEX
Millbrook House, Grange Drive, Hedge End,
Southampton, Hampshire, SO30 2DF
Area of Operation: UK & Ireland
Tel: 0845 600 5111
Fax: 01489 773050
Email: customer.services@glendimplex.com
Web: www.dimplex.co.uk
Product Type: 1, 4, 9 ✿

DIMPLEX
Area of Operation: UK & Ireland
Tel: 0845 600 5111
Fax: 01489 773050
Email: customer.services@glendimplex.com
Web: www.dimplex.co.uk
Product Type: 1, 9 ✿

If you'd like a real fire, but don't want the hassle,
a Dimplex Optiflame electric fire is the solution.
No chimney, no flue - just plug in and go.

DRAYTON PROPERTY
9 Kenilworth Close, Daventry,
Northamptonshire, NN11 4AH
Area of Operation: UK (Excluding Ireland)
Tel: 07754 039272
Email: draytonproperty@aol.com
Web: www.draytonproperty.com ✐
Product Type: 2, 3, 4, 8

DUNSLEY HEAT LTD
Bridge Mills, Huddersfield Road, Holmfirth,
Huddersfield, West Yorkshire, HD9 3TW
Area of Operation: UK & Ireland
Tel: 01484 682635
Fax: 01484 688428
Email: sales@dunsleyheat.co.uk
Web: www.dunsleyheat.co.uk
Product Type: 9 ☐ ●

ELGIN & HALL
Adelphi House, Hunton, Bedale, North Yorkshire, DL8 1LY
Area of Operation: UK (Excluding Ireland)
Tel: 01677 450 100
Fax: 01677 450 713
Email: info@elgin.co.uk
Web: www.elgin.co.uk

EMSWORTH FIREPLACES LIMITED
Unit 3, Station Approach,
Emsworth, Hampshire, PO10 7PW
Tel: 01243 373300   **Fax:** 01243 371023
Email: sales@emsworth.co.uk
Web: www.emsworth.co.uk ✐
Product Type: 1, 2, 3, 4, 5, 6, 7, 8, 9

ENGLISH FIREPLACES
Old Firs, Hillbrow, Liss, Hampshire, GU33 7QE
Tel: 01730 890218   **Fax:** 01730 890218
Email: info@englishfireplaces.co.uk
Web: www.englishfireplaces.co.uk ✐

EUROFLAMES LIMITED
120 Suite, 70 Churchill Square,
Kings Hill, West Malling, Kent, ME19 4YU
Area of Operation: UK & Ireland
Tel: 01732 897919
Email: karolina.barnes@euroflames.com
Web: www.euroflames.com ✐
Product Type: 1, 8 ● ✪

FABER FIRES
Touchstone House, 82 High Street,
Measham , Derbyshire, DE12 7JB
Tel: 0845 130 1862   **Fax:** 01530 274271
Email: sales@faber-fires.co.uk
Web: www.faber-fires.co.uk
Product Type: 1, 9 ★ ■ ●

FIREPLACE & TIMBER PRODUCTS
Unit 2 Holyrood Drive, Skippingdale Industrial Estate,
Scunthorpe, Lincolnshire, DN15 8NN
Area of Operation: UK & Ireland
Tel: 01724 852888   **Fax:** 01724 277255
Email: ftprodcts@yahoo.co.uk
Web: www.fireplaceandtimberproducts.co.uk
Product Type: 1, 2, 3, 4, 5, 6, 8, 9

FIREPLACE CONSULTANTS LTD
The Studio, The Old Rothschild Arms, Buckland Road,
Buckland, Aylesbury, Buckinghamshire, HP22 5LP
Area of Operation: Greater London, Midlands & Mid
Wales, South East England
Tel: 01296 632287   **Fax:** 01296 632287
Email: info@fireplaceconsultants.com
Web: www.fireplaceconsultants.com
Product Type: 1, 2, 3, 4, 5, 6, 7, 8
Other Info: ✐ ✋

FIREPLACE DESIGN CONSULTANCY
Stansley Wood Farm, Dapple Heath,
Rugeley, Staffordshire, WS15 3PH
Tel: 01889 500500   **Fax:** 01889 500500
Email: info@inglenooks.co.uk
Web: www.inglenooks.co.uk

FIRES4U
PO Box 6843, Swadlincote, Derbyshire, DE12 7XX
Area of Operation: Worldwide
Tel: 0845 612 0001
Email: sales@fires4u.co.uk
Web: www.fires4u.co.uk ✐
Product Type: 1, 2, 3, 4, 5, 6, 8 ★ ☐ ● ✪ ✿ ♦

FLAMERITE FIRES LTD
Greenhough Road, Lichfield, West Midlands, WS13 7AU
Tel: 01543 251122   **Fax:** 01543 251133
Email: info@flameritefires.com
Web: www.flameritefires.com
Product Type: 1, 5, 6, 8, 9 ✿   **Other Info:** ✋
Material Type: C) 1, 2, 3, 4, 5, 6, 11, 14

FLAMEWAVE FIRES - DK UK LTD
PO Box 611, Folkestone, Kent, CT18 7WY
Tel: 0845 257 5028   **Fax:** 0845 257 5038
Email: info@flamewavefires.co.uk
Web: www.flamewavefires.co.uk

FRANCIS N. LOWE LTD.
The Marble Works, New Road, Middleton,
Matlock, Derbyshire, DE4 4NA
Tel: 01629 822216   **Fax:** 01629 824348
Email: info@lowesmarble.com
Web: www.lowesmarble.com

GAZCO LTD
Osprey Road, Sowton Industrial Estate,
Exeter, Devon, EX2 7JG
Tel: 01392 261999   **Fax:** 01392 444148
Email: info@gazco.com   **Web:** www.gazco.com
Product Type: 1, 2, 3, 4, 5, 6, 8 ★ ☐ ● ✪ ✿
Other Info: ✐   **Material Type:** C) 2, 3, 5, 11

JETMASTER FIRES LTD
Unit 2 Peacock Trading Estate, Goodwood Road,
Chandlers Ford, Eastleigh, Hampshire, SO50 4NT
Area of Operation: Europe
Tel: 0870 727 0105   **Fax:** 0870 727 0106
Email: jetmastersales@aol.com
Web: www.jetmaster.co.uk   **Other Info:** ✐
Product Type: 1, 2, 3, 4, 5, 6, 7, 8, 9

JETMASTER FIRES LTD
Area of Operation: Europe
Tel: 0870 727 0105   **Fax:** 0870 727 0106
Email: jetmastersales@aol.com
Web: www.jetmaster.co.uk
Product Type: 1,2,3,4,5,6,7,8,9

Jetmaster gas fires are often mistaken for real coal
fires. Flame variation flicker and ember colour
changes combine to produce a completely realistic
effect. Also available with remote control, that ignites
the pilot and controls the fire.

JETMASTER FIRES LTD
Area of Operation: Europe
Tel: 0870 727 0105   **Fax:** 0870 727 0106
Email: jetmastersales@aol.com
Web: www.jetmaster.co.uk
Product Type: 1,2,3,4,5,6,7,8,9

Jetmaster's original two way heating system with
radiant and convective heat, warms the whole
room right into the corners, while the flames and
embers make a natural and effective focal draw.
There's nothing like a real fire!

JETMASTER FIRES LTD
Area of Operation: Europe
Tel: 0870 727 0105   **Fax:** 0870 727 0106
Email: jetmastersales@aol.com
Web: www.jetmaster.co.uk
Product Type: 1, 2, 3, 4, 5, 6 ,7, 8, 9

Jetmaster has been building stylish and efficient,
smoke free fireboxes for wood and coal or gas
since 1951, real fires! real quality! A welcoming
warmth to enhance every home.

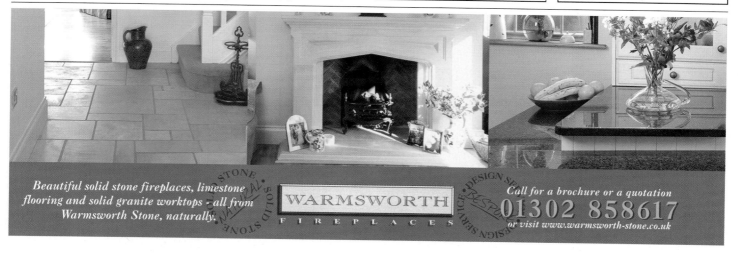
HEATING, PLUMBING & ELECTRICAL

HEATING, PLUMBING & ELECTRICAL

KINGSWORTHY FOUNDRY CO LTD
London Road, Kingsworthy,
Winchester, Hampshire, SO23 7QG
Area of Operation: UK & Ireland
Tel: 01962 883776   **Fax:** 01962 882925
Email: kwf@fsbdial.co.uk
Web: www.kingsworthyfoundry.co.uk
Product Type: 9

LEL FIREPLACES
Tre-Ifan Farmhouse, Caergeiliog,
Holyhead, Anglesey, LL65 3HP
Area of Operation: UK & Ireland
Tel: 01407 742240   **Fax:** 01407 742262
Email: sales@lel-fireplaces.com
Web: www.lel-fireplaces.com ⌂
Product Type: 1, 2, 3, 4, 5, 6, 7, 8, 9 ★ □ ● ✪ ❄

LIVINGSTYLE.CO.UK
Bridge Street, Shotton, Flintshire, CH5 1DU
Area of Operation: UK (Excluding Ireland)
Tel: 0800 2989190
Email: info@livingstyle.co.uk
Web: www.livingstyle.co.uk ⌂
Product Type: 1, 2, 3, 4, 5, 6, 7, 8, 9

MAGIGLO LTD
Lysander Close, Broadstairs, Kent, CT10 2YJ
Area of Operation: UK & Ireland
Tel: 01843 602863
Fax: 01843 860108
Email: info@magiglo.co.uk
Web: www.magiglo.co.uk
Product Type: 1, 2, 4, 5, 6, 8, 9 ★ ❄
Other Info: ✎

MARBLE HART.COM
1 Edwin Street, Daybrook, Arnold,
Nottingham, Nottinghamshire, NG5 6AX
Area of Operation: Worldwide
Tel: 0115 920 3159   **Fax:** 0115 952 5752
Email: chris@cghart.com
Web: www.marblehart.com ⌂

MARBLE HILL FIREPLACES
70-72 Richmond Road, Twickenham,
Greater London, TW1 3BE
Area of Operation: UK (Excluding Ireland)
Tel: 020 8892 1488   **Fax:** 020 8891 6591
Email: sales@marblehill.co.uk
Web: www.marblehill.co.uk

MARK RIPLEY FORGE & FIREPLACES
Robertsbridge, Bridge Bungalow, East Sussex, TN32 5NY
Tel: 01580 880324
Fax: 01580 881927
Email: info@ripleyfireplaces.co.uk
Web: www.ripleyfireplaces.co.uk
Product Type: 2, 4, 6

NATIONAL FIREPLACE ASSOCIATION
6th Floor, McLaren Building, 35 Dale End,
Birmingham, West Midlands, B4 7LN
Area of Operation: UK & Ireland
Tel: 0121 200 1310
Fax: 0121 200 1306
Email: enquiries@nfa.org.uk
Web: www.nfa.org.uk ⌂

NUNNA UUNI LTD
Karelia House, Kenmore Road, Comrie Bridge By
Aberfeldy, Perth and Kinross, PH15 2PF
Area of Operation: UK & Ireland
Tel: 01887 822025
Fax: 01887 822954
Email: sales@enerfoil.com
Web: www.nunnauuni.com

OLDE ENGLANDE REPRODUCTIONS
Fireplace Works, Normacot Road, Longton,
Stoke-on-Trent, Staffordshire, ST3 1PN
Area of Operation: UK (Excluding Ireland)
Tel: 01782 319350
Fax: 01782 593479
Email: sales@oerfireplaces.com
Web: www.oerfireplaces.com
Product Type: 1, 2, 3, 4, 5, 6, 8

PARAGON FIRES
Unit G1 and G2, Halesfield, Telford, Shropshire, TF7 4QJ
Tel: 01952 278020   **Fax:** 01952 278043
Email: info@charltonandjenrick.co.uk
Web: www.paragonfires.co.uk   **Product Type:** 1, 8 ★ ❄

PENDRAGON FIREPLACES.COM
12 Market Street, Stourbridge, West Midlands, DY8 1AD
Tel: 01384 376441   **Fax:** 01384 376441
Email: sales@pendragonfireplaces.co.uk
Web: www.pendragonfireplaces.com ⌂
Product Type: 2, 3, 4, 5, 6, 7

PEPPERS FIREPLACE AND GARDEN CENTRE
70 Avenue Road, Bexley Heath, Kent, DA7 4EG
Tel: 0208 303 2195   **Fax:** 0208 301 1012
Email: sales@peppers.uk.com
Web: www.peppers.uk.com ⌂

PERCY DOUGHTY & CO
Imperial Point, Express Trading Estate, Stonehill
Road, Farnworth, Bolton, Lancashire, BL4 9TN
Area of Operation: Midlands & Mid Wales, North
West England and North Wales
Tel: 01204 868550   **Fax:** 01204 868551
Email: sales@percydoughty.com
Web: www.percydoughty.co.uk
Product Type: 1, 4, 5, 6, 8

PETRA HELLAS
Park Road Business Centre, Bacup, Lancashire, OL13 0BW
Tel: 01706 876102   **Fax:** 01706 876194
Email: info@petrahellas.co.uk
Web: www.petrahellas.co.uk   **Product Type:** 1, 8

PICTURE HOUSE CABINETS
Cherry House, Oakcroft Road,
West Byfleet, Surrey, KT10 0JH
Area of Operation: UK (Excluding Ireland)
Tel: 01932 345184   **Fax:** 01932 402128
Email: info@picturehousecabinets.com
Web: www.picturehousecabinets.com
Product Type: 1

PICTURE HOUSE CABINETS
Area of Operation: UK (Excluding Ireland)
Tel: 01932 345184
Fax: 01932 402128
Email: info@picturehousecabinets.com
Web: www.picturehousecabinets.com

Picture House's patented plasma fireplaces hide
the TV in a working fireplace. Press the remote
and the TV is raised to viewing height. Press it
again and the TV disappears.

R W KNIGHT & SON LTD
Castle Farm, Marshfield, Chippenham, Wiltshire, SN14 8HU
Area of Operation: Midlands & Mid Wales, South
East England, South West England and South Wales
Tel: 01225 891469   **Fax:** 01225 892369
Email: enquiries@knight-stoves.com
Web: www.knight-stoves.co.uk
Product Type: 1, 2, 3, 4, 5 ★ □ ● ✪

REAL FLAME
80 New Kings Road, London, SW6 4LT
Tel: 0207 731 2704   **Email:** info@realflame.co.uk
Web: www.realflame.co.uk ⌂
Product Type: ★   **Other Info:** ✎ ✋

HEATING, PLUMBING & ELECTRICAL

ROBEYS
Belper, Derbyshire, DE56 1BY
Area of Operation: UK & Ireland
Tel: 01773 820940 **Fax:** 01773 821652
Email: info@robeys.co.uk **Web:** www.robeys.co.uk

ROCAL
Falcon Road, Sowton Industrial Estate,
Exeter, Devon, EX2 7LF
Area of Operation: UK & Ireland
Tel: 01392 474055 **Fax:** 01392 219932
Email: rocal@stovax.com **Web:** www.stovax.com
Product Type: 1 ★ ✪ **Material Type:** C) 5

ROCAL FIRES
Touchstone House, 82 High Street, Measham,
Derbyshire, DE12 7JB
Area of Operation: UK (Excluding Ireland)
Tel: 0845 130 1862 **Fax:** 01530 274271
Email: sales@rocal-fires.co.uk
Web: www.rocal-fires.co.uk
Product Type: 1, 9 ★ ■ ●

RUDLOE STONEWORKS LTD
Leafield Stoneyard, Potley Lane,
Corsham, Wiltshire, SN13 9RS
Area of Operation: UK & Ireland
Tel: 01225 816400 **Fax:** 01225 811343
Email: paul@rudloe-stone.com
Web: www.rudloe-stone.com
Product Type: 1, 2, 5, 7

SOLAR FIRES & FIREPLACES LTD
Alyn Works, Mostyn Road,
Holywell, Flintshire, CH8 9DT
Area of Operation: UK & Ireland
Tel: 01745 561685 **Fax:** 01745 580 987
Email: sales@solarfiresandfireplaces.co.uk
Web: www.solarfiresandfireplaces.co.uk

STOVAX LIMITED
Falcon Road, Sowton Industrial Estate,
Exeter, Devon, EX2 7LF
Area of Operation: UK & Ireland
Tel: 01392 474011 **Fax:** 01392 219932
Email: info@stovax.com **Web:** www.stovax.com
Product Type: 1, 2, 3, 4, 5, 6, 7, 8, 9 ■ ● ✪
Other Info: ✍ ✋

SUPERIOR FIRES
Touchstone House, 82 High Street, Measham,
Derbyshire, DE12 7JB
Area of Operation: UK (Excluding Ireland)
Tel: 0845 130 1862 **Fax:** 01530 274271
Email: sales@superior-fires.co.uk
Web: www.superior-fires.co.uk **Product Type:** 1, 9★

TEMPLESTONE
Station Wharf, Castle Cary, Somerset, BA7 7PE
Area of Operation: UK & Ireland
Tel: 01963 350242 **Fax:** 01963 350258
Email: sales@templestone.co.uk
Web: www.templestone.co.uk
Product Type: 1, 3, 8

THE ANTIQUE FIREPLACE COMPANY
Jasmine Cottage, Prees Green,
Nr Whitchurch, Shropshire, SY13 2BL
Area of Operation: Worldwide
Tel: 01948 840666
Email: sales@antiquefireplacecompany.co.uk
Web: www.antiquefireplacecompany.co.uk ✍
Product Type: 2, 3, 4, 5, 6, 7, 8

THE EDWARDIAN FIREPLACE COMPANY
Former All Saints Church, Armoury Way,
Wandsworth, London, SW18 1HZ
Area of Operation: UK & Ireland
Tel: 0208 870 0167 **Fax:** 0208 877 2847
Email: sales@edwardianfires.com
Web: www.edwardianfires.co.uk
Product Type: 1, 2, 3, 4, 5, 6, 7, 8

THE FIREPLACE GALLERY (UK) LTD
Clarence Road, Worksop, Nottinghamshire, S80 1QA
Area of Operation: UK & Ireland
Tel: 01909 500802 **Fax:** 01909 500810
Email: fireplacegallery@btinternet.com
Web: www.fireplacegallery.co.uk **Product Type:** 1, 8

PLEASE MENTION

THE HOMEBUILDER'S HANDBOOK 2007

WHEN YOU CALL

THE FIREPLACE MARKETING COMPANY LIMITED
Haseley Manor, Birmingham Road,
Warwick, Warwickshire, CV35 7LS
Area of Operation: Worldwide
Tel: 02476 247246 **Fax:** 02476 247266
Email: info@fireplace.co.uk
Web: www.fireplace.co.uk ✍
Product Type: 1, 2, 3, 4, 5, 6, 7, 8

THE JRG GROUP
3 Crompton Way, North Newmoor Industrial Estate,
Irvine, Ayrshire, KA11 4HU
Area of Operation: Europe
Tel: 0871 200 8080 **Fax:** 01294 211 222
Email: chris@jrgfiresurrounds.com
Web: www.jrggroup.com **Product Type:** 1, 8 ❋

THE MASON'S YARD
Penhenllan, Cusop, Hay on Wye,
Herefordshire, HR3 5TE
Area of Operation: UK (Excluding Ireland)
Tel: 01497 821333
Email: hugh@themasonsyard.co.uk
Web: www.themasonsyard.co.uk

THE PLATONIC FIREPLACE COMPAY
Phoenix Wharf, Eel Pie Island,
Twickenham, London, TW1 3DY
Area of Operation: UK (Excluding Ireland)
Tel: 0208 891 5904 **Fax:** 0208 892 2590
Email: platonicfireplace@btinternet.com
Web: www.platonicfireplaces.co.uk
Product Type: 1 ★ ❋

THEALE FIREPLACES RDG LTD
Milehouse Farm, Bath Road,
Theale, Berkshire, RG7 5HJ
Area of Operation: UK (Excluding Ireland)
Tel: 0118 930 2232 **Fax:** 0118 932 3344
Email: mail@theale-fireplaces.co.uk
Web: www.theale-fireplaces.co.uk
Product Type: 1, 2, 3, 4, 5

TOWN AND COUNTRY FIRES
1 Enterprise Way, Thornton Road Industrial Estate,
Pickering, North Yorkshire, YO18 7NA
Area of Operation: Europe
Tel: 01751 474803 **Fax:** 01751 475205
Email: sales@townandcountryfires.co.uk
Web: www.townandcountryfires.co.uk

VERINE
52 Broton Drive, Halstead, Essex, CO9 1HB
Area of Operation: UK & Ireland
Tel: 01787 472551 **Fax:** 01787 476589
Email: sales@verine.co.uk
Web: www.verine.co.uk
Product Type: 1, 2, 3, 4, 5, 6, 8 ★ ❋

VERINE AND PORTWAY
52 Broton Drive Industrial Estate,
Halstead, Essex, CO9 1HB
Area of Operation: Europe
Tel: 01787 472551 **Fax:** 01787 476589
Email: sales@portwayfires.com
Web: www.portwayfires.com
Product Type: 1, 2, 3, 4, 6, 8 ★ ❋

WESSEX STONE FIREPLACES
Ilsom Farm, Cirencester Road,
Tetbury, Gloucestershire, GL8 8RX
Area of Operation: UK (Excluding Ireland)
Tel: 01666 504658 **Fax:** 01666 502285
Email: info@wells-group.co.uk
Web: www.wells-group.co.uk

FIREPLACE ACCESSORIES

KEY
PRODUCT TYPES: 1 = Mantel Pieces
2 = Fenders 3 = Fire Curtains
4 = Fire Screens and Canopies 5 = Fire Backs
6 = Fire Baskets 7 = Fireplace Doors
8 = Dampers 9 = Other

OTHER: ▽ Reclaimed ✍ On-line shopping
✏ Bespoke ✋ Hand-made ECO Ecological

A & M ENERGY FIRES
Pool House, Huntley, Gloucestershire, GL19 3DZ
Area of Operation: Europe
Tel: 01452 830662 **Fax:** 01452 830891
Email: am@energyfires.co.uk
Web: www.energyfires.co.uk **Product Type:** 3, 7

ACANTHA LIFESTYLE LTD
32-34 Park Royal Road, Park Royal, London, NW10 7LN
Area of Operation: Worldwide
Tel: 0208 453 1537 **Fax:** 0208 453 1538
Email: sales@acanthalifestyle.com
Web: www.acanthalifestyle.co.uk **Product Type:** 1

ANGLIA FIREPLACES & DESIGN LTD
Anglia House, Kendal Court, Cambridge Road,
Impington, Cambridgeshire, CB4 9YS
Area of Operation: UK & Ireland
Tel: 01223 234713 **Fax:** 01223 235116
Email: info@fireplaces.co.uk
Web: www.fireplaces.co.uk **Product Type:** 1

BD BROOKS FIREPLACES
109 Halifax Road, Ripponden,
Halifax, West Yorkshire, HX6 4DA
Area of Operation: UK (Excluding Ireland)
Tel: 01422 822220 **Fax:** 01422 822220
Email: sales@bdbrooksfireplaces.com
Web: www.bdbrooksfireplaces.com
Product Type: 1, 2, 3, 4, 5, 6, 7, 8, 9

BRILLIANT FIRES
Thwaites Close, Shadsworth Business Park,
Blackburn, Lancashire, BB1 2QQ
Area of Operation: UK & Ireland
Tel: 01254 682384 **Fax:** 01254 672647
Email: info@brilliantfires.co.uk
Web: www.brilliantfires.co.uk **Product Type:** 1

BROSELEY FIRES
Knights Way, Battlefield Enterprise Park,
Shrewsbury, Shropshire, SY1 3AB
Area of Operation: UK & Ireland
Tel: 01743 461444 **Fax:** 01743 461446
Email: sales@broseleyfires.com
Web: www.broseleyfires.com **Product Type:** 4

CENTURION
Westhill Business Park, Arnhall Business Park,
Westhill, Aberdeen, Aberdeenshire, AB32 6UF
Area of Operation: Scotland
Tel: 01224 744440 **Fax:** 01224 744819
Email: info@centurion-solutions.co.uk
Web: www.centurion-solutions.co.uk
Product Type: 3

COBALT BLACKSMITHS
The Forge, English Farm, English Lane,
Nuffield, Oxfordshire, RG9 5TH
Tel: 01491 641990 **Fax:** 01491 640909
Email: enquiries@cobalt-blacksmiths.co.uk
Web: www.cobalt-blacksmiths.co.uk
Product Type: 4, 6

DIMPLEX
Millbrook House, Grange Drive, Hedge End,
Southampton, Hampshire, SO30 2DF
Area of Operation: UK & Ireland
Tel: 0845 600 5111 **Fax:** 01489 773050
Email: customer.services@glendimplex.com
Web: www.dimplex.co.uk **Product Type:** 9

DRAYTON PROPERTY
9 Kenilworth Close, Daventry,
Northamptonshire, NN11 4AH
Area of Operation: UK (Excluding Ireland)
Tel: 07754 039272
Email: draytonproperty@aol.com
Web: www.draytonproperty.com ✍
Product Type: 1, 5, 6

EMSWORTH FIREPLACES LIMITED
Unit 3, Station Approach,
Emsworth, Hampshire, PO10 7PW
Area of Operation: Worldwide
Tel: 01243 373300 **Fax:** 01243 371023
Email: sales@emsworth.co.uk
Web: www.emsworth.co.uk ✍
Product Type: 1, 2, 4, 5, 6, 8

ENCOMPASS FURNITURE & ACCESSORIES
The Pool Room, Stansted House, Stansted Park,
Rowlands Castle, Hampshire, PO9 6DX
Area of Operation: Worldwide
Tel: 02392 410045 **Fax:** 02392 412145
Email: info@encompassco.com
Web: www.encompassco.com
Product Type: 4, 6 **Material Type:** C) 1, 2, 3, 5, 14

ENGLISH FIREPLACES
Old Firs, Hillbrow, Liss, Hampshire, GU33 7QE
Area of Operation: Worldwide
Tel: 01730 890218 **Fax:** 01730 890218
Email: info@englishfireplaces.com
Web: www.englishfireplaces.co.uk ✍
Product Type: 1, 5, 6

EUROFLAMES LIMITED
120 Suite, 70 Churchill Square,
Kings Hill, West Malling, Kent, ME19 4YU
Area of Operation: UK & Ireland
Tel: 01732 897919
Email: karolina.barnes@euroflames.com
Web: www.euroflames.com ✍ **Product Type:** 6

FIREPLACE & TIMBER PRODUCTS
Unit 2 Holyrood Drive, Skippingdale Indstrial Estate,
Scunthorpe, Lincolnshire, DN15 8NN
Area of Operation: UK & Ireland
Tel: 01724 852888 **Fax:** 01724 277255
Email: ftprodcts@yahoo.com
Web: www.fireplaceandtimberproducts.co.uk
Product Type: 1, 2, 3, 4, 5, 6, 7, 8, 9,

FIREPLACE CONSULTANTS LTD
The Studio, The Old Rothschild Arms, Buckland Road,
Buckland, Aylesbury, Buckinghamshire, HP22 5LP
Area of Operation: Greater London, Midlands & Mid
Wales, South East England
Tel: 01296 632287 **Fax:** 01296 632287
Email: info@fireplaceconsultants.com
Web: www.fireplaceconsultants.com
Product Type: 1, 2, 3, 4, 5, 6, 7, 8,

GRENADIER FIRELIGHTERS LIMITED
Unit 3C, Barrowmore Enterprise Estate,
Great Barrow, Chester, Cheshire, CH3 7JS
Area of Operation: Worldwide
Tel: 01829 741649 **Fax:** 01829 741659
Email: enquiries@grenadier.co.uk
Web: www.grenadier.co.uk ✍
Product Type: 9

H W POULTER & SON
279 Fulham Road, Chelsea, London, SW10 9PZ
Area of Operation: Worldwide
Tel: 0207 352 7268
Fax: 0207 351 0984
Email: hwpoulterandson@btconnect.com
Web: www.hwpoulterandson.co.uk

JIM LAWRENCE LTD
Scotland Hall Farm, Stoke by Nayland,
Colchester, Essex, CO6 4QG
Area of Operation: UK (Excluding Ireland)
Tel: 01206 263459
Fax: 01206 262166
Email: sales@jim-lawrence.co.uk
Web: www.jim-lawrence.co.uk ✍
Product Type: 4, 5, 9

HEATING, PLUMBING & ELECTRICAL

KINGSWORTHY FOUNDRY CO LTD
London Road, Kingsworthy,
Winchester, Hampshire, SO23 7QG
Area of Operation: UK & Ireland
Tel: 01962 883776 **Fax:** 01962 882925
Email: kwf@fsbdial.co.uk
Web: www.kingsworthyfoundry.co.uk
Product Type: 2, 4, 5, 6

LEL FIREPLACES
Tre-Ifan Farmhouse, Caergeiliog,
Holyhead, Anglesey, LL65 3HP
Area of Operation: UK & Ireland
Tel: 01407 742240 **Fax:** 01407 742262
Email: sales@lel-fireplaces.com
Web: www.lel-fireplaces.com 🖱
Product Type: 1, 2, 4, 5, 6, 7, 8, 9
Other Info: ECO 🖐 ✍
Material Type: A) 1, 2, 3, 4, 5, 6, 7, 10, 15

LIVINGSTYLE.CO.UK
Bridge Street, Shotton, Flintshire, CH5 1DU
Area of Operation: UK (Excluding Ireland)
Tel: 0800 2989190 **Email:** info@livingstyle.co.uk
Web: www.livingstyle.co.uk 🖱
Product Type: 1, 2, 3, 4, 5, 6, 7, 8, 9

MARBLE HILL FIREPLACES
70-72 Richmond Road,
Twickenham, Greater London, TW1 3BE
Area of Operation: UK (Excluding Ireland)
Tel: 0208 892 1488 **Fax:** 0208 891 6591
Email: sales@marblehill.co.uk
Web: www.marblehill.co.uk **Product Type:** 1, 6

MARK RIPLEY FORGE & FIREPLACES
Robertsbridge, Bridge Bungalow,
East Sussex, TN32 5NY
Tel: 01580 880324 **Fax:** 01580 881927
Email: info@ripleyfireplaces.co.uk
Web: www.ripleyfireplaces.co.uk
Product Type: 1, 2, 5, 6

NIGEL TYAS HANDCRAFTED IRONWORK
Bullhouse Mill, Lee Lane, Millhouse Green,
Penistone, Sheffield, South Yorkshire, S36 6BE
Area of Operation: Worldwide
Tel: 01226 766618 **Email:** sales@nigeltyas.co.uk
Web: www.nigeltyas.co.uk

OAKLEAF
Unit A, Melbourne Mills, Chesham Street,
Keighley, West Yorkshire, BD21 4LG
Area of Operation: Worldwide
Tel: 01535 663274 **Fax:** 01535 661951
Email: jonathan@oakleaf.co.uk
Web: www.oakleaf.co.uk **Product Type:** 1

OLD FLAMES
30 Long Street, Easingwold,
York, North Yorkshire, YO61 3HT
Area of Operation: UK (Excluding Ireland)
Tel: 01347 821188 **Fax:** 01347 821188
Email: philiplynas@aol.com
Web: www.oldflames.co.uk 🖱

OLDE ENGLANDE REPRODUCTIONS
Fireplace Works, Normacot Road, Longton,
Stoke-on-Trent, Staffordshire, ST3 1PN
Area of Operation: UK (Excluding Ireland)
Tel: 01782 319350 **Fax:** 01782 593479
Email: sales@oerfireplaces.com
Web: www.oerfireplaces.com
Product Type: 1, 2, 4, 6

PENDRAGON FIREPLACES.COM
12 Market Street, Stourbridge,
West Midlands, DY8 1AD
Area of Operation: UK & Ireland
Tel: 01384 376441
Fax: 01384 376441
Email: sales@pendragonfireplaces.co.uk
Web: www.pendragonfireplaces.com 🖱
Product Type: 1, 6

PERCY DOUGHTY & CO
Imperial Point, Express Trading Estate, Stonehill
Road, Farnworth, Bolton, Lancashire, BL4 9TN
Area of Operation: Midlands & Mid Wales, North
West England and North Wales
Tel: 01204 868550 **Fax:** 01204 868551
Email: sales@percydoughty.com
Web: www.percydoughty.co.uk
Product Type: 1, 2, 4, 5, 6, 8

R W KNIGHT & SON LTD
Castle Farm, Marshfield,
Chippenham, Wiltshire, SN14 8HU
Area of Operation: Midlands & Mid Wales, South
East England, South West England and South Wales
Tel: 01225 891469 **Fax:** 01225 892369
Email: enquiries@knight-stoves.co.uk
Web: www.knight-stoves.co.uk
Product Type: 1, 2, 4, 5, 6, 8 **Material Type:** B) 2, 13

REAL FLAME
80 New Kings Road, London, SW6 4LT
Area of Operation: Worldwide
Tel: 0207 731 2704
Email: info@realflame.co.uk
Web: www.realflame.co.uk 🖱
Product Type: 1, 2, 4, 5, 6, 8 **Other Info:** ✍ 🖐

ROCKINGHAM FENDER SEATS
Grange Farm, Thorney, Peterborough,
Cambridgeshire, PE6 0PJ
Area of Operation: Worldwide
Tel: 01733 270233 **Fax:** 01733 270512
Email: info@fenderseats.com
Web: www.rockingham-fenderseats.com
Product Type: 2, 4

RUDLOE STONEWORKS LTD
Leafield Stoneyard, Potley Lane,
Corsham, Wiltshire, SN13 9RS
Area of Operation: UK & Ireland
Tel: 01225 816400
Fax: 01225 811343
Email: paul@rudloe-stone.com
Web: www.rudloe-stone.com
Product Type: 1, 2, 3, 4, 5, 6, 7

SCHIEDEL ISOKERN
14 Haviland Road, Ferndown Industrial Estate,
Wimborne, Dorset, BH21 7RF
Area of Operation: UK & Ireland
Tel: 01202 861650 **Fax:** 01202 861632
Email: sales@isokern.co.uk
Web: www.isokern.co.uk **Product Type:** 9

STOVAX LIMITED
Falcon Road, Sowton Industrial Estate,
Exeter, Devon, EX2 7LF
Area of Operation: UK & Ireland
Tel: 01392 474011 **Fax:** 01392 219932
Email: info@stovax.com **Web:** www.stovax.com
Product Type: 1, 2, 4, 5, 6, 7, 8, 9

THE CHIMNEY BALLOON COMAPNY
Victoria House, 209 Guildford Road,
Ash, Aldershot, Hampshire, GU12 6DX
Area of Operation: Worldwide
Tel: 01252 319325 **Fax:** 01252 322216
Product Type: 9

THE EDWARDIAN FIREPLACE COMPANY
Former All Saints Church, Armoury Way,
Wandsworth, London, SW18 1HZ
Area of Operation: UK & Ireland
Tel: 0208 870 0167 **Fax:** 0208 877 2847
Email: sales@edwardianfires.com
Web: www.edwardianfires.com
Product Type: 1, 2, 3, 4, 5, 6, 7, 8

THE FIREPLACE DOOR COMPANY
106 Alfreton Road, Sutton in Ashfield,
Nottinghamshire, NG17 1FQ
Area of Operation: Worldwide
Tel: 01623 477435 **Fax:** 01623 456734
Email: fdc@ntlworld.com **Product Type:** 7
Web: www.fireplacedoorcompany.co.uk

THE FIREPLACE GALLERY (UK) LTD
Clarence Road, Worksop, Nottinghamshire, S80 1QA
Area of Operation: UK & Ireland
Tel: 01909 500802 **Fax:** 01909 500810
Email: fireplacegallery@btinternet.com
Web: www.fireplacegallery.co.uk
Product Type: 1, 2, 6 **Other Info:** ECO ✍ 🖐
Material Type: A) 1, 2, 3, 4, 5, 7, 11

**THE FIREPLACE MARKETING
COMPANY LIMITED**
Haseley Manor, Birmingham Road,
Warwick, Warwickshire, CV35 7LS
Tel: 02476 247246 **Fax:** 02476 247266
Email: info@fireplace.co.uk
Web: www.fireplace.co.uk 🖱
Product Type: 1, 2, 3, 4, 5, 6, 7, 8

THEALE FIREPLACES RDG LTD
Milehouse Farm, Bath Road, Theale, Berkshire, RG7 5HJ
Area of Operation: UK (Excluding Ireland)
Tel: 0118 930 2232 **Fax:** 0118 932 3344
Email: mail@theale-fireplaces.com
Web: www.theale-fireplaces.co.uk
Product Type: 1, 2, 3, 4, 5, 6, 8

THORNHILL GALLERIES
No. 3, 19 Osiers Road, London, SW18 1NL
Area of Operation: Worldwide
Tel: 0208 874 2101 **Fax:** 0208 877 0313
Email: sales@thornhillgalleries.co.uk
Web: www.thornhillgalleries.co.uk

TRADITIONAL OAK & TIMBER COMPANY
PO Stores, Haywards Heath Road,
North Chailey, Nr Lewes, East Sussex, BN8 4EY
Area of Operation: Worldwide
Tel: 01825 723648 **Fax:** 01825 722215
Email: info@tradoak.co.uk
Web: www.tradoak.com **Product Type:** 1

ECO HEATING

KEY

PRODUCT TYPES: 1= Solar Powered
2 = Geothermal   3 = Wind Powered
4 = Other

SEE ALSO: ELECTRICAL - Renewable Energy
Sources

OTHER: ▽ Reclaimed 🖱 On-line shopping
✍ Bespoke 🖐 Hand-made ECO Ecological

ADM
Ling Fields, Gargrave Road, Skipton,
North Yorkshire, BD23 1UX
Area of Operation: Europe
Tel: 01756 701051 **Fax:** 01756 701076
Email: info@admsystems.co.uk
Web: www.admsystems.co.uk **Product Type:** 2

BORDERS UNDERFLOOR HEATING
26 Coopersknowe Crescent,
Galashiels, Borders, TD1 2DS
Area of Operation: UK & Ireland
Tel: 01896 668667 **Fax:** 01896 668678
Email: underfloor@btinternet.com
Web: www.bordersunderfloor.co.uk
Product Type: 1, 2, 4

**BRISTOL & SOMERSET RENEWABLE
ENERGY ADVICE SERVICE**
The CREATE Centre, Smeaton Road, Bristol, BS1 6XN
Area of Operation: South West England and South Wales
Tel: 0800 512012 **Fax:** 0117 929 9114
Email: info@cse.org.uk **Product Type:** 1, 2, 4
Web: www.cse.org.uk/renewables

BTU HEATING
38 Weyside Road, Guildford, Surrey, GU1 1JB
Area of Operation: South East England
Tel: 01483 590600 **Fax:** 01483 590601
Email: enquiries@btu-heating.com
Web: www.btu-group.com

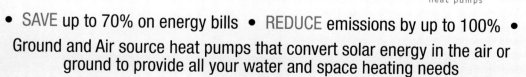
HEATING, PLUMBING & ELECTRICAL

BUILDING & DESIGN SOLUTIONS GERMANY
Auf den Haien 14, 55471 Sargenroth, Germany
Area of Operation: UK (Excluding Ireland)
Tel: 0049 6761 970 871
Email: mail@buildingdesign-germany.eu
Web: www.buildingdesign-germany.eu

CHELMER HEATING SERVICES LTD
Unit 12A, Baddow Park, West Hanningfield Road,
Chelmsford, Essex, CM2 7SY
Area of Operation: UK (Excluding Ireland)
Tel: 01245 471111 **Fax:** 01245 471117
Email: sales@chelmerheating.co.uk
Web: www.chelmerheating.co.uk
Product Type: 1, 2, 4

COMFORT AIR CONDITIONING LTD
Comfort Works, Newchapel Road,
Lingfield, Surrey, RH7 6LE
Area of Operation: East England, Greater London,
Midlands & Mid Wales, South East England, South
West England and South Wales
Tel: 01342 830600 **Fax:** 01342 830605
Email: info@comfort.uk.com
Web: www.comfort.uk.com
Product Type: 2, 3 **Other Info:** ✏

CONSERVATION ENGINEERING LTD
The Street, Troston, Bury St Edmunds, Suffolk, IP31 1EW
Area of Operation: UK & Ireland
Tel: 01359 269360
Email: anne@conservation-engineering.co.uk
Web: www.conservation-engineering.co.uk
Product Type: 1, 2

CONSTRUCTION RESOURCES
16 Great Guildford Street, London, SE1 0HS
Tel: 0207 450 2211
Fax: 0207 450 2212
Email: info@constructionresources.com
Web: www.constructionresources.com
Product Type: 1

DIMPLEX
Millbrook House, Grange Drive, Hedge End,
Southampton, Hampshire, SO30 2DF
Tel: 0845 600 5111 **Fax:** 01489 773050
Email: customer.services@glendimplex.com
Web: www.dimplex.co.uk

DIMPLEX
Area of Operation: UK & Ireland
Tel: 0845 600 5111
Fax: 01489 773050
Email: customer.services@glendimplex.com
Web: www.dimplex.co.uk
Product Type: 2

A range of over 50 heat pumps across ground
source, air source and water source, all supported
by an extensive network of heat pump installer
partners.

EARTHENERGY LIMITED
Falmouth Business Park, Bickland Water Road,
Falmouth, Cornwall, TR11 4SZ
Tel: 01326 310 650 **Fax:** 01326 211 071
Email: enquiries@earthenergy.co.uk
Web: www.earthenergy.co.uk
Product Type: 2

EARTHWISE SCOTLAND LTD
9a Netherton Business Centre,
Kemnay, Aberdeenshire, AB51 5LX
Area of Operation: UK (Excluding Ireland)
Tel: 01467 641640
Email: admin@earthwisescotland.co.uk
Web: www.earthwisescotland.co.uk
Product Type: 2

ECO HEAT PUMPS
Sheffield Technology Park, 60 Shirland Lane,
Sheffield, South Yorkshire, S9 3SP
Area of Operation: UK (Excluding Ireland)
Tel: 0114 296 2227 **Fax:** 0114 296 2229
Email: info@ecoheatpumps.co.uk
Web: www.ecoheatpumps.co.uk
Product Type: 2

ECO HOMETEC UK LTD
Unit 11E, Carcroft Enterprise Park, Carcroft,
Doncaster, South Yorkshire, DN6 8DD
Area of Operation: Europe
Tel: 01302 722266 **Fax:** 01302 728634
Email: Stephen@eco-hometec.co.uk
Web: www.eco-hometec.co.uk **Product Type:** 1, 2

ECO SYSTEMS IRELAND LTD
40 Glenshesk Road, Ballycastle, Co Antrim, BT54 6PH
Area of Operation: UK & Ireland
Tel: 02820 768708 **Fax:** 02820 769781
Email: info@ecosystemsireland.com
Web: www.ecosystemsireland.com
Product Type: 4

ECOLEC
Sharrocks Street, Wolverhampton,
West Midlands, WV1 3RP
Area of Operation: UK & Ireland
Tel: 01902 457575 **Fax:** 01902 457797
Email: sales@ecolec.co.uk
Web: www.ecolec.co.uk ✏
Product Type: 4

ECOWARM SOLAR LTD
Unit 9 Brickworks, Old Stowmarket Road,
Woolpit, Bury St. Edmunds, Suffolk, IP30 9QS
Area of Operation: East England
Tel: 0845 2309190 **Fax:** 0845 2309192
Email: enquiries@ecowarm-solar.co.uk
Web: www.ecowarm-solar.co.uk **Product Type:** 1

ENERGY AND ENVIRONMENT LTD
91 Claude Road, Chorlton, Manchester, M21 8DE
Area of Operation: UK & Ireland
Tel: 0161 881 1383
Email: mail@energyenv.co.uk
Web: www.energyenv.co.uk ✏
Product Type: 1, 2, 3, 4

ENERGY MASTER
Keltic Business Park, Unit 1 Clieveragh Industrial
Estate, Listowel, Ireland
Area of Operation: Ireland Only
Tel: 00353 (0)68 23864
Fax: 00353 (0)68 24533
Email: info@energymaster.ie
Web: www.energymaster.ie **Product Type:** 1, 2

ENERGY SUPERSTORE
3 Wellington Park, Belfast, BT9 6DJ
Area of Operation: UK & Ireland
Tel: 02890 388391
Email: info@energysuperstore.co.uk
Web: www.energysuperstore.co.uk
Product Type: 1, 2, 3

EUROFLAMES LIMITED
120 Suite, 70 Churchill Square,
Kings Hill, West Malling, Kent, ME19 4YU
Area of Operation: UK & Ireland
Tel: 01732 897919
Email: karolina.barnes@euroflames.com
Web: www.euroflames.com ✏
Product Type: 4 **Other Info:** ECO

HEATING, PLUMBING & ELECTRICAL

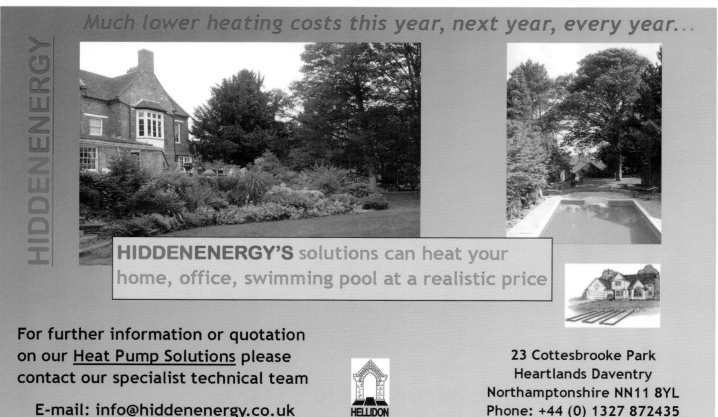

FERROLI UK
Lichfield Road, Branston Industrial Estate,
Burton Upon Trent, Staffordshire, DE14 3HD
Area of Operation: UK (Excluding Ireland)
Tel: 08707 282 882 **Fax:** 08707 282 883
Email: sales@ferroli.co.uk
Web: www.ferroli.co.uk
Product Type: 4

FIRSTLIGHT ENERGY LIMITED
Riverside Business Centre,
River Lawn Road, Tonbridge, Kent, TN9 1EP
Area of Operation: Europe
Tel: 01732 783534 **Fax:** 01732 362626
Email: info@firstlightenergy.com
Web: www.firstlightenergy.com
Product Type: 1, 2

FLOORWARMING (UK) LTD
Warwick Mill, Warwick Bridge,
Carlisle, Cumbria, CA4 8RR
Area of Operation: UK (Excluding Ireland)
Tel: 01228 631300 **Fax:** 01228 631333
Email: michael@floorwarming.co.uk
Web: www.floorwarming.co.uk
Product Type: 2

FOUNDATION FIREWOOD
Sells Close, High Street, Barley,
Royston, Hertfordshire, SG8 8HY
Area of Operation: UK (Excluding Ireland)
Tel: 01763 849468 **Fax:** 05600 765116
Email: info@fbcgroup.co.uk
Web: www.fbcgroup.co.uk
Product Type: 4

GEOTHERMAL INTERNATIONAL LIMITED
Spencer Court, 143 Albany Road,
Coventry, Warwickshire, CV5 6ND
Area of Operation: Europe
Tel: 02476 673 131 **Fax:** 02476 679 999
Email: info@geoheat.co.uk
Web: www.geoheat.co.uk **Product Type:** 2

GEOTHERMAL INTERNATIONAL LIMITED

Area of Operation: UK & Europe
Tel: 02476 673 131
Fax: 02476 679 999
Email: info@geoheat.co.uk
Web: www.geoheat.co.uk
Product Type: 2

UK's market leader in designing and installing ground source heating and cooling systems

Safe, reliable, energy-efficient heating and cooling for commercial and residential buildings

GRANT UK
Hopton House, Hopton Industrial Estate,
Devizes, Wiltshire, SN10 2EU
Area of Operation: UK (Excluding Ireland)
Tel: 0870 777 5553 **Fax:** 0870 777 5559
Email: sales@grantuk.com
Web: www.grantuk.com **Product Type:** 1

GREENSHOP SOLAR LTD
Hullbrook Garage, Bisley, Stroud,
Gloucestershire, GL6 7BX
Area of Operation: UK (Excluding Ireland)
Tel: 01452 772030 **Fax:** 01452 770115
Email: eddie@greenshop.co.uk
Web: www.greenshop-solar.co.uk
Product Type: 1 **Other Info:** ECO

HIDDEN ENERGY LIMITED
23 Cottesbrooke Park, Heartlands,
Daventry, Northamptonshire, NN11 8YL
Area of Operation: UK (Excluding Ireland)
Tel: 01327 872435 **Fax:** 01327 315287
Email: info@hiddenenergy.co.uk
Web: www.hiddenenergy.co.uk
Product Type: 1, 2 **Other Info:** ECO

ICE ENERGY
Unit 2 Oakfields House, Oakfields Industrial Estate,
Eynsham, Oxford, Oxfordshire, OX29 4TH
Area of Operation: UK (Excluding Ireland)
Tel: 01865 882202 **Fax:** 01865 882539
Email: info@iceenergy.co.uk
Web: www.iceenergy.co.uk **Product Type:** 2

INVISIBLE HEATING SYSTEMS
IHS Design Centre, Morefield Industrial Estate,
Ullapool, Highlands, IV26 2SR
Area of Operation: UK & Ireland
Tel: 01854 613161 **Fax:** 01854 613160
Email: design@invisibleheating.co.uk
Web: www.invisibleheating.com
Product Type: 1, 2, 4 **Other Info:**

IPPEC SYSTEMS LTD
66 Rea Street South, Birmingham,
West Midlands, B5 6LB
Area of Operation: UK & Ireland
Tel: 0121 622 4333 **Fax:** 0121 622 5768
Email: info@ippec.co.uk
Web: www.ippec.co.uk **Product Type:** 1

JONES NASH ECO HOMES
12 Lee Street, Louth, Lincolnshire, LN11 9HJ
Area of Operation: UK (Excluding Ireland)
Tel: 01507 609637 **Fax:** 01507 609637
Email: sd@jones-nash.co.uk
Web: www.eco-houses.co.uk **Product Type:** 1

KILTOX CONTRACTS LIMITED
Unit 6 Chiltonian Industrial Estate, 203 Manor Lane,
Lee, London, Greater London, SE12 0TX
Area of Operation: Worldwide
Tel: 0845 166 2040 **Fax:** 0845 166 2050
Email: info@kiltox.co.uk **Web:** www.kiltox.co.uk
Product Type: 4 **Other Info:** ECO

PARAGON SYSTEMS (SCOTLAND) LIMITED
The Office, Corbie Cottage, Maryculter,
Aberdeen, Aberdeenshire, AB12 5FT
Area of Operation: Scotland
Tel: 01224 735536 **Fax:** 01224 735537
Email: info@paragon-systems.co.uk
Web: www.paragon-systems.co.uk
Product Type: 2

POWERGEN
Newstead Court, Sherwood Park, Little Oak Drive,
Annesley, Nottinghamshire, NG15 0DR
Area of Operation: UK (Excluding Ireland)
Tel: 0800 068 6515
Email: whispergen@powergen.co.uk
Web: www.powergen.co.uk
Product Type: 4 **Other Info:** ECO

POWERTECH SOLAR LTD
21 Haviland Road, Forndown Industrial Estate,
Wimborne, Dorset, BH21 7RZ
Area of Operation: UK & Ireland
Tel: 01202 890234 **Fax:** 01202 876252
Email: sales@solar.org.uk
Web: www.solar.org.uk **Product Type:** 1, 2, 3, 4

RADIANT HEATING SOLUTIONS LTD
Mill Farm, Hougham, Grantham, Lincolnshire, NG32 2HZ
Tel: 01400 250572 **Fax:** 01400 251264
Email: sales@heating-solutions.biz
Web: www.heating-solutions.biz **Product Type:** 2

RAYOTEC LTD
Unit 3, Brooklands Close,
Sunbury on Thames, Surrey, TW16 7DX
Area of Operation: UK & Ireland
Tel: 01932 784848 **Fax:** 01932 784849
Email: info@rayotec.com
Web: www.rayotec.com **Product Type:** 1

RENEWABLE ENERGY OPTIONS LTD
Algo Business Centre, Glenearn Road,
Perth, Perth and Kinross, PH2 0NJ
Area of Operation: Scotland
Tel: 08700 801020 **Fax:** 08700 801021
Email: info@reoltd.co.uk
Web: www.reoltd.co.uk **Product Type:** 2

RIOMAY LTD
1 Birch Road, Eastbourne, East Sussex, BN23 6PL
Area of Operation: UK & Ireland
Tel: 01323 648641 **Fax:** 01323 720682
Email: tonybook@riomay.com
Web: www.riomay.com **Product Type:** 1
Other Info: ECO

SECON SOLAR
50 Business & Innovation Centre, Wearfield,
Sunderland, Tyne & Wear, SR5 2TA
Area of Operation: UK & Ireland
Tel: 0191 516 6554 **Fax:** 0191 516 6558
Email: info@seconsolar.com
Web: www.seconsolar.com **Product Type:** 1

SOLAR FIRES & FIREPLACES LTD
Alyn Works, Mostyn Road, Holywell, Flintshire, CH8 9DT
Area of Operation: UK & Ireland
Tel: 01745 561685 **Fax:** 01745 580987
Email: sales@solarfiresandfireplaces.co.uk
Web: www.solarfiresandfireplaces.co.uk
Product Type: 1

SOLAR SENSE
Energy Parc, Sandy Lane,
Pennard, Swansea, SA3 2EN
Area of Operation: Worldwide
Tel: 0845 458 3141 **Fax:** 0870 163 8620
Email: info@solarsense.co.uk
Web: www.solarsense.co.uk
Product Type: 1, 3 **Other Info:** ECO

SOLAR TWIN
2nd Floor, 50 Watergate Street,
Chester, Cheshire, CH1 2LA
Area of Operation: UK & Ireland
Tel: 01244 403407 **Fax:** 01244 403654
Email: hi@solartwin.com
Web: www.solartwin.com **Product Type:** 1

SOLARIS SOLAR ENERGY SYSTEMS
Macroom e-Business Park,
Bowl Road, Macroom, Co. Cork, Ireland
Tel: +353 (0)26 21014 **Fax:** +353 (0)26 46313
Email: info@solaris-energy.ie
Web: www.solaris-energy.ie **Product Type:** 1

SOLARUK
Unit 5, The Estate Yard Buildings,
Eridge Green Road, Tunbridge Wells, Kent, TN3 9JR
Area of Operation: Worldwide
Tel: 01892 667320 **Fax:** 01892 667622
Email: info@solaruk.net
Web: www.solaruk.net **Product Type:** 1

SOUTHERN SOLAR
Unit 6, Allington Farm, Allington Lane,
Offham, Lewes, East Sussex, BN7 3QL
Area of Operation: Greater London, South East
England, South West England and South Wales
Tel: 0845 456 9474 **Fax:** 01273 483928
Email: info@southernsolar.co.uk
Web: www.southernsolar.co.uk
Product Type: 1, 2 **Other Info:**

SPACE AIRCONDITIONING PLC
Willway Court, 1 Opus Park, Moorfield Road,
Guildford, Surrey, GU1 1SZ
Area of Operation: UK & Ireland
Tel: 01483 504883 **Fax:** 01483 574835
Email: marketing@spaceair.co.uk
Web: www.spaceair.co.uk **Product Type:** 3

STREBEL LTD
1F Albany Park Industrial Estate, Frimley Road,
Camberley, Surrey, GU16 7PB
Area of Operation: UK & Ireland
Tel: 01276 685422 **Fax:** 01276 685405
Email: info@strebel.co.uk
Web: www.strebel.co.uk **Product Type:** 1

SUNDWEL SOLAR LTD
Unit 1, Tower Road, Washington,
Sunderland, Tyne & Wear, NE37 2SH
Area of Operation: UK (Excluding Ireland)
Tel: 0191 4163001 **Fax:** 0191 4154297
Email: solar@sundwel.com
Web: www.sundwel.com
Product Type: 1

SUNUSER LTD
157 Buslingthorpe Lane, Leeds, West Yorkshire, LS7 2DQ
Area of Operation: UK (Excluding Ireland)
Tel: 0113 262 0261 **Fax:** 0113 262 3970
Email: solar@sunuser.co.uk
Web: www.sunuser.com
Product Type: 1 **Other Info:** ECO

THE GREEN SHOP
Cheltenham Road, Bisley, Nr Stroud,
Gloucestershire, GL6 7BX
Area of Operation: UK & Ireland
Tel: 01452 770629 **Fax:** 01452 770104
Email: paint@greenshop.co.uk
Web: www.greenshop.co.uk
Product Type: 1, 3

THE HEAT PUMP COMPANY UK LIMITED
2 Evett Close, Stocklake, Aylesbury,
Buckinghamshire, HP20 1DW
Area of Operation: UK (Excluding Ireland)
Tel: 07989 308812 **Fax:** 01494 565689
Email: sales@npsair.com
Web: www.npsair.com
Product Type: 2

THE ORGANIC ENERGY COMPANY
Severn Road, Welshpool, Powys, SY21 7AZ
Area of Operation: UK (Excluding Ireland)
Tel: 0845 4584076 **Fax:** 01938 559222
Email: hbenq@organicenergy.co.uk
Web: www.organicenergy.co.uk
Product Type: 1 **Other Info:** ECO

THE SOLAR TRADE ASSOCIATION
The National Energy Centre, Davy Avenue, Knowlhill,
Milton Keynes, Buckinghamshire, MK5 8NG
Area of Operation: UK (Excluding Ireland)
Tel: 01908 442290
Fax: 01908 665577
Email: enquiries@solartradeassociation.org.uk
Web: www.solartradeassociation.org.uk
Product Type: 1

VIESSMANN LTD
Hortonwood 30, Telford, Shropshire, TF1 7YP
Area of Operation: UK & Ireland
Tel: 01952 675000 **Fax:** 01952 675040
Email: info@viessmann.co.uk
Web: www.viessmann.co.uk
Product Type: 1, 2
Other Info: ECO

WALNEY RADIATORS
The Keys, Latchford Mews,
Wheathampstead, Hertfordshire, AL4 8BB
Area of Operation: Worldwide
Tel: 0870 733 0011 **Fax:** 0870 733 0016
Email: sara.hale@walneyuk.com
Web: www.walneyuk.com
Product Type: 3

WIND AND SUN LIMITED
Humber Marsh, Stoke Prior ,
Leominster, Herefordshire, HR6 0NR
Area of Operation: UK & Ireland
Tel: 01568 760671
Fax: 01568 760484
Email: info@windandsun.co.uk
Web: www.windandsun.co.uk

WORCESTER, BOSCH GROUP
Cotswold Way, Warndon, Worcester, WR4 9SW
Area of Operation: UK & Ireland
Tel: 01905 754624
Fax: 01905 754619
Email: general.worcester@uk.bosch.com
Web: www.worcester-bosch.co.uk
Product Type: 1, 2

HEATING, PLUMBING & ELECTRICAL

FIRE SURROUNDS

KEY

OTHER: ▽ Reclaimed 🛒 On-line shopping
🖋 Bespoke ✋ Hand-made ECO Ecological

A D CALVERT ARCHITECTURAL STONE SUPPLIES LTD
Smithy Lane, Grove Square,
Leyburn, North Yorkshire, DL8 5DZ
Area of Operation: UK & Ireland
Tel: 01969 622515 **Fax:** 01969 624345
Email: stone@calverts.co.uk
Web: www.calverts.co.uk

ARCHITECTURAL TREASURES
The Old Garage, Smarden Road,
Pluckley, Kent, TN27 0RF
Area of Operation: Worldwide
Tel: 01233 840004 **Fax:** 01233 840055
Email: info@architecturaltreasures.co.uk
Web: www.architecturaltreasures.co.uk

ASTRA CEILING FANS & LIGHTING
Unit 6, Lowercroft Industrial Estate,
Bury, Lancashire, BL8 3PA
Area of Operation: Europe
Tel: 0161 7973222 **Fax:** 0161 7973444
Email: support@astra247.com
Web: www.astra247.com 🛒

BRIGHTON MOULDINGS LTD
12 Preston Road, Brighton, East Sussex, BN1 4QF
Area of Operation: East England, Greater London, South East England, South West England and South Wales
Tel: 01273 622230 **Fax:** 01273 622240
Email: info@brightonmouldings.com
Web: www.brightonmouldings.com

BURLEY APPLIANCES LIMITED
Lands End Way, Oakham,
Rutland, Leicestershire, LE15 6RB
Area of Operation: Worldwide
Tel: 01572 756956 **Fax:** 01572 724390
Email: info@burley.co.uk **Web:** www.burley.co.uk

COE STONE LTD
Ty Gwyn, Abernant, Carmarthenshire, SA33 5RR
Area of Operation: UK & Ireland
Tel: 01267 281166 **Fax:** 01267 281166
Email: enquiries@olivercoe.com
Web: www.olivercoe.com

CONSORT EQUIPMENT PRODUCTS LTD
Thornton Industrial Estate, Milford Haven,
Pembrokeshire, SA73 2RT
Tel: 01646 692172 **Fax:** 01646 695195
Email: enquiries@consortepl.com
Web: www.consortepl.com

COSY ROOMS (COSY-HEATING.CO.UK)
17 Chiltern Way, North Hykeham,
Lincoln, Lincolnshire, LN6 9SY
Area of Operation: UK (Excluding Ireland)
Tel: 01522 696002 **Fax:** 01522 696002
Email: keith@cosy-rooms.com
Web: www.cosy-heating.co.uk 🛒

COUNTRY STYLE COOKERS
Unit 8, Oakleys Yard, Gatehouse Road, Rotherwas
Industrial Estate, Hereford, Herefordshire, HR2 6RQ
Tel: 01432 342351 **Fax:** 01432 371331
Email: sales@countrystyle-cookers.com
Web: www.countrystyle-cookers.com
Other Info: ▽

COUNTRYWIDE ENERGY
Defford, Earls Croome, Worcestershire, WR8 9DF
Area of Operation: Midlands & Mid Wales, South West England and South Wales
Tel: 01386 757333 **Fax:** 01386 757341
Email: juliejones-ford@countrywidefarmers.co.uk
Web: www.countrywidefarmers.co.uk

CROWN OIL
The Oil Centre, Bury New Road, Heap Bridge,
Bury, Greater Manchester, BL9 7HY
Area of Operation: UK (Excluding Ireland)
Tel: 0161 764 6622 **Fax:** 0161 762 7685
Email: sales@crownoil.co.uk
Web: www.crownoil.co.uk

EMSWORTH FIREPLACES LIMITED
Unit 3, Station Approach,
Emsworth, Hampshire, PO10 7PW
Area of Operation: Worldwide
Tel: 01243 373300 **Fax:** 01243 371023
Email: sales@emsworth.co.uk
Web: www.emsworth.co.uk 🛒
Other Info: 🖋 🛒 **Material Type:** A) 2, 3, 4, 5, 7, 9, 11

EURO BATHROOMS
102 Annareagh Road, Richhill, Co Armagh, BT61 9JY
Area of Operation: Ireland Only
Tel: 028 3887 9996 **Fax:** 028 3887 9996

FINESSE FIREPLACES
Finesse Fireplaces, Unit 3, The Tannery Industrial
Estate, Holt, Trowbridge, Wiltshire, BA14 6BB
Area of Operation: UK & Ireland
Tel: 01225 783558 **Fax:** 01225 783558
Email: neil@finesse-stone.fsnet.co.uk
Web: www.finessefireplaces.com

H W POULTER & SON
279 Fulham Road, Chelsea, London, SW10 9PZ
Area of Operation: Worldwide
Tel: 0207 352 7268 **Fax:** 0207 351 0984
Email: hwpoulterandson@btconnect.com
Web: www.hwpoulterandson.co.uk

HADDONSTONE LTD
The Forge House, East Haddon,
Northampton, Northamptonshire, NN6 8DB
Area of Operation: Worldwide
Tel: 01604 770711 **Fax:** 01604 770027
Email: info@haddonstone.co.uk
Web: www.haddonstone.com 🛒

HADDONSTONE

Area of Operation: Worldwide
Tel: 01604 770711 **Fax:** 01604 770027
Email: info@haddonstone.co.uk
Web: www.haddonstone.co.uk
Other Info: 🛒 ✋

Haddonstone manufacture cast stone fireplaces from the ornate and traditional to the stylish and contemporary. Extensive range of standard designs. Custom made designs also available.

JETMASTER FIRES LTD
Unit 2 Peacock Trading Estate, Goodwood Road,
Chandlers Ford, Eastleigh, Hampshire, SO50 4NT
Area of Operation: Europe
Tel: 0870 727 0105 **Fax:** 0870 727 0106
Email: jetmastersales@aol.com
Web: www.jetmaster.co.uk

LIONHEART HEATING SERVICES
PO Box 741, Harworth Park,
Doncaster, South Yorkshire, DN11 8WY
Area of Operation: UK (Excluding Ireland)
Tel: 01302 755200 **Fax:** 01302 750155
Email: enquiries@lionheartheating.co.uk
Web: www.lionheartheating.co.uk 🛒

NICAN STONE LTD
Bank House, School Lane,
Bronington, Shropshire, SY13 3HN
Area of Operation: UK (Excluding Ireland)
Tel: 01948 780670 **Fax:** 01948 780679
Email: enquiries@nicanstone.com
Web: www.nicanstone.com

OLD FLAMES
30 Long Street, Easingwold,
York, North Yorkshire, YO61 3HT
Area of Operation: UK (Excluding Ireland)
Tel: 01347 821188
Fax: 01347 821188
Email: philiplynas@aol.com
Web: www.oldflames.co.uk 🛒

PICTURE HOUSE CABINETS
Cherry House, Oakcroft Road,
West Byfleet, Surrey, KT10 0JH
Area of Operation: UK (Excluding Ireland)
Tel: 01932 345184
Fax: 01932 402128
Email: info@picturehousecabinets.com
Web: www.picturehousecabinets.com

PINCKNEY GREEN STONEWORKS
10 Ferndale Road, Larkhall,
Bath, Somerset, BA1 6TD
Area of Operation: UK & Ireland
Tel: 01225 851105 **Fax:** 01225 851105
Email: sales@pinckneygreen.co.uk
Web: www.pinckneygreen.co.uk

ROBERT AAGAARD & CO
Frogmire House, Stockwell Road,
Knaresborough, North Yorkshire, HG5 0JP
Area of Operation: UK (Excluding Ireland)
Tel: 01423 864805 **Fax:** 01423 869356
Email: info@robertaagaard.co.uk
Web: www.robertaagaard.co.uk

STONE ESSENTIALS CO LTD
Mount Spring Works, Off Burnley Road East,
Rossendale, Lancashire, BB4 9LA
Area of Operation: UK (Excluding Ireland)
Tel: 01706 210605
Fax: 01706 228707
Email: ken.howe@btconnect.com
Web: www.stone-essentials.co.uk

TEMPLESTONE
Station Wharf, Castle Cary, Somerset, BA7 7PE
Area of Operation: UK & Ireland
Tel: 01963 350242 **Fax:** 01963 350258
Email: sales@templestone.co.uk
Web: www.templestone.co.uk

THE ANTIQUE FIREPLACE COMPANY
Jasmine Cottage, Prees Green,
Near Whitchurch, Shropshire, SY13 2BL
Area of Operation: Worldwide
Tel: 01948 840666
Email: sales@antiquefireplacecompany.co.uk
Web: www.antiquefireplacecompany.co.uk 🛒

THE EDWARDIAN FIREPLACE COMPANY
Former All Saints Church, Armoury Way,
Wandsworth, London, SW18 1HZ
Area of Operation: UK & Ireland
Tel: 0208 870 0167 **Fax:** 0208 877 2847
Email: sales@edwardianfires.com
Web: www.edwardianfires.com **Other Info:** 🖋 ✋

THE FIREPLACE GALLERY (UK) LTD
Clarence Road, Worksop, Nottinghamshire, S80 1QA
Area of Operation: UK & Ireland
Tel: 01909 500802
Fax: 01909 500810
Email: fireplacegallery@btinternet.com
Web: www.fireplacegallery.co.uk

THE JRG GROUP
3 Crompton Way, North Newmoor Industrial Estate,
Irvine, Ayrshire, KA11 4HU
Area of Operation: Europe
Tel: 0871 200 8080 **Fax:** 01294 211 222
Email: chris@jrgfiresurrounds.com
Web: www.jrggroup.com

THE MASON'S YARD
Penhenllan, Cusop, Hay on Wye,
Herefordshire, HR3 5TE
Area of Operation: UK (Excluding Ireland)
Tel: 01497 821333
Email: hugh@themasonsyard.co.uk
Web: www.themasonsyard.co.uk

THORNHILL GALLERIES
No. 3, 19 Osiers Road, London, SW18 1NL
Area of Operation: Worldwide
Tel: 0208 874 2101
Fax: 0208 877 0313
Email: sales@thornhillgalleries.co.uk
Web: www.thornhillgalleries.co.uk
Material Type: B) 2

HEATING CONTROLS AND VALVES

KEY

PRODUCT TYPES: 1= Thermostats
2 = Time Switches   3 = TRVs
4 = UFH Controls   5 = Zone Controls
6 = Weather Compensation / Optimisation
7 = Other

OTHER: ▽ Reclaimed 🛒 On-line shopping
🖋 Bespoke ✋ Hand-made ECO Ecological

AESTUS
Unit 5 Strawberry Lane Industrial Estate, Strawberry
Lane, Willenhall, West Midlands, WV13 3RS
Area of Operation: UK & Ireland
Tel: 0870 403 0115 **Fax:** 0870 403 0116
Email: melissa@publicityengineers.com

AUTRON PRODUCTS LTD
Unit 17 Second Avenue, Bluebridge Industrial Estate,
Halstead, Essex, CO9 2SU
Tel: 01787 473964 **Fax:** 01787 474061
Email: sales@autron.co.uk
Web: www.autron.co.uk **Product Type:** 3

BAXI HEATING UK
Brooks House, Coventry Road,
Warwick, Warwickshire, CV34 4LL
Area of Operation: UK & Ireland
Tel: 08706 060780 **Fax:** 01926 410006
Web: www.baxi.co.uk
Product Type: 1, 2, 5

BEGETUBE UK LTD
8 Carsegate Road South, Inverness, Highlands, IV3 8LL
Area of Operation: UK & Ireland
Tel: 01463 246600   **Fax:** 01463 246624
Email: rory@begetube.co.uk
Web: www.begetube-uk.co.uk 🛒
Product Type: 1, 2, 3, 4, 5, 6

BISQUE LIMITED
23 Queen Square, Bath, Somerset, BA1 2HX
Area of Operation: Worldwide
Tel: 01225 478500 **Fax:** 01225 478581
Email: marketing@bisque.co.uk
Web: www.bisque.co.uk **Product Type:** 3

BORDERS UNDERFLOOR HEATING
26 Coopersknowe Crescent,
Galashiels, Borders, TD1 2DS
Area of Operation: UK & Ireland
Tel: 01896 668667 **Fax:** 01896 668678
Email: underfloor@btinternet.com
Web: www.bordersunderfloor.co.uk
Product Type: 1, 2, 4, 5, 6

BTU HEATING
38 Weyside Road, Guildford, Surrey, GU1 1JB
Area of Operation: South East England
Tel: 01483 590600 **Fax:** 01483 590601
Email: enquiries@btu-heating.com
Web: www.btu-group.com

CHATSWORTH HEATING PRODUCTS LTD
Unit B Watchmoor Point, Camberley, Surrey, GU15 3EX
Tel: 01276 605880 **Fax:** 01276 605881
Email: enquiries@chatsworth-heating.co.uk
Web: www.chatsworth-heating.co.uk

CONTINENTAL UNDERFLOOR HEATING
Continental House, Kings Hill, Bude, Cornwall, EX23 0LU
Area of Operation: Europe
Tel: 0845 108 1204
Fax: 0845 108 1205
Email: info@continental-ufh.co.uk
Web: www.continental-ufh.co.uk
Product Type: 1, 2, 4, 5, 6 **Other Info:** ECO

COPPERJOB LTD
PO Box 110, Plymouth, Devon, PL7 2ZS
Area of Operation: UK & Ireland
Email: info@copperjob.com
Web: www.centralheatingrepair.co.uk
Product Type: 1, 2, 3, 5, 6

COPPERJOB LTD
Area of Operation: UK & Ireland
Tel: See website
Email: info@copperjob.com
Web: www.centralheatingrepair.co.uk
Product Type: 1, 2, 3, 5, 6

The Industry's newest publication designed to aid installers and engineers of all experience levels. This superb manual helps you to understand domestic Central Heating and Hot Water Systems, quickly trace faults and effect professional repairs. Available online at: www.centralheatingrepair.co.uk

COSY ROOMS (COSY-HEATING.CO.UK)
17 Chiltern Way, North Hykeham,
Lincoln, Lincolnshire, LN6 9SY
Area of Operation: UK (Excluding Ireland)
Tel: 01522 696002 **Fax:** 01522 696002
Email: keith@cosy-rooms.com
Web: www.cosy-heating.co.uk
Product Type: 3

DANFOSS RANDALL LTD
Ampthill Road, Bedford, Bedfordshire, MK42 9ER
Area of Operation: UK & Ireland
Tel: 0845 121 7400 **Fax:** 0845 121 7515
Email: danfossrandall@danfoss.com
Web: www.danfoss-randall.co.uk
Product Type: 1, 2, 3, 4, 5, 6

Don't Forget !

You can use the materials key at the beginning of this Handbook to get much more information from a company's listing.

DCD SYSTEMS LTD
43 Howards Thicket, Gerrards Cross,
Buckinghamshire, SL9 7NU
Area of Operation: UK & Ireland
Tel: 01753 882028 **Fax:** 01753 882029
Email: peter@dcd.co.uk **Web:** www.dcd.co.uk

DCD SYSTEMS LTD
Area of Operation: UK & Ireland
Tel: 01753 882028
Fax: 01753 882029
Email: peter@dcd.co.uk
Web: www.dcd.co.uk

Intelligent Heating Controller with full weather compensating optimisation and room temperature control to within 0.1°C. For water, radiator, underfloor and other heating systems.

E. RICHARDS
PO Box 1115, Winscombe, Somerset, BS25 1WA
Area of Operation: UK & Ireland
Tel: 0845 330 8859 **Fax:** 0845 330 7260
Email: info@e-richards.co.uk
Web: www.e-richards.co.uk

ECO HOMETEC UK LTD
Unit 11E, Carcroft Enterprise Park, Carcroft,
Doncaster, South Yorkshire, DN6 8DD
Tel: 01302 722266 **Fax:** 01302 728634
Email: Stephen@eco-hometec.co.uk
Web: www.eco-hometec.co.uk
Product Type: 1, 2, 4, 5, 6

ECOLEC
Sharrocks Street, Wolverhampton, WV1 3RP
Area of Operation: UK & Ireland
Tel: 01902 457575 **Fax:** 01902 457797
Email: sales@ecolec.co.uk
Web: www.ecolec.co.uk **Product Type:** 1, 2, 5, 7

EURO BATHROOMS
102 Annareagh Road, Richhill, Co Armagh, BT61 9JY
Area of Operation: Ireland Only **Tel:** 028 3887 9996
Fax: 028 3887 9996 **Product Type:** 1, 2, 4, 5

FEATURE RADIATORS
Bingley Railway Station, Wellington Street,
Bingley, West Yorkshire, BD16 2NB
Area of Operation: UK (Excluding Ireland)
Tel: 01274 567789 **Fax:** 01274 561183
Email: contactus@featureradiators.com
Web: www.featureradiators.com
Product Type: 3

FLOORWARMING (UK) LTD
Warwick Mill, Warwick Bridge,
Carlisle, Cumbria, CA4 8RR
Area of Operation: UK (Excluding Ireland)
Tel: 01228 631300 **Fax:** 01228 631333
Email: michael@floorwarming.co.uk
Web: www.floorwarming.co.uk
Product Type: 1, 2, 3, 4, 5, 6, 7

GEMINOX UK
Blenheim House, 1 Blenheim Road,
Epsom, Surrey, KT19 9AP
Area of Operation: UK & Ireland
Tel: 01372 722277 **Fax:** 01372 744477
Email: sales@geminox-uk.com
Web: www.geminox-uk.com
Product Type: 4, 6

GOTO PLUMBING
Area of Operation: UK & Ireland
Email: sales@gotoplumbing.co.uk
Web: www.gotoplumbing.co.uk

GRANT ENGINEERING LTD
Crinkle, Birr, Co. Offaly, Ireland
Area of Operation: Ireland Only
Tel: 00 353 05791 20089 **Fax:** 00 353 05791 21060
Email: info@grantengineering.ie
Web: www.grantengineering.ie **Product Type:** 1

GRUNDFOS PUMPS LTD
Grovebury Road, Leighton Buzzard,
Bedfordshire, LU7 4TL
Area of Operation: Worldwide
Tel: 01525 850000 **Fax:** 01525 850011
Email: uk_sales@grundfos.com
Web: www.grundfos.co.uk **Product Type:** 7

HALSTEAD BOILERS LIMITED
20/22n First Avenue, Bluebridge Industrial Estate,
Halstead, Essex, CO9 2EX
Area of Operation: UK & Ireland
Tel: 01787 272800 **Fax:** 01787 474588
Email: sales@halsteadboilers.co.uk
Web: www.halsteadboilers.co.uk **Product Type:** 1, 7

HEPWORTH PLUMBING PRODUCTS
Edlington Lane, Edlington, Doncaster,
South Yorkshire, DN12 1BY
Area of Operation: Worldwide
Tel: 01709 856300 **Fax:** 01709 856301
Email: info@hepworth.co.uk
Web: www.hepworth.co.uk
Product Type: 4 **Other Info:**

HONEYWELL CONTROL SYSTEMS LTD
Honeywell House, Arlington Business Park, Bracknell,
Berkshire, RG12 1EB
Area of Operation: Worldwide
Tel: 01344 656000 **Fax:** 01344 656054
Email: literature@honeywell.com
Web: www.honeywelluk.com
Product Type: 1, 2, 3, 4, 5, 6, 7

INTERACTIVE HOMES LTD
Unit 43, Centerprise House, New Greenham Park,
Thatcham, Berkshire, RG19 6HP
Area of Operation: UK (Excluding Ireland)
Tel: 01635 49111 **Fax:** 01635 40735
Email: sales@interactivehomes.co.uk
Web: www.interactivehomes.co.uk
Product Type: 1, 2, 3, 4, 5, 6, 7

JIS EUROPE (SUSSEX RANGE)
Warehouse 2, Nash Lane, Scaynes Hill, Haywards
Heath, West Sussex, RH17 7NJ
Area of Operation: Europe
Tel: 01444 831200 **Fax:** 01444 831900
Email: info@jiseurope.co.uk
Web: www.sussexrange.co.uk
Product Type: 1, 3

KV RADIATORS
6 Postle Close, Kilsby, Rugby,
Warwickshire, CV23 8YG
Area of Operation: UK & Ireland
Tel: 01788 823286 **Fax:** 01788 823002
Email: solutions@kvradiators.com
Web: www.kvradiators.com
Product Type: 3, 7

LEEMICK LTD
79 Windermere Drive, Rainham, Kent, ME8 9DX
Area of Operation: UK (Excluding Ireland)
Tel: 01634 351666 **Fax:** 01634 351666
Email: sales@leemick.co.uk
Web: www.leemick.co.uk
Product Type: 1, 2, 4, 5, 6, 7 **Other Info:**

LIONHEART HEATING SERVICES
PO Box 741, Harworth Park,
Doncaster, South Yorkshire, DN11 8WY
Area of Operation: UK (Excluding Ireland)
Tel: 01302 755200
Fax: 01302 750155
Email: enquiries@lionheartheating.co.uk
Web: www.lionheartheating.co.uk

LOBLITE ELECTRIC LTD
Third Avenue, Team Valley Trading Estate,
Gateshead, Tyne & Wear, NE11 0QQ
Area of Operation: Europe
Tel: 0191 487 8103 **Fax:** 0191 491 5541
Email: sales@heatec-rads.com
Web: www.heatec-rads.com
Product Type: 1, 5 **Other Info:** ECO

PARAGON SYSTEMS (SCOTLAND) LIMITED
The Office, Corbie Cottage, Maryculter,
Aberdeen, Aberdeenshire, AB12 5FT
Area of Operation: Scotland
Tel: 01224 735536
Fax: 01224 735537
Email: info@paragon-systems.co.uk
Web: www.paragon-systems.co.uk
Product Type: 1, 4, 5, 6

SOUTHERN SOLAR
Unit 6, Allington Farm, Allington Lane,
Offham, Lewes, East Sussex, BN7 3QL
Area of Operation: Greater London, South East
England, South West England and South Wales
Tel: 0845 456 9474 **Fax:** 01273 483928
Email: info@southernsolar.co.uk
Web: www.southernsolar.co.uk
Product Type: 1, 3, 5

SYSTEMAIR LTD
72 Chestom Road, Birmingham, B7 5EJ
Area of Operation: Worldwide
Tel: 0121 3220850 **Fax:** 0121 3220859
Email: sales@systemair.co.uk
Web: www.systemair.co.uk
Product Type: 1, 2, 3, 4, 5, 6, 7

THERMO-FLOOR (GB) LTD
Unit 1 Babsham Farm, Chichester Road,
Bognor Regis, West Sussex, PO21 5EL
Area of Operation: UK (Excluding Ireland)
Tel: 01243 822058
Fax: 01243 860379
Email: sales@thermo-floor.co.uk
Web: www.thermo-floor.co.uk
Product Type: 1, 2, 4, 5, 6, 7
Other Info:

UNIFIX LTD
St Georges House, Grove Lane,
Smethwick, Birmingham,
West Midlands, B66 2QT
Area of Operation: Europe
Tel: 0800 096 1110 **Fax:** 0800 096 1115
Email: sales@unifix.com
Web: www.unifix-online.co.uk
Product Type: 1, 2, 3

VELTA-THE UNDERFLOOR HEATING COMPANY
Unit 1B Denby Dale Industrial Park,
Wakefield Road, Denby Dale,
Huddersfield, West Yorkshire, HD8 8QH
Area of Operation: Worldwide
Tel: 01484 860811
Fax: 01484 865775
Email: info@velta-uk.com
Web: www.u-h-c.co.uk
Product Type: 1, 2, 4, 5, 6, 7

VOKERA LTD
Borderlake House, Unit 7 Riverside Industrial Estate,
London Colney, Hertfordshire, AL2 1HG
Area of Operation: UK & Ireland
Tel: 0870 333 0220
Fax: 01727 744004
Email: enquiries@vokera.co.uk
Web: www.vokera.co.uk
Product Type: 1, 2, 6

WALNEY RADIATORS
The Keys, Latchford Mews,
Wheathampstead, Hertfordshire, AL 8BB
Area of Operation: Worldwide
Tel: 0870 733 0011
Fax: 0870 733 0016
Email: sara.hale@walneyuk.com
Web: www.walneyuk.com
Product Type: 3, 7

HEATING, PLUMBING & ELECTRICAL

WARMROOMS
24 Corncroft Lane, St Leonards Park,
Gloucester, Gloucestershire, GL4 6XU
Area of Operation: UK (Excluding Ireland)
Tel: 01452 304460
Fax: 01452 304460
Email: sales@warmrooms.co.uk
Web: www.warmrooms.co.uk ⏎
Product Type: 3

WAVIN PLASTICS LTD (OSMA)
Parsonage Way, Chippenham, Wiltshire, SN15 5PN
Area of Operation: UK (Excluding Ireland)
Tel: 01249 766 600
Fax: 01249 443 286
Email: info@wavin.co.uk
Web: www.wavin.co.uk
Product Type: 4, 5

WORCESTER, BOSCH GROUP
Cotswold Way, Warndon,
Worcester, Worcestershire, WR4 9SW
Area of Operation: UK & Ireland
Tel: 01905 754624
Fax: 01905 754619
Email: general.worcester@uk.bosch.com
Web: www.worcester-bosch.co.uk
Product Type: 1, 6

YORKSHIRE FITTINGS
PO Box 166, Leeds, West Yorkshire, LS10 1NA
Tel: 0113 270 1104
Fax: 0113 271 5275
Email: info@yorkshirefittings.co.uk
Web: www.yorkshirefittings.co.uk
Product Type: 3

FLUES AND HEATING ACCESSORIES

KEY

PRODUCT TYPES: 1= Flue Liners
2 = Fan Flues   3 = Boiler Flues
4 = Flue Pipes   5 = Other

OTHER: ▽ Reclaimed ⏎ On-line shopping
✏ Bespoke ✋ Hand-made ECO Ecological

ALPHA BOILERS
Nepicar House, London Road,
Wrotham Heath, Kent, TN15 7RS
Area of Operation: UK (Excluding Ireland)
Tel: 01732 783000 **Fax:** 01732 783080
Email: info@alphatherm.co.uk
Web: www.alpha-boilers.com
Product Type: 3, 4

ANKI CHIMNEY SYSTEMS
Bishops Way, Newport, Isle of Wight, PO30 5WS
Area of Operation: UK (Excluding Ireland)
Tel: 01983 527997 **Fax:** 01983 537788
Email: anki@ajwells.co.uk
Web: www.anki.co.uk **Product Type:** 1

APPLIED HEATING SERVICES LTD
9 Rosse Close, Parsons Industrial Estate,
Washington, Tyne & Wear, NE38 1ET
Area of Operation: North East England
Tel: 0191 4177604
Fax: 0191 4171549
Email: georgecossey1@btconnect.com
Web: www.appliedheat.co.uk
Product Type: 3

CHARNWOOD STOVES & FIRES
Bishops Way, Newport, Isle of Wight, PO30 5WS
Area of Operation: Worldwide
Tel: 01983 537780
Fax: 01983 537788
Email: charnwood@ajwells.co.uk
Web: www.charnwood.com ⏎
Product Type: 1, 3, 4, 5
Other Info: ECO

CHARNWOOD STOVES & ANKI CHIMNEY SYSTEMS
Area of Operation: Worldwide
Tel: 01983 537780 **Fax:** 01983 537788
Email: charnwood@ajwells.co.uk
Web: www.charnwood.com or www.anki.co.uk
Product Type: 1,3, 4, 5

Exceptional wood burning stoves and pumice chimney systems for the perfect combination in highly efficient home heating. Ideal for new build and installation into existing properties.

CLEARVIEW STOVES
More Works, Squilver Hill,
Bishops Castle, Shropshire, SY9 5HH
Area of Operation: Worldwide
Tel: 01588 650401
Fax: 01588 650493
Email: mail@clearviewstoves.com
Web: www.clearviewstoves.com
Product Type: 1, 2, 4

DUNBRIK (YORKS) LIMITED
Ferry Lane, Stanley Ferry,
Wakefield, West Yorkshire, WF3 4LT
Area of Operation: UK & Ireland
Tel: 01924 373694
Fax: 01924 483459
Email: tech@dunbrik.co.uk
Web: www.dunbrik.co.uk
Product Type: 1, 4, 5

ECO HOMETEC UK LTD
Unit 11E, Carcroft Enterprise Park, Carcroft,
Doncaster, South Yorkshire, DN6 8DD
Area of Operation: Europe
Tel: 01302 722266
Fax: 01302 728634
Email: stephen@eco-hometec.co.uk
Web: www.eco-hometec.co.uk
Product Type: 2, 3, 4

EMSWORTH FIREPLACES LIMITED
Unit 3, Station Approach,
Emsworth, Hampshire , PO10 7PW
Area of Operation: Worldwide
Tel: 01243 373300
Fax: 01243 371023
Email: sales@emsworth.co.uk
Web: www.emsworth.co.uk ⏎
Product Type: 1, 2

EUROFLAMES LIMITED
120 Suite, 70 Churchill Square,
Kings Hill, West Malling, Kent, ME19 4YU
Area of Operation: UK & Ireland
Tel: 01732 897919
Email: karolina.barnes@euroflames.com
Web: www.euroflames.com ⏎
Product Type: 4, 5

EXHAUSTO
Unit 3 Lancaster Court, Coronation Road,
Cressex Business Park, High Wycombe,
Buckinghamshire, HP12 3TD
Area of Operation: UK & Ireland
Tel: 01494 465166
Fax: 01494 465163
Email: info@exhausto.co.uk
Web: www.exhausto.co.uk
Product Type: 2, 3, 4

FERROLI UK
Lichfield Road, Branston Industrial Estate,
Burton Upon Trent, Staffordshire, DE14 3HD
Tel: 08707 282 882 **Fax:** 08707 282 883
Email: sales@ferroli.co.uk
Web: www.ferroli.co.uk **Product Type:** 3

FIREPLACE CONSULTANTS LTD
The Studio, The Old Rothschild Arms,
Buckland Road, Buckland, Aylesbury,
Buckinghamshire, HP22 5LP
Area of Operation: Greater London, Midlands & Mid Wales, South East England
Tel: 01296 632287
Fax: 01296 632287
Email: info@fireplaceconsultants.com
Web: www.fireplaceconsultants.com
Product Type: 1, 2, 4

GEMINOX UK
Blenheim House, 1 Blenheim Road,
Epsom, Surrey, KT19 9AP
Area of Operation: UK & Ireland
Tel: 01372 722277 **Fax:** 01372 744477
Email: sales@geminox-uk.com
Web: www.geminox-uk.com
Product Type: 1, 3, 4

GRANT ENGINEERING LTD
Crinkle, Birr, Co. Offaly, Ireland
Area of Operation: Ireland Only
Tel: 00 353 05791 20089
Fax: 00 353 05791 21060
Email: info@grantengineering.ie
Web: www.grantengineering.ie
Product Type: 3

GRANT UK
Hopton House, Hopton Industrial Estate,
Devizes, Wiltshire, SN10 2EU
Area of Operation: UK (Excluding Ireland)
Tel: 0870 777 5553 **Fax:** 0870 777 5559
Email: sales@grantuk.com
Web: www.grantuk.com
Product Type: 3

HALSTEAD BOILERS LIMITED
20/22n First Avenue, Bluebridge Industrial Estate,
Halstead, Essex, CO9 2EX
Area of Operation: UK & Ireland
Tel: 01787 272800
Fax: 01787 474588
Email: sales@halsteadboilers.co.uk
Web: www.halsteadboilers.co.uk
Product Type: 1, 3

HANSON BUILDING PRODUCTS
Stewartby, Bedford, Bedfordshire, MK43 9LZ
Area of Operation: Worldwide
Tel: 08705 258258 **Fax:** 01234 762040
Email: info@hansonbp.com **Web:** www.hanson.biz

HANSON RED BANK MANUFACTURING COMPANY LIMITED
Measham, Swadlincote, Derbyshire, DE12 7EL
Tel: 01530 270333
Fax: 01530 273667
Email: sales@redbankmfg.co.uk
Web: www.redbankmfg.co.uk
Product Type: 1

LIONHEART HEATING SERVICES
PO Box 741, Harworth Park, Doncaster,
South Yorkshire, DN11 8WY
Tel: 01302 755200
Fax: 01302 750155
Email: enquiries@lionheartheating.co.uk
Web: www.lionheartheating.co.uk ⏎

MHS RADIATORS & BOILERS
3 Juniper West, Fenton Way, Southfields Business
Park, Basildon, Essex, SS15 6TD
Area of Operation: UK & Ireland
Tel: 01268 546700
Fax: 01268 888250
Email: sales@modular-heating-group.co.uk
Web: www.mhsradiators.com
Product Type: 3

PERCY DOUGHTY & CO
Imperial Point, Express Trading Estate, Stonehill
Road, Farnworth, Bolton, Lancashire, BL4 9TN
Area of Operation: Midlands & Mid Wales, North
West England and North Wales
Tel: 01204 868550 **Fax:** 01204 868551
Email: sales@percydoughty.com
Web: www.percydoughty.co.uk
Product Type: 4

POUJOULAT UK LTD
Unit 1 Quadrum Park, Old Portsmouth Road,
Guildford, Surrey, GU3 1LU
Area of Operation: UK & Ireland
Tel: 01483 461700
Fax: 01483 533435
Email: sales@poujoulat.co.uk
Web: www.poujoulat.co.uk
Product Type: 1, 4

R W KNIGHT & SON LTD
Castle Farm, Marshfield,
Chippenham, Wiltshire, SN14 8HU
Area of Operation: Midlands & Mid Wales, South
East England, South West England and South Wales
Tel: 01225 891469
Fax: 01225 892369
Email: enquiries@knight-stoves.co.uk
Web: www.knight-stoves.co.uk
Product Type: 1, 2, 3, 4

SCALGON
115 Park Lane, Reading, Berkshire, RG31 4DR
Area of Operation: UK (Excluding Ireland)
Tel: 0118 9424981 **Web:** www.scalgon.co.uk
Email: postmaster@scalgon.co.uk

SCHIEDEL ISOKERN
14 Haviland Road, Ferndown Industrial Estate,
Wimborne, Dorset, BH21 7RF
Area of Operation: UK & Ireland
Tel: 01202 861650 **Fax:** 01202 861632
Email: sales@isokern.co.uk
Web: www.isokern.co.uk
Product Type: 1, 4

SCHIEDEL ISOKERN
Area of Operation: UK & Ireland
Tel: 01202 861650
Fax: 01202 861632
Email: sales@isokern.co.uk
Web: www.isokern.co.uk
Product Type: 1, 4
Secondary Heating under the new Document L. Schiedel Isokern has just released new information on how to minimise the carbon emissions from secondary heating and maintain a real fire at the heart of your home. Schiedel Isokern offer a range of efficient & effective chimney systems to suit all modern appliances.

STOVES ON LINE LTD
Capton, Dartmouth, Devon, TQ6 0JE
Tel: 0845 226 5754
Fax: 0870 220 0920
Email: info@stovesonline.com
Web: www.stovesonline.co.uk

THE CHIMNEY BALLOON COMPANY
Victoria House, 209 Guildford Road,
Ash, Aldershot, Hampshire, GU12 6DX
Area of Operation: Worldwide
Tel: 01252 319325
Fax: 01252 322216

THEALE FIREPLACES RDG LTD
Milehouse Farm, Bath Road,
Theale, Berkshire, RG7 5HJ
Area of Operation: UK (Excluding Ireland)
Tel: 0118 930 2232 **Fax:** 0118 932 3344
Email: mail@theale-fireplaces.co.uk
Web: www.theale-fireplaces.co.uk **Product Type:** 1

THERMOCRETE
Mortimer Street, Bradford, West Yorkshire, BD8 9RL
Area of Operation: Worldwide
Tel: 01274 544442 **Fax:** 01274 484448
Email: info@thermocrete.com
Web: www.thermocrete.com **Product Type:** 1, 3

TRIANCO HEATING PRODUCTS LIMITED
Thorncliffe, Chapeltown, Sheffield,
South Yorkshire, S35 2PH
Tel: 0114 257 2300 **Fax:** 0114 257 1419
Email: info@trianco.co.uk **Web:** www.trianco.co.uk

VOKERA LTD
Borderlake House, Unit 7 Riverside Industrial Estate,
London Colney, Hertfordshire, AL2 1HG
Tel: 0870 333 0220 **Fax:** 01727 744004
Email: enquiries@vokera.co.uk
Web: www.vokera.co.uk **Product Type:** 2, 3, 4

WORCESTER BOSCH GROUP
Cotswold Way, Warndon, Worcester, WR4 9SW
Area of Operation: UK & Ireland
Tel: 01905 754624 **Fax:** 01905 754619
Email: general.worcester@uk.bosch.com
Web: www.worcester-bosch.co.uk
Product Type: 2, 3

FUEL SUPPLIERS AND FUEL TANKS

KEY

ENERGY SOURCES: ★ Gas   ○ Oil
☐ Coal   ● Wood   ✦ Multi-Fuel
✲ Electric   ◗ Gel

OTHER: ▽ Reclaimed   ✌ On-line shopping
✍ Bespoke   ✋ Hand-made   ECO Ecological

BALMORAL TANKS
Balmoral Park, Loirston, Aberdeenshire, AB12 3GY
Area of Operation: Worldwide
Tel: 01224 859100 **Fax:** 01224 859123
Email: tanks@balmoral.co.uk
Web: www.balmoraltanks.com

BALMORAL TANKS

Area of Operation: Worldwide
Tel: 01224 859100
Fax: 01244 859123
Email: tanks@balmoral.co.uk
Web: www.balmoraltanks.com

Balmoral Tanks provides OFTEC approved cost
effective, fuel oil storage solutions c/w electronic
level gauging equipment.

BORDERS UNDERFLOOR HEATING
26 Coopersknowe Crescent,
Galashiels, Borders, TD1 2DS
Area of Operation: UK & Ireland
Tel: 01896 668667 **Fax:** 01896 668678
Email: underfloor@btinternet.com
Web: www.bordersunderfloor.co.uk

BP LPG
1 Cambuslang Way, Cambuslang, Glasgow, G32 8ND
Area of Operation: UK (Excluding Ireland)
Tel: 0845 300 0038 **Fax:** 0141 307 4869
Email: lpg@bp.com **Web:** www.bplpg.co.uk

CALOR GAS LTD
Athena Drive, Tachbrook Park,
Warwick, Warwickshire, CV34 6RL
Area of Operation: UK (Excluding Ireland)
Tel: 01926 330088 **Fax:** 01926 318718
Email: telemarketing@calor.co.uk
Web: www.calor.co.uk ✌

CLEARVIEW STOVES
More Works, Squilver Hill,
Bishops Castle, Shropshire, SY9 5HH
Area of Operation: Worldwide
Tel: 01588 650401 **Fax:** 01588 650493
Email: mail@clearviewstoves.com
Web: www.clearviewstoves.com

COUNTRYWIDE ENERGY
Defford, Earls Croome, Worcestershire, WR8 9DF
Area of Operation: Midlands & Mid Wales, South
West England and South Wales
Tel: 01386 757333 **Fax:** 01386 757341
Email: juliejones-ford@countrywidefarmers.co.uk
Web: www.countrywidefarmers.co.uk

CROWN OIL
The Oil Centre, Bury New Road, Heap Bridge,
Bury, Greater Manchester, BL9 7HY
Area of Operation: UK (Excluding Ireland)
Tel: 0161 764 6622 **Fax:** 0161 762 7685
Email: sales@crownoil.co.uk
Web: www.crownoil.co.uk

OPIES' THE STOVE SHOP
The Stove Shop, The Street, Hatfield Peverel,
Chelmsford, Essex, CM3 2DY
Area of Operation: East England, Greater London,
South East England **Tel:** 01245 380471
Email: enquiries@opie-woodstoves.co.uk
Web: www.opie-woodstoves.co.uk

SHELL GAS LTD
PO Box 1100, Chesterfield, S44 5YQ
Area of Operation: Worldwide
Tel: 0845 076 5544 **Fax:** 0870 128 4541
Email: enquiries@shell.com
Web: www.shellgas.co.uk

SOLID FUEL ASSOCIATION LTD (SFA)
7 Swanwick Court, Alfreton,
Derbyshire, DE55 7AS
Area of Operation: UK (Excluding Ireland)
Tel: 0845 601 4406 **Fax:** 01773 834351
Email: sfa@solidfuel.co.uk
Web: www.solidfuel.co.uk ✌

TITAN ENVIRONMENTAL LIMITED
Barbot Hall Industrial Estate, Mangham Road,
Rotherham, South Yorkshire, S61 4RJ
Area of Operation: Europe
Tel: 01709 538300 **Fax:** 01709 538301
Email: tony.soper@titanenv.com
Web: www.titanenv.com

**Please mention
The Homebuilder's
Handbook
when you call**

HEATING, PLUMBING & ELECTRICAL

All the benefits of gas with an uncompromising view

Many people who live beyond the reach of mains gas also live among some wonderful scenery. By choosing the Nautila vessel from Shell Gas (LPG) you can keep it that way. We can hide your vessel underground so that you needn't compromise the view of your garden or its surrounding area.

Once a suitable position is selected for the vessel, its installation is easy because it doesn't need a sand back fill.

To obtain a free quotation or to arrange a site visit please call us on
0845 076 55 44 or visit **www.shellgas.co.uk**

HEATING, PLUMBING & ELECTRICAL

SPONSORED BY HOMEBUILDING & RENOVATING MAGAZINE ARCHIVE CD-ROM
Tel 01527 834435 Web www.homebuilding.co.uk

Britain's Best Selling Self-Build Magazine

HOMEBUILDING &RENOVATING

Plumbing

What plumbing system is best for your home? And what tasks should your plumber be carrying out? We look at the role of the modern plumber.

The disciplines of plumbing and central heating have seen more changes over the past few years than most other trades, with new materials, equipment and systems flooding the market.Many of these are enthusiastically taken up, and gain acceptance in the self-build market. But when making your choices, make sure that whoever is going to carry out the work understands what you are trying to achieve and is familiar with the selections you have made.

The plumbing trade usually operates on a supply-and-fix basis – labour and materials all in – although most plumbers working within the self-build industry accept that homebuilders may want to specify, if not supply, much of the principle equipment.

Although the bulk of the plumber's work will not take place until the home is well and truly under way – usually once the roof is closed in – it is a good idea to have narrowed down your search, or have a plumber lined up, before work commences, as you'll need a supply of water on site right from the outset. A plumber will need to install a stopcock with a non-return valve, in a lockable position. You may need the plumber again if groundworkers dig the foundations and cut through a previously unknown water pipe.

Green options

You may want to consider energy efficiency before starting your plumbing. A condensing boiler can save up to £60 a year on your heating bills. Another point to bear in mind is modulation. By adjusting the modulator on your boiler you can alter the fuel input and increase efficiency even further, instead of it being on or off. A simple measure such as dual-flush loo will also help by saving water.

Underfloor heating, a relatively recent trend, is also an energy saving option. This is because the emitter (the floor) has a larger surface area than a standard radiator, and the water can therefore be heated at a lower temperature. Running costs of underfloor heating are typically 10-30% cheaper than conventional central heating systems.

For specialist and energy efficient plumbing products, try the IPPEC website www.ippec.co.uk Plumbers should be qualified. Try either OFTEC (Oil Firing Technical Association) members for oil-fired systems, or CORGI (Council for Registered Gas Installers) for those registered for any work to gas appliances or boilers. Visit www.corgi-gas-safety.com or www.oftec.co.uk for more information.

A plumber's tasks can include:

* Installing standpipes for building supply.
* Laying first fix carcassing pipework.
* Placing water tanks in the roof (where applicable)
* Running any gas pipework to boiler and outlets.
* Fixing guttering and downpipes.
* Fitting hot water cylinders.
* Fixing and connecting radiators to the wall.
* Laying underfloor central heating pipework.
* Connecting underfloor heating loops to the manifold.
* Fitting boiler and connecting to system.
* Connecting the boiler to an oil tank (if applicable)
* Fitting sanitaryware.
* Connecting sanitaryware to domestic plumbing and wastes.
* Plumbing in the kitchen and utility sink units, washing machines, dishwashers etc.
* Lagging all exposed pipework.
* Firing up the boiler and testing the system.

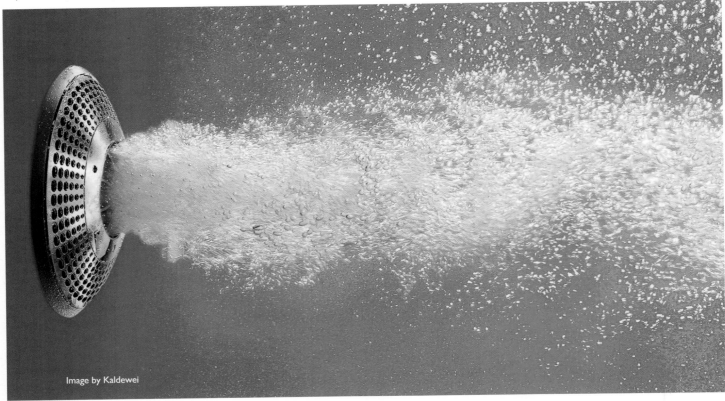

Image by Kaldewei

PLUMBING, PIPES & FITTINGS

KEY

SEE ALSO:

MERCHANTS - Plumbers Merchants,
DRAINAGE - Pipes and Pumps

OTHER: ▽ Reclaimed 🛒 On-line shopping
✎ Bespoke ✋ Hand-made ECO Ecological

ACO BUILDING DRAINAGE
ACO Business Park, Hitchin Road,
Shefford, Bedfordshire, SG17 5TE
Area of Operation: UK & Ireland
Tel: 01462 816666 **Fax:** 01462 851490
Email: buildingdrainage@aco.co.uk
Web: www.acobuildingdrainage.co.uk

AL CHALLIS LTD
Europower House, Lower Road, Cookham,
Maidenhead, Berkshire, SL6 9EH
Area of Operation: UK & Ireland
Tel: 01628 529024 **Fax:** 0870 458 0577
Email: chris@alchallis.com
Web: www.alchallis.com **Other Info:** ECO ✎

ALTON PUMPS
Redwood Lane, Medstead,
Alton, Hampshire, GU34 5PE
Area of Operation: Worldwide
Tel: 01420 561661 **Fax:** 01420 561661
Email: sales@altonpumps.com
Web: www.altonpumps.com

AUTRON PRODUCTS LTD
Unit 17 Second Avenue, Bluebridge Industrial Estate,
Halstead, Essex, C09 2SU
Area of Operation: UK & Ireland
Tel: 01787 473964 **Fax:** 01787 474061
Email: sales@autron.co.uk **Web:** www.autron.co.uk

BTU HEATING
38 Weyside Road, Guildford, Surrey, GU1 1JB
Area of Operation: South East England
Tel: 01483 590600 **Fax:** 01483 590601
Email: enquiries@btu-heating.com
Web: www.btu-group.com

COBURG GUTTER GRID
Little Gunnerby, Hatcliffe,
Grimsby, Lincolnshire, DN37 0SP
Area of Operation: UK & Ireland
Tel: 01472 371406 **Fax:** 01469 560435
Email: sue@guttergrid.com
Web: www.guttergrid.com

COPPERJOB LTD
PO Box 110, Plymouth, Devon, PL7 2ZS
Area of Operation: UK & Ireland
Email: info@copperjob.com
Web: www.centralheatingrepair.co.uk 🛒

DALLMER LTD
4, Norman Way, Lavenham,
Sudbury, Suffolk, CO10 9PY
Area of Operation: Worldwide
Tel: 01787 248244 **Fax:** 01787 248246
Email: sales@dallmer.com **Web:** www.dallmer.com

DECORMASTER LTD
Unit 16, Waterside Industrial Estate,
Wolverhampton, West Midlands, WV2 2RH
Area of Operation: Worldwide
Tel: 01902 406030 **Fax:** 01902 353126
Email: sales@oldcolours.co.uk
Web: www.oldcolours.co.uk

D-LINE (EUROPE) LIMITED
New York Way, New York Industrial Park,
Newcastle upon Tyne, Tyne & Wear, NE27 0QF
Area of Operation: Europe
Tel: 0191 293 0909 **Fax:** 0191 257 7722
Email: keving@d-line-it.co.uk
Web: www.d-line.co.uk 🛒

DMS FLOW MEASURENT & CONTROL LTD
The Lodge, 9 Mansfield Road, Eastwood,
Nottingham, Nottinghamshire, NG16 3AQ
Area of Operation: UK & Ireland
Tel: 01773 534555
Fax: 01773 534666
Email: sales@dmsltd.com **Web:** www.dmsltd.com

DRAINSTORE.COM
Units 1 & 2, Heanor Gate Road,
Heanor Gate Industrial Estate,
Heanor, Derbyshire, DE75 7RJ
Area of Operation: Europe
Tel: 01773 767611 **Fax:** 01773 767613
Email: adrian@drainstore.com
Web: www.drainstore.com 🛒

ECP GROUP
103 Burrell Road, Ipswich, Suffolk, IP2 8AD
Area of Operation: East England, South East England
Tel: 01473 400101 **Fax:** 01473 400103
Email: sales@ecpgroup.com
Web: www.ecpgroup.com

EURO BATHROOMS
102 Annareagh Road, Richhill, Co Armagh, BT61 9JY
Area of Operation: Ireland Only
Tel: 028 3887 9996 **Fax:** 028 3887 9996

EUROCARE SHOWERS LTD
Unit 19, Doncaster Industry Park, Watch House Lane,
Bentley, Doncaster, South Yorkshire, DN5 9LZ
Area of Operation: Worldwide
Tel: 01302 788684
Fax: 01302 780010
Email: sales@eurocare-showers.com
Web: www.eurocare-showers.com
Other Info: ✎

FREERAIN
Millennium Green Business Centre, Rio Drive,
Collingham, Nottinghamshire, NG23 7NB
Area of Operation: UK & Ireland
Tel: 01636 894900 **Fax:** 01636 894909
Email: info@freerain.co.uk
Web: www.freerain.co.uk

GO FIX IT LTD
Unit 10 Castle Industrial Estate, Louvain Street, Off
Oldham Road, Failsworth, Manchester, M35 0HB
Area of Operation: UK (Excluding Ireland)
Tel: 0161 681 4109
Fax: 0161 681 8169
Email: admin@gofixit.co.uk
Web: www.gofixit.co.uk 🛒

GOTO PLUMBING
Area of Operation: UK & Ireland
Email: sales@gotoplumbing.co.uk
Web: www.gotoplumbing.co.uk 🛒

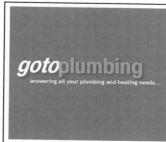

www.gotoplumbing.co.uk

Area of Operation: UK & Ireland
Email: sales@gotoplumbing.co.uk
Web: www.gotoplumbing.co.uk 🛒

This is the Plumbing & Heating Industry as you
have never seen it. For Householders &
Professionals including FAQ's, Technical
Downloads, Products, Regulations, Courses,
Forum and much more.....

GRUNDFOS PUMPS LTD
Groveburry Road, Leighton Buzzard,
Bedfordshire, LU7 4TL
Area of Operation: Worldwide
Tel: 01525 850000 **Fax:** 01525 850011
Email: uk_sales@grundfos.com
Web: www.grundfos.com

HARGREAVES FOUNDRY LTD
Water Lane, South Parade,
Halifax, West Yorkshire, HX3 9HG
Area of Operation: UK & Ireland
Tel: 01422 330607 **Fax:** 01422 320349
Email: info@hargreavesfoundry.co.uk
Web: www.hargreavesfoundry.co.uk

HEPWORTH PLUMBING PRODUCTS
Edlington Lane, Edlington, Doncaster, South
Yorkshire, DN12 1BY
Area of Operation: Worldwide
Tel: 01709 856300 **Fax:** 01709 856301
Email: info@hepworth.co.uk
Web: www.hepworth.co.uk **Other Info:** ✎

HIBERNIA RAINHARVESTING
Unit 530 Storehire, Stanstead Distribution Centre,
Start Hill, Bishops Stortford, Hertfordshire, CM22 7DG
Area of Operation: UK & Ireland
Tel: 02890 249954 **Fax:** 02890 249964
Email: rain@hiberniaeth.com
Web: www.hiberniaeth.com

HIGHWATER (SCOTLAND) LTD
Winewell, Grantown Road, Nairn, Highlands, IV12 5QN
Area of Operation: Scotland
Tel: 01667 451009 **Fax:** 01667 451009
Email: highwater@btinternet.com
Web: www.highwatertechnologies.co.uk
Other Info: ✎

HUNTER PLASTICS
Nathan Way, London, SE28 0AE
Area of Operation: Worldwide
Tel: 0208 855 9851 **Fax:** 0208 317 7764
Email: john.morris@hunterplastics.co.uk
Web: www.hunterplastics.co.uk

HYDRAQUIP
Unit 2 Raleigh Court, Priestley Way,
Crawley, West Sussex, RH10 9PD
Area of Operation: Worldwide
Tel: 01293 615166 **Fax:** 01293 614965
Email: sales@hydraquip.co.uk
Web: www.hydraquip.co.uk 🛒

INTERFLOW UK
Leighton, Shrewsbury, Shropshire, SY5 6SQ
Area of Operation: UK & Ireland
Tel: 01952 510050 **Fax:** 01952 510967
Email: villiers@interflow.co.uk
Web: www.interflow.co.uk

IPPEC SYSTEMS LTD
66 Rea Street South, Birmingham, B5 6LB
Area of Operation: UK & Ireland
Tel: 0121 622 4333 **Fax:** 0121 622 5768
Email: info@ippec.co.uk **Web:** www.ippec.co.uk 🛒

JOHN GUEST SPEEDFIT LTD
Horton Road, West Drayton, Middlesex, UB7 8JL
Area of Operation: Worldwide
Tel: 01895 449233 **Fax:** 01895 420321
Email: info@johnguest.co.uk
Web: www.speedfit.co.uk

LOBLITE ELECTRIC LTD
Third Avenue, Team Valley Trading Estate,
Gateshead, Tyne & Wear, NE11 0QQ
Area of Operation: Europe
Tel: 0191 487 8103 **Fax:** 0191 491 5541
Email: sales@heatec-rads.com
Web: www.heatec-rads.com

MARLEY PLUMBING & DRAINAGE
Lenham, Maidstone, Kent, ME17 2DE
Area of Operation: Europe
Tel: 01622 858888 **Fax:** 01622 858725
Email: marketing@marleyext.com
Web: www.marley.co.uk

MAYFIELD (MANUFACTURING) LTD
Wenden House, New End, Hemingby,
Horncastle, Lincolnshire, LN9 5QQ
Area of Operation: Worldwide
Tel: 01507 578630 **Fax:** 01507 578609
Email: john@aludrain.co.uk
Web: www.aludrain.co.uk

MEKON PRODUCTS
25 Bessemer Park, Milkwood Road, London, SE24 0HG
Area of Operation: UK (Excluding Ireland)
Tel: 0207 733 8011 **Fax:** 0207 737 0840
Email: info@mekon.net **Web:** www.mekon.net

PLUMBING IMPORTS
Dalton Airfield, Dalton, Thirsk,
North Yorkshire, YO7 3HE
Area of Operation: UK (Excluding Ireland)
Tel: 0845 310 80 59 **Fax:** 01845 577838
Email: sales@plumbingimports.co.uk
Web: www.plumbingimports.co.uk

POLYPIPE KITCHENS & BATHROOMS LTD
Warmsworth, Halt Industrial Estate,
Doncaster, South Yorkshire, DN4 9LS
Area of Operation: Worldwide
Tel: 01709 770990 **Fax:** 01302 310602
Email: davery@ppbp.co.uk
Web: www.polypipe.com/bk

PULSAR DIRECT LTD
70 High Park Drive, Mill Park Industrial Estate, Old
Wolverton, Milton Keynes, Buckinghamshire, MK12 5TT
Area of Operation: UK (Excluding Ireland)
Tel: 0800 2988 701 **Fax:** 0800 2988 702
Email: s.hogg@pulsardirect.co.uk
Web: www.pulsardirect.co.uk 🛒

PUMP WORLD LTD
Unit 11, Woodside Road, South Marston Business
Park, Swindon, Wiltshire, SN3 4WA
Area of Operation: UK & Ireland
Tel: 01793 820142 **Fax:** 01793 823800
Email: enquiries@pumpworld.co.uk
Web: www.pumpworld.co.uk 🛒

RADIANT HEATING SOLUTIONS LTD
Mill Farm, Hougham, Grantham, Lincolnshire, NG32 2HZ
Tel: 01400 250572 **Fax:** 01400 251264
Email: sales@heating-solutions.biz
Web: www.heating-solutions.biz

ROCKBOURNE ENVIRONMENTAL
6 Silver Business Park, Airfield Way,
Christchurch, Dorset, BH23 3TA
Area of Operation: UK & Ireland
Tel: 01202 480980 **Fax:** 01202 490590
Email: info@rockbourne.net
Web: www.rockbourne.net

RYTONS BUILDING PRODUCTS LTD
Design House, Kettering Business Park,
Kettering, Northamptonshire, NN15 6NL
Area of Operation: UK & Ireland
Tel: 01536 511874 **Fax:** 01536 310455
Email: admin@rytons.com
Web: www.vents.co.uk

SANIFLO
I D A Industrial Estate, Edenderry, Co Offaly, Ireland
Area of Operation: Ireland Only
Tel: 00353 469733077 **Fax:** 00353 469733078
Email: robin@sanirish.com **Web:** www.saniflo.ie

SANIFLO LTD
Howard House, The Runway,
South Ruislip, Middlesex, HA4 6SE
Area of Operation: UK (Excluding Ireland)
Tel: 0208 842 4040 **Fax:** 0208 842 1671
Email: andrews@saniflo.co.uk
Web: www.saniflo.co.uk

SLIMTRIMS LIMITED
Mitton Mill Industrial Estate, Mill Road,
Stourport-on-Severn, Worcestershire, DY13 9BL
Area of Operation: Europe
Tel: 01299 823824 **Fax:** 01299 823824
Email: info@slimtrims.com
Web: www.slimtrims.com

HEATING, PLUMBING & ELECTRICAL

SMART SHOWERS LTD
Unit 11, Woodside Road, South Marston Business Park, Swindon, Wiltshire, SN3 4WA
Area of Operation: UK & Ireland
Tel: 01793 822775
Fax: 01793 823800
Email: enquiries@smartshowers.co.uk
Web: www.smartshowers.co.uk 🛒

SURE GB LTD
Sure House, Century Park, Starley Way, Bickenhill, Solihull, West Midlands, B37 7HF
Area of Operation: Worldwide
Tel: 0121 782 5666
Fax: 0121 782 4304
Email: sales@surestop.co.uk
Web: www.surestop.co.uk

TAPS SHOP
1 Tristram Road, Ducklington, Whitney, Oxfordshire, OX29 7XH
Area of Operation: Worldwide
Tel: 0845 430 3035 **Fax:** 01993 779653
Email: info@tapsshop.co.uk
Web: www.tapsshop.co.uk 🛒

TECHFLOW PRODUCTS LTD
Unit 7 Sovereign Business Park, Albert Drive, Victoria Industrial Estate, Burgess Hill, West Sussex, RH15 9TY
Area of Operation: UK & Ireland
Tel: 01444 258003
Fax: 01444 258004
Email: rod@techflow.co.uk
Web: www.techflow.co.uk **Other Info:** ECO

TOOLSTATION
Express Park, Bridgwater, Somerset, TA6 4RN
Area of Operation: UK (Excluding Ireland)
Tel: 0808 100 7211
Fax: 0808 100 7210
Email: info@toolstation.com
Web: www.toolstation.com 🛒

UK COPPER BOARD
5 Grovelands Business Centre, Boundary Way, Hemel Hempstead, Hertfordshire, HP2 7TE
Area of Operation: UK & Ireland
Tel: 01442 275700
Fax: 01442 275716
Email: copperboard@copperdev.co.uk
Web: www.ukcopperboard.co.uk

UNIFIX LTD
St Georges House, Grove Lane, Smethwick, Birmingham, West Midlands, B66 2QT
Area of Operation: Europe
Tel: 0800 096 1110 **Fax:** 0800 096 1115
Email: sales@unifix.com
Web: www.unifix-online.co.uk 🛒

UPONOR HOUSING SOLUTIONS LTD
Snapethorpe House, Rugby Road, Lutterworth, Leicestershire, LE17 4HN
Area of Operation: UK & Ireland
Tel: 01455 550355
Fax: 01455 550366
Email: hsenquiries@uponor.co.uk
Web: www.uponorhousingsolutions.co.uk

WAVIN PLASTICS LTD (OSMA)
Parsonage Way, Chippenham, Wiltshire, SN15 5PN
Area of Operation: UK (Excluding Ireland)
Tel: 01249 766 600
Fax: 01249 443 286
Email: info@wavin.co.uk **Web:** www.wavin.co.uk

YEOVIL PLUMBING SUPPLIES
Unit 1, Bartlett Park, Linx Trading Estate, Yeovil, Somerset, BA20 2PJ
Area of Operation: UK (Excluding Ireland)
Tel: 01935 474780
Fax: 01935 432405

YORKSHIRE FITTINGS
PO Box 166, Leeds, West Yorkshire, LS10 1NA
Tel: 0113 270 1104 **Fax:** 0113 271 5275
Email: info@yorkshirefittings.co.uk
Web: www.yorkshirefittings.co.uk

WATER TANKS & CYLINDERS

KEY
PRODUCT TYPES: 1= Vented Hot Water Cylinders 2 = Unvented Hot Water Cylinders 3 = Tanks 4 = Thermal Stores 5 = Other

OTHER: ▽ Reclaimed 🛒 On-line shopping ✏ Bespoke ✋Hand-made ECO Ecological

ACV UK LTD
St Davids Business Park, Dalgety Bay, Fife, KY11 9PF
Tel: 01383 820100 **Fax:** 01383 820180
Email: information@acv-uk.com
Web: www.acv-uk.com **Product Type:** 1, 2, 4

ALBION WATER HEATERS
Shelah Road, Halesowen, West Midlands, B63 3PG
Tel: 0121 585 5151 **Fax:** 0121 585 6117
Email: colin.bland@albionwaterheaters.com
Web: www.albionwaterheaters.com
Product Type: 1, 2, 4

BALMORAL TANKS
Balmoral Park, Loirston, Aberdeenshire, AB12 3GY
Tel: 01224 859100 **Fax:** 01224 859123
Email: tanks@balmoral.co.uk
Web: www.balmoraltanks.com **Product Type:** 3

BAXI HEATING UK
Brooks House, Coventry Road, Warwick, Warwickshire, CV34 4LL
Tel: 08706 060780 **Fax:** 01926 410006
Web: www.baxi.co.uk **Product Type:** 1, 2

BTU HEATING
38 Weyside Road, Guildford, Surrey, GU1 1JB
Area of Operation: South East England
Tel: 01483 590600 **Fax:** 01483 590601
Email: enquiries@btu-heating.com
Web: www.btu-group.com
Product Type: 1, 2, 3, 4

COPPERJOB LTD
PO Box 110, Plymouth, Devon, PL7 2ZS
Email: info@copperjob.com
Web: www.centralheatingrepair.co.uk 🛒
Product Type: 1, 2, 3, 4

DRAYTON TANK & ACCESSORIES LTD
PO Box 435, Tweedale, Telford, Shropshire, TF3 5WH
Area of Operation: UK (Excluding Ireland)
Tel: 0871 288 4213 **Fax:** 0871 288 4214
Email: info@draytontank.co.uk
Web: www.draytontank.co.uk **Product Type:** 3, 4, 5

DRAYTON TANK & ACCESSORIES LTD

Area of Operation: UK (Excluding Ireland)
Tel: 0871 288 4213
Fax: 0871 288 4214
Email: info@draytontank.co.uk
Web: www.draytontank.co.uk
Product Type: 3, 4, 5

WRAS approved GRP Water Storage Tanks up to 90,000 Ltrs, hot water, waste and chemical tanks. GRP Housings, ballvalves, floatvalves, overflows and other fittings available.

DYNO-GROUP (DYNO-ROD & DYNO-SECURE)
Head Office, Sutherland House,
Maple Road, Surbiton, Surrey, KT6 4BJ
Area of Operation: UK & Ireland
Tel: 0800 000 999 **Fax:** 0208 541 1150
Email: postmaster@dyno.com
Web: www.dyno.com **Product Type:** 3

ECO HOMETEC UK LTD
Unit 11E, Carcroft Enterprise Park, Carcroft,
Doncaster, South Yorkshire, DN6 8DD
Tel: 01302 722266 **Fax:** 01302 728634
Email: Stephen@eco-hometec.co.uk
Web: www.eco-hometec.co.uk **Product Type:** 1, 2, 4

ENERGY MASTER
Keltic Business Park, Unit 1 Clieveragh Industrial
Estate, Listowel, Ireland
Area of Operation: Ireland Only
Tel: 00353 (0)68 23864 **Fax:** 00353 (0)68 24533
Email: info@energymaster.ie
Web: www.energymaster.ie **Product Type:** 1, 2, 3, 5

ENVIRONMENTAL CONSTRUCTION SOLUTIONS LIMITED
Head Office, 21 Kielder Road, South Wellfield,
Whitley Bay, Tyne & Wear, NE25 9QW
Area of Operation: Worldwide
Tel: 08456 123332 **Fax:** 08456 123334
Email: enquiries@ecs-sales.co.uk
Web: www.ecs-sales.co.uk **Product Type:** 3

EURO BATHROOMS
102 Annareagh Road, Richhill, Co Armagh, BT61 9JY
Area of Operation: Ireland Only
Tel: 028 3887 9996 **Fax:** 028 3887 9996
Product Type: 1, 3, 4

FABDEC
Grange Road, Ellesmere, Shropshire, SY12 9DG
Area of Operation: UK & Ireland
Tel: 01691 627200 **Fax:** 01691 627222
Email: info@fabdec.com
Web: www.fabdec.com **Product Type:** 2

FREERAIN
Millennium Green Business Centre, Rio Drive,
Collingham, Nottinghamshire, NG23 7NB
Area of Operation: UK & Ireland
Tel: 01636 894900 **Fax:** 01636 894909
Email: info@freerain.co.uk
Web: www.freerain.co.uk **Product Type:** 3

GAH HEATING PRODUCTS
Building 846, Bentwaters Parks, Rendlesham,
Woodbridge, Suffolk, IP12 2TW
Area of Operation: UK (Excluding Ireland)
Tel: 01394 42160 **Fax:** 01394 421170
Email: dcooper@gah.co.uk
Web: www.gah.co.uk **Product Type:** 2

GOTO PLUMBING
Area of Operation: UK & Ireland
Email: sales@gotoplumbing.co.uk
Web: www.gotoplumbing.co.uk

GREENSHOP SOLAR LTD
Hullbrook Garage, Bisley, Stroud,
Gloucestershire, GL6 7BX
Area of Operation: UK (Excluding Ireland)
Tel: 01452 772030 **Fax:** 01452 770115
Email: eddie@greenshop.co.uk
Web: www.greenshop-solar.co.uk
Product Type: 4 **Other Info:** ECO

HEATRAE SADIA HEATING
Hurricane Way, Norwich, Norfolk, NR6 6EA
Area of Operation: Worldwide
Tel: 01603 420110 **Fax:** 01603 420149
Email: sales@heatraesadia.com
Web: www.heatraesadia.com **Product Type:** 2

IPPEC SYSTEMS LTD
66 Rea Street South, Birmingham, B5 6LB
Area of Operation: UK & Ireland
Tel: 0121 622 4333 **Fax:** 0121 622 5768
Email: info@ippec.co.uk **Web:** www.ippec.co.uk
Product Type: 2 **Other Info:** ECO

JOHNSON & STARLEY
Rhosili Road, Brackmills, Northampton, NN4 7LZ
Tel: 01604 762881 **Fax:** 01604 767408
Email: marketing@johnsonandstarleyltd.co.uk
Web: www.johnsonandstarley.co.uk **Product Type:** 2

KESTON BOILERS
34 West Common Road, Hayes, Bromley, Kent, BR2 7BX
Area of Operation: UK & Ireland
Tel: 020 8462 0262 **Fax:** 020 8462 4459
Email: info@keston.co.uk
Web: www.keston.co.uk **Product Type:** 2

POLYPIPE KITCHENS & BATHROOMS LTD
Warmsworth, Halt Industrial Estate,
Doncaster, South Yorkshire, DN4 9LS
Tel: 01709 770990 **Fax:** 01302 310602
Email: davery@ppbp.co.uk
Web: www.polypipe.com/bk **Product Type:** 3

POLYTANK LTD
Naze Lane East, Freckleton,
Preston, Lancashire, PR4 1UN
Tel: 01772 632850 **Fax:** 01772 679615
Email: sales@polytank.co.uk
Web: www.polytank.co.uk **Product Type:** 3

PUMP WORLD LTD
Unit 11, Woodside Road, South Marston Business
Park, Swindon, Wiltshire, SN3 4WA
Tel: 01793 820142 **Fax:** 01793 823800
Email: enquiries@pumpworld.co.uk
Web: www.pumpworld.co.uk **Product Type:** 2, 3

ROCKBOURNE ENVIRONMENTAL
6 Silver Business Park, Airfield Way,
Christchurch, Dorset, BH23 3TA
Tel: 01202 480980 **Fax:** 01202 490590
Email: info@rockbourne.net
Web: www.rockbourne.net **Product Type:** 3

SOUTHERN SOLAR
Unit 6, Allington Farm, Allington Lane,
Offham, Lewes, East Sussex, BN7 3QL
Area of Operation: Greater London, South East
England, South West England and South Wales
Tel: 0845 456 9474 **Fax:** 01273 483928
Email: info@southernsolar.co.uk
Web: www.southernsolar.co.uk
Product Type: 1, 2, 3, 4

TITAN ENVIRONMENTAL LIMITED
Barbot Hall Industrial Estate, Mangham Road,
Rotherham, South Yorkshire, S61 4RJ
Tel: 01709 538300 **Fax:** 01709 538301
Email: tony.soper@titanenv.com
Web: www.titanenv.com **Product Type:** 2, 3

WHIRLPOOL EXPRESS (UK) LTD
61-62 Lower Dock Street, Kingsway, Newport, NP20 1EF
Tel: 01633 244555 **Fax:** 01633 244881
Email: reception@whirlpoolexpress.co.uk
Web: www.whirlpoolexpress.co.uk

WATER TREATMENT

KEY
PRODUCT TYPES: 1= Chlorination
2 = De-alkalisation 3 = Demineralisation
4 = Descaling 5 = Filtration
6 = Water Softening 7 = Other

OTHER: ▽ Reclaimed   On-line shopping
 Bespoke Hand-made   ECO Ecological

AQUA CLEAR WATER TREATMENT
Ballinahinch, Knocklong, Co.Limerick, Ireland
Area of Operation: Ireland Only
Tel: 00353 (0)62 53482
Fax: 00353 (0)62 53484
Email: aquacq@eircom.net
Web: www.aquaclear.ie
Product Type: 1, 2, 3, 4, 5, 6, 7

AQUA CURE PLC
Aqua Cure House, Hall Street,
Southport, Merseyside, PR9 0SE
Tel: 01704 516916 **Fax:** 01704 544916
Email: sales@aquacure.plc.uk
Web: www.aquacure.co.uk
Product Type: 1, 2, 3, 5, 6, 7 **Other Info:**

BIOCLERE TECHNOLOGY LTD
The Oaks, Moons Hill, Frensham, Surrey, GU10 3AW
Area of Operation: Worldwide
Tel: 01252 792688 **Fax:** 01252 794068
Email: adrian@bioclere.co.uk
Web: www.bioclere.co.uk

CISTERMISER LTD
Unit 1 Woodley Park Estate, 59-69 Reading Road,
Woodley, Reading, Berkshire, RG5 3AN
Area of Operation: UK & Ireland
Tel: 0118 969 1611 **Fax:** 0118 944 1426
Email: sales@cistermiser.co.uk
Web: www.cistermiser.co.uk **Product Type:** 4

CLEANWATER SOUTH WEST LTD
Foxfield, Welcombe, Bideford, Devon, EX39 6HF
Area of Operation: South East England, South West
England and South Wales
Tel: 01288 331561
Email: sales@cleanwatersw.co.uk
Web: www.cleanwatersw.co.uk **Product Type:** 7

COPPERJOB LTD
PO Box 110, Plymouth, Devon, PL7 2ZS
Area of Operation: UK & Ireland
Email: info@copperjob.com **Product Type:** 4
Web: www.centralheatingrepair.co.uk

DYNO-GROUP (DYNO-ROD & DYNO-SECURE)
Head Office, Sutherland House,
Maple Road, Surbiton, Surrey, KT6 4BJ
Area of Operation: UK & Ireland
Tel: 0800 000 999 **Fax:** 0208 541 1150
Email: postmaster@dyno.com
Web: www.dyno.com **Product Type:** 4, 5, 6, 7

ECP GROUP
103 Burrell Road, Ipswich, Suffolk, IP2 8AD
Area of Operation: East England, South East England
Tel: 01473 400101 **Fax:** 01473 400103
Email: sales@ecpgroup.com
Web: www.ecpgroup.com **Product Type:** 1, 5, 6, 7

ENVIRONMENTAL CONSTRUCTION SOLUTIONS LIMITED
Head Office, 21 Kielder Road, South Wellfield,
Whitley Bay, Tyne & Wear, NE25 9QW
Tel: 08456 123332 **Fax:** 08456 123334
Email: enquiries@ecs-sales.co.uk
Web: www.ecs-sales.co.uk

FAST SYSTEMS LTD
Dalton House, Newtown Road,
Henley on Thames, Oxfordshire, RG9 1HG
Area of Operation: East England, Greater London, South
East England, South West England and South Wales
Tel: 01491 419200 **Fax:** 01491 419201
Email: sales@scalewatcher.co.uk
Web: www.scalewatcher.co.uk **Product Type:** 4

GAH HEATING PRODUCTS
Building 846, Bentwaters Parks, Rendlesham,
Woodbridge, Suffolk, IP12 2TW
Area of Operation: UK (Excluding Ireland)
Tel: 01394 42160 **Fax:** 01394 421170
Email: dcooper@gah.co.uk
Web: www.gah.co.uk **Product Type:** 6

GREEN ROCK
3 Elmhurst Road, Harwich, Essex, CO12 3SA
Tel: 01255 554055 **Fax:** 01255 554055
Web: www.greenrock.fi

H2ONICS
Anode House, Unit 14 Berkeley Crescent,
Frimley, Camberley, Surrey, GU16 8YN
Tel: 0800 298 5031 **Fax:** 01252 837267
Email: enquiries@h2onics.co.uk
Web: www.h2onics.co.uk
Product Type: 4, 5, 6, 7

HIGHWATER (SCOTLAND) LTD
Winewell, Grantown Road, Nairn, Highlands, IV12 5QN
Area of Operation: Scotland
Tel: 01667 451009 **Fax:** 01667 451009
Email: highwater@btinternet.com
Web: www.highwatertechnologies.co.uk
Product Type: 1, 3, 5, 6 **Other Info:**

HYDROPATH HOLDINGS LIMITED
Unit F, Acorn Park, Redfield Road,
Nottingham, Nottinghamshire, NG7 2TR
Area of Operation: Worldwide
Tel: 0115 986 9966 **Fax:** 0115 986 9944
Email: sales@hydropath.com
Web: www.hydropath.com **Product Type:** 4, 6

KINETICO UK LTD
Bridge House, Park Gate Business Centre,
Park Gate, Hampshire, SO31 1FQ
Area of Operation: UK (Excluding Ireland)
Tel: 0800 015 1380 **Fax:** 01489 566976
Email: info@kinetico.co.uk **Web:** www.kinetico.co.uk

KINETICO UK LTD
Area of Operation: UK (Excluding Ireland)
Tel: 08000 151380
Fax: 01489 566976
Email: info@kinetico.co.uk
Web: www.kinetico.co.uk

Kinetico UK Ltd are the UK's leading supplier of
Water Softeners and Drinking Water Systems.
Call us on our freephone number today for more
information.

LIFESCIENCE PRODUCTS LTD
185 Milton Park, Abingdon, Oxfordshire, OX14 4SR
Tel: 01235 832111 **Fax:** 01235 832129
Email: sales@lifescience.co.uk
Web: www.lifescience.co.uk
Product Type: 4, 5, 6

SALAMANDER ENGINEERING LTD
24 Reddicap Trading Estate,
Sutton Coldfield, West Midlands, B75 7BU
Tel: 0121 378 0952 **Fax:** 0121 3111521
Email: enquiries@salamander-engineering.co.uk
Web: www.salamander-engineering.co.uk
Product Type: 4, 5, 6, 7

THE SOFT WATER SHOP
54 Westfield Road, Harpenden, Hertfordshire, AL5 4HW
Area of Operation: UK (Excluding Ireland)
Tel: 01582 461313 **Fax:** 01582 461313
Email: softwatershop@ntlworld.com
Web: www.softwatershop.co.uk
Product Type: 1, 2, 3, 4, 5, 6, 7

THE WISEMAN GROUP
PO Box 58, Ingatestone, Essex, CM4 9DL
Area of Operation: Worldwide
Tel: 01277 633200 **Fax:** 01277 632700
Email: sales@wisemangroup.co.uk
Web: www.wisemangroup.co.uk
Product Type: 2, 4, 6

WATERMATIC
Unit 24 Reddicap Trading Estate,
Sutton Coldfield, West Midlands, B75 7BU
Tel: 0121 378 1188 **Fax:** 0121 311 1521
Email: info@watermatic.co.uk
Web: www.watermatic.co.uk **Product Type:** 4, 5

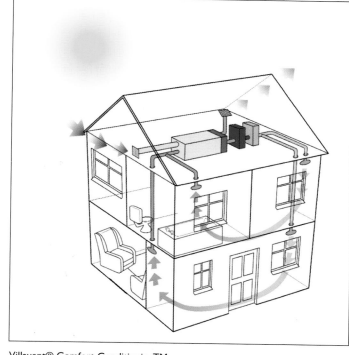

Image courtesy of Villavent Ltd (01993 778481)

Villavent® Comfort ConditioningTM
Villavent's revolutionary new package embracing energy efficiency,
cooling and clean living

HEATING, PLUMBING & ELECTRICAL

SPONSORED BY VILLAVENT LTD
Tel 01993 778481. Web www.villavent.co.uk

Ventilation

Adequate ventilation – the replacement of stale indoor air with fresh outside air – is required under the statutory Building Regulations.

The main purpose of ventilation is that it is essential for controlling moisture levels and indoor air pollutants.

Cheap and simple

If you are building a new house to sell in the near future, or you are on a tight budget, the best option is likely to be the cheapest and simplest. This will usually mean individual extract fans in wet areas and passive vents, or a positive input ventilation system (PIV).

Eco

If you are building an ecological house with a very low heat requirement, then your choice is likely to be between a passive stack system that uses no direct electricity, a PIV system, and a heat recovery ventilation system (HRV). A new option is solar panels, which heat the air rather than water, to pre-warm incoming fresh air, diverting to heat the hot water cylinder when heating is not required.

High-end properties

If you are building or renovating a high value property, then you might consider a system that combines air conditioning with ventilation. The building regulations stipulate some kind of ventilation and most people opt for trickle vents. But if you do not want trickle vents in windows for aesthetic reasons, you should consider a positive input ventilation system, or a mechanical whole-house system that operates continuously. If you require air filtration, to control allergens for instance, a mechanical system with controlled air intake is the best option, although positive input ventilation systems can also filter incoming air.

Renovations

For a typical small renovation project with a single bathroom, the most cost-effective option will be to go for a single wall or ceiling mounted extract fan. For a larger renovation, a single centrally located positive input ventilation system is likely to be more cost-effective than two or more individual extract fans. This will also do away with the need for trickle vents or airbricks, other than those required under Part J for combustion air supply.

Whichever system you opt for, you must include rapid ventilation such as opening windows to all habitable rooms. These must be of a minimum size as dictated by the Building Regulations.

Which solution is best for me?

This will depend on:

- how much you are willing to spend
- aesthetics
- the system maintenance regime acceptable to you
- the relative importance of energy efficiency and ecology
- if you want to filter, pre-warm or cool the incoming fresh air.
- with new build, it will also depend on how energy efficient and airtight the house you are building is, as this will set the effectiveness of features such as heat recovery.

Image, LEFT, by airconwarehouse.com

AIR CONDITIONING

KEY

OTHER: ▽ Reclaimed   ⌐🛒 On-line shopping
✎ Bespoke   🖐 Hand-made   ECO Ecological

ADM
Ling Fields, Gargrave Road,
Skipton, North Yorkshire, BD23 1UX
Area of Operation: Europe
Tel: 01756 701051   **Fax:** 01756 701076
Email: info@admsystems.co.uk
Web: www.admsystems.co.uk   **Other Info:** ✎

AIRCONWAREHOUSE.COM
Unit 2 Chichester Road, Romiley, Cheshire, SK6 4BL
Area of Operation: UK (Excluding Ireland)
Tel: 0161 4307878   **Fax:** 0161 4307979
Email: info@airconwarehouse.com
Web: www.airconwarehouse.com
Other Info: ECO ✎

ALLERGYPLUS LIMITED
65 Stowe Drive, Southam, Warwickshire, CV47 1NZ
Area of Operation: UK & Ireland
Tel: 0870 190 0022   **Fax:** 0870 190 0044
Email: info@allergyplus.co.uk
Web: www.allergyplus.co.uk ⌐🛒

ATB AIR CONDITIONING AND HEATING
67 Melloway Road, Rushden,
Northamptonshire, NN10 6XX
Area of Operation: East England, Greater London,
Midlands & Mid Wales, South East England
Tel: 0870 260 1650   **Fax:** 01933 411731
Email: enquiries@atbairconditioning.co.uk
Web: www.atbairconditioning.co.uk

BTU HEATING
38 Weyside Road, Guildford, Surrey, GU1 1JB
Area of Operation: South East England
Tel: 01483 590600   **Fax:** 01483 590601
Email: enquiries@btu-heating.com
Web: www.btu-group.com

CELSIUS AIR CONDITIONING
1 Well Street, Heywood, Lancashire, OL10 1NT
Area of Operation: UK & Ireland
Tel: 01706 367500   **Fax:** 01706 367355
Email: sales@celsiusair.co.uk
Web: www.celsiusair.co.uk

CLIMATE CENTER
Branches Nationwide
Area of Operation: UK (Excluding Ireland)
Tel: 01282 834498
Web: www.climatecenter.co.uk ⌐🛒

COMFORT AIR CONDITIONING LTD
Comfort Works, Newchapel Road,
Lingfield, Surrey, RH7 6LE
Area of Operation: East England, Greater London,
Midlands & Mid Wales, South East England, South
West England and South Wales
Tel: 01342 830600   **Fax:** 01342 830605
Email: info@comfort.uk.com
Web: www.comfort.uk.com   **Other Info:** ECO ✎

COMFYAIR LTD
Albion Works, Royd Ings Avenue,
Keighley, West Yorkshire, BD21 4BZ
Area of Operation: UK & Ireland
Tel: 01535 611333   **Fax:** 01535 611334
Email: david@comfyair.co.uk
Web: www.comfyair.co.uk   **Other Info:** ✎

COOLANDWARM.COM
Trigger Comfort, t/a cool and warm, 23 Walnut Tree
Close, Guildford, Surrey, GU1 4UL
Area of Operation: Europe
Tel: 01483 30 66 50
Email: info@coolandwarm.com
Web: www.coolandwarm.com ⌐🛒

**CRYOTEC REFRIGERATION &
AIR CONDITIONING**
Unit 4, Wolf Business Park, Alton Road,
Ross on Wye, Herefordshire, HR9 5NB
Area of Operation: South West England and South Wales
Tel: 0800 389 2369   **Fax:** 01989 764401
Email: info@cryotec.co.uk   **Web:** www.cryotec.co.uk

DANFOSS RANDALL LTD
Ampthill Road, Bedford, Bedfordshire, MK42 9ER
Area of Operation: UK & Ireland
Tel: 0845 121 7400   **Fax:** 0845 121 7515
Email: danfossrandall@danfoss.com
Web: www.danfoss-randall.co.uk

DESA UK LTD
11 Beech House, Padgate Business Park,
Green Lane, Warrington, Cheshire, WA1 4JN
Area of Operation: UK (Excluding Ireland)
Tel: 01925 828854   **Fax:** 01925 284124
Email: info@desauk.co.uk   **Web:** www.desauk.co.uk

DRY-IT-OUT LIMITED
The Cwm, Churchstoke, Montgomery, Powys, SY15 6TJ
Area of Operation: Europe
Tel: 0870 011 7987   **Fax:** 01588 620145
Email: enquiries@dry-it-out.com
Web: www.dry-it-out.com ⌐🛒

ENERGY TECHNIQUE PLC
47 Central Avenue, West Molesey, Surrey, KT8 2QZ
Area of Operation: UK (Excluding Ireland)
Tel: 0208 783 0033   **Fax:** 0208 783 0140
Email: rob@etenv.co.uk
Web: www.diffusion-group.co.uk

EU SOLUTIONS
Maghull Business Centre, 1 Liverpool Road North,
Maghull, Liverpool, L31 2HB
Area of Operation: UK & Ireland
Tel: 0870 160 1660   **Fax:** 0151 526 8849
Email: ths@blueyonder.co.uk
Web: www.totalhomesolutions.co.uk
Other Info: ECO

EU SOLUTIONS

Area of Operation: UK & Ireland
Tel: 0870 160 1660
Fax: 0151 526 8849
Email: ths@blueyonder.co.uk
Web: www.totalhomesolutions.co.uk

Vision is a single packaged air conditioning unit
which provides 3.2 kW (11.000 BTU's) of both
cooling and heating, by combining both indoor
and outdoor elements of a traditional system, but
without external equipment or refrigerant pipe
work.

GEA/ SAS AIRCON LTD
Office 9, Cowdray Centre House, Cowdray Centre,
Cowdray Avenue, Colchester, Essex, CO11 QB
Area of Operation: Europe
Tel: 01206 578833   **Fax:** 01206 574061
Email: chris@sasaircon.co.uk
Web: www.gea-acqua.com

HEATLINE
16-19 The Manton Centre, Manton Lane,
Bedford, Bedfordshire, MK41 7PX
Area of Operation: Worldwide
Tel: 0870 777 8323   **Fax:** 0870 777 8320
Email: info@heatline.co.uk
Web: www.heatline.co.uk

HONEYWELL CONTROL SYSTEMS LTD
Honeywell House, Arlington Business Park,
Bracknell, Berkshire, RG12 1EB
Area of Operation: Worldwide
Tel: 01344 656000
Fax: 01344 656054
Email: literature@honeywell.com
Web: www.honeywelluk.com

INTERACTIVE AIR LTD
Wolfelands, High Street, Westerham, Kent, TN16 1RQ
Area of Operation: Worldwide
Tel: 01959 565959   **Fax:** 01959 569933
Email: info@interavtiveair.com
Web: www.interactiveair.com
Other Info: ✎

JOHNSON & STARLEY
Rhosili Road, Brackmills, Northampton,
Northamptonshire, NN4 7LZ
Area of Operation: UK & Ireland
Tel: 01604 762881
Fax: 01604 767408
Email: marketing@johnsonandstarleyltd.co.uk
Web: www.johnsonandstarley.co.uk

SPACE AIRCONDITIONING PLC
Willway Court, 1 Opus Park,
Moorfield Road, Guildford, Surrey, GU1 1SZ
Area of Operation: UK & Ireland
Tel: 01483 504883
Fax: 01483 574835
Email: marketing@spaceair.co.uk
Web: www.spaceair.co.uk
Other Info: ▽ ECO

THE AIR CONDITIONING COMPANY
Unit 4, Bittacy Business Centre,
Mill Hill East, London, NW7 1BA
Area of Operation: Europe
Tel: 020 8346 6000   **Fax:** 020 8346 6002
Email: info@airconco.com
Web: www.airconco.com ⌐🛒
Other Info: ✎

THE HEAT PUMP COMPANY UK LIMITED
2 Evett Close, Stocklake, Aylesbury,
Buckinghamshire, HP20 1DW
Area of Operation: UK (Excluding Ireland)
Tel: 07989 308812   **Fax:** 01494 565689
Email: sales@npsair.com
Web: www.npsair.com
Other Info: ✎

TLC ELECTRICAL WHOLESALERS
TLC Building, Off Fleming Way,
Crawley, West Sussex, RH10 9JY
Area of Operation: Worldwide
Tel: 01293 565630
Fax: 01293 425234
Email: sales@tlc-direct.co.uk
Web: www.tlc-direct.co.uk ⌐🛒

UNICO SYSTEM INTERNATIONAL LIMITED
Unit 3, Ynyshir Industrial Estate, Llanwonno Road,
Porth, Rhondda Cynon Taff, CF39 0HU
Area of Operation: Worldwide
Tel: 01443 684828
Fax: 01443 684838
Email: scott@unicosystem.com
Web: www.unicosystem.co.uk

VENT AXIA
Fleming Way, Crawley, West Sussex, RH10 9YX
Area of Operation: UK (Excluding Ireland)
Tel: 01293 526062
Fax: 01293 552375
Email: sales@vent-axia.com
Web: www.vent-axia.com

WAGNER (GB) LTD
VBH House, Bailey Drive, Gillingham Business Park,
Gillingham, Kent, ME8 0WG
Area of Operation: Worldwide
Tel: 01634 263263
Fax: 01634 263504
Email: sales@wagnergb.com
Web: www.wagnergb.com ⌐🛒

VENTILATION AND HEAT RECOVERY

KEY

PRODUCT TYPES:
1= Mechanical   2 = Passive

OTHER: ▽ Reclaimed   ⌐🛒 On-line shopping
✎ Bespoke   🖐 Hand-made   ECO Ecological

ADM
Ling Fields, Gargrave Road,
Skipton, North Yorkshire, BD23 1UX
Area of Operation: Europe
Tel: 01756 701051   **Fax:** 01756 701076
Email: info@admsystems.co.uk
Web: www.admsystems.co.uk
Product Type: 1, 2   **Other Info:** ▽ ECO ✎

AIRCONWAREHOUSE.COM
Unit 2 Chichester Road, Romiley, Cheshire, SK6 4BL
Area of Operation: UK (Excluding Ireland)
Tel: 0161 4307878
Fax: 0161 4307979
Email: info@airconwarehouse.com
Web: www.airconwarehouse.com
Product Type: 1   **Other Info:** ECO ✎

AIRFLOW DEVELOPMENTS LTD
Lancaster Road, Cressex Business Park,
High Wycombe, Buckinghamshire, HP12 3QP
Area of Operation: Worldwide
Tel: 01494 525252
Fax: 01494 461073
Email: info@airflow.co.uk
Web: www.iconfan.co.uk ⌐🛒

ALLERGYPLUS LIMITED
65 Stowe Drive, Southam, Warwickshire, CV47 1NZ
Area of Operation: UK & Ireland
Tel: 0870 190 0022
Fax: 0870 190 0044
Email: info@allergyplus.co.uk
Web: www.allergyplus.co.uk ⌐🛒
Product Type: 1, 2   **Other Info:** ✎

ATB AIR CONDITIONING AND HEATING
67 Melloway Road, Rushden,
Northamptonshire, NN10 6XX
Area of Operation: East England, Greater London,
Midlands & Mid Wales, South East England
Tel: 0870 260 1650   **Fax:** 01933 411731
Email: enquiries@atbairconditioning.co.uk
Web: www.atbairconditioning.co.uk
Product Type: 1

Villavent Ltd are the brand leaders in whole house environmental solutions. With over 40 years experience in Scandinavia and 20 here in the UK we have both the product quality and expertise to provide an array of services and products to provide a 'one stop' shop, bespoke service to the marketplace.

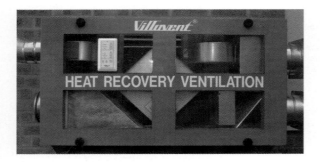

With 20 years experience here in the UK, Villavent strive to provide what we all expect – 'value for money'. It is our experience with what is generally regarded as the quality product in the marketplace and we back this up with an installation service, expert advice, good level of guarantee, extended warranty packages and a clear informative website. As we move forward we can already boost the National Installation Service – a first direct from a manufacturer and a DIY installation booklet for those individuals keen to do it themselves.

Villavent are part of a large European network within the ventilation industry ensuring we remain strong and competitive within this field in a growing international market, and can call upon manufacture from Germany, Norway, Sweden and Canada.

Our product quality is second to none with manufacture to ISO 9002 and the environmental standard 140001.

As the systems are generally a whole house installation complete with piping and ducts the design is of paramount importance with any installation.

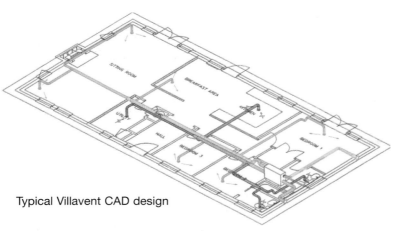

Typical Villavent CAD design

Villavent operate a CAD system, which is drawn in 4 colours and is very clear in its imaging. Generally we provide 3 issues of drawings: For Comment, For Approval and For Construction once all comments and notes have been discussed and agreed. An accurate materials list can then be called off to ensure a smooth installation.

Villavent offer a 2 year guarantee date of invoice and covers all parts. Villavent offer a further 3 year extended warranty, which can be taken out within 12 months of the original invoice. This can be paid monthly, annually by cheque or credit card or up front for 3 years with 5% discount.

Villavent has its own service and maintenance engineers and access to a national network of service engineers. All service queries should be directed to 01993 772270.

So how can we be of assistance to you?

As detailed on the following pages we specialise in:-

- **Central Extract Ventilation**
- **Heat Recovery Ventilation**
- **Comfort Cooling**
- **Villavent® Comfort Conditioning™**
- **Central Vacuum**

Villavent Ltd
Avenue 2, Station Lane Industrial Est,
Witney, Oxon OX28 4YL
Tel: 01993 778481
Fax: 01993 779962
Email: sales@villavent.co.uk
Web: www.villavent.co.uk

on products supplied with EU7 filter

Central Extract

Whole house ventilation from one fan unit providing quiet unobtrusive ventilation with only one external grill and one electrical point.

Villavent
Tel: 01993 778481
Fax: 01993 779962
Email: sales@villavent.co.uk
Web: www.villavent.co.uk

Comfort Cooling

Simplified unit to provide 4kw of cooling at a very modest cost, to the whole house. Can also be retrofitted to the ventilation.

Villavent
Tel: 01993 778481
Fax: 01993 779962
Email: sales@villavent.co.uk
Web: www.villavent.co.uk

Central Vac

One, stationary unit enabling easier more efficient cleaning whilst healthier and no unit noise in the room being cleaned.

Villavent
Tel: 01993 778481
Fax: 01993 779962
Email: sales@villavent.co.uk
Web: www.villavent.co.uk.

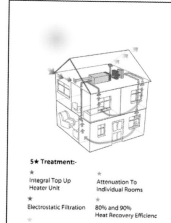

5★ Treatment:-

★ Integral Top Up Heater Unit
★ Attenuation To Individual Rooms
★ Electrostatic Filtration
★ 80% and 90% Heat Recovery Efficienc
★ Comfort Cooling

Villavent® Comfort Conditioning™

The ability to choose the level of comfort within your home.

Heat Recovery – VX400EV

Loft mounted **70% efficient** Heat Recovery unit.

Villavent
Tel: 01993 778481
Fax: 01993 779962
Email: sales@villavent.co.uk
Web: www.villavent.co.uk

Heat Recovery – VX400E

Wall mounted **70% efficient** Heat Recovery unit.

Villavent
Tel: 01993 778481
Fax: 01993 779962
Email: sales@villavent.co.uk
Web: www.villavent.co.uk

Heat Recovery – VM400

Wall or loft mounted **90% efficient** Heat Recovery unit.

Villavent
Tel: 01993 778481
Fax: 01993 779962
Email: sales@villavent.co.uk
Web: www.villavent.co.uk

Heat Recovery – VR400

Wall, ceiling or loft mounted **80% efficient** Heat Recovery unit with rotary wheel and automatic summer by-pass.

Villavent
Tel: 01993 778481
Fax: 01993 779962
Email: sales@villavent.co.uk
Web: www.villavent.co.uk

Retirement Housing

Heat Recovery ventilation to each luxury flat.

Villavent
Tel: 01993 778481
Fax: 01993 779962
Email: sales@villavent.co.uk
Web: www.villavent.co.uk

Health Care

Abingdon Health Care
Heat Recovery ventilation to all areas.

Villavent
Tel: 01993 778481
Fax: 01993 779962
Email: sales@villavent.co.uk
Web: www.villavent.co.uk.

Student Accomodation

Magdalen College - Oxford

Villavent
Tel: 01993 778481
Fax: 01993 779962
Email: sales@villavent.co.uk
Web: www.villavent.co.uk

Residential Development

Hargreaves Homes - West Sussex.
Family house development - South coast.

Villavent
Tel: 01993 778481
Fax: 01993 779962
Email: sales@villavent.co.uk
Web: www.villavent.co.uk

HEATING, PLUMBING & ELECTRICAL

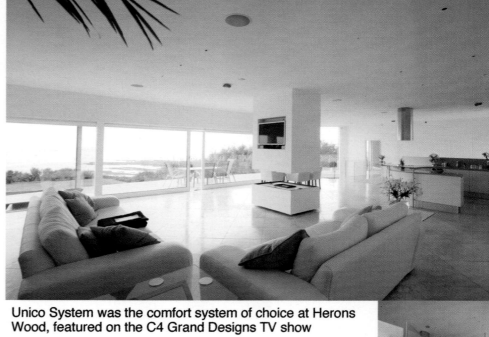

simply
relax

When you choose ADM to handle your heat recovery ventilation systems...

...you know you're in safe hands.

With over 20 years experience ADM provide highly efficient heat recovery ventilation, with options to suit any property.

Using award-winning technology, we provide you with:

• A cleaner, quieter home
• Condensation and odour control
• Over 90% heat recovery
• Energy Savings
• A healthier Home

Couple ADM's leading planning and installation services with flexible, tailored packages – including service contracts – and there simply is no better way to ventilate your home.

Call us now on: **01756 701051**

Ventilation System Specialists

ADM Ltd., Ling Fields,
Gargrave Road, Skipton,
North Yorkshire BD23 1UX

info@admsystems.co.uk
www.admsystems.co.uk

AUTOMATED CONTROL SERVICES LTD
Unit 16, Hightown Industrial Estate,
Crow Arch Lane, Ringwood, Hampshire, BH24 1ND
Area of Operation: UK (Excluding Ireland)
Tel: 01425 461008
Fax: 01425 461009
Email: sales@automatedcontrolservices.co.uk
Web: www.automatedcontrolservices.co.uk
Product Type: 1, 2

BROOK DESIGN HARDWARE LTD
Brook House, Dunmurry Industrial Estate,
Dunmurry, Belfast, Co. Antrim, BT17 9HU
Area of Operation: UK (Excluding Ireland)
Tel: 028 9061 6505
Fax: 028 9061 6518 / 9061 9379
Email: admin@brookvent.co.uk
Web: www.brookvent.co.uk

CATNIC
Pontypandy Industrial Estate, Caerphilly, CF83 3GL
Area of Operation: Worldwide
Tel: 029 2033 7900   **Fax:** 029 2033 7900
Email: barry.jenkins@corusgroup.com
Web: www.catnic.com

CAVITY TRAYS LTD
New Administration Centre,
Boundary Avenue, Yeovil, Somerset, BA22 8HU
Area of Operation: Worldwide
Tel: 01935 474769   **Fax:** 01935 428223
Email: enquiries@cavitytrays.co.uk
Web: www.cavitytrays.com

CLIMATE CENTER
Branches Nationwide
Area of Operation: UK (Excluding Ireland)
Tel: 01282 834498
Web: www.climatecenter.co.uk

COMFORT AIR CONDITIONING LTD
Comfort Works, Newchapel Road,
Lingfield, Surrey, RH7 6LE
Area of Operation: East England, Greater London,
Midlands & Mid Wales, South East England, South
West England and South Wales
Tel: 01342 830600   **Fax:** 01342 830605
Email: info@comfort.uk.com   **Other Info:** ECO
Web: www.comfort.uk.com   **Product Type:** 1

CONSERVATION ENGINEERING LTD
The Street, Troston, Bury St Edmunds, Suffolk, IP31 1EW
Area of Operation: UK & Ireland
Tel: 01359 269360
Email: anne@conservation-engineering.co.uk
Web: www.conservation-engineering.co.uk
Product Type: 1

COOLANDWARM.COM
Trigger Comfort, t/a cool and warm,
23 Walnut Tree Close, Guildford, Surrey, GU1 4UL
Area of Operation: Europe
Tel: 01483 30 66 50 **Email:** info@coolandwarm.com
Web: www.coolandwarm.com

DESA UK LTD
11 Beech House, Padgate Business Park,
Green Lane, Warrington, Cheshire, WA1 4JN
Area of Operation: UK (Excluding Ireland)
Tel: 01925 828854   **Fax:** 01925 284124
Email: info@desauk.co.uk **Web:** www.desauk.co.uk

DOMUS VENTILATION LTD
Bearwarden House, Bearwarden Business Park,
Royston Road, Wendens Ambo, Essex, CB11 4JX
Area of Operation: Worldwide
Tel: 01799 540602   **Fax:** 01799 541143
Email: info@domusventilation.com
Web: www.domusventilation.com
Product Type: 1

DRY-IT-OUT LIMITED
The Cwm, Churchstoke,
Montgomery, Powys, SY15 6TJ
Area of Operation: Europe
Tel: 0870 011 7987   **Fax:** 01588 620145
Email: enquiries@dry-it-out.com
Web: www.dry-it-out.com   **Product Type:** 1

DYER ENVIRONMENTAL CONTROLS LTD
Unit 10, Lawnhurst Trading Estate,
Cheadle Heath, Stockport, Cheshire, SK3 0SD
Area of Operation: UK (Excluding Ireland)
Tel: 0161 491 4840
Fax: 0161 491 4841
Email: enquiry@dyerenvironmental.co.uk
Web: www.dyerenvironmental.co.uk
Product Type: 2

ECO SYSTEMS IRELAND LTD
40 Glenshesk Road, Ballycastle,
Co. Antrim, BT54 6PH
Area of Operation: UK & Ireland
Tel: 02820 768708
Fax: 02820 769781
Email: info@ecosystemsireland.com
Web: www.ecosystemsireland.com
Product Type: 1

ECOLOGICAL BUILDING SYSTEMS UK LTD
The Manse, High Street, Creaton,
Northamptonshire, NN6 8NA
Area of Operation: UK & Ireland
Tel: 05600 758025
Fax: 05600 758026
Email: ecologicalbuild@btconnect.com
Web: www.ecologicalbuildingsystems.co.uk
Product Type: 2

ENERGY SUPERSTORE
3 Wellington Park, Belfast, BT9 6DJ
Area of Operation: UK & Ireland
Tel: 02890 388391
Email: info@energysuperstore.co.uk
Web: www.energysuperstore.co.uk
Product Type: 1

ENERGY TECHNIQUE PLC
47 Central Avenue, West Molesey, Surrey, KT8 2QZ
Area of Operation: UK (Excluding Ireland)
Tel: 0208-783 0033   **Fax:** 0208-783 0140
Email: rob@etenv.co.uk
Web: www.diffusion-group.co.uk

EU SOLUTIONS
Maghull Business Centre, 1 Liverpool Road North,
Maghull, Liverpool, L31 2HB
Area of Operation: UK & Ireland
Tel: 0870 160 1660
Fax: 0151 526 8849
Email: ths@blueyonder.co.uk
Web: www.totalhomesolutions.co.uk
Product Type: 1

EXHAUSTO
Unit 3 Lancaster Court, Coronation Road,
Cressex Business Park, High Wycombe,
Buckinghamshire, HP12 3TD
Area of Operation: UK & Ireland
Tel: 01494 465166
Fax: 01494 465163
Email: info@exhausto.co.uk
Web: www.exhausto.co.uk   **Product Type:** 1

GO FIX IT LTD
Unit 10 Castle Industrial Estate, Louvain Street,
Off Oldham Road, Failsworth, Manchester, M35 0HB
Area of Operation: UK (Excluding Ireland)
Tel: 0161 681 4109   **Fax:** 0161 681 8169
Email: admin@gofixit.co.uk
Web: www.gofixit.co.uk   **Product Type:** 1, 2

HEATLINE
16-19 The Manton Centre, Manton Lane,
Bedford, Bedfordshire, MK41 7PX
Area of Operation: Worldwide
Tel: 0870 777 8323   **Fax:** 0870 777 8320
Email: info@heatline.co.uk
Web: www.heatline.co.uk   **Product Type:** 1

HOME VENTILATION (IRELAND) LIMITED
Units 12-14 Rosevale Industrial Estate,
Moira Road, Lisburn, Co Antrim, BT28 1RW
Area of Operation: Ireland Only
Tel: 028 9267 0363 (ROI 048 9267 0363)
Fax: 028 9267 2980 (ROI 048) 9267 2980)
Email: homeventltd@btconnect.com
Web: www.homevent.co.uk   **Product Type:** 1

HEATING, PLUMBING & ELECTRICAL

Heat Recovery **Ventilation**

BROOK AIRCHANGER

healthy

A Heat Recovery Ventilation System improves the *Indoor Air Quality* throughout the home whilst *Removing Condensation* and *Unpleasant Odours.*

wealthy

The system is *Energy Efficient* and fulfils the latest *Building Control Regulations* for ventilation. As a result *No Trickle Vents* and *No Noisy Extractor Fans* are needed.

wise

Additionally automatic *Humidity Control* and *Pollen Filters* are some of the available options.

Send for your Self Build information pack to

BROOK AIRCHANGER

Tel 028 9061 6505   Fax. 028 9061 6518
www.brookvent.co.uk   E-mail admin@brookvent.co.uk
Brook House, Dunmurry Ind Est, Dunmurry, Belfast BT17 9HU

HONEYWELL CONTROL SYSTEMS LTD
Honeywell House, Arlington Business Park,
Bracknell, Berkshire, RG12 1EB
Area of Operation: Worldwide
Tel: 01344 656000
Fax: 01344 656054
Email: literature@honeywell.com
Web: www.honeywelluk.com
Product Type: 1, 2

JOHNSON & STARLEY
Rhosili Road, Brackmills, Northampton,
Northamptonshire, NN4 7LZ
Area of Operation: UK & Ireland
Tel: 01604 762881
Fax: 01604 767408
Email: marketing@johnsonandstarleyltd.co.uk
Web: www.johnsonandstarley.co.uk
Product Type: 1, 2

KAIR VENTILATION LTD
6 Chiltonian Industrial Estate,
Manor Lane, Lee, London, SE12 0TX
Area of Operation: Worldwide
Tel: 08451 662240 **Fax:** 08451 662250
Email: info@kair.co.uk
Web: www.kair.co.uk
Product Type: 1

KILTOX CONTRACTS LIMITED
Unit 6 Chiltonian Industrial Estate,
203 Manor Lane, Lee, London SE12 0TX
Area of Operation: Worldwide
Tel: 0845 166 2040
Fax: 0845 166 2050
Email: info@kiltox.co.uk
Web: www.kiltox.co.uk
Product Type: 1
Other Info: ECO

KLOBER LTD
Ingleberry Road, Shepshed,
Nr Loughborough, Leicestershire, LE12 9DE
Area of Operation: UK & Ireland
Tel: 01509 500660
Fax: 01509 600061
Email: info@klober.co.uk
Web: www.klober.co.uk

NUAIRE
Western Industrial Estate, Caerphilly, CF83 1NA
Area of Operation: UK & Ireland
Tel: 02920 858441
Fax: 02920 858442
Email: info@nuaire.co.uk
Web: www.nuaireforhomes.co.uk
Product Type: 1

NUAIRE HOLDINGS LIMITED

Area of Operation: UK & Ireland
Tel: 02920 858441
Fax: 02920 858442
Email: info@nuaire.co.uk
Web: www.nuaireforhomes.co.uk
Product Type: 1

Nuaire Group
Complete ventilation solutions from individual extract fans to whole home ventilation, heat recovery and solar thermal air and water pre-heating ventilation systems.

NUAIRE HOLDINGS LIMITED

Area of Operation: UK & Ireland
Tel: 02920 858441
Fax: 02920 858442
Email: info@nuaire.co.uk
Web: www.nuaireforhomes.co.uk
Product Type: 1

Positive Input Ventilation from Nuaire
Nuaire's range of low cost, low energy PIV systems create a healthy living environment for the occupants by introducing fresh filtered air into the home..

NUAIRE HOLDINGS LIMITED

Area of Operation: UK & Ireland
Tel: 02920 858441
Fax: 02920 858442
Email: info@nuaire.co.uk
Web: www.nuaireforhomes.co.uk
Product Type: 1

Heat Recovery from Nuaire
Nuaire offer one of the largest ranges of heat recovery units available in the UK.

PARAGON SYSTEMS (SCOTLAND) LIMITED
The Office, Corbie Cottage, Maryculter,
Aberdeen, Aberdeenshire, AB12 5FT
Area of Operation: Scotland
Tel: 01224 735536
Fax: 01224 735537
Email: info@paragon-systems.co.uk
Web: www.paragon-systems.co.uk
Product Type: 1

PASSIVENT LIMITED
2 Brooklands Way, Sale, Cheshire, M33 3SS
Area of Operation: UK & Ireland
Tel: 0161 962 7113
Fax: 0161 905 2085
Email: davidp@passivent.com
Web: www.passivent.com
Product Type: 1, 2 **Other Info:** ECO

REGA VENTILATION LTD
21-22 Eldon Way, Biggleswade, Bedfordshire, SG18 8NH
Area of Operation: Europe
Tel: 01767 600499
Fax: 01767 600487
Email: sales@rega-uk.com
Web: www.rega-uk.com
Product Type: 1, 2

ROOF VENTILATION SYSTEMS
The Old Forge, Tempsford,
Sandy, Bedfordshire, SG19 2AG
Area of Operation: UK & Ireland
Tel: 01767 640808
Fax: 01767 640561
Email: sales@roofventilationsystems.co.uk
Web: www.roofventilationsystems.co.uk

RYTONS BUILDING PRODUCTS LTD
Design House, Kettering Business Park,
Kettering, Northamptonshire, NN15 6NL
Area of Operation: UK & Ireland
Tel: 01536 511874 **Fax:** 01536 310455
Email: admin@rytons.com
Web: www.vents.co.uk **Product Type:** 2

SOLARIS SOLAR ENERGY SYSTEMS
Macroom e-Business Park, Bowl Road,
Macroom, Co. Cork, Ireland
Area of Operation: UK & Ireland
Tel: +353 (0)26 21014 **Fax:** +353 (0)26 46313
Email: info@solaris-energy.ie
Web: www.solaris-energy.ie **Product Type:** 1

SPACE AIRCONDITIONING PLC
Willway Court, 1 Opus Park,
Moorfield Road, Guildford, Surrey, GU1 1SZ
Area of Operation: UK & Ireland
Tel: 01483 504883 **Fax:** 01483 574835
Email: marketing@spaceair.co.uk
Web: www.spaceair.co.uk **Product Type:** 1

STARKEY SYSTEMS UK LTD
4a St Martins House, St Martins Gate,
Worcester, Worcestershire, WR1 2DT
Area of Operation: UK (Excluding Ireland)
Tel: 01905 611041 **Fax:** 01905 27462
Email: sales@centralvacuums.co.uk
Web: www.centralvacuums.co.uk
Product Type: 1

SYSTEMAIR LTD
72 Chestom Road, Birmingham, B7 5EJ
Area of Operation: Worldwide
Tel: 0121 322 0850 **Fax:** 0121 322 0859
Email: sales@systemair.co.uk
Web: www.systemair.co.uk

THE HEAT PUMP COMPANY UK LIMITED
2 Evett Close, Stocklake, Aylesbury,
Buckinghamshire, HP20 1DW
Area of Operation: UK (Excluding Ireland)
Tel: 07989 308812 **Fax:** 01494 565689
Email: sales@npsair.com
Web: www.npsair.com **Product Type:** 1, 2

TITON
International House, Peartree Road,
Stanway, Colchester, Essex, CO3 0JL
Area of Operation: Worldwide
Tel: 01206 713800 **Fax:** 01206 543126
Email: sales@titon.co.uk
Web: www.titon.co.uk **Product Type:** 1, 2

TLC ELECTRICAL WHOLESALERS
TLC Building, Off Fleming Way,
Crawley,West Sussex, RH10 9JY
Area of Operation: Worldwide
Tel: 01293 565630
Fax: 01293 425234
Email: sales@tlc-direct.co.uk
Web: www.tlc-direct.co.uk
Product Type: 1

Don't Forget !

You can use the materials key at the beginning of the Handbook to get much more information from a company's listing.

HEATING, PLUMBING & ELECTRICAL

So what's the best thing about REGAVENT - the big noise in HRV?

You can't <u>hear</u> it!

Send your plans for FREE DESIGN & QUOTE!

It's True! Rega's unique WhisperFlow™ technology ensures that even when operating at full 'Boost' mode (during the morning bathroom rush hour!) the system remains whisper quiet, unobtrusively, yet effectively, venting stale and damp air and replacing it with air that's gently warmed and filtered.

Ask too about RegaVent's **CENTRAL VACUUM SYSTEMS**
- the ultimate in convenient cleaning!

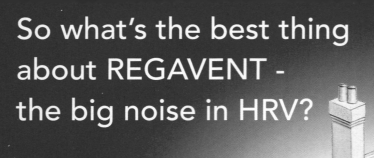

- **Powerful AC or DC electric motors**
- **Fully programmable operation**
- **Acoustically insulated ducting**
- **Filters reduce effects of respiratory allergies**
- **Optional switch systems**
- **Reduces heating bills**
- **Can promote conditions for improved health**
- **Easy to install for DIYer or professional alike**
- **Conforms to Building regulations**

RegaVent HRV systems have been at the forefront of the market for more than 20 years. With thousands of troublefree installations, nationwide, you can be sure of fast, efficient, delivery and installation.

Fresh thinking in the air...

rega vent

www.rega-uk.com

Rega Ventilation Limited   21/22 Eldon Way, Biggleswade, Beds SG18 8NH
Telephone: 01767 600499   fax: 01767 600487   email: sales@rega-uk.com

TOTAL HOME ENVIRONMENT LTD
Swallow House, Cotswold Business Village, London Road, Moreton in Marsh, Gloucestershire, GL56 0JQ
Area of Operation: UK (Excluding Ireland)
Tel: 0845 260 0123 **Fax:** 01608 652490
Email: info@totalhome.co.uk
Web: www.totalhome.co.uk
Product Type: 1 **Other Info:** ECO

UBBINK (UK) LTD
Borough Road, Brackley, Northamptonshire, NN13 7TB
Tel: 01280 700211 **Fax:** 01280 705332
Email: info@ubbink.co.uk
Web: www.ubbink.co.uk **Product Type:** 1, 2

UNICO SYSTEM INTERNATIONAL LIMITED
Unit 3, Ynyshir Industrial Estate, Llanwonno Road, Porth, Rhondda Cynon Taff, CF39 0HU
Tel: 01443 684828 **Fax:** 01443 684838
Email: scott@unicosystem.com
Web: www.unicosystem.co.uk

UNIFIX LTD
St Georges House, Grove Lane, Smethwick, Birmingham, West Midlands, B66 2QT
Area of Operation: Europe
Tel: 0800 096 1110 **Fax:** 0800 096 1115
Email: sales@unifix.com
Web: www.unifix-online.co.uk **Product Type:** 1

VECTAIRE LTD
Lincoln Road, Cressex Business Park, High Wycombe, Buckinghamshire, HP12 3RH
Area of Operation: Worldwide
Tel: 01494 522333 **Fax:** 01494 522337
Email: sales@vectaire.co.uk
Web: www.vectaire.co.uk

VECTAIRE LTD
Area of Operation: Worldwide
Tel: 01494 522333
Fax: 01494 522337
Email: sales@vectaire.co.uk
Web: www.vectaire.co.uk
Ventilation
"Microbox" 2 speed fans for near silent whole house ventilation. From 122mm deep for installation in restricted areas and in sizes to ventilate dwellings up to 400 square metres. Vectaire can design, install and commission.

VENT AXIA
Fleming Way, Crawley, West Sussex, RH10 9YX
Area of Operation: UK (Excluding Ireland)
Tel: 01293 526062 **Fax:** 01293 552375
Email: sales@vent-axia.com
Web: www.vent-axia.com

VILLAVENT LTD
Avenue 2, Station Lane Industrial Estate, Witney, Oxfordshire, OX28 4YL
Area of Operation: UK & Ireland
Tel: 01993 778481 **Fax:** 01993 779962
Email: sales@villavent.co.uk
Web: www.villavent.co.uk
Product Type: 1

EXTRACTOR FANS

KEY
PRODUCT TYPES:
1= Centrifugal Fans   2 = Propellor Fans
OTHER: ▽ Reclaimed   On-line shopping   Bespoke   Hand-made   ECO Ecological

ADM
Ling Fields, Gargrave Road, Skipton, North Yorkshire, BD23 1UX
Area of Operation: Europe
Tel: 01756 701051
Fax: 01756 701076
Email: info@admsystems.co.uk
Web: www.admsystems.co.uk **Product Type:** 1
Other Info: ▽ ECO

ALLERGYPLUS LIMITED
65 Stowe Drive, Southam, Warwickshire, CV47 1NZ
Area of Operation: UK & Ireland
Tel: 0870 190 0022
Fax: 0870 190 0044
Email: info@allergyplus.co.uk
Web: www.allergyplus.co.uk
Product Type: 1, 2 **Other Info:**

CLIMATE CENTER
Branches Nationwide
Area of Operation: UK (Excluding Ireland)
Tel: 01282 834498
Web: www.climatecenter.co.uk

DOMUS VENTILATION LTD
Bearwarden House, Bearwarden Business Park, Royston Road, Wendens Ambo, Essex, CB11 4JX
Area of Operation: Worldwide
Tel: 01799 540602
Fax: 01799 541143
Email: info@domusventilation.com
Web: www.domusventilation.com
Product Type: 1

ELECTRICALSHOP.NET
81 Kinson Road, Wallisdown, Bournemouth, Dorset, BH10 4DG
Area of Operation: UK (Excluding Ireland)
Tel: 0870 027 3730 **Fax:** 0870 027 3731
Email: sales@electricalshop.net
Web: www.electricalshop.net
Product Type: 1, 2

EU SOLUTIONS
Maghull Business Centre, 1 Liverpool Road North, Maghull, Liverpool, L31 2HB
Area of Operation: UK & Ireland
Tel: 0870 160 1660
Fax: 0151 526 8849
Email: ths@blueyonder.co.uk
Web: www.totalhomesolutions.co.uk
Product Type: 1

EXHAUSTO
Unit 3 Lancaster Court, Coronation Road, Cressex Business Park, High Wycombe, Buckinghamshire, HP12 3TD
Area of Operation: UK & Ireland
Tel: 01494 465166
Fax: 01494 465163
Email: info@exhausto.co.uk
Web: www.exhausto.co.uk

GET PLC
Key Point, 3-17 High Street, Potters Bar, Hertfordshire, EN6 5AJ
Area of Operation: Worldwide
Tel: 01707 601601
Fax: 01707 601701
Email: info@getplc.com
Web: www.getplc.com **Product Type:** 1, 2

GET PLC
Area of Operation: Worldwide
Tel: 01707 601601 **Fax:** 01707 601701
Email: info@getplc.com
Web: www.getplc.com
Product Type: 1, 2

Our new slimline 100mm extractor fan has been designed to provide an innovative approach that complements modern styling and fittings and is available in a range of finishes.

GO FIX IT LTD
Unit 10 Castle Industrial Estate, Louvain Street, Off Oldham Road, Failsworth, Manchester, M35 0HB
Area of Operation: UK (Excluding Ireland)
Tel: 0161 681 4109 **Fax:** 0161 681 8169
Email: admin@gofixit.co.uk
Web: www.gofixit.co.uk **Product Type:** 1

KAIR VENTILATION LTD
6 Chiltonian Industrial Estate, Manor Lane, Lee, London, SE12 0TX
Area of Operation: Worldwide
Tel: 08451 662240
Fax: 08451 662250
Email: info@kair.co.uk **Web:** www.kair.co.uk
Product Type: 1, 2

KILTOX CONTRACTS LIMITED
Unit 6 Chiltonian Industrial Estate, 203 Manor Lane, Lee, London, SE12 0TX
Area of Operation: Worldwide
Tel: 0845 166 2040 **Fax:** 0845 166 2050
Email: info@kiltox.co.uk
Web: www.kiltox.co.uk
Product Type: 2 **Other Info:** ECO

ROOF VENTILATION SYSTEMS
The Old Forge, Tempsford, Sandy, Bedfordshire, SG19 2AG
Area of Operation: UK & Ireland
Tel: 01767 640808 **Fax:** 01767 640561
Email: sales@roofventilationsystems.co.uk
Web: www.roofventilationsystems.co.uk
Product Type: 1 **Other Info:** ECO

STARKEY SYSTEMS UK LTD
4a St Martins House, St Martins Gate, Worcester, Worcestershire, WR1 2DT
Area of Operation: UK (Excluding Ireland)
Tel: 01905 611041 **Fax:** 01905 27462
Email: sales@centralvacuums.co.uk
Web: www.centralvacuums.co.uk **Product Type:** 2

SYSTEMAIR LTD
72 Chestom Road, Birmingham, B7 5EJ
Area of Operation: Worldwide
Tel: 0121 3220850 **Fax:** 0121 3220859
Email: sales@systemair.co.uk
Web: www.systemair.co.uk **Product Type:** 1, 2

TLC ELECTRICAL WHOLESALERS
TLC Building, Off Fleming Way, Crawley, West Sussex, RH10 9JY
Area of Operation: Worldwide
Tel: 01293 565630 **Fax:** 01293 425234
Email: sales@tlc-direct.co.uk
Web: www.tlc-direct.co.uk **Product Type:** 1, 2

UBBINK (UK) LTD
Borough Road, Brackley, Northamptonshire, NN13 7TB
Area of Operation: Europe
Tel: 01280 700211 **Fax:** 01280 705332
Email: info@ubbink.co.uk
Web: www.ubbink.co.uk **Product Type:** 1, 2

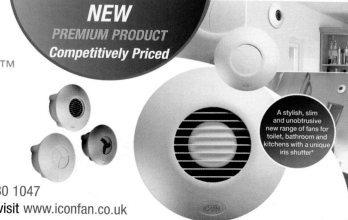

HEATING, PLUMBING & ELECTRICAL

UNIFIX LTD
St Georges House, Grove Lane, Smethwick,
Birmingham, West Midlands, B66 2QT
Tel: 0800 096 1110   **Fax:** 0800 096 1115
Email: sales@unifix.com
Web: www.unifix-online.co.uk
Product Type: 2

VECTAIRE LTD
Lincoln Road, Cressex Business Park,
High Wycombe, Buckinghamshire, HP12 3RH
Area of Operation: Worldwide
Tel: 01494 522333
Fax: 01494 522337
Email: sales@vectaire.co.uk
Web: www.vectaire.co.uk

VECTAIRE LTD
Area of Operation: Worldwide
Tel: 01494 522333
Fax: 01494 522337
Email: sales@vectaire.co.uk
Web: www.vectaire.co.uk

Extractor
"X-Mart" deluxe low profile toilet/
bathroom/kitchen fans finished in stainless steel
or white: in 3 sizes and capacities;
splashproof to IPX4; standard, timer and humidity
control; fixed or automatic opening front cover.

VENT AXIA
Fleming Way, Crawley, West Sussex, RH10 9YX
Area of Operation: UK (Excluding Ireland)
Tel: 01293 526062   **Fax:** 01293 552375
Email: sales@vent-axia.com
Web: www.vent-axia.com

VILLAVENT LTD
Avenue 2, Station Lane Industrial Estate,
Witney, Oxfordshire, OX28 4YL
Area of Operation: UK & Ireland
Tel: 01993 778481   **Fax:** 01993 779962
Email: sales@villavent.co.uk
Web: www.villavent.co.uk

VORTICE LTD
Beeches House, Eastern Avenue,
Burton on Trent, Staffordshire, DE13 0BB
Area of Operation: Worldwide
Tel: 01283 492949   **Fax:** 01283 544121
Email: getit@vortice.ltd.uk
Web: www.vortice.ltd.uk
Product Type: 1

CEILING FANS

KEY
OTHER: ▽ Reclaimed   ⌂ On-line shopping
✎ Bespoke   ✋ Hand-made   ECO Ecological

ASTRA CEILING FANS & LIGHTING
Unit 6, Lowercroft Industrial Estate,
Bury, Lancashire, BL8 3PA
Area of Operation: Europe
Tel: 0161 7973222
Fax: 0161 7973444
Email: support@astra247.com
Web: www.astra247.com

BROUGHTONS OF LEICESTER
The Old Cinema, 69 Cropston Road,
Anstey, Leicester, Leicestershire, LE7 7BP
Area of Operation: Worldwide
Tel: 0116 235 2555   **Fax:** 0116 234 1188
Email: sale@broughtons.com
Web: www.broughtons.com

CLIMATE CENTER
Branches Nationwide
Area of Operation: UK (Excluding Ireland)
Tel: 01282 834498   **Web:** www.climatecenter.co.uk

COMFYAIR LTD
Albion Works, Royd Ings Avenue,
Keighley, West Yorkshire, BD21 4BZ
Area of Operation: UK & Ireland
Tel: 01535 611333   **Fax:** 01535 611334
Email: david@comfyair.co.uk
Web: www.comfyair.co.uk

COOLANDWARM.COM
Trigger Comfort, t/a cool and warm,
23 Walnut Tree Close, Guildford, Surrey, GU1 4UL
Area of Operation: Europe
Tel: 01483 30 66 50
Email: info@coolandwarm.com
Web: www.coolandwarm.com

DOMUS VENTILATION LTD
Bearwarden House, Bearwarden Business Park,
Royston Road, Wendens Ambo, Essex, CB11 4JX
Area of Operation: Worldwide
Tel: 01799 540602   **Fax:** 01799 541143
Email: info@domusventilation.com
Web: www.domusventilation.com

FANTASIA CEILING FANS
Unit B, The Flyers Way, Westerham, Kent, TN16 1DE
Area of Operation: UK (Excluding Ireland)
Tel: 01959 564440   **Fax:** 01959 564829
Email: info@fantasiaceilingfans.com
Web: www.fantasiaceilingfans.com

FANTASIA CEILING FANS
Area of Operation: UK (Excluding Ireland)
Tel: 01959 564440
Fax: 01959 564829
Email: info@fantasiaceilingfans.com
Web: www.fantasiaceilingfans.com

The Viper Ceiling from Fantasia, 137cm
diameter, 100watt halogen light, remote
controlled. Just one of many stunning ceiling
fans available from Fantasia.

THE AMERICAN FAN COMPANY
Unit 8c Castle End Business Park, Ruscombe,
Berkshire, RG10 9XQ
Area of Operation: UK (Excluding Ireland)
Tel: 0870 803 4025   **Fax:** 0870 803 4095
Email: sales@americanfan.co.uk
Web: www.americanfan.co.uk

THE AMERICAN FAN COMPANY
Area of Operation: UK (Excluding Ireland)
Tel: 0870 803 4025
Fax: 0870 803 4095
Email: sales@americanfan.co.uk
Web: www.americanfan.co.uk

The American Fan Company's range of Hunter
ceiling fans not only keep you cool, but are
stylish, energy saving and economical.

TLC ELECTRICAL WHOLESALERS
TLC Building, Off Fleming Way,
Crawley, West Sussex, RH10 9JY
Area of Operation: Worldwide
Tel: 01293 565630   **Fax:** 01293 425234
Email: sales@tlc-direct.co.uk
Web: www.tlc-direct.co.uk

TRIGGER COMFORT LTD
23 Walnut Tree Close, Guildford, Suffolk, GU1 4UL
Area of Operation: Worldwide
Tel: 01483 306650   **Fax:** 01483 303225
Email: info@coolandwarm.com
Web: www.coolandwarm.com

HUNTER CEILING FANS
Area of Operation: Worldwide
Tel: 01483 30 66 50
Fax: 01483 30 32 25
Email: info@coolandwarm.com
Visit: www.coolandwarm.com

Online distributors of Hunter Fan Co - USA, the
world's leading manufacturer of ceiling fans.
Ceiling fans keep you cool in summer. Visit
www.coolandwarm.com for more details/prices
or request a brochure. Ideal in lounges,
bedrooms, kitchens, conservatories, offices,
bars, restaurants and hotels.

VECTAIRE LTD
Lincoln Road, Cressex Business Park, High
Wycombe, Buckinghamshire, HP12 3RH
Area of Operation: Worldwide
Tel: 01494 522333   **Fax:** 01494 522337
Email: sales@vectaire.co.uk
Web: www.vectaire.co.uk

VORTICE LTD
Beeches House, Eastern Avenue,
Burton on Trent, Staffordshire, DE13 0BB
Area of Operation: Worldwide
Tel: 01283 492949   **Fax:** 01283 544121
Email: getit@vortice.ltd.uk
Web: www.vortice.ltd.uk   **Other Info:** ECO

NOTES

Company Name ....
....
Address ....
....
....
email ....
Web ....

Company Name ....
....
Address ....
....
....
email ....
Web ....

Company Name ....
....
Address ....
....
....
email ....
Web ....

Company Name ....
....
Address ....
....
....
email ....
Web ....

Company Name ....
....
Address ....
....
....
email ....
Web ....

SPONSORED BY: How To Renovate A House In France
Tel: 01527 834435 Web: www.homebuilding.co.uk/bookshop

Switches & Sockets

As with many small fittings for the home, switches and sockets are often not given enough thought at the crucial decision-making stage of your self-build or renovation project.

It is not just the style of switches and sockets that is so important, but also the planning that goes into their positioning and the quantity you wish to use in your home.

As with any job involving electrics, safety should come first. You should always seek the services of an electrician – revisions to Part P of the Building Regulations now state that "qualified" installers must complete any electrical works, rather than simply "competent" persons. Contact the National Inspection Council for Electrical Installation Contracting (NICEIC) for details of an approved contractor in your area - www.niceic.org.uk.

Ideally, you should decide where you want your lights early on. Wiring generally consists of a collection of ring circuits, running from the mains consumer unit and circling an area of approximately $100m^2$ before returning to the consumer unit. Although setting this up during the build process should be problem-free, adding them at a later stage is a difficult job.

Images by Switch To Wood

Your fittings can be switched in a number of ways:

- Single-way switches are linked directly to one light

- Two-way means that two switches can operate one light, useful for positioning either end of staircases or long corridors

- Three-way allows you to operate the same light from three separate positions. Only one position can have a dimmer control.

The layout of switches and sockets, and how they are to be switched, should be marked on your plans and presented to your electrician for them to price.

With so many hi-tech devices vying for space in the modern home, it is advisable to

make sure you plan for as many sockets as you can. There is no limit to the number of sockets that you can run off a particular circuit, and installing lots will mean that you are never restricted as to where you can put new equipment or furniture.

Think about the problems you have experienced in past houses, and make sure they don't happen again. Telephone and television sockets in every room will give you freedom of movement and extras, like a shaving point or a feed for an electric kitchen hob, can be installed at a very minor cost. While these extra points are not always necessary, and you may not use them, it is always worth installing them for subsequent owners.

Sockets

The budget choice for socket style is white plastic, which remains the standard in most houses. White isn't the only option however. Coloured plastic sockets are relatively cheap and different, while those with a larger budget can go for clear switch

plates – designed to be 'invisible' against your décor – stone, marble, wood or even patterned plates. Metal plates are also popular, and are readily available in styles from ornate period style – where brass, gold plate and bronze are particularly good – to contemporary minimalist settings, which suit chrome, steel and nickel.

Reclaimed switches and sockets are an excellent choice for those renovating a period property or self-building a traditional style home. However, they can be tricky to install and you may experience difficulties in finding a sufficient number of the matching pieces to fill a room.

ELECTRICAL FITTINGS

KEY

SEE ALSO: LIGHTING - Lighting Controls and Accessories

PRODUCT TYPES: 1= Sockets 2 = Switches
3 = Plugs 4 = Terminal Connectors
5 = Fuse Boxes 6 = Other

OTHER: ▽ Reclaimed ⌐ On-line shopping
✎ Bespoke ✋ Hand-made ECO Ecological

A ALEXANDER & SON (ELECTRICAL) LTD
9 Cathkinview Road, Mount Florida,
Glasgow, Lanarkshire, G42 9EH
Area of Operation: North East England, Scotland
Tel: 0141 632 0868 **Fax:** 0141 636 0020
Email: christine@alexander-electrical.co.uk
Web: www.alexander-electrical.co.uk
Product Type: 1, 2, 3, 4, 5, 6

ABSOLUTE ELECTRICS
47 Tanfield Road, Croydon, Surrey, CR0 1AN
Area of Operation: Greater London, South East England
Tel: 0208 681 7835 **Fax:** 0208 667 9836
Email: mark@absolute-electrics.co.uk
Web: www.absolute-electrics.com
Product Type: 1, 2, 3, 4, 5, 6

ARCHITECTURAL IRONMONGERY LTD
28 Kyrle Street, Ross-on-Wye, Herefordshire, HR9 7DB
Area of Operation: Worldwide
Tel: 01989 567946 **Fax:** 01989 567946
Email: info@arciron.co.uk
Web: www.arciron.com ⌐ **Product Type:** 1, 2, 6

BROMLEIGHS
Unit 12, Goudhurst Road, Marden, Kent, TN12 9NW
Area of Operation: UK (Excluding Ireland)
Tel: 0800 018 3993 **Product Type:** 1, 2, 3

BROUGHTONS OF LEICESTER
The Old Cinema, 69 Cropston Road, Anstey,
Leicester, Leicestershire, LE7 7BP
Area of Operation: Worldwide
Tel: 0116 235 2555 **Fax:** 0116 234 1188
Email: sale@broughtons.com
Web: www.broughtons.com ⌐

BYRON
Byron House, 34 Sherwood Roaad, Aston Fields
Industrial Estate, Bromsgrove, West Midlands, B60 3DR
Area of Operation: Worldwide
Tel: 01527 557700 **Fax:** 01527 557701
Email: info@chbyron.com
Web: www.chbyron.com **Product Type:** 1, 2, 6

CONTACTUM LTD
Victoria Works, Edgeware Road, Cricklewood,
London, Greater London, NW2 6LF
Area of Operation: Worldwide
Tel: 0208 452 6366 **Fax:** 0208 208 3340
Email: info@contactum.co.uk
Web: www.contactum.co.uk
Product Type: 1, 2, 5, 6

DANLERS LIMITED
Vincients Road, Bumpers Farm Industrial Estate,
Chippenham, Wiltshire, SN14 6NQ
Area of Operation: Europe
Tel: 01249 443377 **Fax:** 01249 443388
Email: sales@danlers.co.uk
Web: www.danlers.co.uk **Product Type:** 2

DMS FLOW MEASURENT & CONTROL LTD
The Lodge, 9 Mansfield Road , Eastwood,
Nottingham , Nottinghamshire, NG16 3AQ
Area of Operation: UK & Ireland
Tel: 01773 534 555
Fax: 01773 534 666
Email: sales@dmsltd.com
Web: www.dmsltd.com
Product Type: 6

DORO UK LTD
1 High Street, Chalfont St. Peter,
Buckinghamshire, SL9 9QE
Area of Operation: Europe
Tel: 08708 610200
Email: acsales@doro-uk.com
Web: www.doro-uk.com **Product Type:** 6

ELECTRICALSHOP.NET
81 Kinson Road, Wallisdown,
Bournemouth, Dorset, BH10 4DG
Area of Operation: UK (Excluding Ireland)
Tel: 0870 027 3730 **Fax:** 0870 027 3731
Email: sales@electricalshop.net
Web: www.electricalshop.net ⌐
Product Type: 1, 2, 3, 4, 5, 6

EURO BATHROOMS
102 Annareagh Road, Richhill, Co Armagh, BT61 9JY
Area of Operation: Ireland Only
Tel: 028 3887 9996 **Fax:** 028 3887 9996
Product Type: 1, 2, 3, 4, 5, 6

FOCUS SB
Napier Road, Castleham Industrial Estate,
St-Leonards-on-Sea, East Sussex, TN38 9NY
Area of Operation: Worldwide
Tel: 01424 440734 **Fax:** 01424 853862
Email: sales@focus-sb.co.uk
Web: www.focus-sb.co.uk
Product Type: 1, 2 **Other Info:** ✎

G & H PERIOD FITTINGS
Unit 12, Charles Street, Worcester,
Worcestershire, WR1 2AQ
Area of Operation: UK & Ireland
Tel: 01905 21342 **Fax:** 01905 26161
Email: duncansimpson.gh@btconnect.com
Web: www.gandhperiodfittings.co.uk
Product Type: 1, 2

GET PLC
Key Point, 3-17 High Street, Potters Bar,
Hertfordshire, EN6 5AJ
Area of Operation: Worldwide
Tel: 01707 601601 **Fax:** 01707 601701
Email: info@getplc.com
Web: www.getplc.com **Product Type:** 1, 2, 5, 6

GIBBS AND DANDY PLC
226 Dallow Road, Luton, Bedfordshire, LU1 1YB
Area of Operation: South East England
Tel: 01582 798798 **Fax:** 01582 798799
Email: luton@gibbsanddandy.com
Web: www.gibbsanddandy.com
Product Type: 1, 2, 3, 4, 5, 6

GO FIX IT LTD
Unit 10 Castle Industrial Estate, Louvain Street, Off
Oldham Road, Failsworth, Manchester, M35 0HB
Area of Operation: UK (Excluding Ireland)
Tel: 0161 681 4109 **Fax:** 0161 681 8169
Email: admin@gofixit.co.uk
Web: www.gofixit.co.uk ⌐
Product Type: 1, 2, 3, 4, 6

GREENBROOK ELECTRICAL PLC
West Road, Harlow, Essex, CM20 2BG
Area of Operation: Worldwide
Tel: 01279 772772 **Fax:** 01279 422007
Email: sales@greenbrook.co.uk
Web: www.greenbrook.co.uk
Product Type: 1, 2, 3, 4

HAF DESIGNS LTD
HAF House, Mead Lane, Hertford,
Hertfordshire, SG13 7AP
Area of Operation: UK & Ireland
Tel: 0800 389 8821 **Fax:** 01992 505705
Email: info@hafltd.co.uk
Web: www.hafdesigns.co.uk ⌐ **Product Type:** 1, 2

HAMILTON LITESTAT
Quarry Industrial Estate, Mere, Wiltshire, BA12 6LA
Area of Operation: Worldwide
Tel: 01747 860088 **Fax:** 01747 861032
Email: info@hamilton-litestat.com
Web: www.hamilton-litestat.com
Product Type: 1, 2

HIDDEN HOME AUTOMATION
23 Cottesbrooke Park, Heartlands, Daventry,
Northamptonshire, NN11 8YL
Tel: 01327 872435 **Fax:** 01327 315287
Email: info@hiddenhomeautomation.co.uk
Web: www.hiddenhomeautomation.co.uk

HOUSE OF BRASS
122 North Sherwood Street, Nottingham,
Nottinghamshire, NG1 4EF
Area of Operation: Worldwide
Tel: 0115 947 5430 **Fax:** 0115 947 5430
Email: sales@houseofbrass.co.uk
Web: www.houseofbrass.co.uk ⌐
Product Type: 1, 2

INTELLIGENTHOME
Langham House, Suite 401,
302 Regent Street, London, W1B 3HH
Area of Operation: UK & Ireland
Tel: 0207 394 9344 **Fax:** 0207 252 3879
Email: sales.en@intelligenthome.co.uk
Web: www.intelligenthome.co.uk
Product Type: 1, 2, 6 **Other Info:** ✎

INTERACTIVE HOMES LTD
Unit 43, Centerprise House, New Greenham Park,
Thatcham, Berkshire, RG19 6HP
Area of Operation: UK (Excluding Ireland)
Tel: 01635 49111 **Fax:** 01635 40735
Email: sales@interactivehomes.co.uk
Web: www.interactivehomes.co.uk **Product Type:** 2

IRONMONGERY DIRECT
Unit 2-3 Eldon Way Trading Estate,
Eldon Way, Hockley, Essex, SS5 4AD
Area of Operation: Worldwide
Tel: 01702 562770 **Fax:** 01702 562799
Email: sales@ironmongerydirect.com
Web: www.ironmongerydirect.com ⌐
Product Type: 1, 2

JOHN CLAYTON LIGHTING LTD
Worthingham House, Deep Lane,
Hagworthingham, Lincolnshire, PE23 4LZ
Area of Operation: Europe
Tel: 0800 389 6395 **Fax:** 0870 240 6417
Email: enquiries@jclighting.com
Web: www.flexidim.com **Product Type:** 2, 6

LAMPS & LIGHTING LTD
Bridgewater Court, Network 65 Business Park,
Burnley, Lancashire, BB11 5ST
Area of Operation: UK (Excluding Ireland)
Tel: 01282 448666 **Fax:** 01282 417703
Email: sales@lamps-lighting.co.uk
Web: www.lampslighting.co.uk ⌐
Product Type: 1, 2

LIGHT RIGHT LTD
SBC House, Restmor Way,
Wallington, Surrey, SM6 7AH
Tel: 0208 255 2022 **Fax:** 0208 286 1900
Email: enquiries@lightright.co.uk **Product Type:** 6

LIGHTING DIRECT 2U LIMITED
Venture Court, Broadlands,
Wolverhampton, West Midlands, WV10 6TB
Area of Operation: UK & Ireland
Tel: 0870 600 0076
Email: sales@lightingdirect2u.co.uk
Web: www.lightingdirect2u.co.uk ⌐
Product Type: 1, 2

MR RESISTOR
21 Lydden Road , Wandsworth, London, SW18 4LT
Area of Operation: Worldwide
Tel: 0208 874 2234 **Fax:** 0208 871 2262
Email: info@mr-resistor.co.uk
Web: www.mr-resistor.co.uk ⌐
Product Type: 1, 2, 3, 4, 5, 6

OXFORD LIGHTING & ELECTRICAL SOLUTIONS
Unit 117, Culham Site No 1, Station Road, Culham,
Abingdon, Oxfordshire, OX14 3DA
Area of Operation: UK (Excluding Ireland)
Tel: 01865 408522 **Fax:** 01865 408522
Email: olessales@tiscali.co.uk
Web: www.oles.co.uk ⌐ **Product Type:** 2

PESTWEST ELECTRONICS
Denholme Drive, Ossett, West Yorkshire, WF5 9NB
Area of Operation: Worldwide
Tel: 01924 268500 **Fax:** 01924 273591
Email: info@pestwest.com
Web: www.pestwest.com **Product Type:** 6

PREMIER ELECTRICAL & SECURITY SERVICES LTD
Old Tiles, Water Lane, Storrington,
West Sussex, RH20 3LX
Area of Operation: UK (Excluding Ireland)
Tel: 01903 746697
Fax: 01903 746690
Email: info@premierelectrical.com
Web: www.premierelectrical.com
Product Type: 1, 2, 3, 4, 5, 6

PYRAMID ELECTRICAL & ALARMS LIMITED
68 Forresters Road, Burbage, Hinckley,
Leicestershire, Leicestershire, LE10 2RX
Area of Operation: East England, Greater London,
Midlands & Mid Wales, North East England, North
West England and North Wales
Tel: 01455 458325
Fax: 01455 458 325
Email: pyramid@dotdotnetdot.net
Web: www.pyramidelectrical.net
Product Type: 1, 2, 3, 4, 5, 6

QVS ELECTRICAL
4C The Birches Industrial Estate, Imberhorne Lane,
East Grinstead, West Sussex, RH19 1XZ
Area of Operation: Worldwide
Tel: 0800 197 6565 **Fax:** 0800 197 6566
Email: sales@qvsdirect.co.uk
Web: www.qvs.com ⌐ **Product Type:** 1, 2, 6

ROCOCO SYSTEMS & DESIGN
26 Danbury Street, London, N1 8JU
Area of Operation: Europe
Tel: 0207 454 1234 **Fax:** 0207 870 0888
Email: sales@rococosystems.com
Web: www.rococosystems.com

SCHNEIDER ELECTRIC
Stafford Park 5, Telford, Shropshire, TF3 3BL
Area of Operation: UK (Excluding Ireland)
Tel: 0870 608 8608
Fax: 0870 608 8606
Email: sean.jordan@gb.schneider-electric.com
Web: www.squared.co.uk **Product Type:** 1, 2, 5, 6

SCOLMORE INTERNATIONAL LIMITED
1 Scolmore Park, Landsberg, Lichfield Road
Industrial Estate, Tamworth, Staffordshire, B79 7XB
Area of Operation: UK & Ireland
Tel: 01827 63454 **Fax:** 01827 63362
Email: sales@scolmore.com
Web: www.scolmore.com
Product Type: 1, 2, 3, 4, 5, 6

SETSQUARE LTD
Valley Industries, Hadlow Road,
Tonbridge, Kent, TN11 0AH
Area of Operation: Worldwide
Tel: 01732 851888
Fax: 01732 851853
Email: mah@setsquare.co.uk
Web: www.setsquare.co.uk
Product Type: 2 **Other Info:** ECO

SLIMTRIMS LIMITED
Mitton Mill Industrial Estate, Mill Road,
Stourport-on-Severn, Worcestershire, DY13 9BL
Area of Operation: Europe
Tel: 01299 823824 **Fax:** 01299 823824
Email: info@slimtrims.com
Web: www.slimtrims.com **Product Type:** 6

SUSSEX BRASSWARE
Napier Road, Castleham Industrial Estate, St
Leonards-on-Sea, East Sussex, TN38 9NY
Area of Operation: Worldwide
Tel: 01424 857913 **Fax:** 01424 853862
Email: sales@sussexbrassware.co.uk
Web: www.sussexbrassware.co.uk ⌐
Product Type: 1, 2, 6

**Please mention
The Homebuilder's
Handbook
when you call**

SWITCH TO WOOD
Unit 4, Firsland Park Estate, Henfield Road,
Albourne, West Sussex, BN6 9JJ
Area of Operation: Worldwide
Tel: 01273 495999   **Fax:** 01273 495019
Email: sales@switchtowood.co.uk
Web: www.switchtowood.co.uk
Product Type: 1, 2

TLC ELECTRICAL WHOLESALERS
TLC Building, Off Fleming Way,
Crawley, West Sussex, RH10 9JY
Area of Operation: Worldwide
Tel: 01293 565630   **Fax:** 01293 425234
Email: sales@tlc-direct.co.uk
Web: www.tlc-direct.co.uk
Product Type: 1, 2, 3, 4, 5, 6

DISCOUNTED PRICES FROM TLC ELECTRICAL!

Area of Operation: Worldwide
Tel: 01293 565630
Fax: 01293 425234
Email: sales@tlc-direct.co.uk
Web: www.tlc-direct.co.uk

TLC Electrical Wholesalers offer ' below trade' prices
on over 10,000 products.
22 Warehouses nationwide.
Online website: www.tlc-direct.co.uk
Free Catalogue (24hr Catalogue line) 01293 42 00 00

TOOLSTATION
Express Park, Bridgwater, Somerset, TA6 4RN
Area of Operation: UK (Excluding Ireland)
Tel: 0808 100 7211   **Fax:** 0808 100 7210
Email: info@toolstation.com
Web: www.toolstation.com
Product Type: 1, 2, 3, 4, 5, 6

UNIFIX LTD
St Georges House, Grove Lane, Smethwick,
Birmingham, West Midlands, B66 2QT
Area of Operation: Europe
Tel: 0800 096 1110   **Fax:** 0800 096 1115
Email: sales@unifix.com
Web: www.unifix-online.co.uk
Product Type: 1, 2, 3, 4, 5, 6

WANDSWORTH GROUP LTD
Albert Drive, Sheerwater, Woking, Surrey, GU21 5SE
Area of Operation: UK (Excluding Ireland)
Tel: 01483 713400   **Fax:** 01483 740384
Email: info@wandsworthgroup.com
Web: www.wandsworthgroup.com
Product Type: 1, 2, 3

WANDSWORTH GROUP LTD
Area of Operation: UK
Tel: 01483 713400
Fax: 01483 740384
Email: info@wandsworthgroup.com
Web: www.wandsworthgroup.com
Product Type: 1, 2, 3

Range of high quality electrical accessories
includes light switches, rotary dimmers, wall
sockets, shaver supply units, fused units and
cable and data outlets in 25 elegant finishes

ALTERNATIVE POWER SOURCES

KEY

OTHER: ▽ Reclaimed   On-line shopping
   Bespoke   Hand-made   ECO Ecological

AERODYN-SHOREPOWER
16 Popes Lane, Rockwell Green,
Wellington, Somerset, TA21 9DQ
Area of Operation: UK (Excluding Ireland)
Tel: 01823 666177   **Fax:** 01823 666177
Email: shorepower@ukonline.co.uk

BYRON
Byron House, 34 Sherwood Rd, Aston Fields Industrial
Estate, Bromsgrove, West Midlands, B60 3DR
Area of Operation: Worldwide
Tel: 01527 557700   **Fax:** 01527 557701
Email: info@chbyron.com   **Web:** www.chbyron.com

ENERGY AND ENVIRONMENT LTD
91 Claude Road, Chorlton, Manchester, M21 8DE
Area of Operation: UK & Ireland
Tel: 0161 881 1383
Email: mail@energyenv.co.uk
Web: www.energyenv.co.uk

FIRSTLIGHT ENERGY LIMITED
Riverside Business Centre, River Lawn Road,
Tonbridge, Kent, TN9 1EP
Area of Operation: Europe
Tel: 0172 783534   **Fax:** 01732 362626
Email: info@firstlightenergy.com
Web: www.firstlightenergy.com

GENERATORS NOW
The Birches , Megg Lane, Chipperfield,
Hertfordshire, WD49JW
Area of Operation: UK (Excluding Ireland)
Tel: 01923 262818   **Fax:** 01923 262882
Email: jon@generatorsnow.co.uk
Web: www.generatorsnow.co.uk

JONES NASH ECO HOMES
12 Lee Street, Louth, Lincolnshire, LN11 9HJ
Area of Operation: UK (Excluding Ireland)
Tel: 01507 609637   **Fax:** 01507 609637
Email: sd@jones-nash.co.uk
Web: www.eco-houses.co.uk

POWERCALL UK
Valley View Business Park, Picket Piece,
Andover, Hampshire , SP11 6LU
Area of Operation: UK (Excluding Ireland)
Tel: 0870 758 3210   **Fax:** 0870 758 3215
Email: sales@powersupport.co.uk

POWERTECH SOLAR LTD
21 Haviland Road, Forndown Industrial Estate,
Wimborne, Dorset, BH21 7RZ
Area of Operation: UK & Ireland
Tel: 01202 890234   **Fax:** 01202 876252
Email: sales@solar.org.uk
Web: www.solar.org.uk

SOLARUK
Unit 5, The Estate Yard Buildings, Eridge Green Road,
Tunbridge Wells, Kent, TN3 9JR
Area of Operation: Worldwide
Tel: 01892 667320   **Fax:** 01892 667622
Email: info@SolarUK.net
Web: www.SolarUK.net

THE GREEN SHOP
Cheltenham Road, Bisley, Nr Stroud,
Gloucestershire, GL6 7BX
Area of Operation: UK & Ireland
Tel: 01452 770629   **Fax:** 01452 770104
Email: paint@greenshop.co.uk
Web: www.greenshop.co.uk

WARMFLOORS LTD
Unit1 Aire Street, Cross Hills,
Keighley, West Yorkshire, BD20 7RT
Area of Operation: UK & Ireland
Tel: 0800 0433195   **Fax:** 01535 631196
Email: sales@warmfloorsonline.com
Web: www.warmfloorsonline.com

WIND AND SUN LIMITED
Humber Marsh, Stoke Prior,
Leominster, Herefordshire, HR6 ONR
Area of Operation: UK & Ireland
Tel: 01568 760671   **Fax:** 01568 760484
Email: info@windandsun.co.uk
Web: www.windandsun.co.uk

NOTES

Company Name ....
....
Address ....
....
email ....
Web ....

Company Name ....
....
Address ....
....
email ....
Web ....

Company Name ....
....
Address ....
....
email ....
Web ....

Company Name ....
....
Address ....
....
email ....
Web ....

Company Name ....
....
Address ....
....
email ....
Web ....

HEATING, PLUMBING & ELECTRICAL

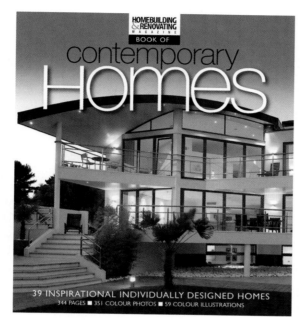

SPONSORED BY: Homebuilding & Renovating Book of Contemporary Homes
Tel: 01527 834435 Web: www.homebuilding.co.uk/bookshop

SMART HOMES & SECURITY

Wireless Technology

Technology in the home – with its long, hanging wires and grey-silver boxes – can be a bit of a nuisance and an eyesore. But today, thanks to the multitude of automated and wireless devices coming onto the market, it's possible to reduce the spaghetti of leads running around your home.

It is possible to hide away a lot of the electronic gubbins in, say, an understairs cupboard or dedicated equipment rack. But you will still need to run wires from the plasma screens and touch-screen control panels back to the equipment. This can be a messy business, requiring pulling up floorboards and channelling cables into walls.

The best solution – and to avoid any disruption at a later date – is to get any pre-wiring done at the very first fix stages.

Indeed, many new homes now feature a Cat5 or Cat5e cable throughout for networking computers/piping music in several rooms as well as co-axial cable for watching TV and video.

However, there is another solution – wireless. While many custom installers are sceptical about the benefits of wireless (partly because it threatens their jobs), it's fair to say that it is already becoming an indispensable function in the hi-tech home.

There are many benefits to going wireless. By using a wireless, or Wi-Fi network, it's possible to connect your home computers without having to trail Ethernet cable around the home. Most laptop computers now come with a wireless chipset built-in but, if not, you can use routers, which distribute the signal to your various computers. Wireless routers cost less than £50.

Another area where wireless is becoming increasingly widespread in the home is the distribution of digital music. Many products, some with built-in hard drives, allow you to listen to different digital tracks in different rooms from the same source.

Despite its advantages, wireless technology still can't do everything in the home. It's fine for home networking and audio distribution, but it's not yet capable of distributing high-quality video or HDTV (High Definition TV) around the home as it requires much greater bandwidth than today's wireless technologies can offer.

Another possible downside of wireless is that, in some cases, it lacks the reliability offered by cables. Wireless signals are more likely to drop out, and are prone to interference from other wireless devices (such as microwave ovens).

Undoubtedly wireless technology is the future, but is it's still relatively early days. For homebuilders, the best option for now would be to pre-wire the home wherever possible and think of wireless as a useful supplementary technology, especially handy for computer and/or audio networking.

Image by Rako Controls Ltd

SMART HOMES & SECURITY

HOME NETWORKING

KEY

OTHER: ▽ Reclaimed 🖱 On-line shopping ✎ Bespoke 🤚 Hand-made ECO Ecological

A.C.E. - AUTOMATION CONTRACTORS & ENGINEERS
126 Heath Hill Avenue, Brighton, East Sussex, BN2 4LS
Area of Operation: UK (Excluding Ireland)
Tel: 01273 665468   **Fax:** 07884 599411
Email: sales@ace-automation.co.uk
Web: www.ace-automation.co.uk

ABITANA NV
4 Myson Way, Raynham Road Industrial Estate,
Bishop's Stortford, Hertfordshire, CM23 5JZ
Area of Operation: Europe
Tel: 01279 757775   **Fax:** 01279 653535
Email: sminns@minitran.co.uk
Web: www.minitran.co.uk 🖱

ADV AUDIO VISUAL INSTALLATIONS LTD
12 York Place, Leeds, West Yorkshire, LS1 2DS
Area of Operation: North East England, North West
England and North Wales
Tel: 0870 199 5755
Email: shaun@adv-installs.co.uk
Web: www.homecinemainstalls.co.uk

ALDOUS SYSTEMS (EUROPE) LTD
Unit 3 Printers End,
Insignia Industrial Estate, Gatehouse Way,
Aylesbury, Buckinghamshire, HP19 8DB
Area of Operation: Europe
Tel: 0870 240 1162   **Fax:** 0207 691 7844
Email: sales@aldoussystems.co.uk
Web: www.aldoussystems.co.uk

ANDROMEDA TELEMATICS LTD
Tec. 6, Byfleet Technical Centre,
Canada Road, Byfleet, Surrey, KT14 7JX
Area of Operation: Europe
Tel: 01932 341200   **Fax:** 01932 331980
Email: sales@andromeda-telematics.com
Web: www.andromeda-telematics.com

AUDIO IMAGES
284 Glossop Road, Sheffield, South Yorkshire, S10 2HS
Area of Operation: Worldwide
Tel: 0114 273 7893   **Fax:** 0114 275 5371
Email: sheffield@audio-images.co.uk
Web: www.audio-images.co.uk

AUDIO T CUSTOM INSTALLATIONS
11 Charter Place, High Street, Egham, Surrey, TW20 9EA
Area of Operation: East England, Greater London,
South East England
Tel: 01784 479423   **Fax:** 01784 479425
Email: custom@audio-t.co.uk
Web: www.audio-t.co.uk/custom

AUDIOVISION
46 Market Square, St Neots, Cambridgeshire, PE19 2AF
Area of Operation: Europe
Tel: 01480 471202   **Fax:** 01480 471115
Email: sales@audiovisiononline.co.uk
Web: www.audiovisiononline.co.uk 🖱

BESPOKE INSTALLATIONS
1 Rogers Close, Tiverton, Devon, EX16 6UW
Area of Operation: South West England and South Wales
Tel: 01884 243497
Email: michael@bespoke.biz
Web: www.bespoke.biz

CUSTOM INSTALLATIONS
Custom House, 51 Baymead Lane,
North Petherton, Bridgwater, Somerset, TA6 6RN
Area of Operation: South West England and South Wales
Tel: 01278 662555   **Fax:** 01278 662975
Email: roger@custom-installations.co.uk
Web: www.custom-installations.co.uk

D&T ELECTRONICS
Unit 9A, Cranborne Industrial Estate, Cranborne
Road, Potters Bar, Hertfordshire, EN6 3JN
Area of Operation: UK (Excluding Ireland)
Tel: 0870 241 5891   **Fax:** 01707 653570
Email: info@dandt.co.uk   **Web:** www.dandt.co.uk

DBCC LIMITED
Woodland View, Winchester Road,
Fair Oak, Eastleigh, Hampshire, SO50 7HD
Area of Operation: UK (Excluding Ireland)
Tel: 02380 692 555
Email: info@dbcc.co.uk   **Web:** www.dbcc.co.uk

DECKORUM LTD
4c Royal Oak Lane, Pirton,
Stevenage, Hertfordshire, SG5 3QT
Area of Operation: East England, Greater London,
South East England
Tel: 08450 204360   **Fax:** 08450 204361
Email: gary.mills@deckorum.com
Web: www.deckorum.com

DESIGN 2 AUTOMATE
Unit 14 Deanfield Court, Link 59 Business Park,
Clitheroe, Lancashire, BB7 1QS
Area of Operation: UK & Ireland
Tel: 01200 444 356   **Fax:** 01200 444 359
Email: info@d2a.co.uk   **Web:** www.d2a.co.uk

DIGITAL DECOR
Sonas House, Button End, Harston,
Cambridge, Cambridgeshire, CB2 5NX
Area of Operation: East England, Greater London
Tel: 01223 870935   **Fax:** 01223 870935
Email: seamus@digital-decor.co.uk
Web: www.digital-decor.co.uk

DIGITAL PLUMBERS
Digital Plumbers, 84 The Chase, London, SW4 0NF
Area of Operation: Greater London
Tel: 0207 819 1730   **Fax:** 0207 819 1731
Email: info@digitalplumbers.com
Web: www.digitalplumbers.com

DISCOVERY SYSTEMS LTD
1 Corn Mill Close, The Spindles,
Ashton in Makerfield, Wigan,
Lancashire, WN4 0PX
Area of Operation: North West England and North Wales
Tel: 01942 723756
Email: mike@discoverysystems.co.uk
Web: www.discoverysystems.co.uk

DOMINTELL
4 Myson Way, Raynham Road Industrial Estate,
Bishop's Stortford, Hertfordshire, CM23 5JZ
Area of Operation: UK (Excluding Ireland)
Tel: 01279 757775
Fax: 01279 653535
Email: njackson@minitran.co.uk
Web: www.minitran.co.uk 🖱

EAST TECHNOLOGY INTEGRATORS
85 Langtons Meadow, Farnham Common,
Slough, Berkshire, SL2 3NS
Area of Operation: Greater London, South East England
Tel: 01753 642367
Email: sales@east-ti.co.uk
Web: www.east-ti.co.uk

EASYCOMM
1 George House, Church Street,
Buntingford, Hertfordshire, SG9 9AS
Area of Operation: UK (Excluding Ireland)
Tel: 0800 389 9459
Email: steve@ezcomm.co.uk
Web: www.ezcomm.co.uk

EASYLIFE AUTOMATION LIMITED
Kullan House,
12 Meadowfield Road,
Stocksfield, Northumberland, NE43 7QX
Area of Operation: UK (Excluding Ireland)
Tel: 01661 844159
Fax: 01661 842594
Email: enquiries@easylifeautomation.com
Web: www.easylifeautomation.com

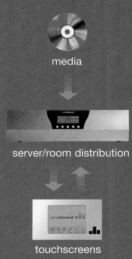

EU SOLUTIONS
Maghull Business Centre,
1 Liverpool Road North, Maghull, Liverpool, L31 2HB
Area of Operation: UK & Ireland
Tel: 0870 160 1660   **Fax:** 0151 526 8849
Email: ths@blueyonder.co.uk
Web: www.totalhomesolutions.co.uk

EU SOLUTIONS
Area of Operation: UK & Ireland
Tel: 0870 160 1660
Fax: 0151 526 8849
Email: ths@blueyonder.co.uk
Web: www.totalhomesolutions.co.uk

NIKO's intelligent management system offers you the possibility to integrate all functions relating to; lighting, audio, entertainment, access control, security, sun blinds, ventilation, heating and cooling.

FAITH & GANTRY LTD
Gainsborough House, 62 Hatfield Road,
Ipswich, Suffolk, IP3 9AF
Area of Operation: East England, Greater London
Tel: 01473 714002   **Fax:** 01473 714060
Email: lindsey@faithandgantry.com
Web: www.faithandgantry.com

FINITE SOLUTIONS - HOME CINEMA AND MULTI ROOM AUDIO
Pavilion Business Centre, Stanningley Road,
Leeds, West Yorkshire, LS28 6NB
Area of Operation: UK (Excluding Ireland)
Tel: 0113 255 4765   **Fax:** 0113 255 4742
Email: info@finitesolutions.co.uk
Web: www.finitesolutions.co.uk

FUSION GROUP
Unit 4 Winston Avenue, Croft,
Leicester, Leicestershire, LE9 3GQ
Tel: 08450 204360   **Fax:** 08450 204361
Email: gary.mills@fusiongroup.uk.com
Web: www.fusiongroup.uk.com

To recommend a company for inclusion in the next edition of The Homebuilder's Handbook, email

customerservice@centaur.co.uk

HELLERMANN TYTON
43-45 Salthouse Road, Brackmills,
Northampton, Northamptonshire, NN4 7EX
Area of Operation: Worldwide
Tel: 01604 707420   **Fax:** 01604 705454
Email: sales@htdata.co.uk
Web: www.homenetworksciences.com

HELLERMANNTYTON
Area of Operation: Worldwide
Tel: 01604 707420
Fax: 01604 705454
Email: sales@htdata.co.uk
Web: www.homenetworksciences.com
Product Type: 1, 2, 3

Hellermann Tyton Home Network Sciences provide a networking infrastructure to support home communications and entertainment. The modular system allows integration of Telephony, Data, TV, CCTV and Audio Solutions.

HIDDEN HOME AUTOMATION
23 Cottesbrooke Park, Heartlands,
Daventry, Northamptonshire, NN11 8YL
Area of Operation: UK (Excluding Ireland)
Tel: 01327 872435 **Fax:** 01327 315287
Email: info@hiddenhomeautomation.co.uk
Web: www.hiddenhomeautomation.co.uk

HOME NETWORKING ONLINE
Unit 3, Printers End, Gethouse Way,
Aylesbury, Buckinghamshire, HP19 8DB
Area of Operation: Europe
Tel: 0870 240 1162   **Fax:** 0207 691 7844
Email: sales@home-networking-online.co.uk
Web: www.home-networking-online.co.uk

HOUSEHOLD AUTOMATION
Foxways, Pinkhurst Lane, Slinfold,
Horsham, West Sussex, RH13 0QR
Tel: 0870 330 0071   **Fax:** 0870 330 0072
Email: ellis-andrew@btconnect.com
Web: www.household-automation.co.uk

IBBD LTD
HomeLifeWorkLife Showroom, Unit 6 Link Trade Park, Penarth Road, Cardiff, CF11 8TQ
Area of Operation: South West England and South Wales
Tel: 029 2071 3460   **Email:** info@ibbd.co.uk
Web: www.homelifeworklife.co.uk

IDOMUS
23 Wornal Park, Menmarsh Road, Worminghall,
Aylesbury, Buckinghamshire, HP18 9PH
Tel: 0845 644 3330   **Fax:** 0845 644 2713
Email: info@iDomus.co.uk **Web:** www.iDomus.co.uk

INTERCONNECTION LTD
12 Chamberlayne Road, Moreton Hall Industrial Estate, Bury St Edmunds, Suffolk, IP32 7EY
Area of Operation: South East England
Tel: 01284 768676   **Fax:** 01284 767161
Email: sales@interconnectionltd.co.uk
Web: www.interconnectionltd.co.uk

IPHOMENET.COM
1045 Stratford Road, Hall Green,
Birmingham, West Midlands, B28 8AS
Area of Operation: UK & Ireland
Tel: 0121 778 6300   **Fax:** 0121 778 1117
Email: info@iphomenet.com
Web: www.iphomenet.com

IQYOURHOME.COM LTD
Unit D10, Chaucer Business Park, Watery Lane,
Kemsing, Sevenoaks, Kent, TN15 6YU
Area of Operation: UK & Ireland
Tel: 01732 763888   **Fax:** 01732 763351
Email: info@iqyourhome.com
Web: www.iqyourhome.com

KENT HOME CINEMA CENTRE
69 London Road, Southborough,
Tunbridge Wells, Kent, TN4 0PA
Area of Operation: UK & Ireland
Tel: 01892 535007   **Fax:** 01892 533334
Email: andrew@kenthomecinema.co.uk
Web: www.av-sales.co.uk

LIVING CONTROL LTD
The Flyer's Way, Westerham, Kent, TN16 1DE
Area of Operation: Worldwide
Tel: 0845 094 0079
Email: thh@livingcontrol.com
Web: www.livingcontrol.com

LIVING CONTROL
Area of Operation: Worldwide
Tel: 0845 094 0079
Email: THH@livingcontrol.com
Web: www.livingcontrol.com

Multi-room Audio and Video systems

The widest choice of entertainment is at your fingertips anywhere in the home. No wires, no gear, no fuss. Living Control is the luxury multi-room system designed for those who value performance and reliability.

LIVING CONTROL

ColourPad

From the kitchen, bathroom, bedroom, living room – even outside on the patio, select CD, MP3, Radio, TV, DVD, even HD video anywhere 'by name' from this full-colour touch-screen, which is no bigger than a double-gang socket and available in a rage of finishes.

LIVING CONTROL

MusicBox-NT

You won't need a degree in IT to experience the freedom and convenience of wireless control from the MusicBox-NT. Equipped with built-in 54MB Wi-Fi networking and compatible with 802.11B/G standards, MusicBox-NT is like MusicBox3 but gives you complete control of room, source and volume from a wireless PC or Pocket PC.

MULTIROOM AUDIO
4 Clement Way, Cawton, Rugby, Warwickshire, CV22 7FH
Area of Operation: UK (Excluding Ireland)
Tel: 01788 521248
Fax: 0870 762 8242
Email: sales@multiroom-audio.co.uk
Web: www.multiroom-audio.co.uk

NODE ZERO LTD
Unit 4a Winston Avenue, Leicester,
Leicestershire, LE9 3GQ
Area of Operation: Europe
Tel: 08700 500248
Fax: 0845 020 4361
Email: jason.neale@nodezero.uk.com
Web: www.nodezero.uk.com

O2M8 LTD
P.O.Box 7716, Newbury, Berkshire, RG20 5WU
Area of Operation: UK (Excluding Ireland)
Tel: 07789 207408
Email: john@o2m8.com **Web:** www.o2m8.com

PARK SYSTEMS INTEGRATION LTD
Unit 3 Queen's Park, Earlsway, Team Valley Trading Estate, Gateshead, Tyne & Wear, NE11 0QD
Area of Operation: UK & Ireland
Tel: 0191 497 0770   **Fax:** 0191 497 0772
Email: elife@psi.uk.com
Web: www.psi.uk.com

SPONSORED BY: HOMEBUILDING & RENOVATING BOOK OF CONTEMPORARY HOMES   www.homebuilding.co.uk/bookshop

PHILLSON LTD
144 Rickerscote Road, Stafford,
Staffordshire, ST17 4HE
Area of Operation: UK & Ireland
Tel: 0845 612 0128   **Fax:** 01477 535090
Email: info@phillson.co.uk
Web: www.phillson.co.uk

ROCOCO SYSTEMS & DESIGN
26 Danbury Street, London, N1 8JU
Area of Operation: Europe
Tel: 0207 454 1234   **Fax:** 0207 870 0888
Email: sales@rococosystems.com
Web: www.rococosystems.com

SEISMIC INTERAUDIO
3 Maypole Drive, Kings Hill,
West Malling, Kent, ME19 4BP
Area of Operation: Europe
Tel: 0870 073 4764   **Fax:** 0870 073 4765
Email: info@seismic.co.uk **Web:** www.seismic.co.uk

SIMPLY AUTOMATE
23 Wornal Park, Menmarsh Road, Worminghall,
Aylesbury, Buckinghamshire, HP18 9PH
Area of Operation: Worldwide
Tel: 0845 644 3330   **Fax:** 0845 644 2713
Email: info@simplyautomate.co.uk
Web: www.simplyautomate.co.uk ⌐

SINGLEPOINT NETWORKS LIMITED
Basford Hurst, Churnet Grange,
Cheddleton, Leek, Staffordshire, ST13 7EP
Area of Operation: Worldwide
Tel: 0870 850 2705
Email: info@singlepointnetworks.co.uk
Web: www.singlepointnetworks.co.uk

SMARTHOME CONTROLS
11 Horsted Square, Bell Lane Business Park,
Uckfield, East Sussex, TN22 1QG
Area of Operation: Europe
Tel: 01825 769812   **Fax:** 01825 769813
Email: sales@smarthomecontrols.co.uk
Web: www.smarthomecontrols.co.uk

SMART HOUSE
23 Wornal Park, Menmarsh Road, Worminghall,
Aylesbury, Buckinghamshire, HP18 9PH
Area of Operation: Europe
Tel: 0845 053 3680   **Fax:** 0845 644 2713
Email: info@smarthouse.co.uk
Web: www.smarthouse.co.uk

SUB SYSTEMS INTEGRATION LTD
Studio 19, Hurlingham Studios,
Ranelagh Gardens, London, SW6 3PA
Area of Operation: Greater London
Tel: 0207 796 1459   **Fax:** 0207 796 1469
Email: info@sub.eu.com **Web:** www.sub.eu.com

SYNCHRO NETWORKS LTD
PO Box 219, Whitstable, CT5 3WZ
Area of Operation: UK & Ireland
Tel: 05511 490058   **Fax:** 05511 490059
Email: info@synchro-networks.co.uk
Web: www.home-networking-solutions.co.uk ⌐

TECCHO
Unit 19W, Kilroot Business Park,
Carrickfergus, Co. Antrim, BT38 7PR
Area of Operation: UK & Ireland
Tel: 0845 890 1150   **Fax:** 0870 063 4120
Email: enquiries@teccho.net **Web:** www.teccho.net ⌐

**THE BIG PICTURE -
AV & HOME CINEMA LIMITED**
51 Sutton Road, Walsall, West Midlands, WS1 2PQ
Area of Operation: UK & Ireland
Tel: 01922 623000
Email: info@getthebigpicture.co.uk
Web: www.getthebigpicture.co.uk

THE PLASMA WAREHOUSE GROUP PLC
Sandy Farm Business Park,
The Sands, Farnham, Surrey, GU10 1PX
Tel: 0870 734 5432
Email: sales@plasmawarehouseuk.com
Web: www.plasmawarehouseuk.com ⌐

THE THINKING HOME
The White House, Wilderspool Park, Greenalls
Avenue, Warrington, Cheshire, WA4 6HL
Area of Operation: UK & Ireland
Tel: 0800 881 8319   **Fax:** 0800 881 8329
Email: info@thethinkinghome.com
Web: www.thethinkinghome.com

TRIBUNE SMART HOME
321 Bolton Road, Manchester, M6 7GU
Tel: 0161 736 4011   **Fax:** 0161 736 8355
Email: info@tribunesmarthome.com
Web: www.tribunesmarthome.com

UNITY CONTROL
Pinkhurst Lane, Slinfold,
Horsham, West Sussex, RH13 0QR
Area of Operation: Worldwide
Tel: 01403 791305
Email: info@unitycontrol.co.uk
Web: www.unitycontrol.co.uk

VALTEK
Ardykeohane, Bruff, Co. Limerick, Ireland
Area of Operation: UK & Ireland
Tel: +353 (0)6138 2116
Fax: +353 (0)6138 2032
Email: sales@valtek.biz **Web:** www.valtek.biz

WISELAN LIMITED
27 Old Gloucester Street, London, WC1N 3XX
Area of Operation: UK & Ireland
Tel: 0870 787 2144   **Fax:** 0870 787 8823
Email: sales@wiselan.com
Web: www.wiselan.com ⌐

X-HOME
Unit W Williamsons Holdings,
Uphall, West Lothian, EH52 6PA
Area of Operation: UK (Excluding Ireland)
Tel: 0845 130 1091   **Fax:** 0845 130 1092
Email: sales@xhome.biz **Web:** www.xhome.biz

WIRELESS NETWORKS

KEY
OTHER: ▽ Reclaimed   ⌐ On-line shopping
✐ Bespoke ✋Hand-made   ECO Ecological

AUDIO IMAGES
284 Glossop Road, Sheffield,
South Yorkshire, S10 2HS
Area of Operation: Worldwide
Tel: 0114 273 7893   **Fax:** 0114 275 5371
Email: sheffield@audio-images.co.uk
Web: www.audio-images.co.uk

AUDIO T CUSTOM INSTALLATIONS
11 Charter Place, High Street, Egham, Surrey, TW20 9EA
Area of Operation: East England, Greater London,
South East England
Tel: 01784 479423   **Fax:** 01784 479425
Email: custom@audio-t.co.uk
Web: www.audio-t.co.uk/custom

AUDIOVISION
46 Market Square, St Neots, Cambridgeshire, PE19 2AF
Area of Operation: Europe
Tel: 01480 471202   **Fax:** 01480 471115
Email: sales@audiovisiononline.co.uk
Web: www.audiovisiononline.co.uk ⌐

BESPOKE INSTALLATIONS
1 Rogers Close, Tiverton, Devon, EX16 6UW
Area of Operation: South West England and South Wales
Tel: 01884 243497   **Email:** michael@bespoke.biz
Web: www.bespoke.biz

D&T ELECTRONICS
Unit 9A, Cranborne Industrial Estate, Cranborne
Road, Potters Bar, Hertfordshire, EN6 3JN
Area of Operation: UK (Excluding Ireland)
Tel: 0870 241 5891   **Fax:** 01707 653570
Email: info@dandt.co.uk
Web: www.dandt.co.uk

DECKORUM LTD
4c Royal Oak Lane, Pirton,
Stevenage, Hertfordshire, SG5 3QT
Area of Operation: East England,
Greater London, South East England
Tel: 08450 204360   **Fax:** 08450 204361
Email: gary.mills@deckorum.com
Web: www.deckorum.com

DIGITAL DECOR
Sonas House, Button End, Harston,
Cambridge, Cambridgeshire, CB2 5NX
Area of Operation: East England, Greater London
Tel: 01223 870935
Fax: 01223 870935
Email: seamus@digital-decor.co.uk
Web: www.digital-decor.co.uk

DORCOM LTD
11 Lyndhurst Road, Hove, East Sussex, BN3 6FA
Area of Operation: UK & Ireland
Tel: 0845 450 2013   **Fax:** 0845 450 2014
Email: sales@teleporter.co.uk
Web: www.teleporter.co.uk

EAST TECHNOLOGY INTEGRATORS
85 Langtons Meadow, Farnham Common,
Slough, Berkshire, SL2 3NS
Area of Operation: Greater London, South East England
Tel: 01753 642367
Email: sales@east-ti.co.uk **Web:** www.east-ti.co.uk

FAITH & GANTRY LTD
Gainsborough House, 62 Hatfield Road,
Ipswich, Suffolk, IP3 9AF
Area of Operation: East England, Greater London
Tel: 01473 714002   **Fax:** 01473 714060
Email: lindsey@faithandgantry.com
Web: www.faithandgantry.com

**FINITE SOLUTIONS - HOME CINEMA
AND MULTI ROOM AUDIO**
Pavilion Business Centre, Stanningley Road,
Leeds, West Yorkshire, LS28 6NB
Area of Operation: UK (Excluding Ireland)
Tel: 0113 255 4765   **Fax:** 0113 255 4742
Email: info@finitesolutions.co.uk
Web: www.finitesolutions.co.uk

FUSION GROUP
Unit 4 Winston Avenue, Croft,
Leicester, Leicestershire, LE9 3GQ
Area of Operation: UK (Excluding Ireland)
Tel: 08450 204360
Fax: 08450 204361
Email: gary.mills@fusiongroup.uk.com
Web: www.fusiongroup.uk.com

HOME NETWORKING ONLINE
Unit 3, Printers End, Gethouse Way,
Aylesbury, Buckinghamshire, HP19 8DB
Area of Operation: Europe
Tel: 0870 240 1162
Fax: 0207 691 7844
Email: sales@home-networking-online.co.uk
Web: www.home-networking-online.co.uk ⌐

IBBD LTD
HomeLifeWorkLife Showroom, Unit 6 Link Trade
Park, Penarth Road, Cardiff, CF11 8TQ
Area of Operation: South West England and South Wales
Tel: 029 2071 3460   **Email:** info@ibbd.co.uk
Web: www.homelifeworklife.co.uk

IDOMUS
23 Wornal Park, Menmarsh Road, Worminghall,
Aylesbury, Buckinghamshire, HP18 9PH
Area of Operation: Worldwide
Tel: 0845 644 3330   **Fax:** 0845 644 2713
Email: info@iDomus.co.uk
Web: www.iDomus.co.uk ⌐

KENT HOME CINEMA CENTRE
69 London Road, Southborough,
Tunbridge Wells, Kent, TN4 0PA
Area of Operation: UK & Ireland
Tel: 01892 535007   **Fax:** 01892 533334
Email: andrew@kenthomecinema.co.uk
Web: www.av-sales.co.uk ⌐

MULTIROOM AUDIO
4 Clement Way, Cawton, Rugby,
Warwickshire, CV22 7FH
Area of Operation: UK (Excluding Ireland)
Tel: 01788 521248   **Fax:** 0870 762 8242
Email: sales@multiroom-audio.co.uk
Web: www.multiroom-audio.co.uk ⌐

NODE ZERO LTD
Unit 4a Winston Avenue,
Leicester, Leicestershire, LE9 3GQ
Area of Operation: UK & Ireland
Tel: 08700 500248   **Fax:** 0845 020 4361
Email: jason.neale@nodezero.uk.com
Web: www.nodezero.uk.com ⌐

O2M8 LTD
P.O.Box 7716, Newbury, Berkshire, RG20 5WU
Area of Operation: UK (Excluding ireland)
Tel: 07789 207408
Email: john@o2m8.com **Web:** www.o2m8.com ⌐

PARK SYSTEMS INTEGRATION LTD
Unit 3 Queen's Park, Earlsway, Team Valley Trading
Estate, Gateshead, Tyne & Wear, NE11 0QD
Area of Operation: UK & Ireland
Tel: 0191 497 0770   **Fax:** 0191 497 0772
Email: elife@psi.uk.com **Web:** www.psi.uk.com

SUB SYSTEMS INTEGRATION LTD
Studio 19, Hurlingham Studios,
Ranelagh Gardens, London, SW6 3PA
Area of Operation: Greater London
Tel: 0207 796 1459   **Fax:** 0207 796 1469
Email: info@sub.eu.com **Web:** www.sub.eu.com

THE PLASMA WAREHOUSE GROUP PLC
Sandy Farm Business Park, The Sands,
Farnham, Surrey, GU10 1PX
Tel: 0870 734 5432
Email: sales@plasmawarehouseuk.com
Web: www.plasmawarehouseuk.com ⌐

THINKINGBRICKS LTD
6 High Street, West Wickham,
Cambridge, Cambridgeshire, CB1 6RY
Area of Operation: UK & Ireland
Tel: 01223 290886 **Email:** ian@thinkingbricks.co.uk
Web: www.thinkingbricks.co.uk

TRIBUNE SMART HOME
321 Bolton Road, Manchester, M6 7GU
Area of Operation: UK (Excluding Ireland)
Tel: 0161 736 4011   **Fax:** 0161 736 8355
Email: info@tribunesmarthome.com
Web: www.tribunesmarthome.com

X-HOME
Unit W Williamsons Holdings,
Uphall, West Lothian, EH52 6PA
Area of Operation: UK (Excluding Ireland)
Tel: 0845 130 1091   **Fax:** 0845 130 1092
Email: sales@xhome.biz **Web:** www.xhome.biz

REMOTE NETWORKING

KEY
OTHER: ▽ Reclaimed   ⌐ On-line shopping
✐ Bespoke ✋Hand-made   ECO Ecological

ALDOUS SYSTEMS (EUROPE) LTD
Unit 3 Printers End, Insignia Industrial Estate,
Gatehouse Way, Aylesbury,
Buckinghamshire, HP19 8DB
Area of Operation: Europe
Tel: 0870 240 1162   **Fax:** 0207 691 7844
Email: sales@aldoussystems.co.uk
Web: www.aldoussystems.co.uk

AUDIO IMAGES
284 Glossop Road, Sheffield, South Yorkshire, S10 2HS
Area of Operation: Worldwide
Tel: 0114 273 7893   **Fax:** 0114 275 5371
Email: sheffield@audio-images.co.uk
Web: www.audio-images.co.uk

Networked PCs

Dial up Broadband

Infrared

UHF/Cable TV Satellite TV* Freeview

Digital Audio

Telephone

Home Cinema Video

1 POINT

1 CABLE

AUDIO T CUSTOM INSTALLATIONS
11 Charter Place, High Street,
Egham, Surrey, TW20 9EA
Area of Operation: East England,
Greater London, South East England
Tel: 01784 479423   **Fax:** 01784 479425
Email: custom@audio-t.co.uk
Web: www.audio-t.co.uk/custom

D&T ELECTRONICS
Unit 9A, Cranborne Industrial Estate, Cranborne
Road, Potters Bar, Hertfordshire, EN6 3JN
Area of Operation: UK (Excluding Ireland)
Tel: 0870 241 5891   **Fax:** 01707 653570
Email: info@dandt.co.uk   **Web:** www.dandt.co.uk

DBCC LIMITED
Woodland View, Winchester Road,
Fair Oak, Eastleigh, Hampshire, SO50 7HD
Area of Operation: UK (Excluding Ireland)
Tel: 02380 692 555
Email: info@dbcc.co.uk   **Web:** www.dbcc.co.uk

DECKORUM LTD
4c Royal Oak Lane, Pirton,
Stevenage, Hertfordshire, SG5 3QT
Area of Operation: East England, Greater London,
South East England
Tel: 08450 204360   **Fax:** 08450 204361
Email: gary.mills@deckorum.com
Web: www.deckorum.com

DOMINTELL
4 Myson Way, Raynham Road Industrial Estate,
Bishop's Stortford, Hertfordshire, CM23 5JZ
Area of Operation: UK (Excluding Ireland)
Tel: 01279 757775   **Fax:** 01279 653535
Email: njackson@minitran.co.uk
Web: www.minitran.co.uk

EAST TECHNOLOGY INTEGRATORS
85 Langtons Meadow, Farnham Common,
Slough, Berkshire, SL2 3NS
Area of Operation: Greater London, South East England
Tel: 01753 642367
Email: sales@east-ti.co.uk   **Web:** www.east-ti.co.uk

EASYLIFE AUTOMATION LIMITED
Kullan House, 12 Meadowfield Road,
Stocksfield, Northumberland, NE43 7QX
Area of Operation: UK (Excluding Ireland)
Tel: 01661 844159
Fax: 01661 842594
Email: enquiries@easylifeautomation.com
Web: www.easylifeautomation.com

FAITH & GANTRY LTD
Gainsborough House, 62 Hatfield Road,
Ipswich, Suffolk, IP3 9AF
Area of Operation: East England, Greater London
Tel: 01473 714002   **Fax:** 01473 714060
Email: lindsey@faithandgantry.com
Web: www.faithandgantry.com

FINITE SOLUTIONS -
HOME CINEMA AND MULTI ROOM AUDIO
Pavilion Business Centre, Stanningley Road,
Leeds, West Yorkshire, LS28 6NB
Area of Operation: UK (Excluding Ireland)
Tel: 0113 255 4765   **Fax:** 0113 255 4742
Email: info@finitesolutions.co.uk
Web: www.finitesolutions.co.uk

FUSION GROUP
Unit 4 Winston Avenue, Croft,
Leicester, Leicestershire, LE9 3GQ
Area of Operation: UK (Excluding Ireland)
Tel: 08450 204360
Fax: 08450 204361
Email: gary.mills@fusiongroup.uk.com
Web: www.fusiongroup.uk.com

IBBD LTD
HomeLifeWorkLife Showroom, Unit 6 Link Trade
Park, Penarth Road, Cardiff, CF11 8TQ
Area of Operation: South West England and South Wales
Tel: 029 2071 3460
Email: info@ibbd.co.uk
Web: www.homelifeworklife.co.uk

IDOMUS
23 Wornal Park, Menmarsh Road, Worminghall,
Aylesbury, Buckinghamshire, HP18 9PH
Area of Operation: Worldwide
Tel: 0845 644 3330
Fax: 0845 644 2713
Email: info@iDomus.co.uk
Web: www.iDomus.co.uk

IQYOURHOME.COM LTD
Unit D10, Chaucer Business Park,
Watery Lane, Kemsing, Sevenoaks, Kent, TN15 6YU
Area of Operation: UK & Ireland
Tel: 01732 763888
Fax: 01732 763351
Email: info@iqyourhome.com
Web: www.iqyourhome.com

NODE ZERO LTD
Unit 4a Winston Avenue,
Leicester, Leicestershire, LE9 3GQ
Area of Operation: Europe
Tel: 08700 500248
Fax: 0845 020 4361
Email: jason.neale@nodezero.co.uk
Web: www.nodezero.co.uk

O2M8 LTD
P.O.Box 7716, Newbury, Berkshire, RG20 5WU
Area of Operation: UK)(Excluding Ireland)
Tel: 07789 207408
Email: john@o2m8.com
Web: www.o2m8.com

PARK SYSTEMS INTEGRATION LTD
Unit 3 Queen's Park, Earlsway,
Team Valley Trading Estate,
Gateshead, Tyne & Wear, NE11 0QD
Area of Operation: UK & Ireland
Tel: 0191 497 0770
Fax: 0191 497 0772
Email: elife@psi.uk.com
Web: www.psi.uk.com

PHILLSON LTD
144 Rickerscote Road, Stafford,
Staffordshire, ST17 4HE
Area of Operation: UK & Ireland
Tel: 0845 612 0128
Fax: 01477 535090
Email: info@phillson.co.uk
Web: www.phillson.co.uk

SUB SYSTEMS INTEGRATION LTD
Studio 19, Hurlingham Studios,
Ranelagh Gardens, London, SW6 3PA
Area of Operation: Greater London
Tel: 0207 796 1459
Fax: 0207 796 1469
Email: info@sub.eu.com
Web: www.sub.eu.com

THE PLASMA WAREHOUSE GROUP PLC
Sandy Farm Business Park,
The Sands, Farnham, Surrey, GU10 1PX
Area of Operation: Europe
Tel: 0870 734 5432
Email: sales@plasmawarehouseuk.com
Web: www.plasmawarehouseuk.com

TRIBUNE SMART HOME
321 Bolton Road, Manchester, M6 7GU
Area of Operation: UK (Excluding Ireland)
Tel: 0161 736 4011
Fax: 0161 736 8355
Email: info@tribunesmarthome.com
Web: www.tribunesmarthome.com

X-HOME
Unit W Williamsons Holdings,
Uphall, West Lothian, EH52 6PA
Area of Operation: UK (Excluding Ireland)
Tel: 0845 130 1091   **Fax:** 0845 130 1092
Email: sales@xhome.biz
Web: www.xhome.biz

Image courtesy of Living Control (0845 094 0079)

SPONSORED BY Living Control
Tel: 0845 094 0079 Web: www.livingcontrol.com

SMART HOMES & SECURITY

Multi-room Audio

From hi-fis to computers, from set-top boxes to TVs, the latest electrical equipment vies for space in most modern households. It's usually easy enough to slot these devices in somewhere – in a cabinet or on a desk, for example – but the associated wires can be trickier to accommodate, often pushed into a tangled heap behind pieces of furniture, or even left strewn across floors.

Thankfully, with the advent of advanced high capacity cable such as cat5 and its successor cat5e, it's now possible to build homes with most of the electronics hidden away. At last homeowners can enjoy the benefits of the latest technology, without having to see the streams of wires that come with it.

One way to hide technology such as speakers, for example, is to paint them to match the décor of the room, and mount the speakers flush to the ceiling. You can also install in-wall keypads or remote controls, which enables you to adjust the volume up and down, toggle between different sound 'sources' (AM/FM radio, digital radio tuner, iPod, CD player, etc.) and even control and view video sources, such as your DVD, VCR or Sky box. Some integrated systems will also show exactly which track or radio station is playing on the keypad display.

Although it is possible to distribute music around the home wirelessly, the technology isn't always particularly stable or easy to control. One of the best options is to use structured cabling, which can be far more robust and reliable. Most multi-room audio systems use industry-standard cat5 or cat5e cable, which is not only affordable, but also ideal for technologies such as connecting up home computers to the internet. This type of 'home networking' is fast growing in popularity for many families, especially those with teenage children or adults working from home. Some multi-room audio systems also require additional runs of speaker cable, but again these are relatively inexpensive.

If you wish to have the installation done professionally, there are benefits of working closely with a recognised installer. For peace of mind, use a member of the trade body CEDIA. Registered electrical contractors can do the first-fix wiring, ensuring there is no hold up in the timing of the construction work, and also bring a degree of comfort while you're undertaking your self-build project.

Home automation is obviously a fast-advancing technology, so homebuilders should make sure that whoever they use, the tradesperson is fully up to speed with the latest hardware and software developments.

CEDIA is an international, not-for-profit trade organisation spanning three continents with a global membership of over 3,500 companies. Members specialise in the planning, design, supply and installation of automated electronic systems for the modern, intelligent home - visit www.cedia.co.uk for more details.

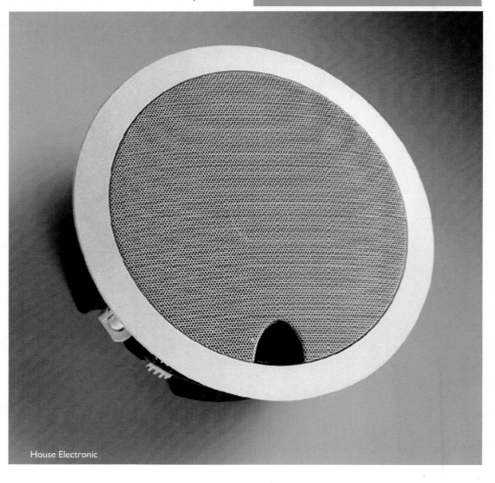

House Electronic

AUDIO SYSTEMS

KEY

OTHER: ▽ Reclaimed 🖐 On-line shopping
✏ Bespoke 🖐 Hand-made ECO Ecological

ABITANA NV
4 Myson Way, Raynham Road Industrial Estate,
Bishop's Stortford, Hertfordshire, CM23 5JZ
Area of Operation: Europe
Tel: 01279 757775 **Fax:** 01279 653535
Email: sminns@minitran.co.uk
Web: www.minitran.co.uk 🖐

ABSOLUTE ELECTRICS
47 Tanfield Road, Croydon, Surrey, CR0 1AN
Area of Operation: Greater London, South East England
Tel: 0208 681 7835 **Fax:** 0208 667 9836
Email: mark@absolute-electrics.co.uk
Web: www.absolute-electrics.com

ACA APEX LIMITED
Apex House, Ivinghoe Way,
Edlesborough, Dunstable, Bedfordshire, LU6 2EL
Area of Operation: UK & Ireland
Tel: 01525 220782 **Fax:** 01525 220782
Email: sales@aca-apex.com
Web: www.aca-apex.com

ACOUSTIC ENERGY
16 Bridge Road, Cirencester, Gloucestershire, GL7 1NJ
Area of Operation: Worldwide
Tel: 01285 654432 **Fax:** 01285 654430
Email: lrettie@hotmail.com
Web: www.acoustic-energy.co.uk 🖐

ADV AUDIO VISUAL INSTALLATIONS LTD
12 York Place, Leeds, West Yorkshire, LS1 2DS
Area of Operation: North East England, North West England and North Wales
Tel: 0870 199 5755
Email: shaun@adv-installs.co.uk
Web: www.homecinemainstalls.co.uk

ALDOUS SYSTEMS (EUROPE) LTD
Unit 3 Printers End, Insignia Industrial Estate, Gatehouse Way, Aylesbury, Buckinghamshire, HP19 8DB
Area of Operation: Europe
Tel: 0870 240 1162 **Fax:** 0207 691 7844
Email: sales@aldoussystems.co.uk
Web: www.aldoussystems.co.uk

AMINA TECHNOLOGIES
Cirrus House, Glebe Road,
Huntingdon, Cambridgeshire, PE29 7DX
Area of Operation: UK (Excluding Ireland)
Tel: 01480 354390 **Fax:** 01480 356564
Email: richard@amina.co.uk
Web: www.amina.co.uk

ARCHANGEL CUSTOM INSTALLATION SPECIALISTS (JERSEY) LIMITED
Les Cotils Farm, Rue Le Cotin,
St. Helier, Jersey, JE2 3FJ
Area of Operation: Europe
Tel: 01534 855584
Email: david.fell@archangelmultimedia.co.uk
Web: www.archangelmultimedia.co.uk

ARMOUR HOME ELECTRONICS
Stortford Hall Industrial Park, Dunmow Road,
Bishops Stortford, Hertfordshire, CM23 5GZ
Area of Operation: Worldwide
Tel: 01279 501111 **Fax:** 01279 501080
Email: info@armourhe.co.uk
Web: www.armourhe.co.uk

AUDIO & CINEMA EXPERIENCE
Callywith Gate Industrial Estate,
Launceston Road, Bodmin, Cornwall, PL31 2RQ
Area of Operation: UK (Excluding Ireland)
Tel: 0870 458 4438
Email: marcus@audio-cinema.co.uk
Web: www.audio-cinema.co.uk

AUDIO DESIGNS CUSTOM INSTALL
7/9 Park Place, Horsham, West Sussex, RH12 1DF
Area of Operation: South East England
Tel: 01403 252255 **Fax:** 01342 328065
Email: horsham@audiodesigns.co.uk
Web: www.audiodesigns.co.uk

AUDIO IMAGES
284 Glossop Road, Sheffield, South Yorkshire, S10 2HS
Area of Operation: Worldwide
Tel: 0114 273 7893 **Fax:** 0114 275 5371
Email: sheffield@audio-images.co.uk
Web: www.audio-images.co.uk **Other Info:** ✏

AUDIO T CUSTOM INSTALLATIONS
11 Charter Place, High Street,
Egham, Surrey, TW20 9EA
Area of Operation: East England, Greater London, South East England
Tel: 01784 479423 **Fax:** 01784 479425
Email: custom@audio-t.co.uk
Web: www.audio-t.co.uk/custom

AUDIOFILE
27 Hockerill Street, Bishops Stortford,
Hertfordshire, CM23 2DH
Area of Operation: UK & Ireland
Tel: 01279 506576 **Fax:** 01279 506638
Email: info@audiofile.co.uk **Web:** www.audiofile.co.uk

AUDIOVISION
46 Market Square, St Neots,
Cambridgeshire, PE19 2AF
Area of Operation: Europe
Tel: 01480 471202 **Fax:** 01480 471115
Email: sales@audiovisiononline.co.uk
Web: www.audiovisiononline.co.uk 🖐

BESPOKE INSTALLATIONS
1 Rogers Close, Tiverton, Devon, EX16 6UW
Area of Operation: South West England and South Wales
Tel: 01884 243497
Email: michael@bespoke.biz
Web: www.bespoke.biz

BEYOND THE INVISIBLE LIMITED
162-164 Arthur Road, London, SW19 8AQ
Area of Operation: Greater London
Tel: 0870 740 5859 **Fax:** 0870 740 5860
Email: info@beyondtheinvisible.com
Web: www.beyondtheinvisible.com

BFT AUTOMATION UK LTD
Unit 8E, Newby Road Industrial Estate,
Hazel Grove, Stockport, Cheshire, SK7 5DA
Area of Operation: UK & Ireland
Tel: 0161 456 0456 **Fax:** 0161 456 9090
Email: info@bftautomation.co.uk
Web: www.bft.co.uk

CHOICE HI-FI
Denehurst Gardens, Richmond, Surrey, TW10
Area of Operation: UK (Excluding Ireland)
Tel: 0208 392 1959
Email: info@choice-hifi.com
Web: www.choice-hifi.com

CIS LTD
Westpoint Business Centre, Westland Square,
Leeds, West Yorkshire, LS11 5SS
Area of Operation: Worldwide
Tel: 08700 240640 **Fax:** 08700 240641
Email: p.hackett@compulock.com
Web: www.compulock.com

CONTROLWISE LTD
Unit 7, St. Davids Industrial Estate,
Pengam, Blackwood, Caerphilly, NP12 3SW
Area of Operation: South West England and South Wales
Tel: 01443 836836 **Fax:** 01443 836502
Email: stuart@controlwise.co.uk
Web: www.controlwise.co.uk

CREO DESIGN
62 North Street, Leeds, West Yorkshire, LS2 7PN
Area of Operation: UK (Excluding Ireland)
Tel: 0113 246 7373 **Fax:** 0113 242 5114
Email: info@creo-designs.co.uk
Web: www.creo-designs.co.uk

CUSTOM INSTALLATIONS
Custom House, 51 Baymead Lane,
North Petherton, Bridgwater, Somerset, TA6 6RN
Area of Operation: South West England and South Wales
Tel: 01278 662555 **Fax:** 01278 662975
Email: roger@custom-installations.co.uk
Web: www.custom-installations.co.uk

D&T ELECTRONICS
Unit 9A, Cranborne Industrial Estate,
Cranborne Road, Potters Bar, Hertfordshire, EN6 3JN
Area of Operation: UK (Excluding Ireland)
Tel: 0870 241 5891 **Fax:** 01707 653570
Email: info@dandt.co.uk
Web: www.dandt.co.uk **Other Info:** ✏

DBCC LIMITED
Woodland View, Winchester Road,
Fair Oak, Eastleigh, Hampshire, SO50 7HD
Area of Operation: UK (Excluding Ireland)
Tel: 02380 692 555
Email: info@dbcc.co.uk **Web:** www.dbcc.co.uk

DECKORUM LTD
4c Royal Oak Lane, Pirton,
Stevenage, Hertfordshire, SG5 3QT
Area of Operation: East England, Greater London, South East England
Tel: 08450 204360 **Fax:** 08450 204361
Email: gary.mills@deckorum.com
Web: www.deckorum.com

DIGITAL DECOR
Sonas House, Button End, Harston,
Cambridge, Cambridgeshire, CB2 5NX
Area of Operation: East England, Greater London
Tel: 01223 870935 **Fax:** 01223 870935
Email: seamus@digital-decor.co.uk
Web: www.digital-decor.co.uk

DISCOVERY SYSTEMS LTD
1 Corn Mill Close, The Spindles,
Ashton in Makerfield, Wigan, Lancashire, WN4 0PX
Area of Operation: North West England and North Wales
Tel: 01942 723756
Email: mike@discoverysystems.co.uk
Web: www.discoverysystems.co.uk

DOMINTELL
4 Myson Way, Raynham Road Industrial Estate,
Bishop's Stortford, Hertfordshire, CM23 5JZ
Area of Operation: UK (Excluding Ireland)
Tel: 01279 757775 **Fax:** 01279 653535
Email: njackson@minitran.co.uk
Web: www.minitran.co.uk 🖐 **Other Info:** ECO ✏

EAST TECHNOLOGY INTEGRATORS
85 Langtons Meadow, Farnham Common,
Slough, Berkshire, SL2 3NS
Area of Operation: Greater London, South East England
Tel: 01753 642367
Email: sales@east-ti.co.uk **Web:** www.east-ti.co.uk

EASYCOMM
1 George House, Church Street,
Buntingford, Hertfordshire, SG9 9AS
Area of Operation: UK (Excluding Ireland)
Tel: 0800 389 9459
Email: steve@ezcomm.co.uk
Web: www.ezcomm.co.uk

EASYLIFE AUTOMATION LIMITED
Kullan House, 12 Meadowfield Road,
Stocksfield, Northumberland, NE43 7QX
Area of Operation: UK (Excluding Ireland)
Tel: 01661 844159 **Fax:** 01661 842594
Email: enquiries@easylifeautomation.com
Web: www.easylifeautomation.com

FAITH & GANTRY LTD
Gainsborough House, 62 Hatfield Road,
Ipswich, Suffolk, IP3 9AF
Area of Operation: East England, Greater London
Tel: 01473 714002
Fax: 01473 714060
Email: lindsey@faithandgantry.com
Web: www.faithandgantry.com

FINITE SOLUTIONS - HOME CINEMA AND MULTI ROOM AUDIO
Pavilion Business Centre, Stanningley Road,
Leeds, West Yorkshire, LS28 6NB
Area of Operation: UK (Excluding Ireland)
Tel: 0113 255 4765
Fax: 0113 255 4742
Email: info@finitesolutions.co.uk
Web: www.finitesolutions.co.uk **Other Info:** ✏

FLAMINGBOX
Perry Farm, Maiden Bradley, Wiltshire, BA12 7JQ
Area of Operation: UK (Excluding Ireland)
Tel: 01985 845440
Fax: 01985 845448
Email: info@flamingbox.com
Web: www.flamingbox.com

FOCUS 21 VISUAL COMMUNICATIONS LIMITED
Tims Boatyard, Timsway, Staines, Surrey, TW18 3JY
Area of Operation: UK & Ireland
Tel: 01784 441153 **Fax:** 01784 225840
Email: info@focus21.co.uk
Web: www.focus21.co.uk

FUSION GROUP
Unit 4 Winston Avenue, Croft,
Leicester, Leicestershire, LE9 3GQ
Area of Operation: UK (Excluding Ireland)
Tel: 08450 204360 **Fax:** 08450 204361
Email: gary.mills@fusiongroup.uk.com
Web: www.fusiongroup.uk.com
Other Info: ✏

GOLDSYSTEM LTD
46 Nightingale Lane, Bromley, Kent, BR1 2SB
Area of Operation: Greater London, South East England
Tel: 0208 313 0485 **Fax:** 0208 313 0665
Email: info@goldsystem.co.uk
Web: www.goldsystem.co.uk

HARRIS GRANT
16 Trinity Church Yard, Guildford, Surrey, GU1 3RR
Area of Operation: UK (Excluding Ireland)
Tel: 01483 885678 **Fax:** 01483 885677
Email: info@harrisgrant.com

HELLERMANN TYTON
43-45 Salthouse Road, Brackmills,
Northampton, Northamptonshire, NN4 7EX
Area of Operation: Worldwide
Tel: 01604 707420 **Fax:** 01604 705454
Email: sales@htdata.co.uk
Web: www.homenetworksciences.com

HIDDEN HOME AUTOMATION
23 Cottesbrooke Park, Heartlands,
Daventry, Northamptonshire, NN11 8YL
Area of Operation: UK (Excluding Ireland)
Tel: 01327 872435
Fax: 01327 315287
Email: info@hiddenhomeautomation.co.uk
Web: www.hiddenhomeautomation.co.uk

HIFI CINEMA
1 Mars House, Calleva Park,
Aldermaston, Berkshire, RG7 8LA
Area of Operation: Greater London, South East England
Tel: 0118 982 0402 **Fax:** 0118 977 3535
Email: experience@hificinema.co.uk
Web: www.hificinema.co.uk

HOME NETWORKING ONLINE
Unit 3, Printers End, Gethouse Way,
Aylesbury, Buckinghamshire, HP19 8DB
Area of Operation: Europe
Tel: 0870 240 1162
Fax: 0207 691 7844
Email: sales@home-networking-online.co.uk
Web: www.home-networking-online.co.uk 🖐

HOUSEHOLD AUTOMATION
Foxways, Pinkhurst Lane, Slinfold,
Horsham, West Sussex, RH13 0QR
Area of Operation: UK & Ireland
Tel: 0870 330 0071 **Fax:** 0870 330 0072
Email: ellis-andrew@btconnect.com
Web: www.household-automation.co.uk

Amaze your guests with a new kind of menu...

It has to be the ultimate home entertainment luxury: an audio/video system that allows you to play your favourite music, DVD or TV channel anywhere in the home.

Living Control has refined the art of multi-room entertainment to a new level, where your entire music collection is available in any room at the touch of a discreet, décor-matching wall panel; where you make selections of audio and HD video by name, and control lights from the same panel; where downloading your play list to your iPod® is a simple joy.

Embracing WiFi® and iPod integration, lighting and home cinema control, Living Control's system will grow with your needs, but will always remain virtually invisible, keeping your interior design as perfect as the day you decorated.

To receive a brochure, please call 0845 094 0079 or email THH@livingcontrol.com

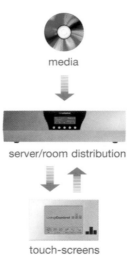

media

server/room distribution

touch-screens

LivingControl

www.livingcontrol.com

LIVING CONTROL

Area of Operation: Worldwide
Tel: 0845 094 0079
Email: THH@livingcontrol.com
Web: www.livingcontrol.com

Multi-room Audio and Video systems

The widest choice of entertainment is at your fingertips anywhere in the home. No wires, no gear, no fuss. Living Control is the luxury multi-room system designed for those who value performance and reliability.

LIVING CONTROL

ColourPad

From the kitchen, bathroom, bedroom, living room – even outside on the patio, select CD, MP3, Radio, TV, DVD, even HD video anywhere 'by name' from this full-colour touch-screen, which is no bigger than a double-gang socket and available in a range of finishes.

LIVING CONTROL

VideoPad

Using the VideoPad is a pure pleasure. Review your entire library alphabetically and make your selection of entertainment with a touch of the screen. VideoPad is available in a range of décor-matching finishes, so it always complements your interior design.

LIVING CONTROL

VideoPadAV

This ultra-sophisticated touch-screen controller has all the virtues of the VideoPad, but has the power to control the performance of your big-screen AV system as well: volume, input, DVD track and so on. It will even control lights, screens and blinds.

LIVING CONTROL

DisplayPad-S

DisplayPad-S is available in a wide range of colours to blend unobtrusively with any bespoke interior. Three buttons and an intuitive display combine to let you select source, disc or station alphabetically. Plates and modules fit snugly into a standard UK wall box for trouble-free installation.

LIVING CONTROL

Rako-S

Gives you the power to set the right mood with music and light from the same discreet in-wall keypad. Powered by the Living Control system, the lighting buttons allow you to design up to four 'scenes' for the room, which can comprise any combination of lights and levels.

LIVING CONTROL

Outdoor DisplayPad

An all-weather DisplayPad for use in the garden, on the patio or by the pool. When used with weather-proof outdoor speakers, an Outdoor DisplayPad installation gives you the wonderfully discreet control and superb sound quality you've enjoyed inside your home, outside the home as well.

LIVING CONTROL

RF Pad

Where wiring is difficult or inconvenient, the RF Pad is the perfect solution. Through this one-way battery powered panel, you'll enjoy control over source and volume, track, preset and disc. Available in black, white or brushed/polished steel.

LIVING CONTROL

MusicBox3

Upload your entire CD collection (up to 7000 disks) to the new super-fast MusicBox3 and they're available all over your home through a Living Control system. Mum, Dad and the kids can listen to three different songs simultaneously. The MusicBox3 is easy to use and fitted with a 400GB hard-disk (upgradable to over 2TB internally).

LIVING CONTROL

MusicBox1

Enjoy all the convenience, quality and reliability of a Living Control system from the single output MusicBox1 - the perfect lower-cost solution for smaller applications using a RoomBox 4 CPU. A 250GB hard drive is fitted, upgradeable to over 2TB internally.

LIVING CONTROL

CVX-S

Marry the CVX-S with a RoomBox6 to enjoy the luxury of choosing six different high-resolution (up to HD 720p/1080i) video sources in six rooms. Watch video from DVD, Sky HD or satellite, TV, video game or VCR when you choose the source on the in-room keypad.

LIVING CONTROL

RoomBox6 and 4

RoomBox6 and 4 are 'invisible' multi-room CPUs (Central Processing Units) designed to be located with our servers and your sources out of sight. RB6 distributes six sources between six rooms and offers extra features such as wake-up calls and control over lights and blinds. RB4 is Living Control's 'entry-level' CPU distributing six sources to four rooms.

Meridian. Hi-fi with hidden benefits.

When we set out to design our new 300 Series installation loudspeakers, we wanted them to offer something special: something unique.

Most important of all, they had to deliver a superb sound to rival our acclaimed stand-alone designs.

So the enclosures incorporate a rigid, bonded sandwich of ply and aluminium, like our flagship DSP8000, minimising wall and cavity resonances. So you hear the loudspeaker – not the wall.

We carefully selected powerful bass drivers, ABRs and a wide-dispersion ribbon tweeter to punch through wall-coverings.

We also wanted our installation speakers to be versatile. So we designed in-wall, flush-mount and on-wall varieties, in three different sizes (the 350, shown here with grille removed, is the largest).

The result? A series of installation speakers that offer real, high fidelity quality – quality like you've never heard before from an in-wall.

Contact Meridian for more details. And specify the hi-fi speakers with hidden benefits: installation loudspeakers from Meridian.

BOOTHROYD STUART
MERIDIAN®

Meridian Audio Lt
Latham Road, Huntingdor
Cambridgeshire PE29 6Y
T 01480 445678 • F 01480 44568
sales@meridian.co.u
www.meridian-audio.com

Illustrated: A350 active in-wall with grille remove
G41 powered crossover/amplifier and G91 DVD syster

IBBD LTD
HomeLifeWorkLife Showroom, Unit 6 Link Trade
Park, Penarth Road, Cardiff, CF11 8TQ
Area of Operation: South West England and South Wales
Tel: 029 2071 3460 **Email:** info@ibbd.co.uk
Web: www.homelifeworklife.co.uk

IKURE (AUDIO VISUAL) LTD
27 Vanalloys Business Park, Busgrove Park, Stoke
Row, Henley-on-Thames, Oxfordshire, RG9 5QW
Area of Operation: Worldwide
Tel: 01491 682981 **Fax:** 01491 682578
Email: timv@ikure.co.uk **Web:** www.ikure.co.uk

INTERCONNECTION
12 Chamberlayne Road, Moreton Hall Industrial
Estate, Bury St Edmunds, Suffolk, IP32 7EY
Area of Operation: East England
Tel: 01284 768676 **Fax:** 01284 767161
Email: info@interconnectionltd.co.uk
Web: www.interconnectionltd.co.uk

IQYOURHOME.COM LTD
Unit D10, Chaucer Business Park, Watery Lane,
Kemsing, Sevenoaks, Kent, TN15 6YU
Area of Operation: UK & Ireland
Tel: 01732 763888 **Fax:** 01732 763351
Email: info@iqyourhome.com
Web: www.iqyourhome.com

J K AUDIO VISUAL
Unit 7 Newport Business Park, Audley Avenue,
Newport, Shropshire, TF10 7DP
Area of Operation: UK (Excluding Ireland)
Tel: 01952 825088
Fax: 01952 814884
Email: sales@jk-audiovisual.co.uk
Web: www.jk-audiovisual.co.uk

JELLYBEAN CTRL LTD
Eagle House, Passfield Business Centre,
Lynchborough Road, Passfield, Hampshire, GU30 7SB
Area of Operation: UK (Excluding Ireland)
Tel: 01428 751729
Fax: 01428 751772
Email: david@jellybeanctrl.com
Web: www.jellybeanctrl.com

KENT HOME CINEMA CENTRE
69 London Road, Southborough,
Tunbridge Wells, Kent, TN4 0PA
Area of Operation: UK & Ireland
Tel: 01892 535007
Fax: 01892 533334
Email: andrew@kenthomecinema.co.uk
Web: www.av-sales.co.uk **Other Info:**

LIFESTYLE ELECTRONICS
Woodview, Castlebridge, County Wexford, Ireland
Area of Operation: Europe
Tel: +353 (0)53 9159880 **Fax:** +353 (0)53 5919844
Email: lifestyle123@eircom.net

LIVING CONTROL LTD
The Flyer's Way, Westerham, Kent, TN16 1DE
Area of Operation: Worldwide
Tel: 0845 094 0079
Email: thh@livingcontrol.com
Web: www.livingcontrol.com
Other Info:

MARANTZ HIFI UK
Kingsbridge House, Padbury Oaks,
581 Bath Road, Longford, Middlesex, UB7 0EH
Area of Operation: Worldwide
Tel: 01753 680868
Fax: 01753 680428
Email: joe.thurston@marantz.co.uk
Web: www.marantz.com

MARQUEE HOME LIMITED
Unit 6, Eversley Way, Thorpe Industrial Estate,
Egham, Surrey, TW20 8RF
Area of Operation: Greater London, South East England
Tel: 07004 567888
Fax: 07004 567788
Email: paulendersby@marqueehome.co.uk
Web: www.marqueehome.co.uk

MARTINS HI-FI
85/87 Ber Street, Norwich, Norfolk, NR1 3EY
Area of Operation: East England
Tel: 01603 627010 **Fax:** 01603 878019
Email: info@martinshifi.co.uk
Web: www.martinshifi.co.uk

MERIDIAN AUDIO LIMITED
Latham Road, Huntingdon, Cambridgeshire, PE29 6YE
Area of Operation: Worldwide
Tel: 01480 445678 **Fax:** 01480 445686
Email: info@meridian-audio.com
Web: www.meridian-audio.com

MERIDIAN - LIFESTYLE ENTERTAINMENT TECHNOLOGY
Area of Operation: Worldwide
Tel: 01480 445678
Fax: 01480 445686
Email: info@meridian-audio.com
Web: www.meridian-audio.com

Meridian's elegant, stylish audio/video components and stand-alone loudspeakers are perfect for any décor – while their in-wall speakers facilitate unobtrusive installation. Meridian systems deliver breathtaking digital stereo or surround sound, and crystal-sharp high-definition digital video from HD or existing sources.

MJ ACOUSTICS
9 Venture Court, Boleness Road,
Wisbech, Cambridgeshire, PE132XQ
Area of Operation: Worldwide
Tel: 01945 467770 **Fax:** 01945 467778
Email: sales@mjacoustics.co.uk
Web: www.mjacoustics.co.uk

MJ ACOUSTICS
Area of Operation: Worldwide
Tel: 01945 467770
Fax: 01945 467778
Email: sales@mjacoustics.co.uk
Web: www.mjacoustics.co.uk

The Purist Audiophile Sound Reproduction. Manufacturing the finest Subwoofers and Stereo Speakers from solid woods and that quintessential English touch. British Audio at its Best!

PRODUCT OF THE YEAR 2005
ACOUSTICS

MJ ACOUSTICS
Area of Operation: Worldwide
Tel: 01945 467770
Fax: 01945 467778
Email: sales@mjacoustics.co.uk
Web: www.mjacoustics.co.uk

The Reference 200 has a feature list as long as two arms. Maximum controllability is available on the Reference 200 and is simple to use via its digital display confirming all your settings. Ask your local dealer for a demonstration today and experience the missing link to your system!

MJ ACOUSTICS
Area of Operation: Worldwide
Tel: 01945 467770
Fax: 01945 467778
Email: sales@mjacoustics.co.uk
Web: www.mjacoustics.co.uk

The diminutive Reference 100 MkII packs a punch equal to subs twice its size, yet it goes almost visually unnoticed due to its small 278mm square cabinet size. Ask your local dealer for a demonstration today and experience the missing link to your system!

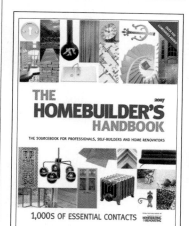

THE HOMEBUILDER'S HANDBOOK 2007
THE SOURCEBOOK FOR PROFESSIONALS, SELF-BUILDERS AND HOME RENOVATORS
1,000S OF ESSENTIAL CONTACTS

MULTIROOM AUDIO
4 Clement Way, Cawton, Rugby, Warwickshire, CV22 7FH
Area of Operation: UK (Excluding Ireland)
Tel: 01788 521248 **Fax:** 0870 762 8242
Email: sales@multiroom-audio.co.uk
Web: www.multiroom-audio.co.uk
Other Info:

Solutions for Whole House Audio Systems

MULTIROOM AUDIO
Area of Operation: UK (Excluding Ireland)
Tel: 01788 521248
Fax: 08707 628242
Email: sales@multiroom-audio.co.uk
Web: www.multiroom-audio.co.uk

- Multiroom Audio Solution
- Sound Servers
- Audio Visual Equipment
- Surround Sounds Systems
- Custom Fit Speakers
- Plasma and LCD TV
- Data Wiring Services

We can provide solutions from simple home networks to full Audio and Video distribution systems, DIY or installed.

MUSICAL APPROACH
111 Wolverhampton Road,
Stafford, Staffordshire, ST17 4AH
Area of Operation: UK (Excluding Ireland)
Tel: 01785 255154
Email: info@musicalapproach.co.uk
Web: www.musicalapproach.co.uk

NODE ZERO LTD
Unit 4a Winston Avenue,
Leicester, Leicestershire, LE9 3GQ
Area of Operation: Europe
Tel: 08700 500248 **Fax:** 0845 020 4361
Email: jason.neale@nodezero.uk.com
Web: www.nodezero.uk.com

O2M8 LTD
P.O.Box 7716, Newbury, Berkshire, RG20 5WU
Area of Operation: UK (Excluding Ireland)
Tel: 07789 207408
Email: john@o2m8.com
Web: www.o2m8.com **Other Info:** ECO

OPUS GB
Gallery Court, Pilgrimage Street, London, SE1 4LL
Area of Operation: Worldwide
Tel: 0207 940 2205 **Fax:** 0207 940 2206
Email: info@opus-technologies.co.uk
Web: www.opus-technologies.co.uk

ORANGES & LEMONS
61/63 Webbs Road, Battersea, London, SW11 6RX
Area of Operation: Greater London, South East England
Tel: 0207 924 2040 **Fax:** 0207 924 3665
Email: oranges.lemons@virgin.net
Web: www.oandlhifi.co.uk

PARK SYSTEMS INTEGRATION LTD
Unit 3 Queen's Park, Earlsway, Team Valley Trading
Estate, Gateshead, Tyne & Wear, NE11 0QD
Area of Operation: UK & Ireland
Tel: 0191 497 0770 **Fax:** 0191 497 0772
Email: elife@psi.uk.com **Web:** www.psi.uk.com

PHILLSON LTD
144 Rickerscote Road,
Stafford, Staffordshire, ST17 4HE
Area of Operation: UK & Ireland
Tel: 0845 612 0128 **Fax:** 01477 535090
Email: info@phillson.co.uk
Web: www.phillson.co.uk

It's a mirror. It's a TV.

At first sight Mirror TV looks familiar. It's a mirror.

With its slim profile and choice of frames, it looks perfectly at home in your bathroom, your kitchen, your living room.

Then you hit the remote control. Suddenly it's not a mirror, it's a flat screen TV.

It can show a pin sharp picture from its built-in TV tuner (HDTV ready) or from satellite, cable, DVD or external PC. It can even have its own optional built-in multimedia computer, so you can access e-mails or internet, play MP3 audio or MPEG video files, or go large on your favourite games.

'Til you zap the off switch. And it's a mirror again.

Available with 6.4" to 55" (as well as custom built sizes) with Hitachi plasma or LCD screens.

Contact us on 0870 3866333 or e-mail sales@mirrormedia.com

www.mirrormedia.com

PRESTIGE AUDIO
12 High Street, Rickmansworth, Hertfordshire, WD3 1ER
Area of Operation: Worldwide
Tel: 01923 711113   **Fax:** 01923 776606
Email: info@prestigeaudio.co.uk
Web: www.prestigeaudio.co.uk

ROCOCO SYSTEMS & DESIGN
26 Danbury Street, London, N1 8JU
Area of Operation: Europe
Tel: 0207 454 1234   **Fax:** 0207 870 0888
Email: sales@rococosystems.com
Web: www.rococosystems.com

SCAN AUDIO
1 Honeycrock Lane, Salford, Redhill, Surrey, RH1 5DG
Area of Operation: UK (Excluding Ireland)
Tel: 01737 778620   **Fax:** 01737 778620
Email: scanaudio@mac.com
Web: www.scanaudio.co.uk

SCION TECHNOLOGY LIMITED
Scion Business Park, Brimpton Common,
Reading, Berkshire, RG7 4RN
Area of Operation: UK & Ireland
Tel: 0118 981 7151   **Fax:** 0118 981 7575
Email: mark.brown@sciontech.com
Web: www.sciontech.com

SEISMIC INTERAUDIO
3 Maypole Drive, Kings Hill,
West Malling, Kent, ME19 4BP
Area of Operation: Europe
Tel: 0870 073 4764   **Fax:** 0870 073 4765
Email: info@seismic.co.uk
Web: www.seismic.co.uk

SENSORY INTERNATIONAL LIMITED
48A London Road, Alderley Edge,
Cheshire, SK9 7DZ
Area of Operation: Worldwide
Tel: 01625 584540   **Fax:** 01625 585789
Email: garyc@sensoryinternational.com
Web: www.sensoryinternational.com

SEVENOAKS SOUND & VISION (LEEDS)
62 North Street, Leeds, West Yorkshire, LS2 7PN
Area of Operation: Midlands & Mid Wales, North
East England, North West England and North Wales
Tel: 0113 245 2775
Fax: 0113 242 5114
Email: leeds@ssav.com   **Web:** www.ssav.com

SEVENOAKS SOUND & VISION (OXFORD)
41 St. Clements Street, Oxford, Oxfordshire, OX4 1AG
Area of Operation: UK (Excluding Ireland)
Tel: 01865 241773   **Fax:** 01865 794904
Email: oxford@ssav.com   **Web:** www.ssav.com

SG SYSTEMS LTD
Unit 38 Elderpark Workspace, 100 Elderpark Street,
Glasgow, Renfrewshire, G51 3TR
Area of Operation: Europe
Tel: 0141 445 4125   **Fax:** 0141 445 4125
Email: info@sgsystems.ltd.uk
Web: www.sgsystems.ltd.uk

SHARP ELECTRONICS (UK) LTD
4 Furzeground Way, Stockley Park, Uxbridge, UB11 1EZ
Area of Operation: UK & Ireland
Tel: 0208 734 2000
Email: mike.gabriel@sharp-uk.co.uk
Web: www.sharp.co.uk

SIMPLY AUTOMATE
23 Wornal Park, Menmarsh Road, Worminghall,
Aylesbury, Buckinghamshire, HP18 9PH
Area of Operation: Worldwide
Tel: 0845 644 3330
Fax: 0845 644 2713
Email: info@simplyautomate.co.uk
Web: www.simplyautomate.co.uk

SIMPLYSONOS
PO Box 237, Hampton, TW12 2WU
Area of Operation: Europe
Tel: 0800 731 7308
Email: enquiry@simplysonos.co.uk
Web: www.simplysonos.co.uk

SINCLAIR YOUNGS LTD
Basingstoke Business Centre, Winchester Road,
Basingstoke, Hampshire, RG22 4AU
Area of Operation: South East England
Tel: 01256 355015   **Fax:** 01256 818344
Email: david.wilson@sinclairyoungs.com
Web: www.sinclairyoungs.com

SMART HOUSE
23 Wornal Park, Menmarsh Road, Worminghall,
Aylesbury, Buckinghamshire, HP18 9PH
Area of Operation: Europe
Tel: 0845 053 3680   **Fax:** 0845 644 2713
Email: info@smarthouse.co.uk
Web: www.smarthouse.co.uk

STONEAUDIO UK LIMITED
Holmead Walk, Poundbury, Dorchester, Dorset, DT1 3GE
Area of Operation: Worldwide
Tel: 01305 257555   **Fax:** 01305 257666
Email: info@stoneaudio.co.uk
Web: www.stoneaudio.co.uk

STUART WESTMORELAND (HOLDINGS) LTD
33 Cattle Market, Loughborough,
Leicestershire, LE11 3DL
Area of Operation: East England, Midlands & Mid Wales
Tel: 01509 230465   **Fax:** 01509 267478
Email: loughborough@stuartwestmoreland.co.uk
Web: www.custom-install.co.uk

SUB SYSTEMS INTEGRATION LTD
Studio 19, Hurlingham Studios,
Ranelagh Gardens, London, SW6 3PA
Area of Operation: Greater London
Tel: 0207 796 1459   **Fax:** 0207 796 1469
Email: info@sub.eu.com   **Web:** www.sub.eu.com

SYNCHRO NETWORKS LTD
PO Box 219, Whitstable, CT5 3WZ
Tel: 05511 490058   **Fax:** 05511 490059
Email: info@synchro-networks.co.uk
Web: www.home-networking-solutions.co.uk

TEC 4 HOME
10 Carver Street, Hockley,
Birmingham, West Midlands, B1 3AS
Area of Operation: UK (Excluding Ireland)
Tel: 0121 693 9292   **Fax:** 0121 693 9293
Email: paul@dareproaudio.com
Web: www.tec4home.com

TECCHO
Unit 19W, Kilroot Business Park,
Carrickfergus, Co. Antrim, BT38 7PR
Area of Operation: UK & Ireland
Tel: 0845 890 1150   **Fax:** 0870 063 4120
Email: enquiries@teccho.net
Web: www.teccho.net

TELESTIAL LTD
109-111 Pope Street, Birmingham, B1 3AG
Area of Operation: UK (Excluding Ireland)
Tel: 0870 855 0010
Email: sales@telestial.biz   **Web:** www.telestial.biz

**THE BIG PICTURE -
AV & HOME CINEMA LIMITED**
51 Sutton Road, Walsall, West Midlands, WS1 2PQ
Area of Operation: UK & Ireland
Tel: 01922 623000
Email: info@getthebigpicture.co.uk
Web: www.getthebigpicture.co.uk

THE EDGE
90-92 Norwich Road, Ipswich, Suffolk, IP1 2NL
Area of Operation: UK (Excluding Ireland)
Tel: 01473 288211   **Fax:** 01473 288255
Email: nick@theedge.eu.com
Web: www.theedge.eu.com

THE IVY HOUSE
The Ivy House, Cherry Trees,
Bridegate Lane, Hickling Pastures,
Melton Mowbray, Leicestershire, LE14 3QA
Area of Operation: East England, Midlands & Mid Wales
Tel: 01664 822628
Email: enquiries@the-ivy-house.com
Web: www.the-ivy-house.com

THE LITTLE CINEMA COMPANY
72 New Bond Street, London, W1S 1RR
Area of Operation: Worldwide
Tel: 0207 385 5521   **Fax:** 0207 385 5524
Email: sales@littlecinema.co.uk
Web: www.littlecinema.co.uk

THE MAJIK HOUSE COMPANY LTD
Unit J Mainline Industrial Estate,
Crooklands Road, Milnthorpe, Cumbria, LA7 7LR
Area of Operation: North East England, North West
England and North Wales
Tel: 0870 240 8350   **Fax:** 0870 240 8350
Email: tim@majikhouse.com
Web: www.majikhouse.com

THE PLASMA WAREHOUSE GROUP PLC
Sandy Farm Business Park,
The Sands, Farnham, Surrey, GU10 1PX
Area of Operation: Europe
Tel: 0870 734 5432
Email: sales@plasmawarehouseuk.com
Web: www.plasmawarehouseuk.com

THE THINKING HOME
The White House, Wilderspool Park, Greenalls
Avenue, Warrington, Cheshire, WA4 6HL
Area of Operation: UK & Ireland
Tel: 0800 881 8319
Fax: 0800 881 8329
Email: info@thethinkinghome.com
Web: www.thethinkinghome.com

THINKINGBRICKS LTD
6 High Street, West Wickham,
Cambridge, Cambridgeshire, CB1 6RY
Area of Operation: UK & Ireland
Tel: 01223 290886
Email: ian@thinkingbricks.co.uk
Web: www.thinkingbricks.co.uk

TRI CUSTOM
Unit 38 Elderpark Workspace, 100 Elderpark Street,
Govan, Glasgow, Lanarkshire, G51 3TR
Area of Operation: UK & Ireland
Tel: 0141 4454195   **Fax:** 0141 4454195
Email: info@tricustom.co.uk
Web: www.tricustom.co.uk

TRIBUNE SMART HOME
321 Bolton Road, Manchester, M6 7GU
Area of Operation: UK (Excluding Ireland)
Tel: 0161 736 4011
Fax: 0161 736 8355
Email: info@tribunesmarthome.com
Web: www.tribunesmarthome.com

UNLIMITED DREAM HOME SYSTEMS
The Long Barn, Wakefield Road, Hampole,
Doncaster, South Yorkshire, DN6 7EU
Area of Operation: UK (Excluding Ireland)
Tel: 01302 727274
Fax: 01302 725550
Email: info@thehifistudios.freeserve.co.uk
Web: www.unlimiteddream.co.uk

VALTEK
Ardykeohane, Bruff, Co. Limerick, Ireland
Area of Operation: UK & Ireland
Tel: +353 (0)6138 2116
Fax: +353 (0)6138 2032
Email: sales@valtek.biz   **Web:** www.valtek.biz

WATERPROOFTV.CO.UK
7 Allandale Road, Stoneygate,
Leicester, Leicestershire, LE2 2DA
Area of Operation: Worldwide
Tel: 0116 270 5777   **Fax:** 0116 274 5777
Email: w@terproof.tv
Web: www.waterprooftv.co.uk

WEBSTRACT LTD
2-4 Place Farm, Wheathampstead,
Hertfordshire, AL4 8SB
Area of Operation: UK (Excluding Ireland)
Tel: 0870 446 0146   **Fax:** 0870 762 6431
Email: info@webstract.co.uk
Web: www.webstract.co.uk

WIRED FOR LIVING
19 Harwood Road, Rishton,
Blackburn, Lancashire, BB1 4DH
Area of Operation: UK (Excluding Ireland)
Tel: 07734 798771   **Fax:** 01254 399078
Email: info@wiredforliving.co.uk
Web: www.wiredforliving.co.uk

X-HOME
Unit W Williamsons Holdings,
Uphall, West Lothian, EH52 6PA
Area of Operation: UK (Excluding Ireland)
Tel: 0845 130 1091   **Fax:** 0845 130 1092
Email: sales@xhome.biz   **Web:** www.xhome.biz

ZEN CUSTOM SOLUTIONS LTD
Unit 9, Brookfield Business Park, Clay Lane, York
Road, Market Weighton, North Yorkshire, YO43 3PU
Area of Operation: UK (Excluding Ireland)
Tel: 01430 803473   **Fax:** 01430 803473
Email: sales@zencs.co.uk
Web: www.zencs.co.uk

VISUAL SYSTEMS

KEY
OTHER: ▽ Reclaimed   🛒 On-line shopping
✎ Bespoke   🖐 Hand-made   ECO Ecological

2TECHVISUALS
Unit 11, EuroLink Business Centre,
49 Effra Road, London, SW2 1BZ
Area of Operation: Europe
Tel: 0207 738 6560   **Fax:** 0207 738 6596
Email: annette@2techvisuals.co.uk
Web: www.2techvisuals.co.uk

ABITANA NV
4 Myson Way, Raynham Road Industrial Estate,
Bishop's Stortford, Hertfordshire, CM23 5JZ
Area of Operation: Europe
Tel: 01279 757775   **Fax:** 01279 653535
Email: sminns@minitran.co.uk
Web: www.minitran.co.uk

ABSOLUTE ELECTRICS
47 Tanfield Road, Croydon, Surrey, CR0 1AN
Area of Operation: Greater London, South East England
Tel: 0208 681 7835   **Fax:** 0208 667 9836
Email: mark@absolute-electrics.co.uk
Web: www.absolute-electrics.com

ACA APEX LIMITED
Apex House, Ivinghoe Way, Edlesborough,
Dunstable, Bedfordshire, LU6 2EL
Area of Operation: UK & Ireland
Tel: 01525 220782   **Fax:** 01525 220782
Email: sales@aca-apex.com
Web: www.aca-apex.com

ADV AUDIO VISUAL INSTALLATIONS LTD
12 York Place, Leeds, West Yorkshire, LS1 2DS
Area of Operation: North East England, North West
England and North Wales
Tel: 0870 199 5755
Email: shaun@adv-installs.co.uk
Web: www.homecinemainstalls.co.uk

ALDOUS SYSTEMS (EUROPE) LTD
Unit 3 Printers End, Insignia Industrial Estate, Gatehouse
Way, Aylesbury, Buckinghamshire, HP19 8DB
Area of Operation: Europe
Tel: 0870 240 1162   **Fax:** 0207 691 7844
Email: sales@aldoussystems.co.uk
Web: www.aldoussystems.co.uk

**ARCHANGEL CUSTOM INSTALLATION
SPECIALISTS (JERSEY) LIMITED**
Les Cotils Farm, Rue Le Cotin,
St. Helier, Jersey, JE2 3FJ
Area of Operation: Europe
Tel: 01534 855584
Email: david.fell@archangelmultimedia.co.uk
Web: www.archangelmultimedia.co.uk

The Reference Range

Our unique combination of state-of-the-art electronics and tuned hand-built sealed cabinets, affords the user the ultimate in sub-bass control. Deep and powerful enough for the most demanding movie sound-track, yet subtle, agile, fast, and accurate for the highest fidelity in music listening. It's just like being there!

PRO 50 MkII

Reference 100MkII

Available in 8 Real Wood Veneers (only 278x278x316mm)

Fully Microprocessor Controlled with DAMP 2nd Gen

4 Memory user presets

Huge 10" driver.

More Features at this price point than ever before.

Remote Control.

High Level Lead included.

Spikes included.

Reference 150 MkII

150 watts, 10" driver.
Digital Display.
Twin Crossovers.
Remote Control.

Reference I MkIII

250 watts, 10" driver.
Twin Crossovers.
Digital Display.
Large fluted port.
Remote Control

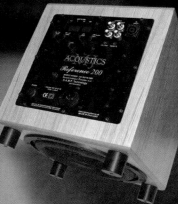

Reference 200

200 watts, 10" driver.
Digital Display.
Twin Crossovers.
Remote Control

Reference 800

800 watts, 18" Radial Driver.
Twin Crossovers, Digital Display.
Digital Power, Remote Control

The Reference series Audiophile Subwoofers add full function remote control, memory presets, choice of real wood finishes and a clutter free and simple panel design with digital display to all audio and AV systems. These Reference grade subwoofers are jaw-dropping adjuncts to complement the most discerning cinema and music system! Power from 120 to 800 watts feeding ultra long-throw super-rigid 10" & 18" sub-bass drivers of exquisite design and finish.

Add to this the battleship construction, beautiful furniture grade finish, and attention to the finest and smallest detail, which ensures the Reference series delivers adroit punch and solid slam – without the dreaded overhang – down to a gut-wrenching 10Hz with an in-room -3db point at 15 to 19Hz.

www.mjacoustics.co.uk

01945 467770

T: 01945 467770
F: 01945 467778
W: www.mjacoustics.co.uk

Hi-fi news

MJ ACOUSTICS SUBLIMINAL S1R

Steve Harris tested the S1R's and below are some of the comments made in his review:

"There have been other Jordan VTL-inspired transmission-lines, from Carolina Audio (USA) and Konus (Bosnia) for example, but even Jordan call MJ's "the best version yet" and it's hard to believe that any could be as nicely built as MJ's. Even the badges are a work of art. A fine speaker, room-friendly and surprisingly satisfying."

"The S1R made me listen with far less jaded ear to the Jennifer Warnes' famous blue raincoat, and in fact I couldn't take it off. "Joan of Arc", a dark song even by Leonard Cohen's standards, came over with amazing power. Words can't describe just how electrifyingly metallic the slide guitar sounded on this track - just as it should do, of course."

The verdict was a resounding thumbs up for MJ Acoustics and the overall rating was 19/20

SPEC/FEATURES	5 / 5
SOUND QUALITY	5 / 5
BUILD QUALITY	5 / 5
VALUE FOR MONEY	4 / 5
OVERALL RATING	19/20

FOR:
Realism, transparency, immediacy, build quality

AGAINST: Not a criticism, but you do need a decent amp

ACOUSTICS

When Speakers Look and Sound this good,
there is truly no alternative.
Made using solid woods
Available in Cherry, Maple and Natural Oak.

100% UK Design
100% UK Manufactured
100% Hand Built
100% UK Dedication

SPONSORED BY: LIVING CONTROL   www.livingcontrol.com

AUDIO & CINEMA EXPERIENCE
Callywith Gate Industrial Estate,
Launceston Road, Bodmin, Cornwall, PL31 2RQ
Area of Operation: UK (Excluding Ireland)
Tel: 0870 458 4438
Email: marcus@audio-cinema.co.uk
Web: www.audio-cinema.co.uk

AUDIO DESIGNS CUSTOM INSTALL
7/9 Park Place, Horsham, West Sussex, RH12 1DF
Area of Operation: South East England
Tel: 01403 252255   **Fax:** 01342 328065
Email: horsham@audiodesigns.co.uk
Web: www.audiodesigns.co.uk

AUDIO IMAGES
284 Glossop Road, Sheffield, South Yorkshire, S10 2HS
Area of Operation: Worldwide
Tel: 0114 273 7893   **Fax:** 0114 275 5371
Email: sheffield@audio-images.co.uk
Web: www.audio-images.co.uk   **Other Info:** ✐

AUDIO T CUSTOM INSTALLATIONS
11 Charter Place, High Street,
Egham, Surrey, TW20 9EA
Area of Operation: East England, Greater London,
South East England
Tel: 01784 479423   **Fax:** 01784 479425
Email: custom@audio-t.co.uk
Web: www.audio-t.co.uk/custom

AUDIOFILE
27 Hockerill Street, Bishops Stortford,
Hertfordshire, CM23 2DH
Area of Operation: UK & Ireland
Tel: 01279 506576   **Fax:** 01279 506638
Email: info@audiofile.co.uk   **Web:** www.audiofile.co.uk

AUDIOVISION
46 Market Square, St Neots,
Cambridgeshire, PE19 2AF
Area of Operation: Europe
Tel: 01480 471202   **Fax:** 01480 471115
Email: sales@audiovisiononline.co.uk
Web: www.audiovisiononline.co.uk ✐

BESPOKE INSTALLATIONS
1 Rogers Close, Tiverton, Devon, EX16 6UW
Area of Operation: South West England and South Wales
Tel: 01884 243497   **Email:** michael@bespoke.biz
Web: www.bespoke.biz

BEYOND THE INVISIBLE LIMITED
162-164 Arthur Road, London, SW19 8AQ
Area of Operation: Greater London
Tel: 0870 740 5859   **Fax:** 0870 740 5860
Email: info@beyondtheinvisible.com
Web: www.beyondtheinvisible.com

BFT AUTOMATION UK LTD
Unit 8E, Newby Road Industrial Estate,
Hazel Grove, Stockport, Cheshire, SK7 5DA
Area of Operation: UK & Ireland
Tel: 0161 456 0456   **Fax:** 0161 456 9090
Email: info@bftautomation.co.uk
Web: www.bft.co.uk

CHOICE HI-FI
Denehurst Gardens, Richmond, Surrey, TW10
Area of Operation: UK (Excluding Ireland)
Tel: 0208 392 1959
Email: info@choice-hifi.com
Web: www.choice-hifi.com

CIS LTD
Westpoint Business Centre, Westland Square,
Leeds, West Yorkshire, LS11 5SS
Area of Operation: Worldwide
Tel: 08700 240640   **Fax:** 08700 240641
Email: p.hackett@compulock.com
Web: www.compulock.com

CONTROLWISE LTD
Unit 7, St. Davids Industrial Estate,
Pengam, Blackwood, Caerphilly, NP12 3SW
Area of Operation: South West England and South Wales
Tel: 01443 836836   **Fax:** 01443 836502
Email: stuart@controlwise.co.uk
Web: www.controlwise.co.uk

CREO DESIGN
62 North Street, Leeds, West Yorkshire, LS2 7PN
Area of Operation: UK (Excluding Ireland)
Tel: 0113 246 7373   **Fax:** 0113 242 5114
Email: info@creo-designs.co.uk
Web: www.creo-designs.co.uk

CUSTOM INSTALLATIONS
Custom House, 51 Baymead Lane,
North Petherton, Bridgwater, Somerset, TA6 6RN
Area of Operation: South West England and South Wales
Tel: 01278 662555
Fax: 01278 662975
Email: roger@custom-installations.co.uk
Web: www.custom-installations.co.uk

D&T ELECTRONICS
Unit 9A, Cranborne Industrial Estate,
Cranborne Road, Potters Bar, Hertfordshire, EN6 3JN
Area of Operation: UK (Excluding Ireland)
Tel: 0870 241 5891   **Fax:** 01707 653570
Email: info@dandt.co.uk
Web: www.dandt.co.uk   **Other Info:** ✐

DBCC LIMITED
Woodland View, Winchester Road,
Fair Oak, Eastleigh, Hampshire, SO50 7HD
Area of Operation: UK (Excluding Ireland)
Tel: 02380 692 555
Email: info@dbcc.co.uk   **Web:** www.dbcc.co.uk

DECKORUM LTD
4c Royal Oak Lane, Pirton,
Stevenage, Hertfordshire, SG5 3QT
Area of Operation: East England, Greater London,
South East England
Tel: 08450 204360   **Fax:** 08450 204361
Email: gary.mills@deckorum.com
Web: www.deckorum.com

DECO LEISURE
10 Carver Street, Birmingham,
West Midlands, B1 3AS
Area of Operation: Worldwide
Tel: 0121 693 9292   **Fax:** 0121 693 9293
Email: paul@dareproaudio.com
Web: www.tec4home.com

DIGITAL DECOR
Sonas House, Button End, Harston,
Cambridge, Cambridgeshire, CB2 5NX
Area of Operation: East England, Greater London
Tel: 01223 870935
Fax: 01223 870935
Email: seamus@digital-decor.co.uk
Web: www.digital-decor.co.uk

DISCOVERY SYSTEMS LTD
1 Corn Mill Close, The Spindles,
Ashton in Makerfield, Wigan, Lancashire, WN4 0PX
Area of Operation: North West England and North Wales
Tel: 01942 723756
Email: mike@discoverysystems.co.uk
Web: www.discoverysystems.co.uk

EAST TECHNOLOGY INTEGRATORS
85 Langtons Meadow, Farnham Common,
Slough, Berkshire, SL2 3NS
Area of Operation: Greater London, South East England
Tel: 01753 642367
Email: sales@east-ti.co.uk
Web: www.east-ti.co.uk

EASYCOMM
1 George House, Church Street,
Buntingford, Hertfordshire, SG9 9AS
Area of Operation: UK (Excluding Ireland)
Tel: 0800 389 9459
Email: steve@ezcomm.co.uk
Web: www.ezcomm.co.uk

EASYLIFE AUTOMATION LIMITED
Kullan House, 12 Meadowfield Road,
Stocksfield, Northumberland, NE43 7QX
Area of Operation: UK (Excluding Ireland)
Tel: 01661 844159   **Fax:** 01661 842594
Email: enquiries@easylifeautomation.com
Web: www.easylifeautomation.com

ECT PROJECTION SCREENS & ACCESSORIES
PO Box 4020, Pangbourne, Berkshire, RG8 8TX
Area of Operation: UK & Ireland
Tel: 0118 984 1141   **Fax:** 0118 984 1847
Email: lucinda@ect-av.com   **Web:** www.ect-av.com

FAITH & GANTRY LTD
Gainsborough House, 62 Hatfield Road,
Ipswich, Suffolk, IP3 9AF
Area of Operation: East England, Greater London
Tel: 01473 714002   **Fax:** 01473 714060
Email: lindsey@faithandgantry.com
Web: www.faithandgantry.com

FINITE SOLUTIONS -
HOME CINEMA AND MULTI ROOM AUDIO
Pavilion Business Centre, Stanningley Road,
Leeds, West Yorkshire, LS28 6NB
Area of Operation: UK (Excluding Ireland)
Tel: 0113 255 4765   **Fax:** 0113 255 4742
Email: info@finitesolutions.co.uk
Web: www.finitesolutions.co.uk   **Other Info:** ✐

FLAMINGBOX
Perry Farm, Maiden Bradley, Wiltshire, BA12 7JQ
Area of Operation: UK (Excluding Ireland)
Tel: 01985 845440   **Fax:** 01985 845448
Email: info@flamingbox.com
Web: www.flamingbox.com

FOCUS 21 VISUAL COMMUNICATIONS LIMITED
Tims Boatyard, Timsway, Staines, Surrey, TW18 3JY
Area of Operation: UK & Ireland
Tel: 01784 441153   **Fax:** 01784 225840
Email: info@focus21.co.uk
Web: www.focus21.co.uk

FUSION GROUP
Unit 4 Winston Avenue, Croft,
Leicester, Leicestershire, LE9 3GQ
Area of Operation: UK (Excluding Ireland)
Tel: 08450 204360   **Fax:** 08450 204361
Email: gary.mills@fusiongroup.uk.com
Web: www.fusiongroup.uk.com   **Other Info:** ✐

GOLDSYSTEM LTD
46 Nightingale Lane, Bromley, Kent, BR1 2SB
Area of Operation: Greater London, South East England
Tel: 0208 313 0485   **Fax:** 0208 313 0665
Email: info@goldsystem.co.uk
Web: www.goldsystem.co.uk

HARRIS GRANT
16 Trinity Church Yard, Guildford, Surrey, GU1 3RR
Area of Operation: UK (Excluding Ireland)
Tel: 01483 885678   **Fax:** 01483 885677
Email: info@harrisgrant.com

HELLERMANN TYTON
43-45 Salthouse Road, Brackmills,
Northampton, Northamptonshire, NN4 7EX
Area of Operation: Worldwide
Tel: 01604 707420   **Fax:** 01604 705454
Email: sales@htdata.co.uk
Web: www.homenetworksciences.com

HIDDEN HOME AUTOMATION
23 Cottesbrooke Park, Heartlands,
Daventry, Northamptonshire, NN11 8YL
Area of Operation: UK (Excluding Ireland)
Tel: 01327 872435   **Fax:** 01327 315287
Email: info@hiddenhomeautomation.co.uk
Web: www.hiddenhomeautomation.co.uk

HIFI CINEMA
1 Mars House, Calleva Park,
Aldermaston, Berkshire, RG7 8LA
Area of Operation: Greater London, South East England
Tel: 0118 982 0402   **Fax:** 0118 977 3535
Email: experience@hificinema.co.uk
Web: www.hificinema.co.uk

HOME NETWORKING ONLINE
Unit 3, Printers End, Gethouse Way,
Aylesbury, Buckinghamshire, HP19 8DB
Area of Operation: Europe
Tel: 0870 240 1162   **Fax:** 0207 691 7844
Email: sales@home-networking-online.co.uk
Web: www.home-networking-online.co.uk ✐

HOUSEHOLD AUTOMATION
Foxways, Pinkhurst Lane, Slinfold,
Horsham, West Sussex, RH13 0QR
Area of Operation: UK (Excluding Ireland)
Tel: 0870 330 0071   **Fax:** 0870 330 0072
Email: ellis-andrew@btconnect.com
Web: www.household-automation.co.uk

IBBD LTD
HomeLifeWorkLife Showroom, Unit 6 Link Trade
Park, Penarth Road, Cardiff, CF11 8TQ
Area of Operation: South West England and South Wales
Tel: 029 2071 3460   **Email:** info@ibbd.co.uk
Web: www.homelifeworklife.co.uk

IKURE (AUDIO VISUAL) LTD
27 Vanalloys Business Park, Busgrove Park,
Stoke Row, Henley-on-Thames, Oxfordshire, RG9 5QW
Area of Operation: Worldwide
Tel: 01491 682981   **Fax:** 01491 682578
Email: timv@ikure.co.uk   **Web:** www.ikure.co.uk

INTERCONNECTION
12 Chamberlayne Road, Moreton Hall Industrial
Estate, Bury St Edmunds, Suffolk, IP32 7EY
Area of Operation: East England
Tel: 01284 768676   **Fax:** 01284 767161
Email: info@interconnectionltd.co.uk
Web: www.interconnectionltd.co.uk

IQYOURHOME.COM LTD
Unit D10, Chaucer Business Park, Watery Lane,
Kemsing, Sevenoaks, Kent, TN15 6YU
Area of Operation: UK & Ireland
Tel: 01732 763888   **Fax:** 01732 763351
Email: info@iqyourhome.com
Web: www.iqyourhome.com

J K AUDIO VISUAL
Unit 7 Newport Business Park,
Audley Avenue, Newport, Shropshire, TF10 7DP
Area of Operation: UK (Excluding Ireland)
Tel: 01952 825088   **Fax:** 01952 814884
Email: sales@jk-audiovisual.co.uk
Web: www.jk-audiovisual.co.uk ✐

JELLYBEAN CTRL LTD
Eagle House, Passfield Business Centre,
Lynchborough Road, Passfield, Hampshire, GU30 7SB
Area of Operation: UK (Excluding Ireland)
Tel: 01428 751729   **Fax:** 01428 751772
Email: david@jellybeanctrl.com
Web: www.jellybeanctrl.com

KENT HOME CINEMA CENTRE
69 London Road, Southborough,
Tunbridge Wells, Torfaen, TN4 0PA
Tel: 01892 535007   **Fax:** 01892 533334
Email: andrew@kenthomecinema.co.uk
Web: www.av-sales.co.uk ✐

LIFESTYLE ELECTRONICS
Woodview, Castlebridge, County Wexford, Ireland
Area of Operation: Europe
Tel: +353 53 9159880   **Fax:** +353 53 5919844
Email: lifestyle123@eircom.net

LIVING CONTROL LTD
The Flyer's Way, Westerham, Kent, TN16 1DE
Area of Operation: Worldwide
Tel: 0845 094 0079
Email: thh@livingcontrol.com
Web: www.livingcontrol.com   **Other Info:** ✐

MARANTZ HIFI UK
Kingsbridge House, Padbury Oaks, 581 Bath Road,
Longford, Middlesex, UB7 0EH
Area of Operation: Worldwide
Tel: 01753 680868   **Fax:** 01753 680428
Email: joe.thurston@marantz.co.uk
Web: www.marantz.com

MARQUEE HOME LIMITED
Unit 6, Eversley Way, Thorpe Industrial Estate,
Egham, Surrey, TW20 8RF
Area of Operation: Greater London, South East England
Tel: 07004 567888   **Fax:** 07004 567788
Email: paulendersby@marqueehome.co.uk
Web: www.marqueehome.co.uk

MARTINS HI-FI
85/87 Ber Street, Norwich, Norfolk, NR1 3EY
Area of Operation: East England
Tel: 01603 627010 **Fax:** 01603 878019
Email: info@martinshifi.co.uk
Web: www.martinshifi.co.uk

MERIDIAN AUDIO LIMITED
Latham Road, Huntingdon, Cambridgeshire, PE29 6YE
Area of Operation: Worldwide
Tel: 01480 445678 **Fax:** 01480 445686
Email: info@meridian-audio.com
Web: www.meridian-audio.com

MIRRORMEDIA LTD
15 Southmill Trading Centre, Southmill Road,
Bishop's Stortford, Hertfordshire, CM23 3DY
Tel: 0870 386 6333 **Fax:** 0870 386 6111
Email: sales@mirrormedia.com
Web: www.mirrormedia.com

MJ ACOUSTICS
9 Venture Court, Boleness Road,
Wisbech, Cambridgeshire, PE132XQ
Tel: 01945 467770 **Fax:** 01945 467778
Email: sales@mjacoustics.co.uk
Web: www.mjacoustics.co.uk

MULTIROOM AUDIO
4 Clement Way, Cawton, Rugby, Warwickshire, CV22 7FH
Area of Operation: UK (Excluding Ireland)
Tel: 01788 521248 **Fax:** 08707628242
Email: sales@multiroom-audio.co.uk
Web: www.multiroom-audio.co.uk
Other Info:

MUSICAL APPROACH
111 Wolverhampton Road,
Stafford, Staffordshire, ST17 4AH
Tel: 01785 255154
Email: info@musicalapproach.co.uk
Web: www.musicalapproach.co.uk

NODE ZERO LTD
Unit 4a Winston Avenue,
eicester, Leicestershire, LE9 3GQ
Area of Operation: Europe
Tel: 08700 500248 **Fax:** 0845 020 4361
Email: jason.neale@nodezero.uk.com
Web: www.nodezero.uk.com

O2M8 LTD
P.O.Box 7716, Newbury, Berkshire, RG20 5WU
Area of Operation: UK (Excluding Ireland)
Tel: 07789 207408
Email: john@o2m8.com **Web:** www.o2m8.com

OPUS GB
Gallery Court, Pilgrmage Street, London, SE1 4LL
Tel: 0207 940 2205 **Fax:** 0207 940 2206
Email: info@opus-technologies.co.uk
Web: www.opus-technologies.com

ORANGES & LEMONS
61/63 Webbs Road, Battersea, London, SW11 6RX
Area of Operation: Greater London, South East England
Tel: 0207 924 2040 **Fax:** 0207 924 3665
Email: oranges.lemons@virgin.net
Web: www.oandlhifi.co.uk

PARK SYSTEMS INTEGRATION LTD
Unit 3 Queen's Park, Earlsway, Team Valley Trading
Estate, Gateshead, Tyne & Wear, NE11 0QD
Tel: 0191 497 0770 **Fax:** 0191 497 0772
Email: elife@psi.uk.com **Web:** www.psi.uk.com

PHILLSON LTD
144 Rickerscote Road, Stafford,
Staffordshire, ST17 4HE
Tel: 0845 612 0128 **Fax:** 01477 535090
Email: info@phillson.co.uk
Web: www.phillson.co.uk

PICTURE HOUSE CABINETS
Cherry House, Oakcroft Road,
West Byfleet, Surrey, KT10 0JH
Tel: 01932 345184 **Fax:** 01932 402128
Email: info@picturehousecabinets.com
Web: www.picturehousecabinets.com

PLASMATVINFO.COM LIMITED
Dorisima House, Ipswich Road,
Brantham, Manningtree, Suffolk, CO11 1NR
Tel: 01206 391001 **Fax:** 01206 391096
Email: info@plasmatvinfo.com
Web: www.plasmatvinfo.com

PRESTIGE AUDIO
12 High Street, Rickmansworth,
Hertfordshire, WD3 1ER
Tel: 01923 711113 **Fax:** 01923 776606
Email: info@prestigeaudio.co.uk
Web: www.prestigeaudio.co.uk

ROCOCO SYSTEMS & DESIGN
26 Danbury Street, London, N1 8JU
Area of Operation: Europe
Tel: 0207 454 1234 **Fax:** 0207 870 0888
Email: sales@rococosystems.com
Web: www.rococosystems.com

SCAN AUDIO
1 Honeycrock Lane, Salford,
Redhill, Surrey, RH1 5DG
Tel: 01737 778620 **Fax:** 01737 778620
Email: scanaudio@mac.com
Web: www.scanaudio.co.uk

SCION TECHNOLOGY LIMITED
Scion Business Park, Brimpton Common,
Reading, Berkshire, RG7 4RN
Tel: 0118 981 7151 **Fax:** 0118 981 7575
Email: mark.brown@sciontech.com
Web: www.sciontech.com

SEISMIC INTERAUDIO
3 Maypole Drive, Kings Hill,
West Malling, Kent, ME19 4BP
Area of Operation: Europe
Tel: 0870 073 4764 **Fax:** 0870 073 4765
Email: info@seismic.co.uk **Web:** www.seismic.co.uk

SENSORY INTERNATIONAL LIMITED
48A London Road, Alderley Edge, Cheshire, SK9 7DZ
Tel: 01625 584540 **Fax:** 01625 585789
Email: garyc@sensoryinternational.com
Web: www.sensoryinternational.com

SEVENOAKS SOUND & VISION (LEEDS)
62 North Street, Leeds, West Yorkshire, LS2 7PN
Area of Operation: Midlands & Mid Wales, North
East England, North West England and North Wales
Tel: 0113 245 2775 **Fax:** 0113 242 5114
Email: leeds@ssav.com **Web:** www.ssav.com

SEVENOAKS SOUND & VISION (OXFORD)
41 St Clements Street, Oxford, Oxfordshire, OX4 1AG
Tel: 01865 241773 **Fax:** 01865 794904
Email: oxford@ssav.com **Web:** www.ssav.com

SG SYSTEMS LTD
Unit 38 Elderpark Workspace, 100 Elderpark Street,
Glasgow, Renfrewshire, G51 3TR
Tel: 0141 445 4125 **Fax:** 0141 445 4125
Email: info@sgsystems.ltd.uk
Web: www.sgsystems.ltd.uk

SHARP ELECTRONICS (UK) LTD.
4 Furzeground Way, Stockley Park, Uxbridge, UB11 1EZ
Area of Operation: UK & Ireland
Tel: 0208 734 2000
Email: mike.gabriel@sharp-uk.co.uk
Web: www.sharp.co.uk

SIMPLY AUTOMATE
23 Wornal Park, Menmarsh Road, Worminghall,
Aylesbury, Buckinghamshire, HP18 9PH
Area of Operation: Worldwide
Tel: 0845 644 3330 **Fax:** 0845 644 2713
Email: info@simplyautomate.co.uk
Web: www.simplyautomate.co.uk

SINCLAIR YOUNGS LTD
Basingstoke Business Centre, Winchester Road,
Basingstoke, Hampshire, RG22 4AU
Area of Operation: South East England
Tel: 01256 355015 **Fax:** 01256 818344
Email: david.wilson@sinclairyoungs.com
Web: www.sinclairyoungs.com

SMART HOUSE
23 Wornal Park, Menmarsh Road, Worminghall,
Aylesbury, Buckinghamshire, HP18 9PH
Area of Operation: Europe
Tel: 0845 053 3680 **Fax:** 0845 644 2713
Email: info@smarthouse.co.uk
Web: www.smarthouse.co.uk

STONEAUDIO UK LIMITED
Holmead Walk, Poundbury,
Dorchester, Dorset, DT1 3GE
Area of Operation: Worldwide
Tel: 01305 257555 **Fax:** 01305 257666
Email: info@stoneaudio.co.uk
Web: www.stoneaudio.co.uk

STUART WESTMORELAND (HOLDINGS) LTD
33 Cattle Market, Loughborough,
Leicestershire, LE11 3DL
Area of Operation: East England, Midlands & Mid Wales
Tel: 01509 230465 **Fax:** 01509 267478
Email: loughborough@stuartwestmoreland.co.uk
Web: www.custom-install.co.uk

SUB SYSTEMS INTEGRATION LTD
Studio 19, Hurlingham Studios,
Ranelagh Gardens, London, SW6 3PA
Area of Operation: Greater London
Tel: 0207 796 1459 **Fax:** 0207 796 1469
Email: info@sub.eu.com **Web:** www.sub.eu.com

SYNCHRO NETWORKS LTD
PO Box 219, Whitstable, CT5 3WZ
Area of Operation: UK & Ireland
Tel: 05511 490058 **Fax:** 05511 490059
Email: info@synchro-networks.co.uk
Web: www.home-networking-solutions.co.uk

TEC 4 HOME
10 Carver Street, Hockley,
Birmingham, West Midlands, B1 3AS
Area of Operation: UK (Excluding Ireland)
Tel: 0121 693 9292 **Fax:** 0121 693 9293
Email: paul@dareproaudio.com
Web: www.tec4home.com

TECCHO
Unit 19W , Kilroot Business Park,
Carrickfergus, Co Antrim, BT38 7PR
Area of Operation: UK & Ireland
Tel: 0845 890 1150 **Fax:** 0870 063 4120
Email: enquiries@teccho.net **Web:** www.teccho.net

TELESTIAL LTD
109-111 Pope Street, Birmingham, B1 3AG
Area of Operation: UK (Excluding Ireland)
Tel: 0870 855 0010
Email: sales@telestial.biz **Web:** www.telestial.biz

**THE BIG PICTURE -
AV & HOME CINEMA LIMITED**
51 Sutton Road, Walsall, West Midlands, WS1 2PQ
Area of Operation: UK & Ireland
Tel: 01922 623000
Email: info@getthebigpicture.co.uk
Web: www.getthebigpicture.co.uk

THE EDGE
90-92 Norwich Road, Ipswich, Suffolk, IP1 2NL
Area of Operation: UK (Excluding Ireland)
Tel: 01473 288211 **Fax:** 01473 288255
Email: nick@theedge.eu.com
Web: www.theedge.eu.com

THE IVY HOUSE
The Ivy House, Cherry Trees,
Bridegate Lane, Hickling Pastures,
Melton Mowbray, Leicestershire, LE14 3QA
Area of Operation: East England, Midlands & Mid Wales
Tel: 01664 822628
Email: enquiries@the-ivy-house.com
Web: www.the-ivy-house.com

THE LITTLE CINEMA COMPANY
72 New Bond Street, London, W1S 1RR
Area of Operation: Worldwide
Tel: 0207 385 5521 **Fax:** 0207 385 5524
Email: sales@littlecinema.com
Web: www.littlecinema.co.uk

THE MAJIK HOUSE COMPANY LTD
Unit J Mainline Industrial Estate,
Crooklands Road, Milnthorpe, Cumbria, LA7 7LR
Area of Operation: North East England, North West
England and North Wales
Tel: 0870 240 8350 **Fax:** 0870 240 8350
Email: tim@majikhouse.com
Web: www.majikhouse.com

THE PLASMA WAREHOUSE GROUP PLC
Sandy Farm Business Park,
The Sands, Farnham, Surrey, GU10 1PX
Area of Operation: Europe
Tel: 0870 734 5432
Email: sales@plasmawarehouseuk.com
Web: www.plasmawarehouseuk.com

THE THINKING HOME
The White House, Wilderspool Park,
Greenalls Avenue, Warrington, Cheshire, WA4 6HL
Tel: 0800 881 8319 **Fax:** 0800 881 8329
Email: info@thethinkinghome.com
Web: www.thethinkinghome.com

THINKINGBRICKS LTD
6 High Street, West Wickham,
Cambridge, Cambridgeshire, CB1 6RY
Tel: 01223 290886
Email: ian@thinkingbricks.co.uk
Web: www.thinkingbricks.co.uk

TRIBUNE SMART HOME
321 Bolton Road, Manchester, M6 7GU
Area of Operation: UK (Excluding Ireland)
Tel: 0161 736 4011 **Fax:** 0161 736 8355
Email: info@tribunesmarthome.com
Web: www.tribunesmarthome.com

UNLIMITED DREAM HOME SYSTEMS
The Long Barn, Wakefield Road, Hampole,
Doncaster, South Yorkshire, DN6 7EU
Area of Operation: UK (Excluding Ireland)
Tel: 01302 727274 **Fax:** 01302 725550
Email: info@thehifistudios.freeserve.co.uk
Web: www.unlimiteddream.co.uk

VALTEK
Ardykeohane, Bruff, Co. Limerick, Ireland
Tel: +353 6138 2116 **Fax:** +353 6138 2032
Email: sales@valtek.biz **Web:** www.valtek.biz

WATERPROOFTV.CO.UK
7 Allandale Road, Stoneygate, Leicester,
Leicestershire, LE2 2DA
Area of Operation: Worldwide
Tel: 0116 270 5777 **Fax:** 0116 274 5777
Email: w@terproof.tv **Web:** www.waterprooftv.co.uk

WEBSTRACT LTD
2-4 Place Farm, Wheathampstead, Hertfordshire, AL4 8SB
Area of Operation: UK (Excluding Ireland)
Tel: 0870 446 0146 **Fax:** 0870 762 6431
Email: info@webstract.co.uk
Web: www.webstract.co.uk

WIRED FOR LIVING
19 Harwood Road, Rishton,
Blackburn, Lancashire, BB1 4DH
Area of Operation: UK (Excluding Ireland)
Tel: 07734 798771 **Fax:** 01254 399078
Email: info@wiredforliving.co.uk
Web: www.wiredforliving.co.uk

X-HOME
Unit W Williamsons Holdings,
Uphall, West Lothian, EH52 6PA
Area of Operation: UK (Excluding Ireland)
Tel: 0845 130 1091 **Fax:** 0845 130 1092
Email: sales@xhome.biz
Web: www.xhome.biz

ZEN CUSTOM SOLUTIONS LTD
Unit 9, Brookfield Business Park, Clay Lane, York
Road, Market Weighton, North Yorkshire, YO43 3PU
Area of Operation: UK (Excluding Ireland)
Tel: 01430 803473 **Fax:** 01430 803473
Email: sales@zencs.co.uk
Web: www.zencs.co.uk

PLOTFINDER.NET
SITEFINDERIRELAND.COM

Searching for your perfect plot of land – be it one with a fantastic view, one in a country hideaway or one close to a buzzing city – is often an uphill struggle. Endless effort and time can be spent trawling through papers, calling estate agents and going to auctions. Which is where **www.plotfinder.net** and **www.sitefinderireland.com** can help you…

www.plotfinder.net is a database which holds details on around 6,000 building plots and properties for renovation currently for sale in the UK, whilst **www.sitefinderireland.com** contains details on thousands of building sites and properties for renovation for sale in Ireland.

Visit the sites for more information.

Unit 2 Sugar Brook Court
Aston Road
Bromsgrove
Worcestershire
B60 3EX

Tel: 01527 834428
Fax: 01527 837810
Email: customerservice@centaur.co.uk
Website: www.plotfinder.net / www.sitefinderireland.com

Image courtesy of VacuDuct (0800 783 6264)

SPONSORED BY: VacuDuct
Tel: 0800 783 6264 Web: www.vacuduct.co.uk

SMART HOMES & SECURITY

Central Vacuum Systems

Central vacuums are designed to remove all the dust and dirt from your house, without the hassle of lugging a heavy unit from room to room.

Built-in vacuums transport dirt out through a pipe in the wall and into a dirt collection canister. Image ABOVE by Total Home Environment.

It is a very simple idea – a central power unit is fitted outside the main living area (usually in a basement, garage or utility room) while inlet valves are positioned at strategic points around the house. You simply take the hose around the house with you, inserting it into the valve for that area

of the house. The valves suck dust and debris into a network of hidden tubes leading to a collection tank or bag, where all waste is deposited. How many inlets you want in your home is based on your own needs - an installer will be able to discuss the best placement for your home.

To ensure proper installation, it is best to leave it to the professionals. There are many companies to choose from, and most will offer a design-and-fit service, including an installation and service warranty. However, many manufacturers do offer complete instructions to help you with your own installation if you prefer, and fitting can usually be completed in a single day by anyone skilled at DIY

Central vacuum systems require little maintenance, but you should empty the dirt canister or replace the bag - once every three to six months is average. Filters may also need changing to ensure the benefits of cleaner air are maintained.

Some benefits of central vacuums:

- **Healthy air** - Central vacuums eliminate the re-circulation of dirty air inside your home, removing smelly particles and allergens like pet hair and dust mites, so central vacuums are especially useful for allergy sufferers.

- **Power** - Central vacuums have up to five times more power than their traditional counterparts; not being portable they can contain a more powerful motor than traditional vacuums.

- **Convenience** - You choose the best locations for wall inlets, so you aren't reliant on the positions of existing electrical sockets.

- **Durability** – Central vacuum systems are stored out of the way, so are less prone to damage than traditional portable vacuums.

- **Noise** - Central vacuums are usually quieter than traditional vacuums, as the power unit is located outside the living area.

- **Home value** - Any permanent appliance in your home should help increase its value upon re-sale.

BUILT-IN VACUUMS

ADM
Ling Fields, Gargrave Road,
Skipton, North Yorkshire, BD23 1UX
Tel: 01756 701051
Fax: 01756 701076
Email: info@admsystems.co.uk
Web: www.admsystems.co.uk

ALLERGYPLUS LIMITED
65 Stowe Drive, Southam, Warwickshire, CV47 1NZ
Area of Operation: UK & Ireland
Tel: 0870 190 0022
Fax: 0870 190 0044
Email: info@allergyplus.co.uk
Web: www.allergyplus.co.uk

BEAM CENTRAL VACUUMS (UK) LTD
Swallow House,
Cotswold Business Village,
London Road, Moreton in Marsh,
Gloucestershire, GL56 0JQ
Area of Operation: UK (Excluding Ireland)
Tel: 0845 260 0123 **Fax:** 01608 652490
Email: info@beamvac.co.uk
Web: www.beamvac.co.uk

BEAM VACUUM SYSTEMS LTD
Opus Business Park,
35 Aughrim Road, Magherafelt, BT45 6BB
Area of Operation: UK & Ireland
Tel: 028 7938 6307   **Fax:** 028 7938 6869
Email: enquiries@beamvacuums.ie
Web: www.beamvacuums.ie

BEL-AIR CENTRAL VACUUM SYSTEMS
1 Kirkhill Gate, Newton Mearns,
East Renfrewshire, G77 5RH
Area of Operation: UK (Excluding Ireland)
Tel: 0141 639 7327
Fax: 0141 639 7827
Email: gordon@centralvacuumsystems.co.uk
Web: www.centralvacuumsystems.co.uk

BESPOKE INSTALLATIONS
1 Rogers Close, Tiverton, Devon, EX16 6UW
Area of Operation: South West England and South Wales
Tel: 01884 243497 **Email:** michael@bespoke.biz
Web: www.bespoke.biz

CENTRAVAC LTD
Unit 6, Mills Hill Trading Estate,
Mills Hill Road, Middleton,
Greater Manchester, M24 2ES
Area of Operation: UK & Ireland
Tel: 08000 13 15 17 **Fax:** 0161 6433377
Email: enquiries@centravac.co.uk
Web: www.centravac.co.uk

COOLANDWARM.COM
Trigger Comfort, t/a Cool and Warm, 23 Walnut Tree Close, Guildford, Surrey, GU1 4UL
Area of Operation: Europe
Tel: 01483 30 66 50
Email: info@coolandwarm.com
Web: www.coolandwarm.com

CVC DIRECT LIMITED
Unit B, The Croft, Whitely Road,
Hithercroft Industrial Estate, Wallingford,
Oxfordshire, OX10 9RG
Area of Operation: Europe
Tel: 01491 836666 **Fax:** 01491 838086
Email: info@cvcdirect.co.uk
Web: www.cvcdirect.co.uk

DUOVAC UK
21 Ellingham Way, Ashford, Kent, TN23 6NF
Area of Operation: UK (Excluding Ireland)
Tel: 01233 664244
Email: info@duovac.co.uk
Web: www.duovac.co.uk

EASYLIFE AUTOMATION LIMITED
Kullan House, 12 Meadowfield Road,
Stocksfield, Northumberland, NE43 7QX
Tel: 01661 844159 **Fax:** 01661 842594
Email: enquiries@easylifeautomation.com
Web: www.easylifeautomation.com

SMART HOMES & SECURITY

EU SOLUTIONS
Maghull Business Centre, 1 Liverpool Road North,
Maghull, Liverpool, L31 2HB
Area of Operation: UK & Ireland
Tel: 0870 160 1660   **Fax:** 0151 526 8849
Email: ths@blueyonder.co.uk
Web: www.totalhomesolutions.co.uk

EU SOLUTIONS

Area of Operation: UK & Ireland
Tel: 0870 160 1660
Fax: 0151 526 8849
Email: ths@blueyonder.co.uk
Web: www.totalhomesolutions.co.uk

Imagine having a fully integrated, versatile
cleaning system within your home or work place,
offering real benefits for every day cleaning,
health and your living environment, without
lugging a heavy portable around.

FUSION GROUP
Unit 4 Winston Avenue, Croft,
Leicester, Leicestershire, LE9 3GQ
Tel: 08450 204360   **Fax:** 08450 204361
Email: gary.mills@fusiongroup.uk.com
Web: www.fusiongroup.uk.com

HOUSEHOLD AUTOMATION
Foxways, Pinkhurst Lane, Slinfold,
Horsham, West Sussex, RH13 0QR
Tel: 0870 330 0071   **Fax:** 0870 330 0072
Email: ellis-andrew@btconnect.com
Web: www.household-automation.co.uk

NUTONE PRODUCTS UK
30 Harmer Street, Gravesend, Kent, DA12 2AX
Tel: 01474 352264   **Fax:** 01474 334438
Email: marionmoney@tiscali.co.uk

PARAGON SYSTEMS (SCOTLAND) LIMITED
The Office, Corbie Cottage,
Maryculter, Aberdeen, Aberdeenshire, AB12 5FT
Area of Operation: Scotland
Tel: 01224 735536   **Fax:** 01224 735537
Email: info@paragon-systems.co.uk
Web: www.paragon-systems.co.uk

SMART CENTRAL VACUUMS LTD
Unit 3, Whitestone Business Park,
Whitestone, Herefordshire, HR1 3SE
Area of Operation: UK (Excluding Ireland)
Tel: 01432 853019   **Fax:** 01432 853070
Email: info@smartvacuums.co.uk
Web: www.smartvacuums.co.uk

STARKEY SYSTEMS UK LTD
4a St Martins House, St Martins Gate,
Worcester, Worcestershire, WR1 2DT
Area of Operation: UK (Excluding Ireland)
Tel: 01905 611041   **Fax:** 01905 27462
Email: sales@centralvacuums.co.uk
Web: www.centralvacuums.co.uk

VACUDUCT LTD
Unit 6, Brynberth Enterprise Park,
Rhayader, Powys, LD6 5EN
Area of Operation: Europe
Tel: 0800 783 6264   **Fax:** 01597 810755
Email: info@vacuduct.co.uk
Web: www.vacuduct.co.uk

NOTES

Company Name ....

....

Address ....

....

....

email ....

Web ....

Company Name ....

....

Address ....

....

....

email ....

Web ....

Company Name ....

....

Address ....

....

....

email ....

Web ....

Company Name ....

....

Address ....

....

....

email ....

Web ....

SMART HOMES & SECURITY

With no heavy, noisy machine to lug about VacuDuct is the answer to an age old problem; efficiently cleaning your home.

House work is a chore and in our increasingly busy lives it's crazy that most of us are still spending hours doing it the same old way that our Grandparents did. Carting a noisy, dirty machine filled with dirt and dust around a house and having to empty it frequently, adding to the dust in the house.

There is a much better way to keep your house clean and if you are planning and building your new home this is the time to include the latest in cleaning technology.

Some years ago a new concept was developed. Instead of dragging a machine around the house why not fix a larger, more powerful vacuum machine in an out of the way place and duct this to a number of inlet points about the house so that vacuum power would always be available through out the house.

To clean the house all that is required is to plug a long hose into the inlet point and as you vacuum all the dirt and debris is sucked through the ducting and back to the vacuum machine. This is the basic concept of a central or built in vacuum.

Great cleaning power

Because a VacuDuct is an integrated appliance it provides up to 5 times the power of a conventional vacuum. It will pick up the dirt others leave behind.

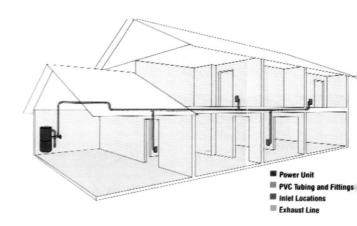

■ Power Unit
■ PVC Tubing and Fittings
■ Inlet Locations
■ Exhaust Line

No Heavy Lifting

Just plug the lightweight hose into a convenient inlet point upstairs or down. Fit the attachment you need and start cleaning.

The system starts at the press of the switch on the handle for added convenience

No stale dusty air

Conventional vacuums push stale dusty air back into the room - a VacuDuct vents it out of your home altogether. Not only is your home cleaner, but it stays cleaner for long

Types of power unit and filtration

There are available today, a wide choice of vacuum power units. The principal components of each are, motor and circuit board, a filter and a dirt collection bucket.

The electric motor spins at around 20,000 RPM and turns a set of fan blades (turbines) that generates the suction power. A circuit board controls when the motor turns on and off. When the motor is running dirt and air is drawn into the collector bucket, the dirt is deposited and the air is exhausted from the machine.

Self cleaning cloth filters, sponge filters, paper cartridges and cyclonic systems are all available as well as the unique Drainvac automatic which uses water. Some use a supplementary bag for dirt collection/ filtration. Sponge filters tend to clog rapidly reducing efficiency. Self cleaning cloth filters eventually need cleaning and can be difficult to remove and refit. Cartridge filters are better than sponge but are expensive to replace and fiddly to clean.

In our opinion cloth filters with a supplementary paper bag are the happy medium. When you come to empty the unit you will have dirt collected over the last few months. With an open bucket this tends to be a dirty operation. With a sealed disposable dust bag you simply remove the bag and throw it away. Fitting a new bag takes only a few moments and cost only a couple of pounds. Each time you replace a bag you are effectively fitting a new filter, which gives an extended life to the motor. Fitting a new bag is also far more hygienic than dealing with a large bucket of months old dirt.

Generally the exhaust from a central vacuum is vented outside. If this is impossible it is still possible to have a central vacuum. The exhaust will terminate on a special disposable filter. VacuDuct use a carbon impregnated filter for added hygiene

ALL THE INSPIRATION AND INFORMATION YOU NEED TO MAKE YOUR PROJECT A SUCCESS

THINKING ABOUT, OR IN THE MIDDLE OF CONVERTING, RENOVATING OR BUILDING YOUR OWN HOME?

Full of inspiration and ideas, including readers' homes, practical features about building or renovating, plus a complete beginner's guide with advice on raising finance, getting planning permission and much more…

SUBSCRIBER BENEFITS:

- Free access to 100s of houseplans, readers' homes, financial and technical articles in the subscriber only area at www.homebuilding.co.uk
- Free tickets to all of the Homebuilding & Renovating Shows (worth £112)
- Save £5 off any book published by *Homebuilding and Renovating* magazine.

ON SALE NOW IN ALL GOOD NEWSAGENTS AND SUPER-MARKETS

SUBSCRIBE TODAY!

VISIT www.homebuilding.co.uk   Call 01527 834 435

CENTAUR SPECIAL INTEREST MEDIA

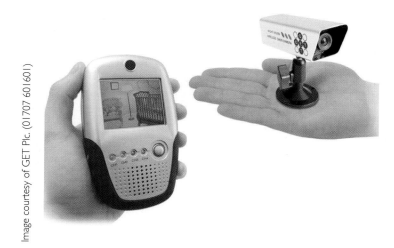

Image courtesy of GET Plc. (01707 601601)

SPONSORED BY: The Smart Home Show
Tel: 0207 970 4249   Web: www.smarthomeshow.co.uk

22-25 March 2007
NEC, Birmingham

SMART HOMES & SECURITY

Security

Security is obviously a major consideration for self-builders, and it's a good idea to think about such measures early into your project

GET Pic.

Although cases of domestic burglary in England and Wales have been falling dramatically in the last ten years – cases fell by 57% between 1995 and 2005 – there is still a real risk of suffering a burglary, with around 3 in 100 households targeted.

To help prevent against burglary, adopt a few simple security measures such as leaving a light on or plugging lamps into a timer switch. These actions will deter the opportunist burglar, but to make your home safer from the professional thief, you may want to consider something a little more hi-tech.

A good place to start is with PIR (Passive Infra Red) security lights at the front and back of your property. These detect movement by monitoring infra-red energy levels and illuminate a certain area for a pre-set time.

Another option is, of course, a burglar alarm. The problem with burglar alarms is, like car alarms, they are often ignored. And even if you do phone the police to report a burglar alarm going off, they probably won't come out to investigate unless it is connected to a professional Central Monitoring Station (CMS), run by a security company. These aren't excessively expensive to fit – generally less than £1,000, but you should remember that there is often a cost implication of a few hundred pounds a year in monitoring these systems.

In recent years closed circuit television (CCTV) has become an important security provision for homes. Simple black and white surveillance systems are now fairly cheap to buy and you can install them yourself quite easily.

But a better option would be one of the newer CCTV systems. They often store images digitally so you don't have to change a tape to manage recordings. The systems can also be linked up to a broadband connection, so you can see what's happening while you are away. Moreover, some images can even be checked from mobile phones.

Generally, monochrome cameras work best in poor light, but a growing number of colour cameras have low-light-level functions and switch automatically to black and white when light levels fall. You can also get moveable pan, tilt and zoom (PTZ) which sit on motorised mounts built inside weatherproof housings,

and static or moveable IP cameras (netcams) which enable you to view your property – or simply keep an eye on the kids – from anywhere in the world via the internet. Using digital recording systems it's also possible to record footage from several cameras at the same time.

And for those after a really hi-tech security solution you can always use fingerprint recognition locks rather than keys. These are capable of storing the individual fingerprints of each family member, and allow you to check exactly when someone entered and left the building.

Finally, it is worth mentioning a cheaper way of keeping your house safe and secure. The neighbourhood watch scheme involves the police, volunteers and local communities to help keep your neighbourhood safe. The website www.neighbourhoodwatch.uk.com contains lots of information about local schemes.

- For the most effective alarm system, conceal all wiring. A professional burglar looks for places where he or she can disconnect the security system.

- If you have a faulty alarm that frequently goes off, get it fixed immediately and tell your neighbours that it's been repaired so they do not ignore it.

ACCESS SYSTEMS

KEY

OTHER: ▽ Reclaimed ⌂ On-line shopping

✎ Bespoke ✋ Hand-made ECO Ecological

A.C.E. - AUTOMATION CONTRACTORS & ENGINEERS
126 Heath Hill Avenue, Brighton,
East Sussex, BN2 4LS
Area of Operation: UK (Excluding Ireland)
Tel: 01273 665468 **Fax:** 07884 599411
Email: sales@ace-automation.co.uk
Web: www.ace-automation.co.uk

A.S.K. SUPPLIES LIMITED
5 Stretton Close, Bridgnorth, Shropshire, WV16 5DB
Area of Operation: UK (Excluding Ireland)
Tel: 01746 768164 **Fax:** 01746 766835
Email: sales@asksupplies.co.uk
Web: www.asksupplies.co.uk

AFM SECURITY
Head Office, The Stables,
Foxes Loke, Loddon, Norfolk, NR14 6UL
Area of Operation: East England, Greater London
Tel: 01508 522078 **Fax:** 01508 522079
Email: sales@afmsecurity.co.uk
Web: www.afmsecurity.co.uk

ANGELL SECURITY & SURVEILLANCE LTD
19 Primrose Drive, Bicester, Oxfordshire, OX26 3WP
Area of Operation: Europe
Tel: 01869 247500 **Fax:** 01869 323601
Email: sales@angellsecurity.com
Web: www.angellsecurity.com ⌂
Other Info: ✎

AUDIO T CUSTOM INSTALLATIONS
11 Charter Place, High Street,
Egham, Surrey, TW20 9EA
Area of Operation: East England, Greater London,
South East England
Tel: 01784 479423 **Fax:** 01784 479425
Email: custom@audio-t.co.uk
Web: www.audio-t.co.uk/custom

AUTOPA LIMITED
Cottage Leap, Rugby, Warwickshire, CV21 3XP
Area of Operation: Worldwide
Tel: 01788 550556 **Fax:** 01788 550265
Email: info@autopa.co.uk
Web: www.autopa.co.uk

BESPOKE INSTALLATIONS
1 Rogers Close, Tiverton, Devon, EX16 6UW
Area of Operation: South West England and South Wales
Tel: 01884 243497
Email: michael@bespoke.biz
Web: www.bespoke.biz

BFT AUTOMATION UK LTD
Unit 8E, Newby Road Industrial Estate,
Hazel Grove, Stockport, Cheshire, SK7 5DA
Area of Operation: UK & Ireland
Tel: 0161 456 0456 **Fax:** 0161 456 9090
Email: info@bftautomation.co.uk
Web: www.bft.co.uk

CIRRUS COMMUNICATION SYSTEMS
Oregon House, 19 Queensway,
New Milton, Hampshire, BH25 5NN
Area of Operation: UK (Excluding Ireland)
Tel: 0845 602 2440 **Fax:** 01425 626345
Email: enquiries@cirruscom.co.uk
Web: www.cirruscom.co.uk **Other Info:** ⌂

CIS LTD
Westpoint Business Centre, Westland Square,
Leeds, West Yorkshire, LS11 5SS
Area of Operation: Worldwide
Tel: 08700 240640 **Fax:** 08700 240641
Email: p.hackett@compulock.com
Web: www.compulock.com

COASTFORM SYSTEMS LTD.
Unit 18 Dinnington Business Centre, Outgang Lane,
Dinnington, Sheffield, South Yorkshire, S25 3QX
Area of Operation: Worldwide
Tel: 01909 561470 **Fax:** 08700 516793
Email: sales@coastform.co.uk
Web: www.coastform.co.uk

COMFORT HOME CONTROLS
Carlton House, Carlton Avenue,
Chester, Cheshire, CH4 8UE
Area of Operation: UK & Ireland
Tel: 08707 605528 **Fax:** 01244 671455
Email: sales@home-control.co.uk
Web: www.home-control.co.uk ⌂

D&T ELECTRONICS
Unit 9A, Cranborne Industrial Estate, Cranborne
Road, Potters Bar, Hertfordshire, EN6 3JN
Area of Operation: UK (Excluding Ireland)
Tel: 0870 241 5891 **Fax:** 01707 653570
Email: info@dandt.co.uk
Web: www.dandt.co.uk **Other Info:** ✎

DBCC LIMITED
Woodland View, Winchester Road,
Fair Oak, Eastleigh, Hampshire, SO50 7HD
Area of Operation: UK (Excluding Ireland)
Tel: 02380 692 555
Email: info@dbcc.co.uk **Web:** www.dbcc.co.uk

DIGITAL DECOR
Sonas House, Button End, Harston,
Cambridge, Cambridgeshire, CB2 5NX
Area of Operation: East England, Greater London
Tel: 01223 870935 **Fax:** 01223 870935
Email: seamus@digital-decor.co.uk
Web: www.digital-decor.co.uk

DISKLOK UK LTD
Disklok House, Preston Road,
Charnock Richard, Lancashire, PR7 5HH
Area of Operation: Worldwide
Tel: 01257 795100 **Fax:** 01257 795101
Email: sales@disklokuk.com
Web: www.disklokuk.com ⌂

DOMINTELL
4 Myson Way, Raynham Road Industrial Estate,
Bishop's Stortford, Hertfordshire, CM23 5JZ
Tel: 01279 757775 **Fax:** 01279 653535
Email: njackson@minitran.co.uk
Web: www.minitran.co.uk ⌂ **Other Info:** ECO ▽

DORCOM LTD
11 Lyndhurst Road, Hove, East Sussex, BN3 6FA
Area of Operation: UK & Ireland
Tel: 0845 450 2013 **Fax:** 0845 450 2014
Email: sales@teleporter.co.uk
Web: www.teleporter.co.uk

DYNO-GROUP (DYNO-ROD & DYNO-SECURE)
Head Office, Sutherland House,
Maple Road, Surbiton, Surrey, KT6 4BJ
Area of Operation: UK & Ireland
Tel: 0800 000 999 **Fax:** 0208 541 1150
Email: postmaster@dyno.com **Web:** www.dyno.com

FARFISA SECURITY PRODUCTS LTD
22 Wolmer Close, Bordon, Hampshire, GU35 9QF
Area of Operation: UK (Excluding Ireland)
Tel: 01420 471400 **Fax:** 01420 476101
Email: info@farfisasecurity.co.uk
Web: www.farfisasecurity.co.uk

FUSION GROUP
Unit 4 Winston Avenue, Croft,
Leicester, Leicestershire, LE9 3GQ
Area of Operation: UK (Excluding Ireland)
Tel: 08450 204360 **Fax:** 08450 204361
Email: gary.mills@fusiongroup.uk.com
Web: www.fusiongroup.uk.com

GOLDSYSTEM LTD
46 Nightingale Lane, Bromley, Kent, BR1 2SB
Area of Operation: Greater London, South East England
Tel: 0208 313 0485 **Fax:** 0208 313 0665
Email: sales@goldsystem.co.uk
Web: www.goldsystem.co.uk

HIDDEN HOME AUTOMATION
23 Cottesbrooke Park, Heartlands,
Daventry, Northamptonshire, NN11 8YL
Area of Operation: UK (Excluding Ireland)
Tel: 01327 872435 **Fax:** 01327 315287
Email: info@hiddenhomeautomation.co.uk
Web: www.hiddenhomeautomation.co.uk

HOUSEHOLD AUTOMATION
Foxways, Pinkhurst Lane, Slinfold,
Horsham, West Sussex, RH13 0QR
Area of Operation: UK & Ireland
Tel: 0870 330 0071 **Fax:** 0870 330 0072
Email: ellis-andrew@btconnect.com
Web: www.household-automation.co.uk

HOYLES ELECTRONIC DEVELOPMENTS LTD
Unit 3 Mill Brook Business Park, Mill Lane,
Rainfod, St Helens, Lancashire, WA11 8LZ
Area of Operation: Worldwide
Tel: 01744 886600 **Fax:** 01744 886607
Email: sales@hedsolutions.co.uk
Web: www.hedsolutions.co.uk ⌂

LADDERS-ONLINE
Penarth Road, Cardiff, CF11 8TD
Area of Operation: Worldwide
Tel: 08450 647647 **Fax:** 02920 702386
Email: sales@tbdavies.co.uk
Web: www.ladders-online.com ⌂

MACO DOOR AND WINDOW HARDWARE (UK) LTD
Castle Road, Eurolink Business Centre,
Sittingbourne, Kent, ME10 8LY
Area of Operation: Europe
Tel: 01795 433900 **Fax:** 01795 433902
Email: enquiry@macouk.net **Web:** www.macouk.net

MEDPAGE LTD
Factor4, Grange Road Industrial Estate,
Geddington, Northamptonshire, NN14 1AL
Area of Operation: Worldwide
Tel: 01536 744 788 **Fax:** 01536 744 988
Email: sales@easylinkuk.co.uk
Web: www.easylinkuk.co.uk

O2M8 LTD
P.O.Box 7716, Newbury, Berkshire, RG20 5WU
Area of Operation: UK (Excluding Ireland)
Tel: 07789 207408
Email: john@o2m8.com **Web:** www.o2m8.com ⌂

PARK SYSTEMS INTEGRATION LTD
Unit 3 Queen's Park, Earlsway, Team Valley Trading
Estate, Gateshead, Tyne & Wear, NE11 0QD
Area of Operation: UK & Ireland
Tel: 0191 497 0770 **Fax:** 0191 497 0772
Email: elife@psi.uk.com **Web:** www.psi.uk.com

PORTICO GB LTD
Unit 9 Windmill Avenue, Woolpit Business Park,
Woolpit, Bury St Edmunds, Suffolk, IP30 9UP
Area of Operation: Greater London, South East England
Tel: 01359 244299 **Fax:** 01359 244232
Email: info@portico-gb.co.uk
Web: www.portico-newbuild.co.uk

THE EDGE
90-92 Norwich Road, Ipswich, Suffolk, IP1 2NL
Area of Operation: UK (Excluding Ireland)
Tel: 01473 288211 **Fax:** 01473 288255
Email: nick@theedge.eu.com
Web: www.theedge.eu.com

THE IVY HOUSE
The Ivy House, Cherry Trees, Bridegate Lane, Hickling
Pastures, Melton Mowbray, Leicestershire, LE14 3QA
Area of Operation: East England, Midlands & Mid Wales
Tel: 01664 822628
Email: enquiries@the-ivy-house.com
Web: www.the-ivy-house.com

VEERMOUNT TECHNOLOGY LTD
15 Ancaster Crescent, New Malden, Surrey, KT3 6BD
Area of Operation: Worldwide
Tel: 020 82416161 **Fax:** 020 82416515
Email: jmoore@veermounttechnology.co.uk
Web: www.veermounttechnology.co.uk

X-HOME
Unit W Williamsons Holdings,
Uphall, West Lothian, EH52 6PA
Area of Operation: UK (Excluding Ireland)
Tel: 0845 130 1091 **Fax:** 0845 130 1092
Email: sales@xhome.biz **Web:** www.xhome.biz

CCTV & SURVEILLANCE SYSTEMS

KEY

OTHER: ▽ Reclaimed ⌂ On-line shopping

✎ Bespoke ✋ Hand-made ECO Ecological

ACA APEX LIMITED
Apex House, Ivinghoe Way,
Edlesborough, Dunstable, Bedfordshire, LU6 2EL
Area of Operation: UK & Ireland
Tel: 01525 220782 **Fax:** 01525 220782
Email: sales@aca-apex.com
Web: www.aca-apex.com

AFM SECURITY
Head Office, The Stables,
Foxes Loke, Loddon, Norfolk, NR14 6UL
Area of Operation: East England, Greater London
Tel: 01508 522078 **Fax:** 01508 522079
Email: sales@afmsecurity.co.uk
Web: www.afmsecurity.co.uk

ALDOUS SYSTEMS (EUROPE) LTD
Unit 3 Printers End, Insignia Industrial Estate, Gatehouse
Way, Aylesbury, Buckinghamshire, HP19 8DB
Area of Operation: Europe
Tel: 0870 240 1162 **Fax:** 0207 691 7844
Email: sales@aldoussystems.co.uk
Web: www.aldoussystems.co.uk

ANGELL SECURITY & SURVEILLANCE LTD
19 Primrose Drive, Bicester, Oxfordshire, OX26 3WP
Area of Operation: Europe
Tel: 01869 247500 **Fax:** 01869 323601
Email: sales@angellsecurity.com
Web: www.angellsecurity.com ⌂
Other Info: ✎

AUDIO T CUSTOM INSTALLATIONS
11 Charter Place, High Street,
Egham, Surrey, TW20 9EA
Area of Operation: East England, Greater London,
South East England
Tel: 01784 479423 **Fax:** 01784 479425
Email: custom@audio-t.co.uk
Web: www.audio-t.co.uk/custom

BESPOKE INSTALLATIONS
1 Rogers Close, Tiverton, Devon, EX16 6UW
Area of Operation: South West England and South Wales
Tel: 01884 243497
Email: michael@bespoke.biz
Web: www.bespoke.biz

BEYOND THE INVISIBLE LIMITED
162-164 Arthur Road, London, SW19 8AQ
Area of Operation: Greater London
Tel: 0870 740 5859 **Fax:** 0870 740 5860
Email: info@beyondtheinvisible.com
Web: www.beyondtheinvisible.com

BYRON
Byron House, 34 Sherwood Rd, Aston Fields Industrial
Estate, Bromsgrove, West Midlands, B60 3DR
Area of Operation: Worldwide
Tel: 01527 557700 **Fax:** 01527 557701
Email: info@chbyron.com **Web:** www.chbyron.com

CCTV (UK) LTD
109-111 Pope Street, Birmingham, B1 3AG
Area of Operation: Worldwide
Tel: 0121 200 1031 **Fax:** 0121 200 1167
Email: sales@cctvgroup.com
Web: www.cctvgroup.com

CIRRUS COMMUNICATION SYSTEMS
Oregon House, 19 Queensway,
New Milton, Hampshire, BH25 5NN
Area of Operation: UK (Excluding Ireland)
Tel: 0845 602 2440   **Fax:** 01425 626345
Email: enquiries@cirruscom.co.uk
Web: www.cirruscom.co.uk   **Other Info:** ✍

CIS LTD
Westpoint Business Centre, Westland Square,
Leeds, West Yorkshire, LS11 5SS
Area of Operation: Worldwide
Tel: 08700 240640   **Fax:** 08700 240641
Email: p.hackett@compulock.com
Web: www.compulock.com

COMFORT HOME CONTROLS
Carlton House, Carlton Avenue,
Chester, Cheshire, CH4 8UE
Area of Operation: UK & Ireland
Tel: 08707 605528   **Fax:** 01244 671455
Email: sales@home-control.co.uk
Web: www.home-control.co.uk ✍

CUSTOM INSTALLATIONS
Custom House, 51 Baymead Lane,
North Petherton, Bridgwater, Somerset, TA6 6RN
Area of Operation: South West England and South Wales
Tel: 01278 662555   **Fax:** 01278 662975
Email: roger@custom-installations.co.uk
Web: www.custom-installations.co.uk

D&T ELECTRONICS
Unit 9A, Cranborne Industrial Estate, Cranborne
Road, Potters Bar, Hertfordshire, EN6 3JN
Area of Operation: UK (Excluding Ireland)
Tel: 0870 241 5891   **Fax:** 01707 653570
Email: info@dandt.co.uk
Web: www.dandt.co.uk   **Other Info:** ✍

DBCC LIMITED
Woodland View, Winchester Road,
Fair Oak, Eastleigh, Hampshire, SO50 7HD
Area of Operation: UK (Excluding Ireland)
Tel: 02380 692 555
Email: info@dbcc.co.uk   **Web:** www.dbcc.co.uk

DECKORUM LTD
4c Royal Oak Lane, Pirton,
Stevenage, Hertfordshire, SG5 3QT
Area of Operation: East England, Greater London,
South East England
Tel: 08450 204360   **Fax:** 08450 204361
Email: gary.mills@deckorum.com
Web: www.deckorum.com

DIGITAL DECOR
Sonas House, Button End, Harston,
Cambridge, Cambridgeshire, CB2 5NX
Area of Operation: East England, Greater London
Tel: 01223 870935
Fax: 01223 870935
Email: seamus@digital-decor.co.uk
Web: www.digital-decor.co.uk

DISCOVERY SYSTEMS LTD
1 Corn Mill Close, The Spindles, Ashton in
Makerfield, Wigan, Lancashire, WN4 0PX
Area of Operation: North West England and North Wales
Tel: 01942 723756
Email: mike@discoverysystems.co.uk
Web: www.discoverysystems.co.uk

DOMINTELL
4 Myson Way, Raynham Road Industrial Estate,
Bishop's Stortford, Hertfordshire, CM23 5JZ
Area of Operation: UK (Excluding Ireland)
Tel: 01279 757775   **Fax:** 01279 653535
Email: njackson@minitran.co.uk
Web: www.minitran.co.uk ✍   **Other Info:** ECO ✍

DYNO-GROUP (DYNO-ROD & DYNO-SECURE)
Head Office, Sutherland House,
Maple Road, Surbiton, Surrey, KT6 4BJ
Area of Operation: UK & Ireland
Tel: 0800 000 999   **Fax:** 0208 541 1150
Email: postmaster@dyno.com
Web: www.dyno.com

EASYCOMM
1 George House, Church Street,
Buntingford, Hertfordshire, SG9 9AS
Area of Operation: UK (Excluding Ireland)
Tel: 0800 389 9459
Email: steve@ezcomm.co.uk
Web: www.ezcomm.co.uk

EASYLIFE AUTOMATION LIMITED
Kullan House, 12 Meadowfield Road,
Stocksfield, Northumberland, NE43 7QX
Area of Operation: UK (Excluding Ireland)
Tel: 01661 844159   **Fax:** 01661 842594
Email: enquiries@easylifeautomation.com
Web: www.easylifeautomation.com

EVEREST LTD
Sopers Road, Cuffley, Hertfordshire, EN6 4SG
Area of Operation: UK & Ireland
Tel: 0800 010123
Web: www.everest.co.uk ✍

FAITH & GANTRY LTD
Gainsborough House, 62 Hatfield Road,
Ipswich, Suffolk, IP3 9AF
Area of Operation: East England, Greater London
Tel: 01473 714002   **Fax:** 01473 714060
Email: lindsey@faithandgantry.com
Web: www.faithandgantry.com

FUSION GROUP
Unit 4 Winston Avenue, Croft,
Leicester, Leicestershire, LE9 3GQ
Area of Operation: UK (Excluding Ireland)
Tel: 08450 204360   **Fax:** 08450 204361
Email: gary.mills@fusiongroup.uk.com
Web: www.fusiongroup.uk.com

HELLERMANN TYTON
43-45 Salthouse Road, Brackmills,
Northampton, Northamptonshire, NN4 7EX
Area of Operation: Worldwide
Tel: 01604 707420   **Fax:** 01604 705454
Email: sales@htdata.co.uk
Web: www.homenetworksciences.com

HOUSEHOLD AUTOMATION
Foxways, Pinkhurst Lane, Slinfold,
Horsham, West Sussex, RH13 0QR
Area of Operation: UK & Ireland
Tel: 0870 330 0071   **Fax:** 0870 330 0072
Email: ellis-andrew@btconnect.com
Web: www.household-automation.co.uk

HOYLES ELECTRONIC DEVELOPMENTS LTD
Unit 3 Mill Brook Business Park, Mill Lane,
Rainford, St Helens, Lancashire, WA11 8LZ
Area of Operation: Worldwide
Tel: 01744 886600   **Fax:** 01744 886607
Email: sales@hedsolutions.co.uk
Web: www.hedsolutions.co.uk ✍

IBBD LTD
HomeLifeWorkLife Showroom, Unit 6 Link Trade
Park, Penarth Road, Cardiff, CF11 8TQ
Area of Operation: South West England and South Wales
Tel: 029 2071 3460   **Email:** info@ibbd.co.uk
Web: www.homelifeworklife.co.uk

MYGARD SAFE & SECURE PLC
Suite 10 Lloyd Berkeley Place, Pebble Lane,
Aylesbury, Buckinghamshire, HP20 2JH
Area of Operation: UK (Excluding Ireland)
Tel: 01296 433746   **Email:** info@mygard.com
Web: www.mygard.com ✍

O2M8 LTD
P.O.Box 7716, Newbury, Berkshire, RG20 5WU
Area of Operation: UK (Excluding Ireland)
Tel: 07789 207408   **Email:** john@o2m8.com
Web: www.o2m8.com ✍

PARK SYSTEMS INTEGRATION LTD
Unit 3 Queen's Park, Earlsway, Team Valley Trading
Estate, Gateshead, Tyne & Wear, NE11 0QD
Area of Operation: UK & Ireland
Tel: 0191 497 0770   **Fax:** 0191 497 0772
Email: elife@psi.uk.com
Web: www.psi.uk.com

PHILLSON LTD
144 Rickerscote Road, Stafford, Staffordshire, ST17 4HE
Area of Operation: UK & Ireland
Tel: 0845 612 0128   **Fax:** 01477 535090
Email: info@phillson.co.uk   **Web:** www.phillson.co.uk

ROCOCO SYSTEMS & DESIGN
26 Danbury Street, London, N1 8JU
Area of Operation: Europe
Tel: 0207 454 1234   **Fax:** 0207 870 0888
Email: sales@rococosystems.com
Web: www.rococosystems.com

SECURITY VISION INTERNATIONAL LTD
Berwick Courtyard, Berwick St Leonard,
Salisbury, Wiltshire, SP3 5SN
Area of Operation: UK & Ireland
Tel: 01747 820820   **Fax:** 01747 820821
Email: charles@securityvision.co.uk
Web: www.securityvision.co.uk

SG SYSTEMS LTD
Unit 38 Elderpark Workspace, 100 Elderpark Street,
Glasgow, Renfrewshire, G51 3TR
Area of Operation: Europe
Tel: 0141 445 4125   **Fax:** 0141 445 4125
Email: info@sgsystems.ltd.uk
Web: www.sgsystems.ltd.uk

SIMPLY AUTOMATE
23 Wornal Park, Menmarsh Road, Worminghall,
Aylesbury, Buckinghamshire, HP18 9PH
Area of Operation: Worldwide
Tel: 0845 644 3330   **Fax:** 0845 644 2713
Email: info@simplyautomate.co.uk
Web: www.simplyautomate.co.uk ✍

SMART HOUSE
23 Wornal Park, Menmarsh Road, Worminghall,
Aylesbury, Buckinghamshire, HP18 9PH
Area of Operation: Europe
Tel: 0845 053 3680   **Fax:** 0845 644 2713
Email: info@smarthouse.co.uk
Web: www.smarthouse.co.uk

SMART HOUSE SOLUTIONS
7 Cricketer's Row, Brentwood, Essex, CM13 3QA
Area of Operation: UK & Ireland
Tel: 01277 264369   **Fax:** 01277 262143
Web: www.smarthousesolutions.co.uk

TECCHO
Unit 19W, Kilroot Business Park,
Carrickfergus, Co. Antrim, BT38 7PR
Area of Operation: UK & Ireland
Tel: 0845 890 1150   **Fax:** 0870 063 4120
Email: enquiries@teccho.net   **Web:** www.teccho.net ✍

THE IVY HOUSE
The Ivy House, Cherry Trees,
Bridegate Lane, Hickling Pastures,
Melton Mowbray, Leicestershire, LE14 3QA
Area of Operation: East England, Midlands & Mid Wales
Tel: 01664 822628
Email: enquiries@the-ivy-house.com
Web: www.the-ivy-house.com

THE THINKING HOME
The White House, Wilderspool Park, Greenalls
Avenue, Warrington, Cheshire, WA4 6HL
Area of Operation: UK & Ireland
Tel: 0800 881 8319   **Fax:** 0800 881 8329
Email: info@thethinkinghome.com
Web: www.thethinkinghome.com

TRIBUNE SMART HOME
321 Bolton Road, Manchester, M6 7GU
Area of Operation: UK (Excluding Ireland)
Tel: 0161 736 4011   **Fax:** 0161 736 8355
Email: info@tribunesmarthome.com
Web: www.tribunesmarthome.com

X-HOME
Unit W Williamsons Holdings,
Uphall, West Lothian, EH52 6PA
Area of Operation: UK (Excluding Ireland)
Tel: 0845 130 1091   **Fax:** 0845 130 1092
Email: sales@xhome.biz
Web: www.xhome.biz

FIRE PROTECTION

KEY

SEE ALSO: DOORS, WINDOWS AND
CONSERVATORIES - Fire Doors,   INSULATION
AND PROOFING MATERIALS - Fire Proofing

OTHER: ▽ Reclaimed   🖐 On-line shopping
✍ Bespoke   🖐 Hand-made   ECO Ecological

AFM SECURITY
Head Office, The Stables, Foxes Loke,
Loddon, Norfolk, NR14 6UL
Area of Operation: East England, Greater London
Tel: 01508 522078   **Fax:** 01508 522079
Email: sales@afmsecurity.co.uk
Web: www.afmsecurity.co.uk

AICO LTD
Mile End Business Park, Maesbury Road,
Oswestry, Shropshire, SY10 8NN
Area of Operation: UK (Excluding Ireland)
Tel: 0870 758 4000   **Fax:** 0870 758 4010
Email: sales@aico.co.uk   **Web:** www.aico.co.uk

CENTURION
Westhill Business Park, Arnhall Business Park,
Westhill, Aberdeen, Aberdeenshire, AB32 6UF
Area of Operation: Scotland
Tel: 01224 744440   **Fax:** 01224 744819
Email: info@centurion-solutions.co.uk
Web: www.centurion-solutions.co.uk

CIRRUS COMMUNICATION SYSTEMS
Oregon House, 19 Queensway,
New Milton, Hampshire, BH25 5NN
Area of Operation: UK (Excluding Ireland)
Tel: 0845 602 2440   **Fax:** 01425 626345
Email: enquiries@cirruscom.co.uk
Web: www.cirruscom.co.uk
Other Info: ✍

COMFORT HOME CONTROLS
Carlton House, Carlton Avenue,
Chester, Cheshire, CH4 8UE
Area of Operation: UK & Ireland
Tel: 08707 605528   **Fax:** 01244 671455
Email: sales@home-control.co.uk
Web: www.home-control.co.uk ✍

DICON SAFETY PRODUCTS (EUROPE) LTD
Javelin 1, Meteor Business Park, Cheltenham Road
East, Gloucester, Gloucestershire, GL2 9QL
Area of Operation: Europe
Tel: 01452 714999   **Fax:** 01452 713103
Email: sales@diconsafety.co.uk
Web: www.diconsafety.co.uk

DIGITAL DECOR
Sonas House, Button End, Harston,
Cambridge, Cambridgeshire, CB2 5NX
Area of Operation: East England, Greater London
Tel: 01223 870935
Fax: 01223 870935
Email: seamus@digital-decor.co.uk
Web: www.digital-decor.co.uk

DOMESTIC SPRINKLERS PLC
6 Kent CLose, Weymouth, Dorset, DT4 9TF
Area of Operation: UK & Ireland
Tel: 01305 765763   **Fax:** 01305 777700
Email: email@domesticsprinklers.co.uk
Web: www.domesticsprinklers.co.uk

DOMINTELL
4 Myson Way, Raynham Road Industrial Estate,
Bishop's Stortford, Hertfordshire, CM23 5JZ
Area of Operation: UK (Excluding Ireland)
Tel: 01279 757775   **Fax:** 01279 653535
Email: njackson@minitran.co.uk
Web: www.minitran.co.uk ✍
Other Info: ✍

FIREANGEL LIMITED
The TechnoCentre, Puma Way,
Coventry, Warwickshire, CV1 2TT
Area of Operation: Worldwide
Tel: 02476 236600   **Email:** info@fireangel.co.uk
Web: www.fireangel.co.uk ⌐

FIRESTOP SPRINKLER SYSTEMS LTD
58 Burns Wynd, Stonehouse,
Larkhall, Lanarkshire, ML9 3DU
Area of Operation: Europe
Tel: 01698 792992   **Fax:** 01698 792992
Email: davidwatson@firestopsprinklers.com
Web: www.firestopsprinklers.com
Other Info: ✎

HOYLES ELECTRONIC DEVELOPMENTS LTD
Unit 3 Mill Brook Business Park, Mill Lane, Rainford,
St Helens, Lancashire, WA11 8LZ
Tel: 01744 886600   **Fax:** 01744 886607
Email: sales@hedsolutions.co.uk
Web: www.hedsolutions.co.uk ⌐

MEDPAGE LTD
Factor4, Grange Road Industrial Estate,
Geddington, Northamptonshire, NN14 1AL
Area of Operation: Worldwide
Tel: 01536 744 788   **Fax:** 01536 744 988
Email: sales@easylinkuk.co.uk
Web: www.easylinkuk.co.uk

MR RESISTOR
21 Lydden Road, Wandsworth, London, SW18 4LT
Area of Operation: Worldwide
Tel: 0208 874 2234   **Fax:** 0208 871 2262
Email: info@mr-resistor.co.uk
Web: www.mr-resistor.co.uk ⌐

O2M8 LTD
P.O.Box 7716, Newbury, Berkshire, RG20 5WU
Area of Operation: UK (Excluding Ireland)
Tel: 07789 207408   **Email:** john@o2m8.com
Web: www.o2m8.com ⌐

PARK SYSTEMS INTEGRATION LTD
Unit 3 Queen's Park, Earlsway, Team Valley Trading
Estate, Gateshead, Tyne & Wear, NE11 0QD
Area of Operation: UK & Ireland
Tel: 0191 497 0770   **Fax:** 0191 497 0772
Email: elife@psi.uk.com   **Web:** www.psi.uk.com

SAFELINCS
Farlesthorpe Road, Unit 1, Alford, Lincolnshire, LN13 9PF
Area of Operation: UK & Ireland
Tel: 01507 462176   **Fax:** 01507 463288
Email: service@safelincs.co.uk
Web: www.safelincs.co.uk ⌐

SIGNS & LABELS LTD
Douglas Bruce House, Corrie Way, Bredbury
Industrial Park, Stockport, Cheshire, SK6 2RR
Area of Operation: Worldwide
Tel: 0800 132323   **Fax:** 0800 389 5311
Email: sales@safetyshop.co.uk
Web: www.safetyshop.com ⌐

INTRUDER ALARMS

KEY
OTHER: ▽ Reclaimed   ⌐ On-line shopping
✐ Bespoke   ✠ Hand-made   ECO Ecological

ANGELL SECURITY & SURVEILLANCE LTD
19 Primrose Drive, Bicester, Oxfordshire, OX26 3WP
Area of Operation: Europe
Tel: 01869 247500   **Fax:** 01869 323601
Email: sales@angellsecurity.com
Web: www.angellsecurity.com ⌐   **Other Info:** ✎

CENTURION
Westhill Business Park, Arnhall Business Park,
Westhill, Aberdeen, Aberdeenshire, AB32 6UF
Area of Operation: Scotland
Tel: 01224 744440   **Fax:** 01224 744819
Email: info@centurion-solutions.co.uk
Web: www.centurion-solutions.co.uk

CHARNOCK ENTERPRISES
Disklok House, Preston Road,
Charnock Richard, Chorley, Lancashire, PR7 5HH
Area of Operation: UK & Ireland
Tel: 01257 792111   **Fax:** 01257 795101
Email: sales@disklokuk.co.uk
Web: www.charnockenterprises.co.uk ⌐

CIRRUS COMMUNICATION SYSTEMS
Oregon House, 19 Queensway,
New Milton, Hampshire, BH25 5NN
Area of Operation: UK (Excluding Ireland)
Tel: 0845 602 2440   **Fax:** 01425 626345
Email: enquiries@cirruscom.co.uk
Web: www.cirruscom.co.uk   **Other Info:** ✎

CIS LTD
Westpoint Business Centre, Westland Square,
Leeds, West Yorkshire, LS11 5SS
Area of Operation: Worldwide
Tel: 08700 240640   **Fax:** 08700 240641
Email: p.hackett@compulock.com
Web: www.compulock.com

COMFORT HOME CONTROLS
Carlton House, Carlton Avenue,
Chester, Cheshire, CH4 8UE
Area of Operation: UK & Ireland
Tel: 08707 605528   **Fax:** 01244 671455
Email: sales@home-control.co.uk
Web: www.home-control.co.uk ⌐

DIGITAL DECOR
Sonas House, Button End, Harston,
Cambridge, Cambridgeshire, CB2 5NX
Area of Operation: East England, Greater London
Tel: 01223 870935   **Fax:** 01223 870935
Email: seamus@digital-decor.co.uk
Web: www.digital-decor.co.uk

DISKLOK UK LTD
Disklok House, Preston Road,
Charnock Richard, Lancashire, PR7 5HH
Area of Operation: Worldwide
Tel: 01257 795100   **Fax:** 01257 795101
Email: sales@disklokuk.co.uk
Web: www.disklokuk.com ⌐

DYNO-GROUP (DYNO-ROD & DYNO-SECURE)
Head Office, Sutherland House,
Maple Road, Surbiton, Surrey, KT6 4BJ
Area of Operation: UK & Ireland
Tel: 0800 000 999   **Fax:** 0208 541 1150
Email: postmaster@dyno.com
Web: www.dyno.com

EVEREST LTD
Sopers Road, Cuffley, Hertfordshire, EN6 4SG
Area of Operation: UK & Ireland
Tel: 0800 010123   **Web:** www.everest.co.uk ⌐

HIDDEN HOME AUTOMATION
23 Cottesbrooke Park, Heartlands,
Daventry, Northamptonshire, NN11 8YL
Area of Operation: UK (Excluding Ireland)
Tel: 01327 872435   **Fax:** 01327 315287
Email: info@hiddenhomeautomation.co.uk
Web: www.hiddenhomeautomation.co.uk

HOUSEHOLD AUTOMATION
Foxways, Pinkhurst Lane, Slinfold,
Horsham, West Sussex, RH13 0QR
Area of Operation: UK & Ireland
Tel: 0870 330 0071   **Fax:** 0870 330 0072
Email: ellis-andrew@btconnect.com
Web: www.household-automation.co.uk

HOYLES ELECTRONIC DEVELOPMENTS LTD
Unit 3 Mill Brook Business Park, Mill Lane,
Rainfod, St Helens, Lancashire, WA11 8LZ
Area of Operation: Worldwide
Tel: 01744 886600   **Fax:** 01744 886607
Email: sales@hedsolutions.co.uk
Web: www.hedsolutions.co.uk ⌐

IBBD LTD
HomeLifeWorkLife Showroom, Unit 6 Link Trade
Park, Penarth Road, Cardiff, CF11 8TQ
Area of Operation: South West England and South Wales
Tel: 029 2071 3460   **Email:** info@ibbd.co.uk
Web: www.homelifeworklife.co.uk

MEDPAGE LTD
Factor4, Grange Road Industrial Estate,
Geddington, Northamptonshire, NN14 1AL
Area of Operation: Worldwide
Tel: 01536 744 788   **Fax:** 01536 744 988
Email: sales@easylinkuk.co.uk
Web: www.easylinkuk.co.uk

MYGARD SAFE & SECURE PLC
Suite 10 Lloyd Berkeley Place, Pebble Lane,
Aylesbury, Buckinghamshire, HP20 2JH
Area of Operation: UK (Excluding Ireland)
Tel: 01296 433746   **Email:** info@mygard.com
Web: www.mygard.com ⌐

O2M8 LTD
P.O.Box 7716, Newbury, Berkshire, RG20 5WU
Area of Operation: UK (Excluding Ireland)
Tel: 07789 207408   **Email:** john@o2m8.com
Web: www.o2m8.com

PARK SYSTEMS INTEGRATION LTD
Unit 3 Queen's Park, Earlsway, Team Valley Trading
Estate, Gateshead, Tyne & Wear, NE11 0QD
Area of Operation: UK & Ireland
Tel: 0191 497 0770   **Fax:** 0191 497 0772
Email: elife@psi.uk.com   **Web:** www.psi.uk.com

PYRAMID ELECTRICAL & ALARMS LIMITED
68 Forresters Road, Burbage, Hinckley,
Leicestershire, Leicestershire, LE10 2RX
Area of Operation: East England, Greater London,
Midlands & Mid Wales, North East England, North
West England and North Wales
Tel: 01455 458325   **Fax:** 01455 458325
Email: pyramid@dotdotnetdot.net
Web: www.pyramidelectrical.net

QUICKSAFE.CO.UK
Unit 272, 12 South Bridge, Edinburgh, Lothian, EH1 1DD
Area of Operation: UK (Excluding Ireland)
Tel: 0800 195 5810
Email: sales@quicksafe.co.uk
Web: www.quicksafe.co.uk ⌐

ROCOCO SYSTEMS & DESIGN
26 Danbury Street, London, N1 8JU
Area of Operation: Europe
Tel: 0207 454 1234   **Fax:** 0207 870 0888
Email: sales@rococosystems.com
Web: www.rococosystems.com

SMART HOUSE SOLUTIONS
7 Cricketer's Row, Brentwood, Essex, CM13 3QA
Area of Operation: UK & Ireland
Tel: 01277 264369   **Fax:** 01277 262143
Web: www.smarthousesolutions.co.uk

THE IVY HOUSE
The Ivy House, Cherry Trees, Bridegate Lane, Hickling
Pastures, Melton Mowbray, Leicestershire, LE14 3QA
Area of Operation: East England, Midlands & Mid Wales
Tel: 01664 822628
Email: enquiries@the-ivy-house.com
Web: www.the-ivy-house.com

TRIBUNE SMART HOME
321 Bolton Road, Manchester, M6 7GU
Area of Operation: UK (Excluding Ireland)
Tel: 0161 736 4011   **Fax:** 0161 736 8355
Email: info@tribunesmarthome.com
Web: www.tribunesmarthome.com

X-HOME
Unit W Williamsons Holdings,
Uphall, West Lothian, EH52 6PA
Area of Operation: UK (Excluding Ireland)
Tel: 0845 130 1091   **Fax:** 0845 130 1092
Email: sales@xhome.biz
Web: www.xhome.biz

Image courtesy of Cottage Craft Spirals (01663 750716)

Flooring Structure

More often than not, the decision of what flooring structure to use in your new home is made without question. If you hire a timber frame company, you will get the floor that comes packaged as part of the system, and if you hire an architect, the chances are they won't even ask what sort of floor you want.

Your choice of flooring system is both critical to the way a house is built and to the performance of the property in years to come, so it's important to assess all the options. We look at the two main choices; beam and block or suspended timber.

Beam & Block

Beam and block is the cheapest and commonest form of precast floor. It consists of a number of evenly spaced concrete beams — similar to timber joists — infilled with normal building blocks. Beam and block has been popular with developers since it first appeared in the 1970s, mainly because it is a fast and largely dry system.

As with all precast options, beam and block floors are provided by specialists who work from drawings supplied. A number of businesses cater for this market and many have links with

builders' merchants who act as middlemen. The floors are designed to work with standard concrete blocks (i.e. 100 x 225 x 440mm) as used in wall construction.

Variations on standard beam and block floors use polystyrene infill blocks to fill the voids between the beams. They have become popular as a ground floor option since changes to the Building Regulations in 2002 brought in a requirement for floor insulation.

The main downside of a precast floor is that each one is manufactured to order, so you may have to wait a number of weeks for delivery.

Timber

Timber floors are simple to build and so tend to be the cheapest choice. Like precast options, the timber floor is suspended, but it uses readily available materials, such as timber joists and

chipboard or plywood covering. However, at ground floor level, timber needs to be both insulated underneath, which is far from straightforward, and also vented below.

The Building Regulations also insist on there being a concrete capping and damp-proof membrane laid over the oversite underneath the suspended floor, which effectively adds around £5/m2 to the costs. Thus a timber ground floor is similar cost-wise to a ground-bearing concrete slab.

Upstairs, no such extra work applies and here timber joisting is easily the cheapest option. However, adding expensive sound-proofing all but eliminates this cost advantage.

Top tips

What many people don't realise is that timber floors can be improved to perform just as well as precast concrete simply by implementing a number of features:

- Insulation within the joist void (mandatory): adds 3-5dB

- Thicker or heavier ceiling boards: adds 3dB

- Mount ceiling board on resilient strips: adds 2dB

- Absorbing strips above the joists: adds 2dB

- Sound-deadening layer under the floor cover: adds 4dB

- Separate floor joists from ceiling joists: adds 3dB

If you incorporated all these options, you would improve sound reduction from around 35dB to around 50dB — close to the party floor standard required in flats and similar to precast systems.

The cost? Similar to switching to precast.

FLOORING STRUCTURE

KEY

PRODUCT TYPES:

1= Beam and Block 2 = Suspended Timber

OTHER: ▽ Reclaimed 🖱 On-line shopping

✎ Bespoke ✋ Hand-made ECO Ecological

AC ROOF TRUSSES LTD

Severn Farm Industrial Estate, Welshpool, Powys, SY21 7DF

Area of Operation: UK & Ireland

Tel: 01938 554881 **Fax:** 01938 556265

Email: info@acrooftrusses.co.uk

Web: www.acrooftrusses.co.uk 🖱 **Product Type:** 3, 4, 6

BOARD CENTRAL

Chiltern Business Centre, Couching Street,
Watlington, Oxfordshire, OX49 5PX

Area of Operation: Greater London, South East England

Tel: 0845 458 8016 **Fax:** 01844 354112

Email: howardmorrice@hotmail.com **Product Type:** 6

FFOREST TIMBER ENGINEERING LTD

Kestrel Way, Garngoch Industrial Estate,
Gorseinon, Swansea, SA4 9WN

Area of Operation: Midlands & Mid Wales, South
West England and South Wales

Tel: 01792 895620 **Fax:** 01792 893969

Email: info@fforest.co.uk

Web: www.fforest.co.uk **Product Type:** 3

FRENCH FLOORS

8 Balmore Wood, Luton, Bedfordshire, LU3 4EP

Area of Operation: UK (Excluding Ireland)

Tel: 07702 322597 **Fax:** 01582 490224

Email: frenchfloors@yahoo.co.uk

Web: www.frenchfloors.co.uk **Product Type:** 2

LAFARGE PLASTERBOARD LTD

Marsh Lane, Easton-in-Gordano, Bristol, BS20 0NF

Area of Operation: Worldwide

Tel: 01275 377777

Email: enquiryline@lafarge-gypsum.lafarge.com

MERSEYBEAMS LTD

Riverbank Road, Bromborough,
Wirral, Merseyside, CH62 3LQ

Area of Operation: UK (Excluding Ireland)

Tel: 0151 334 7346 **Fax:** 0151 334 0600

Email: info@merseybeams.com

Web: www.merseybeams.com

Product Type: 3

MERSEYBEAMS LTD

Area of Operation: UK (Excluding Ireland)

Tel: 0151 334 7346 **Fax:** 0151 334 0600

Email: info@merseybeams.com

Web: www.merseybeams.com

Product Type: 3

We manufacture 150mm & 225mm Deep Beam & Block along with 100mm,150mm,200mm and 225mm Deep Wideslab systems suitable for both ground and upper floors, specialising in self build projects, completing over 100 self build houses each year.

MIDLANDS CEILINGS & PARTITIONS

201 High Street, Harborne, Birmingham, B17 9QG

Area of Operation: UK (Excluding Ireland)

Tel: 0121 694 8258

Fax: 0121 694 3258

Email: deanoneill100@msn.com **Product Type:** 2

MILBANK FLOORS

Earls Colne Business Park,
Earls Colne, Colchester, Essex, CO6 2NS

Area of Operation: UK (Excluding Ireland)

Tel: 01787 223931 **Fax:** 01787 220535

Email: estimating@milbank.co.uk

Web: www.milbank-floors.co.uk

Product Type: 1, 5

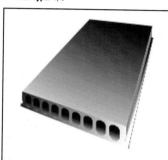

MILBANK FLOORS

Area of Operation: UK (Excluding Ireland)

Tel: 01787 223931

Fax: 01787 220535

Email: estimating@milbank.co.uk

Web: www.milbank-floors.co.uk

Product Type: 1

Milbank are able to offer a variety of economical design solutions by combining their full range of prestressed and precast concrete products.

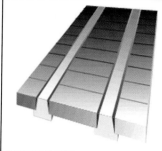

MILBANK FLOORS

Area of Operation: UK (Excluding Ireland)

Tel: 01787 223931

Fax: 01787 220535

Email: estimating@milbank.co.uk

Web: www.milbank-floors.co.uk

Product Type: 1

Milbank Beam and Block floors provide a quick and economical solution for most structural flooring situations, both at ground and upper floor levels.

MITEK INDUSTRIES LTD

Mitek House, Grazebrook Industrial Park,
eartree Lane, Dudley, West Midlands, DY2 0XW

Area of Operation: UK & Ireland

Tel: 01384 451400 **Fax:** 01384 451415

Email: roy.troman@mitek.co.uk

Web: www.mitek.co.uk

OAKBEAMS.COM

Hunterswood Farm, Alfold Road,
Dunsfold, Godalming, Surrey, GU8 4NP

Area of Operation: Worldwide

Tel: 01483 200477 **Email:** info@oakbeams.com

Web: www.oakbeams.com

Product Type: 3 **Other Info:** ▽

Posi-Joist™
Supporting a cleaner Lifestyle

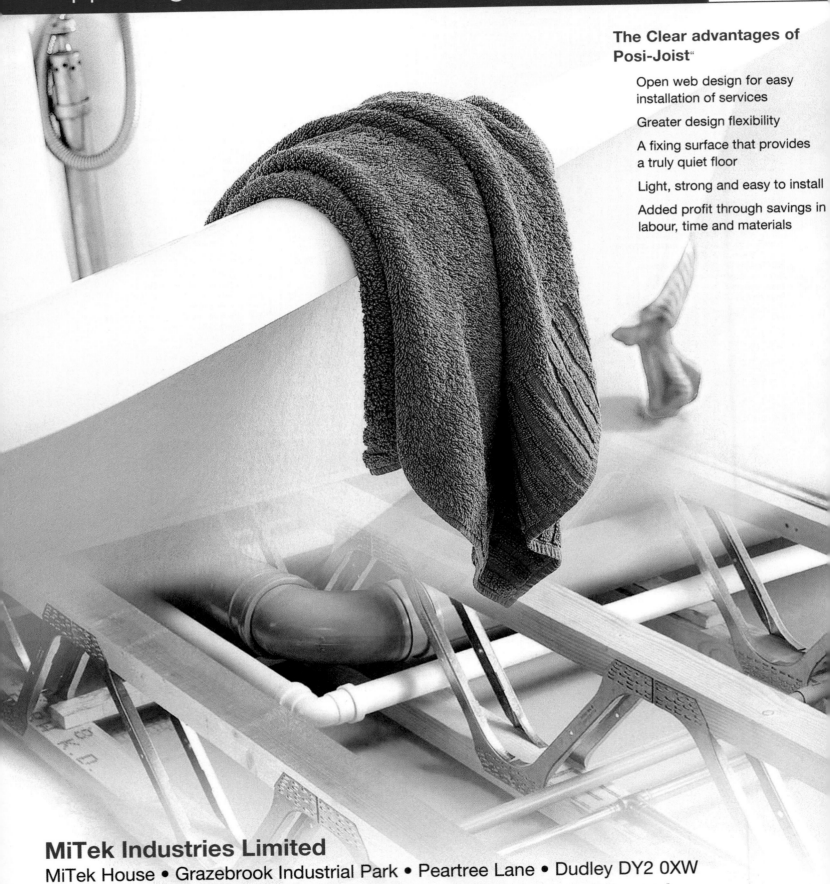

The Clear advantages of Posi-Joist"

Open web design for easy installation of services

Greater design flexibility

A fixing surface that provides a truly quiet floor

Light, strong and easy to install

Added profit through savings in labour, time and materials

MiTek Industries Limited

MiTek House • Grazebrook Industrial Park • Peartree Lane • Dudley DY2 0XW
Telephone: 01384 451400 • Facsimile: 01384 451411 • www.mitek.co.uk

INTERIORS, FIXTURES & FINISHES - **Interior Structure** - Flooring Structure; Lofts & Loft Conversions; Ceilings
SPONSORED BY: MOVE OR IMPROVE MAGAZINE www.moveorimprove.co.uk

INTERIORS, FIXTURES & FINISHES

S.L. HARDWOODS
390 Sydenham Road, Croydon, Surrey, CR0 2EA
Area of Operation: UK (Excluding Ireland)
Tel: 0208 683 0292 **Fax:** 0208 683 0404
Email: info@slhardwoods.co.uk
Web: www.slhardwoods.co.uk **Product Type:** 5

SCHLUTER SYSTEMS LTD
Units 4-5, Bardon 22 Industrial Park, Beveridge Lane,
Coalville, Leicestershire, LE67 1TE
Area of Operation: UK & Ireland
Tel: 01530 813396 **Fax:** 01530 813376
Email: sales@schluter.co.uk
Web: www.schluter.co.uk

SPANCAST CONCRETE FLOORS
Stephenson Way, Barrington Industrial Estate,
Bedlington, Northumberland, NE22 7DL
Area of Operation: East England, North East England,
North West England and North Wales, Scotland
Tel: 01670 531160 **Fax:** 01670 531170
Email: enquiry@spancast.co.uk
Web: www.spancast.co.uk
Product Type: 5 **Material Type:** G) 1

THE CARPENTRY INSIDER - AIRCOMDIRECT
1 Castleton Crescent, Skegness, Lincolnshire, PE25 2TJ
Area of Operation: Worldwide
Tel: 01754 767163
Email: aircom8@hotmail.com
Web: www.easycarpentry.com
Product Type: 4, 6

THE EXPANDED METAL COMPANY LIMITED
PO Box 14, Longhill Industrial Estate (North),
Hartlepool, Durham, TS25 1PR
Area of Operation: Worldwide
Tel: 01429 867388 **Fax:** 01429 866795
Email: paulb@expamet.co.uk
Web: www.expandedmetalcompany.co.uk

LOFTS AND LOFT CONVERSIONS

KEY
PRODUCT TYPES: 1= Loft Installation
2 = Loft Conversion   3 = Loft Doors
4 = Loft Ladders
OTHER: ▽ Reclaimed   On-line shopping
 Bespoke   Hand-made   ECO Ecological

ABBEY ARCHITECTURAL & DESIGN LTD
56 Cheviot Road, London, SE27 0LG
Area of Operation: Greater London
Tel: 0208 676 4393
Email: surveyor@abbeyarch.co.uk
Web: www.abbeyarch.co.uk
Product Type: 2

ABOVE IT ALL
56 Hardman Avenue, Rawtenstall,
Rossendale, Lancashire, BB4 6BB
Area of Operation: North West England and North Wales
Tel: 0800 505 3344
Email: info@above-it-all.co.uk
Web: www.above-it-all.co.uk
Product Type: 2, 4 **Material Type:** B) 2

ASSET LOFT CONVERSIONS
32 Saltwell View, Gateshead,
Tyne & Wear, NE8 4NT
Area of Operation: North East England
Tel: 0191 477 9057
Fax: 0191 420 7057
Web: www.assetlofts.co.uk

ECONOLOFT LTD
Unit 5, Kingfisher Court, South Lancs. Industrial Estate,
Bryn, Ashton in Makerfield, Lancashire, WN4 8DY
Area of Operation: UK (Excluding Ireland)
Tel: 01942 722754
Email: sales@econoloft.co.uk
Web: www.econoloft.co.uk **Product Type:** 2

HALLS STAIRS & LANDING
The Triangle, Paddock, Huddersfield,
West Yorkshire, HD1 4RN
Area of Operation: UK & Ireland
Tel: 01484 451485 **Email:** info@loftaccess.com
Web: www.loftaccess.com **Product Type:** 4

LADDERS-ONLINE
Penarth Road, Cardiff, CF11 8TD
Area of Operation: Worldwide
Tel: 08450 647647 **Fax:** 02920 702386
Email: sales@tbdavies.co.uk
Web: www.ladders-online.com   **Product Type:** 4

LOFT CENTRE PRODUCTS
Thicket Lane, Halnaker, Nr Chichester,
West Sussex, PO18 0QS
Area of Operation: UK & Ireland
Tel: 01243 785246 **Fax:** 01243 533184
Email: sales@loftcentreproducts.co.uk
Web: www.loftcentreproducts.co.uk
Product Type: 4

LOFT CENTRE PRODUCTS
Area of Operation: UK & Ireland
Tel: 01243 785246 **Fax:** 01243 533184
Email: sales@loftcentreproducts.co.uk
Web: www.loftcentreproducts.co.uk

Loft Centre Products comprehensive range of
spirals include all metal, all timber, metal and
timber, round and square to suit most internal
and external applications.

LOFT CONVERSION WAREHOUSE LTD
9 Motcombe Street, London, SW1X 8LA
Area of Operation: UK (Excluding Ireland)
Tel: 0207 7245 1150 **Fax:** 0207 7201 2569
Email: enquiries@loftconversionwarehouse.com
Web: www.loftconversionwarehouse.com
Product Type: 1, 2, 4

LOFT MASTERS
44-46 Seymour Place, London, W1H 5WQ
Area of Operation: UK (Excluding Ireland)
Tel: 0800 917 7532
Email: sales@loftmasters.co.uk
Web: www.loftmasters.co.uk **Product Type:** 1, 2

MIDLANDS CEILINGS & PARTITIONS
201 High Street, Harborne,
Birmingham, West Midlands, B17 9QG
Area of Operation: UK (Excluding Ireland)
Tel: 0121 694 8258 **Fax:** 0121 694 3258
Email: deanoneill100@msn.com
Product Type: 2

SPACE LOFT CONVERSIONS
Halton, 156 Bures Road, Sudbury, Suffolk, CO10 0JG
Area of Operation: East England
Tel: 01787 373570
Email: jesskeyton@yahoo.co.uk
Web: www.spaceloftconversions.co.uk
Product Type: 2

STIRA FOLDING ATTIC STAIRS
Dunmore, Co. Galway, Ireland
Area of Operation: UK & Ireland
Tel: 0800 973 111 **Fax:** 00353 933 8428
Email: enquiry@stira.ie
Web: www.stira.co.uk   **Product Type:** 4

STIRA FOLDING ATTIC STAIRS

Area of Operation: UK & Ireland
Tel: 0800 973 111
Fax: 00353 933 8428
Email: enquiry@stira.ie
Web: www.stira.co.uk

High quality folding attic stairs choose from our
extensive range or request a custom build to your
specifications. All new automatic Stira available.

SYSTEMATTIC LTD
Office 1, 4 Springfield Road,
Altrincham, Cheshire, WA14 1HE
Area of Operation: North West England and North Wales
Tel: 0161 928 0034 **Fax:** 0161 928 0048
Email: contact_us@systemattic.ltd.uk
Web: www.systemattic.ltd.uk **Product Type:** 1, 2

T.B. DAVIES (CARDIFF) LTD
Penarth Road, Cardiff, CF11 8TD
Area of Operation: UK (Excluding Ireland)
Tel: 02920 713000 **Fax:** 02920 702386
Email: sales@tbdavies.co.uk
Web: www.ladders-online.com
Product Type: 4

TEAM TECHNOLOGY
32 High Street, Guilden Morden,
Near Royston, Hertfordshire, SG8 0JR
Area of Operation: UK (Excluding Ireland)
Tel: 01763 853369 **Fax:** 01763 853164
Email: info@teamtechnology.co.uk
Web: www.teamtechnologyltd.co.uk
Product Type: 4

**TELEBEAM LOFT CONVERSION
AND FLOORING SYSTEM**
Cromwell House, 31 Market Place,
Devizes, Wiltshire, SN10 1JG
Area of Operation: UK & Ireland
Tel: 01380 739000 **Fax:** 01380 722205
Email: info@telebeam.co.uk
Web: www.telebeam.co.uk **Product Type:** 2

THE LOFT SHOP
The Loft Shop, Eldon Way,
Littlehampton, West Sussex, BN17 7HE
Area of Operation: UK & Ireland
Tel: 0870 604 0404 **Fax:** 01903 738501
Email: enquiries@loftshop.co.uk
Web: www.loftshop.co.uk   **Product Type:** 4

THE TELESCOPIC LADDER COMPANY
Canal Wharf, Horsenden Lane North,
Greenford, Greater London, UB6 7PH
Area of Operation: Worldwide
Tel: 020 8900 1902 **Fax:** 020 8900 1906
Email: sales@telescopicladders.co.uk
Web: www.telescopicladders.co.uk
Product Type: 4

TRUSS LOFT CONVERSIONS LTD
Bellwood Farm, Harrogate Road,
Ripon, North Yorkshire, HG4 3AA
Area of Operation: UK (Excluding Ireland)
Tel: 0800 195 3855 **Fax:** 01765 692 189
Email: sales@trussloft.co.uk
Web: www.trussloft.co.uk
Product Type: 2

WEST LONDON LOFTS LTD
41 St Margarets Road,
Hanwell, London, W7 2EX
Area of Operation: Greater London
Tel: 0845 456 4699 **Fax:** 0208 567 5725
Email: info@westlondonlofts.com
Web: www.westlondonlofts.com

CEILINGS

KEY
OTHER: ▽ Reclaimed   On-line shopping
 Bespoke   Hand-made   ECO Ecological

BRITISH GYPSUM LIMITED
Head Office, East Leake,
Loughborough, Leicestershire, LE12 6HX
Area of Operation: UK (Excluding Ireland)
Tel: 08705 456123 **Fax:** 08705 456356
Email: bgtechnical.enquiries@bpb.com
Web: www.british-gypsum.com

BURNT ASH CEILINGS
228 Burnt Ash Hill, Lee, London, SE12 0QE
Area of Operation: Greater London, South East England
Tel: 0208 857 4856 **Fax:** 0208 857 7667
Email: info@burntashceilings.co.uk
Web: www.burntashceilings.co.uk

CREATIVE CEILINGS LTD
West Midlands House, Gipsy Lane,
Willenhall, West Midlands, WV13 2HA
Area of Operation: UK (Excluding Ireland)
Tel: 0870 755 7830
Fax: 0121 609 7001
Email: info@creativeceilings.co.uk
Web: www.creativeceilings.co.uk

FIREPLACE & TIMBER PRODUCTS
Unit 2 Holyrood Drive,
Skippingdale Industrial Estate,
Scunthorpe, Lincolnshire, DN15 8NN
Area of Operation: UK & Ireland
Tel: 01724 852888
Fax: 01724 277255
Email: ftprodcts@yahoo.co.uk
Web: www.fireplaceandtimberproducts.co.uk

HERAKLITH
Broadway House, 21 Broadway,
Maidenhead, Berkshire, SL6 1NJ
Area of Operation: UK & Ireland
Tel: 01628 784330
Fax: 01628 633080
Email: muirwork@btinternet.com

LAFARGE PLASTERBOARD LTD
Marsh Lane, Easton-in-Gordano,
Bristol, BS20 0NF
Area of Operation: Worldwide
Tel: 01275 377777
Email: enquiryline@lafarge-gypsum.lafarge.com

Don't Forget ! You can use the materials key
at the beginning of the
Handbook to get
much more information
from a company's listing.

STAIRCASES, STAIRPARTS & WALKWAYS

Image courtesy of Richard Burbidge (01691 655131)

SPONSORED BY RICHARD BURBIDGE
Tel 01691 655131. Web www.richardburbidge.co.uk

Richard Burbidge

Staircases

If windows are the most important external features of a house, then staircases rate highly on the scale of crucial features on a home's interior.

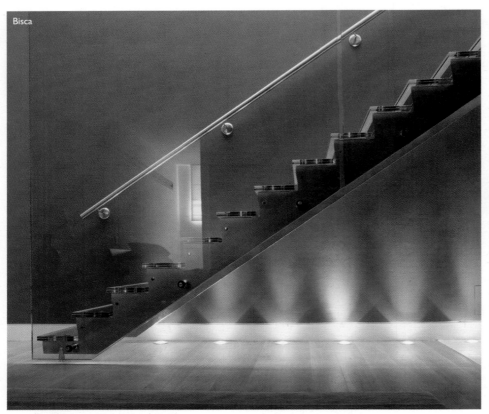

Bisca

Wooden Hill Company

Constructing staircases – in terms of exactness and line – and calculating the space and headroom required for the structure, is one of the greatest challenges to any self-builder. But it is all a question of style and subtlety, which may mean a long search for a joiner you consider capable of the job.

Far too many new self-builds are ruined because the staircase is heavy and peppered with an abundance of newel posts. Another common scenario is when the staircase is too 'grand' for the style of building. Unless your design ideal is pretension, most self-builders would be better off sticking to something more restrained. But it is equally easy to upset your self-build by fitting a staircase that is underplayed. Go for something that is rather more than just a means of getting you up to the next floor. The staircase should do justice to the quality of your interior.

Another potential problem for the self-builder is that today's building regulations do not permit, on grounds of safety, staircases that in the past would have been considered perfectly secure and risk-free. But, with a little imagination and endeavor, it is achievable to create staircases in reasonable keeping with the looks and elegance of the past.

A well-designed staircase can become one of the most important focal points of a house, so don't miss an opportunity to create a really special feature. You can achieve some fabulous results by making the staircase as transparent as possible, providing views through it (to higher level galleries, landings and other rooms). Half landings between two staircases flights can provide space to accommodate a desk or bookshelves.

As for materials, a traditional home generally means a timber staircase. Contemporary homes are likely to use more industrial materials, such as glass or metal, although combinations of these materials with pale wood are also popular.

Many self-builders opt for a straight flight of timber stairs. These, bought off-the-peg, are relatively inexpensive, but in most cases there is no need to compromise on style. Some of the most effective staircases are simple straight flights 'dressed up' by using other components such as balusters, handrails and newel posts.

The most common alternative to a straight flight is to split the staircase into two halves connected by a half or quarter landing. This is cheap to construct, but again needs space if you want an open stairwell design. Staircases with half and quarter landings are far cheaper than curved geometric stairs, but still cost at least twice as much as straight flights.

Spiral staircases are the best option when communication is required between two levels within a confined space. But while less space is taken up there is a certain loss of comfort and general safety, as well as the difficulty of moving large pieces of furniture between levels. Spiral staircases should generally not be used for rises of more than 13ft.

A spiral stair, however, can provide an exciting architectural feature. Position it away from walls so the whole structure can be seen and . appreciated.

STAIRCASES, GENERAL

KEY
OTHER: ▽ Reclaimed ⌐ On-line shopping
✎ Bespoke ✋ Hand-made ECO Ecological

AACORN JOINERY AND DESIGN LTD
2 Balaclava Place, South Street,
Bridport, Dorset, DT6 3PE
Area of Operation: Europe
Tel: 01308 456217 **Fax:** 01308 424511
Email: info@aacornjoinery.co.uk
Web: www.aacornjoinery.co.uk

ANDY THORNTON LTD
Ainleys Industrial Estate,
Elland, West Yorkshire, HX5 9JP
Area of Operation: Worldwide
Tel: 01422 375595 **Fax:** 01422 377455
Email: marketing@ataa.co.uk
Web: www.andythornton.com **Other Info:** ✎

ARC ANGEL
Angel Works, Bendish Farm,
Whitwell, Hitchin, Hertfordshire, SG4 8JD
Area of Operation: Europe
Tel: 01438 871100 **Fax:** 01438 871100
Email: angels@arcangelmetalwork.co.uk
Web: www.arcangelmetalwork.co.uk **Other Info:** ✎ ✋

AVON MANUFACTURING LIMITED
Avon House, Kineton Road, Southam,
Leamington Spa, Warwickshire, CV47 0DG
Area of Operation: UK (Excluding Ireland)
Tel: 01926 817292
Fax: 01926 814156
Email: sales@avonmanufacturing.co.uk
Web: www.avonmanufacturing.co.uk

B ROURKE & CO LTD
Vulcan Works, Accrington Road,
Burnley, Lancashire, BB11 5QD
Area of Operation: Worldwide
Tel: 01282 422841 **Fax:** 01282 458901
Email: info@rourkes.co.uk **Web:** www.rourkes.co.uk
Other Info: **Material Type:** C) 2, 5, 6

BAYFIELD STAIR CO
Unit 4, Praed Road, Trafford Park,
Manchester, M17 1PQ
Area of Operation: Worldwide
Tel: 0161 848 0700 **Fax:** 0161 872 2230
Email: sales@bayfieldstairs.co.uk
Web: www.bayfieldstairs.co.uk

BISCA
Sawmill Lane, Helmsley, North Yorkshire, YO62 5DQ
Area of Operation: UK (Excluding Ireland)
Tel: 01439 771702 **Fax:** 01439 771002
Email: info@bisca.co.uk **Web:** www.bisca.co.uk

BLANC DE BIERGES
Eastrea Road, Whittlesey, Cambridgeshire, PE7 2AG
Area of Operation: Worldwide
Tel: 01733 202566 **Fax:** 01733 205405
Email: info@blancdebierges.com
Web: www.blancdebierges.com **Other Info:** ✎ ✋

BUILDING & DESIGN SOLUTIONS GERMANY
Auf den Haien 14, 55471 Sargenroth, Germany
Area of Operation: UK (Excluding Ireland)
Tel: 0049 6761 970 871
Email: mail@buildingdesign-germany.eu
Web: www.buildingdesign-germany.eu

BURBEARY JOINERY LTD
Units 2, 3 & 4, 47 Robin Lane,
Beighton, Sheffield, South Yorkshire, S20 1BB
Area of Operation: UK (Excluding Ireland)
Tel: 0114 247 5003 **Fax:** 0114 247 5007
Email: info@burbearyjoinery.co.uk
Web: www.burbearyjoinery.co.uk ⌐
Other Info: ECO ✎ ✋ **Material Type:** A) 2, 3, 4, 5, 6, 15

CAMBRIDGE STRUCTURES
2 Huntingdon Street, St. Neots,
Cambridgeshire, PE19 1BG
Area of Operation: Worldwide
Tel: 01480 477700 **Fax:** 01480 477766
Email: info@cambridgestructures.com
Web: www.cambridgestructures.com
Other Info: ECO ✎
Material Type: A) 1, 2, 3, 4, 5, 6, 7, 8, 9, 10, 11, 12, 13, 14, 15

CHRIS TOPP & COMPANY WROUGHT IRONWORKS
Lyndhurst, Carlton Husthwaite,
Thirsk, North Yorkshire, YO7 2BJ
Area of Operation: Worldwide
Tel: 01845 501415
Fax: 01845 501072
Email: enquiry@christopp.co.uk
Web: www.christopp.co.uk **Other Info:** ✎ ✋
Material Type: C) 1, 2, 3, 4, 5, 6, 7, 11, 12, 14, 18

COMPLETE STAIR SYSTEMS LTD
Unit 70, Abbey Enterprise Centre, Premier Way, Abbey
Park Industrial Estate, Romsey, Hampshire, SO51 9DF
Area of Operation: UK & Ireland
Tel: 0845 838 1622
Email: info@completestairsystems.co.uk
Web: www.completestairsystems.co.uk
Other Info: ECO ✎
Material Type: A) 1, 2, 3, 4, 5, 6, 7, 8, 9, 10, 11, 12, 13, 14

COTTAGE CRAFT SPIRALS
The Barn, Gorsley Low Farm, The Wash,
Chapel-En-Le-Frith, Derbyshire, SK23 0QL
Area of Operation: Worldwide
Tel: 01663 750716
Fax: 01663 751093
Email: sales@castspiralstairs.com
Web: www.castspiralstairs.com **Other Info:** ✎ ✋
Material Type: A) 2, 3, 4, 5, 6, 7, 8, 9, 10, 11, 12, 13, 14

COUNTY JOINERY (SOUTH EAST) LTD
Tetley House, Marley Lane Business Park, Marley
Lane, Battle, East Sussex, TN33 0RE
Area of Operation: Greater London, South East England
Tel: 01424 871500
Fax: 01424 871550
Email: info@countyjoinery.co.uk
Web: www.countyjoinery.co.uk

CREATE DESIGN SOLUTIONS LTD
The Wood Yard, Castell Ddu Road,
Waun Gron, Pontarddulais, Swansea, SA4 8DH
Area of Operation: Greater London, Midlands & Mid
Wales, North West England and North Wales, South
East England, South West England and South Wales
Tel: 01792 386677
Fax: 01792 386677
Email: mail@createdesignsolutions.co.uk
Web: www.createdesignsolutions.co.uk

CREATE JOINERY
The Wood Yard, Castell Ddu Road,
Waun Gron , Pontarddulais, Swansea, SA4 8DH
Area of Operation: Greater London, Midlands & Mid
Wales, North West England and North Wales, South
East England, South West England and South Wales
Tel: 01792 386677 **Fax:** 01792 386677
Email: mail@create-joinery.co.uk
Web: www.create-joinery.co.uk

CROXFORD'S JOINERY MANUFACTURERS & WOODTURNERS
Meltham Joinery, Works New Street,
Meltham, Holmfirth, West Yorkshire, HD9 5NT
Area of Operation: UK (Excluding Ireland)
Tel: 01484 850892 **Fax:** 01484 850969
Email: croxford1@btconnect.com
Web: www.croxfords.co.uk
Material Type: A) 2, 3, 6

CUSTOM WOOD PRODUCTS
Cliffe Road, Easton on the Hill,
Stamford, Lincolnshire, PE9 3NP
Area of Operation: East England
Tel: 01780 755711 **Fax:** 01780 480834
Email: customwoodprods@aol.com
Web: www.cwpuk.com **Other Info:** ECO ✎ ✋

DAVID SMITH ST IVES LTD
Marley Road, St Ives, Huntingdon,
Cambridgeshire, PE27 3EX
Area of Operation: East England, Greater London,
Midlands & Mid Wales, South East England
Tel: 01480 309900
Fax: 01480 309949
Email: jeremyenglish@davidsmith.co.uk
Web: www.davidsmith.co.uk
Other Info: ECO ✎
Material Type: A) 2, 4, 5, 6, 7

DEACON & SANDYS
Apple Pie Farm, Cranbrook Road,
Benenden, Kent, TN17 4EU
Area of Operation: Worldwide
Tel: 01580 243331 **Fax:** 01580 243301
Email: pr@deaconandsandys.co.uk
Web: www.deaconandsandys.co.uk
Material Type: A) 2

DRESSER MOULDINGS LTD
Unit 3, Station Road, Blackrod,
Bolton, Lancashire, BL6 5JB
Area of Operation: UK (Excluding Ireland)
Tel: 01204 667667 **Fax:** 01204 667600
Email: mac@dresser.uk.com
Web: www.dresser.uk.com

E.A. HIGGINSON & CO LTD
Unit 1, Carlisle Road, London, NW9 0HD
Area of Operation: UK (Excluding Ireland)
Tel: 0208 200 4848
Fax: 0208 200 8249
Email: sales@higginson.co.uk
Web: www.higginson.co.uk
Material Type: A) 1, 2, 3, 4, 5, 6, 7, 10

ERMINE ENGINEERING COMPANY LTD
Francis House, Silver Birch Park, Great Northern
Terrace, Lincoln, Lincolnshire, LN5 8LG
Area of Operation: UK (Excluding Ireland)
Tel: 01522 510977
Fax: 01522 510929
Email: info@ermineengineering.co.uk
Web: www.ermineengineering.co.uk
Other Info: ✎ ✋
Material Type: A) 1, 2, 3, 4, 5, 6, 15

FAHSTONE LTD
Michaels Stud Farm, Meer End,
Kenilworth, Warwickshire, CV8 1PU
Area of Operation: UK (Excluding Ireland)
Tel: 01676 534226 **Fax:** 01676 532224
Email: sales@meer-end.co.uk
Web: www.meer-end.co.uk

FAIRMITRE WINDOWS & JOINERY LTD
2A Cope Road, Banbury, Oxfordshire, OX16 2EH
Area of Operation: UK (Excluding Ireland)
Tel: 01295 268441 **Fax:** 01295 268468
Email: info@fairmitrewindows.co.uk
Web: www.fairmitrewindows.co.uk

FINNISH WOOD PRODUCTS LTD
Tresparrett Farm Villa, Tresparrett, Cornwall, PL32 9ST
Area of Operation: UK & Ireland
Tel: 01840 261415
Fax: 01840 261415
Email: sales@finnishwoodproducts.com
Web: www.finnishwoodproducts.com

FITZROY JOINERY
Garden Close, Langage Industrial Estate,
Plympton, Plymouth, Devon, PL7 5EU
Area of Operation: UK & Ireland
Tel: 0870 428 9110 **Fax:** 0870 428 9111
Email: admin@fitzroy.co.uk
Web: www.fitzroyjoinery.co.uk ⌐ **Other Info:** ECO ✎
Material Type: A) 1, 2, 3, 4, 5, 6, 7, 8, 9, 10, 11

FLETCHER JOINERY
261 Whessoe Road, Darlington, Durham, DL3 0YL
Area of Operation: North East England
Tel: 01325 357347
Fax: 01325 357347
Email: enquiries@fletcherjoinery.co.uk
Web: www.fletcherjoinery.co.uk

FLIGHT TIMBER PRODUCTS
Earls Colne Business Park, Earls Colne, Essex, CO6 2NS
Area of Operation: East England, Greater London,
South East England
Tel: 01787 222336
Fax: 01787 222359
Email: sales@flighttimber.com
Web: www.flighttimber.com **Other Info:** ✎

G MIDDLETON LTD
Cross Croft Industrial Estate,
Appleby, Cumbria, CA16 6HX
Area of Operation: Europe
Tel: 01768 352067
Fax: 01768 353228
Email: info@graham-middleton.co.uk
Web: www.graham-middleton.co.uk ⌐
Material Type: A) 2

GALLICO CEMENT
3 Mead Court, 52 South Molton Street,
London, W1K 5SE
Area of Operation: Worldwide
Tel: 0207 193 1144
Fax: 0207 491 3539
Email: sales@gallicoservices.co.uk
Web: www.gallicoservices.co.uk
Other Info: ✎ **Material Type:** G) 1, 2

HALDANE UK
Blackwood Way, Bankhead Industrial Estate,
Glenrothes, Fife, KY7 6JF
Area of Operation: UK & Ireland
Tel: 01592 775656
Fax: 01592 775757
Email: sales@haldaneuk.com
Web: www.haldaneuk.com
Other Info: ✎
Material Type: A) 2, 3, 4, 5, 6, 7, 8, 9, 10, 11, 12, 13, 14

HALLS STAIRS & LANDING
The Triangle, Paddock,
Huddersfield, West Yorkshire, HD1 4RN
Area of Operation: UK & Ireland
Tel: 01484 451485
Email: info@loftaccess.com
Web: www.loftaccess.com
Material Type: A) 2, 6

INPUT JOINERY LTD
The Fairground, Weyhill,
Andover, Hampshire, SP11 0ST
Area of Operation: UK (Excluding Ireland)
Tel: 01264 771900
Fax: 01264 771901
Email: info@inputjoinery.co.uk
Web: www.inputjoinery.co.uk
Other Info: ✎ ✋ **Material Type:** A) 2, 4, 5, 6

INTERIOR ASSOCIATES
3 Highfield Road, Windsor, Berkshire, SL4 4DN
Area of Operation: UK & Ireland
Tel: 01753 865339
Fax: 01753 865339
Email: sales@interiorassociates.fsnet.co.uk
Web: www.interiorassociates.co.uk
Other Info: ✎ **Material Type:** C) 2, 3, 14, 17

JAIC LTD
Pattern House, Southwell Business Park,
Portland, Dorset, DT5 2NR
Area of Operation: UK (Excluding Ireland)
Tel: 01305 826991
Fax: 01305 823535
Email: info@jaic.co.uk
Web: www.jaic.co.uk **Other Info:** ✎
Material Type: A) 2, 4, 5

JELD-WEN
Watch House Lane, Doncaster,
South Yorkshire, DN5 9LR
Area of Operation: UK & Ireland
Tel: 0870 126 0000
Fax: 01302 787383
Email: customer-services@jeld-wen.co.uk
Web: www.jeld-wen.co.uk

INTERIORS, FIXTURES & FINISHES

JELD-WEN

Area of Operation: UK & Ireland
Tel: 0870 126 0000
Fax: 01302 787383
Email: customer-services@jeld-wen.co.uk
Web: www.jeld-wen.co.uk

Staircases

JELD-WEN manufactures a wide range of contemporary and more traditional staircases, available as stock flights or bespoke designs, with a wide choice of handrails and balusters available. The company provides a free measuring service and has a number of stairs specialist who can make the whole process simple and straightforward. All JELD-WEN stairs are fully certified and meet with all relevant Building Regulations.

JOHN OWEN JOINERY
Unit 1 Hays Bridge Farm, Brickhouse Lane, South Godstone, Surrey, RH9 8JW
Area of Operation: Greater London, South West England and South Wales
Tel: 01342 844036   **Fax:** 01342 844036
Email: johnowen.joinery@virgin.net
Web: www.johnowen.co.uk

JOINERY-PLUS
Bentley Hall Barn, Alkmonton, Ashbourne, Derbyshire, DE6 3DJ
Area of Operation: UK (Excluding Ireland)
Tel: 07931 386233   **Fax:** 01335 330922
Email: joinery@joinery-plus.co.uk
Web: www.joinery-plus.co.uk
Material Type: A) 2, 6, 7

KASPAR SWANKEY
405, Goldhawk Road, Hammersmith, West London, W6 0SA
Area of Operation: Worldwide
Tel: 020 8746 3586   **Fax:** 020 8746 3586
Email: kaspar@swankeypankey.com
Web: www.swankeypankey.com

KIGI JOINERY LTD
The Workshop, Haileywood Farm, Shiplake, Henley-on-Thames, Oxfordshire, RG9 4BG
Area of Operation: UK (Excluding Ireland)
Tel: 0118 940 4583
Email: enquiries@kigi.co.uk
Web: www.kigi.co.uk   **Other Info:**
Material Type: A) 1, 2, 3, 4, 5, 6, 7

LADDERS-ONLINE
Penarth Road, Cardiff, CF11 8TD
Area of Operation: Worldwide
Tel: 08450 647647
Fax: 02920 702386
Email: sales@tbdavies.co.uk
Web: www.ladders-online.com

LAPPIPORRAS
Tresparrett Farm Villa, Tresparrett, Camelford, Cornwall, PL32 9ST
Area of Operation: UK & Ireland
Tel: 01840 261415   **Fax:** 01840 261415
Email: sales@finnishwoodproducts.com
Web: www.finnishwoodproducts.com
Material Type: A) 9

LAPPIPORRAS STAIRS

Area of Operation: UK & Ireland
Tel: 01840 261415
Fax: 01840 261415
Email: sales@finnishwoodproducts.com
Web: www.finnishwoodproducts.com

Stairs from Finland, manufactured in high-quality Finnish Redwood or Birch.
Factory lacqured in clear of coloured finishes. Various styles and components to create individulisum. Made to your measurements.

LOFT CENTRE PRODUCTS
Thicket Lane, Halnaker, Nr Chichester, West Sussex, PO18 0QS
Area of Operation: UK & Ireland
Tel: 01243 785246   **Fax:** 01243 533184
Email: sales@loftcentreproducts.co.uk
Web: www.loftcentreproducts.co.uk

LOFT CENTRE PRODUCTS

Area of Operation: UK & Ireland
Tel: 01243 785246
Fax: 01243 533184
Email: sales@loftcentreproducts.co.uk
Web: www.loftcentreproducts.co.uk

Loft Centre Products have developed a comprehensive range of staircases both standard and bespoke, offering a wide range of styles and materials to match most applications.

METALCRAFT [TOTTENHAM]
6-40 Durnford Street, Tottenham, London, N15 5NQ
Tel: 0208 802 1715   **Fax:** 0208 802 1258
Email: sales@makingmetalwork.com
Web: www.makingmetalwork.com
Material Type: C) 2, 3, 4, 5

OAKLEAF INDUSTRIES LTD
D5 Flightway Business Park, Dunkeswell, Honiton, Devon, EX14 4RD
Area of Operation: UK & Ireland
Tel: 01404 891902   **Fax:** 01404 891912
Email: info@stairsolutions.co.uk
Web: www.stairsolutions.co.uk
Material Type: A) 2, 3, 4, 5, 6, 9

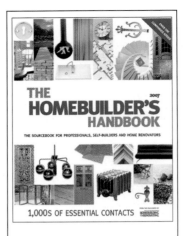

RHONES JOINERY (WREXHAM) LTD
Mold Road Industrial Estate, Gwersyllt, Wrexham, LL11 4AQ
Area of Operation: UK (Excluding Ireland)
Tel: 01978 262488   **Fax:** 01978 262488
Email: info@rhonesjoinery.co.uk
Web: www.rhonesjoinery.co.uk

SANDERSON'S FINE FURNITURE
Unit 5 & 6, The Village Workshop, Four Crosses Business Park, Four Crosses, Powys, SY22 6ST
Area of Operation: UK (Excluding Ireland)
Tel: 01691 830075   **Fax:** 01691 830075
Email: sales@sandersonsfinefurniture.co.uk
Web: www.sandersonsfinefurniture.co.uk

SPIRAL STAIRS LTD
Unit 3, Annington Commercial Centre, Annington Road, Steyning, West Sussex, BN44 3WA
Area of Operation: Europe
Tel: 01903 812310   **Fax:** 01903 812306
Email: sales@spiralstairs.org
Web: www.spiralstairs.org
Other Info: **Material Type:** A) 1, 2, 3, 4, 5, 6, 9, 15

STAIRFLIGHT LTD
Unit 17, Landford Common Industrial Estate, New Road, Landford, Salisbury, Wiltshire, SP5 2AZ
Area of Operation: UK (Excluding Ireland)
Tel: 01794 324150   **Fax:** 01794 324151
Email: sales@stairflightltd.com
Web: www.stairflightltd.com
Other Info: **Material Type:** A) 1, 2, 3, 4, 5, 6

STAIRPLACE LTD
86 Knights Hill, West Norwood, London, SE27 0JD
Area of Operation: UK (Excluding Ireland)
Tel: 0208 761 8844   **Fax:** 0208 761 8855
Email: jon@stairplace.co.uk
Web: www.stairplace.co.uk

STAIRPLAN LTD
Unit C4, Stafford Park 4, Telford, Shropshire, TF3 3BA
Area of Operation: UK (Excluding Ireland)
Tel: 01952 216000   **Fax:** 01952 216021
Email: sales@stairplan.com
Web: www.stairplan.com
Material Type: A) 1, 2, 4, 6, 9

STAIRS DIRECT UK LTD
3 Park Gate Crescent, Guiseley, Leeds, LS20 8AT
Area of Operation: UK & Ireland
Tel: 0870 8147760   **Fax:** 0870 3835426
Email: info@stairs-direct.co.uk
Web: www.stairs-direct.co.uk

STIRA FOLDING ATTIC STAIRS
Dunmore, Co Galway, Ireland
Area of Operation: UK & Ireland
Tel: 0800 973 111   **Fax:** 00353 933 8428
Email: enquiry@stira.ie   **Web:** www.stira.co.uk
Other Info: **Material Type:** B) 2

STIRA FOLDING ATTIC STAIRS

Area of Operation: UK & Ireland
Tel: 0800 973 111
Fax: 00353 933 8428
Email: enquiry@stira.ie
Web: www.stira.co.uk

High quality folding attic stairs choose from our extensive range or request a custom build to your specifications. All new automatic Stira available.

STROUDS WOODWORKING COMPANY LTD
Ashmansworthy, Woolsery, Bideford, Devon, EX39 5RE
Area of Operation: South West England and South Wales
Tel: 01409 241624
Fax: 01409 241769
Email: enquiries@stroudswoodworking.co.uk
Web: www.stroudswoodworking.co.uk
Other Info:
Material Type: A) 1, 2, 3, 4, 5, 6, 8, 10

T.B. DAVIES (CARDIFF) LTD
Penarth Road, Cardiff, CF11 8TD
Area of Operation: UK (Excluding Ireland)
Tel: 02920 713000
Fax: 02920 702386
Email: sales@tbdavies.co.uk
Web: www.ladders-online.com

TEAM TECHNOLOGY
32 High Street, Guilden Morden, Nr Royston, Hertfordshire, SG8 0JR
Area of Operation: UK (Excluding Ireland)
Tel: 01763 853369
Fax: 01763 853164
Email: info@teamtechnology.co.uk
Web: www.teamtechnologyltd.co.uk
Material Type: A) 2, 3, 4, 5, 6, 9, 14

THE GRANITE FACTORY
4 Winchester Drive, Peterlee, Durham, SR8 2RJ
Area of Operation: North East England
Tel: 0191 518 3600
Fax: 0191 518 3600
Email: admin@granitefactory.co.uk
Web: www.granitefactory.co.uk

THE LOFT SHOP
The Loft Shop, Eldon Way, Littlehampton, West Sussex, BN17 7HE
Area of Operation: UK & Ireland
Tel: 0870 604 0404
Fax: 01903 738501
Email: enquiries@loftshop.co.uk
Web: www.loftshop.co.uk

THE WOODEN HILL COMPANY
The Atrium, Curtis Road, Dorking, Surrey, RH4 1XA
Area of Operation: Europe
Tel: 0845 456 1088   **Fax:** 01932 264693
Email: info@the-wooden-hill-company.co.uk
Web: www.the-wooden-hill-company.co.uk
Other Info:
Material Type: A) 1, 2, 3, 4, 7, 15

INTERIORS, FIXTURES & FINISHES - **Staircases, Stairparts & Walkways** - Staircases, General; Spiral & Helical Staircases

SPONSORED BY: RICHARD BURBIDGE   www.richardburbidge.co.uk

INTERIORS, FIXTURES & FINISHES

THE WOODEN HILL COMPANY LTD

Area of Operation: Europe
Tel: 0845 456 1088
Fax: 01932 264693
Email: info@the-wooden-hill-company.co.uk
Web: www.the-wooden-hill-company.co.uk

The stunning "Genius" range in Spiral or Traditional configuration. Transform your staircase into a feature or selling point for your property. **Free drawing and quotation.**

TOMPKINS LTD

High March Close, Long March Industrial Estate, Daventry, Northamptonshire, NN11 4EZ
Area of Operation: UK (Excluding Ireland)
Tel: 01327 877187   **Fax:** 01327 310491
Email: info@tompkinswood.co.uk
Web: www.tompkinswood.co.uk   **Other Info:** ✎ 🖑

TONY HOOPER

Unit 18 Camelot Court, Bancombe Trading Estate, Somerton, TA11 6SB
Area of Operation: UK (Excluding Ireland)
Tel: 01458 274221   **Fax:** 01458 274690
Email: tonyhooper1@aol.com
Web: www.tonyhooper.co.uk

WOODCHESTER KITCHENS & INTERIORS

Unit 18a Chalford Industrial Estate, Chalford, Gloucestershire, GL6 8NT
Area of Operation: UK (Excluding Ireland)
Tel: 01453 886411   **Fax:** 01453 886411
Email: enquiries@woodchesterkitchens.co.uk
Web: www.woodchesterkitchens.co.uk
Other Info: ✎ 🖑

WOODSIDE JOINERY

40 Llantarnam Park, Cwmbran, Torfaen, NP44 3AW
Area of Operation: UK & Ireland
Tel: 01633 875232   **Fax:** 01633 482718
Email: sales@woodsidejoinery.com
Web: www.woodside-joinery.co.uk

SPIRAL & HELICAL STAIRCASES

KEY

OTHER: ▽ Reclaimed   ⌂ On-line shopping
✎ Bespoke   🖑 Hand-made   ECO Ecological

B ROURKE & CO LTD

Vulcan Works, Accrington Road, Burnley, Lancashire, BB11 5QD
Area of Operation: Worldwide
Tel: 01282 422841   **Fax:** 01282 458901
Email: info@rourkes.co.uk
Web: www.rourkes.co.uk
Material Type: C) 2, 5, 6

BARBE & BALD LTD

112 Tudor Way, Hertford, Hertfordshire, SG14 2DL
Area of Operation: Worldwide
Tel: 01992 552783   **Fax:** 01992 552783
Email: mark@baldsbalm.co.uk
Web: www.baldsbalm.co.uk ⌂

BAYFIELD STAIR CO

Unit 4, Praed Road, Trafford Park, Manchester, M17 1PQ
Area of Operation: Worldwide
Tel: 0161 848 0700   **Fax:** 0161 872 2230
Email: sales@bayfieldstairs.co.uk
Web: www.bayfieldstairs.co.uk

BISCA

Sawmill Lane, Helmsley, North Yorkshire, YO62 5DQ
Area of Operation: UK (Excluding Ireland)
Tel: 01439 771702   **Fax:** 01439 771002
Email: info@bisca.co.uk   **Web:** www.bisca.co.uk

BLANC DE BIERGES

Eastrea Road, Whittlesey, Cambridgeshire, PE7 2AG
Area of Operation: Worldwide
Tel: 01733 202566   **Fax:** 01733 205405
Email: info@blancdebierges.com
Web: www.blancdebierges.com   **Other Info:** ✎ 🖑

BLANC DE BIERGES

Area of Operation: Worldwide
Tel: 01733 202566
Fax: 01733 205405
Email: info@blancdebierges.com
Web: www.blancdebierges.com
Other Info: ✎ 🖑

The handcrafted Blanc de Bierges spiral staircase is available in 48 different versions and landings can be made to specific requirements. The non-slip finish coupled with a closed riser are important safety features. All structural components are fully reinforced.

BURBEARY JOINERY LTD

Units 2, 3 & 4, 47 Robin Lane, Beighton, Sheffield, South Yorkshire, S20 1BB
Area of Operation: UK (Excluding Ireland)
Tel: 0114 247 5003   **Fax:** 0114 247 5007
Email: www.burbearyjoinery.co.uk
Web: www.burbearyjoinery.co.uk ⌂
Other Info: ECO ✎ 🖑
Material Type: A) 1, 2, 4, 5, 6, 15

CAMBRIDGE STRUCTURES

2 Huntingdon Street, St. Neots, Cambridgeshire, PE19 1BG
Area of Operation: Worldwide
Tel: 01480 477700   **Fax:** 01480 477766
Email: info@cambridgestructures.com
Web: www.cambridgestructures.com
Other Info: ECO ✎ 🖑
Material Type: A) 1, 2, 3, 4, 5, 6, 7, 8, 9, 10, 11, 12, 13, 14, 15

CHRIS TOPP & COMPANY WROUGHT IRONWORKS

Lyndhurst, Carlton Husthwaite, Thirsk, North Yorkshire, YO7 2BJ
Tel: 01845 501415   **Fax:** 01845 501072
Email: enquiry@christopp.co.uk
Web: www.christopp.co.uk   **Other Info:** ✎ 🖑
Material Type: C) 2, 3, 4, 5, 6, 7, 11, 12, 17

COMPLETE STAIR SYSTEMS LTD

Unit 70, Abbey Enterprise Centre, Premier Way, Abbey Park Industrial Estate, Romsey, Hampshire, SO51 9DF
Area of Operation: UK & Ireland
Tel: 0845 838 1622
Email: info@completestairsystems.co.uk
Web: www.completestairsystems.co.uk
Other Info: ECO ✎ 🖑
Material Type: A) 1, 2, 3, 4, 5, 6, 7, 8, 9, 10, 11, 12, 13, 14

CONSCULPT SPIRAL STAIRS LTD

Ash Close, Par, Cornwall, PL24 2HD
Area of Operation: Worldwide
Tel: 01726 816555   **Fax:** 01726 816555
Email: info@spiralstairs.uk.com
Web: www.spiralstairs.uk.com

COTTAGE CRAFT SPIRALS

The Barn, Gorsley Low Farm, The Wash, Chapel-En-Le-Frith, Derbyshire, SK23 0QL
Area of Operation: Worldwide
Tel: 01663 750716   **Fax:** 01663 751093
Email: sales@castspiralstairs.com
Web: www.castspiralstairs.com
Other Info: ✎ 🖑
Material Type: A) 2, 3, 4, 5, 6, 7, 8, 9, 10, 11, 12, 13, 14

CREATE DESIGN SOLUTIONS LTD

The Wood Yard, Castell Ddu Road, Waun Gron, Pontarddulais, Swansea, SA4 8DH
Area of Operation: Greater London, Midlands & Mid Wales, North West England and North Wales, South East England, South West England and South Wales
Tel: 01792 386677   **Fax:** 01792 386677
Email: mail@createdesignsolutions.co.uk
Web: www.createdesignsolutions.co.uk

CREATE JOINERY

The Wood Yard, Castell Ddu Road, Waun Gron , Pontarddulais, Swansea, SA4 8DH
Area of Operation: Greater London, Midlands & Mid Wales, North West England and North Wales, South East England, South West England and South Wales
Tel: 01792 386677   **Fax:** 01792 386677
Email: mail@create-joinery.co.uk
Web: www.create-joinery.co.uk

DRESSER MOULDINGS LTD

Unit 3, Station Road, Blackrod, Bolton, Lancashire, BL6 5JB
Area of Operation: UK (Excluding Ireland)
Tel: 01204 667667   **Fax:** 01204 667600
Email: mac@dresser.uk.com
Web: www.dresser.uk.com

E.A. HIGGINSON & CO LTD

Unit 1, Carlisle Road, London, NW9 0HD
Area of Operation: UK (Excluding Ireland)
Tel: 0208 200 4848   **Fax:** 0208 200 8249
Email: sales@higginson.co.uk
Web: www.higginson.co.uk
Material Type: A) 2, 4, 5

ERMINE ENGINEERING COMPANY LTD

Francis House, Silver Birch Park, Great Northern Terrace, Lincoln, Lincolnshire, LN5 8LG
Area of Operation: UK (Excluding Ireland)
Tel: 01522 510977   **Fax:** 01522 510929
Email: info@ermineengineering.co.uk
Web: www.ermineengineering.co.uk
Other Info: ✎ 🖑   **Material Type:** A) 1, 2, 3, 4, 5, 6, 15

FAHSTONE LTD

Michaels Stud Farm, Meer End, Kenilworth, Warwickshire, CV8 1PU
Area of Operation: UK (Excluding Ireland)
Tel: 01676 534226   **Fax:** 01676 532224
Email: sales@meer-end.co.uk
Web: www.meer-end.co.uk

FITZROY JOINERY

Garden Close, Langage Industrial Estate, Plympton, Plymouth, Devon, PL7 5EU
Area of Operation: UK & Ireland
Tel: 0870 428 9110   **Fax:** 0870 428 9111
Email: admin@fitzroy.co.uk
Web: www.fitzroyjoinery.co.uk ⌂
Other Info: ECO
Material Type: A) 1, 2, 3, 4, 5, 6, 7, 8, 9, 10, 11, 12, 14

HALDANE UK

Blackwood Way, Bankhead Industrial Estate, Glenrothes, Fife, KY7 6JF
Area of Operation: UK & Ireland
Tel: 01592 775656   **Fax:** 01592 775757
Email: sales@haldaneuk.com
Web: www.haldaneuk.com   **Other Info:** ✎
Material Type: A) 2, 3, 4, 5, 6, 7, 8, 9, 10, 11, 12, 13, 14

HALLS STAIRS & LANDING

The Triangle, Paddock, Huddersfield, West Yorkshire, HD1 4RN
Area of Operation: UK & Ireland
Tel: 01484 451485
Email: info@loftaccess.com
Web: www.loftaccess.com   **Material Type:** A) 4

INPUT JOINERY LTD

The Fairground, Weyhill, Andover, Hampshire, SP11 0ST
Area of Operation: UK (Excluding Ireland)
Tel: 01264 771900
Fax: 01264 771901
Email: info@inputjoinery.co.uk
Web: www.inputjoinery.co.uk
Other Info: ✎ 🖑   **Material Type:** A) 2, 3, 4, 5, 6

JAIC LTD

Pattern House, Southwell Business Park, Portland, Dorset, DT5 2NR
Area of Operation: UK (Excluding Ireland)
Tel: 01305 826991   **Fax:** 01305 823535
Email: info@jaic.co.uk
Web: www.jaic.co.uk

JARABOSKY

Old Station Road, Exley Lane, Elland, West Yorkshire, HX5 0SW
Area of Operation: UK & Ireland
Tel: 01422 311922
Fax: 01422 374053
Email: sales@jarabosky.co.uk
Web: www.jarabosky.co.uk

JARABOSKY

Area of Operation: UK & Ireland
Tel: 01422 311922
Fax: 01422 374053
Email: sales@jarabosky.co.uk
Web: www.jarabosky.co.uk
Product Type: 1, 4

We use French Oak or Australian Jarrah, ecologically sourced, to produce hardwood sleeper treads with wonderful natural imperfections. Character or plain, from 30mm to 100mm, they will enhance any staircase.

JOHN OWEN JOINERY

Unit 1 Hays Bridge Farm, Brickhouse Lane, South Godstone, Surrey, RH9 8JW
Area of Operation: Greater London, South West England and South Wales
Tel: 01342 844036   **Fax:** 01342 844036
Email: johnowen.joinery@virgin.net
Web: www.johnowen.co.uk

KIGI JOINERY LTD

The Workshop, Haileywood Farm, Shiplake, Henley-on-Thames, Oxfordshire, RG9 4BG
Area of Operation: UK (Excluding Ireland)
Tel: 0118 940 4583
Email: enquiries@kigi.co.uk
Web: www.kigi.co.uk   **Other Info:** ✎ 🖑
Material Type: A) 1, 2, 3, 4, 5, 6, 7, 12

LADDERS-ONLINE

Penarth Road, Cardiff, CF11 8TD
Area of Operation: Worldwide
Tel: 08450 647647   **Fax:** 02920 702386
Email: sales@tbdavies.co.uk
Web: www.ladders-online.com ⌂

SPONSORED BY: RICHARD BURBIDGE   www.richardburbidge.co.uk

LOFT CENTRE PRODUCTS
Thicket Lane, Halnaker, Nr Chichester,
West Sussex, PO18 0QS
Area of Operation: UK & Ireland
Tel: 01243 785246   **Fax:** 01243 533184
Email: sales@loftcentreproducts.co.uk
Web: www.loftcentreproducts.co.uk

LOFT CENTRE PRODUCTS
Area of Operation: UK & Ireland
Tel: 01243 785246   **Fax:** 01243 533184
Email: sales@loftcentreproducts.co.uk
Web: www.loftcentreproducts.co.uk

Loft Centre Products comprehensive range of
spirals include all metal, all timber, metal and
timber, round and square to suit most internal
and external applications.

METALCRAFT [TOTTENHAM]
6-40 Durnford Street, Tottenham, London, N15 5NQ
Area of Operation: UK (Excluding Ireland)
Tel: 0208 802 1715   **Fax:** 0208 802 1258
Email: sales@makingmetalwork.com
Web: www.makingmetalwork.com
Material Type: C) 2, 3, 4, 5

OAKLEAF INDUSTRIES LTD
D5 Flightway Business Park,
Dunkeswell, Honiton, Devon, EX14 4RD
Area of Operation: UK & Ireland
Tel: 01404 891902
Fax: 01404 891912
Email: info@stairsolutions.co.uk
Web: www.stairsolutions.co.uk
Material Type: A) 2, 3, 4, 5, 6, 9

RICHARD BURBIDGE LTD
Whittington Road, Oswestry, Shropshire, SY11 1HZ
Area of Operation: UK & Ireland
Tel: 01691 655131   **Fax:** 01691 659091
Email: info@richardburbidge.co.uk
Web: www.richardburbidge.co.uk

SPIRAL CONSTRUCTION LTD
Water-Ma-Trout Industrial Estate,
Helston, Cornwall, TR13 OLW
Area of Operation: UK & Ireland
Tel: 01326 574497   **Fax:** 01326 574760
Email: enquiries@spiral.uk.com
Web: www.spiral.uk.com
Material Type: A) 2, 3, 4, 5, 6, 7, 9

SPIRAL STAIRCASE SYSTEMS
The Mill, Glynde, Near Lewes, East Sussex, BN8 6SS
Area of Operation: Worldwide
Tel: 01273 858341   **Fax:** 01273 858200
Email: sales@spiralstairs.co.uk
Web: www.spiralstairs.co.uk
Material Type: A) 1, 2, 3, 4, 5, 6, 7, 8, 9, 10, 12

SPIRAL STAIRS LTD
Unit 3, Annington Commercial Centre, Annington
Road, Steyning, West Sussex, BN44 3WA
Area of Operation: Europe
Tel: 01903 812310
Fax: 01903 812306
Email: sales@spiralstairs.org
Web: www.spiralstairs.org   **Other Info:** ✎
Material Type: A) 1, 2, 3, 4, 5, 6, 9, 15

STAIRFLIGHT LTD
Unit 17, Landford Common Industrial Estate, New
Road, Landford, Salisbury, Wiltshire, SP5 2AZ
Area of Operation: UK (Excluding Ireland)
Tel: 01794 324150   **Fax:** 01794 324151
Email: sales@stairflightltd.com
Web: www.stairflightltd.com   **Other Info:** ✎
Material Type: A) 1, 2, 3, 4, 5, 6

STAIRPLACE LTD
86 Knights Hill, West Norwood, London, SE27 0JD
Area of Operation: UK (Excluding Ireland)
Tel: 0208 761 8844
Fax: 0208 761 8855
Email: jon@stairplace.co.uk
Web: www.stairplace.co.uk
Material Type: A) 2, 4

STAIRS DIRECT UK LTD
3 Park Gate Crescent, Guiseley, Leeds, LS20 8AT
Area of Operation: UK & Ireland
Tel: 0870 8147760   **Fax:** 0870 3835426
Email: info@stairs-direct.co.uk
Web: www.stairs-direct.co.uk ✍
Other Info: ✎

T.B. DAVIES (CARDIFF) LTD
Penarth Road, Cardiff, CF11 8TD
Area of Operation: UK (Excluding Ireland)
Tel: 02920 713000
Fax: 02920 702386
Email: sales@tbdavies.co.uk
Web: www.ladders-online.com ✍

TEAM TECHNOLOGY
32 High Street, Guilden Morden,
Nr Royston, Hertfordshire, SG8 0JR
Area of Operation: UK (Excluding Ireland)
Tel: 01763 853369
Fax: 01763 853164
Email: info@teamtechnology.co.uk
Web: www.teamtechnologyltd.co.uk
Material Type: A) 2, 3, 4, 5, 6, 9, 14

THE GRANITE FACTORY
4 Winchester Drive, Peterlee, Durham, SR8 2RJ
Area of Operation: North East England
Tel: 0191 518 3600
Fax: 0191 518 3600
Email: admin@granitefactory.co.uk
Web: www.granitefactory.co.uk ✍
Material Type: E) 1, 2, 3, 4, 5, 7, 8, 9, 11

THE LOFT SHOP
The Loft Shop, Eldon Way,
Littlehampton, West Sussex, BN17 7HE
Area of Operation: UK & Ireland
Tel: 0870 604 0404
Fax: 01903 738501
Email: enquiries@loftshop.co.uk
Web: www.loftshop.co.uk ✍

THE WOODEN HILL COMPANY
The Atrium, Curtis Road, Dorking, Surrey, RH4 1XA
Area of Operation: Europe
Tel: 0845 456 1088
Fax: 01932 264693
Email: info@the-wooden-hill-company.co.uk
Web: www.the-wooden-hill-company.co.uk
Other Info: ✎ ✋
Material Type: A) 1, 2, 3, 4, 7, 15

TOMPKINS LTD
High March Close, Long March Industrial Estate,
Daventry, Northamptonshire, NN11 4EZ
Area of Operation: UK (Excluding Ireland)
Tel: 01327 877187
Fax: 01327 310491
Email: info@tompkinswood.co.uk
Web: www.tompkinswood.co.uk
Other Info: ✎ ✋

WOODSIDE JOINERY
40 Llantarnam Park, Cwmbran, Torfaen, NP44 3AW
Area of Operation: UK & Ireland
Tel: 01633 875232
Fax: 01633 482718
Email: sales@woodsidejoinery.com
Web: www.woodside-joinery.co.uk

STAIRPARTS

ARC ANGEL
Angel Works, Bendish Farm, Whitwell,
Hitchin, Hertfordshire, SG4 8JD
Area of Operation: Europe
Tel: 01438 871100   **Fax:** 01438 871100
Email: angels@arcangelmetalwork.co.uk
Web: www.arcangelmetalwork.co.uk

AVON MANUFACTURING LIMITED
Avon House, Kineton Road, Southam,
Leamington Spa, Warwickshire, CV47 0DG
Area of Operation: UK (Excluding Ireland)
Tel: 01926 817292
Fax: 01926 814156
Email: sales@avonmanufacturing.co.uk
Web: www.avonmanufacturing.co.uk

B ROURKE & CO LTD
Vulcan Works, Accrington Road,
Burnley, Lancashire, BB11 5QD
Area of Operation: Worldwide
Tel: 01282 422841
Fax: 01282 458901
Email: info@rourkes.co.uk
Web: www.rourkes.co.uk
Material Type: C) 2, 4, 5, 6

BALCAS TIMBER LTD
Laragh, Enniskillen, Co Fermanagh, BT94 2FQ
Area of Operation: UK & Ireland
Tel: 0286 632 3003   **Fax:** 0286 632 7924
Email: info@balcas.com
Web: www.balcas.com

BAYFIELD STAIR CO
Unit 4, Praed Road, Trafford Park,
Manchester, M17 1PQ
Area of Operation: Worldwide
Tel: 0161 848 0700   **Fax:** 0161 872 2230
Email: sales@bayfieldstairs.co.uk
Web: www.bayfieldstairs.co.uk

BISCA
Sawmill Lane, Helmsley, North Yorkshire, YO62 5DQ
Area of Operation: UK (Excluding Ireland)
Tel: 01439 771702   **Fax:** 01439 771002
Email: info@bisca.co.uk
Web: www.bisca.co.uk

BOB LANE WOODTURNERS
Unit 1, White House Workshop, Old London Road,
Swinfen, Lichfield, Staffordshire, WS14 9QW
Area of Operation: UK (Excluding Ireland)
Tel: 01543 483148
Fax: 01543 481245
Email: info@theturner.co.uk
Web: www.theturner.co.uk

BURBEARY JOINERY LTD
Units 2, 3 & 4, 47 Robin Lane, Beighton,
Sheffield, South Yorkshire, S20 1BB
Area of Operation: UK (Excluding Ireland)
Tel: 0114 247 5003
Fax: 0114 247 5007
Email: info@burbearyjoinery.co.uk
Web: www.burbearyjoinery.co.uk ✍
Other Info: ECO ✎
Material Type: A) 2, 3, 4, 5, 6, 7, 9

CARPETRUNNERS
Somerset House, Clatendon Place,
Leamington Spa, Warwickshire, CV32 5QN
Area of Operation: UK & Ireland
Tel: 01926 885523   **Fax:** 01926 885552
Email: sales@carpetrunners.co.uk
Web: www.carpetrunners.co.uk ✍

CHRIS TOPP & COMPANY WROUGHT IRONWORKS
Lyndhurst, Carlton Husthwaite,
Thirsk, North Yorkshire, YO7 2BJ
Area of Operation: Worldwide
Tel: 01845 501415   **Fax:** 01845 501072
Email: enquiry@christopp.co.uk
Web: www.christopp.co.uk   **Other Info:** ✎ ✋
Material Type: C) 2, 3, 4, 5, 6, 7, 11, 12, 17

CHRISTIE TIMBER SERVICES LTD
New Victoria Sawmills, Bridgeness Road,
Bo'ness, Falkirk, EH51 9SG
Area of Operation: North East England, Scotland
Tel: 01506 828222   **Fax:** 01506 828226
Email: gordon@christie-timber.co.uk
Web: www.christie-timber.co.uk ✍
Material Type: A) 2, 3, 5, 6

COTTAGE CRAFT SPIRALS
The Barn, Gorsley Low Farm, The Wash,
Chapel-En-Le-Frith, Derbyshire, SK23 0QL
Area of Operation: Worldwide
Tel: 01663 750716   **Fax:** 01663 751093
Email: sales@castspiralstairs.com
Web: www.castspiralstairs.com   **Other Info:** ✎ ✋
Material Type: A) 2, 3, 4, 5, 6, 7, 8, 9, 10, 11, 12, 13, 14

COUNTY JOINERY (SOUTH EAST) LTD
Tetley House, Marley Lane Business Park,
Marley Lane, Battle, East Sussex, TN33 0RE
Area of Operation: Greater London, South East
England
Tel: 01424 871500   **Fax:** 01424 871550
Email: info@countyjoinery.co.uk
Web: www.countyjoinery.co.uk

CROXFORD'S JOINERY MANUFACTURERS & WOODTURNERS
Meltham Joinery, Works New Street, Meltham,
Holmfirth, West Yorkshire, HD9 5NT
Area of Operation: UK (Excluding Ireland)
Tel: 01484 850892   **Fax:** 01484 850969
Email: croxford1@btconnect.com
Web: www.croxfords.co.uk

CUSTOM WOOD PRODUCTS
Cliffe Road, Easton on the Hill,
Stamford, Lincolnshire, PE9 3NP
Area of Operation: East England
Tel: 01780 755711   **Fax:** 01780 480834
Email: customwoodprods@aol.com
Web: www.cwpuk.com   **Other Info:** ECO ✎ ✋

DEACON & SANDYS
Apple Pie Farm, Cranbrook Road,
Benenden, Kent, TN17 4EU
Area of Operation: Worldwide
Tel: 01580 243331
Fax: 01580 243301
Email: pr@deaconandsandys.co.uk
Web: www.deaconandsandys.co.uk
Material Type: A) 2

DESIGNS BY DAVID
84 Merlin Avenue, Nuneaton,
Warwickshire, CV10 9JZ
Area of Operation: UK & Ireland
Tel: 02476 744580
Email: david@designsbydavid.co.uk
Web: www.designsbydavid.co.uk   **Other Info:** ✋

DRESSER MOULDINGS LTD
Unit 3, Station Road, Blackrod,
Bolton, Lancashire, BL6 5JB
Area of Operation: UK (Excluding Ireland)
Tel: 01204 667667   **Fax:** 01204 667600
Email: mac@dresser.uk.com
Web: www.dresser.uk.com

FAHSTONE LTD
Michaels Stud Farm, Meer End,
Kenilworth, Warwickshire, CV8 1PU
Area of Operation: UK (Excluding Ireland)
Tel: 01676 534226
Fax: 01676 532224
Email: sales@meer-end.co.uk
Web: www.meer-end.co.uk

FINNISH WOOD PRODUCTS LTD
Tresparrett Farm Villa,
Tresparrett, Cornwall, PL32 9ST
Area of Operation: UK & Ireland
Tel: 01840 261415   **Fax:** 01840 261415
Email: sales@finnishwoodproducts.com
Web: www.finnishwoodproducts.com

HALDANE UK
Blackwood Way, Bankhead Industrial Estate,
Glenrothes, Fife, KY7 6JF
Area of Operation: UK & Ireland
Tel: 01592 775656   **Fax:** 01592 775757
Email: sales@haldaneuk.com
Web: www.haldaneuk.com   **Other Info:** ✎
Material Type: A) 2, 3, 4, 5, 6, 7, 8, 9, 10, 11, 12, 13, 14

HALLS STAIRS & LANDING
The Triangle, Paddock,
Huddersfield, West Yorkshire, HD1 4RN
Area of Operation: UK & Ireland
Tel: 01484 451485
Email: info@loftaccess.com
Web: www.loftaccess.com   **Material Type:** A) 1, 2, 6

HOUSE OF BRASS
122 North Sherwood Street,
Nottingham, Nottinghamshire, NG1 4EF
Area of Operation: Worldwide
Tel: 0115 947 5430   **Fax:** 0115 947 5430
Email: sales@houseofbrass.co.uk
Web: www.houseofbrass.co.uk ⌐🛒

INPUT JOINERY LTD
The Fairground, Weyhill,
Andover, Hampshire, SP11 0ST
Area of Operation: UK (Excluding Ireland)
Tel: 01264 771900   **Fax:** 01264 771901
Email: info@inputjoinery.co.uk
Web: www.inputjoinery.co.uk   **Other Info:** ✎ 🖐
Material Type: A) 1, 2, 4, 5, 6

ION GLASS
PO Box 284, Burgess Hill, West Sussex, RH15 0BN
Area of Operation: UK (Excluding Ireland)
Tel: 0845 658 9988   **Fax:** 0845 658 9989
Email: sales@ionglass.co.uk
Web: www.ionglass.co.uk
Other Info: ✎   **Material Type:** J) 4, 5

JAIC LTD
Pattern House, Southwell Business Park,
Portland, Dorset, DT5 2NR
Area of Operation: UK (Excluding Ireland)
Tel: 01305 826991   **Fax:** 01305 823535
Email: info@jaic.co.uk   **Web:** www.jaic.co.uk

JIM LAWRENCE LTD
Scotland Hall Farm, Stoke by Nayland,
Colchester, Essex, CO6 4QG
Area of Operation: UK (Excluding Ireland)
Tel: 01206 263459   **Fax:** 01206 262166
Email: sales@jim-lawrence.co.uk
Web: www.jim-lawrence.co.uk 🛒

JOHN OWEN JOINERY
Unit 1 Hays Bridge Farm, Brickhouse Lane,
South Godstone, Surrey, RH9 8JW
Area of Operation: Greater London, South West
England and South Wales
Tel: 01342 844036   **Fax:** 01342 844036
Email: johnowen.joinery@virgin.net
Web: www.johnowen.co.uk

JOINERY-PLUS
Bentley Hall Barn, Alkmonton,
Ashbourne, Derbyshire, DE6 3DJ
Area of Operation: UK (Excluding Ireland)
Tel: 07931 386233   **Fax:** 01335 330922
Email: info@joinery-plus.co.uk
Web: www.joinery-plus.co.uk
Material Type: A) 2, 6, 7

KIEVEL.KL-CHEMIE (UK) LTD
Lower Farm, Lower Farm Lane,
Ampfield, Romsey, Hampshire, SO51 9BN
Tel: 01794 368865   **Fax:** 01794 368914
Email: info@kievel.com   **Web:** www.kievel.com
Other Info: 🖐

KIGI JOINERY LTD
The Workshop, Haileywood Farm, Shiplake,
Henley-on-Thames, Oxfordshire, RG9 4BG
Area of Operation: UK (Excluding Ireland)
Tel: 0118 940 4583
Email: enquiries@kigi.co.uk
Web: www.kigi.co.uk   **Other Info:** ✎ 🖐
Material Type: A) 1, 2, 3, 4, 5, 6, 7, 12

M D STAINLESS DESIGNS
79 Verity Cresent, Poole, Dorset, BH17 8TT
Area of Operation: UK (Excluding Ireland)
Tel: 01202 684998
Fax: 01202 684998
Email: stainlessdesigns@onetel.com

M.B.L
55 High Street, Biggleswade,
Bedfordshire, SG18 0JH
Area of Operation: UK (Excluding Ireland)
Tel: 01767 318695   **Fax:** 01767 318695
Email: info@mblai.co.uk
Web: www.mblai.co.uk
Other Info: ▽ ✎ 🖐

METALCRAFT [TOTTENHAM]
6-40 Durnford Street, Tottenham, London, N15 5NQ
Area of Operation: UK (Excluding Ireland)
Tel: 0208 802 1715   **Fax:** 0208 802 1258
Email: sales@makingmetalwork.com
Web: www.makingmetalwork.com
Other Info: ✎   **Material Type:** C) 2, 3, 4, 5

RHONES JOINERY (WREXHAM) LTD
Mold Road Industrial Estate,
Gwersyllt, Wrexham, LL11 4AQ
Area of Operation: UK (Excluding Ireland)
Tel: 01978 262488
Fax: 01978 262488
Email: info@rhonesjoinery.co.uk
Web: www.rhonesjoinery.co.uk

RICHARD BURBIDGE LTD
Whittington Road, Oswestry, Shropshire, SY11 1HZ
Area of Operation: UK & Ireland
Tel: 01691 655131
Fax: 01691 659091
Email: info@richardburbidge.co.uk
Web: www.richardburbidge.co.uk
Material Type: A) 2

SCHLUTER SYSTEMS LTD
Units 4-5, Bardon 22 Industrial Park,
Beveridge Lane, Coalville, Leicestershire, LE67 1TE
Area of Operation: UK & Ireland
Tel: 01530 813396
Fax: 01530 813376
Email: sales@schluter.co.uk
Web: www.schluter.co.uk
Other Info: ✎   **Material Type:** C) 1, 2, 3, 11

STAIRFLIGHT LTD
Unit 17, Landford Common Industrial Estate, New
Road, Landford, Salisbury, Wiltshire, SP5 2AZ
Area of Operation: UK (Excluding Ireland)
Tel: 01794 324150
Fax: 01794 324151
Email: sales@stairflightltd.com
Web: www.stairflightltd.com
Material Type: A) 1, 2, 3, 4, 5, 6

STAIRPLAN LTD
Unit C4, Stafford Park 4, Telford, Shropshire, TF3 3BA
Area of Operation: UK (Excluding Ireland)
Tel: 01952 216000
Fax: 01952 216021
Email: sales@stairplan.com
Web: www.stairplan.com
Material Type: A) 1, 2, 4, 6

STAIRRODS (UK)
Unti 6 Park Road, North Industrial Estate, Blackhill,
Consett, Durham, DH8 5UN
Area of Operation: Worldwide
Tel: 01207 591543
Fax: 01207 591911
Email: sales@stairrods.co.uk
Web: www.stairrods.co.uk

STAIRS DIRECT UK LTD
3 Park Gate Crescent, Guiseley, Leeds, LS20 8AT
Area of Operation: UK (Excluding Ireland)
Tel: 0870 8147760   **Fax:** 0870 3835426
Email: info@stairs-direct.co.uk
Web: www.stairs-direct.co.uk 🛒

STROUDS WOODWORKING COMPANY LTD
Ashmansworthy, Woolsery,
Bideford, Devon, EX39 5RE
Area of Operation: South West England and South Wales
Tel: 01409 241624   **Fax:** 01409 241769
Email: enquiries@stroudswoodworking.co.uk
Web: www.stroudswoodworking.co.uk

SUSSEX BRASSWARE
Napier Road, Castleham Industrial Estate,
St. Leonards-on-Sea, East Sussex, TN38 9NY
Area of Operation: Worldwide
Tel: 01424 857913   **Fax:** 01424 853862
Email: sales@sussexbrassware.co.uk
Web: www.sussexbrassware.co.uk 🛒
Other Info: ✎ 🖐

T.B. DAVIES (CARDIFF) LTD
Penarth Road, Cardiff, CF11 8TD
Area of Operation: UK (Excluding Ireland)
Tel: 02920 713000   **Fax:** 02920 702386
Email: sales@tbdavies.co.uk
Web: www.ladders-online.com 🛒

THE EXPANDED METAL COMPANY LIMITED
PO Box 14, Longhill Industrial Estate (North),
Hartlepool, Durham, TS25 1PR
Area of Operation: Worldwide
Tel: 01429 867388   **Fax:** 01429 866795
Email: paulb@expamet.co.uk
Web: www.expandedmetalcompany.co.uk

THE SPA & WARWICK TIMBER CO LTD
Harriott Drive, Heathcote Industrial Estate,
Warwick, Warwickshire, CV34 6TJ
Area of Operation: Midlands & Mid Wales
Tel: 01926 883876   **Fax:** 01926 450831
Email: spa.warwick@btconnect.com
Web: www.sawhardwood.com

WINTHER BROWNE
75 Bilton Way, Enfield, London, EN3 7ER
Area of Operation: UK (Excluding Ireland)
Tel: 0208 3449050   **Fax:** 0845 612 1894
Email: sales@wintherbrowne.co.uk
Web: www.wintherbrowne.co.uk
Material Type: A) 2, 4

WOODCHESTER KITCHENS & INTERIORS
Unit 18a Chalford Industrial Estate, Chalford,
Gloucestershire, GL6 8NT
Area of Operation: UK (Excluding Ireland)
Tel: 01453 886411   **Fax:** 01453 886411
Email: enquires@woodchesterkitchens.co.uk
Web: www.woodchesterkitchens.co.uk
Material Type: A) 1, 2, 3, 4, 5, 6, 7, 8, 9, 10, 11, 12

WOODHOUSE TIMBER
Unit 15 Quarry Farm Industrial Estate,
Staplecross Road, Bodiam, East Sussex, TN32 5RA
Area of Operation: UK (Excluding Ireland)
Tel: 01580 831700   **Fax:** 01580 830054
Email: info@woodhousetimber.co.uk
Web: www.woodhousetimber.co.uk
Other Info: ✎   **Material Type:** A) 2

WOODSIDE JOINERY
40 Llantarnam Park, Cwmbran, Torfaen, NP44 3AW
Area of Operation: UK & Ireland
Tel: 01633 875232   **Fax:** 01633 482718
Email: sales@woodsidejoinery.com
Web: www.woodside-joinery.co.uk

ZOROUFY UK LTD
Unit A, 8 Capel Hendre Industrial Estate,
Capel Hendre, Ammanford, Carms,
Carmarthenshire, SA18 3SJ
Area of Operation: Europe
Tel: 01269 832244   **Fax:** 01269 841010
Email: enquiries@zoroufy.co.uk
Web: www.zoroufy.co.uk
Material Type: C) 11, 14, 18

WALKWAYS

KEY

OTHER: ▽ Reclaimed   🛒 On-line shopping
✎ Bespoke   🖐 Hand-made   ECO Ecological

B ROURKE & CO LTD
Vulcan Works, Accrington Road,
Burnley, Lancashire, BB11 5QD
Area of Operation: Worldwide
Tel: 01282 422841   **Fax:** 01282 458901
Email: info@rourkes.co.uk
Web: www.rourkes.co.uk
Material Type: C) 2, 4, 5, 6

BAYFIELD STAIR CO
Unit 4, Praed Road, Trafford Park,
Manchester, M17 1PQ
Area of Operation: Worldwide
Tel: 0161 848 0700   **Fax:** 0161 872 2230
Email: sales@bayfieldstairs.co.uk
Web: www.bayfieldstairs.co.uk

BISCA
Sawmill Lane, Helmsley, North Yorkshire, YO62 5DQ
Area of Operation: UK (Excluding Ireland)
Tel: 01439 771702   **Fax:** 01439 771002
Email: info@bisca.co.uk   **Web:** www.bisca.co.uk

BURBEARY JOINERY LTD
Units 2, 3 & 4, 47 Robin Lane, Beighton,
Sheffield, South Yorkshire, S20 1BB
Area of Operation: UK (Excluding Ireland)
Tel: 0114 247 5003
Fax: 0114 247 5007
Email: info@burbearyjoinery.co.uk
Web: www.burbearyjoinery.co.uk 🛒

CAMBRIDGE STRUCTURES
2 Huntingdon Street, St. Neots,
Cambridgeshire, PE19 1BG
Area of Operation: Worldwide
Tel: 01480 477700   **Fax:** 01480 477766
Email: info@cambridgestructures.com
Web: www.cambridgestructures.com
Material Type: A)1, 2, 3, 4, 5, 6, 7, 8, 9, 10, 11, 12, 13, 14, 15

ERMINE ENGINEERING COMPANY LTD
Francis House, Silver Birch Park, Great Northern
Terrace, Lincoln, Lincolnshire, LN5 8LG
Area of Operation: UK (Excluding Ireland)
Tel: 01522 510977
Fax: 01522 510929
Email: info@ermineengineering.co.uk
Web: www.ermineengineering.co.uk
Other Info: ✎ 🖐   **Material Type:** C) 1, 2, 3, 4

FAHSTONE LTD
Michaels Stud Farm, Meer End,
Kenilworth, Warwickshire, CV8 1PU
Area of Operation: UK (Excluding Ireland)
Tel: 01676 534226   **Fax:** 01676 532224
Email: sales@meer-end.co.uk
Web: www.meer-end.co.uk

FLOORS GALORE
Unit 5E, Centurion Park, Kendal Road,
Shrewsbury, Shropshire, SY1 4EH
Area of Operation: UK & Ireland
Tel: 0800 083 0623
Email: info@floors-galore.co.uk
Web: www.floors-galore.co.uk 🛒
Material Type: A) 2, 4, 5, 6, 7, 9

ION GLASS
PO Box 284, Burgess Hill, West Sussex, RH15 0BN
Area of Operation: UK (Excluding Ireland)
Tel: 0845 658 9988
Fax: 0845 658 9989
Email: sales@ionglass.co.uk
Web: www.ionglass.co.uk
Other Info: ✎
Material Type: J) 4, 5

JAIC LTD
Pattern House, Southwell Business Park,
Portland, Dorset, DT5 2NR
Area of Operation: UK (Excluding Ireland)
Tel: 01305 826991
Fax: 01305 823535
Email: info@jaic.co.uk
Web: www.jaic.co.uk

KIRK NATURAL STONE
Bridgend, Fyvie, Turriff, Aberdeenshire, AB53 8LL
Area of Operation: Worldwide
Tel: 01651 891891
Fax: 01651 891794
Email: info@kirknaturalstone.com
Web: www.kirknaturalstone.com
Material Type: E) 1, 2, 3, 4, 5

METALCRAFT [TOTTENHAM]
6-40 Durnford Street, Tottenham, London, N15 5NQ
Area of Operation: UK (Excluding Ireland)
Tel: 0208 802 1715
Fax: 0208 802 1258
Email: sales@makingmetalwork.com
Web: www.makingmetalwork.com
Other Info: ✎
Material Type: C) 2, 3, 4, 5

THE EXPANDED METAL COMPANY LIMITED
PO Box 14, Longhill Industrial Estate (North),
Hartlepool, Durham, TS25 1PR
Area of Operation: Worldwide
Tel: 01429 867388
Fax: 01429 866795
Email: paulb@expamet.co.uk
Web: www.expandedmetalcompany.co.uk

STAIRLIFTS

KEY
OTHER: ▽ Reclaimed 🖱 On-line shopping
✎ Bespoke ✋ Hand-made ECO Ecological

BROOKS STAIRLIFTS
Spring Mills, Norwood Avenue,
Shipley, West Yorkshire, BD18 2AX
Area of Operation: Worldwide
Tel: 01274 717766 **Fax:** 01274 533129
Email: info@stairlifts.co.uk
Web: www.stairlifts.co.uk

DISABILITY ACCESS COMPANY LTD
Access House, 16-18 Chapel Street,
Glossop, Derbyshire, SK13 8AT
Area of Operation: UK & Ireland
Tel: 01457 868547 **Fax:** 0871 733 5071
Email: sales@disabilityaccessco.com
Web: www.disabilityaccessco.com
Other Info: ✎

HOUSE ELECTRONIC LTD
97 Francisco Close, Hollyfields Park,
Chafford Hundred, Essex, RM16 6YE
Area of Operation: UK & Ireland
Tel: 01375 483595 **Fax:** 01375 483595
Email: info@houselectronic.co.uk
Web: www.houselectronic.co.uk

INVALIFTS LIMITED
The Lawns Business Centre,
Hinckley, Leicestershire, LE10 1DY
Area of Operation: UK (Excluding Ireland)
Tel: 0845 468 2543 **Fax:** 01455 891307
Email: joy@invalifts.com
Web: www.invalifts.com

TAURUS (CUSTOM ACCESS SOLUTIONS) LTD
Derwentside Development Business Complex,
Consett Business Park, Consett, Durham, DH8 6BP
Area of Operation: UK (Excluding Ireland)
Tel: 01207 502555 **Fax:** 01207 502444
Email: info@tauruscas.co.uk **Other Info:** ✎
Web: www.tauruscas.co.uk

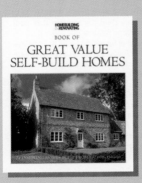 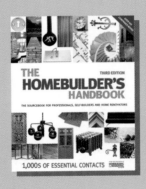 
 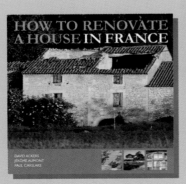

LIGHTING

Image courtesy of All Lit Up (0845 034 5050)

SPONSORED BY www.homebuilding.co.uk
Tel: 01527 834435

Britain's Best Selling Self-Build Magazine & Website

HOMEBUILDING &RENOVATING

Outdoor Lighting

Outdoor lighting is becoming an essential element of a home's exterior. Not only does it enhance security and safety, it is perfect for making the most of the attractive features of your home and garden.

ABOVE: LED lighting combined with fibre optics can create an unusual "starry night" effect. Image by Optic Lighting.
ABOVE RIGHT: Glass stones provide an individual statement and will leave a lasting impression. Image by Cameron Peters.
RIGHT: Lighting paths and steps provides a useful safety feature as well as making your garden a more attractive space at night. Image by All Weather Lighting.

Firstly, decide what you want to achieve with your lighting. Is it purely for security? Are you trying to subtly highlight architectural features and plants? Or are you going all out with a cool contemporary lighting scheme? And what is your budget? Whilst some modest lights will incur only a minor cost, an extensive decorative lighting scheme will cost thousands in fittings and design – and you will almost certainly need to consult a lighting professional.

Accent lighting may be added to create features and effects. A tree is simple to light, requiring a single, powerful uplighter to instantly transform it into the focal point of a garden. By focusing a spotlight onto a solitary object such as a plant, a theatrical effect can be achieved which is far more dramatic than a general light source. Spiked garden uplighters are ideal for this purpose and may be easily moved and repositioned to focus on specific areas. Similarly any water feature should be well lit, as moving water sparkles and reflects when lit, creating a tranquil effect. The best way to arrange this is by using floats, or by installing underwater lights via special fixtures anchored to the bottom of the pond/pool to shine upwards.

A soft wash over a garden wall from a directional flood is very also effective, and you can create a sense of greater depth by using a decorative mirror to bounce light back into the garden. A fully recessed, buried spotlight for concealed lighting of trees or hedges can be scattered with leaves to give a broken effect

similar to a stained glass window. Also, an increasingly popular method is moonlighting. It creates the romantic effect of moonlight filtering through trees placing low-voltage downlighters amongst the branches.

For safety, it is always wise to illuminate paths, steps and decking. This can be done in two ways; either by putting lighting in nearby shrubbery or flowerbeds to light up the surfaces, or by placing walk-over lights inset into the surface itself. Both are highly effective. The decision will be based on your personal style and budget.

Whether your fixtures subtly blend in with the rest of the exterior, or are features in their own right, one thing for sure is that they should be in keeping with the overall external design. You should qe that your fixings won't cause any light pollution – you don't want to light up your neighbour's garden or upset the surrounding wildlife. Choose low-voltage shielded fixtures, which avoid glare and only focus lighting where it is needed.

Outdoor lighting can be run from a mains supply. However, most good garden lighting operates at a low voltage – 12v, which is a safer option for

external lights, and is available in a wide variety of fixings. You will require at least one transformer to convert the mains voltage to 12v, which can be located either outside in a weatherproof box, or indoors. Low-voltage wires can be moved around easily because they are buried only a few inches underground, but you will still need a qualified electrician to undertake any electrical installation.

The eco-friendly, wireless alternative is to install solar-powered lighting. The downside to these products is they may not be as bright as electric-powered lights, and as such are not practical for all applications. The amount of energy they store will also be affected by weather conditions, so they may not be as effective when the weather has been cloudy or dull.

LIGHTING

KEY

PRODUCT TYPES: 1= Downlights
2 = Spotlights   3 = Chandeliers
4 = Wall Lights   5 = Emergency   6 = Security
7 = External   8 = Low Voltage
9 = Waterproof   10 = Fibre Optic   11 = Solar
12 = Fluorescent
OTHER: ▽ Reclaimed   🖐 On-line shopping
✎ Bespoke   ✋ Hand-made   ECO Ecological

A & H BRASS
201-203 Edgware Road, London, W2 1ES
Area of Operation: Worldwide
Tel: 0207 402 1854   **Fax:** 0207 402 0110
Email: ahbrass@btinternet.com
Web: www.aandhbrass.co.uk 🖐
Product Type: 3, 7, 8

ADVANCED LEDS LTD
Unit 14, Bow Court, Fletchworth Gate,
Burnsall Road, Coventry, West Midlands, CV5 6SP
Tel: 02476 716151   **Fax:** 02476 712161
Email: sales@advanced-led.com
Web: www.advanced-led.com
Product Type: 1, 4, 12

ALL WEATHER LIGHTING LTD
Shrubbery Court, Cross Bank,
Bewdley, Worcestershire, DY12 2XF
Area of Operation: Europe
Tel: 01299 269246   **Fax:** 01299 269246
Email: chris@allweatherlighting.co.uk
Web: www.allweatherlighting.co.uk
Product Type: 3, 7, 9, 11

ALL-LIT-UP
PO Box 130, Stevenage, Hertfordshire, SG1 5WF
Area of Operation: UK (Excluding Ireland)
Tel: 0845 034 5050
Fax: 0845 034 5051
Email: email@all-lit-up.co.uk
Web: www.all-lit-up.co.uk 🖐
Product Type: 1, 2, 3, 4, 6, 7, 8, 9, 10, 12, 13

ANDY THORNTON LTD
Ainleys Industrial Estate, Elland,
West Yorkshire, HX5 9JP
Area of Operation: Worldwide
Tel: 01422 375595
Fax: 01422 377455
Email: marketing@ataa.co.uk
Web: www.andythornton.com
Product Type: 1, 3, 4, 7, 8   **Other Info:** ▽ ✎ ✋

ANTIQUARIUS ANTIQUES CENTRE
131-141 Kings Road, Chelsea, London, SW3 5EB
Area of Operation: Worldwide
Tel: 0207 351 5353
Fax: 0207 969 1639
Email: antique@dial.pipex.com
Web: www.antiquarius.co.uk 🖐   **Product Type:** 3

ARC-COMP
Friedrichstr. 3, 12205 Berlin-Lichterfelde, Germany
Area of Operation: Europe
Tel: +49 (0)308 430 9956
Fax: +49 (0)308 430 9957
Email: jvs@arc-comp.com
Web: www.arc-com.com   **Product Type:** 7

ARC-COMP (IRISH BRANCH)
Whitefield Cottage, Lugduff,
Tinahely, Co. Wicklow, Republic of Ireland
Area of Operation: Europe
Tel: +353 (0)868 729 945   **Fax:** +353 (0)402 28900
Email: jvs@arc-comp.com
Web: www.arc-comp.com   **Product Type:** 7

ASHFIELD TRADITIONAL
119 High Street, Needham Market,
Ipswich, Suffolk, IP6 8DQ
Area of Operation: Europe
Tel: 01449 723601   **Fax:** 01449 723602
Email: mail@limelightgb.com
Web: www.limelightgb.com 🖐   **Product Type:** 1, 3

ASTRA CEILING FANS & LIGHTING
Unit 6, Lowercroft Industrial Estate,
Bury, Lancashire, BL8 3PA
Area of Operation: Europe
Tel: 0161 7973222   **Fax:** 0161 7973444
Email: support@astra247.com
Web: www.astra247.com 🖐
Product Type: 3, 5, 6, 7, 8, 9, 10

B ROURKE & CO LTD
Vulcan Works, Accrington Road,
Burnley, Lancashire, BB11 5QD
Area of Operation: Worldwide
Tel: 01282 422841   **Fax:** 01282 458901
Email: info@rourkes.co.uk
Web: www.rourkes.co.uk
Product Type: 1, 2, 3, 4, 6, 7
Material Type: C) 1, 2, 3, 4, 5, 6, 7, 11, 14

BARRY SIMS
11 Bognor Road, Chichester, West Sussex, PO19 7TF
Area of Operation: UK & Ireland
Tel: 07787 987652
Email: info@barrysims.biz
Web: www.barrysims.biz
Product Type: 1, 4, 7, 8, 9, 13

BATHROOM CITY
Seeleys Road, Tyseley Industrial Estate,
Birmingham, West Midlands, B11 2LQ
Area of Operation: UK & Ireland
Tel: 0121 753 0700   **Fax:** 0121 753 1110
Email: sales@bathroomcity.com
Web: www.bathroomcity.com 🖐
Product Type: 3, 8, 9

BESPOKE INSTALLATIONS
1 Rogers Close, Tiverton, Devon, EX16 6UW
Area of Operation: UK (Excluding Ireland)
Tel: 01884 243497
Email: michael@bespokeinstallations.com
Web: www.bespoke.biz
Product Type: 2, 3, 4, 6, 7, 8, 10

BESSELINK & JONES
1.04 Chelsea Harbour Design Centre,
Chelsea Harbour, London, SW10 0XE
Area of Operation: Worldwide
Tel: 0207 351 4669   **Fax:** 0207 352 3898
Email: enquiry@besselink.com
Web: www.besselink.com 🖐
Product Type: 1, 2, 3, 4, 5, 8, 9
Material Type: A) 2, 3, 4, 5, 6, 7, 8, 9, 10, 11, 12, 14

BLOWZONE HOT STUDIO
The Ruskin Glass Centre, Wollaston Road,
Amblecote, West Midlands, DY8 4HF
Area of Operation: Worldwide
Tel: 01384 399464   **Fax:** 01384 377746
Email: sales@blowzone.co.uk
Web: www.blowzone.co.uk   **Product Type:** 10

BLUE BEACON LIGHTING
Intermail Plc - Horizon West, Canal View Road,
Newbury, Berkshire, RG14 5XF
Area of Operation: UK & Ireland
Tel: 0870 241 3992   **Fax:** 01635 41678
Email: michaelm@crescent.co.uk
Web: www.bluebeacon.co.uk 🖐
Product Type: 1, 2, 3, 4, 6, 7, 8, 9, 10, 11

BRETT LANDSCAPING LTD
Salt Lane, Cliffe, Rochester, Kent, ME3 7SZ
Area of Operation: Worldwide
Tel: 01634 222188   **Fax:** 01634 222186
Email: cliffeenquiries@brett.co.uk
Web: www.brett.co.uk/landscaping
Product Type: 7

snaplite

downlighting
withou
comprimis

The award winning Snaplite range of low voltage down lighters have be
designed to maintain the Fire, Acoustic and Airtight properties of you
ceiling in line with the high standards set by Local Authority
Building Regulations.

Easily installed, they provide the safe, attractive lighting solution to
compliment your room design.

0870 4437735   www.snaplite.co.uk

fire and acoustically rated downlighters

Safe and Sound Lighting
Bordesley Hall
Alvechurch
Worcestershire
B48 7QA

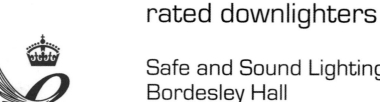

THE QUEEN'S AWARDS
FOR ENTERPRISE:
INNOVATION
2006

BROUGHTONS OF LEICESTER
The Old Cinema, 69 Cropston Road,
Anstey, Leicester, Leicestershire, LE7 7BP
Area of Operation: Worldwide
Tel: 0116 235 2555 **Fax:** 0116 234 1188
Email: sale@broughtons.com
Web: www.broughtons.com **Product Type:** 3

BURWOOD LIGHTING COMPANY LTD
Market Street, Exeter, Devon, EX1 1BW
Area of Operation: UK & Ireland
Tel: 01392 259367
Fax: 01392 210239
Email: sales@burwoodlighting.co.uk
Web: www.burwoodlighting.co.uk
Product Type: 1, 2, 3, 4, 5, 6, 7, 8, 9, 10

BYRON
Byron House, 34 Sherwood Road, Aston Fields
Industrial Estate, Bromsgrove, West Midlands, B60 3DR
Area of Operation: Worldwide
Tel: 01527 557700 **Fax:** 01527 557701
Email: info@chbyron.com **Web:** www.chbyron.com

CAMERON PETERS LTD
The Old Dairy, Home Farm, Ardington,
Wantage, Oxfordshire, OX12 8PD
Area of Operation: Worldwide
Tel: 01235 835000
Fax: 01235 835005
Email: info@cameronpeters.co.uk
Web: www.cameronpeters.co.uk
Product Type: 1, 2, 3, 4, 7, 8, 10

CANDELA LTD
52 Spaces Business Centre,
Ingate Place, London, SW8 3NS
Area of Operation: Worldwide
Tel: 0207 720 4480 **Fax:** 0207 498 0026
Email: mail@candela.ltd.uk
Web: www.candela.ltd.uk
Product Type: 1, 4, 5, 7, 8, 9

CHAOS DESIGN CONSULTANTS LTD
14 Queen Square, Bath, Somerset, BA1 2HN
Area of Operation: Worldwide
Tel: 01225 780044 **Fax:** 01225 780087
Email: sonja@chaosdc.co.uk
Web: www.chaosdc.co.uk
Product Type: 4, 8 **Material Type:** J) 4

CHARLES MASON LTD
Unit 11A Brook Street Mill, Off Goodall Street,
Macclesfield, Cheshire, SK11 7AW
Area of Operation: Worldwide
Tel: 0800 085 3616 **Fax:** 01625 668789
Email: info@charles-mason.com
Web: www.charles-mason.com
Product Type: 1, 2, 3, 4, 7
Material Type: C) 2, 3, 14

CHARNOCK ENTERPRISES
Disklok House, Preston Road, Charnock Richard,
Chorley, Lancashire, PR7 5HH
Area of Operation: UK & Ireland
Tel: 01257 792111 **Fax:** 01257 795101
Email: sales@disklokuk.co.uk
Web: www.charnockenterprises.co.uk

COMMERCIAL ILLUMINATION LTD
Thurleston Hall, Ipswich, Suffolk, IP1 6TD
Area of Operation: Worldwide
Tel: 01473 257813
Email: sales@period-lighting.co.uk
Web: www.period-lighting.co.uk
Product Type: 1, 3, 4, 7, 8, 9, 11 **Other Info:**

CRESCENT LIGHTING LTD
8 Rivermead, Pipers Lane,
Thatcham, Berkshire, RG19 4EP
Area of Operation: Europe
Tel: 01635 87 88 88 **Fax:** 01635 87 38 88
Email: sales@crescent.co.uk
Web: www.crescent.co.uk
Product Type: 10

DEBDEN ANTIQUES & INTERIORS
Elder Street, Debden,
Saffron Walden, Essex, CB11 3JY
Area of Operation: Worldwide
Tel: 01799 543007
Email: info@debden-antiques.co.uk
Web: www.debden-antiques.co.uk
Product Type: 3, 4

DESIGNER-LIGHTS.COM
16 Jamaica Street, North Lane, Edinburgh, EH3 6HQ
Area of Operation: Worldwide
Tel: 0131 225 5279 **Fax:** 0131 226 3922
Email: orders@designer-lights.com
Web: www.designer-lights.com
Product Type: 1, 2, 3, 4, 5, 8, 9, 10, 13

DETAIL LIGHTING LIMITED
30 Stilebrook Road, Olney,
Buckinghamshire, MK46 5EA
Area of Operation: UK (Excluding Ireland)
Tel: 0845 052 4442
Fax: 0845 052 4443
Email: sales@detaillighting.co.uk
Web: www.detaillighting.co.uk
Product Type: 1, 2, 4, 7, 8, 9

DIFFUSE PORCELAIN LIGHTING
1 Jubilee Lane, Langford, Bedfordshire, SG18 9PH
Area of Operation: Worldwide
Tel: 01462 638331 **Fax:** 01462 638332
Email: light@diffuse.co.uk
Web: www.diffuse.co.uk **Product Type:** 3, 4
Other Info: ECO **Material Type:** F) 2

EASYLIGHTING
C/O Aladdins Lighting, The Street,
Long Stratton, Norwich, Norfolk, NR15 2XJ
Area of Operation: UK (Excluding Ireland)
Tel: 01508 532528 **Fax:** 07876 873062
Email: info@easylighting.co.uk
Web: www.easylighting.co.uk

ELECTRICALSHOP.NET
81 Kinson Road, Wallisdown,
Bournemouth, Dorset, BH10 4DG
Area of Operation: UK (Excluding Ireland)
Tel: 0870 027 3730 **Fax:** 0870 027 3731
Email: sales@electricalshop.net
Web: www.electricalshop.net
Product Type: 1, 2, 5, 7, 8, 13

ELECTRO TECHNIK
Bordesley Hall, Alvechurch, Birmingham, B48 7QA
Area of Operation: Worldwide
Tel: 01527 595349 **Fax:** 01527 595092
Email: alan@flpatents.co.uk
Web: www.snaplite.co.uk **Product Type:** 1, 8, 11

Snaplite

ELECTRO TECHNIK
Area of Operation: Worldwide
Tel: 01527 595349
Fax: 01527 595092
Email: alan@flpatents.co.uk
Web: www.snaplite.co.uk
Product Type: 1, 8

The award winning Snaplite range of Downlighters gives complete compliance to all Building Regulations without the need for covers or the removal of insulation. With its high specification, wide range of colours, Snaplite ensures that your installation is safe and attractive.

 picture
 children's
 colourful
  wall lights
 spot lights
ceiling lights
 garden

 contemporary
 traditional
 lampshades
 bathroom
 outdoor
 dining
 mirror

INTERIORS, FIXTURES & FINISHES

F W LIGHTING LTD
Unit 19, The Lays Business Centre, Charlton Road,
Keynsham, Bristol, Somerset, BS31 2SE
Area of Operation: UK & Ireland
Tel: 0117 986 7500
Fax: 0117 986 7600
Email: info@fw-lighting.co.uk
Web: www.fw-lighting.co.uk
Product Type: 1, 7, 8, 9, 11 **Other Info:** ✍ ☺

FLEXION OPTICAL FIBRE LTD
Flexion House, Shaw Wood Business Park, Shaw
Wood Way, Doncaster, South Yorkshire, DN2 5TB
Area of Operation: Worldwide
Tel: 01302 328282 **Fax:** 01302 739922
Email: info@flexionltd.co.uk
Web: www.flexionltd.co.uk **Product Type:** 10

FORMFOLLOWS
35 Matlock Road, Brighton, East Sussex, BN1 5BS
Area of Operation: Worldwide
Tel: 01273 550180 **Fax:** 01273 823995
Email: sk@formfollows.co.uk
Web: www.formfollows.co.uk ✍ **Other Info:** ☺

FUTURISTIC FIBRE OPTICS LTD
The Innovation Centre, Brunswick Street,
Nelson, Lancashire, BB9 0PQ
Area of Operation: UK (Excluding Ireland)
Tel: 01282 877177
Fax: 01282 877178
Email: ejl@f2olighting.com
Web: www.f2olighting.com **Product Type:** 10

GET PLC
Key Point, 3-17 High Street,
Potters Bar, Hertfordshire, EN6 5AJ
Area of Operation: Worldwide
Tel: 01707 601601 **Fax:** 01707 601701
Email: info@getplc.com
Web: www.getplc.com
Product Type: 1, 2, 4, 6, 7, 9, 12, 13

GET PLC
Area of Operation: Worldwide
Tel: 01707 601601 **Fax:** 01707 601701
Email: info @getplc.com
Web: www.getplc.com
Product Type: 1, 2, 4, 6, 7, 9, 11, 12

The new screwless range will add the perfect
finishing touch to a domestic or commercial
environment by offering an ultra slim high quality
alternative.

GIGB LIGHTING LTD
Innovator House, Bickland Water Road,
Falmouth, Cornwall, TR11 4RS
Area of Operation: UK & Ireland
Tel: 0845 402 0673 **Fax:** 01326 377773
Email: sales@gigb.co.uk
Web: www.gigb.co.uk ✍
Product Type: 1, 2, 4, 5, 6, 7, 8, 9, 12, 13

GJD MANUFACTURING LTD
Unit 2, Birch Industrial Estate, Whittle Lane,
Heywood, Lancashire, OL10 2SX
Area of Operation: Worldwide
Tel: 01706 363998 **Fax:** 01706 363991
Email: info@gjd.co.uk
Web: www.gjd.co.uk **Product Type:** 6

GLASS & LIGHTING STUDIO
56 The Tything, Worcester, Worcestershire, WR1 1JT
Area of Operation: UK & Ireland
Tel: 01905 26285 **Fax:** 01905 26285
Email: studio@glass-lighting.co.uk
Web: www.glass-lighting.co.uk **Product Type:** 3, 4

GOBBSMAK DESIGN LTD
Drill Hall, Meadow Place,
Crieff, Perth and Kinross, PH7 4DU
Area of Operation: Worldwide
Tel: 01764 655392 **Fax:** 01764 654300
Email: catrina@gobbsmak.co.uk
Web: www.gobbsmak.co.uk **Other Info:** ECO ✍ ☺

GREENBROOK ELECTRICAL PLC
West Road, Harlow, Essex, CM20 2BG
Area of Operation: Worldwide
Tel: 01279 772772 **Fax:** 01279 422007
Email: sales@greenbrook.co.uk
Web: www.greenbrook.co.uk
Product Type: 1, 2, 4, 5, 6, 7, 8, 12, 13

HOUSE ELECTRONIC LTD
97 Francisco Close, Hollyfields Park,
Chafford Hundred, Essex, RM16 6YE
Area of Operation: UK & Ireland
Tel: 01375 483595
Fax: 01375 483595
Email: info@houselectronic.co.uk
Web: www.houselectronic.co.uk
Product Type: 1, 3, 6, 7, 8, 9, 10

ICA LIGHTING
10 Newton Place, Glasgow, G3 7PR
Area of Operation: Worldwide
Tel: 0141 331 2366 **Fax:** 0141 353 3588
Email: info@icalighting.com
Web: www.icalighting.com
Product Type: 1, 2, 3, 4, 5, 6, 7, 8, 9, 10, 12, 13

IMPACT LIGHTING SERVICES LTD
1 Thatched Cottage, Herd Lane,
Corringham, Essex, SS17 9BH
Area of Operation: East England, Greater London,
South East England
Tel: 01375 361391 **Fax:** 01375 361392
Email: ray@impact-lighting.freeserve.co.uk
Product Type: 1, 2, 3, 4, 5, 6, 7, 8, 9, 10, 11

INTERACTIVE HOMES LTD
Unit 43, Centerprise House, New Greenham Park,
Thatcham, Berkshire, RG19 6HP
Area of Operation: UK (Excluding Ireland)
Tel: 01635 49111
Fax: 01635 40735
Email: sales@interactivehomes.co.uk
Web: www.interactivehomes.co.uk
Product Type: 1, 3, 4, 6, 7, 8, 9, 11
Material Type: C) 2, 3, 7, 9, 11, 12, 13, 14, 15, 16

ISAAC LORD LTD
West End Court, Suffield Road,
High Wycombe, Buckinghamshire, HP11 2JY
Area of Operation: East England, Greater London,
North East England, South East England, South West
England and South Wales
Tel: 01494 462121 **Fax:** 01494 461376
Email: info@isaaclord.co.uk
Web: www.isaaclord.co.uk ✍ **Product Type:** 2, 8

ITALIAN LIGHTING CENTRE
4 Meliden Road, Penarth,
Vale of Glamorgan, CF64 3UG
Area of Operation: Worldwide
Tel: 029 2025 9596 **Fax:** 07043 018474
Email: sales@italian-lighting-centre.co.uk
Web: www.italian-lighting-centre.co.uk ✍
Product Type: 1, 2, 3, 4, 8

JIM LAWRENCE LTD
Scotland Hall Farm, Stoke by Nayland,
Colchester, Essex, CO6 4QG
Area of Operation: UK (Excluding Ireland)
Tel: 01206 263459 **Fax:** 01206 262166
Email: sales@jim-lawrence.co.uk
Web: www.jim-lawrence.co.uk ✍
Product Type: 1, 3, 4, 7, 9

JOHN ARMISTEAD RESTORATIONS
Malham Cottage, Bellingdon,
Nr.Chesham, Buckinghamshire, HP5 2UR
Area of Operation: Worldwide
Tel: 01494 758209 **Fax:** 01494 758209
Email: j.armistead@ntlworld.com
Web: www.john-armistead-restorations.co.uk
Product Type: 3, 4 **Other Info:** ✍ ☺
Material Type: C) 7, 11, 12, 13, 14, 15, 16

JOHN GIBBONS
Montrose House, Willersey Road,
Badsey, Worcestershire, WR11 7HD
Area of Operation: Worldwide
Tel: 01386 830216 **Fax:** 01386 830216
Email: johngibbons@btconnect.com
Web: www.johngibbonslighting.com
Product Type: 3

KANSA LIGHTING
The Flour Mill, Wath Road, Elescar,
Barnsley, South Yorkshire, S74 8HW
Area of Operation: Worldwide
Tel: 01226 351484 **Fax:** 01226 743712
Email: johnd@kansacraft.co.uk
Product Type: 1, 3, 4, 5, 7

KASPAR SWANKEY
405, Goldhawk Road,
Hammersmith, West London, W6 0SA
Area of Operation: Worldwide
Tel: 020 8746 3586 **Fax:** 020 8746 3586
Email: kaspar@swankeypankey.com
Web: www.swankeypankey.com

KITCHEN SUPPLIES
East Chesters, North Way, Hillend Industrial Estate,
Dalgety Bay, Fife, KY11 9JA
Area of Operation: UK (Excluding Ireland)
Tel: 01383 824729
Email: sales@kitchensupplies.co.uk
Web: www.kitchensupplies.co.uk ✍
Product Type: 1, 4, 8

KNIGHT DESIGN LIGHTING
PO Box 15, Brackley, Northamptonshire, NN13 5YN
Area of Operation: UK & Ireland
Tel: 01280 851092
Fax: 01280 851093
Email: knightdesign@btconnect.com
Web: www.knightdesignlighting.co.uk
Product Type: 1, 2, 3, 4, 5, 7, 8, 9

LAMPHOLDER 2000 LTD
Unit 3 TU House, Thorpe Underwood,
Northampton, Northamptonshire, NN6 9PA
Area of Operation: UK (Excluding Ireland)
Tel: 01536 713642
Fax: 01536 713994
Email: bc@lampholder.co.uk
Web: www.lampholder.co.uk
Product Type: 1, 2, 4, 8, 11, 13

LAMPS & LIGHTING LTD
Bridgewater Court, Network 65 Business Park,
Burnley, Lancashire, BB11 5ST
Area of Operation: UK (Excluding Ireland)
Tel: 01282 448666 **Fax:** 01282 417703
Email: sales@lamps-lighting.co.uk
Web: www.lampslighting.co.uk ✍
Product Type: 1, 2, 3, 4, 5, 6, 7, 8, 9, 10, 11

LEAX LIGHTING CONTROLS
11 Mandeville Courtyard,
142 Battersea Park Road, London, SW11 4NB
Area of Operation: Europe
Tel: 0207 501 0880 **Fax:** 0207 501 0890
Email: simonh@leax.co.uk
Web: www.leax.co.uk **Product Type:** 1, 7, 8, 10, 11

LEIGH LIGHTING
1591-93 London Road,
Leigh On Sea, Essex, SS9 2SG
Area of Operation: Worldwide
Tel: 01702 477633 **Fax:** 01702 470112
Email: leighlighting@btconnect.com
Web: www.leighlighting.com
Product Type: 1, 3, 7, 8

LIGHT INNOVATION LTD
362 Kingston Road, Ewell, Epsom, Surrey, KT19 0DT
Area of Operation: Worldwide
Tel: 0208 873 1582 **Fax:** 0208 224 8949
Email: info@lightinnovation.com
Web: www.lightinnovation.com ✍
Product Type: 1, 2, 3, 4, 7, 8, 9, 10, 12, 13

LIGHT IQ LTD
1 Rylett Studios, 77 Rylett Crescent,
London, W12 9RP
Area of Operation: Europe
Tel: 020 87491900 **Fax:** 020 87491999
Email: philip@lightiq.com
Web: www.lightiq.com

LIGHT RIGHT LTD
SBC House, Restmor Way,
Wallington, Surrey, SM6 7AH
Area of Operation: Europe
Tel: 0208 255 2022 **Fax:** 0208 286 1900
Email: enquiries@lightright.co.uk
Product Type: 1, 3, 7, 8, 9

LIGHTING DIRECT 2U LIMITED
Venture Court, Broadlands,
Wolverhampton, West Midlands, WV10 6TB
Area of Operation: UK & Ireland
Tel: 0870 600 0076
Email: sales@lightingdirect2u.co.uk
Web: www.lightingdirect2u.co.uk ✍
Product Type: 3, 6, 7, 8, 9

LIGHTING FOR GARDENS LTD
20 Furmston Court, Letchworth Garden City,
Hertfordshire, SG6 1UJ
Area of Operation: UK (Excluding Ireland)
Tel: 01462 486777 **Fax:** 01462 480344
Email: sales@lightingforgardens.com
Web: www.lightingforgardens.com ✍
Product Type: 7

LIGHTINGFORYOU
Grange Farm, Pinley Green,
Claverdon, Warwickshire, CV35 8NA
Area of Operation: UK (Excluding Ireland)
Tel: 01926 842738 **Fax:** 01926 840114
Email: sales@lightingforyou.co.uk
Web: www.lightingforyou.co.uk ✍

LIGHTINGFORYOU

Area of Operation: UK (Excluding Ireland)
Tel: 01926 842738
Fax: 01926 840114
Email: sales@lightingforyou.co.uk
Web: www.lightingforyou.co.uk

Suppliers of High Quality Lighting.
E-brochure now available featuring: Multiple
Downlights, Fire Rated Downlights, LED Strips,
Light Shelves, Wardrobe Hanging Rail Lights and
much much more.

LIGHTINGWORKS.CO.UK
The Idea Works, New Road,
Gillingham, Dorset, SP8 4JH
Area of Operation: UK (Excluding Ireland)
Tel: 01747 822818
Fax: 01747 824469
Email: sales@lightingworks.co.uk
Web: www.lightingworks.co.uk ✍
Product Type: 1, 4 **Other Info:** ✍ ☺

LINOLITE DIRECT
Unit 25, Red Lion Road Business Park,
Surbiton, Surrey, KT6 7QD
Area of Operation: Worldwide
Tel: 0208 391 7474 **Fax:** 0208 391 7475
Email: linolite@cp-lighting.co.uk
Web: www.linolitedirect.co.uk
Product Type: 1, 2, 4, 8, 9, 13

LINOLITE DIRECT

Area of Operation: Worldwide
Tel: 0208 391 7474
Fax: 0208 391 7475
Email: linolite@cp-lighting.co.uk
Web: www.linolitedirect.co.uk
Product Type: 1, 2, 4, 8, 9, 12

Linolite are the leading manufacturer of quality bathroom light fittings. Now Linolite have introduced a full range of lights for the whole house. Veiw and order direct from the web

LINOLITE: SYLVANIA
Avis Way, Newhaven, East Sussex, BN9 0ED
Tel: 0870 606 2030 **Fax:** 0870 241 0803
Email: tamara.newman@sylvania-lighting.com
Web: www.sylvania-lighting.com
Product Type: 1, 4, 8, 13

LITETEC LTD
Technologies House, 507 Ashingdon Road,
Rochford, Essex, SS4 3HE
Area of Operation: Europe
Tel: 01702 540187 **Fax:** 01702 541049
Email: info@litetec.co.uk
Web: www.litetec.co.uk **Product Type:** 10

MALL ANTIQUES ARCADE
359 Upper Street, Islington, London, N1 0PD
Tel: 0207 351 5353 **Fax:** 0207 969 1639
Email: antique@dial.pipex.com
Web: www.themallantiques.co.uk
Product Type: 3, 4, 7 **Other Info:** ▽

MARL INTERNATIONAL LIMITED
Marl Business Park, Ulverston, Cumbria, LA12 9BN
Area of Operation: Worldwide
Tel: 01229 582430 **Fax:** 01229 585155
Email: sales@marl.co.uk **Web:** www.marl.co.uk ⌁
Product Type: 1, 2, 4, 6, 7, 8, 9

MARL INTERNATIONAL LTD
Area of Operation: Worldwide
Tel: 01229 582430
Fax: 01229 585155
Email: sales@marl.co.uk
Web: www.marl.co.uk

Marl Creative Arc is a groundbreaking concept that offers a total solution to architectural, retail and commercial lighting applications.

Marl Creative Arc has the experience and expertise to assist you in any process from initial concept through to design, manufacture and installation.

METCRAFT LIGHTING LIMITED
13a Gatesway Crescent, Oldham Broadway Business Park, Chadderton, Oldham, Lancashire, OL9 9XB
Area of Operation: Europe
Tel: 0161 683 4298
Fax: 0161 688 8004
Email: info@metcraftlighting.com
Web: www.metcraftlighting.com

MOONLIGHT DESIGN LTD
9 Essex Road, North Chingford,
Greater London, E4 6DG
Area of Operation: UK (Excluding Ireland)
Tel: 0208 925 8639
Email: enquiries@moonlightdesign.co.uk
Web: www.moonlightdesign.co.uk ⌁
Product Type: 7

MR RESISTOR
21 Lydden Road, Wandsworth, London, SW18 4LT
Area of Operation: Worldwide
Tel: 0208 874 2234 **Fax:** 0208 871 2262
Email: info@mr-resistor.co.uk
Web: www.mr-resistor.co.uk ⌁

MYFLOATINGWORLD.COM LIMITED
3 Hartlepool Court, Galleons Lock,
Royal Docks, London, E16 2RL
Area of Operation: Europe
Tel: 0870 777 0728
Fax: 0870 777 0729
Email: info@myfloatingworld.com
Web: www.myfloatingworld.com ⌁
Product Type: 1, 2, 3, 4, 8
Other Info: ✎

NIGEL TYAS HANDCRAFTED IRONWORK
Bullhouse Mill, Lee Lane, Millhouse Green,
Penistone, Sheffield, South Yorkshire, S36 6BE
Area of Operation: Worldwide
Tel: 01226 766618
Email: sales@nigeltyas.co.uk
Web: www.nigeltyas.co.uk **Product Type:** 1, 3, 8
Other Info: ✎ ✋ **Material Type:** C) 2, 6, 11

OLD FLAMES
30 Long Street, Easingwold,
York, North Yorkshire, YO61 3HT
Area of Operation: UK (Excluding Ireland)
Tel: 01347 821188 **Fax:** 01347 821188
Email: philiplynas@aol.com
Web: www.oldflames.co.uk ⌁ **Product Type:** 3

OPTIC LIGHTING LTD
The Innovation Centre, Brunswick Street,
Nelson, Lancashire, BB9 0PQ
Area of Operation: UK & Ireland
Tel: 01282 877171 **Fax:** 01282 877178
Email: info@opticlighting.co.uk
Web: www.opticlighting.co.uk ⌁
Product Type: 10

ORIGINAL
3 Festival Units, The Showground,
Bridgwater, Somerset, TA6 6LS
Area of Operation: South West England and South Wales
Tel: 0870 0110808 **Fax:** 0870 011 0606
Email: enquiries@obsc.co.uk **Web:** www.obsc.co.uk

OXFORD LIGHTING & ELECTRICAL SOLUTIONS
Unit 117, Culham Site No 1, Station Road,
Culham, Abingdon, Oxfordshire, OX14 3DA
Area of Operation: UK (Excluding Ireland)
Tel: 01865 408522 **Fax:** 01865 408522
Email: olessales@tiscali.co.uk
Web: www.oles.co.uk ⌁

PESTWEST ELECTRONICS
Denholme Drive, Ossett, West Yorkshire, WF5 9NB
Area of Operation: Worldwide
Tel: 01924 268500 **Fax:** 01924 273591
Email: info@pestwest.com
Web: www.pestwest.com **Product Type:** 13

PETER CARLSON INTERIORS
Lower Hillgate, Stockport, Cheshire, SK1 3AW
Area of Operation: North West England and North Wales
Tel: 0161 480 8164 **Fax:** 0161 480 0097
Email: petercarlson@petercarlson.co.uk
Web: www.petercarlson.co.uk

PLM ILLUMINATION
Unit 6 Arthur Drive, Hoo Farm Industrial Estate,
Kidderminster, Worcestershire, DY11 7RA
Area of Operation: Worldwide
Tel: 01562 66441
Fax: 01562 829992
Email: info@plmgroup.co.uk
Web: www.plmgroup.co.uk
Product Type: 1, 2, 5, 7, 8, 9, 10

POLARON PLC
26 Greenhill Crescent, Watford Business Park,
Watford, Hertfordshire, WD18 8XG
Area of Operation: UK (Excluding Ireland)
Tel: 01923 495495 **Fax:** 01923 228796
Email: arichards@polaron.co.uk
Web: www.polaron.com **Product Type:** 1, 2, 3, 4, 6, 8

PS INTERIORS
11 Cecil Road, Hale, Altrincham, Cheshire, WA15 9NY
Area of Operation: Europe
Tel: 0161 926 9398 **Fax:** 0161 929 0363
Email: sales@ps-interiors.co.uk
Web: www.ps-interiors.co.uk
Product Type: 2, 3, 4, 7, 8, 9, 11

QVS ELECTRICAL
4C The Birches Industrial Estate, Imberhorne Lane,
East Grinstead, West Sussex, RH19 1XZ
Area of Operation: Worldwide
Tel: 0800 197 6565 **Fax:** 0800 197 6566
Email: sales@qvsdirect.co.uk
Web: www.qvs.com ⌁
Product Type: 1, 2, 3, 4, 7, 8, 13

RAYLIGHT LTD
1 Cherry Trees, Stanbridge Road Terrace,
Leighton Buzzard, Bedfordshire, LU7 4QU
Area of Operation: Europe
Tel: 0845 170 5511 **Fax:** 01525 372255
Email: info@raylight.co.uk **Web:** www.raylight.co.uk
Product Type: 1, 2, 4, 7, 8, 9, 13

REINDEER ANTIQUES LTD
43 Watling Street, Pottersbury,
Northamptonshire, NN12 7QD
Tel: 01908 542407 **Fax:** 01908 542121
Email: sales@reindeerantiques.co.uk
Web: www.reindeerantiques.co.uk **Product Type:** 3

SCA DISTRIBUTORS LIMITED
PO Box 21, Barnet, Hertfordshire, EN5 4PR
Area of Operation: UK (Excluding Ireland)
Tel: 0208 441 2555 **Fax:** 0208 440 7839
Email: mail@scalights.co.uk
Web: www.scalights.co.uk
Product Type: 1, 2, 4, 5, 6, 7, 8, 9, 13

SHELDON COONEY
Chapel Glassworks, Leek Road, Cellarhead,
Werrington, Staffordshire, ST9 0DQ
Area of Operation: UK & Ireland
Tel: 01782 551699
Email: info@sheldoncooney.com
Web: www.sheldoncooney.com

SIMPLY STAINED
7 Farm Mews, Farm Road,
Brighton & Hove, East Sussex, BN3 1GH
Area of Operation: UK (Excluding Ireland)
Tel: 01273 220030
Email: david@simply-stained.co.uk
Web: www.simply-stained.co.uk
Product Type: 1, 3, 4, 7
Other Info: ▽ ✎ ✋ **Material Type:** E) 9

SMART HOUSE SOLUTIONS
7 Cricketer's Row, Brentwood, Essex, CM13 3QA
Area of Operation: UK & Ireland
Tel: 01277 264369 **Fax:** 01277 262143
Web: www.smarthousesolutions.co.uk
Product Type: 6

SMITHBROOK LIGHTING
Manfield Park, Cranleigh, Surrey, GU6 8PT
Area of Operation: UK & Ireland
Tel: 01483 272744 **Fax:** 01483 267863
Email: sales@smithbrooklighting.co.uk
Web: www.smithbrooklighting.co.uk
Product Type: 3, 4 **Material Type:** C) 5, 6, 11

STARSCAPE STAR CEILINGS
7 Main Street, Lowick, Berwick upon Tweed,
Northumberland, TD15 2UD
Area of Operation: Europe
Tel: 01289 388399
Email: enquiries@starceiling.co.uk
Web: www.starceiling.co.uk **Product Type:** 10

SYLVANIA LIGHTING INTERNATIONAL
Avis Way, Newhaven, East Sussex, BN9 0ED
Area of Operation: Europe
Tel: 0870 241 0802 **Fax:** 0870 241 0803
Email: lumiance.uk.info@sylviana-lighting.com
Web: www.sylviana-lighting.com
Product Type: 1, 3, 4, 5, 7, 8, 9

TENTERDEN HOUSE INTERIORS
4 West Cross, Tenterden, Kent, TN30 6JL
Area of Operation: Worldwide
Tel: 01580 764481 **Fax:** 01580 765531
Email: tenterdenhouseinteriors@hotmail.com
Product Type: 1, 3, 4, 7

THE AMERICAN FAN COMPANY
Unit 8c Castle End Business Park,
Ruscombe, Berkshire, RG10 9XQ
Area of Operation: UK (Excluding Ireland)
Tel: 0870 803 4025 **Fax:** 0870 803 4095
Email: sales@americanfan.co.uk
Web: www.americanfan.co.uk

THE BRADLEY COLLECTION
Lion Barn, Maitland Road,
Needham Market, Suffolk, IP6 8NS
Area of Operation: Worldwide
Tel: 01449 722724 **Fax:** 0845 118 7228
Email: claus.fortmann@bradleycollection.co.uk
Web: www.bradleycollection.co.uk
Product Type: 3, 4, 13 **Material Type:** C) 2, 3, 13

THE EXCITING LIGHTING COMPANY LTD
Unit 5 Sandyhill Industrial Estate, 43a Stratford Road,
Shirley, Solihull, West Midlands, B90 3LS
Area of Operation: UK (Excluding Ireland)
Tel: 0845 868 3652 **Fax:** 0845 868 3607
Email: enquiries@theexcitinglightingcompany.com
Web: www.theexcitinglightingcompany.com

THE GREEN SHOP
Cheltenham Road, Bisley,
Nr Stroud, Gloucestershire, GL6 7BX
Area of Operation: UK & Ireland
Tel: 01452 770629 **Fax:** 01452 770104
Email: paint@greenshop.co.uk
Web: www.greenshop.co.uk
Product Type: 7, 8, 12 **Other Info:** ECO

THE HOME & GARDEN CENTRE
Benfield ATT Group, Castle Way,
Caldicot, Monmouthshire, NP26 5PR
Area of Operation: UK (Excluding Ireland)
Tel: 01291 437062 **Fax:** 01291 437051
Email: info@homegardenshop.co.uk
Web: www.home-garden-centre.co.uk
Product Type: 4, 7, 12

TLC ELECTRICAL WHOLESALERS
TLC Building, Off Fleming Way,
Crawley, West Sussex, RH10 9JY
Area of Operation: Worldwide
Tel: 01293 565630 **Fax:** 01293 425234
Email: sales@tlc-direct.co.uk
Web: www.tlc-direct.co.uk
Product Type: 1, 2, 3, 5, 6, 7, 8, 9, 10, 11

VICTORIA HAMMOND INTERIORS
Bury Farm, Church Street, Bovingdon,
Hemel Hempstead, Hertfordshire, HP3 0LU
Area of Operation: UK (Excluding Ireland)
Tel: 01442 831641 **Fax:** 01442 831641
Email: victoria@victoriahammond.com
Web: www.victoriahammond.com
Product Type: 1, 2, 3, 4, 8

ZEN CUSTOM SOLUTIONS LTD
Unit 9, Brookfield Business Park, Clay Lane, York
Road, Market Weighton, North Yorkshire, YO43 3PU
Area of Operation: UK (Excluding Ireland)
Tel: 01430 803473 **Fax:** 01430 803473
Email: sales@zencs.co.uk **Web:** www.zencs.co.uk

LIGHTING ACCESSORIES & CONTROLS

KEY
SEE ALSO: ELECTRICAL - Electrical Fittings
PRODUCT TYPES: 1= Dolly Switches
2 = Rocker Switches 3 = Dimmer Switches
4 = Flat Plates 5 = Smart Lighting Systems
6 = Accessories 7 = Other
OTHER: ▽ Reclaimed ✍ On-line shopping
✍ Bespoke ✋ Hand-made ECO Ecological

ADV AUDIO VISUAL INSTALLATIONS LTD
12 York Place, Leeds, West Yorkshire, LS1 2DS
Area of Operation: North East England, North West
England and North Wales
Tel: 0870 199 5755
Email: shaun@adv-installs.co.uk
Web: www.homecinemainstalls.co.uk
Product Type: 5

ALL WEATHER LIGHTING LTD
Shrubbery Court, Cross Lane,
Bewdley, Worcestershire, DY12 2XF
Area of Operation: Europe
Tel: 01299 269246 **Fax:** 01299 269246
Email: chris@allweatherlighting.co.uk
Web: www.allweatherlighting.co.uk **Product Type:** 5

ARCHITECTURAL IRONMONGERY LTD
28 Kyrle Street, Ross-on-Wye, Herefordshire, HR9 7DB
Area of Operation: Worldwide
Tel: 01989 567946 **Fax:** 01989 567946
Email: info@arciron.co.uk
Web: www.arciron.com **Product Type:** 1, 2, 3, 4

AUDIO VENUE
36 Queen Street, Maidenhead, Berkshire, SL6 1HZ
Area of Operation: Greater London, South East
England, South West England and South Wales
Tel: 0208 567 8703 **Fax:** 01628 633654
Email: info@audiovenue.com
Web: www.audiovenue.co.uk **Product Type:** 3, 5

AUDIOFILE
27 Hockerill Street, Bishops Stortford,
Hertfordshire, CM23 2DH
Area of Operation: UK & Ireland
Tel: 01279 506576 **Fax:** 01279 506638
Email: info@audiofile.co.uk
Web: www.audiofile.co.uk **Product Type:** 5

B ROURKE & CO LTD
Vulcan Works, Accrington Road,
Burnley, Lancashire, BB11 5QD
Area of Operation: Worldwide
Tel: 01282 422841 **Fax:** 01282 458901
Email: info@rourkes.co.uk
Web: www.rourkes.co.uk

BESPOKE INSTALLATIONS
1 Rogers Close, Tiverton, Devon, EX16 6UW
Area of Operation: South West England and South Wales
Tel: 01884 243497
Email: michael@bespoke.biz
Web: www.bespoke.biz **Product Type:** 3, 4, 5, 6

BEYOND THE INVISIBLE LIMITED
162-164 Arthur Road, London, SW19 8AQ
Area of Operation: Greater London
Tel: 0870 740 5859 **Fax:** 0870 740 5860
Email: info@beyondtheinvisible.com
Web: www.beyondtheinvisible.com **Product Type:** 5

BLUE BEACON LIGHTING
Intermail Plc - Horizon West, Canal View Road,
Newbury, Berkshire, RG14 5XF
Area of Operation: UK & Ireland
Tel: 0870 241 3992 **Fax:** 01635 41678
Email: michaelm@crescent.co.uk
Web: www.bluebeacon.co.uk **Product Type:** 5

BLUE RIDGE ELECTRICAL SYSTEMS LTD
18 Ridge Drive, Rugby, Warwickshire, CV21 3FE
Tel: 01788 561701 **Fax:** 01788 536242
Email: sales@blueridge-electrical.com
Web: www.blueridge-electrical.com **Product Type:** 5

BURWOOD LIGHTING COMPANY LTD
Market Street, Exeter, Devon, EX1 1BW
Area of Operation: UK & Ireland
Tel: 01392 259367 **Fax:** 01392 210239
Email: sales@burwoodlighting.co.uk
Web: www.burwoodlighting.co.uk
Product Type: 1, 2, 3, 4, 5

CANDELA LTD
52 Spaces Business Centre,
Ingate Place, London, SW8 3NS
Area of Operation: Worldwide
Tel: 0207 720 4480 **Fax:** 0207 498 0026
Email: mail@candela.ltd.uk
Web: www.candela.ltd.uk
Product Type: 3, 5 **Other Info:** ✍

CHAOS DESIGN CONSULTANTS LTD
14 Queen Square, Bath, Somerset, BA1 2HN
Area of Operation: Worldwide
Tel: 01225 780044 **Fax:** 01225 780087
Email: sonja@chaosdc.co.uk
Web: www.chaosdc.co.uk **Other Info:** ✍

CHARLES MASON LTD
Unit 11A Brook Street Mill, Off Goodall Street,
Macclesfield, Cheshire, SK11 7AW
Area of Operation: Worldwide
Tel: 0800 085 3616 **Fax:** 01625 668789
Email: info@charles-mason.com
Web: www.charles-mason.com
Product Type: 1, 2, 3, 4

CLOUD9 SYSTEMS
87 Bishops Park Road, London, SW6 6DY
Area of Operation: Greater London, South East England
Tel: 0870 420 5495 **Fax:** 0870 402 0121
Email: info@cloud9systems.co.uk
Web: www.cloud9systems.co.uk **Product Type:** 5

COHERE LTD
10 Singleton Scarp, London, N12 7AR
Area of Operation: Europe **Tel:** 0845 456 0695
Email: info@wirefreeliving.com
Web: www.wirefreeliving.com **Product Type:** 5

CREO DESIGN
62 North Street, Leeds, West Yorkshire, LS2 7PN
Area of Operation: UK (Excluding Ireland)
Tel: 0113 246 7373 **Fax:** 0113 242 5114
Email: info@creo-designs.co.uk
Web: www.creo-designs.co.uk **Product Type:** 5

D&T ELECTRONICS
Unit 9A, Cranborne Industrial Estate, Cranborne
Road, Potters Bar, Hertfordshire, EN6 3JN
Area of Operation: UK (Excluding Ireland)
Tel: 0870 241 5891 **Fax:** 01707 653570
Email: info@dandt.co.uk **Web:** www.dandt.co.uk
Product Type: 5 **Other Info:** ✍

DANICO BRASS LTD
31-35 Winchester Road,
Swiss Cottage, London, NW3 3NR
Area of Operation: Worldwide
Tel: 0207 483 4477 **Fax:** 0207 722 7992
Email: sales@danico.co.uk
Product Type: 1, 2, 3, 4, 6, 7 **Other Info:** ✍

DANLERS LIMITED
Vincients Road, Bumpers Farm Industrial Estate,
Chippenham, Wiltshire, SN14 6NQ
Area of Operation: Europe
Tel: 01249 443377
Fax: 01249 443388
Email: sales@danlers.co.uk
Web: www.danlers.co.uk
Product Type: 3, 5

DBCC LIMITED
Woodland View, Winchester Road,
Fair Oak, Eastleigh, Hampshire, SO50 7HD
Area of Operation: UK (Excluding Ireland)
Tel: 02380 692 555
Email: info@dbcc.co.uk
Web: www.dbcc.co.uk
Product Type: 3, 5

DIGITAL DECOR
Sonas House, Button End, Harston,
Cambridge, Cambridgeshire, CB2 5NX
Area of Operation: East England, Greater London
Tel: 01223 870935
Fax: 01223 870935
Email: seamus@digital-decor.co.uk
Web: www.digital-decor.co.uk
Product Type: 5, 6

EAST TECHNOLOGY INTEGRATORS
85 Langtons Meadow, Farnham Common,
Slough, Berkshire, SL2 3NS
Area of Operation: Greater London, South East England
Tel: 01753 642367
Email: sales@east-ti.co.uk
Web: www.east-ti.co.uk
Product Type: 5

EASYLIGHTING
C/O Aladdins Lighting, The Street,
Long Stratton, Norwich, Norfolk, NR15 2XJ
Area of Operation: UK (Excluding Ireland)
Tel: 01508 532528
Fax: 07876 873062
Email: info@easylighting.co.uk
Web: www.easylighting.co.uk

F W LIGHTING LTD
Unit 19, The Lays Business Centre,
Charlton Road, Keynsham,
Bristol, Somerset, BS31 2SE
Area of Operation: UK & Ireland
Tel: 0117 986 7500
Fax: 0117 986 7600
Email: info@fw-lighting.co.uk
Web: www.fw-lighting.co.uk
Product Type: 1, 2, 3, 4, 5, 6
Other Info: ✍ ✋

FLAMINGBOX
Perry Farm, Maiden Bradley,
Wiltshire, BA12 7JQ
Area of Operation: UK (Excluding Ireland)
Tel: 01985 845440 **Fax:** 01985 845448
Email: info@flamingbox.com
Web: www.flamingbox.com
Product Type: 4
Other Info: ✍

FUTRONIX
Futronix House, 143 Croydon Road,
Caterham, Surrey, CR3 6PF
Area of Operation: Worldwide
Tel: 01883 373333
Fax: 01883 373335
Email: sales@futronix.info
Web: www.futronix.info
Product Type: 3, 5

GET PLC
Key Point, 3-17 High Street,
Potters Bar, Hertfordshire, EN6 5AJ
Area of Operation: Worldwide
Tel: 01707 601601
Fax: 01707 601701
Email: info@getplc.com
Web: www.getplc.com
Product Type: 3

GET PLC

Area of Operation: Worldwide
Tel: 01706 601601
Fax: 01707 601701
Email: info@getplc.com
Web: www.getplc.com
Product Type: 3

The stylish new Smart wireless lighting system allows users to control the entire lighting network in their home from one smart remote control unit.

GIGB LIGHTING LTD
Innovator House, Bickland Water Road,
Falmouth, Cornwall, TR11 4RS
Area of Operation: UK & Ireland
Tel: 0845 402 0673 Fax: 01326 377773
Email: sales@gigb.co.uk
Web: www.gigb.co.uk Product Type: 3, 5

GOBBSMAK DESIGN LTD
Drill Hall, Meadow Place,
Crieff, Perth and Kinross, PH7 4DU
Area of Operation: Worldwide
Tel: 01764 655392 Fax: 01764 654300
Email: catrina@gobbsmak.co.uk
Web: www.gobbsmak.co.uk
Product Type: 5 Other Info: ECO

GOLDSYSTEM LTD
46 Nightingale Lane, Bromley, Kent, BR1 2SB
Area of Operation: Greater London, South East England
Tel: 0208 313 0485 Fax: 0208 313 0665
Email: info@goldsystem.co.uk
Web: www.goldsystem.co.uk Product Type: 5

GRAHAMS HI-FI LTD
Canonbury Yard, 190a New North Road, London, N1 7BS
Area of Operation: Europe
Tel: 020 7226 5500 Email: enq@grahams.co.uk
Web: www.grahams.co.uk Product Type: 5

GREENBROOK ELECTRICAL PLC
West Road, Harlow, Essex, CM20 2BG
Area of Operation: Worldwide
Tel: 01279 772772 Fax: 01279 422007
Email: sales@greenbrook.co.uk
Web: www.greenbrook.co.uk Product Type: 2, 3

HAF DESIGNS LTD
HAF House, Mead Lane,
Hertford, Hertfordshire, SG13 7AP
Area of Operation: UK & Ireland
Tel: 0800 389 8821 Fax: 01992 505705
Email: info@hafltd.co.uk Product Type: 2, 3, 4
Web: www.hafdesigns.co.uk

HELVAR
Hawley Mill, Hawley Road, Dartford, Kent, DA2 7SY
Area of Operation: Worldwide
Tel: 01322 222211 Fax: 01322 282216
Email: gary.brown@helvar.com
Web: www.helvar.co.uk Product Type: 5

HOMETECH INTEGRATION LTD
Earlsgate House, 35 St. Ninian's Road,
Stirling, Stirlingshire, FK8 2HE
Area of Operation: UK (Excluding Ireland)
Tel: 0870 7661060 Fax: 0870 7661070
Email: info@hometechintegration.com
Web: www.hometechintegration.com
Product Type: 5

HOUSE ELECTRONIC LTD
97 Francisco Close, Hollyfields Park,
Chafford Hundred, Essex, RM16 6YE
Area of Operation: UK & Ireland
Tel: 01375 483595 Fax: 01375 483595
Email: info@houselectronic.co.uk
Web: www.houselectronic.co.uk
Product Type: 3, 4, 5 Other Info:

HOUSE OF BRASS
122 North Sherwood Street,
Nottingham, Nottinghamshire, NG1 4EF
Area of Operation: Worldwide
Tel: 0115 947 5430 Fax: 0115 947 5430
Email: sales@houseofbrass.co.uk
Web: www.houseofbrass.co.uk
Product Type: 1, 3, 4

ICA LIGHTING
10 Newton Place, Glasgow, G3 7PR
Area of Operation: Worldwide
Tel: 0141 331 2366 Fax: 0141 353 3588
Email: info@icalighting.com
Web: www.icalighting.com
Product Type: 1, 2, 3, 4, 5, 6, 7

IMPACT LIGHTING SERVICES LTD
1 Thatched Cottage, Herd Lane,
Corringham, Essex, SS17 9BH
Area of Operation: East England, Greater London, South East England
Tel: 01375 361391 Fax: 01375 361392
Email: ray@impact-lighting.freeserve.co.uk
Product Type: 3, 4, 5

INTELLIGENTHOME
Langham House, Suite 401,
302 Regent Street, London, W1B 3HH
Area of Operation: UK & Ireland
Tel: 0207 394 9344 Fax: 0207 252 3879
Email: sales.en@intelligenthome.co.uk
Web: www.intelligenthome.co.uk
Product Type: 2, 3, 5, 6

INTERACTIVE HOMES LTD
Unit 43, Centerprise House, New Greenham Park,
Thatcham, Berkshire, RG19 6HP
Area of Operation: UK (Excluding Ireland)
Tel: 01635 49111 Fax: 01635 40735
Email: sales@interactivehomes.co.uk
Web: www.interactivehomes.co.uk
Product Type: 3, 5

INTERCONNECTION
12 Chamberlayne Road, Moreton Hall Industrial
Estate, Bury St Edmunds, Suffolk, IP32 7EY
Area of Operation: East England
Tel: 01284 768676 Fax: 01284 767161
Email: info@interconnectionltd.co.uk
Web: www.interconnectionltd.co.uk
Product Type: 5

IQYOURHOME.COM LTD
Unit D10, Chaucer Business Park, Watery Lane,
Kemsing, Sevenoaks, Kent, TN15 6YU
Area of Operation: UK & Ireland
Tel: 01732 763888 Fax: 01732 763351
Email: info@iqyourhome.com
Web: www.iqyourhome.com Product Type: 5

IRONMONGERY DIRECT
Unit 2-3 Eldon Way Trading Estate,
Eldon Way, Hockley, Essex, SS5 4AD
Area of Operation: Worldwide
Tel: 01702 562770 Fax: 01702 562799
Email: sales@ironmongerydirect.com
Web: www.ironmongerydirect.com
Product Type: 3

JELLYBEAN CTRL LTD
Eagle House, Passfield Business Centre,
Lynchborough Road, Passfield, Hampshire, GU30 7SB
Area of Operation: UK (Excluding Ireland)
Tel: 01428 751729
Fax: 01428 751772
Email: david@jellybeanctrl.com
Web: www.jellybeanctrl.com
Product Type: 5

JIM LAWRENCE LTD
Scotland Hall Farm, Stoke by Nayland,
Colchester, Essex, CO6 4QG
Area of Operation: UK (Excluding Ireland)
Tel: 01206 263459 Fax: 01206 262166
Email: sales@jim-lawrence.co.uk
Web: www.jim-lawrence.co.uk
Product Type:

JOHN CLAYTON LIGHTING LTD
Worthingham House, Deep Lane,
Hagworthingham, Lincolnshire, PE23 4LZ
Area of Operation: Europe
Tel: 0800 389 6395 Fax: 0870 240 6417
Email: enquiries@jclighting.com
Web: www.flexidim.com Product Type: 5

KENT HOME CINEMA CENTRE
69 London Road, Southborough,
Tunbridge Wells, Kent, TN4 0PA
Area of Operation: UK & Ireland
Tel: 01892 535007 Fax: 01892 533334
Email: andrew@kenthomecinema.co.uk
Web: www.av-sales.co.uk
Product Type: 2, 3, 4, 5

KITCHEN SUPPLIES
East Chesters, North Way,
Hillend Industrial Estate, Dalgety Bay, Fife, KY11 9JA
Area of Operation: UK (Excluding Ireland)
Tel: 01383 824729
Email: sales@kitchensupplies.co.uk
Web: www.kitchensupplies.co.uk
Product Type: 6

KNIGHT DESIGN LIGHTING
PO Box 15, Brackley, Northamptonshire, NN13 5YN
Area of Operation: UK & Ireland
Tel: 01280 851092 Fax: 01280 851093
Email: knightdesign@btconnect.com
Web: www.knightdesignlighting.co.uk

LAMPS & LIGHTING LTD
Bridgewater Court, Network 65 Business Park,
Burnley, Lancashire, BB11 5ST
Area of Operation: UK (Excluding Ireland)
Tel: 01282 448666 Fax: 01282 417703
Email: sales@lamps-lighting.co.uk
Web: www.lampslighting.co.uk
Product Type: 3, 5

LEAX LIGHTING CONTROLS
11 Mandeville Courtyard,
142 Battersea Park Road, London, SW11 4NB
Area of Operation: Europe
Tel: 0207 501 0880 Fax: 0207 501 0890
Email: simonh@leax.co.uk
Web: www.leax.co.uk Product Type: 3, 5, 6

LIFESTYLE ELECTRONICS
Woodview, Castlebridge, County Wexfor, Ireland
Area of Operation: Europe
Tel: +353 (0)53 9159880 Fax: +353 (0)53 5919844
Email: lifestyle123@eircom.net
Product Type: 5 Other Info:

LIGHT INNOVATION LTD
362 Kingston Road, Ewell, Epsom, Surrey, KT19 0DT
Area of Operation: Worldwide
Tel: 0208 873 1582 Fax: 0208 224 8949
Email: info@lightinnovation.com
Web: www.lightinnovation.com
Product Type: 3, 6

LIGHTINGWORKS.CO.UK
The Idea Works, New Road,
Gillingham, Dorset, SP8 4JH
Area of Operation: UK (Excluding Ireland)
Tel: 01747 822818 Fax: 01747 824469
Email: sales@lightingworks.co.uk
Web: www.lightingworks.co.uk
Product Type: 6

LINK MEDIA SYSTEMS
68 St. John Street, London, EC1M 4DT
Area of Operation: UK (Excluding Ireland)
Tel: 0207 251 2638 Fax: 0207 251 2487
Email: sohan@linkmediasystems.com
Web: www.linkmediasystems.com
Product Type: 5

LUTRON EA LTD
Lutron House, 6 Sovereign Close,
Wapping, Greater London, E1W 3JF
Area of Operation: Worldwide
Tel: 0207 702 0657 Fax: 0207 480 6899
Email: lutronlondon@lutron.com
Web: www.lutron.com/europe
Product Type: 3, 5

MALL ANTIQUES ARCADE
359 Upper Street, Islington, London, N1 0PD
Area of Operation: Worldwide
Tel: 0207 351 5353 Fax: 0207 969 1639
Email: antique@dial.pipex.com
Web: www.themallantiques.co.uk
Product Type: 6

MARQUEE HOME LIMITED
Unit 6, Eversley Way, Thorpe Industrial Estate,
Egham, Surrey, TW20 8RF
Area of Operation: Greater London, South East England
Tel: 07004 567888 Fax: 07004 567788
Email: paulendersby@marqueehome.co.uk
Web: www.marqueehome.co.uk
Product Type: 2, 3, 4, 5, 6

MODE LIGHTING (UK) LTD
The Maltings, 63 High Street,
Ware, Hertfordshire, SG12 9AD
Area of Operation: Worldwide
Tel: 01920 462121 Fax: 01920 466881
Email: james.king@modelighting.co.uk
Web: www.modelighting.co.uk Product Type: 3, 5

MR RESISTOR
21 Lydden Road , Wandsworth, London, SW18 4LT
Area of Operation: Worldwide
Tel: 0208 874 2234 Fax: 0208 871 2262
Email: info@mr-resistor.co.uk
Web: www.mr-resistor.co.uk

OXFORD LIGHTING & ELECTRICAL SOLUTIONS
Unit 117, Culham Site No 1, Station Road,
Culham, Abingdon, Oxfordshire, OX14 3DA
Area of Operation: UK (Excluding Ireland)
Tel: 01865 408522 Fax: 01865 408522
Email: olessales@tiscali.co.uk
Web: www.oles.co.uk

PHILLSON LTD
144 Rickerscote Road, Stafford,
Staffordshire, ST17 4HE
Area of Operation: UK & Ireland
Tel: 0845 612 0128 Fax: 01477 535090
Email: info@phillson.co.uk
Web: www.phillson.co.uk Product Type: 5

POLARON PLC
26 Greenhill Crescent, Watford Business Park,
Watford, Hertfordshire, WD18 8XG
Area of Operation: UK (Excluding Ireland)
Tel: 01923 495495 Fax: 01923 228790
Email: arichards@polaron.com
Web: www.polaron.com Product Type: 5

PW TECHNOLOGIES
Windy House, Hutton Roof,
Carnforth, Lancashire, LA6 2PE
Area of Operation: UK (Excluding Ireland)
Tel: 01524 272400 Fax: 01524 272402
Email: info@pwtechnologies.co.uk
Web: www.pwtechnologies.co.uk

RAKO CONTROLS LTD
Slip 7, The Historic Dockyard, Chatham, Kent, ME4 4TE
Area of Operation: Worldwide
Tel: 0870 043 3905 Fax: 0870 043 3906
Email: sales@rakocontrols.com
Web: www.rakocontrols.com
Product Type: 4, 5, 6, 7

ROCOCO SYSTEMS & DESIGN
26 Danbury Street, London, N1 8JU
Area of Operation: Europe
Tel: 0207 454 1234 Fax: 0207 870 0888
Email: sales@rococosystems.com
Web: www.rococosystems.com
Product Type: 3, 5

SEISMIC INTERAUDIO
3 Maypole Drive, Kings Hill,
West Malling, Kent, ME19 4BP
Area of Operation: Europe
Tel: 0870 073 4764 **Fax:** 0870 073 4765
Email: info@seismic.co.uk
Web: www.seismic.co.uk **Product Type:** 5

SENSORY INTERNATIONAL LIMITED
48A London Road, Alderley Edge, Cheshire, SK9 7DZ
Area of Operation: Worldwide
Tel: 01625 584540
Fax: 01625 585789
Email: garyc@sensoryinternational.com
Web: www.sensoryinternational.com
Product Type: 5

SETSQUARE LTD
Valley Industries, Hadlow Road,
Tonbridge, Kent, TN11 0AH
Area of Operation: Worldwide
Tel: 01732 851888 **Fax:** 01732 851853
Email: mah@setsquare.co.uk
Web: www.setsquare.co.uk **Product Type:** 5

SMART HOUSE
23 Wornal Park, Menmarsh Road, Worminghall,
Aylesbury, Buckinghamshire, HP18 9PH
Area of Operation: Europe
Tel: 0845 053 3680 **Fax:** 0845 644 2713
Email: info@smarthouse.co.uk
Web: www.smarthouse.co.uk **Product Type:** 5

SMART HOUSE SOLUTIONS
7 Cricketer's Row, Brentwood, Essex, CM13 3QA
Area of Operation: UK & Ireland
Tel: 01277 264369 **Fax:** 01277 262143
Web: www.smarthousesolutions.co.uk
Product Type: 5

SMARTCOMM LTD
45 Cressex Enterprise Centre, Lincoln Road,
Cressex Business Park, High Wycombe,
Buckinghamshire, HP12 3RL
Area of Operation: Worldwide
Tel: 01494 471912 **Fax:** 01494 472464
Email: info@smartcomm.co.uk
Web: www.smartcomm.co.uk

SUB SYSTEMS INTEGRATION LTD
Studio 19, Hurlingham Studios,
Ranelagh Gardens, London, SW6 3PA
Area of Operation: Greater London
Tel: 0207 796 1459 **Fax:** 0207 796 1469
Email: info@sub.eu.com
Web: www.sub.eu.com **Product Type:** 5

TECCHO
Unit 19W, Kilroot Business Park,
Carrickfergus, Co. Antrim, BT38 7PR
Area of Operation: UK & Ireland
Tel: 0845 890 1150 **Fax:** 0870 063 4120
Email: enquiries@teccho.net
Web: www.teccho.net **Product Type:** 3, 5

THE BIG PICTURE -
AV & HOME CINEMA LIMITED
51 Sutton Road, Walsall, West Midlands, WS1 2PQ
Area of Operation: UK & Ireland
Tel: 01922 623000
Email: info@getthebigpicture.co.uk
Web: www.getthebigpicture.co.uk **Product Type:** 5

THE EDGE
90-92 Norwich Road, Ipswich, Suffolk, IP1 2NL
Area of Operation: UK (Excluding Ireland)
Tel: 01473 288211 **Fax:** 01473 288255
Email: nick@theedge.eu.com
Web: www.theedge.eu.com **Product Type:** 5

THE IVY HOUSE
The Ivy House, Cherry Trees,
Bridegate Lane, Hickling Pastures,
Melton Mowbray, Leicestershire, LE14 3QA
Area of Operation: East England, Midlands & Mid Wales
Tel: 01664 822628
Email: enquiries@the-ivy-house.com
Web: www.the-ivy-house.com **Product Type:** 5

THE MAJIK HOUSE COMPANY LTD
Unit J Mainline Industrial Estate,
Crooklands Road, Milnthorpe, Cumbria, LA7 7LR
Area of Operation: North East England, North West
England and North Wales
Tel: 0870 240 8350 **Fax:** 0870 240 8350
Email: tim@majikhouse.com
Web: www.majikhouse.com **Product Type:** 5, 6

THE MULTI ROOM COMPANY LTD
4 Churchill House, Churchill Road,
Cheltenham, Gloucestershire, GL53 7EG
Area of Operation: UK & Ireland
Tel: 01242 539100 **Fax:** 01242 539300
Email: info@multi-room.com
Web: www.multi-room.com **Product Type:** 5

THE THINKING HOME
The White House, Wilderspool Park,
Greenalls Avenue, Warrington, Cheshire, WA4 6HL
Area of Operation: UK & Ireland
Tel: 0800 881 8319 **Fax:** 0800 881 8329
Email: info@thethinkinghome.com
Web: www.thethinkinghome.com **Product Type:** 5

THINKINGBRICKS LTD
6 High Street, West Wickham,
Cambridge, Cambridgeshire, CB1 6RY
Area of Operation: UK & Ireland
Tel: 01223 290886
Email: ian@thinkingbricks.co.uk
Web: www.thinkingbricks.co.uk
Product Type: 5

TLC ELECTRICAL WHOLESALERS
TLC Building, Off Fleming Way,
Crawley, West Sussex, RH10 9JY
Area of Operation: Worldwide
Tel: 01293 565630 **Fax:** 01293 425234
Email: sales@tlc-direct.co.uk
Web: www.tlc-direct.co.uk
Product Type: 1, 2, 3, 4, 5, 6

TRIBUNE SMART HOME
321 Bolton Road, Manchester, M6 7GU
Area of Operation: UK (Excluding Ireland)
Tel: 0161 736 4011 **Fax:** 0161 736 8355
Email: info@tribunesmarthome.com
Web: www.tribunesmarthome.com **Product Type:** 5

VALTEK
Ardykeohane, Bruff, Co. Limerick, Ireland
Area of Operation: UK & Ireland
Tel: +353 (0)6138 2116 **Fax:** +353 (0)6138 2032
Email: sales@valtek.biz **Web:** www.valtek.biz
Product Type: 5

WANDSWORTH GROUP LTD
Albert Drive, Sheerwater, Woking, Surrey, GU21 5SE
Area of Operation: UK (Excluding Ireland)
Tel: 01483 713400 **Fax:** 01483 740384
Email: info@wandsworthgroup.com
Web: www.wandsworthgroup.com
Product Type: 1, 2, 3, 4, 5, 6

WEBSTRACT LTD
2-4 Place Farm, Wheathampstead,
Hertfordshire, AL4 8SB
Area of Operation: UK (Excluding Ireland)
Tel: 0870 446 0146 **Fax:** 0870 762 6431
Email: info@webstract.co.uk
Web: www.webstract.co.uk **Product Type:** 3, 5

WIRED FOR LIVING
19 Harwood Road, Rishton,
Blackburn, Lancashire, BB1 4DH
Area of Operation: UK (Excluding Ireland)
Tel: 07734 798771 **Fax:** 01254 399078
Email: info@wiredforliving.co.uk
Web: www.wiredforliving.co.uk **Product Type:** 5

ZEN CUSTOM SOLUTIONS LTD
Unit 9, Brookfield Business Park, Clay Lane, York
Road, Market Weighton, North Yorkshire, YO43 3PU
Area of Operation: UK (Excluding Ireland)
Tel: 01430 803473 **Fax:** 01430 803473
Email: sales@zencs.co.uk
Web: www.zencs.co.uk
Product Type: 5

NOTES

Company Name ....

Address ....

email ....

Web ....

Company Name ....

Address ....

email ....

Web ....

Company Name ....

Address ....

email ....

Web ....

Company Name ....

Address ....

email ....

Web ....

Company Name ....

Address ....

email ....

Web ....

Company Name ....

Address ....

email ....

Web ....

Company Name ....

Address ....

email ....

Web ....

Company Name ....

Address ....

email ....

Web ....

FLOOR & WALL FINISHES

Image courtesy of Goss Marble (0845 400 4677)

SPONSORED BY GOSS MARBLE
Tel 0845 400 4677 Web www.gossmarble.co.uk

GOSS
marble

Ceramic Floor Tiles

The use of ceramic tiles on the floor is becoming increasingly popular, largely thanks to underfloor heating systems which take away the cold feeling that bare feet dread.

The idea of heated ceramic floors is nothing new – the Romans were doing it 2,000 years ago. So why has it taken so long to catch on again? We can probably, in part, blame the British climate, which can make ceramic floors seem cold and slippery. But in reality, with the addition of underfloor heating, they make an ideal easy-care surface, perfect for the bathroom, kitchen, or conservatory, or even for the lounge, to give a really continental feel to your home.

A number of British manufacturers are now producing a wide and stylish range of floor tiles, which are designed to compete with the larger European factories. Here's a few of the options.

Encaustic tiles

Encaustic tiles are made by a technique similar to marquetry, except the clay is still in a semi-liquid state when the design is formed. First used in mediaeval times, the Victorians revived the skills by adapting ancient patterns, and laid the foundations of a massive tile industry. These designs are enjoying a revival, particularly as encaustic tiles are suitable for areas of heavy wear, such as hallways and kitchens.

Handmade tiles

Ceramic art has also enjoyed somewhat of a renaissance in recent years, which has led to a growth of small ceramic tile manufacturers. As is the nature of handmade tiles, you should expect variations in the colour and form of different tiles: imperfections such as pin holes in the glaze, uneven edges, and differing sizes only add to the uniqueness and desirability of handmade tiles. When choosing the tiles, mix the batch before laying, to prevent unwanted 'blocks' of colour forming on the floor.

Mosaic

One of the oldest forms of ceramic decoration for floors, some remarkable examples from the Roman and mediaeval periods still survive today. Employ a specialist tiler for an intricate, highly decorative effect, or lay your own simpler design.

Marble effect

A cost effective and hardwearing alternative to marble is marble effect tiles, which can look stunning in the right setting. Use them to create classically inspired tiling schemes, perhaps incorporating a border.

BELOW: Mosaics in the bathroom add an interesting detail - this example from Stonell Direct.
BELOW LEFT: For a completely individual finish, use a company who can digitally transfer images or prints of your choice onto tiles - H&R Johnson's *Artile* is an example of such a bespoke service.

Machine made tiles

Machine made tiles are mass produced from a compressed clay compound and display an even glaze, colour and shape. They are usually evenly sized with equal thickness and come at a reasonable price.

Top tips

- Before carrying out any new tiling work, it is essential that the surface to be tiled is sound, flat, dry, dust-free and completely stable. Remove all irregularities, weaknesses or unevenness and, if necessary, lay a sub floor to the receive tiles

- If you're tiling the floor yourself, remember that time spent in preparation is seldom wasted, and putting in the effort at an early stage will pay dividends later

- There are numerous books on the market which contain instructions for laying tiles, but if the design you choose is complicated, or you just don't feel up to tackling the job, employ an experienced tiler who will work to your specification

- When fixing, use a good quality adhesive and plan out your design early on, measuring each tile and remembering that handmade tiles are usually smaller than ones made by machine

- The type of grouting required depends on your choice of tiles. A coarse grain for wide joints will be needed for handmade tiles to compensate for irregular edges. Consider a contrasting grout on plain white tiles for an attractive, decorative effect

- With proper care and attention, a correctly installed, good quality ceramic floor tile should give you many years of trouble-free service. Grit is the biggest enemy of any floor material and a mat adjacent to doors is strongly recommended.

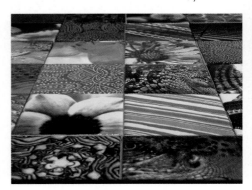

WOODEN FLOORING

KEY

PRODUCT TYPES: 1= Planks 2 = Boards
3 = Parquet 4 = Laminate 5 = Glue Free
Systems 6 = Other
OTHER: ▽ Reclaimed 🖐 On-line shopping
✎ Bespoke ✋ Hand-made ECO Ecological

1926 TRADING COMPANY LTD
2 Daimler Close, Royal Oak, Daventry,
Northamptonshire, NN11 8QJ
Area of Operation: UK & Ireland
Tel: 0800 587 2027 **Fax:** 01327 310123
Email: sales@1926woodflooring.co.uk
Web: www.1926woodflooring.co.uk
Product Type: 1, 2, 3, 4, 5, 6 **Other Info:** ECO ✎ ✋
Material Type: A) 1, 2, 3, 4, 5, 6, 7, 8, 9, 10, 14

AARDVARK WHOLESALE LTD
PO Box 3733, Dronfield, Derbyshire, S18 9AD
Area of Operation: UK (Excluding Ireland)
Tel: 07050 244219 **Fax:** 07050 323630
Email: aardvark@inbox.com
Product Type: 1, 2, 4, 5, 6 **Other Info:** ✎

AMTICO INTERNATIONAL
Solar Park, Southside, Solihull, West Midlands, B90 4SH
Area of Operation: Worldwide
Tel: 0121 745 0800 **Fax:** 0121 745 0888
Email: samples@amtico.com
Web: www.amtico.com

AMTICO INTERNATIONAL
Area of Operation: Worldwide
Tel: 0121 745 0800
Fax: 0121 745 0888
Email: samples@amtico.com
Web: www.amtico.com

Amtico International is the dominant supplier of
premium, resilient flooring in the UK, combining
the look of natural materials with the
performance benefits of vinyl

ATC (MONMOUTHSHIRE) LTD
Unit 2, Mayhill Industrial Estate,
Monmouth, Monmouthshire, NP25 3LX
Area of Operation: Worldwide
Tel: 01600 713036 **Fax:** 01600 715512
Email: info@floorsanddecking.com
Web: www.floorsanddecking.com 🖐
Product Type: 1, 2, 3, 6
Material Type: A) 2, 3, 5, 6, 7, 8, 9, 10, 12, 13

ATKINSON & KIRBY
2 Burscough Road, Ormskirk, Lancashire, L39 2XG
Area of Operation: UK & Ireland
Tel: 01695 573234 **Fax:** 01695 586902
Email: sales@akirby.co.uk
Web: www.akirby.co.uk
Product Type: 1, 2, 3, 5
Material Type: A) 1, 2, 3, 4, 5, 6, 7, 9, 10

ATKINSON & KIRBY LTD
Unit 4 Inwood Business Park,
Whitton Road, Hounslow, TW3 2EB
Area of Operation: UK (Excluding Ireland)
Tel: 0208 577 1100
Fax: 0208 577 0400
Email: james.double@akirby.co.uk
Web: www.akirby.co.uk **Product Type:** 1, 2, 3, 5, 6

BARBE & BALD LTD
112 Tudor Way, Hertford, Hertfordshire, SG14 2DL
Area of Operation: Worldwide
Tel: 01992 552783 **Fax:** 01992 552783
Email: mark@baldsbalm.co.uk
Web: www.baldsbalm.co.uk 🖐
Product Type: 1, 2, 3

BARHAM & SONS
58 Finchley Avenue, Mildenhall, Suffolk, IP28 7BG
Area of Operation: UK (Excluding Ireland)
Tel: 01638 711611
Fax: 01638 716688
Email: info@barhamwoodfloors.com
Web: www.barhamwoodfloors.com
Product Type: 1, 2

BATONS TO BEAMS
Unit 4, Pool Bank Park, Tarvin,
Chester, Cheshire, CH3 8JH
Area of Operation: UK & Ireland
Tel: 01829 741900 **Fax:** 01829 741101
Email: info@floor-works.co.uk
Web: www.floor-works.co.uk
Product Type: 1, 2, 3, 5, 6
Other Info: ▽ ECO ✎ ✋

BAYFIELD STAIR CO
Unit 4, Praed Road, Trafford Park,
Manchester, M17 1PQ
Area of Operation: Worldwide
Tel: 0161 848 0700
Fax: 0161 872 2230
Email: sales@bayfieldstairs.co.uk
Web: www.bayfieldstairs.co.uk
Product Type: 1, 2, 3, 5, 6

BHK FLOORING LTD
Davy Drive, North West Industrial Estate,
Peterlee, Durham, SR8 2JF
Area of Operation: UK & Ireland
Tel: 0191 518 6538 **Fax:** 0191 518 6536
Email: eleanor.smith@peterlee.bhk.de
Web: www.bhkonline.com
Product Type: 1, 2, 4, 5 **Other Info:** ECO

BLACK MOUNTAIN QUARRIES LTD
Howton Court, Pontrilas, Herefordshire, HR2 0BG
Area of Operation: UK & Ireland
Tel: 01981 241541
Email: info@blackmountainquarries.com
Web: www.blackmountainquarries.com 🖐

BONAKEMI LIMITED
1 Radian Court, Davy Avenue, Knowlhill,
Milton Keynes, Buckinghamshire, MK5 8PJ
Area of Operation: UK & Ireland
Tel: 01908 399740 **Fax:** 01908 232722
Email: info.uk@bona.com
Web: www.bona.com **Product Type:** 6

BROADLEAF TIMBER
Llandeilo Road Industrial Estate,
Carms, Carmarthenshire, SA18 3JG
Area of Operation: UK & Ireland
Tel: 01269 851910
Fax: 01269 851911
Email: sales@broadleaftimber.com
Web: www.broadleaftimber.com
Product Type: 1, 2, 3
Material Type: A) 2, 5, 7, 8, 10

CAMPBELL MARSON & COMPANY LTD
34 Wimbledon Business Centre,
Riverside Road, London, SW17 0BA
Area of Operation: UK & Ireland
Tel: 0871 222 7292
Fax: 0208 946 9395
Email: pippa@campbellmarson.com
Web: www.campbellmarson.com 🖐
Product Type: 1, 2, 3, 5

CANADA WOOD UK
PO Box 1, Farnborough, Hampshire, GU14 6WE
Area of Operation: UK & Ireland
Tel: 01252 522545
Fax: 01252 522546
Email: office@canadawooduk.org
Web: www.canadawood.info
Product Type: 1, 2
Material Type: A) 2, 3, 4, 5, 6, 7, 9

CHRISTIE TIMBER SERVICES LTD
New Victoria Sawmills, Bridgeness Road,
Bo'ness, Falkirk, EH51 9SG
Area of Operation: North East England, Scotland
Tel: 01506 828222
Fax: 01506 828226
Email: gordon@christie-timber.co.uk
Web: www.christie-timber.co.uk 🖐
Product Type: 2
Other Info: ✎ **Material Type:** A) 2, 3, 4, 5, 6

CITY BATHROOMS & KITCHENS
158 Longford Road, Longford,
Coventry, West Midlands, CV6 6DR
Area of Operation: UK & Ireland
Tel: 02476 365877
Fax: 02476 644992
Email: citybathrooms@hotmail.com
Web: www.citybathrooms.co.uk

CONSTRUCTION RESOURCES
16 Great Guildford Street, London, SE1 0HS
Area of Operation: UK (Excluding Ireland)
Tel: 0207 450 2211
Fax: 0207 450 2212
Email: info@constructionresources.com
Web: www.constructionresources.com
Product Type: 2, 3, 5

COUNTY HARDWOODS
Creech Mill, Mill Lane, Creech Saint Michael,
Taunton, Somerset, TA3 5PX
Area of Operation: UK & Ireland
Tel: 01823 443760
Fax: 01823 443940
Email: sales@countyhardwoods.co.uk
Web: www.countyhardwoods.co.uk 🖐
Product Type: 1, 2, 3, 5
Material Type: A) 2

**CRONINS RECLAMATION &
SOLID WOOD FLOORING**
Preston Farm Court, Lower Road,
Little Bookham, Surrey, KT23 4EF
Area of Operation: Worldwide
Tel: 0208 614 4370 **Fax:** 01932 241918
Email: dfc1@supanet.com
Web: www.croninsreclamation.co.uk
Product Type: 2

CSM CARPETS & FLOORING LTD
Brickmakers Arms Lane, Doddington,
Cambridgeshire, PE15 0TR
Area of Operation: East England
Tel: 01354 740727 **Fax:** 01354 740078
Email: alan.csm@virgin.net
Web: www.csm-flooring.co.uk
Product Type: 2, 4

DEACON & SANDYS
Apple Pie Farm, Cranbrook Road,
Benenden, Kent, TN17 4EU
Area of Operation: Worldwide
Tel: 01580 243331
Fax: 01580 243301
Email: pr@deaconandsandys.co.uk
Web: www.deaconandsandys.co.uk
Product Type: 2 **Material Type:** A) 2

DEVON HARDWOODS LTD
Dotton, Colaton Raleigh, Sidmouth, Devon, EX10 0JH
Area of Operation: South West England and South Wales
Tel: 01395 568991 **Fax:** 01395 567881
Email: sales@devonhardwoods.ltd.uk
Material Type: A) 2

THE ULTIMATE FINISHING TOUCH

marble ■ travertine ■ applestone ■ slate ■ granite ■ limestone

INTERIORS, FIXTURES & FINISHES - Floor & Wall Finishes - Wooden Flooring
SPONSORED BY: GOSS MARBLE   www.gossmarble.co.uk

INTERIORS, FIXTURES & FINISHES

DISNEY FLOORING LTD
Albert Avenue, Weston-Super-Mare,
Somerset, BS23 1YJ
Area of Operation: UK (Excluding Ireland)
Tel: 01934 615005
Fax: 01934 615006
Email: enquiries@disney-flooring.com
Web: www.disney-flooring.com
Product Type: 1, 2, 3, 4, 5   **Other Info:** ECO

E&B QUALITY FLOORING SUPPLIES
6 Beatrice Avenue, Dereham,
Yaxham Road, Norfolk, NR19 1AQ
Area of Operation: East England
Tel: 01362 695081   **Fax:** 01362 695088
Email: info@laminateafloor.co.uk
Web: www.laminateafloor.co.uk
Product Type: 4

ECO IMPACT LTD
50a Kew Green, Richmond,
Greater London, TW9 3BB
Area of Operation: UK & Ireland
Tel: 0208 940 7072
Fax: 0208 332 1218
Email: sales@ecoimpact.co.uk
Web: www.ecoimpact.co.uk
Product Type: 2, 3, 6   **Other Info:** ECO

ECOCHOICE TIMBER PRODUCTS
18 Charlton Lodge, Temple Fortune Lane,
London, NW11 7TY
Area of Operation: UK & Ireland
Tel: 0845 638 1340   **Fax:** 0870 286 3680
Email: info@ecochoice.co.uk
Web: www.ecochoice.co.uk
Other Info: ECO

EDEN NATURAL FLOORING
64 Wyle Cop, Shrewsbury, Shropshire, SY1 1UX
Area of Operation: Midlands & Mid Wales
Tel: 01743 340077
Email: hello@edennaturalflooring.com
Web: www.edennaturalflooring.com
Product Type: 1, 2, 3, 5, 6
Material Type: A) 1, 2, 3, 4, 5, 6, 7, 9, 10

EGGER (UK) LIMITED
Anick Grange Road, Hexham,
Northumberland, NE46 4JS
Area of Operation: UK & Ireland
Tel: 01434 602191
Fax: 01434 605103
Email: building.uk@egger.com
Web: www.egger.co.uk
Product Type: 6   **Material Type:** H) 1, 6

ENGLISH TIMBERS LTD
1A Main Street, Kirkburn, Driffield,
East Riding of Yorks, YO25 8NT
Area of Operation: UK & Ireland
Tel: 01377 229301   **Fax:** 01377 229303
Email: info@englishtimbers.co.uk
Web: www.englishtimbers.co.uk
Product Type: 1, 2   **Material Type:** A) 2, 3, 5, 6, 7

EUROPEAN HERITAGE
48-54 Dawes Road, Fulham, London, SW6 7EN
Area of Operation: Worldwide
Tel: 0207 381 6063   **Fax:** 0207 381 9534
Email: fulham@europeanheritage.co.uk
Web: www.europeanheritage.co.uk
Product Type: 1, 2, 5, 6
Material Type: A) 2, 3, 4, 5, 6, 9, 10

EVANS FLOORING
Pontyclerc, Penybanc Road, Ammanford,
Carmarthenshire, SA18 3HP
Area of Operation: UK & Ireland
Tel: 01269 591600
Fax: 01269 596116
Email: enquiries@evanshardwoodflooring.co.uk
Web: www.evanshardwoodflooring.co.uk
Product Type: 1, 2, 3, 5, 6

EXAKT PRECISION TOOLS LTD
Midmill Business Park, Tumulus Way,
Kintore, Aberdeenshire, AB51 0TG
Area of Operation: Europe
Tel: 01467 633800   **Fax:** 01467 633900
Email: info@exaktpt.com
Web: www.exaktpt.com   **Product Type:** 3, 4, 6

FIBRE - NATURAL FLOOR COVERINGS
149 London Road, Worcester,
Worcestershire, WR5 2ED
Area of Operation: UK (Excluding Ireland)
Tel: 01905 728 111 ·
Fax: 01905 764 766
Email: sales@fibretrading.co.uk
Web: www.fibretrading.co.uk
Product Type: 1, 2   **Material Type:** A) 2

FINE OAK FLOORING
94 Kings Road, London Colney,
St Albans, Hertfordshire, AL2 1EP
Area of Operation: UK (Excluding Ireland)
Tel: 01727 826500
Fax: 01727 826500
Email: erik@fineoakflooring.co.uk
Web: www.fineoakflooring.co.uk
Product Type: 1

FITZROY JOINERY
Garden Close, Langage Industrial Estate,
Plympton, Plymouth, Devon, PL7 5EU
Area of Operation: UK & Ireland
Tel: 0870 428 9110
Fax: 0870 428 9111
Email: admin@fitzroy.co.uk
Web: www.fitzroyjoinery.co.uk   **Product Type:** 4
Other Info: ECO   **Material Type:** A) 2

FLOORBRAND
Cavendish Business Centre, High Street Green,
Sible Hedingham, Essex, CO9 3LH
Area of Operation: Europe
Tel: 0845 1668001   **Fax:** 0845 166 8002
Email: sales@floorbrand.com
Web: www.floorbrand.com   **Product Type:** 3, 4, 5

FLOORCO
Aston House, Higham Business Park, Bury Close,
Higham Ferrers, Northamptonshire, NN10 8HQ
Area of Operation: UK (Excluding Ireland)
Tel: 01933 418899   **Fax:** 01933 417470

FLOORS AND DOORS DIRECT
Unit 7 Blaydon Trade Park, Toll Bridge Road,
Blaydob, Tyne & Wear, NE21 5TR
Area of Operation: North East England
Tel: 0191 414 5055   **Fax:** 0191 414 5066
Email: fddbleydon@aol.co.uk
Web: www.floorsanddoorsdirect.co.uk
Product Type: 1, 2, 4

FLOORS GALORE
Unit 5E, Centurion Park, Kendal Road,
Shrewsbury, Shropshire, SY1 4EH
Area of Operation: UK & Ireland
Tel: 0800 083 0623
Email: info@floors-galore.co.uk
Web: www.floors-galore.co.uk
Product Type: 1, 2, 3, 4, 5, 6
Material Type: A) 1, 2, 3, 4, 5, 6, 7, 8, 9, 10, 11, 12, 13, 14

FLOORS-2-GO
140 Stores Nationwide
Area of Operation: UK & Ireland
Tel: 08000 830330   **Email:** info@floors2go.co.uk
Web: www.floors2go.co.uk
Product Type: 1, 2, 3, 4, 5

FLOORSDIRECT
Unit 6, Fountain Drive, Hertford,
Hertfordshire, SG13 7UB
Area of Operation: UK (Excluding Ireland)
Tel: 01992 552447   **Fax:** 01992 558760
Email: jenny@floorsdirect.co.uk
Web: www.floorsdirect.co.uk
Product Type: 1, 4, 5, 6
Material Type: A) 1, 2, 3, 4, 5, 6, 7, 9

FLOORTECK LTD
10 Reservoir Close, Northfield, Northfield,
Birmingham, West Midlands, B31 1TW
Area of Operation: UK (Excluding Ireland)
Tel: 0121 476 6271   **Fax:** 0121 476 6271
Email: sarahcollier@go.com
Product Type: 1, 2, 3, 4, 5, 6

FLOORZ.CO.UK
Unit 13 Spa Industrial Estate, Longfield Road, North
Farm Estate, Tunbridge Wells, Kent, TN2 3EY
Area of Operation: UK & Ireland
Tel: 01892 678866   **Fax:** 01892 678856
Email: info@floorz.co.uk   **Web:** www.floorz.co.uk
Product Type: 1, 2, 6   **Other Info:**

FORBO FLOORING
PO Box 1, Den Road, Kirkclady, Fife, KY1 2SB
Area of Operation: Worldwide
Tel: 01592 643777   **Fax:** 01592 643999
Email: info.uk@forbo.com
Web: www.forbo-flooring.co.uk

FOREST INSIGHT
East Farm, Knook, Warminster, Wiltshire, BA12 0JG
Area of Operation: UK (Excluding Ireland)
Tel: 01985 850 088   **Fax:** 01985 850185
Email: nick@forestinsight.co.uk
Web: www.forestinsight.co.uk

FRENCH FLOORS
8 Balmore Wood, Luton, Bedfordshire, LU3 4EP
Area of Operation: UK (Excluding Ireland)
Tel: 07702 322597
Fax: 01582 490224
Email: frenchfloors@yahoo.co.uk
Web: www.frenchfloors.co.uk
Product Type: 1, 2, 3

FRENCH PARQUET DIRECT LTD.
Woodhead House, Sorn, Ayrshire, KA5 6JA
Area of Operation: Europe
Tel: 01290 559028   **Fax:** 01290 559188
Email: enquiries@frenchparquet.com
Web: www.frenchparquet.com
Product Type: 1, 2, 3
Other Info: ECO   **Material Type:** A) 2, 8

HARDWOOD FLOOR STORE
North Way, Hillend Industrial Estate,
Dalgety Bay, Fife, KY11 9JA
Area of Operation: UK (Excluding Ireland)
Tel: 01383 824729
Email: sales@hardwoodfloorstore.co.uk
Web: www.hardwoodfloorstore.co.uk
Product Type: 1, 2, 3, 4

HENRY VENABLES TIMBER LTD
Tollgate Drive, Tollgate Industrial Estate,
Stafford, Staffordshire, ST16 3HS
Area of Operation: UK (Excluding Ireland)
Tel: 01785 270600   **Fax:** 01785 270626
Email: enquiries@henryvenables.co.uk
Web: www.henryvenables.co.uk   **Product Type:** 1, 2

HITT OAK LTD
10 Park Parade, Gunnersbury Avenue, London, W3 9BD
Area of Operation: UK (Excluding Ireland)
Tel: 0208 8961900   **Fax:** 0208 8961900
Email: zhitas@yahoo.co.uk   **Product Type:** 1, 2, 3, 4

HONEYSUCKLE BOTTOM SAWMILL LTD
Honeysuckle Bottom, Green Dene, East Horsley,
Leatherhead, Surrey, KT24 5TD
Area of Operation: Greater London, South East England
Tel: 01483 282394   **Fax:** 01483 282394
Email: honeysucklemill@aol.com
Web: www.easisites.co.uk/honeysucklebottomsawmill
Product Type: 2

HOPPINGS SOFTWOOD PRODUCTS
The Woodyard, Epping Road,
Epping, Essex, CM16 6TT
Area of Operation: South East England
Tel: 01992 578877   **Fax:** 01992 563185
Email: sales@hoppings.co.uk
Web: www.hoppings.co.uk
Product Type: 1   **Other Info:** ECO

INTERIORS, FIXTURES & FINISHES - Floor & Wall Finishes - Wooden Flooring
SPONSORED BY: GOSS MARBLE www.gossmarble.co.uk

INTERIORS, FIXTURES & FINISHES

Designed for Generations

The original laminate flooring from Sweden with real guarantee.

For a brochure on flooring ideas and stockist list, call 0800 374771.

www.pergo.com

PERGO Expression

Floors with a bevelled edge for a new and modern expression .

PERGO Country

A modern rustic with bevelled edges.

PERGO Naturaltouch

A wooden floor feeling without the worries.

PERGO Vintage

A floor with an antique textured surface.

PERGO Modern Tile

Mix, match and design your own floor.

PERGO Exotic

Exotic designs with an exclusive ploished finish,

PERGO Original

Pure and elegant floors with the spirit of Scandinavian design

PERGO Classic Plus

The essential elegance of classic wood designs

4-in-1 Molding

4 different flooring transitions in a single package; T-moldings, hard surafce reducer, acrpet transition amd end moldings.
No glue necessary. Just snap parts together and push the assembly into the track.

simple
SOLUTIONS
FLOORING ACCESSORIES

PERGO quality goes beyond the installed floor. With our complete accessory assortment we offer that perfect look you can expect from a PERGO floor.

HYPERION TILES
67 High Street , Ascot, Berkshire, SL5 7HP
Area of Operation: Greater London, South East England
Tel: 01344 620211 **Fax:** 01344 620100
Email: graham@hyperiontiles.com
Web: www.hyperiontiles.com
Product Type: 1, 2, 3, 4, 5, 6

JOHN FLEMING & CO LTD
Silverburn Place, Bridge of Don,
Aberdeen, Aberdeenshire, AB23 8EG
Area of Operation: Scotland
Tel: 0800 085 8728 **Fax:** 01224 825377
Email: info@johnfleming.co.uk
Web: www.johnfleming.co.uk **Product Type:** 2, 4

JUNCKERS LTD
Unit A,1 Wheaton Road, Witham, Essex, CM8 3UJ
Area of Operation: UK & Ireland
Tel: 01376 534700 **Fax:** 01376 514401
Email: sales@junckers.co.uk
Web: www.junckers.com **Product Type:** 1, 2, 3, 5
Other Info: ECO **Material Type:** A) 2, 4, 6, 11

KAHRS (UK) LTD
Unit 2 West, 68 Bognor Road,
Chichester, West Sussex, PO19 8NS
Area of Operation: UK & Ireland
Tel: 01243 778747 **Fax:** 01243 531237
Email: sales@kahrs.co.uk
Web: www.kahrs.co.uk
Product Type: 1, 2, 3, 5 **Other Info:** ECO
Material Type: A) 2, 3, 4, 5, 6, 7, 9, 14

KARELIA WOOD FLOORING
Havenhurst Mill, Bexhill Road, St Leonards-on-Sea,
East Sussex, TN38 0AJ
Area of Operation: UK (Excluding Ireland)
Tel: 01424 456805 **Fax:** 01424 440505
Email: enquiries@kareliawoodflooring-uk.com
Web: www.kareliaparketti.com
Product Type: 1, 2, 3, 4, 5

KITCHEN SUPPLIES
East Chesters, North Way,
Hillend Industrial Estate, Dalgety Bay, Fife, KY11 9JA
Area of Operation: UK (Excluding Ireland)
Tel: 01383 824729
Email: sales@kitchensupplies.co.uk
Web: www.kitchensupplies.co.uk
Product Type: 1, 2, 3, 4, 5

LAMBETH DIXON
Unit 5, Drury Drive, Wood Hall Business Park,
Sudbury, Suffolk, CO10 1WH
Area of Operation: UK (Excluding Ireland)
Tel: 01787 379311
Fax: 01787 379344
Email: lambeth.dixon@btconnect.com
Product Type: 1, 2, 3, 4

LAWSONS
Gorst Lane, Off New Lane,
Burscough, Ormskirk, Lancashire, L40 0RS
Area of Operation: Worldwide
Tel: 01704 893998
Fax: 01704 892526
Email: info@traditionaltimber.co.uk
Web: www.traditionaltimber.co.uk

LEGACY FLOORS
Grange Lane, Winsford, Cheshire, CW7 2PS
Area of Operation: Worldwide
Tel: 0870 607 9080 **Web:** www.legacyfloors.com
Product Type: 2, 3, 6

MCKAY FLOORING LTD
8 Harmony Square, Govan, City of Glasgow, G51 3LW
Area of Operation: UK & Ireland
Tel: 0141 440 1586 **Fax:** 0141 425 1020
Email: enquiries@mckayflooring.co.uk
Web: www.mckayflooring.co.uk
Product Type: 1, 2, 3, 4, 5, 6
Other Info: ▽ ECO
Material Type: A)1, 2, 3, 4, 5, 6, 7, 8, 9, 10, 11, 12, 13, 14, 15

Don't Forget !

You can use the materials key at the beginning of this Handbook to get much more information from a company's listing.

MERCIA FLOORING
59 The Square, Dunchurch,
Rugby, Warwickshire, CV22 6NU
Area of Operation: UK (Excluding Ireland)
Tel: 01788 522168 **Fax:** 01788 811847
Email: sales@merciaflooring.co.uk
Web: www.merciaflooring.co.uk
Product Type: 1, 2, 3, 4, 5

MIDLANDS SLATE & TILE
Units 9-12, Star Industrial Estate,
Chadwell St Mary, Essex, RM16 4LR
Area of Operation: UK & Ireland
Tel: 0871 4743185 **Fax:** 01375 846478
Email: mark@slate-tile-brick.co.uk
Web: www.slate-tile-brick.co.uk
Product Type: 1, 2, 3, 4
Material Type: A) 1, 2, 5, 7

MIDLANDS SLATE & TILE
Area of Operation: UK & Ireland
Tel: 0871 4743185
Fax: 01375 846478
Email: mark@slate-tile-brick.co.uk
Web: www.slate-tile-brick.co.uk

A solid wooden floor in oak or pine, is an enhancement to any property and will mature and adapt to any future change in style.

MULTITOP FLOOR LTD
Transpoint, Doncaster Road, Kirk Sandall,
Doncaster, South Yorkshire, DN3 1HT
Tel: 01302 888800 **Fax:** 01302 888899
Email: info@multitopfloorltd.com
Web: www.multitopfloorltd.com
Product Type: 1, 5 **Material Type:** A) 1, 2, 3, 5, 7

N&C NICOBOND
41-51 Freshwater Road,
Chadwell Heath, Romford, Essex, RM8 1SP
Tel: 0208 586 4600 **Fax:** 0208 586 4646
Email: info@nichollsandclarke.com
Web: www.ncdirect.co.uk

FLOORS-2-GO
WORKING WITH YOUR BUSINESS

engineered wood: OAK COGNAC

With **interest free credit*** and **low prices**, your dream floor's closer than you think

As the UK's largest real wood and laminate flooring specialist, we stock over 100 beautiful floors. What's more, we guarantee that we won't be beaten on price, and offer a range of finance options to make the floor of your dreams even more accessible.

To find out more call freephone 08000 830 830 or visit us at www.floors2go.co.uk to find your local store.

*0% APR (Typical) Finance available on orders over £280. Subject to status, terms and conditions apply.

More than 140 stores across the uk
www.floors2go.co.uk

NATURAL FLOORING
152-154 Wellingborough Road,
Northampton, Northamptonshire, NN1 4DT
Area of Operation: UK (Excluding Ireland)
Tel: 01604 239238
Fax: 01604 627799
Email: sales@naturalflooring.co.uk
Web: www.naturalflooring.co.uk

NATURAL IMAGE (GRANITE, MARBLE, STONE)
Station Road, Staplehurst, Kent, TN12 0QD
Area of Operation: UK & Ireland
Tel: 01580 895489 **Fax:** 01580 893720
Web: www.naturalimage.co.uk
Product Type: 1, 2

NORTH YORKSHIRE TIMBER
Standard House, Thurston Road,
Northallerton Business Park,
Northallerton, North Yorkshire, DL6 2NA
Area of Operation: UK (Excluding Ireland)
Tel: 01609 780777 **Fax:** 01609 777888
Email: sales@nytimber.co.uk
Web: www.nytimber.co.uk

OAKBEAMS.COM
Hunterswood Farm, Alfold Road,
Dunsfold, Godalming, Surrey, GU8 4NP
Area of Operation: Worldwide
Tel: 01483 200477
Email: info@oakbeams.com
Web: www.oakbeams.com **Product Type:** 2

ORIGINAL
3 Festival Units, The Showground,
Bridgwater, Somerset, TA6 6LS
Area of Operation: South West England and South Wales
Tel: 0870 0110808 **Fax:** 0870 011 0606
Email: enquiries@obsc.co.uk
Web: www.obsc.co.uk

ORIGINAL OAK
Ashlands, Burwash, East Sussex, TN19 7HS
Area of Operation: UK (Excluding Ireland)
Tel: 01435 882228 **Fax:** 01435 882228
Web: www.originaloak.co.uk **Material Type:** A) 2

OSMO UK LTD
Unit 24 Anglo Business Park, Smeaton Close,
Aylesbury, Buckinghamshire, HP19 8UP
Area of Operation: UK & Ireland
Tel: 01296 481220 **Fax:** 01296 424090
Email: info@osmouk.com
Web: www.osmouk.com **Product Type:** 1, 2, 3, 4, 5

PARQUET & GENERAL FLOORING CO. LTD.
Grange Lane, Winsford, Cheshire, CW7 2PS
Area of Operation: UK (Excluding Ireland)
Tel: 01606 861442 **Fax:** 01606 861445
Email: floors@wideboards.com
Web: www.wideboards.com
Product Type: 1, 2, 3, 5, 6
Material Type: A) 2, 3, 4, 5, 6, 7, 8, 9, 10, 11, 12, 13, 14

PENNY BRICKS & TIMBER LIMITED
The Old Timber Yard, York Road,
Wetherby, West Yorkshire, LS22 5EF
Area of Operation: UK (Excluding Ireland)
Tel: 01937 580580 **Fax:** 01937 580587
Email: pw@penny-bricks.co.uk
Web: www.penny-bricks.co.uk
Product Type: 1, 2, 4, 5

PERGO LTD
PO Box 13113, Kingsbury Link,
Piccadilly, Tamworth, Staffordshire, B77 9DJ
Area of Operation: Worldwide
Tel: 01827 871840 **Fax:** 01827 871850
Email: cc.uk@pergo.com **Web:** www.pergo.com
Product Type: 1, 4, 5, 6 **Other Info:** ECO

PETER CARLSON INTERIORS
Lower Hillgate, Stockport, Cheshire, SK1 3AW
Area of Operation: North West England and North Wales
Tel: 0161 480 8164 **Fax:** 0161 480 0097
Email: petercarlson@petercarlson.co.uk
Web: www.petercarlson.co.uk
Product Type: 1, 2, 3, 4, 5

PETERSONS NATURAL FLOORINGS
Unit 10/11 Woodlands Park Industrial Estate,
Short Thorn Road, Stratton Strawless,
Norwich, Norfolk, NR10 5NU
Area of Operation: UK & Ireland
Tel: 01603 755511
Fax: 01603 755019
Email: office@petersons-natural-floorings.co.uk
Web: www.petersons-natural-floorings.co.uk
Product Type: 2 **Other Info:** ECO
Material Type: A) 2, 4, 6, 8

PILKINGTON'S TILES GROUP
PO Box 4, Clifton Junction, Manchester, M27 8LP
Area of Operation: UK (Excluding Ireland)
Tel: 0161 727 1000 **Fax:** 0161 727 1122
Email: sales@pilkingtons.com
Web: www.pilkingtons.com **Other Info:** ✐

PRIORY HARDWOODS LIMITED
Unit 57 Bowers Mill, Branch Road,
Barkisland, West Yorkshire, HX4 0AD
Area of Operation: UK (Excluding Ireland)
Tel: 01422 311 700 **Fax:** 01422 311 118
Email: info@prioryhardwoods.com
Web: www.prioryhardwoods.com

PURE PROJECTS
Repose Toi, Huberts Lane, Doyle Road,
St Peter Port, Guernsey, GY1 1RG
Area of Operation: Europe
Tel: 01481 730773 **Fax:** 01481 730773
Email: info@pure-projects.co.uk
Web: www.pure-projects.co.uk
Product Type: 1, 2, 3

R&D MARKETING (DEMISTA) LTD
Land House, Anyards Road,
Cobham, Surrey, KT11 2LW
Area of Operation: Worldwide
Tel: 01932 866600 **Fax:** 01932 866 688
Email: rd@demista.co.uk **Web:** www.demista.co.uk

ECOMAT™

Area of Operation: Worldwide
Tel: 01932 866600 **Fax:** 01932 866688
Email: rd@demista.co.uk
Web: www.demista.co.uk
Product Type: 1, 2, 4, 6

ECOMAT™ ultra thin heating elements are ideal
beneath laminate and wood floor surfaces.
Advantages include: even distribution giving
gentle overall warmth; simple installation;
maintenance free; 10 year guarantee.

RED ROSE PLASTICS (BURNLEY) LTD
Parliament Street, Burnley, Lancashire, BB11 3JT
Area of Operation: East England, North East
England, North West England and North Wales
Tel: 01282 724600 **Fax:** 01282 724644
Email: info@redroseplastics.co.uk
Web: www.redroseplastics.co.uk
Product Type: 1, 4, 5 **Other Info:** ECO

REDLAM TIMBERS LTD
PO Box 1908, Meriden,
Coventry, Warwickshire, CV7 7YR
Area of Operation: UK (Excluding Ireland)
Tel: 01676 521222 **Fax:** 01676 521221
Email: darrenwabrown@btinternet.com
Web: www.redlam-flooring.co.uk
Other Info: ECO **Material Type:** A) 2, 4, 5

FLOORS-2-GO
WORKING WITH YOUR BUSINESS

real wood: MAPLE

With the **UK's largest range** of laminate & real wood floors, and **140 stores nationwide** we've got the floor you're looking for

With hundreds of laminate and real wood flooring to choose from, we have floors to cater for every taste and budget. What's more, we're right on your doorstep so our specialist advice is at hand to help you make the best decision.

To find out more call freephone 08000 830 830 or visit us at www.floors2go.co.uk to find your local store.

**More than 140 stores across the uk
www.floors2go.co.uk**

RICHARD BURBIDGE LTD
Whittington Road, Oswestry, Shropshire, SY11 1HZ
Area of Operation: UK & Ireland
Tel: 01691 655131
Fax: 01691 659091
Email: info@richardburbidge.co.uk
Web: www.richardburbidge.co.uk

RUSTIC WOOD FLOORING LIMITED
Rustic House, Thongsbridge Mills, Miry Lane,
Thongsbridge, Holmfirth, West Yorkshire, HD9 7RW
Area of Operation: East England, Greater London,
North East England
Tel: 01484 685222 **Fax:** 01484 685222
Email: rusticwfc@tiscali.co.uk
Web: www.warmawood.co.uk
Product Type: 1, 2, 4

S.L. HARDWOODS
390 Sydenham Road, Croydon, Surrey, CR0 2EA
Area of Operation: UK (Excluding Ireland)
Tel: 0208 683 0292
Fax: 0208 683 0404
Email: info@slhardwoods.co.uk
Web: www.slhardwoods.co.uk

SCANDAFLOOR LIMITED
7 Folkestone Road, Lytham St Annes,
Lancashire, FY8 3EQ
Area of Operation: UK (Excluding Ireland)
Tel: 01253 714907 **Fax:** 01253 729348
Email: info@scandafloor.co.uk
Web: www.scandafloor.co.uk
Product Type: 1, 2, 3

SIESTA CORK TILE CO
Unit 21, Tait Road, Gloucester Road,
Croydon, Surrey, CR0 2DP
Area of Operation: UK (Excluding Ireland)
Tel: 0208 683 4055 **Fax:** 0208 663 4480
Email: info@siestacorktile.co.uk
Web: www.siestacorktile.com **Product Type:** 6

Don't Forget !

You can use the materials key at the beginning of this Handbook to get much more information from a company's listing.

SOLID FLOOR
53 Pembridge Rd, Notting Hill, London, W11 3HG
Area of Operation: Worldwide
Tel: 020 7221 9166
Fax: 020 7221 8193
Email: nottinghill@solidfloor.co.uk
Web: www.solidfloor.co.uk
Product Type: 1, 2, 3, 6
Other Info: ▽ ✍ ✋
Material Type: A) 1, 2, 3, 5, 6, 7, 8, 9, 10

SONAE (UK) LTD
Moss Lane, Knowsley Industrial Park,
Knowsley, Liverpool, Merseyside, L33 7XQ
Area of Operation: UK & Ireland
Tel: 0151 545 4000
Fax: 0151 545 4090
Email: sonaeuklink@sonae.co.uk
Web: www.sonaeuk.com
Product Type: 1, 4

SONAE (UK) LTD
Area of Operation: UK and Ireland
Tel: 0151 545 4000
Fax: 0151 545 4090
Email: sonaeuklink@sonae.co.uk
Web: www.sonaeuk.com
Product Type: 1, 4

Evermore and First Parquet engineered wood
flooring in 8 species including Walnut, Oak and
Pine in either 7" or 5" wide planks and smooth
or rustic surfaces.

SOUTH WESTERN FLOORING SERVICES
145-147 Park Lane, Frampton Cotterell, Bristol, BS36 2ES
Tel: 01454 880982 **Fax:** 01454 880982
Email: mikeflanders@blueyonder.co.uk
Web: www.southwesternflooring.co.uk
Product Type: 1, 2, 3, 5

STRATHEARN STONE AND TIMBER LTD
Glenearn, Bridge of Earn, Perth, PH2 9HL
Area of Operation: North East England, Scotland
Tel: 01738 813215 **Fax:** 01738 815946
Email: info@stoneandoak.com
Web: www.stoneandoak.com
Product Type: 2 **Material Type:** A) 2, 10

SURFACE SOLUTIONS
33 Alma Road, Herne Bay, Kent, CT6 6JJ
Area of Operation: UK (Excluding Ireland)
Tel: 01227 362775

SWIFTWOOD IMPORTS LTD
Quay House, Nene Parade,
Wisbech, Cambridgeshire, PE13 3BY
Area of Operation: UK (Excluding Ireland)
Tel: 01945587000
Fax: 01945 581203
Email: timber.floors@swiftwood.co.uk
Web: www.basecofloors.co.uk
Product Type: 1, 2
Material Type: B) 2, 8, 10

THE CARPENTRY INSIDER - AIRCOMDIRECT
1 Castleton Crescent, Skegness,
Lincolnshire, PE25 2TJ
Area of Operation: Worldwide
Tel: 01754 767163
Email: aircom8@hotmail.com
Web: www.easycarpentry.com ✍
Product Type: 1, 6

THE FLOORING STUDIO
149a High Street, Brentwood, Essex, CM14 4SA
Area of Operation: Worldwide
Tel: 08700 332022
Fax: 08700 332023
Email: sales@theflooringstudio.com
Product Type: 1, 2, 3

THE NATURAL FLOORING WAREHOUSE
East Building, Former All Saints Church,
Armoury Way, Wandsworth, London, SW18 1HZ
Area of Operation: UK (Excluding Ireland)
Tel: 0208 870 5555
Fax: 0208 877 2847
Email: natalie@edwardianfires.com
Web: www.natural-floors.net
Product Type: 1, 2, 3, 5, 6

A nationwide trade service you can rely on

- Exclusive trade prices
- Specialist products
- Up to 60 days interest free credit
- Instant credit available
- 140 Stores nationwide
- Fantastic loyalty scheme

To find out more call 08000 156 015
or visit www.floors2go.co.uk

THE NATURAL WOOD FLOOR COMPANY
Unit 6B, Freshfields Business Park,
Stevenson Road, Brighton, East Sussex, BN2 0DF
Area of Operation: Worldwide
Tel: 01273 605800 **Fax:** 01273 605799
Email: sales@naturalwoodfloor.co.uk
Web: www.naturalwoodfloor.co.uk
Product Type: 1, 2, 3, 5, 6

**THE NATURAL WOOD
FLOORING COMPANY LTD**
20 Smugglers Way, Wandsworth, London, SW18 1EQ
Area of Operation: Worldwide
Tel: 0208 871 9771 **Fax:** 0208 877 0273
Email: sales@naturalwoodfloor.co.uk
Web: www.naturalwoodfloor.co.uk
Product Type: 1, 2, 3, 5, 6

THE REAL DOOR COMPANY
Unit 5, Cadwell Lane, Hitchen,
Hertfordshire, SG4 0SA
Area of Operation: UK & Ireland
Tel: 01462 451230 **Fax:** 01462 440459
Email: sales@realdoor.co.uk
Web: www.realdoor.co.uk

THE ROUNDWOOD TIMBER COMPANY LTD
Roundwood, Newick Lane,
Mayfield, East Sussex, TN20 6RG
Area of Operation: UK & Ireland
Tel: 01435 867072 **Fax:** 01435 864708
Email: sales@roundwoodtimber.com
Web: www.roundwoodtimber.com

THE SPA & WARWICK TIMBER CO LTD
Harriott Drive, Heathcote Industrial Estate,
Warwick, Warwickshire, CV34 6TJ
Area of Operation: Midlands & Mid Wales
Tel: 01926 883876 **Fax:** 01926 450831
Email: spa.warwick@btconnect.com
Web: www.sawhardwood.co.uk
Product Type: 1, 2, 5

THE WORLDWIDE WOOD COMPANY LIMITED
154 Colney Hatch Lane,
Muswell Hill, London, N10 1ER
Area of Operation: Worldwide
Tel: 0800 458 3366 **Fax:** 0208 365 3965
Email: info@solidwoodflooring.com
Web: www.solidwoodflooring.com
Product Type: 1, 2, 3, 5, 6

THOROGOOD TIMBER PLC
Colchester Road, Ardleigh, Colchester, Essex, CO7 7PQ
Area of Operation: East England
Tel: 01206 233100 **Fax:** 01206 233115
Email: barry@thorogood.co.uk
Web: www.thorogood.co.uk **Product Type:** 1, 2

TONGLING BAMBOO FLOORING
6 Camellia Drive, Priorslee,
Telford, Shropshire, TF2 9UA
Area of Operation: UK & Ireland
Tel: 01952 200032 **Fax:** 01952 291938
Email: sales@tlflooring.co.uk
Web: www.tlflooring.co.uk **Product Type:** 1, 2

TOPPS TILES
Thorpe Way, Grove Park,
Enderby, Leicestershire, LE19 1SU
Area of Operation: UK (Excluding Ireland)
Tel: 0116 282 8000 **Fax:** 0116 282 8100
Email: mlever@toppstiles.co.uk
Web: www.toppstiles.co.uk

TOPPS TILES
Area of Operation: UK (Excluding Ireland)
Tel: 0116 282 8000 **Fax:** 0116 282 8100
Email: mlever@toppstiles.co.uk
Web: www.toppstiles.co.uk

Topps Tiles is Britain's biggest tile and wood flooring specialist, with over 200 stores nationwide. For details of your nearest store or free brochure call 0800 138 1673 www.toppstiles.co.uk.

TRADITIONAL OAK & TIMBER COMPANY
P O Stores , Haywards Heath Road, North Chailey, Nr
Lewes, East Sussex, BN8 4EY
Area of Operation: Worldwide
Tel: 01825 723648 **Fax:** 01825 722215
Email: info@tradoak.co.uk
Web: www.tradoak.com **Product Type:** 2
Other Info: ▽ **Material Type:** A) 2

TREEWORK FLOORING LTD
Cheston Combe, Church Town,
Backwell, Bristol, BS48 3JQ
Area of Operation: UK (Excluding Ireland)
Tel: 01275 790049 **Fax:** 01275 463078
Email: johnemery@treeworkflooring.co.uk
Web: www.treeworkflooring.co.uk
Product Type: 1, 2, 3

UK HARDWOODS LTD
Wade Mill, Molland, South Molton, Devon, EX36 3NL
Area of Operation: UK (Excluding Ireland)
Tel: 01769 550526 **Product Type:** 1, 2, 3

UK HARDWOODS LTD T/A BEDFORD TIMBERS
Wade Mill, Molland, South Molton, Devon, EX36 3NL
Area of Operation: Europe
Tel: 01769 550526
Email: bedfordtimbers@talk21.com
Product Type: 2 **Material Type:** A) 2, 6, 8

UK WOOD FLOORS LTD
Unit 8 Arrow Industrial Estate, Farnborough,
Hampshire , GU14 7QH
Area of Operation: UK (Excluding Ireland)
Tel: 01252 520520
Fax: 01252 520440
Email: info@ukwoodfloors.co.uk
Web: www.ukwoodfloors.co.uk
Product Type: 1, 2, 3, 5 **Other Info:** ECO
Material Type: A) 2, 3, 4, 5, 6, 7, 9

VICTORIA HAMMOND INTERIORS
Bury Farm, Church Street, Bovingdon, Hemel
Hempstead, Hertfordshire, HP3 0LU
Area of Operation: UK (Excluding Ireland)
Tel: 01442 831641
Fax: 01442 831641
Email: victoria@victoriahammond.com
Web: www.victoriahammond.com
Product Type: 2, 3, 5, 6 **Other Info:** ▽ ✎

VICTORIAN WOOD WORKS LTD
54 River Road, Creekmouth,
Barking, Essex, IG11 0DW
Area of Operation: Worldwide
Tel: 0208 534 1000 **Fax:** 0208 534 2000
Email: sales@victorianwoodworks.co.uk
Web: www.victorianwoodworks.co.uk
Product Type: 1, 2, 3, 6 **Other Info:** ▽ ✎ ✍

VISION ASSOCIATES
Demita House, North Orbital Road,
Denham, Buckinghamshire, UB9 5EY
Area of Operation: UK & Ireland
Tel: 01895 831600 **Fax:** 01895 835323
Email: info@visionassociates.co.uk
Web: www.visionassociates.co.uk
Product Type: 1, 2, 3

WAXMAN CERAMICS LTD
Grove Mills, Elland, West Yorkshire, HX5 9DZ
Tel: 01422 311331 **Fax:** 01422 370360
Email: sales@waxmanceramics.co.uk
Web: www.waxmanceramics.co.uk

WOOD YOU LIKE
School Road, Charing, Ashford, Kent, TN27 0JW
Area of Operation: East England
Tel: 01233 713725
Email: info@wood-you-like.co.uk
Web: www.wood-you-like.co.uk ⌁ **Other Info:** ECO ✎
Material Type: A) 1, 2, 3, 4, 5, 6, 7, 9, 10

WOOD2U
26 Waring Way, Dunchurch,
Rugby, Warwickshire, CV22 6PH
Area of Operation: UK (Excluding Ireland)
Tel: 0870 241 8847
Email: sales@wood2u.com
Web: www.wood2u.co.uk ⌁
Product Type: 1, 2, 3, 4, 5, 6

WOODHOUSE TIMBER
Unit 15 Quarry Farm Industrial Estate,
Staplecross Road, Bodiam, East Sussex, TN32 5RA
Area of Operation: UK (Excluding Ireland)
Tel: 01580 831700 **Fax:** 01580 830054
Email: info@woodhousetimber.co.uk
Web: www.woodhousetimber.co.uk
Product Type: 1, 2 **Material Type:** A) 2

WOODLINE FLOORS LTD
Unit 3, Brook Farm, Horsham Road,
Cowfold, Horsham, West Sussex, RH13 8AH
Area of Operation: UK & Ireland
Tel: 0870 840 8484 **Fax:** 0870 840 0040
Email: sales@woodlinefloors.co.uk
Web: www.woodlinefloors.co.uk ⌁
Product Type: 1, 5
Material Type: A) 1, 2, 3, 4, 5, 6, 7, 9

CERAMIC FLOORING, INCLUDING MOSAICS

ALISTAIR MACKINTOSH LTD
Bannerley Road, Garretts Green,
Birmingham, West Midlands, B33 0SL
Area of Operation: UK & Ireland
Tel: 0121 784 6800 **Fax:** 0121 789 7068
Email: info@alistairmackintosh.co.uk
Web: www.alistairmackintosh.co.uk

AMTICO INTERNATIONAL
Solar Park, Southside, Solihull,
West Midlands, B90 4SH
Area of Operation: Worldwide
Tel: 0121 745 0800 **Fax:** 0121 745 0888
Email: samples@amtico.com
Web: www.amtico.com

AMTICO INTERNATIONAL
Area of Operation: Worldwide
Tel: 0121 745 0800
Fax: 0121 745 0888
Email: samples@amtico.com
Web: www.amtico.com

Amtico International is the dominant supplier of
premium, resilient flooring in the UK, combining
the look of natural materials with the
performance benefits of vinyl

BRITISH CERAMIC TILE
Heathfield, Newton Abbot, Devon, TQ12 6RF
Area of Operation: UK & Ireland
Tel: 01626 831480 **Fax:** 01626 831465
Email: sales@bctltd.co.uk
Web: www.candytiles.com
Material Type: F) 1, 2, 4

CAPITAL MARBLE DESIGN
Unit 1 Pall Mall Deposit,
124-128 Barlby Road, London, W10 6BL
Area of Operation: UK & Ireland
Tel: 0208 968 5340
Fax: 0208 968 8827
Email: stonegallery@capitalmarble.co.uk
Web: www.capitalmarble.co.uk
Other Info: ECO ✎ **Material Type:** J) 5, 6

CERAMIQUE INTERNATIONALE LTD
Unit 1 Royds Lane, Lower Wortley Ring Road,
Leeds, West Yorkshire, LS12 6DU
Area of Operation: UK & Ireland
Tel: 0113 231 0218 **Fax:** 0113 231 0353
Email: cameron@ceramiqueinternationale.co.uk
Web: www.ceramiqueinternationale.co.uk
Other Info: ✎

CITY BATHROOMS & KITCHENS
158 Longford Road, Longford,
Coventry, West Midlands, CV6 6DR
Area of Operation: UK & Ireland
Tel: 02476 365877 **Fax:** 02476 644992
Email: citybathrooms@hotmail.com
Web: www.citybathrooms.co.uk

CONCEPT TILING LIMITED
Unit 3, Jones Court, Jones Square,
Stockport, Cheshire, SK1 4LJ
Area of Operation: UK & Ireland
Tel: 0161 480 0994 **Fax:** 0161 480 0911
Email: enquiries@concept-tiles.com
Web: www.concept-tiles.com
Material Type: E) 1, 2, 3, 4, 5, 8, 9, 11, 13

CRAVEN DUNNILL
Stourbridge Road, Bridgnorth, Shropshire, WV15 6AS
Area of Operation: UK (Excluding Ireland)
Tel: 01746 761611 **Fax:** 01746 767007
Email: info@cravendunnill.co.uk
Web: www.cravendunnill.co.uk

CRAVEN DUNNILL JACKFIELD
Jackfield Tile Museum,
Ironbridge Gorge, Shropshire, TF8 7LJ
Area of Operation: Worldwide
Tel: 01952 884124
Fax: 01952 884487
Email: sales@cravendunnill-jackfield.co.uk
Web: www.cravendunnill-jackfield.co.uk

CTD SCOTLAND
72 Hydepark Street, Glasgow,
Dunbartonshire, G3 8BW
Area of Operation: Scotland
Tel: 0141 221 4591 **Fax:** 0141 221 8442
Email: info@ctdscotland.co.uk
Web: www.ctdscotland.co.uk

DAR INTERIORS
Arch 11, Miles Street, London, SW8 1RZ
Area of Operation: Worldwide
Tel: 020 7720 9678
Fax: 020 7627 5129
Email: enquiries@darinteriors.com
Web: www.darinteriors.com

DECORUM TILE STUDIO LTD
5 Leekbrook Industrial Estate,
Cheadle Road, Leek, Staffordshire, ST13 7AP
Area of Operation: UK & Ireland
Tel: 01538 372500 **Fax:** 01538 399916
Email: sales@decorum-ceramics.co.uk
Web: www.decorumtilestudio.co.uk
Other Info: ✎

DISNEY FLOORING LTD
Albert Avenue, Weston-Super-Mare,
Somerset, BS23 1YJ
Area of Operation: UK (Excluding Ireland)
Tel: 01934 615005 **Fax:** 01934 615006
Email: enquiries@disney-flooring.com
Web: www.disney-flooring.com

DOMUS
3 Molesey Business Centre, Central Avenue,
West Molesey, Surrey, KT8 2QZ
Area of Operation: UK (Excluding Ireland)
Tel: 0208 481 9500 **Fax:** 0208 481 9501
Email: info@domustiles.com
Web: www.domustiles.com
Other Info: ✎ **Material Type:** C) 2, 3

DROSTLE
40 Strand House, Merbury Close, London, SE28 0LU
Area of Operation: Worldwide
Tel: 020 8316 7734 **Fax:** 020 8316 7734
Email: mosaics@drostle.com
Web: http://www.drostle.com
Other Info: ✎ ✋ **Material Type:** E) 2

EUROPEAN HERITAGE
48-54 Dawes Road, Fulham, London, SW6 7EN
Area of Operation: Worldwide
Tel: 0207 381 6063 **Fax:** 0207 381 9534
Email: fulham@europeanheritage.co.uk
Web: www.europeanheritage.co.uk ⌁
Material Type: F) 1, 2, 3

EXAKT PRECISION TOOLS LTD
Midmill Business Park, Tumulus Way,
Kintore, Aberdeenshire, AB51 0TG
Area of Operation: Europe
Tel: 01467 633800 **Fax:** 01467 633900
Email: info@exaktpt.com
Web: www.exaktpt.com

FIRED EARTH
3 Twyford Mill, Oxford Road,
Adderbury, Banbury, Oxfordshire, OX17 3SX
Area of Operation: Worldwide
Tel: 01295 812088 **Fax:** 01295 810832
Email: enquiries@firedearth.com
Web: www.firedearth.com ⌁

FLOORTECK LTD
10 Reservoir Close, Northfield,
Birmingham, West Midlands, B31 1TW
Area of Operation: UK (Excluding Ireland)
Tel: 0121 476 6271 **Fax:** 0121 476 6271
Email: sarahcollier@go.com

FRENCH FLOORS
8 Balmore Wood, Luton, Bedfordshire, LU3 4EP
Area of Operation: UK (Excluding Ireland)
Tel: 07702 322597
Fax: 01582 490224
Email: frenchfloors@yahoo.co.uk
Web: www.frenchfloors.co.uk

GLASSWORK
73 Victor Road, Teddington, Middlesex, TW11 8SP
Area of Operation: UK (Excluding Ireland)
Tel: 0208 943 3177
Email: michaelwnewby@yahoo.com
Web: www.glassworkteddington.co.uk

H & R JOHNSON TILES LTD
Harewood Street, Tunstall,
Stoke on Trent, Staffordshire, ST6 5JZ
Area of Operation: Worldwide
Tel: 01782 575575 **Fax:** 01782 524138
Email: sales @johnson-tiles.com
Web: www.johnson-tiles .com ⌁
Material Type: F) 1, 2, 4

HERITAGE TILE CONSERVATION LTD
The Studio, 2 Harris Green,
Broseley, Shropshire, TF12 5HJ
Area of Operation: UK & Ireland
Tel: 01746 785025 **Fax:** 01746 785025
Email: heritagetile@msn.com
Web: www.heritagetile.co.uk
Material Type: F) 1, 2, 3, 4, 5

HITT OAK LTD
10 Park Parade,
Gunnersbury Avenue, London, W3 9BD
Area of Operation: UK (Excluding Ireland)
Tel: 0208 8961900 **Fax:** 0208 8961900
Email: zhitas@yahoo.co.uk

HYPERION TILES
67 High Street, Ascot, Berkshire, SL5 7HP
Area of Operation: Greater London, South East England
Tel: 01344 620211 **Fax:** 01344 620100
Email: graham@hyperiontiles.com
Web: www.hyperiontiles.com

KIEVEL.KL-CHEMIE (UK) LTD
Lower Farm, Lower Farm Lane
Ampfield, Romsey, Hampshire, SO51 9BN
Area of Operation: UK & Ireland
Tel: 01794 368865 **Fax:** 01794 368914
Email: info@kievel.com
Web: www.kievel.com **Other Info:** ✎
Material Type: E) 1, 2, 3, 4, 5, 7, 8, 9

LAWLEY CERAMICS
8 Stourbridge Road, Bromsgrove,
Worcestershire, B61 0AB
Area of Operation: UK (Excluding Ireland)
Tel: 01527 570455 **Fax:** 01527 570455
Email: lawleyceramics@hotmail.com

MANOR ARCHITECTURAL CERAMICS LTD
16 Charles Street, Warwick, Warwickshire, CV34 5LE
Area of Operation: Worldwide
Tel: 01926 400946
Fax: 01926 400272
Email: mike@manorceramic.co.uk
Web: www.manorceramic.co.uk ⌁
Other Info: ✎ ✋ **Material Type:** F) 1, 2, 3, 4, 5

MARIA STARLING MOSAICS
40 Strand House, Merbury Close, London, SE28 0LU
Area of Operation: UK (Excluding Ireland)
Tel: 07775 517409
Email: mosaics@mariastarling.com
Web: www.mariastarling.com
Other Info: ✎ ✋

MARLBOROUGH TILES LTD.
Elcot Lane, Marlborough, Wiltshire, SN8 2AY
Area of Operation: UK & Ireland
Tel: 01672 512422
Fax: 01672 515791
Email: admin@marlboroughtiles.com
Web: www.marlboroughtiles.com

MERCIA FLOORING
59 The Square, Dunchurch,
Rugby, Warwickshire, CV22 6NU
Area of Operation: UK (Excluding Ireland)
Tel: 01788 522168
Fax: 01788 811847
Email: sales@merciaflooring.co.uk
Web: www.merciaflooring.co.uk

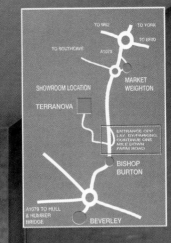

Please visit our stunning showroom spread over 5,000 sq ft containing one of the most comprehensive displays of stone products in the country.

Place your order before the end of December and we will give you a

25% discount
off your materials!

natural wall & floor coverings

Terranova have supplied and fitted wall and floor coverings in some of the finest interiors in the area.

As one of the country's largest importers of natural stone, slate, terracotta, and ceramics. We can offer our customers the best prices in the region. We also design and fit using our craftsmen to guarantee the best value and finest installation.

TERRANOVA
marble • stone • slate • terracotta • ceramics • glass

N&C NICOBOND
41-51 Freshwater Road, Chadwell Heath,
Romford, Essex, RM8 1SP
Area of Operation: Worldwide
Tel: 0208 586 4600 **Fax:** 0208 586 4646
Email: info@nichollsandclarke.com
Web: www.ncdirect.co.uk

NATURAL FLOORING
152-154 Wellingborough Road,
Northampton, Northamptonshire, NN1 4DT
Area of Operation: UK (Excluding Ireland)
Tel: 01604 239238 **Fax:** 01604 627799
Email: sales@naturalflooring.co.uk
Web: www.naturalflooring.co.uk

ORIGINAL OAK
Ashlands, Burwash, East Sussex, TN19 7HS
Area of Operation: UK (Excluding Ireland)
Tel: 01435 882228 **Fax:** 01435 882228
Web: www.originaloak.co.uk **Material Type:** F) 3

ORIGINAL STYLE
Falcon Road, Sowton Industrial Estate,
Exeter, Devon, EX2 7LF
Area of Operation: Worldwide
Tel: 01392 474011 **Fax:** 01392 219932
Email: eboalch@originalstyle.com
Web: www.originalstyle.com
Other Info: ✋ **Material Type:** E) 2, 11

PARKSIDE TILES
49-51 Highmeres Road, Thurmeston,
Leicester, Leicestershire, LE4 9LZ
Area of Operation: UK (Excluding Ireland)
Tel: 0116 276 2532 **Fax:** 0116 246 0649
Email: info@parksidetiles.co.uk
Web: www.parksidetiles.co.uk

PILKINGTON'S TILES GROUP
PO Box 4, Clifton Junction, Manchester, M27 8LP
Area of Operation: UK (Excluding Ireland)
Tel: 0161 727 1000 **Fax:** 0161 727 1122
Email: sales@pilkingtons.com
Web: www.pilkingtons.com

RAK CERAMICS
The Tile House, Easebourne Lane,
Easebourne, West Sussex, GU29 9AZ
Tel: 01730 815507 **Fax:** 01730 815007
Email: info@rakceramics.co.uk
Web: www.rakceramics.co.uk

RUSTICA LTD
154c Milton Park, Oxfordshire, OX14 4SD
Area of Operation: UK & Ireland
Tel: 01235 834192 **Fax:** 01235 835162
Email: sales@rustica.co.uk
Web: www.rustica.co.uk **Other Info:** ✋
Material Type: E) 2, 3, 4, 5, 8, 9

**SHARON JONES HANDMADE
ARCHITECTURAL CERAMIC TILES**
Trevillian Cottage, Barrington,
Nr Ilminster, Somerset, TA19 0JB
Area of Operation: UK (Excluding Ireland)
Tel: 01460 259074
Email: info@handmadearchitecturaltiles.co.uk
Web: www.handmadearchitecturaltiles.co.uk

STONE AND SLATE
Coney Green Farm, Lower Market Street,
Claycross, Chesterfield, Derbyshire, S45 9NE
Area of Operation: UK & Ireland
Tel: 01246 250088 **Fax:** 01246 250099
Email: sales@stoneandslate.ltd.uk
Web: www.stoneandslate.co.uk

SURFACE SOLUTIONS
33 Alma Road, Herne Bay, Kent, CT6 6JJ
Area of Operation: UK (Excluding Ireland)
Tel: 01227 362775

TERRA OMNIA
39 Shortheath Road, Farnham, Surrey, GU9 8SH
Area of Operation: UK & Ireland
Tel: 01252 716661 **Fax:** 01252 716661
Email: info@terromnia.com **Other Info:** ✋
Material Type: E) 1, 2, 3, 4, 5, 7, 8, 9, 11, 13, 14

TERRANOVA CERAMICS LTD
Lings Farm, York Road, Bishop Burton,
East Riding of Yorks, HU17 7RU
Area of Operation: UK (Excluding Ireland)
Tel: 01964 551555
Web: www.terranova.uk.com

THE CANDY TILE COMPANY
The Candy Tile Company, Heathfield,
Newton Abbot, Devon, TQ12 6RF
Area of Operation: UK (Excluding Ireland)
Tel: 01626 834774 **Fax:** 01626 834775
Email: sales@candytiles.com
Web: www.candytiles.com
Material Type: F) 1

**THE MOSAIC RESTORATION
COMPANY LIMITED**
Verwood House, High Street,
West Haddon, Northamptonshire, NN6 7AP
Area of Operation: UK (Excluding Ireland)
Tel: 01788 510000
Fax: 01788 510222
Email: gary@mosaicrestoration.co.uk
Web: www.mosaicrestoration.co.uk

THE NATURAL FLOORING WAREHOUSE
East Building, Former All Saints Church,
Armoury Way, Wandsworth, London, SW18 1HZ
Area of Operation: UK (Excluding Ireland)
Tel: 0208 870 5555
Fax: 0208 877 2847
Email: natalie@edwardianfires.com
Web: www.natural-floors.net

THE ORIGINAL TILE COMPANY
23A Howe Street, Lothian, EH3 6TF
Area of Operation: UK & Ireland
Tel: 0131 556 2013
Fax: 0131 558 3172
Email: info@originaltile.freeserve.co.uk
Web: www.originaltilecompany.co.uk
Other Info: ✏ ✋
Material Type: E) 1, 2, 3, 4, 5, 7, 8, 12

**THE REALLY SAFE
FLOORING COMPANY LIMITED**
Brown Oak Workshops, Arlesford Road,
Wivenhoe, Essex, CO7 9JX
Area of Operation: UK & Ireland
Tel: 01206 827870
Fax: 01206 827881
Email: sales@realsafe.co.uk
Web: www.realsafe.co.uk

THE STONE AND CERAMIC WAREHOUSE
51-55 Stirling Road, Chiswick, London, W3 8DJ
Area of Operation: Worldwide
Tel: 0208 993 5545
Fax: 0208 752 0281
Email: wespalmer@sacw.co.uk
Web: www.sacw.co.uk

THE TILE ASSOCIATION
Forum Court, 83 Copers Cope Road,
Beckenham, Kent, BR3 1NR
Area of Operation: UK & Ireland
Tel: 020 8663 0946
Fax: 0208 663 0949
Email: info@tiles.org.uk
Web: www.tiles.org.uk

TILES UK LTD
1-13 Montford Street, Off South Langworthy Road,
Salford, Greater Manchester, M50 2XD
Area of Operation: UK (Excluding Ireland)
Tel: 0161 872 5155
Fax: 0161 848 7948
Email: info@tilesuk.com
Web: www.tilesuk.com ✏

TOPPS TILES
Thorpe Way, Grove Park,
Enderby, Leicestershire, LE19 1SU
Area of Operation: UK (Excluding Ireland)
Tel: 0116 282 8000
Fax: 0116 282 8100
Email: mlever@toppstiles.co.uk
Web: www.toppstiles.co.uk

TOPPS TILES

Area of Operation: UK (Excluding Ireland)
Tel: 0116 282 8000 **Fax:** 0116 282 8100
Email: mlever@toppstiles.co.uk
Web: www.toppstiles.co.uk

Topps Tiles is Britain's biggest tile and wood flooring specialist, with over 200 stores nationwide. For details of your nearest store or free brochure call 0800 138 1673 www.toppstiles.co.uk.

TRADEMARK TILES
Tile Store, Somersham Road, St Ives,
Huntingdon, Cambridgeshire, PE27 3WR
Area of Operation: UK (Excluding Ireland)
Tel: 01480 498123
Email: info@tilestoreplus.co.uk
Web: www.tilestoreplus.co.uk ✏

WAXMAN CERAMICS LTD
Grove Mills, Elland, West Yorkshire, HX5 9DZ
Tel: 01422 311331 **Fax:** 01422 370360
Email: sales@waxmanceramics.co.uk
Web: www.waxmanceramics.co.uk

WILTON STUDIOS
Cleethorpes Business Centre, Wilton Road Industrial
Estate, Grimsby, Lincolnshire, DN36 4AS
Area of Operation: UK (Excluding Ireland)
Tel: 01472 210820 **Fax:** 01472 812602
Email: postbox@wiltonstudios.co.uk
Web: www.wiltonstudios.co.uk **Other Info:** ✏ ✋
Material Type: C) 1, 2, 3, 4, 12, 14, 15, 16

WORLD'S END TILES
Silverthorne Road, Battesea, Greater London, SW8 3HE
Tel: 0207 819 2100 **Fax:** 0207 819 2101
Email: info@worldsendtiles.co.uk
Web: www.worldsendtiles.co.uk
Material Type: F) 1, 2, 3, 4, 5

STONE & SLATE FLOORING - INCLUDING MARBLE, GRANITE, TRAVERTINE & TERRAZZO

KEY

OTHER: ▽ Reclaimed 🖱 On-line shopping
✏ Bespoke ✋ Hand-made ECO Ecological

AFFORDABLE GRANITE LTD
Unit 5 John Lory Farm, Charlwood Place,
Norwood Hill Road, Charlwwod, Surrey, RH6 0EB
Area of Operation: UK (Excluding Ireland)
Tel: 0845 330 1692 **Fax:** 0845 330 1260
Email: sales@affordablegranite.co.uk
Web: www.affordablegranite.co.uk

AFFORDABLE GRANITE LTD
Unit 5 Charlwood Place,
Norwood Hill Road, Surrey, RH6 0EB
Tel: 0845 330 1692 **Fax:** 0845 330 1260
Email: sales@affordablegranite.co.uk
Web: www.affordablegranite.co.uk
Material Type: E) 1

ALDRIDGE STONE FLOORING COMPANY
Noble House, 50 Military Road,
Colchester, Essex, CO1 2AD
Area of Operation: UK & Ireland
Tel: 01206 541535 **Fax:** 01206 541535
Email: jonathan.afc@btopenworld.com
Web: www.aldridgeflooring.co.uk
Material Type: E) 5, 11, 13

ALICANTE STONE
Damaso Navarro, 6 Bajo,
03610 Petrer (Alicante), P.O. Box 372, Spain
Area of Operation: Europe
Tel: +34 966 31 96 97 **Fax:** +34 966 31 96 98
Email: info@alicantestone.com
Web: www.alicantestone.com
Material Type: E) 1, 2, 4, 5, 8

ALISTAIR MACKINTOSH LTD
Bannerley Road, Garretts Green,
Birmingham, West Midlands, B33 0SL
Tel: 0121 784 6800 **Fax:** 0121 789 7068
Email: info@alistairmackintosh.co.uk
Web: www.alistairmackintosh.co.uk
Material Type: E) 1, 2, 5, 8

ALLAN HARRIS & SONS LIMITED
Station Road, St Georges,
Weston-Super-Mare, Somerset, BS22 7XN
Area of Operation: UK & Ireland
Tel: 01934 511166 **Fax:** 01934 513066
Email: allanharrisslate@hotmail.com
Web: www.allanharrisslate.co.uk
Material Type: E) 1, 3, 4, 5, 8, 9

AMTICO INTERNATIONAL
Solar Park, Southside, Solihull,
West Midlands, B90 4SH
Area of Operation: Worldwide
Tel: 0121 745 0800 **Fax:** 0121 745 0888
Email: samples@amtico.com **Web:** www.amtico.com

AMTICO INTERNATIONAL

Area of Operation: Worldwide
Tel: 0121 745 0800
Fax: 0121 745 0888
Email: samples@amtico.com
Web: www.amtico.com

Amtico International is the dominant supplier of premium, resilient flooring in the UK, combining the look of natural materials with the performance benefits of vinyl

ASHLAR MASON
Manor Building, Manor Road, London, W13 0JB
Area of Operation: East England, Greater London,
Midlands & Mid Wales, South East England, South
West England and South Wales
Tel: 0208 997 0002 **Fax:** 0208 997 0008
Email: enquiries@ashlarmason.co.uk
Web: www.ashlarmason.co.uk
Material Type: E) 1, 2, 3, 4, 5, 8, 9, 11, 13

BANBURY BRICKS LTD
83a Yorke Street, Mansfield Woodhouse,
Nottinghamshire, NG19 9NH
Area of Operation: UK & Ireland
Tel: 0845 230 0941 **Fax:** 0845 230 0942
Email: enquires@banburybricks.co.uk
Web: www.banburybricks.co.uk **Material Type:** E) 3

INTERIORS, FIXTURES & FINISHES - Floor & Wall Finishes - Stone & Slate Flooring (Marble, Granite, Travertine & Terrazzo)

SPONSORED BY: GOSS MARBLE www.gossmarble.co.uk

INTERIORS, FIXTURES & FINISHES

BARHAM & SONS
58 Finchley Avenue, Mildenhall, Suffolk, IP28 7BG
Area of Operation: UK (Excluding Ireland)
Tel: 01638 711611 **Fax:** 01638 716688
Email: info@barhamwoodfloors.com
Web: www.barhamwoodfloors.com

BLACK MOUNTAIN QUARRIES LTD
Howton Court, Pontrilas, Herefordshire, HR2 0BG
Area of Operation: UK & Ireland
Tel: 01981 241541
Email: info@blackmountainquarries.com
Web: www.blackmountainquarries.com

BLANC DE BIERGES
Eastrea Road, Whittlesey, Cambridgeshire, PE7 2AG
Area of Operation: Worldwide
Tel: 01733 202566 **Fax:** 01733 205405
Email: info@blancdebierges.com
Web: www.blancdebierges.com **Other Info:**

BRETT LANDSCAPING LTD
Salt Lane, Cliffe, Rochester, Kent, ME3 7SZ
Area of Operation: Worldwide
Tel: 01634 222188 **Fax:** 01634 222186
Email: cliffenquiries@brett.co.uk
Web: www.brett.co.uk/landscaping

BRITISH CERAMIC TILE
Heathfield, Newton Abbot, Devon, TQ12 6RF
Area of Operation: UK & Ireland
Tel: 01626 831480 **Fax:** 01626 831465
Email: sales@bctltd.co.uk
Web: www.candytiles.com
Material Type: F) 1, 2, 4

CAPITAL GROUP (M/CR) LIMITED
Victoria Mills, Highfield Road,
Little Hulton, Manchester, M38 9ST
Area of Operation: Worldwide
Tel: 0161 799 7555 **Fax:** 0161 799 7666
Email: leigh@choosecapital.co.uk
Web: www.choosecapital.co.uk

CAPITAL MARBLE DESIGN
Unit 1 Pall Mall Deposit,
124-128 Barlby Road, London, W10 6BL
Area of Operation: UK (Excluding Ireland)
Tel: 0208 968 5340 **Fax:** 0208 968 8827
Email: stonegallery@capitalmarble.co.uk
Web: www.capitalmarble.co.uk
Other Info: ECO

CED LTD
728 London Road, West Thurrock,
Grays, Essex, RM20 3LU
Area of Operation: UK (Excluding Ireland)
Tel: 01708 867 237
Email: sales@ced.ltd.uk **Web:** www.ced.ltd.uk
Material Type: E) 1, 2, 3, 4, 5, 6, 8, 9

CERAMIQUE INTERNATIONALE LTD
Unit 1 Royds Lane, Lower Wortley Ring Road,
Leeds, West Yorkshire, LS12 6DU
Area of Operation: UK & Ireland
Tel: 0113 231 0218
Fax: 0113 231 0353
Email: cameron@ceramiqueinternationale.co.uk
Web: www.ceramiqueinternationale.co.uk

CITY BATHROOMS & KITCHENS
158 Longford Road, Longford,
Coventry, West Midlands, CV6 6DR
Area of Operation: UK & Ireland
Tel: 02476 365877 **Fax:** 02476 644992
Email: citybathrooms@hotmail.com
Web: www.citybathrooms.co.uk

CLASSICAL FLAGSTONES LTD
Lower Ledge Farm, Dyrham, Wiltshire, SN14 8EY
Area of Operation: UK & Ireland
Tel: 0117 937 1960
Fax: 0117 303 9088
Email: info@classical-flagstones.com
Web: www.classical-flagstones.com
Material Type: E) 11

CONCEPT TILING LIMITED
Unit 3, Jones Court, Jones Square,
Stockport, Cheshire, SK1 4LJ
Area of Operation: UK & Ireland
Tel: 0161 480 0994 **Fax:** 0161 480 0911
Email: enquiries@concept-tiles.com
Web: www.concept-tiles.com
Material Type: E) 1, 2, 3, 4, 5, 8, 9, 11, 13

CORE AND ORE LTD
16 Portland Street, Clifton, Bristol, BS8 4JH
Area of Operation: UK (Excluding Ireland)
Tel: 01179 042408 **Fax:** 01179 094010
Email: sales@coreandore.com
Web: www.coreandore.com

COUNTRY FLOORING
16 Julian Road, Orpington, Kent, BR6 6HU
Tel: 01689 619044
Email: naturalstone2000@aol.com
Web: www.naturalstone2000.co.uk
Material Type: E) 2, 3, 4, 5, 8, 9

COUNTY GRANITE AND MARBLE
Mill Lane, Creech Saint Michael,
Taunton, Somerset, TA3 5PX
Area of Operation: UK (Excluding Ireland)
Tel: 01823 444554 **Fax:** 01823 445013
Web: www.countygranite.co.uk

CRAVEN DUNNILL
Stourbridge Road, Bridgnorth, Shropshire, WV15 6AS
Area of Operation: UK (Excluding Ireland)
Tel: 01746 761611 **Fax:** 01746 767007
Email: info@cravendunnill.co.uk
Web: www.cravendunnill.co.uk

CTD SCOTLAND
72 Hydepark Street, Glasgow, Dunbartonshire, G3 8BW
Area of Operation: Scotland
Tel: 0141 221 4591 **Fax:** 0141 221 8442
Email: info@ctdscotland.co.uk
Web: www.ctdscotland.co.uk

D F FIXINGS
15 Aldham Gardens, Rayleigh, Essex, SS6 9TB
Area of Operation: UK (Excluding Ireland)
Tel: 07956 674673 **Fax:** 01268 655072

DECORUM TILE STUDIO LTD
5 Leekbrook Industrial Estate,
Cheadle Road, Leek, Staffordshire, ST13 7AP
Area of Operation: UK & Ireland
Tel: 01538 372500 **Fax:** 01538 399916
Email: sales@decorum-ceramics.co.uk
Web: www.decorumtilestudio.co.uk

DELABOLE SLATE COMPANY
Pengelly, Delabole, Cornwall, PL33 9AZ
Area of Operation: UK & Ireland
Tel: 01840 212242 **Fax:** 01840 212948
Email: sales@delaboleslate.co.uk
Web: www.delaboleslate.co.uk

DEVON STONE LTD
8 Pilot Road, Pierhead, Exmouth, Devon, EX8 1XA
Area of Operation: UK (Excluding Ireland)
Tel: 01395 222525
Email: amy@devonstone.com
Web: www.devonstone.com
Material Type: E) 1, 2, 3, 4, 5, 8

DOMUS
3 Molesey Business Centre,
Central Avenue, West Molesey, Surrey, KT8 2QZ
Area of Operation: UK (Excluding Ireland)
Tel: 0208 481 9500 **Fax:** 0208 481 9501
Email: info@domustiles.com
Web: www.domustiles.com

ELON
12 Silver Road, London, W12 7SG
Area of Operation: UK & Ireland
Tel: 0208 932 3000 **Fax:** 0208 932 3001
Email: marketing@elon.co.uk
Web: www.elon.co.uk
Material Type: E) 2, 3

INTERIORS, FIXTURES & FINISHES - Floor & Wall Finishes - Stone & Slate Flooring (Marble, Granite, Travertine & Terrazzo)

SPONSORED BY: GOSS MARBLE   www.gossmarble.co.uk

INTERIORS, FIXTURES & FINISHES

EUROPEAN HERITAGE
48-54 Dawes Road, Fulham, London, SW6 7EN
Area of Operation: Worldwide
Tel: 0207 381 6063   **Fax:** 0207 381 9534
Email: fulham@europeanheritage.co.uk
Web: www.europeanheritage.co.uk
Material Type: E) 1, 2, 3, 4, 5, 7, 8

EXAKT PRECISION TOOLS LTD
Midmill Business Park, Tumulus Way,
Kintore, Aberdeenshire, AB51 0TG
Area of Operation: Europe
Tel: 01467 633800
Fax: 01467 633900
Email: info@exaktpt.com
Web: www.exaktpt.com

FIBRE - NATURAL FLOOR COVERINGS
149 London Road, Worcester,
Worcestershire, WR5 2ED
Area of Operation: UK (Excluding Ireland)
Tel: 01905 728 111
Fax: 01905 764 766
Email: sales@fibretrading.co.uk
Web: www.fibretrading.co.uk

FIRED EARTH
3 Twyford Mill, Oxford Road, Adderbury,
Banbury, Oxfordshire, OX17 3SX
Area of Operation: Worldwide
Tel: 01295 812088   **Fax:** 01295 810832
Email: enquiries@firedearth.com
Web: www.firedearth.com

FLOORTECK LTD
10 Reservoir Close, Northfield,
Birmingham, West Midlands, B31 1TW
Area of Operation: UK (Excluding Ireland)
Tel: 0121 476 6271   **Fax:** 0121 476 6271
Email: sarahcollier@go.com

GOSS MARBLE TRADING LTD
Unit 2 Hurstwood Court, Raikes Lane Industrial
Estate, Bolton, Lancashire, BL3 2NH
Area of Operation: North West England and North
Wales, Scotland
Tel: 0845 400 4677   **Fax:** 01204 364010
Email: info@gossmarble.co.uk
Web: www.gossmarble.co.uk
Material Type: E) 1, 2, 3, 5, 8

GREYSLATE & STONE SUPPLIES
Unit 1 Cae Pawb Industrial Estate, Off Madog Street,
Port Madog, Nr. Blaenau Ffestiniog, Gwynedd, LL49 9EE
Area of Operation: UK & Ireland
Tel: 01766 514700   **Fax:** 01766 515200
Email: greyslate@slateandstone.net
Web: www.slateandstone.net   **Material Type:** E) 3

GWRHYD SPECIALIST STONE QUARRY
Gwrhyd Road, Rhiwfawr, Swansea, Neath, SA9 2SB
Area of Operation: UK & Ireland
Tel: 01639 830743   **Fax:** 01639 830930
Email: enquiries@specialiststone.com
Web: www.specialiststone.com

GWRHYD SPECIALIST STONE QUARRY

Area of Operation: UK & Ireland
Tel: 01639 830743
Fax: 01639 830930
Email: enquiries@specialiststone.com
Web: www.specialiststone.com

The almost square shape of the stone itself,
combined with the astonishingly attractive
surface pattern and long-standing reputation for
durability and slip-resistance, make it a must for
those seeking traditional charm and beauty
without compromising quality.

HARD ROCK FLOORING
Fleet Marston Farm, Fleet Marston,
Aylesbury, Buckinghamshire, HP18 0PZ
Area of Operation: Europe
Tel: 01296 658755
Fax: 01296 655735
Email: paul@hardrockflooring.co.uk
Web: www.hardrockflooring.co.uk
Material Type: E) 2, 3, 4, 5, 8, 9

HYPERION TILES
67 High Street, Ascot, Berkshire, SL5 7HP
Area of Operation: Greater London, South East England
Tel: 01344 620211
Fax: 01344 620100
Email: graham@hyperiontiles.com
Web: www.hyperiontiles.com

INDIGENOUS LTD
Cheltenham Road, Burford, Oxfordshire, OX18 4JA
Area of Operation: Worldwide
Tel: 01993 824200   **Fax:** 01993 824300
Email: enquiries@indigenoustiles.com
Web: www.indigenoustiles.com
Other Info:
Material Type: A) 2, 4, 6

J & R MARBLE COMPANY LTD
Unit 9, Period Works, Lammas Road,
Leyton, London, E10 7QT
Area of Operation: UK (Excluding Ireland)
Tel: 0208 539 6471   **Fax:** 0208 539 9264
Email: sales@jrmarble.co.uk
Web: www.jrmarble.co.uk   **Other Info:**
Material Type: E) 1, 2, 3, 4, 5, 8, 9, 13, 14

KEYSTONE NATURAL STONE FLOORING
204 Duggins Lane, Tile Hill,
Coventry, West Midlands, CV4 9GP
Area of Operation: Worldwide
Tel: 02476 422580   **Fax:** 02476 695794

KIEVEL.KL-CHEMIE (UK) LTD
Lower Farm, Lower Farm Lane,
Ampfield, Romsey, Hampshire, SO51 9BN
Area of Operation: UK & Ireland
Tel: 01794 368865   **Fax:** 01794 368914
Email: info@kievel.com
Web: www.kievel.com   **Other Info:**
Material Type: E) 1, 2, 3, 4, 5, 8, 9

KIRK NATURAL STONE
Bridgend, Fyvie, Turriff, Aberdeenshire, AB53 8LL
Area of Operation: Worldwide
Tel: 01651 891891   **Fax:** 01651 891794
Email: info@kirknaturalstone.com
Web: www.kirknaturalstone.com
Material Type: E) 1, 2, 3, 4, 5

KIRKSTONE QUARRIES LIMITED
Skelwith Bridge, Ambleside, Cumbria, LA22 9NN
Area of Operation: UK & Ireland
Tel: 01539 433296   **Fax:** 01539 434006
Email: info@kirkstone.com
Web: www.kirkstone.com
Material Type: E) 1, 2, 3, 5, 8, 9

LAPICIDA
Killinghall Stone Quarry, Ripon Road, Killinghall,
Harrogate, North Yorkshire, HG3 2BA
Area of Operation: Worldwide
Tel: 01423 560262   **Fax:** 01423 529517
Email: sales@lapicida.co.uk
Web: www.lapicida.com

MANDARIN
Unit 1 Wonastow Road Industrial Estate,
Monmouth, Monmouthshire, NP25 5JB
Area of Operation: Europe
Tel: 01600 715444   **Fax:** 01600 715494
Email: info@mandarinstone.com
Web: www.mandarinstone.com

MARBLE CLASSICS
Unit 3, Station Approach,
Emsworth, Hampshire, PO10 7PW
Area of Operation: UK & Ireland
Tel: 01243 370011   **Fax:** 01243 371023
Email: info@marbleclassics.co.uk
Web: www.marbleclassics.co.uk
Material Type: E) 1, 2, 3, 5, 8, 13

MARBLE HART.COM
1 Edwin Street, Daybrook, Arnold,
Nottingham, Nottinghamshire, NG5 6AX
Area of Operation: Worldwide
Tel: 0115 920 3159
Fax: 0115 952 5752
Email: chris@cghart.com
Web: www.marblehart.com

MARIA STARLING MOSAICS
40 Strand House, Merbury Close, London, SE28 0LU
Area of Operation: UK (Excluding Ireland)
Tel: 07775 517409
Email: mosaics@mariastarling.com
Web: www.mariastarling.com

MARLBOROUGH TILES LTD
Elcot Lane, Marlborough, Wiltshire, SN8 2AY
Area of Operation: UK & Ireland
Tel: 01672 512422   **Fax:** 01672 515791
Email: admin@marlboroughtiles.com
Web: www.marlboroughtiles.com

MARSHALLS
Birkby Grange, Birkby Hall Road, Birkby,
Huddersfield, West Yorkshire, HD2 27A
Area of Operation: UK (Excluding Ireland)
Tel: 01422 306400
Web: www.marshalls.co.uk

MGLW
44 Linford Street, London, SW8 4UN
Area of Operation: Greater London
Tel: 0207 720 9944
Email: contact@naturalstonefloor.com
Web: www.naturalstonefloor.com
Material Type: E) 1, 2, 3, 4, 5, 6, 7, 8, 9, 10, 11, 12, 13, 14

MIDLANDS SLATE & TILE
Units 9-12, Star Industrial Estate,
Chadwell St. Mary, Essex, RM16 4LR
Area of Operation: UK & Ireland
Tel: 0871 474 3185   **Fax:** 01375 846478
Email: mark@slate-tile-brick.co.uk
Web: www.slate-tile-brick.co.uk
Material Type: E) 3, 4, 5, 8

MIDLANDS SLATE & TILE

Area of Operation: UK & Ireland
Tel: 0871 4743185
Fax: 01375 846478
Email: mark@slate-tile-brick.co.uk
Web: www.slate-tile-brick.co.uk

Our extensive range of hand split and dressed
sandstone and limestone paving has the timeless
look and durability that has brought natural stone
back to the forefront of today's creative design
culture. Ideal for landscaping and also interior
projects such as conservatories or kitchens.

INTERIORS, FIXTURES & FINISHES - Floor & Wall Finishes - Stone & Slate Flooring (Marble, Granite, Travertine & Terrazzo)

SPONSORED BY: GOSS MARBLE www.gossmarble.co.uk

INTERIORS, FIXTURES & FINISHES

N&C NICOBOND
41-51 Freshwater Road, Chadwell Heath,
Romford, Essex, RM8 1SP
Area of Operation: Worldwide
Tel: 0208 586 4600 **Fax:** 0208 586 4646
Email: info@nichollsandclarke.com
Web: www.ncdirect.co.uk

NATURAL IMAGE (GRANITE, MARBLE, STONE)
Station Road, Staplehurst, Kent, TN12 0QD
Area of Operation: UK & Ireland
Tel: 01580 895489 **Fax:** 01580 893720
Web: www.naturalimage.co.uk

NICAN STONE LTD
Bank House, School Lane,
Bronington, Shropshire, SY13 3HN
Tel: 01948 780670 **Fax:** 01948 780679
Email: enquiries@nicanstone.com
Web: www.nicanstone.com

ORCHARD STONEMASONS
48 West Street, Axbridge, Somerset, BS26 2AD
Area of Operation: UK (Excluding Ireland)
Tel: 01934 732718 **Fax:** 01934 732718
Email: info@orchardstonemasons.co.uk
Web: www.orchardstonemasons.co.uk

ORIGINAL
3 Festival Units, The Showground,
Bridgwater, Somerset, TA6 6LS
Area of Operation: South West England and South Wales
Tel: 0870 0110808 **Fax:** 0870 011 0606
Email: enquiries@obsc.co.uk **Web:** www.obsc.co.uk

ORIGINAL OAK
Ashlands, Burwash, East Sussex, TN19 7HS
Area of Operation: UK (Excluding Ireland)
Tel: 01435 882228 **Fax:** 01435 882228
Web: www.originaloak.co.uk
Other Info: ▽ ♨ **Material Type:** E) 1, 2

ORIGINAL STYLE
Falcon Road, Sowton Industrial Estate,
Exeter, Devon, EX2 7LF
Area of Operation: Worldwide
Tel: 01392 474011 **Fax:** 01392 219932
Email: eboalch@originalstyle.com
Web: www.originalstyle.com
Material Type: E) 2, 3, 5, 8, 11

PILKINGTON'S TILES GROUP
PO Box 4, Clifton Junction, Manchester, M27 8LP
Tel: 0161 727 1000 **Fax:** 0161 727 1122
Email: sales@pilkingtons.com
Web: www.pilkingtons.com **Material Type:** G) 1, 5

RANSFORDS
Drayton Way, Drayton Fields Industrial Estate,
Daventry, Northamptonshire, NN11 8XW
Area of Operation: Worldwide
Tel: 01327 705310 **Fax:** 01327 706831
Email: sales@ransfords.com
Web: www.ransfords.com /
www.stoneflooringandpaving.com

RED ROSE PLASTICS (BURNLEY) LTD
Parliament Street, Burnley, Lancashire, BB11 3JT
Area of Operation: East England, North East
England, North West England and North Wales
Tel: 01282 724600 **Fax:** 01282 724644
Email: info@redroseplastics.co.uk
Web: www.redroseplastics.co.uk

RIVERSTONE LTD
301 Elveden Road, Park Royal,
Greater London, NW10 7SS
Tel: 0208 961 7725 **Fax:** 0208 965 7013
Email: alain@ssq.co.uk **Web:** www.ssq.co.uk
Other Info: ✎ **Material Type:** E) 3

ROCK UNIQUE LTD
c/o Select Garden and Pet Centre,
Main Road, Sundridge, Kent, TN14 6ED
Area of Operation: Europe
Tel: 01959 565608 **Fax:** 01959 569312
Email: stone@rock-unique.com
Web: www.rock-unique.com

RUSTIC WOOD FLOORING LIMITED
Rustic House, Thongsbridge Mills, Miry Lane,
Thongsbridge, Holmfirth, West Yorkshire, HD9 7RW
Area of Operation: East England, Greater London,
North East England
Tel: 01484 685222 **Fax:** 01484 685222
Email: rusticwfc@tiscali.co.uk
Web: www.warmawood.co.uk

RUSTICA LTD
154c Milton Park, Oxfordshire, OX14 4SD
Area of Operation: UK & Ireland
Tel: 01235 834192 **Fax:** 01235 835162
Email: sales@rustica.co.uk
Web: www.rustica.co.uk
Material Type: E) 2, 3, 4, 5, 8, 9

SIMALI STONE FLOORING
40E Wincombe Business Park,
Shaftesbury, Dorset, SP7 9QJ
Area of Operation: Europe
Tel: 01747 852557 **Fax:** 01747 852557
Email: stonefloors@aol.com
Web: www.stoneflooringonline.com
Material Type: E) 1, 2, 3, 4, 5, 6, 7, 8, 9

SLATE WORLD LTD
Westmoreland Road, Kingsbury,
Greater London, NW9 9RN
Area of Operation: Europe
Tel: 0208 204 3444 **Fax:** 0208 204 3311
Email: kingsbury@slateworld.com
Web: www.slateworld.com ✎
Material Type: E) 3, 4, 5, 9

SLATE WORLD LTD

Area of Operation: Europe
Tel: 0208 2043444 / 014 8345 9115
Fax: 0208 2043311 / 014 8345 9117
Email: kingsbury@slateworld.com
Web: www.slateworld.com
Material Type: E) 3, 4, 5, 9

Suppliers of the most comprehensive range of
QUARRY-DIRECT, non-slip and low maintenance
natural slate flooring tiles in the UK.

SOUTH WESTERN FLOORING SERVICES
145-147 Park Lane,
Frampton Cotterell, Bristol, BS36 2ES
Area of Operation: UK & Ireland
Tel: 01454 880982 **Fax:** 01454 880982
Email: mikeflanders@blueyonder.co.uk
Web: www.southwesternflooring.co.uk
Other Info: ▽ **Material Type:** E) 1, 2, 3, 4, 5, 7, 8

STONE AND SLATE
Coney Green Farm, Lower Market Street,
Claycross, Chesterfield, Derbyshire, S45 9NE
Area of Operation: UK & Ireland
Tel: 01246 250088 **Fax:** 01246 250099
Email: sales@stoneandslate.ltd.uk
Web: www.stoneandslate.co.uk

STONE FLOOR TILES LIMITED
The Nurseries, 221 Halifax Road,
Brighouse, West Yorkshire, HX3 8DH
Area of Operation: UK (Excluding Ireland)
Tel: 01484 402454 **Fax:** 01484 402454
Email: simon@stone-floor-tiles.co.uk
Web: www.stone-floor-tiles.co.uk
Material Type: E) 1, 2, 3, 4, 5, 8, 9, 10

STONE TILES ONLINE
Boxted Farm, Berkhamsted Road,
Hemel Hempstead, Hertfordshire, HP1 2SQ
Area of Operation: UK & Ireland
Tel: 0845 308 1100 **Fax:** 01442 229282
Email: info@stonetilesonline.co.uk
Web: www.stonetilesonline.co.uk ✎
Material Type: E) 1, 2, 3, 4, 5, 8

STONEHOUSE TILES (LONDON) LTD
2 Ossory Road, London, SE1 5AN
Area of Operation: UK (Excluding Ireland)
Tel: 0207 237 5375 **Fax:** 0207 231 7597
Email: info@stonehousetiles.co.uk
Web: www.stonehousetiles.co.uk

STONELL DIRECT
7 showrooms nationwide - see website for details
Area of Operation: Worldwide
Tel: 08000 832283 **Fax:** 01283 501098
Email: info@stonelldirect.com
Web: www.stonelldirect.com

STONEVILLE (UK) LTD
Unit 12, Set Star Estate, Transport Avenue, Great
West Road, Brentford, Greater London, TW8 9HF
Area of Operation: Europe
Tel: 0208 560 1000 **Fax:** 0208 560 4060
Email: info@stoneville.co.uk
Web: www.stoneville.co.uk
Material Type: E) 1, 2, 3, 5, 8

STONEWAYS LTD
Railside Works, Marlbrook,
Leominster, Herefordshire, HR6 0PH
Area of Operation: UK (Excluding Ireland)
Tel: 01568 616818 **Fax:** 01568 620085
Email: stoneways@msn.com
Web: www.stoneways.co.uk

STRATHEARN STONE AND TIMBER LTD
Glenearn, Bridge of Earn, Perth,
Perth and Kinross, PH2 9HL
Area of Operation: North East England, Scotland
Tel: 01738 813215 **Fax:** 01738 815946
Email: info@stoneandoak.com
Web: www.stoneandoak.com **Material Type:** E) 3, 5

STUDIO STONE
The Stone Yard, Alton Lane,
Four Marks, Hampshire, GU34 5AJ
Area of Operation: UK (Excluding Ireland)
Tel: 01420 562500
Fax: 01420 563192
Email: sales@studiostone.co.uk
Web: www.studiostone.co.uk
Other Info: ✎ **Material Type:** E) 1, 2, 3, 4, 5, 8

SURFACE SOLUTIONS
33 Alma Road, Herne Bay, Kent, CT6 6JJ
Area of Operation: UK (Excluding Ireland)
Tel: 01227 362775

TERRA OMNIA
39 Shortheath Road, Farnham, Surrey, GU9 8SH
Area of Operation: UK & Ireland
Tel: 01252 716661 **Fax:** 01252 716661
Email: info@terraomnia.com
Other Info: ✎ ♨

TERRANOVA CERAMICS LTD
Lings Farm, York Road, Bishop Burton,
East Riding of Yorks, HU17 7RU
Area of Operation: UK (Excluding Ireland)
Tel: 01964 551555 **Web:** www.terranova.uk.com

THE GRANITE FACTORY
4 Winchester Drive, Peterlee, Durham, SR8 2RJ
Area of Operation: North East England
Tel: 0191 518 3600 **Fax:** 0191 518 3600
Email: admin@granitefactory.co.uk
Web: www.granitefactory.co.uk ✎

THE HOME OF STONE
Boot Barn, Newcastle,
Monmouth, Monmouthshire, NP25 5NU
Area of Operation: UK (Excluding Ireland)
Tel: 01600 750462 **Fax:** 01600 750462

THE NATURAL FLOORING WAREHOUSE
East Building, Former All Saints Church,
Armoury Way, Wandsworth, London, SW18 1HZ
Area of Operation: UK (Excluding Ireland)
Tel: 0208 870 5555
Fax: 0208 877 2847
Email: natalie@edwardianfires.com
Web: www.natural-floors.net

THE NATURAL SLATE COMPANY LTD
161 Ballards Lane, Finchley, London, N3 1LJ
Area of Operation: Worldwide
Tel: 0845 177 5008 **Fax:** 0870 429 9891
Email: sales@theslatecompany.net
Web: www.theslatecompany.net
Other Info: ECO ♨ **Material Type:** E) 3, 5, 8

THE ORIGINAL TILE COMPANY
23A Howe Street, Lothian, EH3 6TF
Area of Operation: UK & Ireland
Tel: 0131 556 2013 **Fax:** 0131 558 3172
Email: info@originaltile.freeserve.co.uk
Web: www.originaltilecompany.co.uk
Other Info: ✎

THE REALLY SAFE
FLOORING COMPANY LIMITED
Brown Oak Workshops, Arlesford Road,
Wivenhoe, Essex, CO7 9JX
Area of Operation: UK & Ireland
Tel: 01206 827870
Fax: 01206 827881
Email: sales@realsafe.co.uk
Web: www.realsafe.co.uk

THE STONE AND CERAMIC WAREHOUSE
51-55 Stirling Road, Chiswick, London, W3 8DJ
Area of Operation: Worldwide
Tel: 0208 993 5545 **Fax:** 0208 752 0281
Email: wespalmer@sacw.co.uk
Web: www.sacw.co.uk
Material Type: E) 2, 3, 4, 5, 8, 9, 13

TILES UK LTD
1-13 Montford Street, Off South Langworthy Road,
Salford, Greater Manchester, M50 2XD
Area of Operation: UK (Excluding Ireland)
Tel: 0161 872 5155 **Fax:** 0161 848 7948
Email: info@tilesuk.com
Web: www.tilesuk.com ✎

TOPPS TILES
Thorpe Way, Grove Park,
Enderby, Leicestershire, LE19 1SU
Area of Operation: UK (Excluding Ireland)
Tel: 0116 282 8000
Fax: 0116 282 8100
Email: mlever@toppstiles.co.uk
Web: www.toppstiles.co.uk

TOPPS TILES

Area of Operation: UK (Excluding Ireland)
Tel: 0116 282 8000 **Fax:** 0116 282 8100
Email: mlever@toppstiles.co.uk
Web: www.toppstiles.co.uk

Topps Tiles is Britain's biggest tile and wood
flooring specialist, with over 200 stores
nationwide. For details of your nearest store
or free brochure call 0800 138 1673
www.toppstiles.co.uk

INTERIORS, FIXTURES & FINISHES - Floor & Wall Finishes - Stone & Slate Flooring; Clay & Quarry Tiles, including Terracotta

SPONSORED BY: GOSS MARBLE www.gossmarble.co.uk

TRADEMARK TILES
Tile Store, Somersham Road, St Ives,
Huntingdon, Cambridgeshire, PE27 3WR
Tel: 01480 498123 **Email:** info@tilestoreplus.co.uk
Web: www.tilestoreplus.co.uk

WALLS AND FLOORS LTD
Wilson Terrace, Kettering, Northamptonshire, NN16 9RT
Area of Operation: UK (Excluding Ireland)
Tel: 01536 410484
Email: sales@wallsandfloors.uk.com
Web: www.wallsandfloors.uk.com

WELSH SLATE
Business Design Centre, Unit 205,
52 Upper Street, London, N1 0QH
Area of Operation: Worldwide
Tel: 0207 354 0306 **Fax:** 0207 354 8485
Email: enquiries@welshslate.com
Web: www.welshslate.com **Material Type:** E) 3

WILTON STUDIOS
Cleethorpes Business Centre, Wilton Road Industrial
Estate, Grimsby, Lincolnshire, DN36 4AS
Tel: 01472 210820 **Fax:** 01472 812602
Email: postbox@wiltonstudios.co.uk
Web: www.wiltonstudios.co.uk **Other Info:** ✋

ZARKA MARBLE
43 Belsize Lane, Hampstead, London, NW3 5AU
Area of Operation: South East England
Tel: 0207 431 3042 **Fax:** 0207 431 3879
Email: enquiries@zarkamarble.co.uk
Web: www.zarkamarble.co.uk **Material Type:** E) 1, 2, 5

CLAY & QUARRY TILES, INCLUDING TERRACOTTA

KEY
OTHER: ▽ Reclaimed ⌂ On-line shopping
✎ Bespoke ✋ Hand-made ECO Ecological

ALDERSHAW HANDMADE CLAY TILES LTD
Pokehold Wood, Kent Street,
Sedlescombe, Nr Battle, East Sussex, TN33 0SD
Tel: 01424 756777 **Fax:** 01424 756888
Email: tiles@aldershaw.co.uk
Web: www.aldershaw.co.uk
Other Info: ✎ ✋ **Material Type:** F) 1, 3, 4, 5

AMTICO INTERNATIONAL
Solar Park, Southside, Solihull, West Midlands, B90 4SH
Area of Operation: Worldwide
Tel: 0121 745 0800 **Fax:** 0121 745 0888
Email: samples@amtico.com **Web:** www.amtico.com

AMTICO INTERNATIONAL
Area of Operation: Worldwide
Tel: 0121 745 0800
Fax: 0121 745 0888
Email: samples@amtico.com
Web: www.amtico.com

Amtico International is the dominant supplier of
premium, resilient flooring in the UK, combining
the look of natural materials with the
performance benefits of vinyl

ASHLAR MASON
Manor Building, Manor Road, London, W13 0JB
Area of Operation: East England, Greater London,
Midlands & Mid Wales, South East England, South
West England and South Wales
Tel: 0208 997 0002 **Fax:** 0208 997 0008
Email: enquiries@ashlarmason.co.uk
Web: www.ashlarmason.co.uk

BLACK MOUNTAIN QUARRIES LTD
Howton Court, Pontrilas, Herefordshire, HR2 0BG
Area of Operation: UK & Ireland **Tel:** 01981 241541
Email: info@blackmountainquarries.com
Web: www.blackmountainquarries.com ⌂

BODJ FAIR TRADE FLOORING
Bishops Way, Newport, Isle of Wight, PO30 5WS
Area of Operation: Europe
Tel: 01983 537760 **Fax:** 01983 537788
Email: bodj@ajwells.co.uk **Web:** www.bodj.co.uk
Other Info: ECO ✋ **Material Type:** F) 3

CERAMIQUE INTERNATIONALE LTD
Unit 1 Royds Lane, Lower Wortley Ring Road,
Leeds, West Yorkshire, LS12 6DU
Area of Operation: UK & Ireland
Tel: 0113 231 0218 **Fax:** 0113 231 0353
Email: cameron@ceramiqueinternationale.co.uk
Web: www.ceramiqueinternationale.co.uk

CITY BATHROOMS & KITCHENS
158 Longford Road, Longford,
Coventry, West Midlands, CV6 6DR
Area of Operation: UK & Ireland
Tel: 02476 365877 **Fax:** 02476 644992
Email: citybathrooms@hotmail.com
Web: www.citybathrooms.co.uk

CONQUIRA LTD
2 Central Buildings, Warwick Road,
Coventry, Warwickshire, CV8 1FQ
Area of Operation: Midlands & Mid Wales
Tel: 02476 222255 **Fax:** 02476 552211
Email: gary@conquira.freeserve.co.uk
Web: www.conquira.co.uk

CRAVEN DUNNILL
Stourbridge Road, Bridgnorth, Shropshire, WV15 6AS
Area of Operation: UK (Excluding Ireland)
Tel: 01746 761611 **Fax:** 01746 767007
Email: info@cravendunnill.co.uk
Web: www.cravendunnill.co.uk

DAR INTERIORS
Arch 11, Miles Street, London, SW8 1RZ
Area of Operation: Worldwide
Tel: 020 7720 9678 **Fax:** 020 7627 5129
Email: enquiries@darinteriors.com
Web: www.darinteriors.com

ELON
12 Silver Road, London, W12 7SG
Area of Operation: UK & Ireland
Tel: 0208 932 3000 **Fax:** 0208 932 3001
Email: marketing@elon.co.uk
Web: www.elon.co.uk ⌂ **Material Type:** F) 3

EUROPEAN HERITAGE
48-54 Dawes Road, Fulham, London, SW6 7EN
Area of Operation: Worldwide
Tel: 0207 381 6063 **Fax:** 0207 381 9534
Email: fulham@europeanheritage.co.uk
Web: www.europeanheritage.co.uk ⌂
Other Info: ✋ **Material Type:** F) 1, 2, 3

FIRED EARTH
3 Twyford Mill, Oxford Road,
Adderbury, Banbury, Oxfordshire, OX17 3SX
Area of Operation: Worldwide
Tel: 01295 812088 **Fax:** 01295 810832
Email: enquiries@firedearth.com
Web: www.firedearth.com ⌂

FLOORTECK LTD
10 Reservoir Close, Northfield,
Birmingham, West Midlands, B31 1TW
Area of Operation: UK (Excluding Ireland)
Tel: 0121 476 6271 **Fax:** 0121 476 6271
Email: sarahcollier@go.com

FRANCIS N. LOWE LTD
The Marble Works, New Road,
Middleton, Matlock, Derbyshire, DE4 4NA
Tel: 01629 822216 **Fax:** 01629 824348
Email: info@lowesmarble.com
Web: www.lowesmarble.com

HARD ROCK FLOORING
Fleet Marston Farm, Fleet Marston,
Aylesbury, Buckinghamshire, HP18 0PZ
Area of Operation: Europe
Tel: 01296 658755 **Fax:** 01296 655735
Email: paul@hardrockflooring.co.uk
Web: www.hardrockflooring.co.uk

HERITAGE TILE CONSERVATION LTD
The Studio, 2 Harris Green,
Broseley, Shropshire, TF12 5HJ
Area of Operation: UK & Ireland
Tel: 01746 785025 **Fax:** 01746 785025
Email: heritagetile@msn.com
Web: www.heritagetile.co.uk

HYPERION TILES
67 High Street, Ascot, Berkshire, SL5 7HP
Area of Operation: Greater London, South East England
Tel: 01344 620211 **Fax:** 01344 620100
Email: graham@hyperiontiles.com
Web: www.hyperiontiles.com

INDIGENOUS LTD
Cheltenham Road, Burford, Oxfordshire, OX18 4JA
Area of Operation: Worldwide
Tel: 01993 824200 **Fax:** 01993 824300
Email: enquiries@indigenoustiles.com
Web: www.indigenoustiles.com **Other Info:** ✎ ✋

KIEVEL.KL-CHEMIE (UK) LTD
Lower Farm, Lower Farm Lane,
Ampfield, Romsey, Hampshire, SO51 9BN
Area of Operation: UK & Ireland
Tel: 01794 368865 **Fax:** 01794 368914
Email: info@kievel.com **Web:** www.kievel.com

LAWLEY CERAMICS
8 Stourbridge Road, Bromsgrove,
Worcestershire, B61 0AB
Area of Operation: UK (Excluding Ireland)
Tel: 01527 570455 **Fax:** 01527 570455
Email: lawleyceramics@hotmail.com

MANOR ARCHITECTURAL CERAMICS LTD
16 Charles Street, Warwick, Warwickshire, CV34 5LE
Area of Operation: Worldwide
Tel: 01926 400946 **Fax:** 01926 400272
Email: mike@manorceramic.co.uk
Web: www.manorceramic.co.uk ⌂
Other Info: ✎ ✋ **Material Type:** F) 1, 2, 3, 5

MARLBOROUGH TILES LTD
Elcot Lane, Marlborough, Wiltshire, SN8 2AY
Area of Operation: UK & Ireland
Tel: 01672 512422 **Fax:** 01672 515791
Email: admin@marlboroughtiles.com
Web: www.marlboroughtiles.com

MIDLANDS SLATE & TILE
Units 9-12, Star Industrial Estate,
Chadwell St. Mary, Essex, RM16 4LR
Area of Operation: UK & Ireland
Tel: 0871 474 3185 **Fax:** 01375 846478
Email: mark@slate-tile-brick.co.uk
Web: www.slate-tile-brick.co.uk **Material Type:** F) 3

NATURAL FLOORING
152-154 Wellingborough Road,
Northampton, Northamptonshire, NN1 4DT
Area of Operation: UK (Excluding Ireland)
Tel: 01604 239238 **Fax:** 01604 627799
Email: sales@naturalflooring.co.uk
Web: www.naturalflooring.co.uk

ORIGINAL STYLE
Falcon Road, Sowton Industrial Estate,
Exeter, Devon, EX2 7LF
Area of Operation: Worldwide
Tel: 01392 474011 **Fax:** 01392 219932
Email: eboalch@originalstyle.com
Web: www.originalstyle.com **Material Type:** F) 3

RUSTICA LTD
154c Milton Park, Oxfordshire, OX14 4SD
Area of Operation: UK & Ireland
Tel: 01235 834192 **Fax:** 01235 835162
Email: sales@rustica.co.uk **Web:** www.rustica.co.uk
Other Info: ✳ ✋ **Material Type:** F) 3

SIMALI STONE FLOORING
40E Wincombe Business Park,
Shaftesbury, Dorset, SP7 9QJ
Area of Operation: Europe
Tel: 01747 852557 **Fax:** 01747 852557
Email: stonefloors@aol.com
Web: www.stoneflooringonline.com

SOUTH WESTERN FLOORING SERVICES
145-147 Park Lane,
Frampton Cotterell, Bristol, BS36 2ES
Area of Operation: UK & Ireland
Tel: 01454 880982 **Fax:** 01454 880982
Email: mikeflanders@blueyonder.co.uk
Web: www.southwesternflooring.co.uk
Material Type: E) 1, 2, 3, 4, 5, 7, 8

STONE AND SLATE
Coney Green Farm, Lower Market Street,
Claycross, Chesterfield, Derbyshire, S45 9NE
Area of Operation: UK & Ireland
Tel: 01246 250088 **Fax:** 01246 250099
Email: sales@stoneandslate.ltd.uk
Web: www.stoneandslate.co.uk

STONE FLOOR TILES LIMITED
The Nurseries, 221 Halifax Road,
Brighouse, West Yorkshire, HX3 8DH
Area of Operation: UK (Excluding Ireland)
Tel: 01484 402454 **Fax:** 01484 402454
Email: simon@stone-floor-tiles.co.uk
Web: www.stone-floor-tiles.co.uk

SURFACE SOLUTIONS
33 Alma Road, Herne Bay, Kent, CT6 6JJ
Area of Operation: UK (Excluding Ireland)
Tel: 01227 362775

TERRA OMNIA
39 Shortheath Road, Farnham, Surrey, GU9 8SH
Area of Operation: UK & Ireland
Tel: 01252 716661 **Fax:** 01252 716661
Email: info@terraomnia.com **Other Info:** ✋

THE ORIGINAL TILE COMPANY
23A Howe Street, Lothian, EH3 6TF
Area of Operation: UK & Ireland
Tel: 0131 556 2013 **Fax:** 0131 558 3172
Email: info@originaltile.freeserve.co.uk
Web: www.originaltilecompany.co.uk
Material Type: F) 3, 5

THE REALLY SAFE FLOORING COMPANY LIMITED
Brown Oak Workshops,
Arlesford Road, Wivenhoe, Essex, CO7 9JX
Area of Operation: UK & Ireland
Tel: 01206 827870 **Fax:** 01206 827881
Email: sales@realsafe.co.uk
Web: www.realsafe.co.uk

THE STONE AND CERAMIC WAREHOUSE
51-55 Stirling Road, Chiswick, London, W3 8DJ
Area of Operation: Worldwide
Tel: 0208 993 5545 **Fax:** 0208 752 0281
Email: wespalmer@sacw.co.uk
Web: www.sacw.co.uk

THE TILE ASSOCIATION
Forum Court, 83 Copers Cope Road,
Beckenham, Kent, BR3 1NR
Area of Operation: UK & Ireland
Tel: 0208 663 0946 **Fax:** 0208 663 0949
Email: info@tiles.org.uk **Web:** www.tiles.org.uk

TILEASY LTD
Unit 10a, Railway Triangle, Walton Road,
Portsmouth, Hampshire, PO6 1TN
Tel: 02392 220077 **Fax:** 02392 220088
Email: enquiries@craftceramics.com
Web: www.craftceramics.com
Material Type: F) 1

INTERIORS, FIXTURES & FINISHES - Floor & Wall Finishes - Clay & Quarry Tiles; Concrete Flooring; Linoleum, Vinyl & Rubber Flooring

SPONSORED BY: GOSS MARBLE www.gossmarble.co.uk

INTERIORS, FIXTURES & FINISHES

TILES UK LTD
1-13 Montfort Street, Off South Langworthy Road,
Salford, Greater Manchester, M50 2XD
Area of Operation: UK (Excluding Ireland)
Tel: 0161 872 5155 **Fax:** 0161 848 7948
Email: info@tilesuk.com **Web:** www.tilesuk.com ⌐🖰

TOPPS TILES
Thorpe Way, Grove Park,
Enderby, Leicestershire, LE19 1SU
Area of Operation: UK (Excluding Ireland)
Tel: 0116 282 8000 **Fax:** 0116 282 8100
Email: mlever@toppstiles.co.uk
Web: www.toppstiles.co.uk

TOPPS TILES

Area of Operation: UK (Excluding Ireland)
Tel: 0116 282 8000 **Fax:** 0116 282 8100
Email: mlever@toppstiles.co.uk
Web: www.toppstiles.co.uk

Topps Tiles is Britain's biggest tile and wood flooring specialist, with over 200 stores nationwide. For details of your nearest store or free brochure call 0800 138 1673 www.toppstiles.co.uk.

TRADEMARK TILES
Tile Store, Somersham Road, St Ives,
Huntingdon, Cambridgeshire, PE27 3WR
Area of Operation: UK (Excluding Ireland)
Tel: 01480 498123 **Email:** info@tilestoreplus.co.uk
Web: www.tilestoreplus.co.uk ⌐🖰

VICTORIAN WOOD WORKS LTD
54 River Road, Creekmouth,
Barking, Essex, IG11 0DW
Area of Operation: Worldwide
Tel: 0208 534 1000 **Fax:** 0208 534 2000
Email: sales@victorianwoodworks.co.uk
Web: www.victorianwoodworks.co.uk
Other Info: ▽

WALLS AND FLOORS LTD
Wilson Terrace, Kettering,
Northamptonshire, NN16 9RT
Area of Operation: UK (Excluding Ireland)
Tel: 01536 410484
Email: sales@wallsandfloors.uk.com
Web: www.wallsandfloors.uk.com ⌐🖰

WAXMAN CERAMICS LTD
Grove Mills, Elland, West Yorkshire, HX5 9DZ
Tel: 01422 311331 **Fax:** 01422 370360
Email: sales@waxmanceramics.co.uk
Web: www.waxmanceramics.co.uk

WILTON STUDIOS
Cleethorpes Business Centre, Wilton Road Industrial
Estate, Grimsby, Lincolnshire, DN36 4AS
Area of Operation: UK (Excluding Ireland)
Tel: 01472 210820 **Fax:** 01472 812602
Email: postbox@wiltonstudios.co.uk
Web: www.wiltonstudios.co.uk

WORLD'S END TILES
Silverthorne Road, Battesea, London, SW8 3HE
Area of Operation: UK (Excluding Ireland)
Tel: 0207 819 2100 **Fax:** 0207 819 2101
Email: info@worldsendtiles.co.uk
Web: www.worldsendtiles.co.uk
Material Type: E) 1, 2, 3, 5

YORK HANDMADE BRICK CO LTD
Forest Lane, Alne, York, North Yorkshire, YO61 1TU
Area of Operation: Worldwide
Tel: 01347 838881
Fax: 01347 838885
Email: sales@yorkhandmade.co.uk
Web: www.yorkhandmade.co.uk
Material Type: F) 3

CONCRETE FLOORING

AMTICO INTERNATIONAL
Solar Park, Southside,
Solihull, West Midlands, B90 4SH
Area of Operation: Worldwide
Tel: 0121 745 0800 **Fax:** 0121 745 0888
Email: samples@amtico.com
Web: www.amtico.com

AMTICO INTERNATIONAL

Area of Operation: Worldwide
Tel: 0121 745 0800
Fax: 0121 745 0888
Email: samples@amtico.com
Web: www.amtico.com

Amtico International is the dominant supplier of premium, resilient flooring in the UK, combining the look of natural materials with the performance benefits of vinyl

DEGUSSA CONSTRUCTION CHEMICALS (UK)
Albany House, Swinton Hall Road,
Swinton, Manchester, M27 4DT
Area of Operation: Worldwide
Tel: 0161 794 7411
Fax: 0161 727 8547
Email: mbtfeb@basf.com
Web: www.degussa-cc.co.uk

FLOORTECK LTD
10 Reservoir Close, Northfield,
Birmingham, West Midlands, B31 1TW
Area of Operation: UK (Excluding Ireland)
Tel: 0121 476 6271 **Fax:** 0121 476 6271
Email: sarahcollier@go.com

GALLICO CEMENT
3 Mead Court, 52 South Molton Street,
London, W1K 5SE
Area of Operation: Worldwide
Tel: 0207 193 1144 **Fax:** 0207 491 3539
Email: sales@gallicoservices.co.uk
Web: www.gallicoservices.co.uk **Other Info:** 🖊

INSTARMAC GROUP PLC
Kingsbury Link, Trinity Road,
Tamworth, Staffordshire, B78 2EX
Area of Operation: Europe
Tel: 01827 872244 **Fax:** 01827 874466
Email: email@instarmac.co.uk
Web: www.instarmac.co.uk

NATURAL FLOORING
152-154 Wellingborough Road,
Northampton, Northamptonshire, NN1 4DT
Area of Operation: UK (Excluding Ireland)
Tel: 01604 239238
Fax: 01604 627799
Email: sales@naturalflooring.co.uk
Web: www.naturalflooring.co.uk

PERMANENT FLOORING LTD
Britannia House, High Street,
Bagillt, Flintshire, CH6 6HE
Area of Operation: UK & Ireland
Tel: 01352 714869 **Fax:** 01352 713666
Email: info@permanentflooring.com
Web: www.permanentflooringltd.com

SPANCAST CONCRETE FLOORS
Stephenson Way, Barrington Industrial Estate,
Bedlington, Northumberland, NE22 7DL
Area of Operation: East England, North East England,
North West England and North Wales, Scotland
Tel: 01670 531160 **Fax:** 01670 531170
Email: enquiry@spancast.co.uk
Web: www.spancast.co.uk

LINOLEUM, VINYL AND RUBBER FLOORING

AARDVARK WHOLESALE LTD
PO Box 3733, Dronfield, Derbyshire, S18 9AD
Area of Operation: UK (Excluding Ireland)
Tel: 07050 244219 **Fax:** 07050 323630
Email: aardvark@inbox.com

AMTICO INTERNATIONAL
Solar Park, Southside, Solihull,
West Midlands, B90 4SH
Area of Operation: Worldwide
Tel: 0121 745 0800 **Fax:** 0121 745 0888
Email: samples@amtico.com
Web: www.amtico.com

AMTICO INTERNATIONAL

Area of Operation: Worldwide
Tel: 0121 745 0800
Fax: 0121 745 0888
Email: samples@amtico.com
Web: www.amtico.com

Amtico International is the dominant supplier of premium, resilient flooring in the UK, combining the look of natural materials with the performance benefits of vinyl

CSM CARPETS & FLOORING LTD
Brickmakers Arms Lane, Doddington,
Cambridgeshire, PE15 0TR
Area of Operation: East England
Tel: 01354 740727 **Fax:** 01354 740078
Email: alan.csm@virgin.net
Web: www.csm-flooring.co.uk

DALSOUPLE
Unit 1 Showground Road,
Bridgwater, Somerset, TA6 6AJ
Area of Operation: Worldwide
Tel: 01278 727733 **Fax:** 01278 727766
Email: info@dalsouple.com
Web: www.dalsouple.com **Other Info:** ECO 🖊

DISNEY FLOORING LTD
Albert Avenue, Weston-Super-Mare,
Somerset, BS23 1YJ
Area of Operation: UK (Excluding Ireland)
Tel: 01934 615005 **Fax:** 01934 615006
Email: enquiries@disney-flooring.com
Web: www.disney-flooring.com
Other Info: ECO **Material Type:** D) 4

FIBRE - NATURAL FLOOR COVERINGS
149 London Road, Worcester,
Worcestershire, WR5 2ED
Area of Operation: UK (Excluding Ireland)
Tel: 01905 728111 **Fax:** 01905 764766
Email: sales@fibretrading.co.uk
Web: www.fibretrading.co.uk

FIRST FLOOR (FULHAM) LTD
174 Wandsworth Bridge Road,
Fulham, London, SW6 2UQ
Area of Operation: UK (Excluding Ireland)
Tel: 0207 736 1123 **Fax:** 0207 371 9812
Email: annie@firstfloor.uk.com
Web: www.firstfloor.uk.com

FLOORBRAND
Cavendish Business Centre, High Street Green,
Sible Hedingham, Essex, CO9 3LH
Area of Operation: Europe
Tel: 0845 166 8001 **Fax:** 0845 166 8002
Email: sales@floorbrand.com
Web: www.floorbrand.com ⌐🖰

FLOORS-2-GO
140 Stores Nationwide
Area of Operation: UK & Ireland
Tel: 08000 830 330
Email: info@floors2go.co.uk
Web: www.floors2go.co.uk ⌐🖰

FLOORSDIRECT
Unit 6, Fountain Drive, Hertford,
Hertfordshire, SG13 7UB
Area of Operation: UK (Excluding Ireland)
Tel: 01992 552447 **Fax:** 01992 558760
Email: jenny@floorsdirect.co.uk
Web: www.floorsdirect.co.uk ⌐🖰
Material Type: D) 1, 4

FLOORTECK LTD
10 Reservoir Close, Northfield,
Birmingham, West Midlands, B31 1TW
Area of Operation: UK (Excluding Ireland)
Tel: 0121 476 6271 **Fax:** 0121 476 6271
Email: sarahcollier@go.com

FORBO FLOORING
PO Box 1, Den Road, Kirkclady, Fife, KY1 2SB
Area of Operation: Worldwide
Tel: 01592 643777 **Fax:** 01592 643999
Email: info.uk@forbo.com
Web: www.forbo-flooring.co.uk **Other Info:** ECO

HARVEY MARIA LTD
Acorn House, 74-94 Cherry Orchard Road,
Croydon, Greater London, CR0 6BA
Area of Operation: UK & Ireland
Tel: 0208 688 4700
Fax: 0208 688 4800
Email: info@harveymaria.co.uk
Web: www.harveymaria.co.uk ⌐🖰
Material Type: D) 4

JAYMART RUBBER & PLASTICS LTD
Woodlands Trading Estate, Eden Vale Road,
Westbury, Wiltshire, BA13 3QS
Area of Operation: UK & Ireland
Tel: 01373 864926 **Fax:** 01373 858454
Email: sales@jaymart.co.uk
Web: www.jaymart.net

Amtico

feel
comfortable

Low-maintenance flooring

An Amtico floor not only looks absolutel
stunning in any room of the home, it
unique Multiple Performance Syster
(comprising five distinct performanc
layers) provides unrivalled dent, stain, sli
and water resistance. And because it
warm, quiet and low-maintenance, livin
with a beautiful natural replica, Amtico floc
is a real pleasure too – it's even better tha
the real thing. Call now to find out more o
0800 667766 or visit www.amtico.com

Amtico floors. So much to feel good about.

NATURAL FLOORING
152-154 Wellingborough Road,
Northampton, Northamptonshire, NN1 4DT
Area of Operation: UK (Excluding Ireland)
Tel: 01604 239238
Fax: 01604 627799
Email: sales@naturalflooring.co.uk
Web: www.naturalflooring.co.uk

RTC SAFETY SURFACES
Woodland House, Chestnut Business Park,
Smallshaw Lane, Burnley, Lancashire, BB11 5SQ
Area of Operation: Worldwide
Tel: 01282 414131 **Fax:** 01282 414133
Email: emma.bradley@rtcsafety.co.uk
Web: www.rtcsafety.co.uk ⌐🖰

THE NATURAL FLOORING WAREHOUSE
East Building, Former All Saints Church,
Armoury Way, Wandsworth, London, SW18 1HZ
Area of Operation: UK (Excluding Ireland)
Tel: 0208 870 5555 **Fax:** 0208 877 2847
Email: natalie@edwardianfires.com
Web: www.natural-floors.net

THEISSEN GARDINEN-RAUMAUSSTATTUNG
Virchowstraße 18, Essen, Germany, 45147
Area of Operation: Europe
Tel: 0049 201 734 011 **Fax:** 0049 201 701 871
Email: naturcom-theissen@t-online.de
Other Info: ECO

UNNATURAL FLOORING
PO Box 80, Salcombe, Devon, TQ8 8WW
Area of Operation: UK & Ireland
Tel: 0870 766 1088 **Fax:** 01548 821707
Email: info@unnaturalflooring.co.uk
Web: www.unnaturalflooring.com

SOFT FLOOR COVERINGS

KEY

PRODUCT TYPES: 1= Carpets 2 = Rugs
3 = Natural Matting 4 = Carpet Accessories
and Underlays 5 = Oriental Carpets
6 = Other
OTHER: ▽ Reclaimed ⌐🖰 On-line shopping
✏ Bespoke 🖐Hand-made ECO Ecological

AARDVARK WHOLESALE LTD
PO Box 3733, Dronfield, Derbyshire, S18 9AD
Area of Operation: UK (Excluding Ireland)
Tel: 07050 244219 **Fax:** 07050 323630
Email: aardvark@inbox.com **Product Type:** 1, 4

ANNETTE NIX
150a Camden Street, London, NW1 9PA
Area of Operation: Worldwide
Tel: 07956 451719 **Email:** annette.n@virgin.net
Web: www.annettenix.com **Product Type:** 1, 2

AXMINSTER CARPETS
Axminster, Devon, EX13 5PQ
Area of Operation: UK & Ireland
Tel: 01297 630650 **Fax:** 01297 35241
Email: sales@axminster-carpets.co.uk
Web: www.axminster-carpets.co.uk
Product Type: 1

BIRCH INTERNATIONAL CARPETS
Hazel Park Mills, 318 Coleford Road,
Sheffield, South Yorkshire, S9 5PH
Area of Operation: UK & Ireland
Tel: 0114 243 1240 **Fax:** 0114 243 5118
Email: info@birchinternational.co.uk
Web: www.birchinternational.co.uk **Product Type:** 1

BLENHEIM CARPETS
41 Pimlico Road, London, SW1 8NE
Area of Operation: Worldwide
Tel: 0207 823 6333 **Fax:** 0207 823 5210
Email: admin@blenheim-carpets.com
Web: www.blenheim-carpets.com
Product Type: 1, 2, 3, 4

BRINTONS LTD
PO Box 16, Exchange Street,
Kidderminster, Worcestershire, DY10 1AG
Area of Operation: UK & Ireland
Tel: 01562 820000 **Fax:** 01562 634523
Email: selfbuild@brintons.co.uk
Web: www.brintons.net **Product Type:** 1, 2

BRONTE CARPETS
Bankfield Mill, Greenfield Road,
Colne, Lancashire, BB8 9PD
Area of Operation: Europe
Tel: 01282 862736 **Fax:** 01282 868307
Email: office@brontecarpets.co.uk
Web: www.brontecarpets.co.uk
Product Type: 1, 2

CARPETRUNNERS
Somerset House, Clatendon Place,
Leamington Spa, Warwickshire, CV32 5QN
Area of Operation: UK & Ireland
Tel: 01926 885523 **Fax:** 01926 885552
Email: sales@carpetrunners.co.uk
Web: www.carpetrunners.co.uk ⌐🖰 **Product Type:** 4, 6

CAVALIER CARPETS LTD
Thompson Street Industrial Estate,
Dixon Street, Blackburn, Lancashire, BB2 1TX
Area of Operation: Worldwide
Tel: 01254 268000 **Fax:** 01254 268001
Email: sales@cavalier-carpets.co.uk
Web: www.cavaliercarpets.co.uk **Product Type:** 1

CHANTRY HOUSE OAK LTD
28 North Street, Chichester, West Sussex, PO20 2BT
Area of Operation: South East England
Tel: 01243 776811
Email: shop@chantryhouseoak.co.uk
Web: www.chantryhouseoak.co.uk **Product Type:** 2

CONSTRUCTION RESOURCES
16 Great Guildford Street, London, SE1 0HS
Area of Operation: UK (Excluding Ireland)
Tel: 0207 450 2211 **Fax:** 0207 450 2212
Email: info@constructionresources.com
Web: www.constructionresources.com
Product Type: 1, 2, 4

CORE AND ORE LTD
16 Portland Street, Clifton, Bristol, BS8 4JH
Area of Operation: UK (Excluding Ireland)
Tel: 01179 042408 **Fax:** 01179 094010
Email: sales@coreandore.com
Web: www.coreandore.com
Product Type: 6 **Material Type:** (M) 4

CRAIGIE STOCKWELL CARPETS LIMITED
81 York Street, London, W1H 1QH
Area of Operation: Worldwide
Tel: 0207 224 8380 **Fax:** 0207 224 8381
Email: craigiestockwell@aol.com
Web: www.craigiestockwellcarpets.com
Product Type: 1, 2, 6 **Other Info:** ✏ 🖐

CRUCIAL TRADING
PO Box 10469, Birmingham,
West Midlands, B46 1WB
Area of Operation: Worldwide
Tel: 01562 743747 **Fax:** 01675 433521
Email: sales@crucial-trading.com
Web: www.crucial-trading.com
Product Type: 1, 2, 3 **Other Info:** ✏

CSM CARPETS & FLOORING LTD
Brickmakers Arms Lane, Doddington,
Cambridgeshire, PE15 0TR
Area of Operation: East England
Tel: 01354 740727 **Fax:** 01354 740078
Email: alan.csm@virgin.net
Web: www.csm-flooring.co.uk **Product Type:** 1

DISNEY FLOORING LTD
Albert Avenue, Weston-Super-Mare,
Somerset, BS23 1YJ
Area of Operation: UK (Excluding Ireland)
Tel: 01934 615005 **Fax:** 01934 615006
Email: enquiries@disney-flooring.com
Web: www.disney-flooring.com
Product Type: 1, 2, 3, 4 **Other Info:** ECO ✏

FIBRE - NATURAL FLOOR COVERINGS
149 London Road, Worcester,
Worcestershire, WR5 2ED
Area of Operation: UK (Excluding Ireland)
Tel: 01905 728111 **Fax:** 01905 764766
Email: sales@fibretrading.co.uk
Web: www.fibretrading.co.uk
Product Type: 1, 2, 3, 4, 6 **Other Info:** ✏

FIRST FLOOR (FULHAM) LTD
174 Wandsworth Bridge Road,
Fulham, London, SW6 2UQ
Area of Operation: UK (Excluding Ireland)
Tel: 0207 736 1123 **Fax:** 0207 371 9812
Email: annie@firstfloor.uk.com
Web: www.firstfloor.uk.com **Product Type:** 1

FLOORSDIRECT
Unit 6, Fountain Drive,
Hertford, Hertfordshire, SG13 7UB
Area of Operation: UK (Excluding Ireland)
Tel: 01992 552447 **Fax:** 01992 558760
Email: jenny@floorsdirect.co.uk
Web: www.floorsdirect.co.uk ⌐🖰
Product Type: 1, 3, 4, 6

FLOORTECK LTD
10 Reservoir Close, Northfield,
Birmingham, West Midlands, B31 1TW
Area of Operation: UK (Excluding Ireland)
Tel: 0121 476 6271 **Fax:** 0121 476 6271
Email: sarahcollier@go.com
Product Type: 1, 3, 4, 5, 6

FORBO FLOORING
PO Box 1, Den Road, Kirkclady, Fife, KY1 2SB
Area of Operation: Worldwide
Tel: 01592 643777 **Fax:** 01592 643999
Email: info.uk@forbo.com
Web: www.forbo-flooring.co.uk

GIANO DESIGNS LTD
7 Blakedown Road, Halesowen,
Birmingham, West Midlands, B63 4NE
Area of Operation: UK (Excluding Ireland)
Tel: 0121 550 2071 **Email:** info@giano.co.uk
Web: www.giano.co.uk **Product Type:** 2

J W JENNINGS ORIENTAL RUGS
10 Church Street, Tewkesbury,
Gloucestershire, GL20 5PA
Area of Operation: Midlands & Mid Wales, South
West England and South Wales
Tel: 01684 292033 **Fax:** 01684 290292
Email: jwjennings@btconnect.com
Web: www.jenningsrugs.co.uk **Product Type:** 2

JAYMART RUBBER & PLASTICS LTD
Woodlands Trading Estate, Eden Vale Road,
Westbury, Wiltshire, BA13 3QS
Area of Operation: UK & Ireland
Tel: 01373 864926 **Fax:** 01373 858454
Email: sales@jaymart.co.uk
Web: www.jaymart.net **Product Type:** 1, 3

MADE TO MEASURE RUGS
278 Holly Lodge Mansions,
Oakeshott Avenue, Highgate, London, N6 6EB
Area of Operation: UK & Ireland
Tel: 0208 341 6856 **Fax:** 0208 340 2678
Email: sales@made-to-measure-rugs.co.uk
Web: www.made-to-measure-rugs.co.uk ⌐🖰
Product Type: 2 **Other Info:** ✏

NATURAL FLOORING
152-154 Wellingborough Road,
Northampton, Northamptonshire, NN1 4DT
Area of Operation: UK (Excluding Ireland)
Tel: 01604 239238 **Fax:** 01604 627799
Email: sales@naturalflooring.co.uk
Web: www.naturalflooring.co.uk

OLLERTON HALL DECOR
Ollerton Hall, Ollerton, Knutsford, Cheshire, WA16 8SF
Area of Operation: UK & Ireland
Tel: 01565 650222 **Fax:** 01565 754411
Email: sales@ollertonhalldiscountcarpets.co.uk
Web: www.ollertonhalldiscountcarpets.co.uk
Product Type: 1, 2, 3, 4

PERIOD FLOORING
Commerce House, 4 High Street,
Nutfield, Surrey, RH1 4HQ
Tel: 01737 823053 **Fax:** 01737 822862
Email: periodflooring@aol.com
Web: www.periodflooring.co.uk
Product Type: 1, 2, 3, 4, 6

PETER CARLSON INTERIORS
Lower Hillgate, Stockport, Cheshire, SK1 3AW
Area of Operation: North West England and North Wales
Tel: 0161 480 8164 **Fax:** 0161 480 0097
Email: petercarlson@petercarlson.co.uk
Web: www.petercarlson.co.uk
Product Type: 1, 2, 3, 4

POWNALL CARPETS
Ensor Mill, Queensway, Castleton,
Rochdale, Lancashire, OL12 7GB
Area of Operation: Europe
Tel: 01706 716000 **Email:** dneville@ryalux.com
Web: www.pownallcarpets.com **Product Type:** 1

PRIORY
Unit 57, Bowers Mill, Branch Road,
Barkisland, West Yorkshire, HX4 0AD
Area of Operation: Europe
Tel: 01422 311700 **Fax:** 01422 311118
Email: tom.bentley@prioryhardwoods.com
Product Type: 1, 2, 3 **Other Info:** ✏ 🖐

RENEWAL CARPET TILE LTD
P.O.Box 428, Blackburn, Lancashire, BB2 2WQ
Area of Operation: Europe
Tel: 0870 350 2602
Email: timwright@renewalcarpettiles.com
Web: www.renewalcarpettiles.com
Product Type: 1 **Other Info:** ECO ✏

RTC SAFETY SURFACES
Woodland House, Chestnut Business Park,
Smallshaw Lane, Burnley, Lancashire, BB11 5SQ
Area of Operation: Worldwide
Tel: 01282 414131 **Fax:** 01282 414133
Email: emma.bradley@rtcsafety.co.uk
Web: www.rtcsafety.co.uk ⌐🖰 **Product Type:** 6

RUG DESIGN CO
98 Morningside Road, Edinburgh, EH10 4BY
Area of Operation: Worldwide
Tel: 0845 345 1744 **Fax:** 0871 989 5421
Email: info@rugdesign.co.uk
Web: www.rugdesign.co.uk **Product Type:** 1, 2

SELECT FIRST
4 Ridgmount Street, London, WC1E 7AA
Area of Operation: UK & Ireland
Tel: 0207 580 6960 **Fax:** 0207 580 4173
Email: myles@selectfirst.com
Web: www.carpetinfo.co.uk **Product Type:** 1

STAIRRODS (UK)
Unit 6 Park Road, North Industrial Estate,
Blackhill, Consett, Durham, DH8 5UN
Area of Operation: Worldwide
Tel: 01207 591543 **Fax:** 01207 591911
Email: sales@stairrods.co.uk
Web: www.stairrods.co.uk **Product Type:** 4

SWIFTEC
Pennine House, Tilson Road,
Roundthorn Estate, Manchester, M23 9GF
Area of Operation: UK & Ireland
Tel: 0800 074 4145 **Fax:** 0800 074 0005
Product Type: 6

TENTERDEN HOUSE INTERIORS
4 West Cross, Tenterden, Kent, TN30 6JL
Area of Operation: Worldwide
Tel: 01580 764481 **Fax:** 01580 765531
Email: tenterdenhouseinteriors@hotmail.com
Product Type: 2

THE ALTERNATIVE FLOORING COMPANY
3b Stephenson Close, East Portway,
Andover, Hampshire, SP10 3RU
Area of Operation: UK & Ireland
Tel: 01264 335111 **Fax:** 01264 336445
Email: sales@alternativeflooring.com
Web: www.alternativeflooring.com
Product Type: 2, 3, 6 **Other Info:** ECO ✏

THE BRAIDED RUG COMPANY
2 Cliffside, Aberdovey, Gwynedd, LL35 0LR
Area of Operation: Worldwide
Tel: 01654 767248   **Fax:** 01654 767248
Email: info@braided-rug.co.uk
Web: www.braided-rug.co.uk   **Product Type:** 2

THE CANE STORE
Wash Dyke Cottage, 1 Witham Road,
Long Bennington, Lincolnshire, NG23 5DS
Area of Operation: Worldwide
Tel: 01400 282271   **Fax:** 01400 281103
Email: jaki@canestore.co.uk
Web: www.canestore.co.uk   **Product Type:** 3

THE CARPET FOUNDATION
MCF Complex, 60 New Road,
Kidderminster, Worcestershire, DY10 1AQ
Area of Operation: UK & Ireland
Tel: 01562 755 568   **Fax:** 01562 865405
Email: info@carpetfoundation.com
Web: www.comebacktocarpet.com   **Product Type:** 1, 2

THE FLOORING STUDIO
149a High Street, Brentwood, Essex, CM14 4SA
Area of Operation: Worldwide
Tel: 08700 332022   **Fax:** 08700 332023
Email: sales@theflooringstudio.com
Product Type: 1, 2

THEISSEN GARDINEN-RAUMAUSSTATTUNG
Virchowstraße 18, Essen, Germany, 45147
Area of Operation: Europe
Tel: 0049 201 734 011   **Fax:** 0049 201 701 871
Email: naturcom-theissen@t-online.de
Product Type: 1, 3, 4, 5, 6

UNNATURAL FLOORING
PO Box 80, Salcombe, Devon, TQ8 8WW
Tel: 0870 766 1088   **Fax:** 01548 821707
Email: info@unnaturalflooring.com
Web: www.unnaturalflooring.com   **Product Type:** 3

VICTORIA CARPETS LIMITED
Worcester Road, Kidderminster,
Worcestershire, DY10 1HL
Area of Operation: Europe
Tel: 01562 749300   **Fax:** 01562 749349
Email: sales@victoriacarpets.com
Web: www.victoriacarpets.com   **Product Type:** 1

VICTORIA HAMMOND INTERIORS
Bury Farm, Church Street, Bovingdon,
Hemel Hempstead, Hertfordshire, HP3 0LU
Tel: 01442 831641   **Fax:** 01442 831641
Email: victoria@victoriahammond.com
Web: www.victoriahammond.com
Product Type: 1, 2, 3, 4, 6

WOOLS OF NEW ZEALAND
International Development Centre,
Little Lane, Ilkley, West Yorkshire, LS29 8UG
Area of Operation: Worldwide
Tel: 01943 603888   **Fax:** 01943 817083
Email: info.uk@canesis.co.uk
Web: www.woolcarpet.com   **Product Type:** 1, 2

WALL TILES AND BACKING BOARDS

KEY
PRODUCT TYPES: 1= Hand Painted Tiles
2 = Mirrored Tiles   3 = Matt Tiles
4 = Satin Tiles   5 = High Gloss Tiles
6 = Backing Boards
OTHER: ▽ Reclaimed   ⌐🖐 On-line shopping
✐ Bespoke 🖐 Hand-made   ECO Ecological

AFFORDABLE GRANITE LTD
Unit 5 John Lory Farm, Charlwood Place,
Norwood Hill Road, Charlwood, Surrey, RH6 0EB
Area of Operation: UK (Excluding Ireland)
Tel: 0845 330 1692   **Fax:** 0845 330 1260
Email: sales@affordablegranite.co.uk
Web: www.affordablegranite.co.uk

ALDERSHAW HANDMADE CLAY TILES LTD
Pokehold Wood, Kent Street, Sedlescombe,
Nr Battle, East Sussex, TN33 0SD
Area of Operation: Europe
Tel: 01424 756777   **Fax:** 01424 756888
Email: tiles@aldershaw.co.uk
Web: www.aldershaw.co.uk   **Product Type:** 1, 3, 5
Other Info: 🖐   **Material Type:** F) 1

ALICANTE STONE
Damaso Navarro, 6 Bajo,
03610 Petrer (Alicante), P.O. Box 372, Spain
Area of Operation: Europe
Tel: +34 966 31 96 97   **Fax:** +34 966 31 96 98
Email: info@alicantestone.com
Web: www.alicantestone.com
Product Type: 2, 3, 4   **Material Type:** E) 2, 4, 5, 8

ALISTAIR MACKINTOSH LTD
Bannerley Road, Garretts Green,
Birmingham, West Midlands, B33 0SL
Area of Operation: UK & Ireland
Tel: 0121 784 6800   **Fax:** 0121 789 7068
Email: info@alistairmackintosh.co.uk
Web: www.alistairmackintosh.co.uk

AMABIS TILES
Ubique Park, March Way, Battlefield Enterprise Park,
Shrewsbury, Shropshire, SY1 3JE
Area of Operation: Europe
Tel: 01743 440860   **Fax:** 01743 462440
Email: info@amabis.co.uk
Web: www.amabis.co.uk   **Product Type:** 5
Other Info: 🖐   **Material Type:** F) 1

ART ON TILES
2 Orchard Terrace, The Street,
Walberton, Arundel, West Sussex, BN18 0PH
Area of Operation: Worldwide
Tel: 01243 552346   **Email:** info@artontiles.co.uk
Web: www.artontiles.co.uk
Product Type: 1   **Other Info:** ✐

ASHLAR MASON
Manor Building, Manor Road, London, W13 0JB
Area of Operation: East England, Greater London,
Midlands & Mid Wales, South East England, South
West England and South Wales
Tel: 0208 997 0002   **Fax:** 0208 997 0008
Email: enquiries@ashlarmason.co.uk
Web: www.ashlarmason.co.uk   **Product Type:** 3

AZTEC METAL TILES
Bowl Road, Charing, Kent, TN27 0HB
Tel: 01233 712332   **Fax:** 01233 714994
Email: enquiries@aztecmetaltiles.co.uk
Web: www.aztecmetaltiles.co.uk   **Product Type:** 2, 3, 4

BATHROOM CITY
Seeleys Road, Tyseley Industrial Estate,
Birmingham, West Midlands, B11 2LQ
Area of Operation: UK & Ireland
Tel: 0121 753 0700   **Fax:** 0121 753 1110
Email: sales@bathroomcity.com
Web: www.bathroomcity.com ⌐🖐

BRITISH CERAMIC TILE
Heathfield, Newton Abbot, Devon, TQ12 6RF
Area of Operation: UK & Ireland
Tel: 01626 831480   **Fax:** 01626 831465
Email: sales@bctltd.co.uk
Web: www.candytiles.co.uk   **Product Type:** 3, 4, 5

CAPITAL MARBLE DESIGN
Unit 1 Pall Mall Deposit,
124-128 Barlby Road, London, W10 6BL
Area of Operation: UK & Ireland
Tel: 0208 968 5340   **Fax:** 0208 968 8827
Email: stonegallery@capitalmarble.co.uk
Web: www.capitalmarble.co.uk
Product Type: 1, 2, 3, 4, 5   **Other Info:** ECO ✐

CERAMIQUE INTERNATIONALE LTD
Unit 1 Royds Lane, Lower Wortley Ring Road,
Leeds, West Yorkshire, LS12 6DU
Area of Operation: UK & Ireland
Tel: 0113 231 0218   **Fax:** 0113 231 0353
Email: cameron@ceramiqueinternationale.co.uk
Web: www.ceramiqueinternationale.co.uk

CITY BATHROOMS & KITCHENS
158 Longford Road, Longford,
Coventry, West Midlands, CV6 6DR
Area of Operation: UK & Ireland
Tel: 02476 365877   **Fax:** 02476 644992
Email: citybathrooms@hotmail.com
Web: www.citybathrooms.co.uk

CLOTH
North Street, Huthwaite, Nottinghamshire, NG17 2PE
Area of Operation: UK & Ireland
Tel: 0870 777 5100
Fax: 0870 777 5101
Email: info@clothuk.com

CONCEPT TILING LIMITED
Unit 3, Jones Court, Jones Square,
Stockport, Cheshire, SK1 4LJ
Area of Operation: UK & Ireland
Tel: 0161 480 0994
Fax: 0161 480 0911
Email: enquiries@concept-tiles.com
Web: www.concept-tiles.com

CRAVEN DUNNILL
Stourbridge Road, Bridgnorth, Shropshire, WV15 6AS
Area of Operation: UK (Excluding Ireland)
Tel: 01746 761611
Fax: 01746 767007
Email: info@cravendunnill.co.uk
Web: www.cravendunnill.co.uk
Product Type: 2, 3, 4, 5

CRAVEN DUNNILL JACKFIELD
Jackfield Tile Museum,
Ironbridge Gorge, Shropshire, TF8 7LJ
Area of Operation: Worldwide
Tel: 01952 884124
Fax: 01952 884487
Email: sales@cravendunnill-jackfield.co.uk
Web: www.cravendunnill-jackfield.co.uk
Product Type: 1, 3, 4, 5

CTD SCOTLAND
72 Hydepark Street, Glasgow, G3 8BW
Area of Operation: Scotland
Tel: 0141 221 4591   **Fax:** 0141 221 8442
Email: info@ctdscotland.co.uk
Web: www.ctdscotland.co.uk
Product Type: 1, 2, 3, 4, 5
Material Type: E) 1, 2, 3, 7, 8

D F FIXINGS
15 Aldham Gardens, Rayleigh, Essex, SS6 9TB
Area of Operation: UK (Excluding Ireland)
Tel: 07956 674673   **Fax:** 01268 655072

DAR INTERIORS
Arch 11, Miles Street, London, SW8 1RZ
Area of Operation: Worldwide
Tel: 020 7720 9678   **Fax:** 020 7627 5129
Email: enquiries@darinteriors.com
Web: www.darinteriors.com
Product Type: 1, 3, 4   **Other Info:** ✐ 🖐

DECORUM TILE STUDIO LTD
5 Leekbrook Industrial Estate,
Cheadle Road, Leek, Staffordshire, ST13 7AP
Area of Operation: UK & Ireland
Tel: 01538 372500
Fax: 01538 399916
Email: sales@decorum-ceramics.co.uk
Web: www.decorumtilestudio.co.uk

DEGUSSA CONSTRUCTION CHEMICALS (UK)
Albany House, Swinton Hall Road,
Swinton, Manchester, M27 4DT
Area of Operation: Worldwide
Tel: 0161 794 7411   **Fax:** 0161 727 8547
Email: mbtfeb@basf.com
Web: www.degussa-cc.co.uk   **Product Type:** 2

DEVON STONE LTD
8 Pilot Road, Pierhead, Exmouth, Devon, EX8 1XA
Area of Operation: UK (Excluding Ireland)
Tel: 01395 222525
Email: amy@devonstone.com
Web: www.devonstone.com

DOMUS
3 Molesey Business Centre, Central Avenue,
West Molesey, Surrey, KT8 2QZ
Area of Operation: UK (Excluding Ireland)
Tel: 0208 481 9500   **Fax:** 0208 481 9501
Email: info@domustiles.com
Web: www.domustiles.com   **Product Type:** 3, 4, 5

ELON
12 Silver Road, London, W12 7SG
Area of Operation: UK & Ireland
Tel: 0208 932 3000   **Fax:** 0208 932 3001
Email: marketing@elon.co.uk
Web: www.elon.co.uk ⌐🖐   **Product Type:** 1

EUROFORM PRODUCTS LIMITED
The Heliport, Lyncastle Road,
Appleton, Warrington, Cheshire, WA4 4SN
Area of Operation: Worldwide
Tel: 01925 860999   **Fax:** 01925 860066
Email: info@euroform.co.uk
Web: www.euroform.co.uk

EUROFORM PRODUCTS LTD
Area of Operation: Worldwide
Tel: 01925 860999
Fax: 01925 860066
Email: info@euroform.co.uk
Web: www.euroform.co.uk

Versaliner™ JPM is a high performance high impact, moisture Resistant, Class '0' stable fibreboard, that can be used for a wide range of dry lining applications.

Versaliner™ JPM is also a good strong substrate for ceramic tiling.

EUROPEAN HERITAGE
48-54 Dawes Road, Fulham, London, SW6 7EN
Area of Operation: Worldwide
Tel: 0207 381 6063   **Fax:** 0207 381 9534
Email: fulham@europeanheritage.co.uk
Web: www.europeanheritage.co.uk ⌐🖐
Product Type: 2, 3, 4, 5

EXAKT PRECISION TOOLS LTD
Midmill Business Park, Tumulus Way, Kintore,
Aberdeenshire, AB51 0TG
Area of Operation: Europe
Tel: 01467 633800   **Fax:** 01467 633900
Email: info@exaktpt.com   **Web:** www.exaktpt.com

FINE ART TILES
Seaspray, The Crescent, Walcott,
Norwich, Norfolk, NR12 0NH
Area of Operation: Worldwide
Tel: 01692 650620   **Email:** info@finearttiles.co.uk
Web: www.finearttiles.co.uk ⌐🖐

FIRED EARTH
3 Twyford Mill, Oxford Road,
Adderbury, Banbury, Oxfordshire, OX17 3SX
Area of Operation: Worldwide
Tel: 01295 812088   **Fax:** 01295 810832
Email: enquiries@firedearth.com
Web: www.firedearth.com ⌐🖐

FLORIAN TILES
PO Box 4684, Sturminster Neton, Dorset, DT10 2SX
Area of Operation: UK (Excluding Ireland)
Tel: 01963 251025   **Fax:** 01963 251025
Email: enquiries@floriantiles.co.uk
Web: www.floriantiles.co.uk   **Product Type:** 1

GLASS & LIGHTING STUDIO
56 The Tything, Worcester, Worcestershire, WR1 1JT
Area of Operation: UK & Ireland
Tel: 01905 26285 **Fax:** 01905 26285
Email: Studio@glass-lighting.co.uk
Web: www.glass-lighting.co.uk **Product Type:** 5

H & R JOHNSON TILES LTD
Harewood Street, Tunstall,
Stoke-on-Trent, Staffordshire, ST6 5JZ
Area of Operation: Worldwide
Tel: 01782 575575
Fax: 01782 524138
Email: sales @johnson-tiles.com
Web: www.johnson-tiles .com
Product Type: 3, 4, 5

HERITAGE TILE CONSERVATION LTD
The Studio, 2 Harris Green,
Broseley, Shropshire, TF12 5HJ
Area of Operation: UK & Ireland
Tel: 01746 785025 **Fax:** 01746 785025
Email: heritagetile@msn.com
Web: www.heritagetile.co.uk
Product Type: 1, 3, 5

HITT OAK LTD
10 Park Parade,
Gunnersbury Avenue, London, W3 9BD
Area of Operation: UK (Excluding Ireland)
Tel: 0208 896 1900
Fax: 0208 896 1900
Email: zhitas@yahoo.co.uk

HOT GLASS DESIGN
Unit 24 Crosby Yard Industrial Estate,
Bridgend, Mid Glamorgan, CF31 1JZ
Area of Operation: Europe
Tel: 01656 659884
Fax: 01656 659884
Email: info@hotglassdesign.co.uk
Web: www.hotglassdesign.co.uk
Material Type: J) 1, 2, 4, 5, 6

HUNTER ART & TILE STUDIO
Craft Courtyard, Harestanes,
Ancrum, Jedburgh, Borders, TD8 6UQ
Area of Operation: UK & Ireland
Tel: 01835 830 328
Email: enquiries@hunterartandtilestudio.co.uk
Web: www.hunterartandtilestudio.co.uk
Product Type: 1

HYPERION TILES
67 High Street, Ascot, Berkshire, SL5 7HP
Area of Operation: Greater London, South East England
Tel: 01344 620211 **Fax:** 01344 620100
Email: graham@hyperiontiles.com
Web: www.hyperiontiles.com
Product Type: 1, 2, 3, 4, 5

INDIGENOUS LTD
Cheltenham Road, Burford, Oxfordshire, OX18 4JA
Area of Operation: Worldwide
Tel: 01993 824200
Fax: 01993 824300
Email: enquiries@indigenoustiles.com
Web: www.indigenoustiles.com
Product Type: 1

KIEVEL.KL-CHEMIE (UK) LTD
Lower Farm, Lower Farm Lane,
Ampfield, Romsey, Hampshire, SO51 9BN
Area of Operation: UK & Ireland
Tel: 01794 368865 **Fax:** 01794 368914
Email: info@kievel.com
Web: www.kievel.com **Product Type:** 3, 4

KIRK NATURAL STONE
Bridgend, Fyvie, Turriff, Aberdeenshire, AB53 8LL
Area of Operation: Worldwide
Tel: 01651 891891
Fax: 01651 891794
Email: info@kirknaturalstone.com
Web: www.kirknaturalstone.com

LAWLEY CERAMICS
8 Stourbridge Road, Bromsgrove,
Worcestershire, B61 0AB
Area of Operation: UK (Excluding Ireland)
Tel: 01527 570455
Fax: 01527 570455
Email: lawleyceramics@hotmail.com

MAGGIE JONES HAND PAINTED TILES
19 Langland Road, Mumbles,
Swansea, SA3 4ND
Area of Operation: Europe
Tel: 01792 360551
Email: maggie@maggiejonestiles.co.uk
Web: www.maggiejonestiles.co.uk
Product Type: 1

MANDARIN
Unit 1 Wonastow Road Industrial Estate,
Monmouth, Monmouthshire, NP25 5JB
Area of Operation: Europe
Tel: 01600 715444
Fax: 01600 715494
Email: info@mandarinstone.com
Web: www.mandarinstone.com

MANOR ARCHITECTURAL CERAMICS LTD
16 Charles Street, Warwick,
Warwickshire, CV34 5LE
Area of Operation: Worldwide
Tel: 01926 400946
Fax: 01926 400272
Email: mike@manorceramic.co.uk
Web: www.manorceramic.co.uk
Product Type: 1, 5

MARIA STARLING MOSAICS
40 Strand House, Merbury Close, London, SE28 0LU
Area of Operation: UK (Excluding Ireland)
Tel: 07775 517409
Email: mosaics@mariastarling.com
Web: www.mariastarling.com

MARLBOROUGH TILES LTD
Elcot Lane, Marlborough, Wiltshire, SN8 2AY
Area of Operation: UK & Ireland
Tel: 01672 512422
Fax: 01672 515791
Email: admin@marlboroughtiles.com
Web: www.marlboroughtiles.com
Product Type: 1, 3, 4

METAL TILES LTD
6c Waterloo Works, Gorsey Mount Street,
Stockport, Cheshire, SK1 3BU
Area of Operation: UK (Excluding Ireland)
Tel: 0161 480 1166 **Fax:** 0161 480 2838
Email: info@metaltiles.ltd.uk
Web: www.metaltiles.ltd.uk
Material Type: C) 3, 7, 11

MIRRORKOOL LTD
89 High Street, Earith, Cambridgeshire, PE28 3PN
Area of Operation: Worldwide
Tel: 01487 741300 **Fax:** 08712 367554
Email: sam@mirrorkool.com
Web: www.mirrorkool.com
Product Type: 2

N&C NICOBOND
41-51 Freshwater Road,
Chadwell Heath, Romford, Essex, RM8 1SP
Area of Operation: Worldwide
Tel: 0208 586 4600 **Fax:** 0208 586 4646
Email: info@nichollsandclarke.com
Web: www.ncdirect.co.uk

NICAN STONE LTD
Bank House, School Lane,
Bronington, Shropshire, SY13 3HN
Area of Operation: UK (Excluding Ireland)
Tel: 01948 780670
Fax: 01948 780679
Email: enquiries@nicanstone.com
Web: www.nicanstone.com

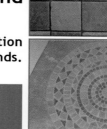

NORTON TILE COMPANY LIMITED
The Coach House, Norton Lane, Norton,
Chichester, West Sussex, PO20 3NH
Area of Operation: UK (Excluding Ireland)
Tel: 01243 544224   **Fax:** 01243 544033
Email: information@norton-tile.co.uk
Web: www.norton-tile.co.uk   **Product Type:** 1

ORIGINAL STYLE
Falcon Road, Sowton Industrial Estate,
Exeter, Devon, EX2 7LF
Area of Operation: Worldwide
Tel: 01392 474011   **Fax:** 01392 219932
Email: eboalch@originalstyle.com
Web: www.originalstyle.com
Product Type: 1, 3, 4, 5
Other Info: ✋   **Material Type:** F) 1, 3

PARKSIDE TILES
49-51 Highmeres Road, Thurmeston,
Leicester, Leicestershire, LE4 9LZ
Area of Operation: UK (Excluding Ireland)
Tel: 0116 276 2532   **Fax:** 0116 246 0649
Email: info@parksidetiles.co.uk
Web: www.parksidetiles.co.uk
Product Type: 1, 2, 3, 4, 5
Material Type: F) 1, 2, 4

PHOENIX TILE STUDIO
Unit 3 Winkhill Mill, Swan Street,
Stoke on Trent, Staffordshire, ST4 7RH
Area of Operation: Worldwide
Tel: 01782 745599   **Fax:** 01782 745599
Email: info@phoenixtilestudio.co.uk
Web: www.phoenixtilestudio.co.uk
Product Type: 1, 3, 4, 5   **Material Type:** F) 1

PILKINGTON'S TILES GROUP
PO Box 4, Clifton Junction, Manchester, M27 8LP
Area of Operation: UK (Excluding Ireland)
Tel: 0161 727 1000   **Fax:** 0161 727 1122
Email: sales@pilkingtons.com
Web: www.pilkingtons.com   **Product Type:** 3, 4, 5

RAK CERAMICS
The Tile House, Easebourne Lane,
Easebourne, West Sussex, GU29 9AZ
Area of Operation: Worldwide
Tel: 01730 815507   **Fax:** 01730 815007
Email: info@rakceramics.co.uk
Web: www.rakceramics.co.uk
Product Type: 3, 4, 5

ROCK UNIQUE LTD
c/o Select Garden and Pet Centre,
Main Road, Sundridge, Kent, TN14 6ED
Area of Operation: Europe
Tel: 01959 565608   **Fax:** 01959 569312
Email: stone@rock-unique.com
Web: www.rock-unique.com
Product Type: 3, 4, 5   **Other Info:** ECO ✎ ✋
Material Type: E) 1, 2, 3, 4, 5, 9

RUPERT SCOTT LTD
The Glass Studio, Mytton Mill, Montford Bridge,
Shrewsbury, Shropshire, SY4 1HA
Area of Operation: UK (Excluding Ireland)
Tel: 01743 851393   **Fax:** 01743 851393
Email: info@rupertscott.co.uk
Web: www.rupertscott.com
Other Info: ✋   **Material Type:** J) 5

RUSTICA LTD
154c Milton Park, Oxfordshire, OX14 4SD
Area of Operation: UK & Ireland
Tel: 01235 834192   **Fax:** 01235 835162
Email: sales@rustica.co.uk
Web: www.rustica.co.uk   **Product Type:** 1, 3, 4, 5

**SHARON JONES HANDMADE
ARCHITECTURAL CERAMIC TILES**
Trevillian Cottage, Barrington,
Nr Ilminster, Somerset, TA19 0JB
Area of Operation: UK (Excluding Ireland)
Tel: 01460 259074
Email: info@handmadearchitecturaltiles.co.uk
Web: www.handmadearchitecturaltiles.co.uk
Product Type: 1, 3, 4, 5   **Other Info:** ✎ ✋

SIMALI STONE FLOORING
40E Wincombe Business Park,
Shaftesbury, Dorset, SP7 9QJ
Area of Operation: Europe
Tel: 01747 852557
Fax: 01747 852557
Email: stonefloors@aol.com
Web: www.stoneflooringonline.com

SPECIALIST TILING SUPPLIES
Unit 5, Wortley Moor Lane Trading Estate,
Leeds, West Yorkshire, LS12 4HX
Area of Operation: UK & Ireland
Tel: 0800 781 8384   **Fax:** 0113 202 2015

STONE AND SLATE
Coney Green Farm, Lower Market Street,
Claycross, Chesterfield, Derbyshire, S45 9NE
Area of Operation: UK & Ireland
Tel: 01246 250088   **Fax:** 01246 250099
Email: sales@stoneandslate.ltd.uk
Web: www.stoneandslate.co.uk
Product Type: 1, 2, 4, 5

STONE FLOOR TILES LIMITED
The Nurseries, 221 Halifax Road,
Brighouse, West Yorkshire, HX3 8DH
Area of Operation: UK (Excluding Ireland)
Tel: 01484 402454   **Fax:** 01484 402454
Email: simon@stone-floor-tiles.co.uk
Web: www.stone-floor-tiles.co.uk
Product Type: 2, 3, 4, 5

STONE TILES ONLINE
Boxted Farm, Berkhamsted Road,
Hemel Hempstead, Hertfordshire, HP1 2SQ
Area of Operation: UK & Ireland
Tel: 0845 308 1100
Fax: 01442 229282
Email: info@stonetilesonline.co.uk
Web: www.stonetilesonline.co.uk ✎
Product Type: 3

STONELL DIRECT
7 showrooms nationwide - see website for details
Area of Operation: Worldwide
Tel: 08000 832283   **Fax:** 01283 501098
Email: info@stonelldirect.com
Web: www.stonelldirect.com

STONEVILLE (UK) LTD
Unit 12, Set Star Estate, Transport Avenue, Great
West Road, Brentford, Greater London, TW8 9HF
Area of Operation: Europe
Tel: 0208 560 1000
Fax: 0208 560 4060
Email: info@stoneville.co.uk
Web: www.stoneville.co.uk
Material Type: E) 1, 2, 5, 8

STUDIO STONE
The Stone Yard, Alton Lane,
Four Marks, Hampshire, GU34 5AJ
Area of Operation: UK (Excluding Ireland)
Tel: 01420 562500
Fax: 01420 563192
Email: info@studiostone.co.uk
Web: www.studiostone.co.uk

SURFACE SOLUTIONS
33 Alma Road, Herne Bay, Kent, CT6 6JJ
Area of Operation: UK (Excluding Ireland)
Tel: 01227 362775

TERRA OMNIA
39 Shortheath Road, Farnham, Surrey, GU9 8SH
Area of Operation: UK & Ireland
Tel: 01252 716661   **Fax:** 01252 716661
Email: info@terraomnia.com
Web: www.terraomnia.com
Product Type: 1, 2, 3, 4, 5

TERRANOVA CERAMICS LTD
Lings Farm, York Road, Bishop Burton,
East Riding of Yorks, HU17 7RU
Area of Operation: UK (Excluding Ireland)
Tel: 01964 551555
Web: www.terranova.uk.com

THE CANDY TILE COMPANY
Heathfield, Newton Abbot, Devon, TQ12 6RF
Area of Operation: UK (Excluding Ireland)
Tel: 01626 834774
Fax: 01626 834775
Email: sales@candytiles.com
Web: www.candytiles.com
Product Type: 3, 4, 5

THE GRANITE FACTORY
4 Winchester Drive, Peterlee, Durham, SR8 2RJ
Area of Operation: North East England
Tel: 0191 518 3600
Fax: 0191 518 3600
Email: admin@granitefactory.co.uk
Web: www.granitefactory.co.uk ✎

THE ORIGINAL TILE COMPANY
23A Howe Street, Lothian, EH3 6TF
Area of Operation: UK & Ireland
Tel: 0131 556 2013   **Fax:** 0131 558 3172
Email: info@originaltile.freeserve.co.uk
Web: www.originaltilecompany.co.uk
Product Type: 1, 2, 3, 4, 5
Other Info: ✎ ✋   **Material Type:** C) 1, 3, 14, 17

THE STONE AND CERAMIC WAREHOUSE
51-55 Stirling Road, Chiswick, London, W3 8DJ
Area of Operation: Worldwide
Tel: 0208 993 5545   **Fax:** 0208 752 0281
Email: wespalmer@sacw.co.uk
Web: www.sacw.co.uk
Product Type: 3, 4, 5

THE TILE ASSOCIATION
Forum Court, 83 Copers Cope Road,
Beckenham, Kent, BR3 1NR
Area of Operation: UK & Ireland
Tel: 0208 663 0946   **Fax:** 0208 663 0949
Email: info@tiles.org.uk
Web: www.tiles.org.uk

TILEASY LTD
Unit 10a, Railway Triangle, Walton Road,
Portsmouth, Hampshire, PO6 1TN
Area of Operation: UK & Ireland
Tel: 02392 220077   **Fax:** 02392 220088
Email: enquiries@craftceramics.com
Web: www.craftceramics.com
Product Type: 1, 3, 4, 5

TILES UK LTD
1-13 Montford Street, Off South Langworthy Road,
Salford, Greater Manchester, M50 2XD
Area of Operation: UK (Excluding Ireland)
Tel: 0161 872 5155   **Fax:** 0161 848 7948
Email: info@tilesuk.com
Web: www.tilesuk.com ✎
Product Type: 1, 2, 3, 4, 5

TOPPS TILES
Thorpe Way, Grove Park,
Enderby, Leicestershire, LE19 1SU
Area of Operation: UK (Excluding Ireland)
Tel: 0116 282 8000
Fax: 0116 282 8100
Email: mlever@toppstiles.co.uk
Web: www.toppstiles.co.uk

TOPPS TILES

Area of Operation: UK (Excluding Ireland)
Tel: 0116 282 8000   **Fax:** 0116 282 8100
Email: mlever@toppstiles.co.uk
Web: www.toppstiles.co.uk

Topps Tiles is Britain's biggest tile and wood
flooring specialist, with over 200 stores
nationwide. For details of your nearest store
or free brochure call 0800 138 1673
www.toppstiles.co.uk.

TRADEMARK TILES
Tile Store, Somersham Road, St Ives,
Huntingdon, Cambridgeshire, PE27 3WR
Area of Operation: UK (Excluding Ireland)
Tel: 01480 498123
Email: info@tilestoreplus.co.uk
Web: www.tilestoreplus.co.uk ✎
Product Type: 1, 3, 4, 5

UK TILES DIRECT LTD
42 Bestwall Road, Wareham, Dorset, BH20 4JA
Area of Operation: UK (Excluding Ireland)
Tel: 01929 556169
Email: admin@uktilesdirect.co.uk
Web: www.uktilesdirect.co.uk

WALLS AND FLOORS LTD
Wilson Terrace, Kettering,
Northamptonshire, NN16 9RT
Area of Operation: UK (Excluding Ireland)
Tel: 01536 410484
Email: sales@wallsandfloors.uk.com
Web: www.wallsandfloors.uk.com ✎

WAXMAN CERAMICS LTD
Grove Mills, Elland, West Yorkshire, HX5 9DZ
Tel: 01422 311331   **Fax:** 01422 370360
Email: sales@waxmanceramics.co.uk
Web: www.waxmanceramics.co.uk

WILTON STUDIOS
Cleethorpes Business Centre, Wilton Road Industrial
Estate, Grimsby, Lincolnshire, DN36 4AS
Area of Operation: UK (Excluding Ireland)
Tel: 01472 210820
Fax: 01472 812602
Email: postbox@wiltonstudios.co.uk
Web: www.wiltonstudios.co.uk
Product Type: 1, 2, 3, 4, 5   **Other Info:** ✎ ✋

WORLD'S END TILES
Silverthorne Road, Battersea, London, SW8 3HE
Area of Operation: UK (Excluding Ireland)
Tel: 0207 819 2100   **Fax:** 0207 819 2101
Email: info@worldsendtiles.co.uk
Web: www.worldsendtiles.co.uk
Product Type: 1, 3, 4, 5
Other Info: 🖰   **Material Type:** E) 2

WALLPAPER

KEY
PRODUCT TYPES: 1= Flock   2 = Paper
3 = Paperweave   4 = Stretch Fabric
5 = Suede Effect   6 = Textile   7 = Other
OTHER: ▽ Reclaimed   🖰 On-line shopping
✎ Bespoke   🖐 Hand-made   ECO Ecological

CHAMELEON COLLECTION
8 High Street, Alcester, Warwickshire, B49 5AD
Area of Operation: Worldwide
Tel: 01789 762857   **Fax:** 01789 400592
Email: andymills@chameleoncollection.co.uk
Web: www.chameleoncollection.co.uk
Product Type: 1, 2, 5, 6

FARROW & BALL
Uddens Estate, Wimborne, Dorset, BH21 7NL
Area of Operation: Worldwide
Tel: 01202 876141   **Fax:** 01202 873793
Email: sales@farrow-ball.com
Web: www.farrow-ball.com 🖰
Product Type: 2

HAMILTON WESTON WALLPAPERS
18 St Marys Grove, Richmond, Surrey, TW9 1UY
Area of Operation: UK & Ireland
Tel: 020 8940 4850   **Fax:** 020 8332 0296
Email: info@hamiltonweston.com
Web: www.hamiltonweston.com
Product Type: 2   **Other Info:** ✎

ID-WALL LTD
90 New North Road, Huddersfield,
West Yorkshire, HD1 5NE
Area of Operation: Worldwide
Tel: 01484 543210
Email: info@id-wall.com
Web: www.id-wall.com 🖰   **Product Type:** 2, 7

PETER CARLSON INTERIORS
Lower Hillgate, Stockport, Cheshire, SK1 3AW
Area of Operation: North West England and North Wales
Tel: 0161 480 8164   **Fax:** 0161 480 0097
Email: petercarlson@petercarlson.co.uk
Web: www.petercarlson.co.uk
Product Type: 1, 2, 3, 4, 5, 6

RAY MUNN LTD
861-863 Fulham Road, London, SW6 5HP
Area of Operation: UK (Excluding Ireland)
Tel: 0207 736 9876
Email: rishi@raymunn.com
Web: www.raymunn.com
Product Type: 1, 2, 3, 5, 7

REDCOW IMAGING
17 Eaton Mews, Chester, Cheshire, CH4 7EJ
Area of Operation: Worldwide
Tel: 08708 810670   **Fax:** 08708 810670
Email: info@redcowimaging.com
Web: www.redcowimaging.com 🖰
Product Type: 7

ROOMS FOR KIDS LTD
Unit 20 Argyle Industrial Estate, Argyle Street South,
Birkenhead, Cheshire, CH41 4HH
Area of Operation: Worldwide
Tel: 0151 650 2401   **Fax:** 0151 650 2403
Email: roger@friezeframe.com
Web: www.friezeframe.com 🖰
Product Type: 2, 7

TENTERDEN HOUSE INTERIORS
4 West Cross, Tenterden, Kent, TN30 6JL
Area of Operation: UK (Excluding Ireland)
Tel: 01580 764481   **Fax:** 01580 765531
Email: tenterdenhouseinteriors@hotmail.com
Product Type: 2

THE WORLDWIDE WOOD COMPANY LIMITED
154 Colney Hatch Lane,
Muswell Hill, London, N10 1ER
Area of Operation: Worldwide
Tel: 0800 458 3366   **Fax:** 0208 365 3965
Email: info@solidwoodflooring.com
Web: www.solidwoodflooring.com
Product Type: 7

THEISSEN GARDINEN-RAUMAUSSTATTUNG
Virchowstraße 18, Essen, Germany, 45147
Area of Operation: Europe
Tel: 0049 201 734 011
Fax: 0049 201 701 871
Email: naturcom-theissen@t-online.de
Product Type: 2, 6

VICTORIA HAMMOND INTERIORS
Bury Farm, Church Street, Bovingdon,
Hemel Hempstead, Hertfordshire, HP3 0LU
Area of Operation: UK (Excluding Ireland)
Tel: 01442 831641   **Fax:** 01442 831641
Email: victoria@victoriahammond.com
Web: www.victoriahammond.com
Product Type: 1, 2, 3, 4, 5, 6, 7   **Other Info:** ✎

WALLPAPERORDERS.CO.UK
Oozewood Road, Royton,
Oldham, Lancashire, OL2 5SQ
Area of Operation: UK (Excluding Ireland)
Tel: 0870 170 9660   **Fax:** 0161 627 4459
Email: sales@wallpaperorders.co.uk
Web: www.wallpaperorders.co.uk

WILLIAM ROBINSON INTERNATIONAL
Daleside Road, Nottinghamshire, NG2 4DH
Area of Operation: UK (Excluding Ireland)
Tel: 0115 979 9790   **Fax:** 0115 959 9590
Email: sales@williamrobinson.co.uk
Web: www.williamrobinson.co.uk

WALL PANELLING

KEY
PRODUCT TYPES: 1= Laminated
2 = Wood Veneered   3 = Timber Effect
4 = Other
OTHER: ▽ Reclaimed   🖰 On-line shopping
✎ Bespoke   🖐 Hand-made   ECO Ecological

ARCHITECTURAL HERITAGE
Taddington Manor, Taddington, Nr Cutsdean,
Cheltenham, Gloucestershire, GL54 5RY
Area of Operation: Worldwide
Tel: 01386 584414   **Fax:** 01386 584236
Email: puddy@architectural-heritage.co.uk
Web: www.architectural-heritage.co.uk
Other Info: ▽ ✎ 🖐

BHK FLOORING LTD
Davy Drive, North West Industrial Estate,
Peterlee, Durham, SR8 2JF
Area of Operation: UK & Ireland
Tel: 0191 518 6538   **Fax:** 0191 518 6536
Email: eleanor.smith@peterlee.bhk.de
Web: www.bhkonline.com
Product Type: 1, 2, 3   **Other Info:** ECO

CANADA WOOD UK
PO Box 1, Farnborough, Hampshire, GU14 6WE
Area of Operation: UK & Ireland
Tel: 01252 522545   **Fax:** 01252 522546
Email: office@canadawooduk.org
Web: www.canadawood.info
Product Type: 4   **Material Type:** A) 12

CITY BATHROOMS & KITCHENS
158 Longford Road, Longford,
Coventry, West Midlands, CV6 6DR
Area of Operation: UK & Ireland
Tel: 02476 365877   **Fax:** 02476 644992
Email: citybathrooms@hotmail.com
Web: www.citybathrooms.co.uk

CORE AND ORE LTD
16 Portland Street, Clifton, Bristol, BS8 4JH
Area of Operation: UK (Excluding Ireland)
Tel: 01179 042408   **Fax:** 01179 094010
Email: sales@coreandore.com
Web: www.coreandore.com
Product Type: 4   **Material Type:** M) 4

DEACON & SANDYS
Apple Pie Farm, Cranbrook Road,
Benenden, Kent, TN17 4EU
Area of Operation: Worldwide
Tel: 01580 243331   **Fax:** 01580 243301
Email: pr@deaconandsandys.co.uk
Web: www.deaconandsandys.co.uk
Product Type: 4   **Material Type:** A) 2

ECO IMPACT LTD
50a Kew Green, Richmond,
Greater London, TW9 3BB
Area of Operation: UK & Ireland
Tel: 0208 940 7072   **Fax:** 0208 332 1218
Email: sales@ecoimpact.co.uk
Web: www.ecoimpact.co.uk   **Product Type:** 4

FORMICA LIMITED
Coast Road, North Shields, Tyne & Wear, NE29 8RE
Area of Operation: UK & Ireland
Tel: 0191 259 3000   **Fax:** 0191 2582719
Email: info@formica.co.uk
Web: www.formica.co.uk   **Product Type:** 1

HALLIDAYS UK LTD
Queen Street, Dorchester On Thames,
Oxfordshire, OX10 7HL
Area of Operation: Worldwide
Tel: 01865 340028   **Fax:** 01865 341149
Email: info@hallidays.com
Web: www.hallidays.com   **Product Type:** 1, 2, 3, 4

HANNAH WHITE
Area of Operation: Worldwide
Tel: 01372 806703   **Fax:** 01372 806703
Email: info@hannahwhite.co.uk
Web: www.hannahwhite.co.uk
Product Type: 4   **Other Info:** ✎ 🖐
Material Type: M) 4

HERAKLITH
Broadway House, 21 Broadway,
Maidenhead, Berkshire, SL6 1NJ
Area of Operation: UK & Ireland
Tel: 01628 784330   **Fax:** 01628 633080
Email: muirwork@btinternet.com
Product Type: 4   **Other Info:** ECO
Material Type: H) 8

ION GLASS
PO Box 284, Burgess Hill, West Sussex, RH15 0BN
Area of Operation: UK (Excluding Ireland)
Tel: 0845 658 9988   **Fax:** 0845 658 9989
Email: sales@ionglass.co.uk
Web: www.ionglass.co.uk
Product Type: 4   **Other Info:** ✎
Material Type: J) 1, 4, 5, 6

LAWSONS
Gorst Lane, Off New Lane, Burscough,
Ormskirk, Lancashire, L40 0RS
Area of Operation: Worldwide
Tel: 01704 893998   **Fax:** 01704 892526
Email: info@traditionaltimber.co.uk
Web: www.traditionaltimber.co.uk

NATURAL BUILDING TECHNOLOGIES
The Hangar, Worminghall Road,
Oakley, Buckinghamshire, HP18 9UL
Area of Operation: UK & Ireland
Tel: 01844 338338   **Fax:** 01844 338525
Email: info@natural-building.co.uk
Web: www.natural-building.co.uk

NORSKE INTERIORS
Estate Road One, South Humberside Industrial
Estate, Grimsby, Lincolnshire, DN31 2TA
Area of Operation: UK (Excluding Ireland)
Tel: 01472 240832   **Fax:** 01472 360112
Email: sales@norske-int.co.uk
Web: www.norske-int.co.uk   **Product Type:** 4

OAKLEAF
Unit A , Melbourne Mills, Chesham Street,
Keighley, West Yorkshire, BD21 4LG
Area of Operation: Worldwide
Tel: 01535 663274   **Fax:** 01535 661951
Email: jonathan@oakleaf.co.uk
Web: www.oakleaf.co.uk

ORCHARD STONEMASONS
48 West Street, Axbridge, Somerset, BS26 2AD
Area of Operation: UK (Excluding Ireland)
Tel: 01934 732718   **Fax:** 01934 732718
Email: info@orchardstonemasons.co.uk
Web: www.orchardstonemasons.co.uk
Product Type: 4

PANEL MASTER UK LIMITED
Unit 7, Spring Vale Mill, Waterside Road,
Haslingden, Rossendale, Lancashire, BB4 5EZ
Area of Operation: UK & Ireland
Tel: 01706 219196   **Fax:** 01706 222173
Email: www.panelmaster.co.uk
Web: www.panelmaster.co.uk 🖰
Product Type: 1, 2, 3, 4

PANELITDIRECT.COM
Unit 1, Oldhall Industrial Estate,
Bromborough, Wirral, Cheshire, CH62 3QA
Area of Operation: UK & Ireland
Tel: 0845 466 0123   **Fax:** 0870 170 9870
Email: info@panelitdirect.co.uk
Web: www.panelitdirect.com
Product Type: 4   **Material Type:** D) 1

PLASTIVAN LTD
Unit 4 Bonville Industrial Estate,
Bonville Road, Brislington, Bristol, BS4 5QU
Area of Operation: Worldwide
Tel: 0117 300 5625
Fax: 0117 971 5028
Email: sales@plastivan.co.uk
Web: www.plastivan.co.uk
Product Type: 1, 3, 4   **Other Info:** ▽

STEVENSONS OF NORWICH LIMITED
Roundtree Way, Norwich, Norfolk, NR7 8SQ
Area of Operation: Worldwide
Tel: 01603 400824   **Fax:** 01603 405113
Email: info@stevensons-of-norwich.co.uk
Web: www.stevensons-of-norwich.co.uk
Product Type: 4

STUART INTERIORS
Barrington Court, Barrington,
Ilminster, Somerset, TA19 0NQ
Area of Operation: Worldwide
Tel: 01460 240349
Fax: 01460 242069
Email: design@stuartinteriors.com
Web: www.stuartinteriors.com
Product Type: 2, 4   **Other Info:** ✎ 🖐
Material Type: A) 2

SWISH BUILDING PRODUCTS LTD
Pioneer House, Mariner, Litchfield Road Industrial
Estate, Tamworth, Staffordshire, B79 7TF
Area of Operation: UK & Ireland
Tel: 01827 317200   **Fax:** 01827 317201
Email: info@swishbp.co.uk
Web: www.swishbp.co.uk   **Material Type:** D) 1

TBS FABRICATIONS
Martens Road, Northbank Industrial Park,
rlam, Manchester, M44 5AX.
Area of Operation: UK & Ireland
Tel: 0161 775 1871   **Fax:** 0161 775 8929.
Email: info@tbs-fabrications.co.uk
Web: www.tbs-fabrications.co.uk
Product Type: 1, 2, 3, 4
Material Type: C) 1, 3

THE CARPENTRY INSIDER - AIRCOMDIRECT
1 Castleton Crescent, Skegness,
Lincolnshire, PE25 2TJ
Area of Operation: Worldwide
Tel: 01754 767163
Email: aircom8@hotmail.com
Web: www.easycarpentry.com
Product Type: 3, 4

THE GRANITE FACTORY
4 Winchester Drive, Peterlee, Durham, SR8 2RJ
Area of Operation: North East England
Tel: 0191 518 3600   **Fax:** 0191 518 3600
Email: admin@granitefactory.co.uk
Web: www.granitefactory.co.uk
Product Type: 2

THE WORLDWIDE WOOD COMPANY LIMITED
154 Colney Hatch Lane,
Muswell Hill, London, N10 1ER
Area of Operation: Worldwide
Tel: 0800 458 3366   **Fax:** 0208 365 3965
Email: info@solidwoodflooring.com
Web: www.solidwoodflooring.com
Product Type: 2

THORNHILL GALLERIES
No. 3, 19 Osiers Road, London, SW18 1NL
Area of Operation: Worldwide
Tel: 0208 874 2101   **Fax:** 0208 877 0313
Email: sales@thornhillgalleries.co.uk
Web: www.thornhillgalleries.co.uk

VICTORIAN WOOD WORKS LTD
54 River Road, Creekmouth,
Barking, Essex, IG11 0DW
Area of Operation: Worldwide
Tel: 0208 534 1000   **Fax:** 0208 534 2000
Email: sales@victorianwoodworks.co.uk
Web: www.victorianwoodworks.co.uk

VISION ASSOCIATES
Demita House, North Orbital Road,
Denham, Buckinghamshire, UB9 5EY
Area of Operation: UK & Ireland
Tel: 01895 831600   **Fax:** 01895 835323
Email: info@visionassociates.co.uk
Web: www.visionassociates.co.uk
Product Type: 2

WOODHOUSE TIMBER
Unit 15 Quarry Farm Industrial Estate,
Staplecross Road, Bodiam, East Sussex, TN32 5RA
Area of Operation: UK (Excluding Ireland)
Tel: 01580 831700   **Fax:** 01580 830054
Email: info@woodhousetimber.co.uk
Web: www.woodhousetimber.co.uk
Material Type: A) 2

PAINTS, STAINS AND VARNISHES

KEY
PRODUCT TYPES: 1= Interior Paint
2 = Exterior Paint   3 = Stains and Varnishes
OTHER: ▽ Reclaimed   On-line shopping
Bespoke   Hand-made   ECO Ecological

AURO UK - NATURAL PAINTS
Cheltenham Road, Bisley, Gloucestershire, GL6 7BX
Area of Operation: UK (Excluding Ireland)
Tel: 01452 772020   **Fax:** 01452 770104
Email: sales@auro.co.uk
Web: www.auro.co.uk
Product Type: 1, 2, 3

BEDEC PRODUCT LTD
Units 1 & 2 Poplars Farm, Aythorpe Roding,
Dunmow, Essex, CM6 1RY
Area of Operation: Worldwide
Tel: 01279 876657   **Fax:** 01279 876008
Email: info@bedec.co.uk
Web: www.bedec.co.uk

BIOFA UK
Gloucester House,
45 Gloucester Street, Brighton, BN14EW
Area of Operation: UK & Ireland
Tel: 01273 685800
Fax: 01273 699304
Email: laurentcoltrane@villanatura.co.uk
Web: www.biofa.co.uk   **Product Type:** 1, 2, 3

BONAKEMI LIMITED
1 Radian Court, Davy Avenue, Knowlhill,
Milton Keynes, Buckinghamshire, MK5 8PJ
Area of Operation: UK & Ireland
Tel: 01908 399740
Fax: 01908 232722
Email: info.uk@bona.com
Web: www.bona.com   **Product Type:** 3

CENTRE FOR ALTERNATIVE TECHNOLOGY
Llwyngwren Quarry, Machynlleth, Powys, SY20 9AZ
Area of Operation: Worldwide
Tel: 01654 705 950   **Fax:** 01654 702 782
Email: lucy.stone@cat.org.uk
Web: www.cat.org.uk   **Other Info:** ECO

CONSTRUCTION RESOURCES
16 Great Guildford Street, London, SE1 0HS
Area of Operation: UK (Excluding Ireland)
Tel: 0207 450 2211
Fax: 0207 450 2212
Email: info@constructionresources.com
Web: www.constructionresources.com
Product Type: 1, 2, 3

DYEBRICK
Ripley House, Keycol Hill, Newington, Kent, ME9 8NE
Area of Operation: Worldwide
Tel: 01795 871972   **Fax:** 01795 871077
Email: mail@dyebrick.com
Web: www.dyebrick.com   **Product Type:** 3

DYECRETE
Ripley House, Keycol Hill, Newington, Kent, ME9 8NE
Area of Operation: Worldwide
Tel: 01795 871972   **Fax:** 01795 871077
Email: mail@dyebrick.com
Web: www.dyecrete.com   **Product Type:** 3

EARTHBORN PAINTS
Frodsham Business Centre, Bridge Lane,
Frodsham, Cheshire, WA6 7FZ
Area of Operation: UK & Ireland
Tel: 0207 566 5650
Web: www.earthbornpaints.co.uk
Product Type: 1, 2, 3

ECOSHOP
Unit 1, Glen of the Downs Garden Centre,
Kilmacanogue, Co. Wicklow, Republic of Ireland
Area of Operation: Ireland Only
Tel: +353 01 488 0400
Fax: +353 01 201 6480
Email: info@ecoshop.ie   **Web:** www.ecoshop.ie

FARROW & BALL
Uddens Estate, Wimborne, Dorset, BH21 7NL
Area of Operation: Worldwide
Tel: 01202 876141   **Fax:** 01202 873793
Email: sales@farrow-ball.com
Web: www.farrow-ball.com
Product Type: 1, 2, 3

FIRED EARTH
3 Twyford Mill, Oxford Road,
Adderbury, Banbury, Oxfordshire, OX17 3SX
Area of Operation: Worldwide
Tel: 01295 812088   **Fax:** 01295 810832
Email: enquiries@firedearth.com
Web: www.firedearth.com

HOLKHAM LINSEED PAINTS
The Clock Tower, Longlands, Holkham Park,
Wells-next-the-Sea, Norfolk, NR23 1RU
Area of Operation: UK & Ireland
Tel: 01328 711348   **Fax:** 01328 710368
Email: linseedpaint@holkham.co.uk
Web: www.holkhamlinseedpaints.co.uk
Product Type: 1, 2   **Other Info:** ECO

ICI PAINTS
Wexham Road, Slough, Berkshire, SL2 5DS
Area of Operation: Worldwide
Tel: 01753 550000
Web: www.cuprinoltrade.co.uk /
www.duluxtrade.co.uk   **Product Type:** 3

INTERNATIONAL PAINTS
Meadow Lane, St. Ives, Cambridgeshire, PE27 4UY
Area of Operation: UK & Ireland
Tel: 01480 484285
Web: www.international-paints.co.uk
Product Type: 1, 2

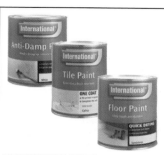

INTERNATIONAL PAINTS

Area of Operation: UK & Ireland
Tel: 01480 484285
Web: www.international-paints.co.uk
Product Type: 1, 2
International's range of paints provide tough, decorative protection against wear and tear. Paints are available in a choice of finishes and colours. From floor finishes to radiator finishes and exterior protection International has specialist paint for every occasion. Whenever you need outstanding performance in demanding conditions, International has the solution

JOHNSTONE'S PAINTS
Huddersfield Road, Birstall,
Batley, West Yorkshire, WF17 9XA
Area of Operation: UK & Ireland
Tel: 01924 354000
Fax: 01924 354001
Email: enquiries@sigmakalon.co.uk
Web: www.johnstones-paints.co.uk
Product Type: 1, 2, 3

KEIM MINERAL PAINTS LTD
Muckley Cross, Morville, Nr Bridgnorth,
Shropshire, WV16 4RR
Area of Operation: Worldwide
Tel: 01746 714543
Fax: 01746 714526
Email: sales@keimpaints.co.uk
Web: www.keimpaints.co.uk
Product Type: 1, 2   **Other Info:** ECO

MALABAR PAINTWORKS
31-33 The South Bank Business Centre,
Ponton Road, London, SW8 4B
Area of Operation: Europe
Tel: 0207 501 4200   **Fax:** 0207 501 4210
Email: info@malabar.co.uk
Web: www.malabar.co.uk
Product Type: 1   **Other Info:**

MIKE WYE & ASSOCIATES
Buckland Filleigh Sawmills, Buckland Filleigh,
Beaworthy, Devon, EX21 5RN
Area of Operation: Worldwide
Tel: 01409 281644   **Fax:** 01409 281669
Email: sales@mikewye.co.uk
Web: www.mikewye.co.uk
Product Type: 1, 2, 3   **Other Info:** ECO

MOULD GROWTH CONSULTANTS LTD
McMillan House, Cheam Common Road,
Worcester Park, Surrey, KT4 8RH
Area of Operation: UK & Ireland
Tel: 0208 337 0731   **Fax:** 0208 337 3739
Email: info@mgcltd.co.uk
Web: www.mgcltd.co.uk   **Product Type:** 2, 3

NATURAL BUILDING TECHNOLOGIES
The Hangar, Worminghall Road,
Oakley, Buckinghamshire, HP18 9UL
Area of Operation: UK & Ireland
Tel: 01844 338338   **Fax:** 01844 338525
Email: info@natural-building.co.uk
Web: www.natural-building.co.uk
Other Info: ECO

NEVER PAINT AGAIN INTERNATIONAL
2nd Floor, 145-157 St John's Street,
London, EC1V 4PY
Area of Operation: Worldwide
Tel: 0800 970 4928
Email: info@neverpaintagain.co.uk
Web: www.neverpaintagain.co.uk
Product Type: 1, 2, 3

NUTSHELL NATURAL PAINTS
PO Box 72, South Brent, Devon, TQ10 9YR
Area of Operation: Worldwide
Tel: 0870 033 1140   **Fax:** 01752 692200
Email: info@nutshellpaints.com
Web: www.nutshellpaints.com
Product Type: 1, 2, 3

OLD HOUSE STORE LTD
Hampstead Farm, Binfield Heath,
Henley on Thames, Oxfordshire, RG9 4LG
Area of Operation: Worldwide
Tel: 0118 969 7711   **Fax:** 0118 969 8822
Email: info@oldhousestore.co.uk
Web: www.oldhousestore.co.uk
Other Info: ECO

OLD HOUSE STORE LTD

Area of Operation: Worldwide
Tel: 0118 969 7711
Fax: 0118 969 8822
Email: info@oldhousestore.co.uk
Web: www.oldhousestore.co.uk
Other Info: ECO

Quality exterior masonry paint and decorating products, many made by hand using traditional techniques. Wood treatments and finishes, lime washes and paints, natural pigments and tinters.

ORIGINAL STYLE
Falcon Road, Sowton Industrial Estate,
Exeter, Devon, EX2 7LF
Area of Operation: Worldwide
Tel: 01392 474011   **Fax:** 01392 219932
Email: eboalch@originalstyle.com
Web: www.originalstyle.com   **Product Type:** 1

OSMO UK LTD
Unit 24 Anglo Business Park, Smeaton Close,
Aylesbury, Buckinghamshire, HP19 8UP
Area of Operation: UK & Ireland
Tel: 01296 481220   **Fax:** 01296 424090
Email: info@osmouk.com
Web: www.osmouk.com

PAINT MAGIC SHREWSBURY
16 Barrow Street, Much Wenlock,
Shropshire, TF13 6EN
Area of Operation: Worldwide
Tel: 01952 728768   **Fax:** 01952 728768
Email: ndesalis@btinternet.com
Web: www.paintmagic.net
Product Type: 1, 2, 3

RAY MUNN LTD
861-863 Fulham Road, London, SW6 5HP
Area of Operation: UK (Excluding Ireland)
Tel: 0207 736 9876
Email: rishi@raymunn.com
Web: www.raymunn.com
Product Type: 1, 2, 3 **Other Info:** ECO

SANDED FLOORS
7 Pleydell Avenue, Upper Norwood,
London, SE19 2LN
Area of Operation: UK (Excluding Ireland)
Tel: 0208 653 6283
Email: peter-weller@sandedfloors.co.uk
Web: www.sandedfloors.co.uk
Product Type: 3

TENTERDEN HOUSE INTERIORS
4 West Cross, Tenterden, Kent, TN30 6JL
Area of Operation: Worldwide
Tel: 01580 764481 **Fax:** 01580 765531
Email: tenterdenhouseinteriors@hotmail.com
Product Type: 1

THE GREEN SHOP
Cheltenham Road, Bisley, Nr Stroud,
Gloucestershire, GL6 7BX
Area of Operation: UK & Ireland
Tel: 01452 770629 **Fax:** 01452 770104
Email: paint@greenshop.co.uk
Web: www.greenshop.co.uk
Product Type: 3 **Other Info:** ECO

TRADITIONAL LIME CO
The Salvage Yard, Rath, Shillelagh Road,
Tullow, Co.Carlow, Ireland
Area of Operation: Ireland Only
Tel: 00353 599 151 750
Fax: 00353 599 152 113
Email: admin@traditionallime.com
Web: www.traditionallime.com
Product Type: 1, 2, 3

TY-MAWR LIME LTD
Ty-Mawr, Llangasty, Brecon, Powys, LD3 7PJ
Area of Operation: UK & Ireland
Tel: 01874 658000
Email: joyce.gervis@lime.org.uk
Web: www.lime.org.uk
Product Type: 1, 2, 3 **Other Info:** ECO

WILTON STUDIOS
Cleethorpes Business Centre, Wilton Road Industrial
Estate, Grimsby, Lincolnshire, DN36 4AS
Area of Operation: UK (Excluding Ireland)
Tel: 01472 210820 **Fax:** 01472 812602
Email: postbox@wiltonstudios.co.uk
Web: www.wiltonstudios.co.uk

ACCESS COVERS

KEY
OTHER: ▽ Reclaimed ᕦ On-line shopping
✎ Bespoke ✋Hand-made ECO Ecological

ACO BUILDING DRAINAGE
ACO Business Park, Hitchin Road,
Shefford, Bedfordshire, SG17 5TE
Area of Operation: UK & Ireland
Tel: 01462 816666
Fax: 01462 851490
Email: buildingdrainage@aco.co.uk
Web: www.acobuildingdrainage.co.uk

D-LINE (EUROPE) LIMITED
New York Way, New York Industrial Park,
Newcastle upon Tyne, Tyne & Wear, NE27 0QF
Area of Operation: Europe
Tel: 0191 293 0909 **Fax:** 0191 257 7722
Email: keving@d-line-it.co.uk
Web: www.d-line.co.uk

D-LINE (EUROPE) LTD

Area of Operation: Europe
Tel: 0191 293 0909
Fax: 0191 257 7722
Email: keving@d-line-it.co.uk
Web: www.d-line.co.uk

Use D-Line for the fastest and decorative way of
concealing surface wiring. Also available is a
socket fixing kit that requires no electrical
competence or certification.

EGGER (UK) LIMITED
Anick Grange Road, Hexham,
Northumberland, NE46 4JS
Area of Operation: UK & Ireland
Tel: 01434 602191 **Fax:** 01434 605103
Email: building.uk@egger.com **Web:** www.egger.co.uk

INTERFLOW UK
Leighton, Shrewsbury, Shropshire, SY5 6SQ
Area of Operation: UK & Ireland
Tel: 01952 510050 **Fax:** 01952 510967
Email: villiers@interflow.co.uk **Web:**
www.interflow.co.uk

TILE ADHESIVES AND GROUT

KEY
OTHER: ▽ Reclaimed ᕦ On-line shopping
✎ Bespoke ✋Hand-made ECO Ecological

AURO UK - NATURAL PAINTS
Cheltenham Road, Bisley, Gloucestershire, GL6 7BX
Area of Operation: UK (Excluding Ireland)
Tel: 01452 772020 **Fax:** 01452 770104
Email: sales@auro.co.uk **Web:** www.auro.co.uk

BUILDING ADHESIVES LTD
Longton Road, Trentham,
Stoke on Trent, Staffordshire, ST4 8JB
Area of Operation: Worldwide
Tel: 01782 591100 **Fax:** 01782 591101
Email: info@building-adhesives.com
Web: www.building-adhesives.com

CERAMIQUE INTERNATIONALE LTD
Unit 1 Royds Lane, Lower Wortley Ring Road,
Leeds, West Yorkshire, LS12 6DU
Area of Operation: UK & Ireland
Tel: 0113 231 0218 **Fax:** 0113 231 0353
Email: cameron@ceramiqueinternationale.co.uk
Web: www.ceramiqueinternationale.co.uk

CRAVEN DUNNILL
Stourbridge Road, Bridgnorth, Shropshire, WV15 6AS
Tel: 01746 761611 **Fax:** 01746 767007
Email: info@cravendunnill.co.uk
Web: www.cravendunnill.co.uk

DEGUSSA CONSTRUCTION CHEMICALS (UK)
Albany House, Swinton Hall Road, Swinton,
Manchester, M27 4DT
Area of Operation: Worldwide
Tel: 0161 794 7411 **Fax:** 0161 727 8547
Email: mbtfeb@basf.com
Web: www.degussa-cc.co.uk

DEVON STONE LTD
8 Pilot Road, Pierhead, Exmouth, Devon, EX8 1XA
Area of Operation: UK (Excluding Ireland)
Tel: 01395 222525
Email: amy@devonstone.com
Web: www.devonstone.com

EUROPEAN HERITAGE
48-54 Dawes Road, Fulham, London, SW6 7EN
Area of Operation: Worldwide
Tel: 0207 381 6063 **Fax:** 0207 381 9534
Email: fulham@europeanheritage.co.uk
Web: www.europeanheritage.co.uk

H & R JOHNSON TILES LTD
Harewood Street, Tunstall,
Stoke on Trent, Staffordshire, ST6 5JZ
Area of Operation: Worldwide
Tel: 01782 575575 **Fax:** 01782 524138
Email: sales @johnson-tiles.com
Web: www.johnson-tiles .com

INDIGENOUS LTD
Cheltenham Road, Burford, Oxfordshire, OX18 4JA
Area of Operation: Worldwide
Tel: 01993 824200 **Fax:** 01993 824300
Email: enquiries@indigenoustiles.com
Web: www.indigenoustiles.com

N&C NICOBOND
41-51 Freshwater Road,
Chadwell Heath, Romford, Essex, RM8 1SP
Area of Operation: Worldwide
Tel: 0208 586 4600 **Fax:** 0208 586 4646
Email: info@nichollsandclarke.com
Web: www.ncdirect.co.uk

ROCK UNIQUE LTD
c/o Select Garden and Pet Centre,
Main Road, Sundridge, Kent, TN14 6ED
Area of Operation: Europe
Tel: 01959 565 608 **Fax:** 01959 569 312
Email: stone@rock-unique.com
Web: www.rock-unique.com

STONE FLOOR TILES LIMITED
The Nurseries, 221 Halifax Road,
Brighouse, West Yorkshire, HX3 8DH
Area of Operation: UK (Excluding Ireland)
Tel: 01484 402454 **Fax:** 01484 402454
Email: simon@stone-floor-tiles.co.uk
Web: www.stone-floor-tiles.co.uk

STONE TILES ONLINE
Boxted Farm, Berkhamsted Road,
Hemel Hempstead, Hertfordshire, HP1 2SQ
Area of Operation: UK & Ireland
Tel: 0845 308 1100 **Fax:** 01442 229282
Email: info@stonetilesonline.co.uk
Web: www.stonetilesonline.co.uk

STONELL DIRECT
7 showrooms nationwide - see website for details,
Area of Operation: Worldwide
Tel: 08000 832283 **Fax:** 01283 501098
Email: info@stonelldirect.com
Web: www.stonelldirect.com

TERRA OMNIA
39 Shortheath Road, Farnham, Surrey, GU9 8SH
Area of Operation: UK & Ireland
Tel: 01252 716661 **Fax:** 01252 716661
Email: info@terraomnia.co.uk

THE STONE AND CERAMIC WAREHOUSE
51-55 Stirling Road, Chiswick, London, W3 8DJ
Area of Operation: Worldwide
Tel: 0208 993 5545 **Fax:** 0208 752 0281
Email: wespalmer@sacw.co.uk
Web: www.sacw.co.uk

TOPPS TILES
Thorpe Way, Grove Park,
Enderby, Leicestershire, LE19 1SU
Area of Operation: UK (Excluding Ireland)
Tel: 0116 282 8000 **Fax:** 0116 282 8100
Email: mlever@toppstiles.co.uk
Web: www.toppstiles.co.uk

TOPPS TILES

Area of Operation: UK (Excluding Ireland)
Tel: 0116 282 8000 **Fax:** 0116 282 8100
Email: mlever@toppstiles.co.uk
Web: www.toppstiles.co.uk

Topps Tiles is Britain's biggest tile and wood
flooring specialist, with over 200 stores
nationwide. For details of your nearest store
or free brochure call 0800 138 1673
www.toppstiles.co.uk.

PLASTER, PLASTERBOARD AND DRY LINING

KEY
PRODUCT TYPES: 1= Resin Bonded Plaster
2 = Gypsum Based Plaster
3 = Lightweight Plaster 4 = Textured Coatings
5 = Plaster Bonding 6 = Other Plasters
7 = Square-edged Plasterboard
8 = Feather-edged Plasterboard
9 = Fibre-reinforced Plasterboard
10 = Insulation-backed Plasterboard
OTHER: ▽ Reclaimed ᕦ On-line shopping
✎ Bespoke ✋Hand-made ECO Ecological

ALLTEK UK
(INTERNATIONAL COATING PRODUCTS LTD)
52 St. Johns Street, Ashbourne, Derbyshire, DE6 1GH
Area of Operation: UK & Ireland
Tel: 07963 723024 **Fax:** 01438 214162
Email: info@alltekuk.com
Web: www.alltekuk.com / www.icp-alltek.com
Product Type: 4, 6

ANDREW WILSON
184 Upper Shoreham Road, Shoreham-by-the-Sea,
West Sussex, BN43 6BG
Area of Operation: South East England
Tel: 01273 880257 **Fax:** 01273 232241

ARTIKA ORNAMENTAL PLASTERERS
6 The Retreat, Foxcote, Radstock, Somerset, BA3 5YF
Area of Operation: Worldwide
Tel: 01761 433740
Email: mark@artika.f9.co.uk
Web: www.bathbusinessfinder.co.uk/artika/index.php

B.WILLIAMSON & DAUGHTERS
Copse Cottage, Ford Manor Road,
Dormansland, Lingfield, Surrey, RH7 6NZ
Area of Operation: Greater London, South East England
Tel: 01342 834829 **Fax:** 01342 834829
Email: bryan.williamson@btclick.com
Web: www.specialistcleaning4me.co.uk
Product Type: 1, 3, 4, 5, 6

BPB ARTEX LTD
Pasture Lane, Ruddington, Nottingham,
Nottinghamshire, NG11 6AE
Area of Operation: UK (Excluding Ireland)
Tel: 0115 984 5679 **Fax:** 0115 940 5240
Email: info@bpb.com **Web:** www.bpbartex.co.uk

BRITISH GYPSUM LIMITED
Head Office, East Leake,
Loughborough, Leicestershire, LE12 6HX
Area of Operation: UK (Excluding Ireland)
Tel: 08705 456123 **Fax:** 08705 456356
Email: bgtechnical.enquiries@bpb.com
Web: www.british-gypsum.com
Product Type: 2, 3, 5, 7, 8, 9, 10

CENTREPIECE MOULDINGS
The Plaster Shop, C6 Bersham Enterprise Park,
Wrexham, LL14 4EG
Area of Operation: North West England and North Wales
Tel: 01978 363923
Email: plasterware@yahoo.co.uk **Product Type:** 2
Web: www.centrepiecemouldings.co.uk

CORNERCARE LIMITED
Units 3 & 4, Walter Nash Road,
Birchen Coppice Trading Estate,
Kidderminster, Worcestershire, DY11 7QY
Area of Operation: UK & Ireland
Tel: 01562 820213 **Fax:** 01562 822012
Email: info@cornercare.co.uk
Web: www.cornercare.com

DEESIDE HOMES TIMBERFRAME
Broomhill Road, Spurryhillock Industrial Estate,
Stonehaven, Near Aberdeen, Aberdeenshire, AB39 2NH
Area of Operation: UK (Excluding Ireland)
Tel: 01569 767123 **Fax:** 01569 767766
Email: john.wright@bancon.co.uk
Web: www.bancon.co.uk

ELLIOTTS INSULATION AND DRYLINING
Unit 8 Goodwood Road, Boyatt Wood Industrial
Estate, Eastleigh, Hampshire, SO50 4NT
Area of Operation: South East England, South West
England and South Wales
Tel: 02380 623960 **Fax:** 02380 623965
Email: insulation@elliott-brothers.co.uk
Web: www.elliotts.uk.com
Product Type: 2, 3, 4, 5, 7, 8, 9, 10

EUROFORM PRODUCTS LIMITED
The Heliport, Lyncastle Road, Appleton,
Warrington, Cheshire, WA4 4SN
Area of Operation: Worldwide
Tel: 01925 860999 **Fax:** 01925 860066
Email: info@euroform.co.uk
Web: www.euroform.co.uk

EUROFORM PRODUCTS LTD
Area of Operation: Worldwide
Tel: 01925 860999
Fax: 01925 860066
Email: info@euroform.co.uk
Web: www.euroform.co.uk

Versaliner™ JPM is a high performance high
impact, moisture Resistant, Class '0' stable
fibreboard, that can be used for a wide range of
dry lining applications.

Versaliner™ JPM is also a good strong substrate
for ceramic tiling.

FIBERTECH
11 James Terrace, Malahide, Dublin, Ireland
Area of Operation: UK & Ireland
Tel: +353 1 8168450 **Fax:** +353 1 8168455
Email: info@fibertech.ie
Web: www.fibertech.ie **Product Type:** 1, 2, 3, 6

**HEATHFIELD SPECIALIST
FINISHES & COATINGS LTD**
Unit 3, 41 Church Road, Bexleyheath, Kent, DA7 4DD
Area of Operation: UK (Excluding Ireland)
Tel: 0800 019 4718
Fax: 0208 303 3072
Email: info@plasterer.co.uk
Web: www.plasterer.co.uk

HERAKLITH
Broadway House, 21 Broadway,
Maidenhead, Berkshire, SL6 1NJ
Area of Operation: UK & Ireland
Tel: 01628 784330
Fax: 01628 633080
Email: muirwork@btinternet.com
Product Type: 6 **Other Info:** ECO

J & A PLASTERING
34 Moore Crescent, Netley Abbey,
Southampton, Hampshire , SA31 1PZ
Area of Operation: South East England
Tel: 02380 560762
Email: crosbykriss@aol.com
Product Type: 2, 3, 5, 6

LAFARGE PLASTERBOARD LTD
Marsh Lane, Easton-in-Gordano, Bristol, BS20 0NF
Area of Operation: Worldwide
Tel: 01275 377777
Email: enquiryline@lafarge-gypsum.lafarge.com
Product Type: 4, 5, 6, 7, 8, 9, 10

LIME TECHNOLOGY LIMITED
Unit 126, Milton Park, Abingdon,
Oxfordshire, OX14 4SA
Area of Operation: Worldwide
Tel: 0845 603 1143
Fax: 0845 634 1560
Email: info@limetechnology.co.uk
Web: www.limetechnology.co.uk
Product Type: 4, 6

LIME TECHNOLOGY LIMITED
Area of Operation: Worldwide
Tel: 0845 603 1143
Fax: 0845 634 1560
Email: info@limetechnology.co.uk
Web: www.limetechnology.co.uk
Product Type: 6
Other Info: ECO

Limetec hydraulic lime-based plasters and
renders designed for spray or hand application.
Suitable for brickwork, blockwork or concrete.
Enhanced breathability, flexibility and fast
installation. Available in 25kg bags.

MIKE WYE & ASSOCIATES
Buckland Filleigh Sawmills, Buckland Filleigh,
Beaworthy, Devon, EX21 5RN
Tel: 01409 281644 **Fax:** 01409 281669
Email: sales@mikewye.co.uk
Web: www.mikewye.co.uk **Other Info:** ECO

OLD HOUSE STORE LTD
Hampstead Farm, Binfield Heath,
Henley on Thames, Oxfordshire, RG9 4LG
Area of Operation: Worldwide
Tel: 0118 969 7711 **Fax:** 0118 969 8822
Email: info@oldhousestore.co.uk
Web: www.oldhousestore.co.uk

ORNATE INTERIORS LIMITED
534 Broad Lane, Stanningley,
Leeds, West Yorkshire, LS28 6PA
Area of Operation: UK & Ireland
Tel: 0113 236 0864 **Fax:** 0113 236 3706
Email: sales@ornateinteriors.co.uk
Web: www.ornateinteriors.co.uk

RAY MUNN LTD
861-863 Fulham Road, London, SW6 5HP
Area of Operation: UK (Excluding Ireland)
Tel: 0207 736 9876 **Email:** rishi@raymunn.com
Web: www.raymunn.com
Product Type: 4, 6 **Other Info:** ✍

SURFACE SOLUTIONS
33 Alma Road, Herne Bay, Kent, CT6 6JJ
Area of Operation: UK (Excluding Ireland)
Tel: 01227 362775

Don't Forget !

You can use the materials key at the beginning of this Handbook to get much more information from a company's listing.

Surface Solutions

decoration
plastering
tiling

Chris Hollidge

Mobile: **07951 722 115**

SURFACE SOLUTIONS

Area of Operation: UK (Excluding Ireland)
Tel: 01227 362775
Mobile: 07951 722 115

Fine Finishes & Materials to Adore

THE ARTFUL PLASTERER
Unit 1 Lovedere Farm, Goathurst,
Bridgewater, Somerset, TA5 2DD
Area of Operation: Worldwide
Tel: 0870 333 6335 **Fax:** 0870 333 6339
Email: colour@theartfulplasterer.co.uk
Web: www.theartfulplasterer.co.uk

THE POLISHED PLASTER COMPANY
Unit 13, Valley Road Business Park, Gas Works Road,
Keighley, West Yorkshire, BD21 4LZ
Tel: 07789 861315 **Fax:** 0870 762 3738
Email: info@polishedplaster.co.uk
Web: www.polishedplaster.co.uk
Product Type: 4, 6 **Other Info:** ✍ ✋

TY-MAWR LIME LTD
Ty-Mawr, Llangasty, Brecon, Powys, LD3 7PJ
Tel: 01874 658000 **Email:** joyce.gervis@lime.org.uk
Web: www.lime.org.uk ⬈

MOULDINGS AND ARCHITRAVE

KEY

PRODUCT TYPES: 1= Ceiling Centres
2 = Beams   3 = Cornices   4 = Coving
5 = Dado Rails   6 = Edge Trims
7 = Panel Mouldings   8 = Picture Rails
9 = Skirting   10 = Window Boards   11 = Other
OTHER: ▽ Reclaimed ⬈ On-line shopping
✍ Bespoke ✋ Hand-made   ECO Ecological

ARTIKA ORNAMENTAL PLASTERERS
6 The Retreat, Foxcote, Radstock, Somerset, BA3 5YF
Tel: 01761 433740   **Email:** mark@artika.f9.co.uk
Web: www.bathbusinessfinder.co.uk/artika/index.php
Product Type: 1, 2, 3, 4, 5, 6, 7, 8

BALCAS TIMBER LTD
Laragh, Enniskillen, Co. Fermanagh, BT94 2FQ
Tel: 0286 632 3003 **Fax:** 0286 632 7924
Email: info@balcas.com **Web:** www.balcas.com

BRIGHTON MOULDINGS LTD
12 Preston Road, Brighton, East Sussex, BN1 4QF
Area of Operation: East England, Greater London, South
East England, South West England and South Wales
Tel: 01273 622230 **Fax:** 01273 622240
Email: info@brightonmouldings.com
Web: www.brightonmouldings.com
Product Type: 1, 3, 4, 5, 6, 7, 8, 9

CENTREPIECE MOULDINGS
The Plaster Shop, C6 Bersham Enterprise Park,
Wrexham, LL14 4EG
Area of Operation: North West England and North Wales
Tel: 01978 363923
Email: plasterware@yahoo.co.uk
Web: www.centrepiecemouldings.co.uk
Product Type: 1, 3, 4, 5, 7, 8

COPLEY DECOR LTD
Leyburn Business Park, Leyburn,
North Yorkshire, DL8 5QA
Area of Operation: UK & Ireland
Tel: 01969 623410 **Fax:** 01969 624398
Email: mouldings@copleydecor.co.uk
Web: www.copleydecor.co.uk ⬈
Product Type: 1, 3, 4, 5, 7, 11

CORNICES CENTRE
1-7 Scraps Lane, Harlesden, London, NW10
Area of Operation: Greater London
Tel: 0208 962 6938 **Fax:** 0208 962 6939
Email: info@cornicescentre.co.uk
Web: www.cornicescentre.co.uk
Product Type: 1, 3, 4, 5, 7, 8, 9, 11

DAVUKA GROUP LTD
2C The Wend, Coulsdon, Surrey, CR5 2AX
Area of Operation: UK (Excluding Ireland)
Tel: 0208 660 2854 **Fax:** 0208 645 2556
Email: info@davuka.co.uk
Web: www.decorative-coving.co.uk ⬈
Product Type: 1, 3, 4, 5, 6, 7, 8, 9

DAVUKA GROUP LTD

Area of Operation: UK (Excluding Ireland)
Tel: 0208 660 2854 **Fax:** 0208 645 2556
Email: info@davuka.co.uk
Web: www.decorative-coving.co.uk
Product Type: 1,3,4,5,6,7,8,9
Complete range of high quality decorative mouldings, internal & external application. Profiles viewable in 3D on our website: www.decorative-coving.co.uk or call for brochure: 020 8660 2854 (Davuka GRP Ltd)

D-LINE (EUROPE) LIMITED
New York Way, New York Industrial Park,
Newcastle upon Tyne, Tyne & Wear, NE27 0QF
Area of Operation: Europe
Tel: 0191 293 0909 **Fax:** 0191 257 7722
Email: keving@d-line-it.co.uk
Web: www.d-line.co.uk

DRESSER MOULDINGS LTD
Unit 3, Station Road, Blackrod,
Bolton, Lancashire, BL6 5JB
Area of Operation: UK (Excluding Ireland)
Tel: 01204 667667 **Fax:** 01204 667600
Email: mac@dresser.uk.com
Web: www.dresser.uk.com **Product Type:** 3, 5, 7, 8, 9

E J HARMER & CO LIMITED
19a Birkbeck Hill, London, SE21 8JS
Tel: 0208 670 1017 **Fax:** 0208 766 6026
Email: ejharmer@aol.com
Web: www.ejharmer.co.uk

HAYLES & HOWE LTD
25 Picton Street, Montpelier, Bristol, BS6 5PZ
Tel: 0117 924 6673 **Fax:** 0117 924 3928
Email: info@haylesandhowe.co.uk
Web: www.haylesandhowe.co.uk
Product Type: 1, 3, 4, 5, 6, 7, 8, 9, 11

HOPPINGS SOFTWOOD PRODUCTS
The Woodyard, Epping Road, Epping, Essex, CM16 6TT
Area of Operation: South East England
Tel: 01992 578877 **Fax:** 01992 563185
Email: sales@hoppings.co.uk
Web: www.hoppings.co.uk
Product Type: 4, 5, 6, 7, 8, 9, 10, 11

J & A PLASTERING
34 Moore Crescent, Netley Abbey,
Southampton, Hampshire, SA31 1PZ
Area of Operation: South East England
Tel: 02380 560762 **Email:** crosbykriss@aol.com
Product Type: 1, 3, 4, 5, 6, 7, 8, 9

LANCASHIRE PLASTER PRODUCTS
167 Chorley New Road, Horwich,
Bolton, Lancashire, BL6 5QE
Area of Operation: UK (Excluding Ireland)
Tel: 01204 693900
Email: plasterproducts@gahope.com
Web: www.gahope.com **Product Type:** 1, 3, 5, 6, 7, 11

LEEWAY LTD
Dept OIN, 27 Woodbridge Road, Moseley,
Birmingham, West Midlands, B13 8EH
Area of Operation: UK & Ireland
Tel: 0121 449 8525
Email: dave@ukhomeinteriors.co.uk
Web: www.ukhomeinteriors.co.uk
Product Type: 1, 3, 4, 5, 6, 7, 9, 10

LOCKER & RILEY
(FIBROUS PLASTERING) LIMITED
Capital House, Hawk Hill, Battlebridge,
Wickford, Essex, SS11 7RJ
Area of Operation: UK (Excluding Ireland)
Tel: 01268 574100 **Fax:** 01268 574101
Email: enquiries@lockerandriley.com
Web: www.lockerandriley.com
Product Type: 1, 2, 3, 4, 5, 6, 7, 8, 9

LONDON FINE ART PLASTER
Unit 3, Romeo Business Centre,
Juliet Way, Purfleet, Essex, RM15 4YD
Area of Operation: UK (Excluding Ireland)
Tel: 01708 252400 **Fax:** 01708 252401
Email: heritage@lfap.co.uk **Web:** www.lfap.co.uk
Product Type: 1, 2, 3, 4, 5, 6, 7, 8, 9, 11

NATIONAL DOOR COMPANY
Unit 55 Dinting Vale Business Park,
Dinting Vale, Glossop, Derbyshire, SK13 6JD
Area of Operation: UK (Excluding Ireland)
Tel: 01457 867079 **Fax:** 01457 868795
Email: sales@nationaldoor.co.uk
Web: www.nationaldoor.co.uk **Product Type:** 9

NMC (UK) LTD
Tafarnaubach Industrial Estate,
Tredegar, Blaenau Gwent, NP22 3AA
Area of Operation: UK & Ireland
Tel: 01495 713252 **Fax:** 01495 713277
Email: enquiries@nmc-uk.com
Web: www.nmc-uk.com **Product Type:** 1, 2, 3, 4, 5

OAKLEAF
Unit A , Melbourne Mills, Chesham Street,
Keighley, West Yorkshire, BD21 4LG
Area of Operation: Worldwide
Tel: 01535 663274 **Fax:** 01535 661951
Email: jonathan@oakleaf.co.uk
Web: www.oakleaf.co.uk **Product Type:** 2

OAKLEAF (GLASGOW)
Birch Court, Doune, Stirlingshire, FK16 6JD
Area of Operation: Scotland
Tel: 01786 842216 **Fax:** 01786 842216
Email: sales@oakleaf.co.uk
Web: www.oakleaf.co.uk
Product Type: 1, 2, 3, 4, 5, 6, 7, 8, 9

OAKLEY BESPOKE REPRODUCTION BEAMS
31 Fort, Picklecombe Maker,
Torpoint, Cornwall, PL10 1JB
Area of Operation: Worldwide
Tel: 01752 829 299 **Fax:** 01752 829299
Email: shaun@repro-beams.freeserve.co.uk
Web: www.reproduction-beams.co.uk
Product Type: 2

OCTAVEWARD LIMITED
Balle Street, Darwen, Lancashire, BB3 2AZ
Area of Operation: UK (Excluding Ireland)
Tel: 01254 773300 **Fax:** 01254 773950
Email: info@octaveward.com
Web: www.octaveward.com

ORAC (UK) LIMITED
Unit 5, Hewitts Estate, Elmbridge Road,
Cranleigh, Surrey, GU6 8LW
Area of Operation: Worldwide
Tel: 01483 271211 **Fax:** 01483 278317
Email: stewart@oracdecor.com
Web: www.oracdecor.com
Product Type: 1, 3, 4, 5, 6, 7, 9, 11

ORNATE INTERIORS LIMITED
534 Broad Lane, Stanningley,
Leeds, West Yorkshire, LS28 6PA
Area of Operation: UK & Ireland
Tel: 0113 236 0864 **Fax:** 0113 236 3706
Email: sales@ornateinteriors.co.uk
Web: www.ornateinteriors.co.uk

REVIVAL DECORATIVE MOULDINGS
2 Park Street, Ampthill, Bedfordshire, MK45 2LR
Area of Operation: Worldwide
Tel: 01525 862717 **Fax:** 01525 406690
Email: sales@revivalplaster.co.uk
Web: www.revivalplaster.co.uk
Product Type: 1, 2, 3, 4, 5, 7, 8, 9, 11 **Other Info:**

RICHARD BURBIDGE LTD
Whittington Road, Oswestry, Shropshire, SY11 1HZ
Area of Operation: UK & Ireland
Tel: 01691 655131
Fax: 01691 659091
Email: info@richardburbidge.co.uk
Web: www.richardburbidge.co.uk

RUSTIC WOOD FLOORING LIMITED
Rustic House, Thongsbridge Mills, Miry Lane,
Thongsbridge, Holmfirth, West Yorkshire, HD9 7RW
Area of Operation: East England, Greater London,
North East England
Tel: 01484 685222 **Fax:** 01484 685222
Email: rusticwfc@tiscali.co.uk
Web: www.warmawood.co.uk **Product Type:** 6, 9

STEVENSONS OF NORWICH LIMITED
Roundtree Way, Norwich, Norfolk, NR7 8SQ
Area of Operation: Worldwide
Tel: 01603 400824 **Fax:** 01603 405113
Email: info@stevensons-of-norwich.co.uk
Web: www.stevensons-of-norwich.co.uk
Product Type: 1, 3, 4, 5, 7, 8

STUART INTERIORS
Barrington Court, Barrington,
Ilminster, Somerset, TA19 0NQ
Area of Operation: Worldwide
Tel: 01460 240349 **Fax:** 01460 242069
Email: design@stuartinteriors.com
Web: www.stuartinteriors.com
Product Type: 7 **Other Info:**

THE NATURAL WOOD FLOOR COMPANY
Unit 6B, Freshfields Business Park, Stevenson Road,
Brighton, East Sussex, BN2 0DF
Tel: 01273 605800 **Fax:** 01273 605799
Email: sales@naturalwoodfloor.co.uk
Web: www.naturalwoodfloor.co.uk
Product Type: 6, 9

THE NATURAL WOOD
FLOORING COMPANY LTD
20 Smugglers Way, Wandsworth, London, SW18 1EQ
Area of Operation: Worldwide
Tel: 0208 871 9771 **Fax:** 0208 877 0273
Email: sales@naturalwoodfloor.co.uk
Web: www.naturalwoodfloor.co.uk
Product Type: 6, 9

THE ROUNDWOOD TIMBER COMPANY LTD
Roundwood, Newick Lane,
Mayfield, East Sussex, TN20 6RG
Tel: 01435 867072 **Fax:** 01435 864708
Email: sales@roundwoodtimber.com
Web: www.roundwoodtimber.com

THE SPA & WARWICK TIMBER CO LTD
Harriott Drive, Heathcote Industrial Estate,
Warwick, Warwickshire, CV34 6TJ
Area of Operation: Midlands & Mid Wales
Tel: 01926 883876 **Fax:** 01926 450831
Email: spa.warwick@btconnect.com
Web: www.sawhardwood.com
Product Type: 5, 8, 9, 10, 11

WINTHER BROWNE
75 Bilton Way, Enfield, London, EN3 7ER
Area of Operation: UK (Excluding Ireland)
Tel: 0208 3449050 **Fax:** 0845 612 1894
Email: sales@wintherbrowne.co.uk
Web: www.wintherbrowne.co.uk

WOODHOUSE TIMBER
Unit 15 Quarry Farm Industrial Estate,
Staplecross Road, Bodiam, East Sussex, TN32 5RA
Tel: 01580 831700 **Fax:** 01580 830054
Email: info@woodhousetimber.co.uk
Web: www.woodhousetimber.co.uk **Product Type:** 9

BATHROOMS

SPONSORED BY MOVE OR IMPROVE? MAGAZINE
Tel 01527 834435 Web www.moveorimprove.co.uk

Wetrooms

While the debate among architects continues over the benefits and practicalities of the contemporary wetroom, the key question for homeowners is how much time and money are they willing to invest to gain the ultimate bathroom luxury.

The idea behind a wetroom is simple. It uses available space in the most flexible way possible, and can be designed to suit your individual needs – rather than being based around the positioning of bathroom furniture.

The doorless entry and level threshold are ideal for the elderly and children. The sleek, clean lines are perfect in a contemporary-style home. It is also a perfect solution for those with small bathrooms, as it will maximize the space and make it look much bigger.

But there are downsides. A wetroom means that the whole area is exposed to water, so in order for the design to work,

the room must be absolutely watertight, requiring an expertly laid waterproof membrane to be installed underneath the floor and wall tiles.

The floor may also need to be strengthened, and will almost certainly need to be raised in order to accommodate waste fittings for drainage, with a slight slope incorporated towards the waste outlet. This is a costly and potentially tricky process, especially when fitting into an existing home rather than a new build.

Design is also crucial when it comes to installing your sanitaryware, which must be far enough away from the shower to prevent perpetual soakings. The alternative is to install a glass screen to segregate the rest of your bathroom furniture from the shower area, although some argue that this interferes with the aesthetics of the room.

The question that many self-builders ask is "should you build a wetroom upstairs?", but the answer is unfortunately not a simple yes or no. The ground floor is ideal for a wetroom, as upstairs timber floors can cause problems due to joist shrinkage. Some architects say this is fine so long as sufficient waterproofing is used, while others are more sceptical. However, in a new build project this can be factored in, and a beam and block floor can be specified for the necessary area. It is also worth considering putting an upstairs wetroom above a kitchen or utility room, to avoid vulnerable living areas in case of any problems.

Wetrooms often have a sleek, contemporary appearance due to their doorless entry and level threshold. IMAGE ABOVE RIGHT by Ideal Standard, and LEFT by Hansgrohe.

Top Tips

- Position the shower fittings away from the door to ensure that the water drains back into the room

- Think about your floor covering carefully; opt for non-slip surfaces

- Consider installing wall-hung sanitaryware to free up floor space and add to the spacious feel

- A luxury shower with body jets, or an opulent rain/waterfall style mixer, will add to the quality finish of your wetroom

INTERIORS, FIXTURES & FINISHES - **Bathrooms** - Basins
SPONSORED BY: MOVE OR IMPROVE MAGAZINE www.moveorimprove.co.uk

INTERIORS, FIXTURES & FINISHES

BASINS

KEY

OTHER: ▽ Reclaimed 👆 On-line shopping
🖋 Bespoke 🖐 Hand-made ECO Ecological

A & H BRASS
201-203 Edgware Road, London, W2 1ES
Area of Operation: Worldwide
Tel: 0207 402 1854 **Fax:** 0207 402 0110
Email: ahbrass@btinternet.com
Web: www.aandhbrass.co.uk 👆

ALEXANDERS
Unit 3, 1/1A Spilsby Road,
Harold Hill, Romford, Essex, RM3 8SB
Area of Operation: UK & Ireland
Tel: 01708 384574 **Fax:** 01708 384089
Email: sales@alexanders-uk.net
Web: www.alexanders-uk.net **Material Type:** J) 5

ALICANTE STONE
Damaso Navarro, 6 Bajo,
03610 Petrer (Alicante), P.O. Box 372, Spain
Area of Operation: Europe
Tel: +34 966 31 96 97 **Fax:** +34 966 31 96 98
Email: info@alicantestone.com
Web: www.alicantestone.com
Material Type: E) 2, 5, 8

AMBIANCE BAIN
Cumberland House, 80 Scrubs Lane, London, NW10 6RF
Area of Operation: UK & Ireland
Tel: 0870 902 1313 **Fax:** 0870 902 1312
Email: sghirardello@mimea.com
Web: www.ambiancebain.com

ANTIQUE BATHS OF IVYBRIDGE LTD
Emebridge Works, Ermington Road,
Ivybridge, Devon, PL21 9DE
Area of Operation: UK (Excluding Ireland)
Tel: 01752 698250 **Fax:** 01752 698266
Email: sales@antiquebaths.com
Web: www.antiquebaths.com 👆

AQUAPLUS SOLUTIONS
Unit 106, Indiana Building, London, SE13 7QD
Area of Operation: UK & Ireland
Tel: 0870 201 1915 **Fax:** 0870 201 1916
Email: info@aquaplussolutions.com
Web: www.aquaplussolutions.com

ASHLEY BATHROOMS
Duffield Road Industrial Estate,
Little Eaton, Derby, Derbyshire, DE21 5DR
Area of Operation: UK & Ireland
Tel: 01332 830404 **Fax:** 01332 830202
Email: info@ashleybathrooms.com
Web: www.ashleybathrooms.com

AVANTE BATHROOMS
Thistle House, Thistle Way,
Gildersome Spur, Wakefield Road,
Morley, Leeds, West Yorkshire, LS27 7JZ
Area of Operation: UK & Ireland
Tel: 0113 201 2240 **Fax:** 0113 253 0717
Email: sales@avantebathrooms.com
Web: www.avantebathrooms.com 👆
Material Type: E) 5, 8

BARRHEAD SANITARYWARE PLC
15-17 Nasmyth Road, Hillington Industrial Estate,
Hillington, Glasgow, Renfrewshire, G52 4RG
Area of Operation: UK & Ireland
Tel: 0141 883 0066 **Fax:** 0141 883 0077
Email: sales@barrhead.co.uk

BATHROOM BARN
The Bathroom Barn, Uplands Industrial Estate, Mere
Way, Wyton, Huntingdon, Cambridgeshire, PE28 2JZ
Area of Operation: UK (Excluding Ireland)
Tel: 01480 458900
Email: sales@bathroom-barn.co.uk
Web: www.bathroombarn.co.uk

BATHROOM CITY
Seeleys Road, Tyseley Industrial Estate,
Birmingham, West Midlands, B11 2LQ
Area of Operation: UK & Ireland
Tel: 0121 753 0700 **Fax:** 0121 753 1110
Email: sales@bathroomcity.com
Web: www.bathroomcity.com 👆

BATHROOM DISCOUNT CENTRE
297 Munster Road, Fulham, Greater London, SW6 6BW
Area of Operation: UK (Excluding Ireland)
Tel: 0207 381 4222 **Fax:** 0207 381 6792
Email: bathdisc@aol.co.uk
Web: www.bathroomdiscount.co.uk

BATHROOMS PLUS LTD
222 Malmesbury Park Road,
Bournemouth, Dorset, BH8 8PR
Area of Operation: South West England and South Wales
Tel: 01202 294417 **Fax:** 01202 316425
Email: info@bathrooms-plus.co.uk
Web: www.bathrooms-plus.co.uk
Material Type: C) 3, 13, 14, 16, 18

BATHROOMSTUFF.CO.UK
326 London Road, Hilsea,
Portsmouth, Hampshire, PO2 9JT
Area of Operation: UK (Excluding Ireland)
Tel: 08450 580 540 **Fax:** 08451 274125
Email: sales@bathroomstuff.co.uk
Web: www.bathroomstuff.co.uk 👆

BROOK-WATER DESIGNER
BATHROOMS & KITCHENS
The Downs, Woodhouse Hill,
Uplyme, Lyme Regis, Dorset, DT7 3SL
Area of Operation: Worldwide
Tel: 0870 851 9739
Email: sales@brookwater.co.uk
Web: www.brookwater.co.uk 👆
Other Info: 🖋

CAPITAL MARBLE DESIGN
Unit 1 Pall Mall Deposit,
124-128 Barlby Road, London, W10 6BL
Area of Operation: UK (Excluding Ireland)
Tel: 0208 968 5340 **Fax:** 0208 968 8827
Email: stonegallery@capitalmarble.co.uk
Web: www.capitalmarble.co.uk
Other Info: 🖋 🖐

CASTELLO LUXURY BATHS LTD
Unit 3 Diamond Industrial Centre, Works Road,
Letchworth, Hertfordshire, SG6 4BS
Area of Operation: UK & Ireland
Tel: 01462 483131 **Fax:** 01462 670939
Email: sales@castellobaths.co.uk
Web: www.castellobaths.co.uk

CIFIAL UK LTD
7 Faraday Court, Park Farm Industrial Estate,
Wellingborough, Northamptonshire, NN8 6XY
Area of Operation: UK & Ireland
Tel: 01933 402008 **Fax:** 01933 402063
Email: sales@cifial.co.uk **Web:** www.cifial.co.uk

CITY BATHROOMS & KITCHENS
158 Longford Road, Longford,
Coventry, West Midlands, CV6 6DR
Area of Operation: UK & Ireland
Tel: 02476 365877 **Fax:** 02476 644992
Email: citybathrooms@hotmail.com
Web: www.citybathrooms.co.uk

COSY ROOMS (THE-BATHROOM-SHOP.CO.UK)
17 Chiltern Way, North Hykeham,
Lincoln, Lincolnshire, LN6 9SY
Area of Operation: UK (Excluding Ireland)
Tel: 01522 696002 **Fax:** 01522 696002
Email: keith@cosy-rooms.com
Web: www.the-bathroom-shop.co.uk 👆

COUNTY GRANITE AND MARBLE
Mill Lane, Creech Saint Michael,
Taunton, Somerset, TA3 5PX
Area of Operation: UK (Excluding Ireland)
Tel: 01823 444554 **Fax:** 01823 445013
Web: www.countygranite.co.uk

CP HART GROUP
Newnham Terrace, Hercules Road, London, SE1 7DR
Area of Operation: Greater London
Tel: 0845 600 1950 **Fax:** 01322 422101
Email: sales@cphart.co.uk **Web:** www.cphart.co.uk

CROSSWATER
Unit 5 Butterly Avenue, Questor,
Dartford, Kent, DA1 1JG
Area of Operation: UK & Ireland
Tel: 01322 628270 **Fax:** 01322 628280
Email: sales@crosswater.co.uk
Web: www.crosswater.co.uk **Material Type:** J) 5

CYMRU KITCHENS
63 Caerleon Road, Newport, NP19 7BX
Area of Operation: UK (Excluding Ireland)
Tel: 01633 676767 **Fax:** 01633 212512
Email: sales@cymrukitchens.com
Web: www.cymrukitchens.com

DART VALLEY SYSTEMS LIMITED
Kemmings Close, Long Road,
Paignton, Devon, TQ4 7TW
Area of Operation: UK & Ireland
Tel: 01803 529021 **Fax:** 01803 559016
Email: sales@dartvalley.co.uk
Web: www.dartvalley.co.uk

DECORLUX LTD
18 Ghyll Industrial Estate,
Ghyll Road, Heathfield, East Sussex, TN21 8AW
Area of Operation: UK (Excluding Ireland)
Tel: 01435 866638 **Fax:** 01435 866641
Email: info@decorlux.co.uk
Web: www.decorlux.co.uk **Other Info:** ▽ 🖐

DECORMASTER LTD
Unit 16, Waterside Industrial Estate,
Wolverhampton, West Midlands, WV2 2RH
Area of Operation: Worldwide
Tel: 01902 406030 **Fax:** 01902 353126
Email: sales@oldcolours.co.uk
Web: www.oldcolours.co.uk

DEEP BLUE SHOWROOM
299-313 Lewisham High Street,
Lewisham, London, SE13 6NW
Area of Operation: UK (Excluding Ireland)
Tel: 0208 690 3401 **Fax:** 0208 690 1408

DEVON STONE LTD
8 Pilot Road, Pierhead, Exmouth, Devon, EX8 1XA
Area of Operation: UK (Excluding Ireland)
Tel: 01395 222525
Email: amy@devonstone.com
Web: www.devonstone.com **Other Info:** 🖋 🖐
Material Type: E) 1, 2, 3, 4, 5, 8

DISCONTINUED BATHROOMS
140-142 Pogmoor Road, Pogmoor,
Barnsley, North Yorkshire, S75 2DX
Area of Operation: UK (Excluding Ireland)
Tel: 01226 280200
Fax: 01226 733273
Email: sales@discontinuedbathrooms.co.uk
Web: www.discontinuedbathrooms.co.uk

DUPONT CORIAN & ZODIAQ
10 Quarry Court, Pitstone Green Business Park,
Pitstone, nr. Tring, Buckinghamshire, LU7 9GW
Area of Operation: UK & Ireland
Tel: 01296 663555 **Fax:** 01296 663599
Email: sales@corian.co.uk
Web: www.corian.co.uk

DURAVIT
Unit 7, Stratus Park, Brudenell Drive, Brinklow,
Milton Keynes, Buckinghamshire, MK10 0DE
Area of Operation: UK & Ireland
Tel: 0870 730 7787 **Fax:** 0870 730 7786
Email: info@uk.duravit.com
Web: www.duravit.co.uk

EURO BATHROOMS
102 Annareagh Road, Richhill, Co Armagh, BT61 9JY
Area of Operation: Ireland Only
Tel: 028 3887 9996 **Fax:** 028 3887 9996

EUROBATH INTERNATIONAL LIMITED
Eurobath House, Wedmore Road,
Cheddar, Somerset, BS27 3EB
Area of Operation: UK & Ireland
Tel: 01934 744466 **Fax:** 01934744345
Email: sales@eurobath.co.uk
Web: www.eurobath.co.uk/www.ilbagno.co.uk

VADO EURO BATH

EUROBATH INTERNATIONAL LTD
Area of Operation: Worldwide
Tel: 01934 744466
Fax: 01934 744345
Email: sales@eurobath.co.uk
Web: www.eurobath.co.uk

VADO® Origins range, complete with patented
handles with natural stone quarried from the Pisa
region of Italy, brings striking aesthetics,
performance and reliability to the bathroom
environment.

GALLICO CEMENT
3 Mead Court, 52 South Molton Street,
London, W1K 5SE
Area of Operation: Worldwide
Tel: 0207 193 1144 **Fax:** 0207 491 3539
Email: sales@gallicoservices.com
Web: www.gallicoservices.co.uk **Other Info:** 🖐

GOODWOOD BATHROOMS LTD
Church Road, North Mundham,
Chichester, West Sussex, PO20 1JU
Area of Operation: UK (Excluding Ireland)
Tel: 01243 532121 **Fax:** 01243 533423
Email: sales@goodwoodbathrooms.co.uk
Web: www.goodwoodbathrooms.co.uk

HERITAGE BATHROOMS
Princess Street, Bedminster, Bristol, BS3 4AG
Area of Operation: UK & Ireland **Tel:** 0117 963 3333
Email: marketing@heritagebathrooms.com
Web: www.heritagebathrooms.com

HOMESTYLE BATHROOMS
Unit 21 Hainault Works, Hainault Road,
Little Heath, Romford, Essex, RM6 5SS
Area of Operation: UK (Excluding Ireland)
Tel: 0208 599 8080 **Fax:** 0208 599 7070
Email: info@homestyle-bathrooms.co.uk
Web: www.homestyle-bathrooms.co.uk

IDEAL STANDARD
The Bathroom Works, National Avenue, Kingston
Upon Hull, East Riding of Yorks, HU5 4HS
Area of Operation: Worldwide
Tel: 0800 590311 **Fax:** 01482 445886
Email: ideal-standard@aseur.com
Web: www.ideal-standard.co.uk

INDESIGN
Kiran House, 53 Park Royal Road, London, NW10 7LQ
Area of Operation: UK & Ireland
Tel: 0208 963 5841 **Fax:** 0208 965 6261
Email: dhanja.bhudia@akshars.co.uk
Web: www.akshars.co.uk

INSPIRED BATHROOMS
Unit R4, Innsworth Technology Park, Innsworth Lane,
Gloucester, Gloucestershire, GL3 1DL
Area of Operation: UK & Ireland
Tel: 01452 559121 **Fax:** 01452 530908
Email: sales@inspired-bathrooms.co.uk
Web: www.inspired-bathrooms.co.uk 👆

ION GLASS
PO Box 284, Burgess Hill, West Sussex, RH15 0BN
Area of Operation: UK (Excluding Ireland)
Tel: 0845 658 9988 **Fax:** 0845 658 9989
Email: sales@ionglass.co.uk **Web:** www.ionglass.co.uk

J & R MARBLE COMPANY LTD
Unit 9,Period Works, Lammas Road,
Leyton, London, E10 7QT
Area of Operation: UK (Excluding Ireland)
Tel: 0208 539 6471 **Fax:** 0208 539 9264
Email: sales@jrmarble.co.uk
Web: www.jrmarble.co.uk **Other Info:** ✐
Material Type: E) 1, 2, 3, 4, 5, 8, 9, 13, 14

JACUZZI UK
Silverdale Road, Newcastle Under Lyme,
Staffordshire, ST5 6EL
Area of Operation: UK & Ireland
Tel: 01782 717175 **Fax:** 01782 717166
Email: jacuzzisalesdesk@jacuzziuk.com
Web: www.jacuzzi.co.uk **Material Type:** F) 1

JACUZZI UK - BC SANITAN
Silverdale Road, Newcastle Under Lyme,
Staffordshire, ST5 6EL
Area of Operation: UK & Ireland
Tel: 01782 717175 **Fax:** 01782 717166
Email: jacuzzisalesdesk@jacuzziuk.com
Web: www.jacuzziuk.com **Material Type:** F) 1

JOHN LEWIS OF HUNGERFORD
Grove Technology Park, Downsview Road,
Wantage, Oxfordshire, OX12 9FA
Area of Operation: UK (Excluding Ireland)
Tel: 01235 774300 **Fax:** 01235 769031
Email: park.street@john-lewis.co.uk
Web: www.john-lewis.co.uk

KENSINGTON STUDIO
13c/d Kensington Road, Earlsdon,
Coventry, West Midlands, CV5 6GG
Area of Operation: UK (Excluding Ireland)
Tel: 02476 713326 **Fax:** 02476 713136
Email: sales@kensingtonstudio.com
Web: www.kensingtonstudio.com ✐

KERAMAG WAVENEY LTD
London Road, Beccles, Suffolk, NR34 8TS
Area of Operation: UK & Ireland
Tel: 01502 716600 **Fax:** 01502 717767
Email: info@keramagwaveney.co.uk
Web: www.keramag.com

KIRKSTONE QUARRIES LIMITED
Skelwith Bridge, Ambleside, Cumbria, LA22 9NN
Area of Operation: UK & Ireland
Tel: 01539 433296 **Fax:** 01539 434006
Email: info@kirkstone.com **Web:** www.kirkstone.com

LECICO PLC
Unit 47a Hobbs Industrial Estate,
Newchapel, Nr Lingfield, Surrey, RH7 6HN
Area of Operation: UK & Ireland
Tel: 01342 834777 **Fax:** 01342 834783
Email: info@lecico.co.uk **Web:** www.lecico.co.uk

M & O BATHROOM CENTRE
174-176 Goswell Road,
Clarkenwell, London, EC1V 7DT
Area of Operation: East England, Greater London,
South East England
Tel: 0207 608 0111 **Fax:** 0207 490 3083
Email: mando@lineone.net

MARBLE CLASSICS
Unit 3, Station Approach,
Emsworth, Hampshire, PO10 7PW
Area of Operation: UK & Ireland
Tel: 01243 370011 **Fax:** 01243 371023
Email: info@marbleclassics.co.uk
Web: www.marbleclassics.co.uk
Material Type: E) 1, 2, 3, 5, 8

MEKON PRODUCTS
25 Bessemer Park, Milkwood Road, London, SE24 0HG
Area of Operation: UK (Excluding Ireland)
Tel: 0207 733 8011 **Fax:** 0207 737 0840
Email: info@mekon.net **Web:** www.mekon.net

MEREWAY CONTRACTS
Unit 1 Wharfdale Road, Tysely,
Birmingham, West Midlands, B11 2DE
Area of Operation: UK (Excluding Ireland)
Tel: 0121 764 7180 **Fax:** 0121 764 7199
Email: info@merewaycontracts.co.uk
Web: www.merewaycontracts.co.uk

MILLER FROM SWEDEN
Unit 18 Thorne Park Business Centre,
Wenman Road, Thame, Oxfordshire, OX9 3XA
Area of Operation: Worldwide
Tel: 01844 264800 **Fax:** 01844 261134
Email: sales@millerbathrooms.co.uk
Web: www.millerbathrooms.co.uk
Material Type: F) 2, 4

**MISCELLANEA DISCONTINUED
BATHROOMWARE**
Churt Place Nurseries, Tilford Road,
Churt, Farnham, Surrey, GU10 2LN
Area of Operation: Worldwide
Tel: 01428 608164 **Fax:** 01428 608165
Email: email@brokenbog.com
Web: www.brokenbog.com

MOODS BATHROOMS
PJH Group, Alder House, Kearsley,
Bolton, Lancashire, BL4 8SL
Area of Operation: UK & Ireland
Tel: 01204 707070 **Fax:** 01204 573140
Email: info@pjh.co.uk
Web: ww.bathroom-moods.com

MWD
Clutton Hill Estate, King Lane,
Clutton Hill, Bristol, BS39 5QQ
Area of Operation: Midlands & Mid Wales, South
West England and South Wales
Tel: 0870 0332288 **Fax:** 0800 1976593
Email: sales@mwdretail.co.uk
Web: www.mikewalker.co.uk

NICHOLAS ANTHONY LTD
42-44 Wigmore Street, London, W1U 2RX
Area of Operation: East England, Greater London,
South East England
Tel: 0800 068 3603 **Fax:** 01206 762698
Email: info@nicholas-anthony.co.uk
Web: www.nicholas-anthony.co.uk

NO CODE
Larkwhistle Farm Road,
Micheldever, Hampshire, SO21 3BG
Area of Operation: UK & Ireland
Tel: 01962 870078 **Fax:** 01962 870077
Email: sales@nocode.co.uk
Web: www.nocode.co.uk

OLD FASHIONED BATHROOMS LTD
Foresters Hall, 52 High Street, Debenham,
Stowmarket, Suffolk, IP14 6QW
Area of Operation: UK (Excluding Ireland)
Tel: 01728 860926 **Fax:** 01728 860446
Email: ofbshop@yahoo.co.uk
Web: www.oldfashionedbathrooms.co.uk
Other Info: ▽ **Material Type:** F) 1, 2, 4

QUALCERAM SHIRES PLC
South Quay, Arklow, Co. Wicklow
Area of Operation: UK & Ireland
Tel: 00353 402 31288 **Fax:** 00353 402 31292
Email: omoriarty@qualceram-shires.com
Web: www.qualceram-shires.com

QUALITY MARBLE
41 Lockfield Avenue, Enfield, Middlesex, EN3 7PY
Area of Operation: UK & Ireland
Tel: 0208 805 6600 **Fax:** 0208 804 9825
Email: deane@qualitymarble.co.uk

RAK CERAMICS
The Tile House, Easebourne Lane,
Easebourne, West Sussex, GU29 9AZ
Area of Operation: Worldwide
Tel: 01730 815507 **Fax:** 01730 815007
Email: info@rakceramics.co.uk
Web: www.rakceramics.co.uk

REGINOX UK LTD
Radnor Park Trading Estate,
Congleton, Cheshire, CW12 4XJ
Area of Operation: UK & Ireland
Tel: 01260 280033 **Fax:** 01260 298889
Email: sales@reginoxuk.co.uk
Web: www.reginox.com ✐

ROSCO COLLECTIONS
Stone Allerton, Axbridge, Somerset, BS26 2NS
Area of Operation: UK & Ireland
Tel: 01934 712299 **Fax:** 01934 713222
Email: jonathan@roscobathrooms.demon.co.uk

SHIRES
Uttoxeter Road, Longton,
Stoke-on-Trent, Staffordshire, ST3 1NA
Area of Operation: UK & Ireland
Tel: 01782 599099 **Fax:** 01782 599295
Email: hkiddle@qualceram-shires.com
Web: www.shires-bathrooms.com ✐

SHOWERLUX UK LTD
Sibree Road, Coventry, West Midlands, CV3 4FD
Area of Operation: UK & Ireland
Tel: 02476 882515 **Fax:** 02476 305457
Email: sales@showerlux.co.uk
Web: www.showerlux.co.uk

SMART SHOWERS LTD
Unit 11, Woodside Road, South Marston Business
Park, Swindon, Wiltshire, SN3 4WA
Area of Operation: UK & Ireland
Tel: 01793 822775 **Fax:** 01793 823800
Email: enquiries@smartshowers.co.uk
Web: www.smartshowers.co.uk ✐

SOGA LTD
41 Mayfield Street, Hull,
East Riding of Yorks, HU3 1NT
Area of Operation: Worldwide
Tel: 01482 327025 **Email:** info@soga.co.uk
Web: www.soga.co.uk ✐

SPLASH
113 High Street, Cuckfield, West Sussex, RH17 5JX
Area of Operation: UK & Ireland
Tel: 01444 473 355 **Fax:** 01444 473 366

STIFFKEY BATHROOMS
89 Upper Saint Giles Street, Norwich, Norfolk, NR2 1AB
Area of Operation: Worldwide
Tel: 01603 627850 **Fax:** 01603 619775
Email: stiffkeybathrooms.norwich@virgin.net
Web: www.stiffkeybathrooms.com

STONELL DIRECT
7 showrooms nationwide - see website for details
Area of Operation: Worldwide
Tel: 08000 832283 **Fax:** 01283 501098
Email: info@stonelldirect.com
Web: www.stonelldirect.com

STONEVILLE (UK) LTD
Unit 12, Set Star Estate,
Transport Avenue, Great West Road,
Brentford, Greater London, TW8 9HF
Area of Operation: Europe
Tel: 0208 560 1000 **Fax:** 0208 560 4060
Email: info@stoneville.co.uk
Web: www.stoneville.co.uk

STUDIO STONE
The Stone Yard, Alton Lane,
Four Marks, Hampshire, GU34 5AJ
Area of Operation: UK (Excluding Ireland)
Tel: 01420 562500 **Fax:** 01420 563192
Email: sales@studiostone.co.uk
Web: www.studiostone.co.uk
Material Type: E) 1, 2, 3, 5, 8

SVEDBERGS
4E Wilsons Park, Monsall Road, Newton Heath,
Manchester, Greater Manchester, M40 8WN
Area of Operation: UK & Ireland
Tel: 0161 2051200 **Fax:** 0161 251212
Email: info@svedbergs.co.uk
Web: www.svedbergs.co.uk **Material Type:** F) 1, 2

TAPS SHOP
1 Tristram Road, Ducklington,
Whitney, Oxfordshire, OX29 7XH
Area of Operation: Worldwide
Tel: 0845 4303035 **Fax:** 01993 779653
Email: info@tapsshop.co.uk
Web: www.tapsshop.co.uk ✐

THE KITCHEN AND BATHROOM COLLECTION
Nelson House, Nelson Road,
Salisbury, Wiltshire, SP1 3LT
Area of Operation: South West England and South Wales
Tel: 01722 334800 **Fax:** 01722 412252
Email: info@kbc.co.uk **Web:** www.kbc.co.uk
Other Info: ✐

THE WATER MONOPOLY
16/18 Lonsdale Road, London, NW6 6RD
Area of Operation: UK (Excluding Ireland)
Tel: 0207 624 2636 **Fax:** 0207 624 2631
Email: enquiries@watermonopoly.com
Web: www.watermonopoly

THOMAS CRAPPER & CO. LTD
The Stable Yard, Alscot Park,
Stratford-on-Avon, Warwickshire, CV37 8BL
Area of Operation: Worldwide
Tel: 01789 450522 **Fax:** 01789 450523
Email: wc@thomas-crapper.com
Web: www.thomas-crapper.com ✐

TIMELESS BATHROOMS LTD
394 Ringwood Road, Ferndown, Dorset, BH22 9AU
Area of Operation: South East England
Tel: 01202 897110 **Fax:** 01202 892252
Email: bathroom@options394.fsnet.co.uk
Web: www.timelessbathrooms.co.uk

TRADEMARK TILES
Tile Store, Somersham Road, St Ives,
Huntingdon, Cambridgeshire, PE27 3WR
Area of Operation: UK (Excluding Ireland)
Tel: 01480 498123
Email: info@tilestoreplus.co.uk
Web: www.tilestoreplus.co.uk ✐

TWYFORD BATHROOMS
Lawton Road, Alsager,
Stoke On Trent, Staffordshire, ST7 2DF
Area of Operation: Worldwide
Tel: 01270 879777
Web: www.twyfordbathrooms.com
Material Type: F) 1, 4

UNICOM
Kingdom House, 219 Gleniffer Road,
Paisley, Renfrewshire, PA2 8UL
Area of Operation: UK & Ireland
Tel: 0845 330 7642 **Fax:** 0845 330 7641
Email: george@unicom-direct.com
Web: www.unicom-direct.com ✐

VICTORIAN BATHROOMS
Ings Mill Complex, Dale Street,
Ossett , West Yorkshire, WF5 9HQ
Area of Operation: UK (Excluding Ireland)
Tel: 01924 267736 **Fax:** 01924 261232
Email: sales@vb-bathrooms.com
Web: www.vb-bathrooms.com ✐

WALTON BATHROOMS
The Hersham Centre, The Green, Molesey Road,
Hersham, Walton on Thames, Surrey, KT12 4HL
Area of Operation: UK (Excluding Ireland)
Tel: 01932 224784
Fax: 01932 253447
Email: sales@waltonbathrooms.co.uk
Web: www.waltonbathrooms.co.uk ✐

WATER FRONT
All Worcester Buildings, Birmingham Road,
Redditch, Worcestershire, B97 6DY
Area of Operation: UK & Ireland
Tel: 01527 584244
Fax: 01527 61127
Email: info@waterfrontbathrooms.com
Web: www.waterfrontbathrooms.com
Other Info: ✐ **Material Type:** E) 2, 5

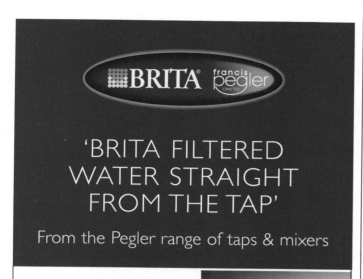

WHIRLPOOL EXPRESS (UK) LTD
61-62 Lower Dock Street, Kingsway, Newport, NP20 1EF
Area of Operation: Europe
Tel: 01633 244555 **Fax:** 01633 244881
Email: reception@whirlpoolexpress.co.uk
Web: www.whirlpoolexpress.co.uk

WILLIAM GARVEY
Leyhill, Payhembury, Honiton, Devon, EX14 3JG
Area of Operation: Worldwide
Tel: 01404 841430 **Fax:** 01404 841626
Email: webquery@williamgarvey.co.uk
Web: www.williamgarvey.co.uk
Other Info: ✏ ✋ **Material Type:** A) 10

TAPS

KEY
SEE ALSO: MERCHANTS - Plumbers Merchants; KITCHENS- Taps
OTHER: ▽ Reclaimed ⬆ On-line shopping ✏ Bespoke ✋ Hand-made ECO Ecological

A & H BRASS
201-203 Edgware Road, London, W2 1ES
Area of Operation: Worldwide
Tel: 0207 402 1854
Fax: 0207 402 0110
Email: ahbrass@btinternet.com
Web: www.aandhbrass.co.uk
Material Type: C) 14, 16

AL CHALLIS LTD
Europower House, Lower Road, Cookham, Maidenhead, Berkshire, SL6 9EH
Area of Operation: UK & Ireland
Tel: 01628 529024
Fax: 0870 458 0577
Email: chris@alchallis.com
Web: www.alchallis.com

ALEXANDERS
Unit 3, 1/1A Spilsby Road, Harold Hill, Romford, Essex, RM3 8SB
Area of Operation: UK & Ireland
Tel: 01708 384574 **Fax:** 01708 384089
Email: sales@alexanders-uk.net
Web: www.alexanders-uk.net

AMBIANCE BAIN
Cumberland House, 80 Scrubs Lane, London, NW10 6RF
Area of Operation: UK & Ireland
Tel: 0870 902 1313
Fax: 0870 902 1312
Email: sghirardello@mimea.com
Web: www.ambiancebain.com

ANTIQUE BATHS OF IVYBRIDGE LTD
Emebridge Works, Ermington Road, Ivybridge, Devon, PL21 9DE
Area of Operation: UK (Excluding Ireland)
Tel: 01752 698250 **Fax:** 01752 698266
Email: sales@antiquebaths.com
Web: www.antiquebaths.com

AQUAAQUA LTD
Melin Maes Dulais, Porthyrhyd, Carmarthenshire, SA32 8BT
Area of Operation: UK (Excluding Ireland)
Tel: 01267 275255
Fax: 01267 275597
Email: jamie@aquaaqua.co.uk
Web: www.aquaaqua.co.uk

AQUALISA PRODUCTS LTD
The Flyers Way, Westerham, Kent, TN16 1DE
Area of Operation: UK & Ireland
Tel: 01959 560000 **Fax:** 01959 560030
Email: sue.anderson@aqualisa.co.uk
Web: www.aqualisa.co.uk

AQUAPLUS SOLUTIONS
Unit 106, Indiana Building, London, SE13 7QD
Area of Operation: UK & Ireland
Tel: 0870 201 1915 **Fax:** 0870 201 1916
Email: info@aquaplussolutions.com
Web: www.aquaplussolutions.com

ASHLEY BATHROOMS
Duffield Road Industrial Estate, Little Eaton, Derby, Derbyshire, DE21 5DR
Area of Operation: UK & Ireland
Tel: 01332 830404
Fax: 01332 830202
Email: info@ashleybathrooms.com
Web: www.ashleybathrooms.com

AVANTE BATHROOMS
Thistle House, Thistle Way, Gildersome Spur, Wakefield Road, Morley, Leeds, West Yorkshire, LS27 7JZ
Area of Operation: UK (Excluding Ireland)
Tel: 0113 201 2240 **Fax:** 0113 253 0717
Email: info@avantebathrooms.com
Web: www.avantebathrooms.com

BARRHEAD SANITARYWARE PLC
15-17 Nasmyth Road, Hillington Industrial Estate, Hillington, Glasgow, Renfrewshire, G52 4RG
Area of Operation: UK & Ireland
Tel: 0141 883 0066 **Fax:** 0141 883 0077
Email: sales@barrhead.co.uk

BATHROOM BARN
The Bathroom Barn, Uplands Industrial Estate, Mere Way, Wyton, Huntingdon, Cambridgeshire, PE28 2JZ
Area of Operation: UK (Excluding Ireland)
Tel: 01480 458900
Email: sales@bathroom-barn.co.uk
Web: www.bathroombarn.co.uk

BATHROOM CITY
Seeleys Road, Tyseley Industrial Estate, Birmingham, West Midlands, B11 2LQ
Area of Operation: UK & Ireland
Tel: 0121 753 0700 **Fax:** 0121 753 1110
Email: sales@bathroomcity.com
Web: www.bathroomcity.com

BATHROOM DISCOUNT CENTRE
297 Munster Road, Fulham, Greater London, SW6 6BW
Area of Operation: UK (Excluding Ireland)
Tel: 0207 381 4222 **Fax:** 0207 381 6792
Email: bathdisc@aol.co.uk
Web: www.bathroomdiscount.co.uk

BATHROOM EXPRESS
61-62 Lower Dock Street, Kingsway, Newport, NP20 1EF
Area of Operation: UK & Ireland
Tel: 0845 130 2000
Fax: 01633 244881
Email: sales@bathroomexpress.co.uk
Web: www.bathroomexpress.co.uk

BATHROOM HEAVEN
25 Eccleston Square, London, SW1V 1NS
Area of Operation: UK & Ireland
Tel: 0845 121 6700 **Fax:** 0207 233 6074
Email: laura@bathroomheaven.com
Web: www.bathroomheaven.com

BATHROOMS PLUS LTD
222 Malmesbury Park Road, Bournemouth, Dorset, BH8 8PR
Area of Operation: South West England and South Wales
Tel: 01202 294417
Fax: 01202 316425
Email: info@bathrooms-plus.co.uk
Web: www.bathrooms-plus.co.uk

BATHROOMSTUFF.CO.UK
326 London Road, Hilsea, Portsmouth, Hampshire, PO2 9JT
Area of Operation: UK (Excluding Ireland)
Tel: 08450 580 540 **Fax:** 08451 274125
Email: sales@bathroomstuff.co.uk
Web: www.bathroomstuff.co.uk

BRISTAN
Birch Coppice Business Park,
Dordon, Tamworth, Staffordshire, B78 1SG
Area of Operation: Worldwide
Tel: 08704 425556 **Fax:** 0808 1611 002
Email: enquiries@bristan.com
Web: www.bristan.com **Material Type:** C) 11, 14

**BROOK-WATER DESIGNER
BATHROOMS & KITCHENS**
The Downs, Woodhouse Hill,
Uplyme, Lyme Regis, Dorset, DT7 3SL
Area of Operation: Worldwide
Tel: 0870 851 9739 **Email:** sales@brookwater.co.uk
Web: www.brookwater.co.uk

CHADDER & CO.
Blenheim Studio, London Road,
Forest Row, East Sussex, RH18 5EZ
Area of Operation: Worldwide **Tel:** 01342 823243
Fax: 01342 823097 **Web:** www.chadder.com

CHARLES MASON LTD
Unit 11A Brook Street Mill, Off Goodall Street,
Macclesfield, Cheshire, SK11 7AW
Area of Operation: Worldwide
Tel: 0800 085 3616 **Fax:** 01625 668789
Email: info@charles-mason.com
Web: www.charles-mason.com
Material Type: C) 2, 3, 14

CIFIAL UK LTD
7 Faraday Court, Park Farm Industrial Estate,
Wellingborough, Northamptonshire, NN8 6XY
Area of Operation: UK & Ireland
Tel: 01933 402008 **Fax:** 01933 402063
Email: sales@cifial.co.uk **Web:** www.cifial.co.uk

CIFIAL UK
Area of Operation: UK & Ireland
Tel: 01933 402008
Fax: 01933 402063
Email: sales@cifial.co.uk
Web: www.cifial.co.uk

Cifial's new contemporary TECHNOvation 35 range
offers solutions for both high & low water pressure.
Designed exclusively for Cifial by international award
winning designer, Carlos Aquiar.

CITY BATHROOMS & KITCHENS
158 Longford Road, Longford,
Coventry, West Midlands, CV6 6DR
Area of Operation: UK & Ireland
Tel: 02476 365877 **Fax:** 02476 644992
Email: citybathrooms@hotmail.com
Web: www.citybathrooms.co.uk

COLOURWASH LTD
165 Chamberlayne Road, London, NW10 3NU
Area of Operation: UK & Ireland
Tel: 0208 830 2992 **Fax:** 0208 830 2317
Email: sales@colourwash.co.uk
Web: www.colourwash.co.uk

COSY ROOMS (THE-BATHROOM-SHOP.CO.UK)
17 Chiltern Way, North Hykeham,
Lincoln, Lincolnshire, LN6 9SY
Area of Operation: UK (Excluding Ireland)
Tel: 01522 696002 **Fax:** 01522 696002
Email: keith@cosy-rooms.com
Web: www.the-bathroom-shop.co.uk

To recommend a
company for inclusion in
the next edition of
The Homebuilder's
Handbook,
email

customerservice@centaur.co.uk

CROSSWATER
Unit 5 Butterly Avenue, Questor,
Dartford, Kent, DA1 1JG
Area of Operation: UK & Ireland
Tel: 01322 628270 **Fax:** 01322 628280
Email: sales@crosswater.co.uk
Web: www.crosswater.co.uk

CYMRU KITCHENS
63 Caerleon Road, Newport, NP19 7BX
Area of Operation: UK (Excluding Ireland)
Tel: 01633 676767 **Fax:** 01633 212512
Email: sales@cymrukitchens.com
Web: www.cymrukitchens.com

DANICO BRASS LTD
31-35 Winchester Road,
Swiss Cottage, London, NW3 3NR
Area of Operation: Worldwide
Tel: 0207 483 4477 **Fax:** 0207 722 7992
Email: sales@danico.co.uk

DART VALLEY SYSTEMS LIMITED
Kemmings Close, Long Road,
Paignton, Devon, TQ4 7TW
Area of Operation: UK & Ireland
Tel: 01803 529021 **Fax:** 01803 559016
Email: sales@dartvalley.co.uk
Web: www.dartvalley.co.uk

DECORLUX LTD
18 Ghyll Industrial Estate, Ghyll Road,
Heathfield, East Sussex, TN21 8AW
Area of Operation: UK (Excluding Ireland)
Tel: 01435 866638 **Fax:** 01435 866641
Email: info@decorlux.co.uk
Web: www.decorlux.co.uk

DEEP BLUE SHOWROOM
299-313 Lewisham High Street,
Lewisham, London, SE13 6NW
Area of Operation: UK (Excluding Ireland)
Tel: 0208 690 3401 **Fax:** 0208 690 1408

DISCONTINUED BATHROOMS
140-142 Pogmoor Road, Pogmoor,
Barnsley, North Yorkshire, S75 2DX
Area of Operation: UK (Excluding Ireland)
Tel: 01226 280200 **Fax:** 01226 733273
Email: sales@discontinuedbathrooms.co.uk
Web: www.discontinuedbathrooms.co.uk

EURO BATHROOMS
102 Annareagh Road, Richhill, Co Armagh, BT61 9JY
Area of Operation: Ireland Only
Tel: 028 3887 9996 **Fax:** 028 3887 9996

EUROBATH INTERNATIONAL LIMITED
Eurobath House, Wedmore Road,
Cheddar, Somerset, BS27 3EB
Area of Operation: Worldwide
Tel: 01934 744466 **Fax:** 01934744345
Email: sales@eurobath.co.uk
Web: www.eurobath.co.uk/www.ilbagno.co.uk

IL BAGNO

IL BAGNO
Area of Operation: Worldwide
Tel: 01934 744466
Fax: 01934 744345
Email: sales@eurobath.co.uk
Web: www.ilbagno.co.uk
www.eurobath.co.uk

Il Bagno collates an exclusive portfolio of design-led
quality bathroom products from across Europe. With
high standards of production involved, the Il Bagno
collection represents supreme quality.

IL BAGNO

IL BAGNO
Area of Operation: Worldwide
Tel: 01934 744466
Fax: 01934 744345
Email: sales@eurobath.co.uk
Web: www.ilbagno.co.uk
www.eurobath.co.uk

ACQUAVIVA has shaken the industry with its
unique design and impeccable quality. The
channel spout feature generates a waterfall
impression that produces a relaxing ambience.

IL BAGNO
Area of Operation: Worldwide
Tel: 01934 744466
Fax: 01934 744345
Email: sales@eurobath.co.uk
Web: www.ilbagno.co.uk
www.eurobath.co.uk

Ethos: the latest exciting innovation to the
expanding VADO® portfolio by Eurobath. A
completely self-contained dynamo unit creating
illuminated red (hot) or blue (cold) water flow.

EUROBATH INTERNATIONAL LTD
Area of Operation: Worldwide
Tel: 01934 744466
Fax: 01934 744345
Email: sales@eurobath.co.uk
Web: www.eurobath.co.uk

With 20 years of experience in the bathroom
industry, Eurobath work only with the highest
quality of innovative designs whilst achieving the
ultimate level of service.

GEBERIT LTD
New Hythe Business Park, New Hythe Lane,
Aylesford, Kent, ME20 7PJ
Area of Operation: UK & Ireland
Tel: 01622 717 811 **Fax:** 01622 716 920
Web: www.geberit.co.uk

GO FIX IT LTD
Unit 10 Castle Industrial Estate, Louvain Street,
Off Oldham Road, Failsworth, Manchester, M35 0HB
Area of Operation: UK (Excluding Ireland)
Tel: 0161 681 4109 **Fax:** 0161 681 8169
Email: admin@gofixit.co.uk **Web:** www.gofixit.co.uk

GROHE UK
1 River Road, Barking, Essex, IG11 0HD
Area of Operation: Worldwide
Tel: 020 8594 7292 **Fax:** 020 8594 8898
Email: info@grohe.co.uk **Web:** www.grohe.co.uk

GUMMERS
Unit H, Redfern Park Way, Tyseley,
Birmingham, West Midlands, B11 2DN
Area of Operation: Worldwide
Tel: 0121 706 2241 **Fax:** 0121 706 2960
Email: sales@gummers.com
Web: www.sirrusshowers.com

HANSGROHE
Units D1 and D2, Sandown Park Trading Estate,
Royal Mills, Esher, Surrey, KT10 8BL
Area of Operation: Worldwide
Tel: 0870 770 1972 **Fax:** 0870 770 1973
Email: sales@hansgrohe.co.uk
Web: www.hansgrohe.co.uk
Material Type: C) 1, 2, 3, 11, 14

HERITAGE BATHROOMS
Princess Street, Bedminster, Bristol, BS3 4AG
Area of Operation: UK & Ireland
Tel: 0117 963 3333
Email: marketing@heritagebathrooms.com
Web: www.heritagebathrooms.com

HUDSON REED
Rylands Street, Burnley, Lancashire, BB10 1RG
Area of Operation: Worldwide
Tel: 01282 418000 **Fax:** 01282 428915
Email: info@ultra-group.com
Web: www.hudsonreed.info
Material Type: C) 3, 11, 14, 16

IDEAL STANDARD
The Bathroom Works, National Avenue,
Kingston Upon Hull, East Riding of Yorks, HU5 4HS
Area of Operation: Worldwide
Tel: 0800 590311 **Fax:** 01482 445886
Email: ideal-standard@aseur.com
Web: www.ideal-standard.co.uk

INDESIGN
Kiran House, 53 Park Royal Road, London, NW10 7LQ
Area of Operation: UK & Ireland
Tel: 0208 963 5841 **Fax:** 0208 965 6261
Email: dhanja.bhudia@akshars.co.uk
Web: www.akshars.co.uk

INSPIRED BATHROOMS
Unit R4, Innsworth Technology Park, Innsworth Lane,
Gloucester, Gloucestershire, GL3 1DL
Area of Operation: UK & Ireland
Tel: 01452 559121 **Fax:** 01452 530908
Email: sales@inspired-bathrooms.co.uk
Web: www.inspired-bathrooms.co.uk

ITFITZ
11-12 Woodlands Farm, Spring Lane,
Cookham Dean, Berkshire, SL6 9PN
Area of Operation: UK (Excluding Ireland)
Tel: 01628 890432
Fax: 0870 133 7955
Email: sales@itfitz.co.uk
Web: www.itfitz.co.uk

JACUZZI UK
Silverdale Road, Newcastle Under Lyme,
Staffordshire, ST5 6EL
Area of Operation: UK & Ireland
Tel: 01782 717175 **Fax:** 01782 717166
Email: jacuzzisalesdesk@jacuzziuk.com
Web: www.jacuzzi.co.uk

JOHN LEWIS OF HUNGERFORD
Grove Technology Park, Downsview Road,
Wantage, Oxfordshire, OX12 9FA
Area of Operation: UK (Excluding Ireland)
Tel: 01235 774300
Fax: 01235 769031
Email: park.street@john-lewis.co.uk
Web: www.john-lewis.co.uk

KENSINGTON STUDIO
13c/d Kensington Road, Earlsdon,
Coventry, West Midlands, CV5 6GG
Area of Operation: UK (Excluding Ireland)
Tel: 02476 713326
Fax: 02476 713136
Email: sales@kensingtonstudio.com
Web: www.kensingtonstudio.com

KERAMAG WAVENEY LTD
London Road, Beccles, Suffolk, NR34 8TS
Area of Operation: UK & Ireland
Tel: 01502 716600 **Fax:** 01502 717767
Email: info@keramagwaveney.co.uk
Web: www.keramag.com

KEUCO (UK)
2 Claridge Court, Lower Kings Road,
Berkhamsted, Hertfordshire, HP42AF
Area of Operation: Worldwide
Tel: 01442 865220
Fax: 01442 865260
Email: klaus@keuco.co.uk **Web:** www.keuco.de
Material Type: C) 3, 14, 17

KOHLER MIRA LIMITED
Barnett Way, Barnwood,
Gloucester, Gloucestershire, GL4 3RT
Area of Operation: UK & Ireland
Tel: 0870 850 5551 **Fax:** 0870 850 5552
Email: info@kohleruk.com
Web: www.kohleruk.com

LECICO PLC
Unit 47a Hobbs Industrial Estate,
Newchapel, Nr Lingfield, Surrey, RH7 6HN
Area of Operation: UK & Ireland
Tel: 01342 834777 **Fax:** 01342 834783
Email: info@lecico.co.uk
Web: www.lecico.co.uk **Material Type:** C) 3, 14, 16

M & O BATHROOM CENTRE
174-176 Goswell Road, Clarkenwell, London, EC1V 7DT
Area of Operation: East England, Greater London,
South East England
Tel: 0207 608 0111 **Fax:** 0207 490 3083
Email: mando@lineone.net

MEKON PRODUCTS
25 Bessemer Park, Milkwood Road, London, SE24 0HG
Area of Operation: UK (Excluding Ireland)
Tel: 0207 733 8011 **Fax:** 0207 737 0840
Email: info@mekon.net **Web:** www.mekon.net

MEREWAY CONTRACTS
Unit 1 Wharfdale Road, Tysely,
Birmingham, West Midlands, B11 2DE
Area of Operation: UK (Excluding Ireland)
Tel: 0121 764 7180 **Fax:** 0121 764 7199
Email: info@merewaycontracts.co.uk
Web: www.merewaycontracts.co.uk

MILLER FROM SWEDEN
Unit 18 Thorne Park Business Centre,
Wenman Road, Thame, Oxfordshire, OX9 3XA
Area of Operation: Worldwide
Tel: 01844 264800
Fax: 01844 261134
Email: sales@millerbathrooms.co.uk
Web: www.millerbathrooms.co.uk
Material Type: C) 11, 14

MOODS BATHROOMS
PJH Group, Alder House, Kearsley,
Bolton, Lancashire, BL4 8SL
Area of Operation: UK & Ireland
Tel: 01204 707070 **Fax:** 01204 573140
Email: info@pjh.co.uk
Web: ww.bathroom-moods.com

MWD
Clutton Hill Estate, King Lane,
Clutton Hill, Bristol, BS39 5QQ
Area of Operation: Midlands & Mid Wales, South
West England and South Wales
Tel: 0870 0332288 **Fax:** 0800 1976593
Email: sales@mwdretail.co.uk
Web: www.mikewalker.co.uk

NICHOLAS ANTHONY LTD
42-44 Wigmore Street, London, W1U 2RX
Area of Operation: East England, Greater London,
South East England
Tel: 0800 068 3603 **Fax:** 01206 762698
Email: info@nicholas-anthony.co.uk
Web: www.nicholas-anthony.co.uk

NO CODE
Larkwhistle Farm Road,
Micheldever, Hampshire, SO21 3BG
Area of Operation: UK & Ireland
Tel: 01962 870078 **Fax:** 01962 870077
Email: sales@nocode.co.uk
Web: www.nocode.co.uk

OLD FASHIONED BATHROOMS LTD
Foresters Hall, 52 High Street, Debenham,
Stowmarket, Suffolk, IP14 6QW
Area of Operation: UK (Excluding Ireland)
Tel: 01728 860926 **Fax:** 01728 860446
Email: ofbshop@yahoo.co.uk
Web: www.oldfashionedbathrooms.co.uk
Other Info: ▽

PEGLER LIMITED
St Catherine's Avenue, Doncaster,
South Yorkshire, DN4 8DF
Area of Operation: Worldwide
Tel: 0870 1200281 **Fax:** 01302 560108
Email: uk.sales@pegler.co.uk
Web: www.pegler.co.uk/francis

PERRIN & ROWE
Gateway XIII, Ferry Lane,
Rainham, Essex, RM13 9JY
Area of Operation: Worldwide
Tel: 01708 526361 **Fax:** 01708 550220
Web: www.perrinandrowe.co.uk **Other Info:** ✐ ✑
Material Type: C) 13, 14, 16, 17, 18

POLYPIPE KITCHENS & BATHROOMS LTD
Warmsworth, Halt Industrial Estate,
Doncaster, South Yorkshire, DN4 9LS
Area of Operation: Worldwide
Tel: 01709 770990 **Fax:** 01302 310602
Email: davery@ppbp.co.uk
Web: www.polypipe.com/bk

QUALCERAM SHIRES PLC
South Quay, Arklow, Co. Wicklow, Ireland
Area of Operation: UK & Ireland
Tel: 00353 402 31288
Fax: 00353 402 31292
Email: omoriarty@qualceram-shires.com
Web: www.qualceram-shires.com

REGINOX UK LTD
Radnor Park Trading Estate,
Congleton, Cheshire, CW12 4XJ
Area of Operation: UK & Ireland
Tel: 01260 280033 **Fax:** 01260 298889
Email: sales@reginoxuk.co.uk
Web: www.reginox.com

RELICS OF WITNEY LTD
1 Tristram Road, Ducklington,
Witney, Oxfordshire, OX29 7HX
Area of Operation: Worldwide
Tel: 0845 430 3035 **Fax:** 01993 779653
Email: sales@lightsshop.co.uk
Web: www.lightsshop.co.uk

ROOTS KITCHENS BEDROOMS BATHROOMS
Vine Farm, Stockers Hill, Boughton under Blean,
Faversham, Kent, ME13 9AB
Area of Operation: South East England
Tel: 01227 751130 **Fax:** 01227 750033
Email: showroom@rootskitchens.co.uk
Web: www.rootskitchens.co.uk

ROSCO COLLECTIONS
Stone Allerton, Axbridge, Somerset, BS26 2NS
Area of Operation: UK & Ireland
Tel: 01934 712299 **Fax:** 01934 713222
Email: jonathan@roscobathrooms.demon.co.uk

SAMUEL HEATH
Leopold Street, Birmingham, West Midlands, B12 0UJ
Area of Operation: Worldwide
Tel: 0121 772 2303 **Fax:** 0121 772 3334
Email: info@samuel-heath.com
Web: www.samuel-heath.com
Material Type: C) 11, 13, 14, 16

SHIRES
Uttoxeter Road, Longton,
Stoke-on-Trent, Staffordshire, ST3 1NA
Tel: 01782 599099
Fax: 01782 599295
Email: hkiddle@qualceram-shires.com
Web: www.shires-bathrooms.com

SMART SHOWERS LTD
Unit 11, Woodside Road, South Marston Business
Park, Swindon, Wiltshire, SN3 4WA
Tel: 01793 822775 **Fax:** 01793 823800
Email: enquiries@smartshowers.co.uk
Web: www.smartshowers.co.uk

SOGA LTD
41 Mayfield Street, Hull, East Riding of Yorks, HU3 1NT
Area of Operation: Worldwide
Tel: 01482 327025
Email: info@soga.co.uk **Web:** www.soga.co.uk

STIFFKEY BATHROOMS
89 Upper Saint Giles Street, Norwich, Norfolk, NR2 1AB
Tel: 01603 627850 **Fax:** 01603 619775
Email: stiffkeybathrooms.norwich@virgin.net
Web: www.stiffkeybathrooms.com

SVEDBERGS
4E Wilsons Park, Monsall Road,
Newton Heath, Manchester, M40 8WN
Tel: 0161 2051200
Fax: 0161 251212
Email: info@svedbergs.co.uk
Web: www.svedbergs.co.uk

SWADLING BRASSWARE - A MATKI COMPANY
Churchward Road, Yate, Bristol, BS37 5PL
Area of Operation: Europe
Tel: 01454 322888 **Fax:** 01454 315284
Email: helpline@matki.co.uk
Web: www.swadlingbrassware.com

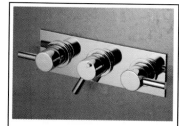

SWADLING BRASSWARE
A MATKI COMPANY

Area of Operation: Europe
Tel: 01454 322888 **Fax:** 01454 315284
Email: enquiries@swadlingbrassware.com
Web: www.swadlingbrassware.com

Swadling shower roses and valves combine
advanced thermostatic technology with cutting
edge design and are suitable for use in domestic
or commercial situations. Most Swadling shower
valves are TMV2 approved.

TAPS SHOP
1 Tristram Road, Ducklington,
Whitney, Oxfordshire, OX29 7XH
Area of Operation: Worldwide
Tel: 0845 4303035 **Fax:** 01993 779653
Email: info@tapsshop.co.uk
Web: www.tapsshop.co.uk

THE KITCHEN AND BATHROOM COLLECTION
Nelson House, Nelson Road,
Salisbury, Wiltshire, SP1 3LT
Area of Operation: South West England and South Wales
Tel: 01722 334800 **Fax:** 01722 412252
Email: info@kbc.co.uk
Web: www.kbc.co.uk **Other Info:** ✐

THE WATER MONOPOLY
16/18 Lonsdale Road, London, NW6 6RD
Area of Operation: UK (Excluding Ireland)
Tel: 0207 624 2636 **Fax:** 0207 624 2631
Email: enquiries@watermonopoly.com
Web: www.watermonopoly.com

THOMAS CRAPPER & CO. LTD
The Stable Yard, Alscot Park,
Stratford-on-Avon, Warwickshire, CV37 8BL
Area of Operation: Worldwide
Tel: 01789 450522 **Fax:** 01789 450523
Email: wc@thomas-crapper.com
Web: www.thomas-crapper.com

TIMELESS BATHROOMS LTD
394 Ringwood Road, Ferndown, Dorset, BH22 9AU
Area of Operation: South East England
Tel: 01202 897110
Fax: 01202 892252
Email: bathroom@options394.fsnet.co.uk
Web: www.timelessbathrooms.co.uk

TRADEMARK TILES
Tile Store, Somersham Road, St. Ives,
Huntingdon, Cambridgeshire, PE27 3WR
Area of Operation: UK (Excluding Ireland)
Tel: 01480 498123 **Email:** info@tilestoreplus.co.uk
Web: www.tilestoreplus.co.uk

TRITON PLC
Triton House, Shepperton Business Park,
Caldwell Road, Nuneaton, Warwickshire, CV11 4NR
Area of Operation: UK & Ireland
Tel: 02476 344441 **Fax:** 02476 6349828
Web: www.tritonshowers.co.uk

TWYFORD BATHROOMS
Lawton Road, Alsager,
Stoke On Trent, Staffordshire, ST7 2DF
Area of Operation: Worldwide
Tel: 01270 879777
Web: www.twyfordbathrooms.com
Material Type: C) 9, 11, 14, 16

UNICOM
Kingdom House, 219 Gleniffer Road,
Paisley, Renfrewshire, PA2 8UL
Tel: 0845 330 7642
Fax: 0845 330 7641
Email: george@unicom-direct.com
Web: www.unicom-direct.com ⌐

VICTORIAN BATHROOMS
Victorian Bathrooms, Ings Mill Complex,
Dale Street, Ossett , West Yorkshire, WF5 9HQ
Area of Operation: UK (Excluding Ireland)
Tel: 01924 267736   Fax: 01924 261232
Email: sales@vb-bathrooms.com
Web: www.vb-bathrooms.com ⌐

WALTON BATHROOMS
The Hersham Centre, The Green, Molesey Road,
Hersham, Walton on Thames, Surrey, KT12 4HL
Tel: 01932 224784   Fax: 01932 253447
Email: sales@waltonbathrooms.co.uk
Web: www.waltonbathrooms.co.uk ⌐

WATER FRONT
All Worcester Buildings, Birmingham Road,
Redditch, Worcestershire, B97 6DY
Area of Operation: UK & Ireland
Tel: 01527 584244   Fax: 01527 61127
Email: info@waterfrontbathrooms.com
Web: www.waterfrontbathrooms.com

WHIRLPOOL EXPRESS (UK) LTD
61-62 Lower Dock Street, Kingsway, Newport, NP20 1EF
Area of Operation: Europe
Tel: 01633 244555   Fax: 01633 244881
Email: reception@whirlpoolexpress.co.uk
Web: www.whirlpoolexpress.co.uk ⌐

BATHS

KEY

PRODUCT TYPES: 1= Standard Baths
2 = Roll Top Baths   3 = Whirlpool Baths
4 = Corner Baths   5 = Double Baths
6 = Shower Baths   7 = Inset Baths
8 = Round Baths   9 = Other

OTHER: ▽ Reclaimed   ⌐ On-line shopping
✎ Bespoke   ✋ Hand-made   ECO Ecological

A & H BRASS
201-203 Edgware Road, London, W2 1ES
Area of Operation: Worldwide
Tel: 0207 402 1854   Fax: 0207 402 0110
Email: ahbrass@btinternet.com
Web: www.aandhbrass.co.uk ⌐   Product Type: 1

AIRBATH APPOLLO LIMITED
Swinnow Lane, Leeds, West Yorkshire, LS13 4TY
Area of Operation: Worldwide
Tel: 0113 255 6666   Fax: 0113 3869176
Email: sales@airbath.co.uk
Web: www.airbath.co.uk
Product Type: 1, 3, 4, 5, 6, 7, 8

ALEXANDERS
Unit 3, 1/1A Spilsby Road,
Harold Hill, Romford, Essex, RM3 8SB
Area of Operation: UK & Ireland
Tel: 01708 384574
Fax: 01708 384089
Email: sales@alexanders-uk.net
Web: www.alexanders-uk.net
Product Type: 1, 3, 4, 5, 7, 8, 9

ALTHEA UK LTD
Concept House, Blanche Street,
Bradford, West Yorkshire, BD4 8DA
Area of Operation: UK (Excluding Ireland)
Tel: 01274 660770   Fax: 01274 667929
Email: sales@altheauk.com
Web: www.periodbathrooms.co.uk

AMBIANCE BAIN
Cumberland House,
80 Scrubs Lane, London, NW10 6RF
Area of Operation: UK & Ireland
Tel: 0870 902 1313   Fax: 0870 902 1312
Email: sghirardello@mimea.com
Web: www.ambiancebain.com

ANTIQUE BATHS OF IVYBRIDGE LTD
Emebridge Works, Ermington Road,
Ivybridge, Devon, PL21 9DE
Area of Operation: UK (Excluding Ireland)
Tel: 01752 698250
Fax: 01752 698266
Email: sales@antiquebaths.com
Web: www.antiquebaths.com ⌐
Product Type: 1, 2, 3, 5, 6, 7

ASHLEY BATHROOMS
Duffield Road Industrial Estate,
Little Eaton, Derby, Derbyshire, DE21 5DR
Area of Operation: UK & Ireland
Tel: 01332 830404   Fax: 01332 830202
Email: info@ashleybathrooms.com
Web: www.ashleybathrooms.com
Product Type: 1, 2, 4, 7

BARRHEAD SANITARYWARE PLC
15-17 Nasmyth Road, Hillington Industrial Estate,
Hillington, Glasgow, Renfrewshire, G52 4RG
Area of Operation: UK & Ireland
Tel: 0141 883 0066   Fax: 0141 883 0077
Email: sales@barrhead.co.uk   Product Type: 1, 4

BATHROOM BARN
The Bathroom Barn, Uplands Industrial Estate, Mere
Way, Wyton, Huntingdon, Cambridgeshire, PE28 2JZ
Area of Operation: UK (Excluding Ireland)
Tel: 01480 458900
Email: sales@bathroom-barn.co.uk
Web: www.bathroombarn.co.uk

BATHROOM CITY
Seeleys Road, Tyseley Industrial Estate,
Birmingham, West Midlands, B11 2LQ
Area of Operation: UK & Ireland
Tel: 0121 753 0700
Fax: 0121 753 1110
Email: sales@bathroomcity.com
Web: www.bathroomcity.com ⌐
Product Type: 1, 2, 3, 4, 5, 6, 7, 8, 9

BATHROOM DISCOUNT CENTRE
297 Munster Road, Fulham,
Greater London, SW6 6BW
Area of Operation: UK (Excluding Ireland)
Tel: 0207 381 4222
Fax: 0207 381 6792
Email: bathdisc@aol.co.uk
Web: www.bathroomdiscount.co.uk

BATHROOM EXPRESS
61-62 Lower Dock Street,
Kingsway, Newport, NP20 1EF
Area of Operation: UK & Ireland
Tel: 0845 130 2000
Fax: 01633 244881
Email: sales@bathroomexpress.co.uk
Web: www.bathroomexpress.co.uk ⌐
Product Type: 1, 2, 3, 4, 5, 6, 7, 8

BATHROOM HEAVEN
25 Eccleston Square, London, SW1V 1NS
Area of Operation: UK & Ireland
Tel: 0845 121 6700
Fax: 0207 233 6074
Email: laura@bathroomheaven.com
Web: www.bathroomheaven.com ⌐
Product Type: 1, 2, 4, 9   Material Type: C) 2

BATHROOMS PLUS LTD
222 Malmesbury Park Road,
Bournemouth, Dorset, BH8 8PR
Area of Operation: South West England and South Wales
Tel: 01202 294417   Fax: 01202 316425
Email: info@bathrooms-plus.co.uk
Web: www.bathrooms-plus.co.uk
Product Type: 1, 2, 3, 4, 5, 6, 7, 8, 9
Material Type: C) 2

BATHROOMSTUFF.CO.UK
326 London Road, Hilsea,
Portsmouth, Hampshire, PO2 9JT
Area of Operation: UK (Excluding Ireland)
Tel: 08450 580 540   Fax: 08451 274125
Email: sales@bathroomstuff.co.uk
Web: www.bathroomstuff.co.uk ⌐
Product Type: 1, 2, 4, 5, 6, 7, 8, 9

BRONTE WHIRLPOOLS
Unit 10, Ryefield Way,
Silsden, West Yorkshire, BD20 0EF
Area of Operation: UK (Excluding Ireland)
Tel: 01535 656524   Fax: 01535 658823
Email: info@brontewhirlpools.co.uk
Web: www.brontewhirlpools.co.uk
Product Type: 3

CABUCHON BATHFORMS
Whitegate, White Lund Estate,
Lancaster, Lancashire, LA3 3BT
Area of Operation: Worldwide
Tel: 01524 66022   Fax: 01524 844927
Email: info@cabuchon.com
Web: www.cabuchon.com
Product Type: 3, 4, 5, 7, 9   Other Info: ✎

CAPITAL MARBLE DESIGN
Unit 1 Pall Mall Deposit,
124-128 Barlby Road, London, W10 6BL
Area of Operation: UK & Ireland
Tel: 0208 968 5340   Fax: 0208 968 8827
Email: stonegallery@capitalmarble.co.uk
Web: www.capitalmarble.co.uk   Product Type: 1, 8

CASACHI HYDROTHERAPY LTD
Unit A Wanborough Business Park, West Flexford
Lane, Wanborough, Guildford, Surrey, GU3 2JS
Area of Operation: UK & Ireland
Tel: 01483 813 181   Fax: 01483 813 182
Email: info@casachi-hydrotherapy.com
Web: www.casachi-hydrotherapy.com
Product Type: 1, 3, 4, 5, 7, 8, 9

CASTELLO LUXURY BATHS LTD
Unit 3 Diamond Industrial Centre, Works Road,
Letchworth, Hertfordshire, SG6 4BS
Area of Operation: UK & Ireland
Tel: 01462 483131   Fax: 01462 670939
Email: sales@castellobaths.co.uk
Web: www.castellobaths.co.uk   Product Type: 5, 9

CHADDER & CO.
Blenheim Studio, London Road,
Forest Row, East Sussex, RH18 5EZ
Area of Operation: Worldwide
Tel: 01342 823243   Fax: 01342 823097
Web: www.chadder.com

CITY BATHROOMS & KITCHENS
158 Longford Road, Longford,
Coventry, West Midlands, CV6 6DR
Area of Operation: UK & Ireland
Tel: 02476 365877
Fax: 02476 644992
Email: citybathrooms@hotmail.com
Web: www.citybathrooms.co.uk

CLEARWATER COLLECTION
Enterprise House, Iron Works Park, Bowling Back
Lane, Bradford, West Yorkshire, BD4 8SX
Area of Operation: UK (Excluding Ireland)
Tel: 01274 738140   Fax: 01274 732461
Email: enquiries@clearwater-collection.com
Web: www.clearwater-collection.com
Product Type: 2

COUNTY GRANITE AND MARBLE
Mill Lane, Creech Saint Michael,
Taunton, Somerset, TA3 5PX
Area of Operation: UK (Excluding Ireland)
Tel: 01823 444554   Fax: 01823 445013
Web: www.countygranite.co.uk

CP HART GROUP
Newnham Terrace, Hercules Road, London, SE1 7DR
Area of Operation: Greater London
Tel: 0845 600 1950   Fax: 01322 422101
Email: sales@cphart.co.uk   Web: www.cphart.co.uk

C.P.HART GROUP
Area of Operation: UK
Tel: 0845 600 1950
Fax: 01322 422 101
Email: sales@cphart.co.uk
Web: www.cphart.co.uk

C.P. Hart is one of the UK's leading bathroom
retailers. There are five exquisite C.P. Hart
showrooms across the country displaying the
latest products from the bathroom industry, many
exclusively sold by C.P. Hart.

CYMRU KITCHENS
63 Caerleon Road, Newport, NP19 7BX
Tel: 01633 676767   Fax: 01633 212512
Email: sales@cymrukitchens.com
Web: www.cymrukitchens.com

DECORMASTER LTD
Unit 16, Waterside Industrial Estate,
Wolverhampton, West Midlands, WV2 2RH
Area of Operation: Worldwide
Tel: 01902 406030   Fax: 01902 353126
Email: sales@oldcolours.co.uk
Web: www.oldcolours.co.uk
Product Type: 1, 2, 3, 4, 5, 6, 7, 8

DEEP BLUE SHOWROOM
299-313 Lewisham High Street,
Lewisham, London, SE13 6NW
Area of Operation: UK (Excluding Ireland)
Tel: 0208 690 3401   Fax: 0208 690 1408

DISCONTINUED BATHROOMS
140-142 Pogmoor Road, Pogmoor,
Barnsley, North Yorkshire, S75 2DX
Area of Operation: UK (Excluding Ireland)
Tel: 01226 280200   Fax: 01226 733273
Email: sales@discontinuedbathrooms.co.uk
Web: www.discontinuedbathrooms.co.uk
Product Type: 1, 2, 3, 4, 5, 6, 7, 8, 9

DURAVIT
Unit 7, Stratus Park, Brudenell Drive, Brinklow,
Milton Keynes, Buckinghamshire, MK10 0DE
Tel: 0870 730 7787   Fax: 0870 730 7786
Email: info.uk@duravit.com   Web: www.duravit.co.uk
Product Type: 1, 3, 4, 5, 7   Material Type: D) 5

ELLIOTT BROTHERS LTD
Millbank Wharf, Northam,
Southampton, Hampshire, SO14 5AG
Area of Operation: South East England, South West
England and South Wales
Tel: 02380 226852   Fax: 02380 638780
Email: laurenh@elliott-brothers.co.uk
Web: www.elliotts.uk.com
Product Type: 1, 2, 3, 4, 5, 6, 8

EURO BATHROOMS
102 Annareagh Road, Richhill, Co Armagh, BT61 9JY
Area of Operation: Ireland Only
Tel: 028 3887 9996   Fax: 028 3887 9996

EUROBATH INTERNATIONAL LIMITED
Eurobath House, Wedmore Road, Cheddar,
Somerset, BS27 3EB
Area of Operation: Worldwide
Tel: 01934 744466   Fax: 01934744345
Email: sales@eurobath.co.uk
Web: www.eurobath.co.uk/www.ilbagno.co.uk
Product Type: 1

INTERIORS, FIXTURES & FINISHES - **Bathrooms** - Baths
SPONSORED BY: MOVE OR IMPROVE MAGAZINE   www.moveorimprove.co.uk

INTERIORS, FIXTURES & FINISHES

EUROCARE SHOWERS LTD
Unit 19, Doncaster Industry Park, Watch House Lane,
Bentley, Doncaster, South Yorkshire, DN5 9LZ
Area of Operation: Worldwide
Tel: 01302 788684
Fax: 01302 780010
Email: sales@eurocare-showers.com
Web: www.eurocare-showers.com
Product Type: 3

HAROLD MOORE & SON LTD
Rawson Spring Road, Hillsborough,
Sheffield, South Yorkshire, S6 1PD
Area of Operation: UK & Ireland
Tel: 0114 233 6161
Fax: 0114 232 6375
Email: admin@haroldmoorebaths.co.uk
Web: www.haroldmoorebaths.co.uk
Product Type: 1, 3, 4, 8

HERITAGE BATHROOMS
Princess Street, Bedminster, Bristol, BS3 4AG
Area of Operation: UK & Ireland
Tel: 0117 963 3333
Email: marketing@heritagebathrooms.com
Web: www.heritagebathrooms.com
Product Type: 1, 2, 3, 4, 5, 6, 7, 8

IDEAL STANDARD
The Bathroom Works, National Avenue,
Kingston Upon Hull, East Riding of Yorks, HU5 4HS
Area of Operation: Worldwide
Tel: 0800 590311   **Fax:** 01482 445886
Email: ideal-standard@aseur.com
Web: www.ideal-standard.co.uk

INSPIRED BATHROOMS
Unit R4, Innsworth Technology Park, Innsworth Lane,
Gloucester, Gloucestershire, GL3 1DL
Area of Operation: UK & Ireland
Tel: 01452 559121
Fax: 01452 530908
Email: sales@inspired-bathrooms.co.uk
Web: www.inspired-bathrooms.co.uk
Product Type: 1, 2, 3, 4, 5, 6, 7, 8

JACUZZI UK
Silverdale Road, Newcastle Under Lyme,
Staffordshire, ST5 6EL
Area of Operation: UK & Ireland
Tel: 01782 717175   **Fax:** 01782 717166
Email: jacuzzisalesdesk@jacuzziuk.com
Web: www.jacuzzi.co.uk   **Product Type:** 3, 4, 6, 7, 9

JACUZZI UK - BC SANITAN
Silverdale Road, Newcastle Under Lyme,
Staffordshire, ST5 6EL
Area of Operation: UK & Ireland
Tel: 01782 717175   **Fax:** 01782 717166
Email: jacuzzisalesdesk@jacuzziuk.com
Web: www.jacuzziuk.com
Product Type: 2

JOHN FLEMING & CO LTD
Silverburn Place, Bridge of Don,
Aberdeen, Aberdeenshire, AB23 8EG
Area of Operation: Scotland
Tel: 0800 085 8728   **Fax:** 01224 825377
Email: info@johnfleming.co.uk
Web: www.johnfleming.co.uk

JOHN LEWIS OF HUNGERFORD
Grove Technology Park, Downsview Road,
Wantage, Oxfordshire, OX12 9FA
Area of Operation: UK (Excluding Ireland)
Tel: 01235 774300
Fax: 01235 769031
Email: park.street@john-lewis.co.uk
Web: www.john-lewis.co.uk

JUST ADD WATER
202 - 228 York Way, Kings Cross, London, N7 9AZ
Area of Operation: UK (Excluding Ireland)
Tel: 0207 697 3161
Fax: 0207 697 3162
Email: kingscoss.sales@justaddwater.co.uk
Web: www.justaddwater.co.uk
Product Type: 1

KALDEWEI
Unit 7, Sundial Court, Tolworth Rise South,
Surbiton, Surrey, KT5 9RN
Area of Operation: Worldwide
Tel: 0870 777 2223
Fax: 0870 777 2225
Email: info@kaldewei-uk.com
Web: www.kaldewei.com
Product Type: 1, 3, 4, 5, 6, 7, 8, 9

KALDEWEI

Area of Operation: Worldwide
Tel: 0870 777 2223
Fax: 0870 777 2225
Email: info@kaldewei-uk.com
Web: www.kaldewei.com
Product Type: 1, 3, 4, 5, 6, 7, 9, 8

Kaldewei is Europe's largest producer of steel
enamel baths and showers tray with over 260
models to choose from for all budgets.

KENSINGTON STUDIO
13 c & d Kensington Road, Earlsdon,
Coventry, West Midlands, CV5 6GG
Area of Operation: UK (Excluding Ireland)
Tel: 02476 713326
Fax: 02476 713136
Email: sales@kensingtonstudio.com
Web: www.kensingtonstudio.com
Product Type: 1, 2, 3, 4, 5, 6, 7, 8, 9

KERAMAG WAVENEY LTD
London Road, Beccles, Suffolk, NR34 8TS
Area of Operation: UK & Ireland
Tel: 01502 716600
Fax: 01502 717767
Email: info@keramagwaveney.co.uk
Web: www.keramag.com
Product Type: 1, 2, 3, 4, 5, 6, 7, 9

KIRKSTONE QUARRIES LIMITED
Skelwith Bridge, Ambleside, Cumbria, LA22 9NN
Area of Operation: UK & Ireland
Tel: 01539 433296   **Fax:** 01539 434006
Email: info@kirkstone.com
Web: www.kirkstone.com   **Product Type:** 9

KOHLER MIRA LIMITED
Barnett Way, Barnwood,
Gloucester, Gloucestershire, GL4 3RT
Area of Operation: UK & Ireland
Tel: 0870 850 5551   **Fax:** 0870 850 5552
Email: info@kohleruk.com
Web: www.kohleruk.com

LECICO PLC
Unit 47a Hobbs Industrial Estate,
Newchapel, Nr Lingfield, Surrey, RH7 6HN
Area of Operation: UK & Ireland
Tel: 01342 834777   **Fax:** 01342 834783
Email: info@lecico.co.uk
Web: www.lecico.co.uk   **Product Type:** 1

M & O BATHROOM CENTRE
174-176 Goswell Road,
Clarkenwell, London, EC1V 7DT
Area of Operation: East England, Greater London,
South East England
Tel: 0207 608 0111   **Fax:** 0207 490 3083
Email: mando@lineone.net
Product Type: 1, 2, 3, 4, 5, 6, 7

MARBLE CLASSICS
Unit 3, Station Approach,
Emsworth, Hampshire, PO10 7PW
Area of Operation: UK & Ireland
Tel: 01243 370011   **Fax:** 01243 371023
Email: info@marbleclassics.co.uk
Web: www.marbleclassics.co.uk
Product Type: 9   **Material Type:** E) 2, 5, 8

MEREWAY CONTRACTS
Unit 1 Wharfdale Road, Tysely,
Birmingham, West Midlands, B11 2DE
Area of Operation: UK (Excluding Ireland)
Tel: 0121 764 7180   **Fax:** 0121 764 7199
Email: info@merewaycontracts.co.uk
Web: www.merewaycontracts.co.uk

**MISCELLANEA DISCONTINUED
BATHROOMWARE**
Churt Place Nurseries, Tilford Road,
Churt, Farnham, Surrey, GU10 2LN
Area of Operation: Worldwide
Tel: 01428 608164   **Fax:** 01428 608165
Email: email@brokenbog.com
Web: www.brokenbog.com
Product Type: 1, 2, 3, 4, 5, 6, 7, 8, 9

MOODS BATHROOMS
PJH Group, Alder House, Kearsley,
Bolton, Lancashire, BL4 8SL
Area of Operation: UK & Ireland
Tel: 01204 707070   **Fax:** 01204 573140
Email: info@pjh.co.uk
Web: ww.bathroom-moods.com
Product Type: 1, 2, 3, 4, 5, 6, 7

N&C NICOBOND
41-51 Freshwater Road, Chadwell Heath,
Romford, Essex, RM8 1SP
Area of Operation: Worldwide
Tel: 0208 586 4600   **Fax:** 0208 586 4646
Email: info@nichollsandclarke.com
Web: www.ncdirect.co.uk

NICHOLAS ANTHONY LTD
42-44 Wigmore Street, London, W1U 2RX
Area of Operation: East England, Greater London,
South East England
Tel: 0800 068 3603   **Fax:** 01206 762698
Email: info@nicholas-anthony.co.uk
Web: www.nicholas-anthony.co.uk
Product Type: 1, 3, 4, 6, 7

NO CODE
Larkwhistle Farm Road,
Micheldever, Hampshire, SO21 3BG
Area of Operation: UK & Ireland
Tel: 01962 870078   **Fax:** 01962 870077
Email: sales@nocode.co.uk
Web: www.nocode.co.uk
Product Type: 1, 2, 3, 4, 5, 7

OLD FASHIONED BATHROOMS LTD
Foresters Hall, 52 High Street, Debenham,
Stowmarket, Suffolk, IP14 6QW
Area of Operation: UK (Excluding Ireland)
Tel: 01728 860926   **Fax:** 01728 860446
Email: ofbshop@yahoo.co.uk
Web: www.oldfashionedbathrooms.co.uk
Product Type: 1, 2, 3, 5, 6, 7, 9
Other Info: ▽   **Material Type:** C) 1, 2, 5

OLD FASHIONED BATHROOMS LTD
Area of Operation: UK (Excluding Ireland)
Tel: 01728 860926
Fax: 01728 860446
Email: ofbshop@yahoo.co.uk
Web: www.oldfashionedbathrooms.co.uk

Spacious showroom displaying period &
contemporary bathrooms. Good selection of
reclaimed baths, sanitary ware & taps also
reproduction suites. Carriage arranged (mainland).

OMNITUB
The Bothy, Lays Lane, Blagdon, Somerset, BS40 7RQ
Area of Operation: UK & Ireland
Tel: 01761 462 641   **Fax:** 01761 462 641
Email: info@omnitub.co.uk
Web: www.omnitub.co.uk   **Product Type:** 6, 9

PRETTY SWIFT LTD
Units 7&8, 51 Chancery Lane,
Debenham, Suffolk, IP14 6PJ
Area of Operation: UK (Excluding Ireland)
Tel: 01728 861818   **Fax:** 01728 861919
Email: prettyswiftltd@yahoo.co.uk

QUALCERAM SHIRES PLC
South Quay, Arklow, Co. Wicklow, Ireland
Area of Operation: UK & Ireland
Tel: 00353 402 31288   **Fax:** 00353 402 31292
Email: omoriarty@qualceram-shires.com
Web: www.qualceram-shires.com
Product Type: 1, 2, 3, 4, 5, 6, 7, 8, 9

RAK CERAMICS
The Tile House , Easebourne Lane,
Easebourne, West Sussex, GU29 9AZ
Tel: 01730 815507   **Fax:** 01730 815007
Email: info@rakceramics.co.uk
Web: www.rakceramics.co.uk   **Product Type:** 1, 4

RELAXAIR
Tiber House, Hall Lane, Off Lostock Lane,
Lostock, Bolton, Lancashire, BL6 4BR
Tel: 01204 675804   **Fax:** 01204 675809
Email: info@relaxair.co.uk
Web: www.relaxair.co.uk   **Product Type:** 3

RIVERBED
Priory Park, Chewton Mendip, Bath, Somerset, BA3 4NT
Area of Operation: UK & Ireland
Tel: 01761 241133   **Fax:** 01761 241134
Email: sales@riverbed.ltd.uk
Web: www.riverbed.ltd.uk
Product Type: 1, 2, 4, 5, 6, 7, 8, 9
Other Info: ✎   **Material Type:** K) 11

ROSCO COLLECTIONS
Stone Allerton, Axbridge, Somerset, BS26 2NS
Area of Operation: UK & Ireland
Tel: 01934 712299   **Fax:** 01934 713222
Email: jonathan@roscobathrooms.demon.co.uk
Product Type: 1, 2, 3, 4, 5, 6, 8

SHIRES
Uttoxeter Road, Longton,
Stoke-on-Trent, Staffordshire, ST3 1NA
Area of Operation: UK & Ireland
Tel: 01782 599099   **Fax:** 01782 599295
Email: hkiddle@qualceram-shires.com
Web: www.shires-bathrooms.com
Product Type: 1, 2, 3, 4, 6, 7

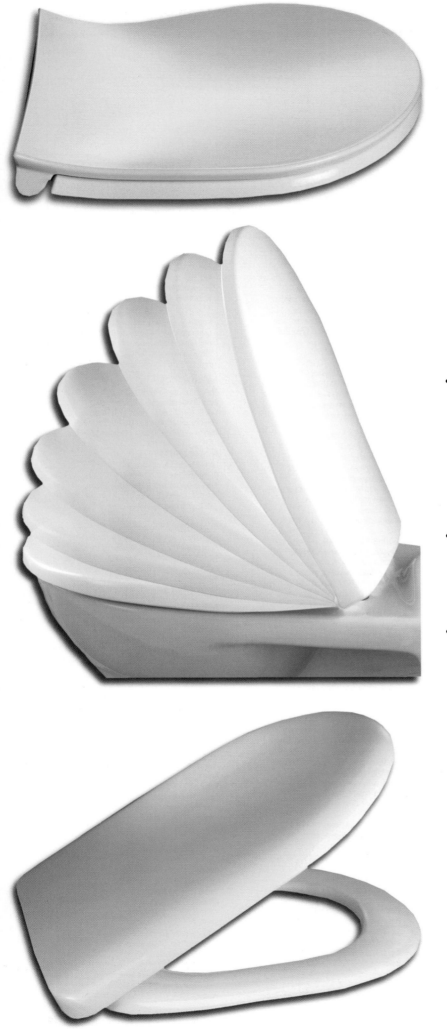

SANITARY

INNOVATION FROM HARO

Leading German WC seat manufacturer, Haro Sanitar
produces a **wide selection of high quality WC se**
offering innovative design solutions with the highest
standards of comfort, hygiene and quality.

- The **SoftClose system** is typical of Haro's desire to
  challenge existing standards in the market. SoftClose
  allows just a touch of the fingertip to bring the lid do
  softly and reliably every time. This unique and patente
  system now also comes with a **ten-year guarante**
  on the soft close action and is the only product in th
  market place to offer this.

- **Homeline range** – offers a large selection of mod
  in a wide range of materials, offering a combination o
  hygiene and comfort. Also offer innovative assembly a
  care solutions including SoftClose, Easyfix and FastFix

- **Careline range** - Designed specifically to meet
  even the toughest hygiene safety standards in both
  private homes and the public and welfare sector.
  All CareLine WC seats come with ActiveShield - a
  specially developed protective hygiene coating that o
  maximum resistance to bacteria and germs and yet is
  odourless and kind to skin.

Haro WC seats are available from all good bathroom
specialists on the high street. For more information v
www.haro-sanitary.com or contact our sales
representative Tel: 01204 707070

**Haro Sanitary is the largest manufacturer of h
plastic WC seats in Europe** and is part of the
Hamberger group which is also well known for being o
of the biggest parquet and laminate floors manufactur

SHOWERLUX UK LTD
Sibree Road, Coventry, West Midlands, CV3 4FD
Area of Operation: UK & Ireland
Tel: 02476 882515 **Fax:** 02476 305457
Email: sales@showerlux.co.uk
Web: www.showerlux.com
Product Type: 1, 3, 4, 5, 6

SMART SHOWERS LTD
Unit 11, Woodside Road, South Marston Business
Park, Swindon, Wiltshire, SN3 4WA
Area of Operation: UK & Ireland
Tel: 01793 822775 **Fax:** 01793 823800
Email: enquiries@smartshowers.co.uk
Web: www.smartshowers.co.uk
Product Type: 3

SOGA LTD
41 Mayfield Street, Hull,
East Riding of Yorks, HU3 1NT
Area of Operation: Worldwide
Tel: 01482 327025
Email: info@soga.co.uk **Web:** www.soga.co.uk
Product Type: 2, 3, 4, 6, 8

STIFFKEY BATHROOMS
89 Upper Saint Giles Street, Norwich, Norfolk, NR2 1AB
Area of Operation: Worldwide
Tel: 01603 627850 **Fax:** 01603 619775
Email: stiffkeybathrooms.norwich@virgin.net
Web: www.stiffkeybathrooms.com
Product Type: 2, 5, 6 **Other Info:** ▽

STONELL DIRECT
7 showrooms nationwide - see website for details.
Area of Operation: Worldwide
Tel: 08000 832283 **Fax:** 01283 501098
Email: info@stonelldirect.com
Web: www.stonelldirect.com

SVEDBERGS
4E Wilsons Park, Monsall Road, Newton Heath,
Manchester, Greater Manchester, M40 8WN
Area of Operation: UK & Ireland
Tel: 0161 2051200 **Fax:** 0161 251212
Email: info@svedbergs.co.uk
Web: www.svedbergs.co.uk
Product Type: 1, 2, 3, 4, 5, 8, 9

THE GRANITE FACTORY
4 Winchester Drive, Peterlee, Durham, SR8 2RJ
Area of Operation: North East England
Tel: 0191 518 3600 **Fax:** 0191 518 3600
Email: admin@granitefactory.co.uk
Web: www.granitefactory.co.uk
Product Type: 7

THE KITCHEN AND BATHROOM COLLECTION
Nelson House, Nelson Road,
Salisbury, Wiltshire, SP1 3LT
Area of Operation: South West England and South Wales
Tel: 01722 334800 **Fax:** 01722 412252
Email: info@kbc.co.uk **Web:** www.kbc.co.uk
Product Type: 1, 2, 3, 4, 5, 6, 7

THE MANTALEDA BATHROOM CO. LTD
Thurston Road, Northallerton Business Park,
Northallerton, North Yorkshire, DL6 2NA
Area of Operation: Worldwide
Tel: 01609 771211 **Fax:** 01609 760100
Email: baths@mantaleda.fsnet.co.uk
Web: www.mantaleda.fsnet.co.uk
Product Type: 3, 4, 5, 6, 7, 8

THE WATER MONOPOLY
16/18 Lonsdale Road, London, NW6 6RD
Area of Operation: UK (Excluding Ireland)
Tel: 0207 624 2636 **Fax:** 0207 624 2631
Email: enquiries@watermonopoly.com
Web: www.watermonopoly.com

THOMAS CRAPPER & CO. LTD
The Stable Yard, Alscot Park,
Stratford-on-Avon, Warwickshire, CV37 8BL
Area of Operation: Worldwide
Tel: 01789 450522 **Fax:** 01789 450523
Email: wc@thomas-crapper.com
Web: www.thomas-crapper.com
Product Type: 2, 6, 7

TIMELESS BATHROOMS LTD
394 Ringwood Road, Ferndown, Dorset, BH22 9AU
Area of Operation: South East England
Tel: 01202 897110 **Fax:** 01202 892252
Email: bathroom@options394.fsnet.co.uk
Web: www.timelessbathrooms.co.uk
Product Type: 1, 2, 3, 4, 5, 6, 7, 8, 9

TRADEMARK TILES
Tile Store, Somersham Road, St Ives,
Huntingdon, Cambridgeshire, PE27 3WR
Tel: 01480 498123
Email: info@tilestoreplus.co.uk
Web: www.tilestoreplus.co.uk
Product Type: 1, 2, 3, 4, 5, 6, 7, 8

TWYFORD BATHROOMS
Lawton Road, Alsager,
Stoke On Trent, Staffordshire, ST7 2DF
Area of Operation: Worldwide
Tel: 01270 879777
Web: www.twyfordbathrooms.com
Product Type: 1, 2, 3, 4, 5, 6, 7, 8, 9
Material Type: C) 2

UNICOM
Kingdom House, 219 Gleniffer Road,
Paisley, Renfrewshire, PA2 8UL
Area of Operation: UK & Ireland
Tel: 0845 330 7642 **Fax:** 0845 330 7641
Email: george@unicom-direct.com
Web: www.unicom-direct.com
Product Type: 1, 2, 3, 4, 5, 6, 7, 8, 9

VASCO
Clitheroe Works, Clitheroe Street,
Skipton, North Yorkshire, BD23 1SU
Area of Operation: UK (Excluding Ireland)
Tel: 0870 027 4528 **Fax:** 0870 027 4531
Email: vascobathrooms@yahoo.co.uk
Web: www.amazingbathrooms.co.uk

VICTORIA & ALBERT BATHS
Waterloo Road, Ketley, Telford, Shropshire, TF1 4AY
Area of Operation: Worldwide
Tel: 01952 221100 **Fax:** 01952 221111
Web: www.vandabaths.com
Product Type: 2, 4, 5, 6, 7

VICTORIAN BATHROOMS
Victorian Bathrooms, Ings Mill Complex,
Dale Street, Ossett, West Yorkshire, WF5 9HQ
Area of Operation: UK (Excluding Ireland)
Tel: 01924 267736 **Fax:** 01924 261232
Email: sales@vb-bathrooms.com
Web: www.vb-bathrooms.com
Product Type: 1, 2, 3, 4, 5, 6, 7, 8

WALTON BATHROOMS
The Hersham Centre, The Green, Molesey Road,
Hersham, Walton on Thames, Surrey, KT12 4HL
Area of Operation: UK (Excluding Ireland)
Tel: 01932 224784 **Fax:** 01932 253447
Email: sales@waltonbathrooms.co.uk
Web: www.waltonbathrooms.co.uk
Product Type: 1, 2, 3, 4, 6

WATTS & WRIGHT (THE JOINERY SHOP)
PO Box 4251, Walsall, West Midlands, WS5 3WY
Area of Operation: Worldwide
Tel: 01922 610800 / 020 70437619
Fax: 0870 7626387
Email: sales@wattsandwright.com
Web: www.wattsandwright.com

WAVENEY BATHS LTD
London Road, Beccles, Suffolk, NR34 8TS
Tel: 01502 717516 **Fax:** 01502 716867
Email: kerrina@waveneybaths.co.uk
Web: www.waveneybaths.co.uk
Product Type: 1, 2, 3, 4, 5, 7, 9
Material Type: D) 5, 6

WHIRLPOOL EXPRESS (UK) LTD
61-62 Lower Dock Street, Kingsway, Newport, NP20 1EF
Area of Operation: Europe
Tel: 01633 244555 **Fax:** 01633 244881
Email: reception@whirlpoolexpress.co.uk
Web: www.whirlpoolexpress.co.uk
Product Type: 1, 2, 3, 4, 5, 6, 7, 8

WICKES
Wickes Customer Services, Wickes House, 120-138
Station Road, Harrow, Middlesex, HA1 2QB
Area of Operation: UK (Excluding Ireland)
Tel: 0870 608 9001 **Fax:** 0208 863 6225
Web: www.wickes.co.uk

LAVATORIES

ALEXANDERS
Unit 3, 1/1A Spilsby Road,
Harold Hill, Romford, Essex, RM3 8SB
Area of Operation: UK & Ireland
Tel: 01708 384574 **Fax:** 01708 384089
Email: sales@alexanders-uk.net
Web: www.alexanders-uk.net

ANTIQUE BATHS OF IVYBRIDGE LTD
Emebridge Works, Ermington Road,
Ivybridge, Devon, PL21 9DE
Area of Operation: UK (Excluding Ireland)
Tel: 01752 698250 **Fax:** 01752 698266
Email: sales@antiquebaths.com
Web: www.antiquebaths.com

BARRHEAD SANITARYWARE PLC
15-17 Nasmyth Road, Hillington Industrial Estate,
Hillington, Glasgow, Renfrewshire, G52 4RG
Area of Operation: UK & Ireland
Tel: 0141 883 0066 **Fax:** 0141 883 0077
Email: sales@barrhead.co.uk

BATHROOM BARN
The Bathroom Barn, Uplands Industrial Estate, Mere
Way, Wyton, Huntingdon, Cambridgeshire, PE28 2JZ
Area of Operation: UK (Excluding Ireland)
Tel: 01480 458900
Email: sales@bathroom-barn.co.uk
Web: www.bathroombarn.co.uk

BATHROOM CITY
Seeleys Road, Tyseley Industrial Estate,
Birmingham, West Midlands, B11 2LQ
Area of Operation: UK (Excluding Ireland)
Tel: 0121 753 0700 **Fax:** 0121 753 1110
Email: sales@bathroomcity.com
Web: www.bathroomcity.com

BATHROOM DISCOUNT CENTRE
297 Munster Road, Fulham,
Greater London, SW6 6BW
Area of Operation: UK (Excluding Ireland)
Tel: 0207 381 4222 **Fax:** 0207 381 6792
Email: bathdisc@aol.co.uk
Web: www.bathroomdiscount.co.uk

BATHROOMS PLUS LTD
222 Malmesbury Park Road,
Bournemouth, Dorset, BH8 8PR
Area of Operation: South West England and South Wales
Tel: 01202 294417 **Fax:** 01202 316425
Email: info@bathrooms-plus.co.uk
Web: www.bathrooms-plus.co.uk

BATHROOMSTUFF.CO.UK
326 London Road, Hilsea,
Portsmouth, Hampshire , PO2 9JT
Area of Operation: UK (Excluding Ireland)
Tel: 08450 580 540 **Fax:** 08451 274125
Email: sales@bathroomstuff.co.uk
Web: www.bathroomstuff.co.uk

CIFIAL UK LTD
7 Faraday Court, Park Farm Industrial Estate,
Wellingborough, Northamptonshire, NN8 6XY
Area of Operation: UK & Ireland
Tel: 01933 402008 **Fax:** 01933 402063
Email: sales@cifial.co.uk **Web:** www.cifial.co.uk

CIFIAL UK
Area of Operation: UK & Ireland
Tel: 01933 402008
Fax: 01933 402063
Email: sales@cifial.co.uk
Web: www.cifial.co.uk

Cifial's new TECHNOvation C1 & C4 collection of
pure white designer ceramics has strong, chunky
styling yet is space efficient suitable for large &
small bathrooms.

CISTERMISER LTD
Unit 1 Woodley Park Estate, 59-69 Reading Road,
Woodley, Reading, Berkshire, RG5 3AN
Area of Operation: UK & Ireland
Tel: 0118 969 1611 **Fax:** 0118 944 1426
Email: sales@cistermiser.co.uk
Web: www.cistermiser.co.uk

CITY BATHROOMS & KITCHENS
158 Longford Road, Longford,
Coventry, West Midlands, CV6 6DR
Area of Operation: UK & Ireland
Tel: 02476 365877 **Fax:** 02476 644992
Email: citybathrooms@hotmail.com
Web: www.citybathrooms.co.uk

COSY ROOMS (THE-BATHROOM-SHOP.CO.UK)
17 Chiltern Way, North Hykeham,
Lincoln, Lincolnshire, LN6 9SY
Area of Operation: UK (Excluding Ireland)
Tel: 01522 696002 **Fax:** 01522 696002
Email: keith@cosy-rooms.com
Web: www.the-bathroom-shop.co.uk

CYMRU KITCHENS
63 Caerleon Road, Newport, NP19 7BX
Area of Operation: UK (Excluding Ireland)
Tel: 01633 676767 **Fax:** 01633 212512
Email: sales@cymrukitchens.com
Web: www.cymrukitchens.com

DART VALLEY SYSTEMS LIMITED
Kemmings Close, Long Road,
Paignton, Devon, TQ4 7TW
Area of Operation: UK & Ireland
Tel: 01803 529021 **Fax:** 01803 559016
Email: sales@dartvalley.co.uk
Web: www.dartvalley.co.uk

DECORMASTER LTD
Unit 16, Waterside Industrial Estate,
Wolverhampton, West Midlands, WV2 2RH
Area of Operation: Worldwide
Tel: 01902 406030 **Fax:** 01902 353126
Email: sales@oldcolours.co.uk
Web: www.oldcolours.co.uk

DEEP BLUE SHOWROOM
299-313 Lewisham High Street,
Lewisham, London, SE13 6NW
Area of Operation: UK (Excluding Ireland)
Tel: 0208 690 3401 **Fax:** 0208 690 1408

DISCONTINUED BATHROOMS
140-142 Pogmoor Road, Pogmoor,
Barnsley, North Yorkshire, S75 2DX
Area of Operation: UK (Excluding Ireland)
Tel: 01226 280200 **Fax:** 01226 733273
Email: sales@discontinuedbathrooms.co.uk
Web: www.discontinuedbathrooms.co.uk

DURAVIT
Unit 7, Stratus Park, Brudenell Drive, Brinklow,
Milton Keynes, Buckinghamshire, MK10 0DE
Area of Operation: UK & Ireland
Tel: 0870 730 7787 **Fax:** 0870 730 7786
Email: info@uk.duravit.com **Web:** www.duravit.co.uk

EURO BATHROOMS
102 Annareagh Road, Richhill, Co Armagh, BT61 9JY
Area of Operation: Ireland Only
Tel: 028 3887 9996 **Fax:** 028 3887 9996

GEBERIT LTD
New Hythe Business Park,
New Hythe Lane, Aylesford, Kent, ME20 7PJ
Area of Operation: UK & Ireland
Tel: 01622 717 811 **Fax:** 01622 716 920
Web: www.geberit.co.uk

GOODWOOD BATHROOMS LTD
Church Road, North Mundham,
Chichester, West Sussex, PO20 1JU
Area of Operation: UK (Excluding Ireland)
Tel: 01243 532121 **Fax:** 01243 533423
Email: sales@goodwoodbathrooms.co.uk
Web: www.goodwoodbathrooms.co.uk

HARO SANITARY
(PART OF THE HAMBERGER GROUP)
PJH Group - Distributor, Alder House, Slackey Brow,
Kearsley, Bolton, Lancashire, BL4 8SL
Area of Operation: UK (Excluding Ireland)
Tel: 01204 707070 **Fax:** 01204 573140
Email: info@pjh.co.uk **Web:** www.haro-sanitary.com

HERITAGE BATHROOMS
Princess Street, Bedminster, Bristol, BS3 4AG
Area of Operation: UK & Ireland
Tel: 0117 963 3333
Email: marketing@heritagebathrooms.com
Web: www.heritagebathrooms.com

IDEAL STANDARD
The Bathroom Works, National Avenue,
Kingston Upon Hull, East Riding of Yorks, HU5 4HS
Area of Operation: Worldwide
Tel: 0800 590311 **Fax:** 01482 445886
Email: ideal-standard@aseur.com
Web: www.ideal-standard.co.uk

INSPIRED BATHROOMS
Unit R4, Innsworth Technology Park, Innsworth Lane,
Gloucester, Gloucestershire, GL3 1DL
Area of Operation: UK & Ireland
Tel: 01452 559121 **Fax:** 01452 530908
Email: sales@inspired-bathrooms.co.uk
Web: www.inspired-bathrooms.co.uk

JACUZZI UK
Silverdale Road, Newcastle Under Lyme,
Staffordshire, ST5 6EL
Area of Operation: UK & Ireland
Tel: 01782 717175 **Fax:** 01782 717166
Email: jacuzzisalesdesk@jacuzziuk.com
Web: www.jacuzzi.co.uk **Material Type:** F) 1

JOHN LEWIS OF HUNGERFORD
Grove Technology Park, Downsview Road,
Wantage, Oxfordshire, OX12 9FA
Area of Operation: UK (Excluding Ireland)
Tel: 01235 774300 **Fax:** 01235 769031
Email: park.street@john-lewis.co.uk
Web: www.john-lewis.co.uk

KENSINGTON STUDIO
13c/d Kensington Road, Earlsdon,
Coventry, West Midlands, CV5 6GG
Area of Operation: UK (Excluding Ireland)
Tel: 02476 713326 **Fax:** 02476 713136
Email: sales@kensingtonstudio.com
Web: www.kensingtonstudio.com

KERAMAG WAVENEY LTD
London Road, Beccles, Suffolk, NR34 8TS
Area of Operation: UK & Ireland
Tel: 01502 716600
Fax: 01502 717767
Email: info@keramagwaveney.co.uk
Web: www.keramag.com

LECICO PLC
Unit 47a Hobbs Industrial Estate,
Newchapel, Nr Lingfield, Surrey, RH7 6HN
Area of Operation: UK & Ireland
Tel: 01342 834777 **Fax:** 01342 834783
Email: info@lecico.co.uk
Web: www.lecico.co.uk

M & O BATHROOM CENTRE
174-176 Goswell Road,
Clarkenwell, London, EC1V 7DT
Area of Operation: East England, Greater London,
South East England
Tel: 0207 608 0111 **Fax:** 0207 490 3083
Email: mando@lineone.net

MEREWAY CONTRACTS
Unit 1 Wharfdale Road, Tysely,
Birmingham, West Midlands, B11 2DE
Area of Operation: UK (Excluding Ireland)
Tel: 0121 764 7180
Fax: 0121 764 7199
Email: info@merewaycontracts.co.uk
Web: www.merewaycontracts.co.uk

MISCELLANEA DISCONTINUED
BATHROOMWARE
Churt Place Nurseries, Tilford Road,
Churt, Farnham, Surrey, GU10 2LN
Area of Operation: Worldwide
Tel: 01428 608164 **Fax:** 01428 608165
Email: email@brokenbog.com
Web: www.brokenbog.com

MOODS BATHROOMS
PJH Group, Alder House, Kearsley,
Bolton, Lancashire, BL4 8SL
Area of Operation: UK & Ireland
Tel: 01204 707070 **Fax:** 01204 573140
Email: info@pjh.co.uk
Web: ww.bathroom-moods.com

NICHOLAS ANTHONY LTD
42-44 Wigmore Street, London, W1U 2RX
Area of Operation: East England, Greater London,
South East England
Tel: 0800 068 3603 **Fax:** 01206 762698
Email: info@nicholas-anthony.co.uk
Web: www.nicholas-anthony.co.uk

NO CODE
Larkwhistle Farm Road,
Micheldever, Hampshire, SO21 3BG
Area of Operation: UK & Ireland
Tel: 01962 870078 **Fax:** 01962 870077
Email: sales@nocode.co.uk
Web: www.nocode.co.uk

OLD FASHIONED BATHROOMS LTD
Foresters Hall, 52 High Street, Debenham,
Stowmarket, Suffolk, IP14 6QW
Area of Operation: UK (Excluding Ireland)
Tel: 01728 860926 **Fax:** 01728 860446
Email: ofbshop@yahoo.co.uk
Web: www.oldfashionedbathrooms.co.uk
Other Info: ▽   **Material Type:** F) 1, 2, 4

ROSCO COLLECTIONS
Stone Allerton, Axbridge, Somerset, BS26 2NS
Area of Operation: UK & Ireland
Tel: 01934 712299 **Fax:** 01934 713222
Email: jonathan@roscobathrooms.demon.co.uk

SANIFLO LTD
Howard House, The Runway,
South Ruislip, Middlesex, HA4 6SE
Area of Operation: UK (Excluding Ireland)
Tel: 0208 842 4040
Fax: 0208 842 1671
Email: andrews@saniflo.co.uk
Web: www.saniflo.co.uk

STIFFKEY BATHROOMS
89 Upper Saint Giles Street, Norwich, Norfolk, NR2 1AB
Area of Operation: Worldwide
Tel: 01603 627850 **Fax:** 01603 619775
Email: stiffkeybathrooms.norwich@virgin.net
Web: www.stiffkeybathrooms.com

SVEDBERGS
4E Wilsons Park, Monsall Road, Newton Heath,
Manchester, Greater Manchester, M40 8WN
Area of Operation: UK & Ireland
Tel: 0161 2051200 **Fax:** 0161 251212
Email: info@svedbergs.co.uk
Web: www.svedbergs.co.uk **Other Info:** ECO

TAPS SHOP
1 Tristram Road, Ducklington,
Whitney, Oxfordshire, OX29 7XH
Area of Operation: Worldwide
Tel: 0845 4303035 **Fax:** 01993 779653
Email: info@tapsshop.co.uk
Web: www.tapsshop.co.uk

THE KITCHEN AND BATHROOM COLLECTION
Nelson House, Nelson Road,
Salisbury, Wiltshire, SP1 3LT
Area of Operation: South West England and South Wales
Tel: 01722 334800 **Fax:** 01722 412252
Email: info@kbc.co.uk
Web: www.kbc.co.uk **Other Info:** ✎

THE WATER MONOPOLY
16/18 Lonsdale Road, London, NW6 6RD
Area of Operation: UK (Excluding Ireland)
Tel: 0207 624 2636 **Fax:** 0207 624 2631
Email: enquiries@watermonopoly.com
Web: www.watermonopoly.com

THOMAS CRAPPER & CO. LTD
The Stable Yard, Alscot Park,
Stratford-on-Avon, Warwickshire, CV37 8BL
Tel: 01789 450522 **Fax:** 01789 450523
Email: wc@thomas-crapper.com
Web: www.thomas-crapper.com

TIMELESS BATHROOMS LTD
394 Ringwood Road, Ferndown, Dorset, BH22 9AU
Area of Operation: South East England
Tel: 01202 897110 **Fax:** 01202 892252
Email: bathroom@options394.fsnet.co.uk
Web: www.timelessbathrooms.co.uk

TRADEMARK TILES
Tile Store, Somersham Road,
St Ives, Huntingdon, Cambridgeshire, PE27 3WR
Area of Operation: UK (Excluding Ireland)
Tel: 01480 498123 **Email:** info@tilestoreplus.com
Web: www.tilestoreplus.co.uk

TWYFORD BATHROOMS
Lawton Road, Alsager,
Stoke On Trent, Staffordshire, ST7 2DF
Area of Operation: Worldwide
Tel: 01270 879777 **Material Type:** F) 1, 4
Web: www.twyfordbathrooms.com

UK BATHROOM INTERIORS
Units 3-4, The Old Laundry,
Fishergreen, Ripon, North Yorkshire, HG4 1NL
Tel: 01765 608822 **Fax:** 01765 608892
Email: mark@ukbathroominteriors.com
Web: www.ukbathroominteriors.com

VICTORIAN BATHROOMS
Ings Mill Complex, Dale Street,
Ossett , West Yorkshire, WF5 9HQ
Area of Operation: UK (Excluding Ireland)
Tel: 01924 267736 **Fax:** 01924 261232
Email: sales@vb-bathrooms.com
Web: www.vb-bathrooms.com

WALTON BATHROOMS
The Hersham Centre, The Green, Molesey Road,
Hersham, Walton on Thames, Surrey, KT12 4HL
Area of Operation: UK (Excluding Ireland)
Tel: 01932 224784 **Fax:** 01932 253447
Email: sales@waltonbathrooms.co.uk
Web: www.waltonbathrooms.co.uk

WHIRLPOOL EXPRESS (UK) LTD
61-62 Lower Dock Street,
Kingsway, Newport, NP20 1EF
Area of Operation: Europe
Tel: 01633 244555 **Fax:** 01633 244881
Email: reception@whirlpoolexpress.co.uk
Web: www.whirlpoolexpress.co.uk

SHOWERS

KEY
PRODUCT TYPES: 1= Enclosures 2 = Trays
3 = Heads 4 = Shower Pumps 5 = Other
OTHER: ▽ Reclaimed ✋ On-line shopping
✎ Bespoke 🖐 Hand-made ECO Ecological

A & H BRASS
201-203 Edgware Road, London, W2 1ES
Area of Operation: Worldwide
Tel: 0207 402 1854 **Fax:** 0207 402 0110
Email: ahbrass@btinternet.com
Web: www.aandhbrass.co.uk
Product Type: 1, 2, 3, 4

AIRBATH APPOLLO LIMITED
Swinnow Lane, Leeds, West Yorkshire, LS13 4TY
Area of Operation: Worldwide
Tel: 0113 255 6666 **Fax:** 0113 3869176
Email: sales@airbath.co.uk
Web: www.airbath.co.uk **Product Type:** 1, 2

AL CHALLIS LTD
Europower House, Lower Road,
Cookham, Maidenhead, Berkshire, SL6 9EH
Area of Operation: UK & Ireland
Tel: 01628 529024 **Fax:** 0870 458 0577
Email: chris@alchallis.com
Web: www.alchallis.com **Product Type:** 3

ALEXANDERS
Unit 3, 1/1A Spilsby Road,
Harold Hill, Romford, Essex, RM3 8SB
Area of Operation: UK & Ireland
Tel: 01708 384574 **Fax:** 01708 384089
Email: sales@alexanders-uk.net
Web: www.alexanders-uk.net
Product Type: 1, 2, 3, 4, 5

AMBIANCE BAIN
Cumberland House,
80 Scrubs Lane, London, NW10 6RF
Area of Operation: UK & Ireland
Tel: 0870 902 1313 **Fax:** 0870 902 1312
Email: sghirardello@mimea.com
Web: www.ambiancebain.com **Product Type:** 1

ANTIQUE BATHS OF IVYBRIDGE LTD
Emebridge Works, Ermington Road,
Ivybridge, Devon, PL21 9DE
Area of Operation: UK (Excluding Ireland)
Tel: 01752 698250 **Fax:** 01752 698266
Email: sales@antiquebaths.com
Web: www.antiquebaths.com
Product Type: 1, 2, 3, 4, 5

AQATA SHOWER ENCLOSURES
Brookfield, Harrowbrook Industrial Estate,
Hinckley, Leicestershire, LE10 3DU
Area of Operation: UK & Ireland
Tel: 01455 896500 **Fax:** 01455 896501
Email: sales@aqata.co.uk
Web: www.aqata.co.uk **Product Type:** 1, 2
Other Info: ✎ 🖐   **Material Type:** C) 1

AQUAAQUA LTD
Melin Maes Dulais, Porthyrhyd,
Carmarthenshire, SA32 8BT
Area of Operation: UK (Excluding Ireland)
Tel: 01267 275255 **Fax:** 01267 275597
Email: jamie@aquaaqua.co.uk
Web: www.aquaaqua.co.uk **Product Type:** 3

AQUALISA PRODUCTS LTD
The Flyers Way, Westerham, Kent, TN16 1DE
Area of Operation: UK & Ireland
Tel: 01959 560000
Fax: 01959 560030
Email: sue.anderson@aqualisa.co.uk
Web: www.aqualisa.co.uk   **Product Type:** 3, 4

AQUALUX PRODUCTS LTD
Universal Point, Steelmans Road, off Park Lane,
Wednesbury, West Midlands, WS10 9UZ
Area of Operation: Europe
Tel: 0870 241 6131   **Fax:** 0870 241 6132
Email: colin.henderson@aqualux.co.uk
Web: www.aqualux.co.uk   **Product Type:** 1, 2, 5

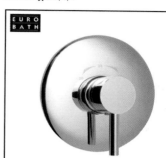

AQUALUX
Area of Operation: Europe
Tel: 0870 241 6131
Fax: 0870 241 6132
Email: colin.henderson@aqualux.co.uk
Web: www.aqualux.co.uk
Product Type: 1, 2, 5

The UK's leading manufacturer of shower surrounds and bath screens provides a wide range of products including its award winning Walk-in with Wet Room option.

AQUAPLUS SOLUTIONS
Unit 106, Indiana Building, London, SE13 7QD
Area of Operation: UK & Ireland
Tel: 0870 201 1915   **Fax:** 0870 201 1916
Email: info@aquaplussolutions.com
Web: www.aquaplussolutions.com
Product Type: 1, 3

BATHROOM BARN
The Bathroom Barn, Uplands Industrial Estate, Mere Way, Wyton, Huntingdon, Cambridgeshire, PE28 2JZ
Area of Operation: UK (Excluding Ireland)
Tel: 01480 458900
Email: sales@bathroom-barn.co.uk
Web: www.bathroombarn.co.uk

BATHROOM CITY
Seeleys Road, Tyseley Industrial Estate,
Birmingham, West Midlands, B11 2LQ
Area of Operation: UK & Ireland
Tel: 0121 753 0700
Fax: 0121 753 1110
Email: sales@bathroomcity.com
Web: www.bathroomcity.com
Product Type: 1, 2, 3, 4, 5

BATHROOM DISCOUNT CENTRE
297 Munster Road, Fulham,
Greater London, SW6 6BW
Area of Operation: UK (Excluding Ireland)
Tel: 0207 381 4222   **Fax:** 0207 381 6792
Email: bathdisc@aol.co.uk
Web: www.bathroomdiscount.co.uk

BATHROOM EXPRESS
61-62 Lower Dock Street,
Kingsway, Newport, NP20 1EF
Area of Operation: UK & Ireland
Tel: 0845 130 2000
Fax: 01633 244881
Email: sales@bathroomexpress.co.uk
Web: www.bathroomexpress.co.uk
Product Type: 1, 3, 4

BATHROOM HEAVEN
25 Eccleston Square, London, SW1V 1NS
Area of Operation: UK & Ireland
Tel: 0845 121 6700   **Fax:** 0207 233 6074
Email: laura@bathroomheaven.com
Web: www.bathroomheaven.com
Product Type: 1, 2, 3, 4, 5

BATHROOMS PLUS LTD
222 Malmesbury Park Road,
Bournemouth, Dorset, BH8 8PR
Area of Operation: South West England and South Wales
Tel: 01202 294417   **Fax:** 01202 316425
Email: info@bathrooms-plus.co.uk
Web: www.bathrooms-plus.co.uk
Product Type: 1, 2, 3, 4, 5

BATHROOMSTUFF.CO.UK
326 London Road, Hilsea,
Portsmouth, Hampshire , PO2 9JT
Tel: 08450 580 540   **Fax:** 08451 274125
Email: sales@bathroomstuff.co.uk
Web: www.bathroomstuff.co.uk
Product Type: 1, 2, 3, 5

BOUNDARY BATHROOMS
Ainsworth & Dent House,
Regent Street, Colne, Lancashire, BB8 8LD
Area of Operation: UK & Ireland
Tel: 01282 862509   **Fax:** 01282 871192
Email: sales@boundarybathrooms.co.uk
Product Type: 1, 2, 3, 4, 5

BRISTAN
Birch Coppice Business Park,
Dordon, Tamworth, Staffordshire, B78 1SG
Area of Operation: Worldwide
Tel: 08704 425556   **Fax:** 0808 1611 002
Email: enquiries@bristan.com
Web: www.bristan.com
Product Type: 3, 4, 5   **Material Type:** C) 11, 14

BROOK-WATER DESIGNER BATHROOMS & KITCHENS
The Downs, Woodhouse Hill,
Uplyme, Lyme Regis, Dorset, DT7 3SL
Area of Operation: Worldwide
Tel: 0870 851 9739
Email: sales@brookwater.co.uk
Web: www.brookwater.co.uk   **Product Type:** 1

CHADDER & CO.
Blenheim Studio, London Road,
Forest Row, East Sussex, RH18 5EZ
Area of Operation: Worldwide
Tel: 01342 823243   **Fax:** 01342 823097
Web: www.chadder.com

CHARLES MASON LTD
Unit 11A Brook Street Mill, Off Goodall Street,
Macclesfield, Cheshire, SK11 7AW
Area of Operation: Worldwide
Tel: 0800 085 3616   **Fax:** 01625 668789
Email: info@charles-mason.com
Web: www.charles-mason.com
Product Type: 3, 4   **Material Type:** C) 2, 3, 14

CHROMA INTERNATIONAL GLASS LTD
Unit 200 Bridgwater Business Park,
Bridgwater, Somerset, TA6 4TB
Tel: 01278 426226   **Fax:** 01278 450088
Email: info@chroma-glass.com
Web: www.chroma-glass.com
Product Type: 1, 2   **Material Type:** C) 3

CIFIAL UK LTD
7 Faraday Court, Park Farm Industrial Estate,
Wellingborough, Northamptonshire, NN8 6XY
Area of Operation: UK & Ireland
Tel: 01933 402008   **Fax:** 01933 402063
Email: sales@cifial.co.uk   **Web:** www.cifial.co.uk

CITY BATHROOMS & KITCHENS
158 Longford Road, Longford,
Coventry, West Midlands, CV6 6DR
Area of Operation: UK & Ireland
Tel: 02476 365877   **Fax:** 02476 644992
Email: citybathrooms@hotmail.com
Web: www.citybathrooms.co.uk

CORAM SHOWERS LIMITED
Stanmore Industrial Estate,
Bridgnorth, Shropshire, WV15 5HP
Area of Operation: UK (Excluding Ireland)
Tel: 01746 766466   **Fax:** 01746 764140
Email: sales@coram.co.uk
Web: www.coram.co.uk   **Product Type:** 1, 2, 5

CORE AND ORE LTD
16 Portland Street, Clifton, Bristol, BS8 4JH
Tel: 01179 042408   **Fax:** 01179 094010
Email: sales@coreandore.com
Web: www.coreandore.com   **Product Type:** 2

COSY ROOMS (THE-BATHROOM-SHOP.CO.UK)
17 Chiltern Way, North Hykeham,
Lincoln, Lincolnshire, LN6 9SY
Area of Operation: UK (Excluding Ireland)
Tel: 01522 696002   **Fax:** 01522 696002
Email: keith@cosy-rooms.com
Web: www.the-bathroom-shop.co.uk
Product Type: 1, 4

CROSSWATER
Unit 5 Butterly Avenue, Questor,
Dartford, Kent, DA1 1JG
Area of Operation: UK & Ireland
Tel: 01322 628270   **Fax:** 01322 628280
Email: sales@crosswater.co.uk
Web: www.crosswater.co.uk   **Product Type:** 3

CYMRU KITCHENS
63 Caerleon Road, Newport, NP19 7BX
Area of Operation: UK (Excluding Ireland)
Tel: 01633 676767   **Fax:** 01633 212512
Email: sales@cymrukitchens.com
Web: www.cymrukitchens.com

DART VALLEY SYSTEMS LIMITED
Kemmings Close, Long Road,
Paignton, Devon, TQ4 7TW
Area of Operation: UK & Ireland
Tel: 01803 529021   **Fax:** 01803 559016
Email: sales@dartvalley.co.uk
Web: www.dartvalley.co.uk   **Product Type:** 3, 5

DECORMASTER LTD
Unit 16, Waterside Industrial Estate,
Wolverhampton, West Midlands, WV2 2RH
Area of Operation: Worldwide
Tel: 01902 406030   **Fax:** 01902 353126
Email: sales@oldcolours.co.uk
Web: www.oldcolours.co.uk   **Product Type:** 1, 2, 4

DEEP BLUE SHOWROOM
299-313 Lewisham High Street,
Lewisham, London, SE13 6NW
Area of Operation: UK (Excluding Ireland)
Tel: 0208 690 3401   **Fax:** 0208 690 1408

DISCONTINUED BATHROOMS
140-142 Pogmoor Road, Pogmoor,
Barnsley, North Yorkshire, S75 2DX
Tel: 01226 280200   **Fax:** 01226 733273
Email: sales@discontinuedbathrooms.co.uk
Web: www.discontinuedbathrooms.co.uk
Product Type: 1, 2, 3, 4   **Other Info:**

DIYWETROOM.COM
Oakstone House, Middleton,
Youlgrave, Bakewell, Derbyshire, DE45 1LS
Area of Operation: Worldwide
Tel: 01629 636109   **Fax:** 01629 636109
Email: sales@diywetroom.com
Web: www.diywetroom.com

DORMA UK LIMITED
Wilbury Way, Hitchin, Hertfordshire, SG4 0AB
Tel: 01462 477600   **Fax:** 01462 477601
Email: info@dorma-uk.co.uk
Web: www.dorma-uk.co.uk   **Product Type:** 1

DUPONT CORIAN & ZODIAQ
10 Quarry Court, Pitstone Green Business Park,
Pitstone, nr. Tring, Buckinghamshire, LU7 9GW
Area of Operation: UK & Ireland
Tel: 01296 663555   **Fax:** 01296 663599
Email: sales@corian.co.uk   **Web:** www.corian.co.uk
Product Type: 2   **Other Info:**

EURO BATHROOMS
102 Annareagh Road, Richhill, Co Armagh, BT61 9JY
Area of Operation: Ireland Only
Tel: 028 3887 9996   **Fax:** 028 3887 9996

EUROBATH INTERNATIONAL LIMITED
Eurobath House, Wedmore Road,
Cheddar, Somerset, BS27 3EB
Area of Operation: Worldwide
Tel: 01934 744466   **Fax:** 01934744345
Email: sales@eurobath.co.uk
Web: www.eurobath.co.uk/www.ilbagno.co.uk
Product Type: 2, 3, 4

EUROBATH INTERNATIONAL LTD
Area of Operation: Worldwide
Tel: 01934 744466
Fax: 01934 744345
Email: sales@eurobath.co.uk
Web: www.eurobath.co.uk

The stylish ZOO single lever thermostatic shower mixer is a new addition to Eurobath's extensive 2006 portfolio. With innovative "Axio:Therm" technology, complete the look with matching taps and accessories.

EUROCARE SHOWERS LTD
Unit 19, Doncaster Industry Park, Watch House Lane,
Bentley, Doncaster, South Yorkshire, DN5 9LZ
Area of Operation: Worldwide
Tel: 01302 788684   **Fax:** 01302 780010
Email: sales@eurocare-showers.com
Web: www.eurocare-showers.com
Product Type: 1, 2, 4

FLAIR INTERNATIONAL
Bailieborough, Co.Cavan, Ireland
Area of Operation: Europe
Tel: 01344 467342
Fax: +353 42 966 5516
Email: flairshowers@aol.com
Web: www.flairshowers.com
Product Type: 1   **Material Type:** C) 1

FLAIR INTERNATIONAL LTD
Area of Operation: Europe
Tel: 01344 467342
Fax: 00 353 429 665516
Email: flairshowers@aol.com
Web: www.flairshowers.com
Product Type: 1

Flair International is Ireland's market leader in the production of high quality glass shower enclosures and bath screens to create the perfect shower space.

nal glass doors
glass shower cubicles:
benefits are clearly visible

ng new trends in interior design. Ideal for the creation of light and spacious living areas,
stylish element to your home. And where size matters, glass makes even small rooms
nd generously proportioned.

a wide range of discrete fittings available for sliding and pivoting doors, shower and wet
res. Load bearing fittings are also available for internal and external structural glazing.

lass solutions, talk to DORMA.

imited · Tel 01462 477600 · Fax 01462 477601
dorma-uk.co.uk · www.dorma-uk.co.uk

GROHE UK
1 River Road, Barking, Essex, IG11 0HD
Area of Operation: Worldwide
Tel: 020 8594 7292 **Fax:** 020 8594 8898
Email: info@grohe.co.uk
Web: www.grohe.co.uk **Product Type:** 3

GUMMERS
Unit H, Redfern Park Way, Tyseley,
Birmingham, West Midlands, B11 2DN
Area of Operation: Worldwide
Tel: 0121 706 2241 **Fax:** 0121 706 2960
Email: sales@gummers.com
Web: www.sirrusshowers.com
Product Type: 1, 2, 3, 4, 5

HANSGROHE
Units D1 and D2, Sandown Park Trading Estate,
Royal Mills, Esher, Surrey, KT10 8BL
Area of Operation: Worldwide
Tel: 0870 770 1972 **Fax:** 0870 770 1973
Email: sales@hansgrohe.co.uk
Web: www.hansgrohe.co.uk
Product Type: 1, 3, 4
Other Info: ✍ **Material Type:** C) 2, 3, 11, 14

HANSGROHE

Area of Operation: Worldwide
Tel: 0870 7701972 **Fax:** 0870 7701973
Email: sales@hansgrohe.co.uk
Web: www.hansgrohe.co.uk
Product Type: 1, 3, 4
Materials Type: C) 2, 3, 11, 14 **Other Info:** ✍

Europe's largest manufacturer of design-led
showers, mixer taps, thermostatic valves and
accessories, plus a range of wellbeing products
like steam cabins.

HAROLD MOORE & SON LTD
Rawson Spring Road, Hillsborough,
Sheffield, South Yorkshire, S6 1PD
Area of Operation: UK & Ireland
Tel: 0114 233 6161 **Fax:** 0114 232 6375
Email: admin@haroldmoorebaths.co.uk
Web: www.haroldmoorebaths.co.uk
Product Type: 2

HEATRAE SADIA HEATING
Hurricane Way, Norwich, Norfolk, NR6 6EA
Area of Operation: Worldwide
Tel: 01603 420110 **Fax:** 01603 420149
Email: sales@heatraesadia.com
Web: www.heatraesadia.com **Product Type:** 4

HERITAGE BATHROOMS
Princess Street, Bedminster, Bristol, BS3 4AG
Area of Operation: UK & Ireland
Tel: 0117 963 3333
Email: marketing@heritagebathrooms.com
Web: www.heritagebathrooms.com
Product Type: 1, 2, 3

HOT GLASS DESIGN
Unit 24 Crosby Yard Industrial Estate,
Bridgend, Mid Glamorgan, CF31 1JZ
Area of Operation: Europe
Tel: 01656 659884
Fax: 01656 659884
Email: info@hotglassdesign.co.uk
Web: www.hotglassdesign.co.uk
Product Type: 1 **Material Type:** J) 1, 2, 4, 5, 6

HUDSON REED
Rylands Street, Burnley, Lancashire, BB10 1RG
Area of Operation: Worldwide
Tel: 01282 418000 **Fax:** 01282 428915
Email: info@ultra-group.co.uk
Web: www.hudsonreed.info **Product Type:** 3, 4, 5
Material Type: C) 1, 3, 11, 14, 16, 17

IDEAL STANDARD
The Bathroom Works, National Avenue,
Kingston Upon Hull, East Riding of Yorks, HU5 4HS
Area of Operation: Worldwide
Tel: 0800 590311 **Fax:** 01482 445886
Email: ideal-standard@aseur.com
Web: www.ideal-standard.co.uk

INDESIGN
Kiran House, 53 Park Royal Road, London, NW10 7LQ
Area of Operation: UK & Ireland
Tel: 0208 963 5841 **Fax:** 0208 965 6261
Email: dhanja.bhudia@akshars.co.uk
Web: www.akshars.co.uk

INDIGO SHOWERS
17 The Rise, Tadworth, Surrey, KT20 5PT
Area of Operation: UK & Ireland
Tel: 0845 226 0321
Email: sales@indigoshowers.co.uk
Web: www.indigoshowers.com ☝
Product Type: 1, 2, 3, 4, 5

INSPIRED BATHROOMS
Unit R4, Innsworth Technology Park, Innsworth Lane,
Gloucester, Gloucestershire, GL3 1DL
Area of Operation: UK & Ireland
Tel: 01452 559121 **Fax:** 01452 530908
Email: sales@inspired-bathrooms.co.uk
Web: www.inspired-bathrooms.co.uk ☝
Product Type: 1, 2, 3, 4, 5

ION GLASS
PO Box 284, Burgess Hill, West Sussex, RH15 0BN
Area of Operation: UK (Excluding Ireland)
Tel: 0845 658 9988 **Fax:** 0845 658 9989
Email: sales@ionglass.co.uk
Web: www.ionglass.co.uk
Product Type: 1, 2 **Other Info:** ✍

ITFITZ
11-12 Woodlands Farm, Spring Lane,
Cookham Dean, Berkshire, SL6 9PN
Area of Operation: UK (Excluding Ireland)
Tel: 01628 890432 **Fax:** 0870 133 7955
Email: sales@itfitz.co.uk
Web: www.itfitz.co.uk ☝ **Product Type:** 3

JACUZZI UK
Silverdale Road, Newcastle Under Lyme,
Staffordshire, ST5 6EL
Area of Operation: UK & Ireland
Tel: 01782 717175 **Fax:** 01782 717166
Email: jacuzzisalesdesk@jacuzziuk.com
Web: www.jacuzzi.co.uk **Product Type:** 1, 2, 3, 5

JOHN LEWIS OF HUNGERFORD
Grove Technology Park, Downsview Road,
Wantage, Oxfordshire, OX12 9FA
Area of Operation: UK (Excluding Ireland)
Tel: 01235 774300 **Fax:** 01235 769031
Email: park.street@john-lewis.co.uk
Web: www.john-lewis.co.uk

KALDEWEI
Unit 7, Sundial Court, Tolworth Rise South,
Surbiton, Surrey, KT5 9RN
Area of Operation: Worldwide
Tel: 0870 777 2223 **Fax:** 0870 777 2225
Email: info@kaldewei-uk.com
Web: www.kaldewei.com **Product Type:** 2

KENSINGTON STUDIO
13 c & d Kensington Road, Earlsdon,
Coventry, West Midlands, CV5 6GG
Area of Operation: UK (Excluding Ireland)
Tel: 02476 713326 **Fax:** 02476 713316
Email: sales@kensingtonstudio.com
Web: www.kensingtonstudio.com ☝
Product Type: 1, 2, 3, 4, 5

KERAMAG WAVENEY LTD
London Road, Beccles, Suffolk, NR34 8TS
Area of Operation: UK & Ireland
Tel: 01502 716600
Fax: 01502 717767
Email: info@keramagwaveney.co.uk
Web: www.keramag.com **Product Type:** 1, 2, 3, 4

KERMI (UK) LTD
7 Brunel Road, Corby, Northamptonshire, NN17 4JW
Area of Operation: UK & Ireland
Tel: 01536 400004 **Fax:** 01536 446614
Email: cradcliff@kermi.co.uk
Web: www.kermi.co.uk **Product Type:** 1

KEUCO (UK)
2 Claridge Court, Lower Kings Road,
Berkhamsted, Hertfordshire, HP42AF
Area of Operation: Worldwide
Tel: 01442 865220
Fax: 01442 865260
Email: klaus@keuco.co.uk
Web: www.keuco.de **Product Type:** 5
Material Type: C) 3, 14, 17

KOHLER DARYL/DARYL SHOWERING
Alfred Road, Wallasey, Merseyside, CH44 7HY
Area of Operation: UK & Ireland
Tel: 0151 606 5000
Email: daryl@daryl-showers.co.uk
Web: www.daryl-showers.co.uk
Product Type: 1, 2, 3, 5 **Other Info:** ✋

KOHLER MIRA LIMITED
Barnett Way, Barnwood,
Gloucester, Gloucestershire, GL4 3RT
Area of Operation: UK & Ireland
Tel: 0870 850 5551
Fax: 0870 850 5552
Email: info@kohleruk.com
Web: www.kohleruk.com

LONGMEAD GROUP PLC
Millwey Industrial Estate, Axminster, Devon, EX13 5HU
Area of Operation: Europe
Tel: 01297 32578 **Fax:** 01297 32710
Email: info@longmead-group.co.uk
Web: www.longmead-group.co.uk
Product Type: 3

M & O BATHROOM CENTRE
174-176 Goswell Road,
Clarkenwell, London, EC1V 7DT
Area of Operation: East England, Greater London,
South East England
Tel: 0207 608 0111 **Fax:** 0207 490 3083
Email: mando@lineone.net **Product Type:** 1, 2, 3, 4

MANHATTAN
Marsden Mill, Brunswick Street,
Nelson, Lancashire, BB9 0LY
Area of Operation: UK & Ireland
Tel: 01282 605000
Fax: 012282 604762
Email: thealy@manhattanshowers.co.uk
Web: www.manhattanshowers.co.uk
Product Type: 1, 2

MARBLE CLASSICS
Unit 3, Station Approach,
Emsworth, Hampshire, PO10 7PW
Area of Operation: UK & Ireland
Tel: 01243 370011
Fax: 01243 371023
Email: info@marbleclassics.co.uk
Web: www.marbleclassics.co.uk
Product Type: 2 **Material Type:** E) 1, 2, 5

MATKI PLC
Churchward Road, Yate, Bristol, BS37 5PL
Area of Operation: UK & Ireland
Tel: 01454 322888
Fax: 01454 315284
Email: helpline@matki.co.uk
Web: www.matki.co.uk **Product Type:** 1, 2, 3

MATKI SHOWERING

Area of Operation: UK & Ireland
Tel: 01454 322888
Fax: 01454 315284
Email: helpline@matki.co.uk
Web: www.matki.co.uk
Product Type: 1, 2, 3

Matki has been a major innovator in the high
quality shower enclosure market for the past 30
years. Their shower doors and trays have a 10
year guarantee.

MEKON PRODUCTS
25 Bessemer Park, Milkwood Road, London, SE24 0HG
Area of Operation: UK (Excluding Ireland)
Tel: 0207 733 8011 **Fax:** 0207 737 0840
Email: info@mekon.net
Web: www.mekon.net **Product Type:** 1, 2, 3

MEREWAY CONTRACTS
Unit 1 Wharfdale Road, Tysely,
Birmingham, West Midlands, B11 2DE
Area of Operation: UK (Excluding Ireland)
Tel: 0121 764 7180
Fax: 0121 764 7199
Email: info@merewaycontracts.co.uk
Web: www.merewaycontracts.co.uk

METROPOLITAN SHOWERS
Marsden Mill, Brunswick Street,
Nelson, Lancashire, BB9 0LY
Area of Operation: UK & Ireland
Tel: 01282 60 60 70
Fax: 01282 60 60 65
Email: info@metropolitanshowers.co.uk
Web: www.metropolitanshowers.co.uk
Product Type: 1, 2

MOODS BATHROOMS
PJH Group, Alder House, Kearsley,
Bolton, Lancashire, BL4 8SL
Area of Operation: UK & Ireland
Tel: 01204 707070 **Fax:** 01204 573140
Email: info@pjh.co.uk
Web: ww.bathroom-moods.com
Product Type: 1, 2, 3, 5

N&C NICOBOND
41-51 Freshwater Road, Chadwell Heath,
Romford, Essex, RM8 1SP
Area of Operation: Worldwide
Tel: 0208 586 4600 **Fax:** 0208 586 4646
Email: info@nichollsandclarke.com
Web: www.ncdirect.co.uk

NICHOLAS ANTHONY LTD
42-44 Wigmore Street, London, W1U 2RX
Area of Operation: East England, Greater London,
South East England
Tel: 0800 068 3603 **Fax:** 01206 762698
Email: info@nicholas-anthony.co.uk
Web: www.nicholas-anthony.co.uk
Product Type: 1, 2, 3, 4

NO CODE
Larkwhistle Farm Road,
Micheldever, Hampshire , SO21 3BG
Area of Operation: UK & Ireland
Tel: 01962 870078 **Fax:** 01962 870077
Email: sales@nocode.co.uk
Web: www.nocode.co.uk **Product Type:** 1, 2, 3

NORDIC
Unit 5, Trading Estate, Holland Road,
Oxted, Surrey, RH8 9BZ
Area of Operation: UK (Excluding Ireland)
Tel: 01883 732400 **Fax:** 01883 716970
Email: info@nordic.co.uk
Web: www.nordic.co.uk
Product Type: 1, 2

OLD FASHIONED BATHROOMS LTD
Foresters Hall, 52 High Street, Debenham,
Stowmarket, Suffolk, IP14 6QW
Area of Operation: UK (Excluding Ireland)
Tel: 01728 860926
Fax: 01728 860446
Email: ofbshop@yahoo.co.uk
Web: www.oldfashionedbathrooms.co.uk
Product Type: 1, 2, 3, 4 **Other Info:** ▽ ✎
Material Type: C) 7, 13, 14, 16

POLYPIPE KITCHENS & BATHROOMS LTD
Warmsworth, Halt Industrial Estate,
Doncaster, South Yorkshire, DN4 9LS
Area of Operation: Worldwide
Tel: 01709 770990 **Fax:** 01302 310602
Email: davery@ppbp.co.uk
Web: www.polypipe.com/bk
Product Type: 2

PUMP WORLD LTD
Unit 11, Woodside Road, South Marston Business
Park, Swindon, Wiltshire, SN3 4WA
Area of Operation: UK & Ireland
Tel: 01793 820142
Fax: 01793 823800
Email: enquiries@pumpworld.co.uk
Web: www.pumpworld.co.uk ✍
Product Type: 3, 4, 5

QUALCERAM SHIRES PLC
South Quay, Arklow, Co. Wicklow
Area of Operation: UK & Ireland
Tel: 00353 402 31288
Fax: 00353 402 31292
Email: omoriarty@qualceram-shires.com
Web: www.qualceram-shires.com
Product Type: 1, 2, 3, 4, 5

RELICS OF WITNEY LTD
1 Tristram Road, Ducklington,
Witney, Oxfordshire, OX29 7HX
Area of Operation: Worldwide
Tel: 0845 430 3035 **Fax:** 01993 779653
Email: sales@lightsshop.co.uk
Web: www.lightsshop.co.uk ✍

RIVERBED
Priory Park, Chewton Mendip, Bath, Somerset, BA3 4NT
Area of Operation: UK & Ireland
Tel: 01761 241133 **Fax:** 01761 241134
Email: sales@riverbed.ltd.uk
Web: www.riverbed.ltd.uk
Product Type: 1, 2, 5 **Material Type:** D) 2

WET ROOMS KITS by RIVERBED

Area of Operation: UK & Ireland
Tel: 01761 241133
Fax: 01761 241134
Email: sales@riverbed.ltd.uk
Web: www.riverbed.ltd.uk

Our German made wet room systems are simple,
quick & easy to install.
No mistakes, No mess, No hassle, No problem.
Peace of mind & complete confidence from
Riverbed

ROMAN
Whitworth Avenue, Aycliffe Industrial Estate,
Newton Aycliffe, Durham, DL5 6YN
Area of Operation: Worldwide
Tel: 0845 050 4032 **Fax:** 01325 319889
Email: brochures@roman-showers.com
Web: www.roman-showers.com
Product Type: 1, 2, 3, 4, 5

ROOTS KITCHENS BEDROOMS BATHROOMS
Vine Farm, Stockers Hill, Boughton under Blean,
Faversham, Kent, ME13 9AB
Area of Operation: South East England
Tel: 01227 751130
Fax: 01227 750033
Email: showroom@rootskitchens.co.uk
Web: www.rootskitchens.co.uk ✍
Product Type: 1, 2, 3, 4, 5

ROSCO COLLECTIONS
Stone Allerton, Axbridge, Somerset, BS26 2NS
Area of Operation: UK & Ireland
Tel: 01934 712299 **Fax:** 01934 713222
Email: jonathan@roscobathrooms.demon.co.uk
Product Type: 1, 2

RSJ ASSOCIATES LTD
Unit 5, Greenfield Road, Greenfield Farm Industrial
Estate, Congleton, Cheshire, CW12 4TR
Area of Operation: UK & Ireland
Tel: 01260 276188
Fax: 01260 280889
Email: info@rsjassociates.co.uk
Web: www.hueppe.com
Product Type: 1, 2, 3

SAMUEL HEATH
Leopold Street, Birmingham, West Midlands, B12 0UJ
Area of Operation: Worldwide
Tel: 0121 772 2303 **Fax:** 0121 772 3334
Email: info@samuel-heath.com
Web: www.samuel-heath.com **Product Type:** 3, 5
Material Type: C) 11, 13, 14, 16

SANIFLO LTD
Howard House, The Runway,
South Ruislip, Middlesex, HA4 6SE
Area of Operation: UK (Excluding Ireland)
Tel: 0208 842 4040 **Fax:** 0208 842 1671
Email: andrews@saniflo.co.uk
Web: www.saniflo.co.uk **Product Type:** 4

SHIRES
Uttoxeter Road, Longton,
Stoke-on-Trent, Staffordshire, ST3 1NA
Area of Operation: UK & Ireland
Tel: 01782 599099 **Fax:** 01782 599295
Email: hkiddle@qualceram-shires.com
Web: www.shires-bathrooms.com ✍

SHOWERLUX UK LTD
Sibree Road, Coventry, West Midlands, CV3 4FD
Area of Operation: UK & Ireland
Tel: 02476 882515
Fax: 02476 305457
Email: sales@showerlux.co.uk
Web: www.showerlux.com **Product Type:** 1, 2

SMART SHOWERS LTD
Unit 11, Woodside Road, South Marston Business
Park, Swindon, Wiltshire, SN3 4WA
Area of Operation: UK & Ireland
Tel: 01793 822775
Fax: 01793 823800
Email: enquiries@smartshowers.co.uk
Web: www.smartshowers.co.uk ✍
Product Type: 1, 2, 3, 4, 5

SOGA LTD
41 Mayfield Street, Hull,
East Riding of Yorks, HU3 1NT
Area of Operation: Worldwide
Tel: 01482 327025 **Email:** info@soga.co.uk
Web: www.soga.co.uk ✍ **Product Type:** 1

SPECIALIST TILING SUPPLIES
Unit 5, Wortley Moor Lane Trading Estate,
Leeds, West Yorkshire, LS12 4HX
Area of Operation: UK & Ireland
Tel: 0800 781 8384 **Fax:** 0113 202 2015
Product Type: 2

STEAM DIRECT
187 London Road, Southend-on-Sea,
Essex, SS1 1PW
Area of Operation: UK & Ireland
Tel: 01702 433445 **Fax:** 01702 433449
Email: steamdirect@aol.com
Web: www.steam-direct.co.uk
Product Type: 1

STIFFKEY BATHROOMS
89 Upper Saint Giles Street,
Norwich, Norfolk, NR2 1AB
Area of Operation: Worldwide
Tel: 01603 627850
Fax: 01603 619775
Email: stiffkeybathrooms.norwich@virgin.net
Web: www.stiffkeybathrooms.com
Product Type: 3, 5 **Other Info:** ▽

STUDIO STONE
The Stone Yard, Alton Lane,
Four Marks, Hampshire, GU34 5AJ
Area of Operation: UK (Excluding Ireland)
Tel: 01420 562500
Fax: 01420 563192
Email: sales@studiostone.co.uk
Web: www.studiostone.co.uk
Product Type: 1, 2 **Other Info:** ✎
Material Type: E) 1, 2, 3, 5

SVEDBERGS
4E Wilsons Park, Monsall Road, Newton Heath,
Manchester, Greater Manchester, M40 8WN
Area of Operation: UK & Ireland
Tel: 0161 2051200
Fax: 0161 251212
Email: info@svedbergs.co.uk
Web: www.svedbergs.co.uk
Product Type: 1, 3, 5

SWADLING BRASSWARE - A MATKI COMPANY
Churchward Road, Yate, Bristol, BS37 5PL
Area of Operation: Europe
Tel: 01454 322888
Fax: 01454 315284
Email: helpline@matki.co.uk
Web: www.swadlingbrassware.com

TAB UK LIMITED
Brewery Lane, Felling,
Gateshead, Tyne & Wear, NE10 0EY
Area of Operation: UK & Ireland
Tel: 0191 4695500 **Fax:** 0191 4695828
Email: sales@tab-uk.com
Web: www.tab-uk.co.uk
Product Type: 1 **Material Type:** C) 1, 11, 14

TAPS SHOP
1 Tristram Road, Ducklington,
Whitney, Oxfordshire, OX29 7XH
Area of Operation: Worldwide
Tel: 0845 4303035 **Fax:** 01993 779653
Email: info@tapsshop.co.uk
Web: www.tapsshop.co.uk ✍
Product Type: 3, 4, 5

TECHFLOW PRODUCTS LTD
Unit 7 Sovereign Business Park, Albert Drive, Victoria
Industrial Estate, Burgess Hill, West Sussex, RH15 9TY
Area of Operation: UK & Ireland
Tel: 01444 258003 **Fax:** 01444 258004
Email: rod@techflow.co.uk
Web: www.techflow.co.uk **Product Type:** 4

THE KITCHEN AND BATHROOM COLLECTION
Nelson House, Nelson Road,
Salisbury, Wiltshire, SP1 3LT
Area of Operation: South West England and South Wales
Tel: 01722 334800 **Fax:** 01722 412252
Email: info@kbc.co.uk **Web:** www.kbc.co.uk
Product Type: 1, 2, 3, 4, 5
Other Info: ✐ **Material Type:** E) 1, 2, 5

THE WATER MONOPOLY
16/18 Lonsdale Road, London, NW6 6RD
Area of Operation: UK (Excluding Ireland)
Tel: 0207 624 2636
Fax: 0207 624 2631
Email: enquiries@watermonopoly.com
Web: www.watermonopoly.com

THOMAS CRAPPER & CO. LTD
The Stable Yard, Alscot Park,
Stratford-on-Avon, Warwickshire, CV37 8BL
Area of Operation: Worldwide
Tel: 01789 450522 **Fax:** 01789 450523
Email: wc@thomas-crapper.com
Web: www.thomas-crapper.com ✐
Product Type: 3

TIMELESS BATHROOMS LTD
394 Ringwood Road, Ferndown, Dorset, BH22 9AU
Area of Operation: South East England
Tel: 01202 897110 **Fax:** 01202 892252
Email: bathroom@options394.fsnet.co.uk
Web: www.timelessbathrooms.co.uk
Product Type: 1, 2, 3, 4, 5

TRADEMARK TILES
Tile Store, Somersham Road, St Ives,
Huntingdon, Cambridgeshire, PE27 3WR
Area of Operation: UK (Excluding Ireland)
Tel: 01480 498123
Email: info@tilestoreplus.co.uk
Web: www.tilestoreplus.co.uk ✐
Product Type: 1, 2, 3, 4

TRITON PLC
Triton Road, Shepperton Business Park,
Caldwell Road, Nuneaton, Warwickshire, CV11 4NR
Area of Operation: UK & Ireland
Tel: 02476 344441 **Fax:** 02476 6349828
Web: www.tritonshowers.co.uk
Product Type: 3, 4

TWYFORD BATHROOMS
Lawton Road, Alsager,
Stoke On Trent, Staffordshire, ST7 2DF
Area of Operation: Worldwide
Tel: 01270 879777
Web: www.twyfordbathrooms.com
Product Type: 1, 2 **Material Type:** C) 14

UK BATHROOM INTERIORS
Units 3-4, The Old Laundry, Fishergreen,
Ripon, North Yorkshire, HG4 1NL
Area of Operation: UK (Excluding Ireland)
Tel: 01765 608822 **Fax:** 01765 608892
Email: mark@ukbathroominteriors.com
Web: www.ukbathroominteriors.com ✐
Product Type: 1, 2, 3, 4

Don't Forget !

You can use the materials key at the beginning of this Handbook to get much more information from a company's listing.

UK TILES DIRECT LTD
42 Bestwall Road, Wareham, Dorset, BH20 4JA
Area of Operation: UK (Excluding Ireland)
Tel: 01929 556169
Email: admin@uktilesdirect.co.uk
Web: www.uktilesdirect.co.uk

UK TILES DIRECT LTD
Area of Operation: UK (Excluding Ireland)
Tel: 01929 556169
Email: admin@uktilesdirect.co.uk
Web: www.uktilesdirect.co.uk

Add style and value to your property with the ultimate showering experience. . . . a Wetroom! UK Tiles Direct can design, design and supply or just simply supply all of your Wetroom requirements. From preformed wet-room bases to bespoke stainless steel drainage systems. They can also advise you on the best non-slip tiles and waterproofing systems.

UNICOM
Kingdom House, 219 Gleniffer Road,
Paisley, Renfrewshire, PA2 8UL
Tel: 0845 330 7642 **Fax:** 0845 330 7641
Email: george@unicom-direct.com
Web: www.unicom-direct.com ✐
Product Type: 1, 2, 3, 4, 5

VICTORIAN BATHROOMS
Ings Mill Complex, Dale Street,
Ossett, West Yorkshire, WF5 9HQ
Area of Operation: UK (Excluding Ireland)
Tel: 01924 267736 **Fax:** 01924 261232
Email: sales@vb-bathrooms.com
Web: www.vb-bathrooms.com ✐
Product Type: 1, 2, 3, 4

WALTON BATHROOMS
The Hersham Centre, The Green, Molesey Road,
Hersham, Walton on Thames, Surrey, KT12 4HL
Area of Operation: UK (Excluding Ireland)
Tel: 01932 224784 **Fax:** 01932 253447
Email: sales@waltonbathrooms.co.uk
Web: www.waltonbathrooms.co.uk ✐
Product Type: 1

WATER FRONT
All Worcester Buildings, Birmingham Road,
Redditch, Worcestershire, B97 6DY
Area of Operation: UK & Ireland
Tel: 01527 584244 **Fax:** 01527 61127
Email: info@waterfrontbathrooms.com
Web: www.waterfrontbathrooms.com
Product Type: 3, 5 **Material Type:** C) 11, 14

WATERMILL PRODUCTS LTD
Gemini House, Enterprise Way,
Hurst Green, Edenbridge, Kent, TN8 6HF
Area of Operation: UK & Ireland
Tel: 0845 2000 912 **Fax:** 0845 2000 913
Email: sales@watermillshowers.co.uk
Web: www.watermillshowers.co.uk
Product Type: 3, 4

WHALE
277-279 Old Belfast Road,
Bangor, Co Down, BT19 1LT
Area of Operation: Worldwide
Tel: 028 9127 0531 **Fax:** 028 9146 6421
Email: dry-deck@whalepumps.com
Web: www.whalepumps.com **Product Type:** 4

WHIRLPOOL EXPRESS (UK) LTD
61-62 Lower Dock Street,
Kingsway, Newport, NP20 1EF
Area of Operation: Europe
Tel: 01633 244555 **Fax:** 01633 244881
Email: reception@whirlpoolexpress.co.uk
Web: www.whirlpoolexpress.co.uk

HEATED TOWEL RAILS

KEY

SEE ALSO: HEATING - Radiators
OTHER: ▽ Reclaimed 🔲 On-line shopping
🖐 Bespoke ✋ Hand-made ECO Ecological

AESTUS
Unit 5 Strawberry Lane Industrial Estate, Strawberry
Lane, Willenhall, West Midlands, WV13 3RS
Area of Operation: UK & Ireland
Tel: 0870 403 0115 **Fax:** 0870 403 0116
Email: melissa@publicityengineers.com

AL CHALLIS LTD
Europower House, Lower Road, Cookham,
Maidenhead, Berkshire, SL6 9EH
Area of Operation: UK & Ireland
Tel: 01628 529024 **Fax:** 0870 458 0577
Email: chris@alchallis.com
Web: www.alchallis.com

ALEXANDERS
Unit 3, 1/1A Spilsby Road,
Harold Hill, Romford, Essex, RM3 8SB
Area of Operation: UK & Ireland
Tel: 01708 384574 **Fax:** 01708 384089
Email: sales@alexanders-uk.net
Web: www.alexanders-uk.net

ANTIQUE BATHS OF IVYBRIDGE LTD
Emebridge Works, Ermington Road,
Ivybridge, Devon, PL21 9DE
Tel: 01752 698250 **Fax:** 01752 698266
Email: sales@antiquebaths.com
Web: www.antiquebaths.com ▽ 🔲

BATHROOM CITY
Seeleys Road, Tyseley Industrial Estate,
Birmingham, West Midlands, B11 2LQ
Area of Operation: UK & Ireland
Tel: 0121 753 0700 **Fax:** 0121 753 1110
Email: sales@bathroomcity.com
Web: www.bathroomcity.com 🔲

BATHROOM DISCOUNT CENTRE
297 Munster Road, Fulham, Greater London, SW6 6BW
Area of Operation: UK (Excluding Ireland)
Tel: 0207 381 4222 **Fax:** 0207 381 6792
Email: bathdisc@aol.com
Web: www.bathroomdiscount.co.uk

BATHROOM EXPRESS
61-62 Lower Dock Street,
Kingsway, Newport, NP20 1EF
Area of Operation: UK & Ireland
Tel: 0845 130 2000 **Fax:** 01633 244881
Email: sales@bathroomexpress.co.uk
Web: www.bathroomexpress.co.uk 🔲

BATHROOM HEAVEN
25 Eccleston Square, London, SW1V 1NS
Tel: 0845 121 6700 **Fax:** 0207 233 6074
Email: laura@bathroomheaven.com
Web: www.bathroomheaven.com 🔲

BATHROOMS PLUS LTD
222 Malmesbury Park Road,
Bournemouth, Dorset, BH8 8PR
Area of Operation: South West England and South Wales
Tel: 01202 294417 **Fax:** 01202 316425
Email: info@bathrooms-plus.co.uk
Web: www.bathrooms-plus.co.uk

BATHROOMSTUFF.CO.UK
326 London Road, Hilsea,
Portsmouth, Hampshire, PO2 9JT
Area of Operation: UK (Excluding Ireland)
Tel: 08450 580 540 **Fax:** 08451 274125
Email: sales@bathroomstuff.co.uk
Web: www.bathroomstuff.co.uk 🔲

BOUNDARY BATHROOMS
Ainsworth & Dent House, Regent Street,
Colne, Lancashire, BB8 8LD
Area of Operation: UK & Ireland
Tel: 01282 862509 **Fax:** 01282 871192
Email: sales@boundarybathrooms.co.uk

CHADDER & CO.
Blenheim Studio, London Road,
Forest Row, East Sussex, RH18 5EZ
Area of Operation: Worldwide
Tel: 01342 823243 **Fax:** 01342 823097
Web: www.chadder.com

CHATSWORTH HEATING PRODUCTS LTD
Unit B Watchmoor Point,
Camberley, Surrey, GU15 3EX
Area of Operation: UK (Excluding Ireland)
Tel: 01276 605880 **Fax:** 01276 605881
Email: enquiries@chatsworth-heating.co.uk
Web: www.chatsworth-heating.co.uk

CITY BATHROOMS & KITCHENS
158 Longford Road, Longford,
Coventry, West Midlands, CV6 6DR
Area of Operation: UK & Ireland
Tel: 02476 365877 **Fax:** 02476 644992
Email: citybathrooms@hotmail.com
Web: www.citybathrooms.co.uk

CLASSIC WARMTH DIRECT LTD
Unit 8, Brunel Workshops, Ashburton Industrial
Estate, Ross-on-Wye, Herefordshire, HR9 7DX
Tel: 01989 565555 **Fax:** 01989 561058
Email: patbur@tiscali.co.uk

COLOURWASH LTD
165 Chamberlayne Road, London, NW10 3NU
Tel: 0208 830 2992 **Fax:** 0208 830 2317
Email: sales@colourwash.co.uk
Web: www.colourwash.co.uk

COMFOOT FLOORING
Walnut Tree, Redgrave Road,
South Lopham, Diss, Norfolk, IP22 2HN
Area of Operation: Europe
Tel: 01379 688516 **Fax:** 01379 688517
Email: sales@comfoot.com
Web: www.comfoot.com 🔲

CONSORT EQUIPMENT PRODUCTS LTD
Thornton Industrial Estate,
Milford Haven, Pembrokeshire, SA73 2RT
Area of Operation: Worldwide
Tel: 01646 692172 **Fax:** 01646 695195
Email: enquiries@consortepl.com
Web: www.consortepl.com

COOLANDWARM.COM
Trigger Comfort, t/a Cool and Warm,
23 Walnut Tree Close, Guildford, Surrey, GU1 4UL
Area of Operation: Europe
Tel: 01483 30 66 50 **Email:** info@coolandwarm.com
Web: www.coolandwarm.com 🔲

COSY ROOMS (THE-BATHROOM-SHOP.CO.UK)
17 Chiltern Way, North Hykeham,
Lincoln, Lincolnshire, LN6 9SY
Area of Operation: UK (Excluding Ireland)
Tel: 01522 696002 **Fax:** 01522 696002
Email: keith@cosy-rooms.com
Web: www.the-bathroom-shop.co.uk 🔲

CYMRU KITCHENS
63 Caerleon Road, Newport, NP19 7BX
Area of Operation: UK (Excluding Ireland)
Tel: 01633 676767 **Fax:** 01633 212512
Email: sales@cymrukitchens.com
Web: www.cymrukitchens.com

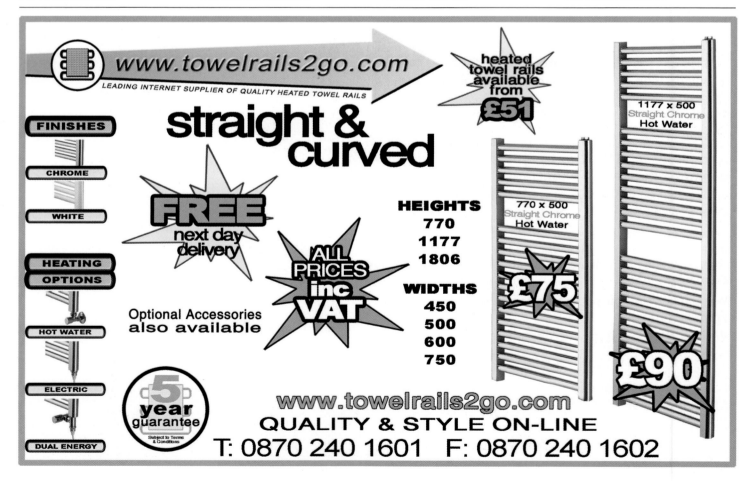

DEEP BLUE SHOWROOM
299-313 Lewisham High Street,
Lewisham, London, SE13 6NW
Area of Operation: UK (Excluding Ireland)
Tel: 0208 690 3401 **Fax:** 0208 690 1408

DESIGNER RADIATORS
Regent Street, Colne, Lancashire, BB8 8LD
Area of Operation: UK & Ireland
Tel: 01282 862509 **Fax:** 01282 871192
Email: sales@boundarybathrooms.co.uk
Web: www.designer-radiators.com ⌐

DIMPLEX
Millbrook House, Grange Drive, Hedge End,
Southampton, Hampshire, SO30 2DF
Area of Operation: UK & Ireland
Tel: 0845 600 5111 **Fax:** 01489 773050
Email: customer.services@glendimplex.com
Web: www.dimplex.co.uk

DOUGH-HEAT LTD
Unit 8 Strawberry Lane Industrial Estate,
Willenhall, West Midlands, WV13 3RS
Area of Operation: Worldwide
Tel: 0870 403 0103 **Fax:** 0870 403 0104
Email: sales@dough-heat.com
Web: www.dough-heat.com
Other Info: ✋ **Material Type:** C) 3

ECOLEC
Sharrocks Street, Wolverhampton, WV1 3RP
Area of Operation: UK & Ireland
Tel: 01902 457575 **Fax:** 01902 457797
Email: sales@ecolec.co.uk
Web: www.ecolec.co.uk ⌐ **Other Info:** ✎

ESKIMO DESIGN LTD.
51-53 Llull, Barcelona, 08005, Spain
Area of Operation: Worldwide **Tel:** 020 7117 0110
Email: ed@eskimodesign.co.uk
Web: www.eskimodesign.co.uk **Other Info:** ✎ ✋
Material Type: C) 1, 2, 3, 7, 11, 14, 15, 16

HERITAGE BATHROOMS
Princess Street, Bedminster, Bristol, BS3 4AG
Area of Operation: UK & Ireland
Tel: 0117 963 3333
Email: marketing@heritagebathrooms.com
Web: www.heritagebathrooms.com

HUDSON REED
Rylands Street, Burnley, Lancashire, BB10 1RG
Area of Operation: Worldwide
Tel: 01282 418000 **Fax:** 01282 428915
Email: info@ultra-group.co.uk
Web: www.hudsonreed.info
Material Type: C) 3, 11, 14, 16

INDESIGN
Kiran House, 53 Park Royal Road, London, NW10 7LQ
Area of Operation: UK & Ireland
Tel: 0208 963 5841 **Fax:** 0208 965 6261
Email: dhanja.bhudia@akshars.co.uk
Web: www.akshars.co.uk

INSPIRED BATHROOMS
Unit R4, Innsworth Technology Park, Innsworth Lane,
Gloucester, Gloucestershire, GL3 1DL
Area of Operation: UK & Ireland
Tel: 01452 559121 **Fax:** 01452 530908
Email: sales@inspired-bathrooms.co.uk
Web: www.inspired-bathrooms.co.uk ⌐

JIS EUROPE (SUSSEX RANGE)
Warehouse 2, Nash Lane, Scaynes Hill,
Haywards Heath, West Sussex, RH17 7NJ
Area of Operation: Europe
Tel: 01444 831200 **Fax:** 01444 831900
Email: info@jiseurope.co.uk
Web: www.sussexrange.co.uk

JOHN LEWIS OF HUNGERFORD
Grove Technology Park, Downsview Road,
Wantage, Oxfordshire, OX12 9FA
Area of Operation: UK (Excluding Ireland)
Tel: 01235 774300 **Fax:** 01235 769031
Email: park.street@john-lewis.co.uk
Web: www.john-lewis.co.uk

KALIREL UK
32 Riverside Way, Brandon, Suffolk, IP27 0AN
Area of Operation: UK & Ireland
Tel: 01842 814489 **Fax:** 01842 814489
Email: contactuk@kalirel.com
Web: www.calo-confort.co.uk

KEELING HEATING PRODUCTS
Cranbourne Road, Gosport, Hampshire, PO12 1RJ
Area of Operation: UK & Ireland
Tel: 02392 796633 **Fax:** 02392 425028
Email: sales@keeling.co.uk
Web: www.keeling.co.uk
Material Type: C) 2, 7, 11, 13, 14, 16

KENSINGTON STUDIO
13 c & d Kensington Road, Earlsdon,
Coventry, West Midlands, CV5 6GG
Area of Operation: UK (Excluding Ireland)
Tel: 02476 713326 **Fax:** 02476 713136
Email: sales@kensingtonstudio.com
Web: www.kensingtonstudio.com ⌐

KERMI (UK) LTD
7 Brunel Road, Corby, Northamptonshire, NN17 4JW
Area of Operation: UK & Ireland
Tel: 01536 400004 **Fax:** 01536 446614
Email: cradcliff@kermi.co.uk
Web: www.kermi.co.uk

M & O BATHROOM CENTRE
174-176 Goswell Road,
Clarkenwell, London, EC1V 7DT
Area of Operation: East England, Greater London,
South East England
Tel: 0207 608 0111 **Fax:** 0207 490 3083
Email: mando@lineone.net

MEKON PRODUCTS
25 Bessemer Park, Milkwood Road, London, SE24 0HG
Area of Operation: UK (Excluding Ireland)
Tel: 0207 733 8011 **Fax:** 0207 737 0840
Email: info@mekon.net **Web:** www.mekon.net

MEREWAY CONTRACTS
Unit 1 Wharfdale Road, Tysely,
Birmingham, West Midlands, B11 2DE
Area of Operation: UK (Excluding Ireland)
Tel: 0121 764 7180 **Fax:** 0121 764 7199
Email: info@merewaycontracts.co.uk
Web: www.merewaycontracts.co.uk

MYSON TOWEL WARMERS
Victoria Works, Nelson Street,
Bolton, Lancashire, BL3 2DW
Area of Operation: Worldwide
Tel: 0870 428 0836 **Email:** sales@myson.co.uk
Web: www.myson.co.uk **Other Info:** ✎ ✋

NICHOLAS ANTHONY LTD
42-44 Wigmore Street, London, W1U 2RX
Area of Operation: East England, Greater London,
South East England
Tel: 0800 068 3603 **Fax:** 01206 762698
Email: info@nicholas-anthony.co.uk
Web: www.nicholas-anthony.co.uk

NO CODE
Larkwhistle Farm Road,
Micheldever, Hampshire, SO21 3BG
Area of Operation: UK & Ireland
Tel: 01962 870078 **Fax:** 01962 870077
Email: sales@nocode.co.uk
Web: www.nocode.co.uk

RADIANT RADIATORS LTD
7 Allandale Road, Stoneygate,
Leicester, Leicestershire, LE2 2DA
Tel: 0116 270 5777 **Fax:** 0116 274 5777
Email: sales@radiant-radiators.co.uk
Web: www.radiant-radiators.co.uk

RADIATING STYLE
Unit 15 Thompon Road, Hounslow,
Middlesex, Greater London, TW3 3UH
Area of Operation: UK (Excluding Ireland)
Tel: 0870 072 3428 **Fax:** 0208 577 9222
Email: sales@radiatingstyle.com
Web: www.radiatingstyle.com

SVEDBERGS
4E Wilsons Park, Monsall Road,
Newton Heath, Manchester, M40 8WN
Area of Operation: UK & Ireland
Tel: 0161 2051200 **Fax:** 0161 251212
Email: info@svedbergs.co.uk
Web: www.svedbergs.co.uk

THE KITCHEN AND BATHROOM COLLECTION
Nelson House, Nelson Road,
Salisbury, Wiltshire, SP1 3LT
Area of Operation: South West England and South Wales
Tel: 01722 334800 **Fax:** 01722 412252
Email: info@kbc.co.uk
Web: www.kbc.co.uk **Other Info:** ✎

TIMELESS BATHROOMS LTD
394 Ringwood Road, Ferndown, Dorset, BH22 9AU
Area of Operation: South East England
Tel: 01202 897110 **Fax:** 01202 892252
Email: bathroom@options394.fsnet.co.uk
Web: www.timelessbathrooms.co.uk

TIVOLIS DESIGN
No 1 Islington Business Centre,
3-5 Islington High Street, London, N1 9LQ
Area of Operation: UK & Ireland
Tel: 0207 745 2375 **Fax:** 0207 745 2376
Email: sales@tivolidesign.com

TOWEL RAILS 2 GO LTD
Unit 4 Paper Mill End, Great Barr,
Birmingham, West Midlands, B44 8NH
Area of Operation: UK & Ireland
Tel: 0870 240 1601 **Fax:** 0870 240 1602
Email: sales@towelrails2go.com
Web: www.towelrails2go.com ⌐

TRADEMARK TILES
Tile Store, Somersham Road, St Ives,
Huntingdon, Cambridgeshire, PE27 3WR
Area of Operation: UK (Excluding Ireland)
Tel: 01480 498123
Email: info@tilestoreplus.co.uk
Web: www.tilestoreplus.co.uk ⌐

UK BATHROOM INTERIORS
Units 3-4, The Old Laundry, Fishergreen,
Ripon, North Yorkshire, HG4 1NL
Area of Operation: UK (Excluding Ireland)
Tel: 01765 608822 **Fax:** 01765 608892
Email: mark@ukbathroominteriors.com
Web: www.ukbathroominteriors.com ⌐

UNICOM
Kingdom House, 219 Gleniffer Road,
Paisley, Renfrewshire, PA2 8UL
Area of Operation: UK & Ireland
Tel: 0845 330 7642
Fax: 0845 330 7641
Email: george@unicom-direct.com
Web: www.unicom-direct.com ⌐

VICTORIAN BATHROOMS
Ings Mill Complex, Dale Street,
Ossett , West Yorkshire, WF5 9HQ
Area of Operation: UK (Excluding Ireland)
Tel: 01924 267736 **Fax:** 01924 261232
Email: sales@vb-bathrooms.com
Web: www.vb-bathrooms.com ⌐

VOGUE UK
Units 6-10, Strawberry Lane Industrial Estate,
Strawberry Lane, Willenhall, West Midlands, WV13 3RS
Area of Operation: UK & Ireland
Tel: 0870 403 0101
Fax: 0870 403 0102
Email: sales@vogue-uk.com
Web: www.vogue-uk.com

WALTON BATHROOMS
The Hersham Centre, The Green, Molesey Road,
Hersham, Walton on Thames, Surrey, KT12 4HL
Area of Operation: UK (Excluding Ireland)
Tel: 01932 224784
Fax: 01932 253447
Email: sales@waltonbathrooms.co.uk
Web: www.waltonbathrooms.co.uk ⌐

WARMROOMS
24 Corncroft Lane, St Leonards Park,
Gloucester, Gloucestershire, GL4 6XU
Area of Operation: UK (Excluding Ireland)
Tel: 01452 304460 **Fax:** 01452 304460
Email: sales@warmrooms.co.uk
Web: www.warmrooms.co.uk ⌐

WHIRLPOOL EXPRESS (UK) LTD
61-62 Lower Dock Street,
Kingsway, Newport, NP20 1EF
Area of Operation: Europe
Tel: 01633 244555 **Fax:** 01633 244881
Email: reception@whirlpoolexpress.co.uk
Web: www.whirlpoolexpress.co.uk ⌐
Product Type: 1, 2, 3, 4, 5

BATHROOM FURNITURE

KEY
PRODUCT TYPES: 1= Vanity Units
2 = Cabinets 3 = Washstands 4 = Other
OTHER: ▽ Reclaimed ⌐ On-line shopping
✎ Bespoke ✋ Hand-made ECO Ecological

ALEXANDERS
Unit 3, 1/1A Spilsby Road,
Harold Hill, Romford, Essex, RM3 8SB
Area of Operation: UK & Ireland
Tel: 01708 384574 **Fax:** 01708 384089
Email: sales@alexanders-uk.net
Web: www.alexanders-uk.net
Product Type: 1, 2, 3, 4

ALICANTE STONE
Damaso Navarro, 6 Bajo,
03610 Petrer (Alicante), P.O. Box 372, Spain
Area of Operation: Europe
Tel: +34 966 31 96 97 **Fax:** +34 966 31 96 98
Email: info@alicantestone.com
Web: www.alicantestone.com
Product Type: 1 **Material Type:** E) 1, 2, 5, 8

ALLMILMO UK
Briff Well, Little Lane, Reading, Berkshire, RG7 6QX
Area of Operation: UK & Ireland
Tel: 01635 868181 **Fax:** 01635 869693
Email: allmilmo@aol.com
Web: www.allmilmo.com
Product Type: 1, 2, 3, 4

ALTHEA UK LTD
Concept House, Blanche Street,
Bradford, West Yorkshire, BD4 8DA
Area of Operation: UK (Excluding Ireland)
Tel: 01274 660770 **Fax:** 01274 667929
Email: sales@altheauk.com
Web: www.periodbathrooms.co.uk

AMBIANCE BAIN
Cumberland House,
80 Scrubs Lane, London, NW10 6RF
Area of Operation: UK & Ireland
Tel: 0870 902 1313 **Fax:** 0870 902 1312
Email: sghirardello@mimea.com
Web: www.ambiancebain.com
Product Type: 1, 2, 3

ANTIQUE BATHS OF IVYBRIDGE LTD
Emebridge Works, Ermington Road,
Ivybridge, Devon, PL21 9DE
Area of Operation: UK (Excluding Ireland)
Tel: 01752 698250 **Fax:** 01752 698266
Email: sales@antiquebaths.com
Web: www.antiquebaths.com ⌐
Product Type: 1, 3

AQUAPLUS SOLUTIONS
Unit 106, Indiana Building, London, SE13 7QD
Area of Operation: UK & Ireland
Tel: 0870 201 1915 **Fax:** 0870 201 1916
Email: info@aquaplussolutions.com
Web: www.aquaplussolutions.com

ARTICHOKE (KITCHEN AND CABINET MAKERS)
Hortswood, Long Lane, Wrington, Somerset, BS40 5SP
Area of Operation: Worldwide
Tel: 01934 863840 **Fax:** 01934 863841
Email: mail@artichoke-ltd.com
Web: www.artichoke-ltd.com
Product Type: 1, 2, 3

ASHLEY BATHROOMS
Duffield Road Industrial Estate,
Little Eaton, Derby, Derbyshire, DE21 5DR
Area of Operation: UK & Ireland
Tel: 01332 830404
Fax: 01332 830202
Email: info@ashleybathrooms.com
Web: www.ashleybathrooms.com

AVANTE BATHROOMS
Thistle House, Thistle Way,
Gildersome Spur, Wakefield Road,
Morley, Leeds, West Yorkshire, LS27 7JZ
Area of Operation: UK (Excluding Ireland)
Tel: 0113 201 2240 **Fax:** 0113 253 0717
Email: info@avantebathrooms.com
Web: www.avantebathrooms.com
Product Type: 1, 2, 3

B ROURKE & CO LTD
Vulcan Works, Accrington Road,
Burnley, Lancashire, BB11 5QD
Area of Operation: Worldwide
Tel: 01282 422841 **Fax:** 01282 458901
Email: info@rourkes.co.uk
Web: www.rourkes.co.uk
Product Type: 3, 4 **Material Type:** C) 2, 4, 5, 6

BARRHEAD SANITARYWARE PLC
15-17 Nasmyth Road, Hillington Industrial Estate,
Hillington, Glasgow, Renfrewshire, G52 4RG
Area of Operation: UK & Ireland
Tel: 0141 883 0066 **Fax:** 0141 883 0077
Email: sales@barrhead.co.uk
Product Type: 1, 2

BATHROOM BARN
The Bathroom Barn, Uplands Industrial Estate, Mere
Way, Wyton, Huntingdon, Cambridgeshire, PE28 2JZ
Area of Operation: UK (Excluding Ireland)
Tel: 01480 458900
Email: sales@bathroom-barn.co.uk
Web: www.bathroombarn.co.uk

BATHROOM CITY
Seeleys Road, Tyseley Industrial Estate,
Birmingham, West Midlands, B11 2LQ
Area of Operation: UK & Ireland
Tel: 0121 753 0700 **Fax:** 0121 753 1110
Email: sales@bathroomcity.com
Web: www.bathroomcity.com
Product Type: 1, 2, 3, 4

BATHROOMS PLUS LTD
222 Malmesbury Park Road,
Bournemouth, Dorset, BH8 8PR
Area of Operation: South West England and South Wales
Tel: 01202 294417
Fax: 01202 316425
Email: info@bathrooms-plus.co.uk
Web: www.bathrooms-plus.co.uk
Product Type: 1, 2, 3, 4
Material Type: A) 1, 2, 4, 5, 9

BOUNDARY BATHROOMS
Ainsworth & Dent House,
Regent Street, Colne, Lancashire, BB8 8LD
Area of Operation: UK & Ireland
Tel: 01282 862509 **Fax:** 01282 871192
Email: sales@boundarybathrooms.co.uk
Product Type: 2

BROOKMANS OF RICKMANSWORTH LTD
1 Moneyhill Parade, Uxbridge Road,
Rickmansworth, Hertfordshire, WD3 7BQ
Area of Operation: Worldwide
Tel: 01923 773906 **Fax:** 01923 896098
Email: celia.warbrick@brookmans.co.uk
Web: www.brookmans.co.uk **Product Type:** 2

**BROOK-WATER DESIGNER
BATHROOMS & KITCHENS**
The Downs, Woodhouse Hill,
Uplyme, Lyme Regis, Dorset, DT7 3SL
Area of Operation: Worldwide
Tel: 0870 851 9739
Email: sales@brookwater.co.uk
Web: www.brookwater.co.uk ⌁ **Product Type:** 2

BUSHBOARD LTD
9-29 Rixon Road, Wellingborough,
Northamptonshire, NN8 4BA
Area of Operation: UK & Ireland
Tel: 01933 232200
Email: washrooms@bushboard.co.uk
Web: www.bushboard.co.uk

BUYDESIGN
Monteviot Nurseries, Ancrum,
Jedburgh, Borders, TD8 6TU
Area of Operation: Scotland
Tel: 01835 830740
Email: enquries@buydesign-furniture.com
Web: www.buydesign-furniture.com
Product Type: 2
Material Type: A) 1, 2, 3, 4, 5, 6, 8, 9, 11

CAPITAL MARBLE DESIGN
Unit 1 Pall Mall Deposit,
124-128 Barlby Road, London, W10 6BL
Area of Operation: UK & Ireland
Tel: 0208 968 5340 **Fax:** 0208 968 8827
Email: stonegallery@capitalmarble.co.uk
Web: www.capitalmarble.co.uk
Product Type: 1, 2, 3

CITY BATHROOMS & KITCHENS
158 Longford Road, Longford,
Coventry, West Midlands, CV6 6DR
Area of Operation: UK & Ireland
Tel: 02476 365877 **Fax:** 02476 644992
Email: citybathrooms@hotmail.com
Web: www.citybathrooms.co.uk

COLOURWASH LTD
165 Chamberlayne Road, London, NW10 3NU
Area of Operation: UK & Ireland
Tel: 0208 830 2992 **Fax:** 0208 830 2317
Email: sales@colourwash.co.uk
Web: www.colourwash.co.uk
Product Type: 1, 2, 3, 4

COSY ROOMS (THE-BATHROOM-SHOP.CO.UK)
17 Chiltern Way, North Hykeham,
Lincoln, Lincolnshire, LN6 9SY
Area of Operation: UK (Excluding Ireland)
Tel: 01522 696002 **Fax:** 01522 696002
Email: keith@cosy-rooms.com
Web: www.the-bathroom-shop.co.uk ⌁
Product Type: 2

COTTAGE FARM ANTIQUES
Stratford Road, Aston Sub Edge,
Chipping Campden, Gloucestershire, GL55 6PZ
Area of Operation: Worldwide
Tel: 01386 438263 **Fax:** 01386 438263
Email: info@cottagefarmantiques.co.uk
Web: www.cottagefarmantiques.co.uk ⌁
Product Type: 2, 4
Other Info: ▽ ECO ⌁ 🖑
Material Type: B) 2

COUNTESS(KITCHENS & BEDROOMS) LTD
Mounsey Road, Bamber Bridge,
Preston, Lancashire, PR6 7RA
Area of Operation: North West England and North Wales
Tel: 01772 321218 **Fax:** 01772 316165
Email: sales@countessinteriors.co.uk
Web: www.countessinteriors.co.uk
Product Type: 1, 2, 4 **Other Info:** ⌁ 🖑
Material Type: H) 1, 2, 7

CYMRU KITCHENS
63 Caerleon Road, Newport, NP19 7BX
Area of Operation: UK (Excluding Ireland)
Tel: 01633 676767 **Fax:** 01633 212512
Email: sales@cymrukitchens.co.uk
Web: www.cymrukitchens.com

D.A FURNITURE LTD
Woodview Workshop, Pitway Lane,
Farrington Gurney, Bristol, BS39 6TX
Area of Operation: South West England and South Wales
Tel: 01761 453117
Email: enquiries@dafurniture.co.uk
Web: www.dafurniture.co.uk
Product Type: 1, 2, 3 **Other Info:** ⌁ 🖑
Material Type: A) 2, 3, 4, 5, 6, 7, 8, 9, 10, 11, 12, 13, 14, 15

DECORLUX LTD
18 Ghyll Industrial Estate, Ghyll Road,
Heathfield, East Sussex, TN21 8AW
Area of Operation: UK (Excluding Ireland)
Tel: 01435 866638
Fax: 01435 866641
Email: info@decorlux.co.uk
Web: www.decorlux.co.uk
Product Type: 1, 2, 3

DECORMASTER LTD
Unit 16, Waterside Industrial Estate,
Wolverhampton, West Midlands, WV2 2RH
Area of Operation: Worldwide
Tel: 01902 406030 **Fax:** 01902 353126
Email: sales@oldcolours.co.uk
Web: www.oldcolours.co.uk **Product Type:** 1, 2, 3

DEEP BLUE SHOWROOM
299-313 Lewisham High Street,
Lewisham, London, Greater London, SE13 6NW
Area of Operation: UK (Excluding Ireland)
Tel: 0208 690 3401 **Fax:** 0208 690 1408
Product Type: 1, 2, 3

DISCONTINUED BATHROOMS
140-142 Pogmoor Road, Pogmoor,
Barnsley, North Yorkshire, S75 2DX
Area of Operation: UK (Excluding Ireland)
Tel: 01226 280200
Fax: 01226 733273
Email: sales@discontinuedbathrooms.co.uk
Web: www.discontinuedbathrooms.co.uk
Product Type: 1, 2, 3, 4

DUPONT CORIAN & ZODIAQ
10 Quarry Court, Pitstone Green Business Park,
Pitstone, nr. Tring, Buckinghamshire, LU7 9GW
Area of Operation: UK & Ireland
Tel: 01296 663555 **Fax:** 01296 663599
Email: sales@corian.co.uk
Web: www.corian.co.uk
Product Type: 1 **Other Info:** ⌁

DURAVIT
Unit 7, Stratus Park, Brudenell Drive, Brinklow,
Milton Keynes, Buckinghamshire, MK10 0DE
Area of Operation: UK & Ireland
Tel: 0870 730 7787 **Fax:** 0870 730 7786
Email: info@uk.duravit.com
Web: www.duravit.com
Product Type: 1, 2, 3, 4
Material Type: A) 1, 2, 3, 4, 5, 6, 7, 9

EMCO
Centre Point Distribution Ltd, Unit A5 Regent Park,
Booth Drive, Park Farm Industrial Estate,
Wellingborough, Northamptonshire, NN8 6GR
Area of Operation: UK & Ireland
Tel: 01933 403786
Fax: 01933 403789
Email: k.pedrick@mailcity.com
Web: www.emco-bath.com
Product Type: 1, 2, 3, 4

ESKIMO DESIGN LTD.
51-53 Llull, Barcelona, 08005, Spain
Area of Operation: Worldwide
Tel: 020 7117 0110
Email: ed@eskimodesign.com
Web: www.eskimodesign.com
Product Type: 1, 2 **Other Info:** 🖑
Material Type: A) 1, 6, 7, 12

EURO BATHROOMS
102 Annareagh Road, Richhill, Co Armagh, BT61 9JY
Area of Operation: Ireland Only
Tel: 028 3887 9996 **Fax:** 028 3887 9996

FRANCIS N. LOWE LTD.
The Marble Works, New Road,
Middleton, Matlock, Derbyshire, DE4 4NA
Area of Operation: Europe
Tel: 01629 822216 **Fax:** 01629 824348
Email: info@lowesmarble.com
Web: www.lowesmarble.com
Product Type: 1

G MIDDLETON LTD
Cross Croft Industrial Estate,
Appleby, Cumbria, CA16 6HX
Area of Operation: Europe
Tel: 01768 352067
Fax: 01768 353228
Email: info@graham-middleton.co.uk
Web: www.graham-middleton.co.uk ⌁
Product Type: 1, 2 **Material Type:** A) 2, 3, 4, 5, 9

GOODWOOD BATHROOMS LTD
Church Road, North Mundham,
Chichester, West Sussex, PO20 1JU
Area of Operation: UK (Excluding Ireland)
Tel: 01243 532121
Fax: 01243 533423
Email: sales@goodwoodbathrooms.co.uk
Web: www.goodwoodbathrooms.co.uk
Product Type: 1, 2, 3

HERITAGE BATHROOMS
Princess Street, Bedminster, Bristol, BS3 4AG
Area of Operation: UK & Ireland
Tel: 0117 963 3333
Email: marketing@heritagebathrooms.com
Web: www.heritagebathrooms.com
Product Type: 1, 2, 3

HIB LTD
Castle House, 21-23 Station Road,
New Barnet, Herefordshire, EN5 1PH
Area of Operation: UK & Ireland
Tel: 0208 441 0352 **Fax:** 0208 441 0219
Email: sales@hib.co.uk **Web:** www.hib.co.uk

HOMESTYLE BATHROOMS
Unit 21 Hainault Works, Hainault Road,
Little Heath, Romford, Essex, RM6 5SS
Area of Operation: UK (Excluding Ireland)
Tel: 0208 599 8080
Fax: 0208 599 7070
Email: info@homestyle-bathrooms.co.uk
Web: www.homestyle-bathrooms.co.uk
Product Type: 1, 2, 3, 4

HYGROVE
152/154 Merton Road, Wimbledon, London, SW19 1EH
Area of Operation: South East England
Tel: 0208 543 1200 **Fax:** 0208 543 6521
Email: sales@hygrove.fsnet.co.uk
Web: www.hygrovefurniture.co.uk
Product Type: 1, 2, 3, 4

IDEAL STANDARD
The Bathroom Works, National Avenue,
Kingston Upon Hull, East Riding of Yorks, HU5 4HS
Area of Operation: Worldwide
Tel: 0800 590311 **Fax:** 01482 445886
Email: ideal-standard@aseur.com
Web: www.ideal-standard.co.uk

INSPIRED BATHROOMS
Unit R4, Innsworth Technology Park, Innsworth Lane,
Gloucester, Gloucestershire, GL3 1DL
Area of Operation: UK & Ireland
Tel: 01452 559121 **Fax:** 01452 530908
Email: sales@inspired-bathrooms.co.uk
Web: www.inspired-bathrooms.co.uk ⌁
Product Type: 1, 2, 3

JACUZZI UK
Silverdale Road, Newcastle Under Lyme,
Staffordshire, ST5 6EL
Area of Operation: UK & Ireland
Tel: 01782 717175
Fax: 01782 717166
Email: jacuzzisalesdesk@jacuzziuk.com
Web: www.jacuzzi.co.uk
Product Type: 1, 2, 4

INTERIORS, FIXTURES & FINISHES - **Bathrooms** - Bathroom Furniture
SPONSORED BY: MOVE OR IMPROVE MAGAZINE www.moveorimprove.co.uk

INTERIORS, FIXTURES & FINISHES

JOHN LEWIS OF HUNGERFORD
Grove Technology Park, Downsview Road,
Wantage, Oxfordshire, OX12 9FA
Area of Operation: UK (Excluding Ireland)
Tel: 01235 774300 **Fax:** 01235 769031
Email: park.street@john-lewis.co.uk
Web: www.john-lewis.co.uk

JUST ADD WATER
202 - 228 York Way , Kings Cross, London, N7 9AZ
Area of Operation: UK (Excluding Ireland)
Tel: 0207 697 3161 **Fax:** 0207 697 3162
Email: kingscoss.sales@justaddwater.co.uk
Web: www.justaddwater.co.uk

KENSINGTON STUDIO
13 c & d Kensington Road, Earlsdon,
Coventry, West Midlands, CV5 6GG
Area of Operation: UK (Excluding Ireland)
Tel: 02476 713326
Fax: 02476 713136
Email: sales@kensingtonstudio.com
Web: www.kensingtonstudio.com
Product Type: 1, 2, 3, 4

KERAMAG WAVENEY LTD
London Road, Beccles, Suffolk, NR34 8TS
Area of Operation: UK & Ireland
Tel: 01502 716600 **Fax:** 01502 717767
Email: info@keramagwaveney.co.uk
Web: www.keramag.com **Product Type:** 1, 2, 3, 4

KEUCO (UK)
2 Claridge Court, Lower Kings Road,
Berkhamsted, Hertfordshire, HP42AF
Area of Operation: Worldwide
Tel: 01442 865220 **Fax:** 01442 865260
Email: klaus@keuco.co.uk **Web:** www.keuco.de
Product Type: 1, 2 **Material Type:** H) 1, 2, 5

KOHLER MIRA LIMITED
Barnett Way, Barnwood, Gloucester,
Gloucestershire, GL4 3RT
Area of Operation: UK & Ireland
Tel: 0870 850 5151 **Fax:** 0870 850 5552
Email: info@kohleruk.com
Web: www.kohleruk.com

LECICO PLC
Unit 47a Hobbs Industrial Estate,
Newchapel, Nr Lingfield, Surrey, RH7 6HN
Area of Operation: UK & Ireland
Tel: 01342 834777 **Fax:** 01342 834783
Email: info@lecico.co.uk
Web: www.lecico.co.uk **Product Type:** 1

LONGMEAD GROUP PLC
Millwey Industrial Estate, Axminster, Devon, EX13 5HU
Area of Operation: Europe
Tel: 01297 32578 **Fax:** 01297 32710
Email: info@longmead-group.co.uk
Web: www.longmead-group.co.uk
Product Type: 1, 2, 3, 4

M & O BATHROOM CENTRE
174-176 Goswell Road,
Clarkenwell, London, EC1V 7DT
Area of Operation: East England, Greater London,
South East England
Tel: 0207 608 0111 **Fax:** 0207 490 3083
Email: mando@lineone.net **Product Type:** 1, 2, 3

MEKON PRODUCTS
25 Bessemer Park,
Milkwood Road, London, SE24 0HG
Area of Operation: UK (Excluding Ireland)
Tel: 0207 733 8011 **Fax:** 0207 737 0840
Web: www.mekon.net **Product Type:** 1, 2, 3

MEREWAY CONTRACTS
Unit 1 Wharfdale Road, Tysely,
Birmingham, West Midlands, B11 2DE
Area of Operation: UK (Excluding Ireland)
Tel: 0121 764 7180
Fax: 0121 764 7199
Email: info@merewaycontracts.co.uk
Web: www.merewaycontracts.co.uk

MILLER FROM SWEDEN
Unit 18 Thorne Park Business Centre,
Wenman Road, Thame, Oxfordshire, OX9 3XA
Area of Operation: Worldwide
Tel: 01844 264800
Fax: 01844 261134
Email: sales@millerbathrooms.co.uk
Web: www.millerbathrooms.co.uk
Product Type: 1, 2, 3, 4
Other Info: ECO **Material Type:** A) 2, 9

MOODS BATHROOMS
PJH Group, Alder House, Kearsley,
Bolton, Lancashire, BL4 8SL
Area of Operation: UK & Ireland
Tel: 01204 707070 **Fax:** 01204 573140
Email: info@pjh.co.uk
Web: ww.bathroom-moods.com
Product Type: 1, 2, 3

MWD
Clutton Hill Estate, King Lane,
Clutton Hill, Bristol, BS39 5QQ
Area of Operation: Midlands & Mid Wales, South
West England and South Wales
Tel: 0870 033 2288
Fax: 0800 197 6593
Email: sales@mwdretail.co.uk
Web: www.mikewalker.com

NICHOLAS ANTHONY LTD
42-44 Wigmore Street, London, W1U 2RX
Area of Operation: East England, Greater London,
South East England
Tel: 0800 068 3603 **Fax:** 01206 762698
Email: info@nicholas-anthony.co.uk
Web: www.nicholas-anthony.co.uk
Product Type: 1, 2, 3

NO CODE
Larkwhistle Farm Road,
Micheldever, Hampshire, SO21 3BG
Area of Operation: UK & Ireland
Tel: 01962 870078 **Fax:** 01962 870077
Email: sales@nocode.co.uk
Web: www.nocode.co.uk **Product Type:** 1, 2, 3

PANELS PLUS
22-24 Mill Place,
Kingston Upon Thames, Surrey, KT1 2RJ
Area of Operation: Greater London
Tel: 0208 399 6343
Fax: 0208 399 6343
Email: sales@panelspluslttd.com
Web: www.panelspluslttd.com
Product Type: 1, 2

PARLOUR FARM
Unit 12b, Wilkinson Road, Love Lane Industrial
Estate, Cirencester, Gloucestershire, GL7 1YT
Area of Operation: Europe
Tel: 01285 885336 **Fax:** 01285 643189
Email: info@parlourfarm.com
Web: www.parlourfarm.com

PRETTY SWIFT LTD
Units 7&8, 51 Chancery Lane,
Debenham, Suffolk, IP14 6PJ
Area of Operation: UK (Excluding Ireland)
Tel: 01728 861818 **Fax:** 01728 861919
Email: prettyswiftltd@yahoo.co.uk

R&D MARKETING (DEMISTA) LTD
Land House, Anyards Road,
Cobham, Surrey, KT11 2LW
Area of Operation: Worldwide
Tel: 01932 866600 **Fax:** 01932 866 688
Email: rd@demista.co.uk
Web: www.demista.co.uk **Product Type:** 2

RICHARD BAKER FURNITURE LTD
Wimbledon Studios, 257 Burlington Road,
New Malden, Surrey, KT3 4NE
Area of Operation: Europe
Tel: 0208 336 1777 **Fax:** 0208 336 1666
Email: richard@richardbakerfurniture.co.uk
Web: www.richardbakerfurniture.co.uk
Product Type: 1, 2

ROSCO COLLECTIONS
Stone Allerton, Axbridge, Somerset, BS26 2NS
Area of Operation: UK & Ireland
Tel: 01934 712299 **Fax:** 01934 713222
Email: jonathan@roscobathrooms.demon.co.uk
Product Type: 1, 2, 3

SAMUEL HEATH
Leopold Street, Birmingham, B12 0UJ
Area of Operation: Worldwide
Tel: 0121 772 2303 **Fax:** 0121 772 3334
Email: info@samuel-heath.com
Web: www.samuel-heath.com **Product Type:** 4

SHIRES
Uttoxeter Road, Longton,
Stoke-on-Trent, Staffordshire, ST3 1NA
Area of Operation: UK & Ireland
Tel: 01782 599099 **Fax:** 01782 599295
Email: hkiddle@qualceram-shires.com
Web: www.shires-bathrooms.com
Product Type: 2

SIMON TAYLOR FURNITURE LIMITED
Cane End Lane, Bierton, Aylesbury,
Buckinghamshire, HP22 5BH
Area of Operation: UK & Ireland
Tel: 01296 488207 **Fax:** 01296 398722
Email: information@simon-taylor.co.uk
Web: www.simon-taylor.co.uk
Product Type: 1, 2, 4 **Other Info:** ✎ 👆

SMART SHOWERS LTD
Unit 11, Woodside Road, South Marston Business
Park, Swindon, Wiltshire, SN3 4WA
Area of Operation: UK & Ireland
Tel: 01793 822775 **Fax:** 01793 823800
Email: enquiries@smartsshowers.co.uk
Web: www.smartsshowers.co.uk
Product Type: 1, 2

SOGA LTD
41 Mayfield Street, Hull,
East Riding of Yorks, HU3 1NT
Area of Operation: Worldwide
Tel: 01482 327025 **Email:** info@soga.co.uk
Web: www.soga.co.uk **Product Type:** 1, 3

STIFFKEY BATHROOMS
89 Upper Saint Giles Street, Norwich, Norfolk, NR2 1AB
Area of Operation: Worldwide
Tel: 01603 627850 **Fax:** 01603 619775
Email: stiffkeybathrooms.norwich@virgin.net
Web: www.stiffkeybathrooms.com **Product Type:** 3

SVEDBERGS
4E Wilsons Park, Monsall Road,
Newton Heath, Manchester, M40 8WN
Area of Operation: UK & Ireland
Tel: 0161 2051200 **Fax:** 0161 251212
Email: info@svedbergs.co.uk
Web: www.svedbergs.co.uk
Product Type: 1, 2, 3, 4 **Material Type:** A) 1, 2, 9

TAB UK LIMITED
Brewery Lane, Felling,
Gateshead, Tyne & Wear, NE10 0EY
Area of Operation: UK & Ireland
Tel: 0191 4695500 **Fax:** 0191 4695828
Email: sales@tab-uk.com
Web: www.tab-uk.co.uk
Product Type: 1, 2 **Material Type:** D) 5

TAPS SHOP
1 Tristram Road, Ducklington,
Whitney, Oxfordshire, OX29 7XH
Area of Operation: Worldwide
Tel: 0845 4303035 **Fax:** 01993 779653
Email: info@tapsshop.co.uk
Web: www.tapsshop.co.uk **Product Type:** 2, 3

TBS FABRICATIONS
Martens Road, Northbank Industrial Park, Irlam,
Manchester, Greater Manchester, M44 5AX.
Area of Operation: UK & Ireland
Tel: 0161 775 1871 **Fax:** 0161 775 8929.
Email: info@tbs-fabrications.co.uk
Web: www.tbs-fabrications.co.uk
Product Type: 1, 2

THE KITCHEN AND BATHROOM COLLECTION
Nelson House, Nelson Road,
Salisbury, Wiltshire, SP1 3LT
Area of Operation: South West England and South Wales
Tel: 01722 334800 **Fax:** 01722 412252
Email: info@kbc.co.uk **Web:** www.kbc.co.uk
Product Type: 1, 2, 3 **Other Info:** ✎

THE WATER MONOPOLY
16/18 Lonsdale Road, London, NW6 6RD
Area of Operation: UK (Excluding Ireland)
Tel: 0207 624 2636 **Fax:** 0207 624 2631
Email: enquiries@watermonopoly.com
Web: www.watermonopoly.com

THOMAS CRAPPER & CO. LTD
The Stable Yard, Alscot Park,
Stratford-on-Avon, Warwickshire, CV37 8BL
Area of Operation: Worldwide
Tel: 01789 450522 **Fax:** 01789 450523
Email: wc@thomas-crapper.com
Web: www.thomas-crapper.com
Product Type: 2, 3

TIMELESS BATHROOMS LTD
394 Ringwood Road, Ferndown, Dorset, BH22 9AU
Area of Operation: South East England
Tel: 01202 897110 **Fax:** 01202 892252
Email: bathroom@options394.fsnet.co.uk
Web: www.timelessbathrooms.co.uk
Product Type: 1, 2, 3, 4

TOUCHSTONE - MARBLE SURFACES
Touchstone House, 82 High Street,
Measham, Derbyshire, DE12 7JB
Area of Operation: UK (Excluding Ireland)
Tel: 0845 130 1862
Fax: 01530 274271
Email: sales@touchstone-uk.com
Web: www.touchstone-uk.com

TRADEMARK TILES
Tile Store, Somersham Road, St Ives,
Huntingdon, Cambridgeshire, PE27 3WR
Area of Operation: UK (Excluding Ireland)
Tel: 01480 498123
Email: info@tilestoreplus.co.uk
Web: www.tilestoreplus.co.uk
Product Type: 1, 2, 3

TURNER FURNITURE
The Old Dairy, Manor Farm,
Sipilly Handley, Salisbury, SP5 5NU
Area of Operation: Greater London, South East
England, South West England and South Wales
Tel: 01725 516990
Fax: 01725 516991
Email: nick@turner-furniture.co.uk
Web: www.turner-furniture.co.uk
Product Type: 1, 2, 3 **Other Info:** ✎

UK BATHROOM INTERIORS
Units 3-4, The Old Laundry,
Fishergreen, Ripon, North Yorkshire, HG4 1NL
Area of Operation: UK (Excluding Ireland)
Tel: 01765 608822 **Fax:** 01765 608892
Email: mark@ukbathroominteriors.com
Web: www.ukbathroominteriors.com
Product Type: 1, 2, 3

VICTORIAN BATHROOMS
Ings Mill Complex, Dale Street,
Ossett , West Yorkshire, WF5 9HQ
Area of Operation: UK (Excluding Ireland)
Tel: 01924 267736
Fax: 01924 261232
Email: sales@vb-bathrooms.com
Web: www.vb-bathrooms.com
Product Type: 1, 2, 3

WALTON BATHROOMS
The Hersham Centre, The Green, Molesey Road,
Hersham, Walton on Thames, Surrey, KT12 4HL
Area of Operation: UK (Excluding Ireland)
Tel: 01932 224784 **Fax:** 01932 253447
Email: sales@waltonbathrooms.co.uk
Web: www.waltonbathrooms.co.uk
Product Type: 2

WATTS & WRIGHT (THE JOINERY SHOP)
Watts & Wright, PO Box 4251,
Walsall, West Midlands, WS5 3WY
Area of Operation: Worldwide
Tel: 01922 610800 / 020 70437619
Fax: 0870 7626387
Email: sales@wattsandwright.com
Web: www.wattsandwright.com **Product Type:** 1, 2

WICKES
Wickes House, 120-138 Station Road,
Harrow, Middlesex, HA1 2QB
Area of Operation: UK (Excluding Ireland)
Tel: 0870 608 9001 **Fax:** 0208 863 6225
Web: www.wickes.co.uk

WILLIAM GARVEY
Leyhill, Payhembury, Honiton, Devon, EX14 3JG
Area of Operation: Worldwide
Tel: 01404 841430 **Fax:** 01404 841626
Email: webquery@williamgarvey.co.uk
Web: www.williamgarvey.co.uk
Product Type: 1, 2, 3, 4 **Other Info:** ✍ ✋

BATHROOM ACCESSORIES

KEY
PRODUCT TYPES: 1= Mirrors 2 = Heated
Mirrors 3 = Containers and Organisers
4 = Shelving 5 = Toilet Seats 6 = Other

OTHER: ▽ Reclaimed ᵔ On-line shopping
✍ Bespoke ✋ Hand-made ECO Ecological

A & H BRASS
201-203 Edgware Road, London, W2 1ES
Area of Operation: Worldwide
Tel: 0207 402 1854 **Fax:** 0207 402 0110
Email: ahbrass@btinternet.com
Web: www.aandhbrass.co.uk ᵔ
Product Type: 1, 4, 5 **Material Type:** C) 14, 16

ALEXANDER INTERIORS
Head Office, 10 Woodberry Avenue, Harrow, HA2 6AU
Area of Operation: UK & Ireland
Tel: 07980 191825 **Fax:** 0208 933 1127
Email: juliana.alexander@talk21.com
Web: www.alexanderinteriors.co.uk

ALEXANDERS
Unit 3, 1/1A Spilsby Road,
Harold Hill, Romford, Essex, RM3 8SB
Area of Operation: UK & Ireland
Tel: 01708 384574 **Fax:** 01708 384089
Email: sales@alexanders-uk.net
Web: www.alexanders-uk.net
Product Type: 1, 3, 4, 5, 6

ALTHEA UK LTD
Concept House, Blanche Street,
Bradford, West Yorkshire, BD4 8DA
Area of Operation: UK (Excluding Ireland)
Tel: 01274 660770 **Fax:** 01274 667929
Email: sales@altheauk.com
Web: www.periodbathrooms.co.uk

AMBIANCE BAIN
Cumberland House,
80 Scrubs Lane, London, NW10 6RF
Area of Operation: UK & Ireland
Tel: 0870 902 1313 **Fax:** 0870 902 1312
Email: sghirardello@mimea.com
Web: www.ambiancebain.com
Product Type: 1, 3, 4

ANTIQUE BATHS OF IVYBRIDGE LTD
Emebridge Works, Ermington Road,
Ivybridge, Devon, PL21 9DE
Area of Operation: UK (Excluding Ireland)
Tel: 01752 698250 **Fax:** 01752 698266
Email: sales@antiquebaths.com
Web: www.antiquebaths.com ᵔ
Product Type: 1, 3, 5, 6

AQUACREST UK LTD
Haven Light Industrial Estate, Gilbey Road,
Grimsby, Lincolnshire, DN31 2SJ
Area of Operation: UK & Ireland
Tel: 01472 241233 **Fax:** 01472 241233
Email: aquatop@aquatop.co.uk
Web: www.aquatop.co.uk **Product Type:** 6

ARCHITECTURAL COMPONENTS LTD
4-8 Exhibition Road,
South Kensington, London, SW7 2HF
Area of Operation: Worldwide
Tel: 0207 581 2401
Fax: 0207 589 4928
Email: sales@knobs.co.uk
Web: www.doorhandles.co.uk ᵔ **Product Type:** 6
Material Type: C) 3, 5, 11, 12, 14, 16, 17

ARCHITECTURAL IRONMONGERY LTD
28 Kyrle Street, Ross-on-Wye, Herefordshire, HR9 7DB
Area of Operation: Worldwide
Tel: 01989 567946 **Fax:** 01989 567946
Email: info@arciron.com
Web: www.arciron.com ᵔ **Product Type:** 6

ASHLEY BATHROOMS
Duffield Road Industrial Estate,
Little Eaton, Derby, Derbyshire, DE21 5DR
Area of Operation: UK & Ireland
Tel: 01332 830404 **Fax:** 01332 830202
Email: info@ashleybathrooms.co.uk
Web: www.ashleybathrooms.com
Product Type: 1, 4, 5

AVANTE BATHROOMS
Thistle House, Thistle Way,
Gildersome Spur, Wakefield Road,
Morley, Leeds, West Yorkshire, LS27 7JZ
Area of Operation: UK (Excluding Ireland)
Tel: 0113 201 2240
Fax: 0113 253 0717
Email: info@avantebathrooms.com
Web: www.avantebathrooms.com ᵔ
Product Type: 1, 3, 4, 6

B ROURKE & CO LTD
Vulcan Works, Accrington Road,
Burnley, Lancashire, BB11 5QD
Area of Operation: Worldwide
Tel: 01282 422841 **Fax:** 01282 458901
Email: info@rourkes.co.uk
Web: www.rourkes.co.uk
Product Type: 1, 4, 6 **Material Type:** C) 2

BARRHEAD SANITARYWARE PLC
15-17 Nasmyth Road, Hillington Industrial Estate,
Hillington, Glasgow, Renfrewshire, G52 4RG
Area of Operation: UK & Ireland
Tel: 0141 883 0066 **Fax:** 0141 883 0077
Email: sales@barrhead.co.uk **Product Type:** 5

BATHROOM CITY
Seeleys Road, Tyseley Industrial Estate,
Birmingham, West Midlands, B11 2LQ
Area of Operation: UK & Ireland
Tel: 0121 753 0700 **Fax:** 0121 753 1110
Email: sales@bathroomcity.com
Web: www.bathroomcity.com ᵔ
Product Type: 1, 5, 6

BATHROOM EXPRESS
61-62 Lower Dock Street,
Kingsway, Newport, NP20 1EF
Area of Operation: UK & Ireland
Tel: 0845 130 2000 **Fax:** 01633 244881
Email: sales@bathroomexpress.co.uk
Web: www.bathroomexpress.co.uk ᵔ
Product Type: 1, 3, 4, 5, 6

BATHROOM MANUFACTURERS ASSOCIATION
Federation House, Station Road,
Stoke on Trent, Staffordshire, ST4 2RT
Area of Operation: UK & Ireland
Tel: 01782 747123
Fax: 01782 747161
Email: info@bathroom-association.org.uk
Web: www.bathroom-association.org.uk
Product Type: 1, 2, 3, 4, 5

BATHROOMS PLUS LTD
222 Malmesbury Park Road,
Bournemouth, Dorset, BH8 8PR
Area of Operation: South West England and South Wales
Tel: 01202 294417 **Fax:** 01202 316425
Email: sales@bathrooms-plus.co.uk
Web: www.bathrooms-plus.co.uk
Product Type: 1, 2, 5

BETTER LIVING PRODUCTS UK LTD
14 Riverside Business Park,
Stansted, Essex, CM24 8PL
Tel: 01279 812958 **Fax:** 01279 817771
Email: info@dispenser.co.uk
Web: www.dispenser.co.uk ᵔ
Product Type: 1, 3, 4, 6 **Material Type:** C) 3

BOUNDARY BATHROOMS
Ainsworth & Dent House, Regent Street,
Colne, Lancashire, BB8 8LD
Area of Operation: UK & Ireland
Tel: 01282 862509 **Fax:** 01282 871192
Email: sales@boundarybathrooms.co.uk
Product Type: 1, 3

BRISTAN
Birch Coppice Business Park, Dordon,
Tamworth, Staffordshire, B78 1SG
Area of Operation: Worldwide
Tel: 08704 425556 **Fax:** 0808 1611 002
Email: enquiries@bristan.com
Web: www.bristan.com
Product Type: 3, 4, 6 **Material Type:** C) 11, 14

CAPITAL MARBLE DESIGN
Unit 1 Pall Mall Deposit,
124-128 Barlby Road, London, W10 6BL
Area of Operation: UK & Ireland
Tel: 0208 968 5340 **Fax:** 0208 968 8827
Email: stonegallery@capitalmarble.co.uk
Web: www.capitalmarble.co.uk **Product Type:** 1

CARLISLE BRASS
Park House Road, Carlisle, Cumbria, CA3 0JU
Area of Operation: UK & Ireland
Tel: 01228 511770 **Fax:** 01228 815306
Email: enquiries@carlislebrass.com
Web: www.carlislebrass.com

CHADDER & CO.
Blenheim Studio, London Road,
Forest Row, East Sussex, RH18 5EZ
Area of Operation: Worldwide
Tel: 01342 823243 **Fax:** 01342 823097
Web: www.chadder.com

CHARLES MASON LTD
Unit 11A Brook Street Mill, Off Goodall Street,
Macclesfield, Cheshire, SK11 7AW
Area of Operation: Worldwide
Tel: 0800 085 3616 **Fax:** 01625 668789
Email: info@charles-mason.com
Web: www.charles-mason.com ᵔ
Product Type: 3, 4, 6 **Material Type:** C) 2, 3, 13, 14

CHROMA INTERNATIONAL GLASS LTD
Unit 200 Bridgwater Business Park,
Bridgwater, Somerset, TA6 4TB
Area of Operation: Europe
Tel: 01278 426226 **Fax:** 01278 450088
Email: info@chroma-glass.com
Web: www.chroma-glass.com
Product Type: 1, 4, 6 **Material Type:** J) 4, 5, 6

CITY BATHROOMS & KITCHENS
158 Longford Road, Longford,
Coventry, West Midlands, CV6 6DR
Tel: 02476 365877 **Fax:** 02476 644992
Email: citybathrooms@hotmail.com
Web: www.citybathrooms.co.uk

COLOURWASH LTD
165 Chamberlayne Road, London, NW10 3NU
Area of Operation: UK & Ireland
Tel: 0208 830 2992 **Fax:** 0208 830 2317
Email: sales@colourwash.co.uk
Web: www.colourwash.co.uk
Product Type: 1, 2, 3, 4, 5, 6

COSY ROOMS (THE-BATHROOM-SHOP.CO.UK)
17 Chiltern Way, North Hykeham,
Lincoln, Lincolnshire, LN6 9SY
Area of Operation: UK (Excluding Ireland)
Tel: 01522 696002
Fax: 01522 696002
Email: keith@cosy-rooms.com
Web: www.the-bathroom-shop.co.uk ᵔ
Product Type: 3, 4, 5, 6

CROSSWATER
Unit 5 Butterly Avenue, Questor,
Dartford, Kent, DA1 1JG
Area of Operation: UK & Ireland
Tel: 01322 628270 **Fax:** 01322 628280
Email: sales@crosswater.co.uk
Web: www.crosswater.co.uk
Product Type: 1, 3, 4

CYMRU KITCHENS
63 Caerleon Road, Newport, NP19 7BX
Area of Operation: UK (Excluding Ireland)
Tel: 01633 676767 **Fax:** 01633 212512
Email: sales@cymrukitchens.com
Web: www.cymrukitchens.com

DANICO BRASS LTD
31-35 Winchester Road,
Swiss Cottage, London, NW3 3NR
Area of Operation: Worldwide
Tel: 0207 483 4477
Fax: 0207 722 7992
Email: sales@danico.co.uk
Product Type: 1, 3, 4

DART VALLEY SYSTEMS LIMITED
Kemmings Close, Long Road,
Paignton, Devon, TQ4 7TW
Area of Operation: UK & Ireland
Tel: 01803 529021 **Fax:** 01803 559016
Email: sales@dartvalley.co.uk
Web: www.dartvalley.co.uk
Product Type: 6

DECORLUX LTD
18 Ghyll Industrial Estate, Ghyll Road,
Heathfield, East Sussex, TN21 8AW
Area of Operation: UK (Excluding Ireland)
Tel: 01435 866638 **Fax:** 01435 866641
Email: info@decorlux.co.uk
Web: www.decorlux.co.uk
Product Type: 1, 3, 4

DECORMASTER LTD
Unit 16, Waterside Industrial Estate,
Wolverhampton, West Midlands, WV2 2RH
Area of Operation: Worldwide
Tel: 01902 406030 **Fax:** 01902 353126
Email: sales@oldcolours.co.uk
Web: www.oldcolours.co.uk **Product Type:** 5

DISCONTINUED BATHROOMS
140-142 Pogmoor Road, Pogmoor,
Barnsley, North Yorkshire, S75 2DX
Area of Operation: UK (Excluding Ireland)
Tel: 01226 280200
Fax: 01226 733273
Email: sales@discontinuedbathrooms.co.uk
Web: www.discontinuedbathrooms.co.uk
Product Type: 1, 2, 3, 4, 5, 6

EMCO
Centre Point Distribution Ltd , Unit A5 Regent Park,
Booth Drive, Park Farm Industrial Estate,
Wellingborough, Northamptonshire, NN8 6GR
Area of Operation: UK & Ireland
Tel: 01933 403786 **Fax:** 01933 403789
Email: k.pedrick@mailcity.com
Web: www.emco-bath.com
Product Type: 1, 2, 3, 4, 6 **Material Type:** C) 11

ENERFOIL MAGNUM LTD
Kenmore Road, Comrie Bridge,
Kenmore, Aberfeldy, Perthshire, PH15 2LS
Area of Operation: Europe
Tel: 01887 822999 **Fax:** 01887 822954
Email: sales@enerfoil.com
Web: www.enerfoil.com ᵔ **Product Type:** 2

INTERIORS, FIXTURES & FINISHES - Bathrooms - Bathroom Accessories
SPONSORED BY: MOVE OR IMPROVE MAGAZINE www.moveorimprove.co.uk

INTERIORS, FIXTURES & FINISHES

EUROBATH INTERNATIONAL LIMITED
Eurobath House, Wedmore Road,
Cheddar, Somerset, BS27 3EB
Area of Operation: Worldwide
Tel: 01934 744466 **Fax:** 01934744345
Email: sales@eurobath.co.uk
Web: www.eurobath.co.uk/www.ilbagno.co.uk
Product Type: 1, 3, 4

FIRED EARTH
3 Twyford Mill, Oxford Road, Adderbury,
Banbury, Oxfordshire, OX17 3SX
Area of Operation: Worldwide
Tel: 01295 812088 **Fax:** 01295 810832
Email: enquiries@firedearth.com
Web: www.firedearth.com

GO FIX IT LTD
Unit 10 Castle Industrial Estate, Louvain Street, Off
Oldham Road, Failsworth, Manchester, M35 0HB
Area of Operation: UK (Excluding Ireland)
Tel: 0161 681 4109 **Fax:** 0161 681 8169
Email: admin@gofixit.co.uk
Web: www.gofixit.co.uk **Product Type:** 5, 6

HAF DESIGNS LTD
HAF House, Mead Lane,
Hertford, Hertfordshire, SG13 7AP
Area of Operation: UK & Ireland
Tel: 0800 389 8821 **Fax:** 01992 505705
Email: info@hafltd.co.uk
Web: www.hafdesigns.co.uk **Product Type:** 3, 4

HANSGROHE
Units D1 and D2, Sandown Park Trading Estate,
Royal Mills, Esher, Surrey, KT10 8BL
Area of Operation: Worldwide
Tel: 0870 770 1972 **Fax:** 0870 770 1973
Email: sales@hansgrohe.co.uk
Web: www.hansgrohe.co.uk
Product Type: 1, 3, 4, 6 **Material Type:** C) 2, 3, 11, 14

HARBRINE LTD
27-31 Payne Road, London, E3 2SP
Area of Operation: Worldwide
Tel: 0208 980 8000 **Fax:** 0208 980 6050
Email: info@harbrine.co.uk
Web: www.harbrine.co.uk

HARO SANITARY
(PART OF THE HAMBERGER GROUP)
PJH Group - Distributor, Alder House, Slackey Brow,
Kearsley, Bolton, Lancashire, BL4 8SL
Area of Operation: UK (Excluding Ireland)
Tel: 01204 707070 **Fax:** 01204 573140
Email: info@pjh.co.uk
Web: www.haro-sanitary.com **Product Type:** 5

HERITAGE BATHROOMS
Princess Street, Bedminster, Bristol, BS3 4AG
Area of Operation: UK & Ireland
Tel: 0117 963 3333
Email: marketing@heritagebathrooms.com
Web: www.heritagebathrooms.com
Product Type: 1, 2, 3, 4, 5

HIB LTD
Castle House, 21-23 Station Road,
New Barnet, Herefordshire, EN5 1PH
Tel: 0208 441 0352 **Fax:** 0208 441 0219
Email: sales@hib.co.uk
Web: www.hib.co.uk **Product Type:** 1, 3, 6

HICKS SHARP & CO.
Grange Close, Milton Ernest,
Bedfordshire, MK44 1RR
Tel: 01234 822843 **Fax:** 01234 822843
Email: tom@hickssharp.freeserve.co.uk
Web: www.perioddoorfurniture.com
Product Type: 6

HOMESTYLE BATHROOMS
Unit 21 Hainault Works, Hainault Road,
Little Heath, Romford, Essex, RM6 5SS
Area of Operation: UK (Excluding Ireland)
Tel: 0208 599 8080 **Fax:** 0208 599 7070
Email: sales@homestyle-bathrooms.co.uk
Web: www.homestyle-bathrooms.co.uk
Product Type: 1, 3, 4, 5, 6

HUDSON REED
Rylands Street, Burnley, Lancashire, BB10 1RG
Area of Operation: Worldwide
Tel: 01282 418000 **Fax:** 01282 428915
Email: info@ultra-group.co.uk
Web: www.hudsonreed.info
Product Type: 1, 3, 6 **Material Type:** A) 15

IDEAL STANDARD
The Bathroom Works, National Avenue,
Kingston Upon Hull, East Riding of Yorks, HU5 4HS
Area of Operation: Worldwide
Tel: 0800 590311 **Fax:** 01482 445886
Email: ideal-standard@aseur.com
Web: www.ideal-standard.co.uk

INSPIRED BATHROOMS
Unit R4, Innsworth Technology Park, Innsworth Lane,
Gloucester, Gloucestershire, GL3 1DL
Area of Operation: UK & Ireland
Tel: 01452 559121 **Fax:** 01452 530908
Email: sales@inspired-bathrooms.co.uk
Web: www.inspired-bathrooms.co.uk
Product Type: 1, 2, 3, 4, 5

ION GLASS
PO Box 284, Burgess Hill, West Sussex, RH15 0BN
Area of Operation: UK (Excluding Ireland)
Tel: 0845 658 9988 **Fax:** 0845 658 9989
Email: sales@ionglass.co.uk
Web: www.ionglass.co.uk

ITFITZ
11-12 Woodlands Farm, Spring Lane,
Cookham Dean, Berkshire, SL6 9PN
Area of Operation: UK (Excluding Ireland)
Tel: 01628 890432 **Fax:** 0870 133 7955
Email: sales@itfitz.co.uk
Web: www.itfitz.co.uk **Product Type:** 1, 6

JACUZZI UK
Silverdale Road, Newcastle Under Lyme,
Staffordshire, ST5 6EL
Area of Operation: UK & Ireland
Tel: 01782 717175 **Fax:** 01782 717166
Email: jacuzzisalesdesk@jacuzziuk.com
Web: www.jacuzzi.co.uk **Product Type:** 1, 4, 5, 6

JACUZZI UK - BC SANITAN
Silverdale Road, Newcastle Under Lyme,
Staffordshire, ST5 6EL
Area of Operation: UK & Ireland
Tel: 01782 717175 **Fax:** 01782 717166
Email: jacuzzisalesdesk@jacuzziuk.com
Web: www.jacuzziuk.com **Product Type:** 1, 4, 5, 6

JOHN LEWIS OF HUNGERFORD
Grove Technology Park, Downsview Road,
Wantage, Oxfordshire, OX12 9FA
Area of Operation: UK (Excluding Ireland)
Tel: 01235 774300 **Fax:** 01235 769031
Email: park.street@john-lewis.co.uk
Web: www.john-lewis.co.uk

JUST ADD WATER
202 - 228 York Way, Kings Cross, London, N7 9AZ
Area of Operation: UK (Excluding Ireland)
Tel: 0207 697 3161 **Fax:** 0207 697 3162
Email: kingscross.sales@justaddwater.co.uk
Web: www.justaddwater.co.uk

KENSINGTON STUDIO
13 c & d Kensington Road, Earlsdon,
Coventry, West Midlands, CV5 6GG
Area of Operation: UK (Excluding Ireland)
Tel: 02476 713326 **Fax:** 02476 713136
Email: sales@kensingtonstudio.com
Web: www.kensingtonstudio.com
Product Type: 1, 2, 3, 4, 5, 6

KEUCO (UK)
2 Claridge Court, Lower Kings Road,
Berkhamsted, Hertfordshire, HP42AF
Area of Operation: Worldwide
Tel: 01442 865220 **Fax:** 01442 865260
Email: klaus@keuco.co.uk
Web: www.keuco.de **Product Type:** 1, 3, 4, 6
Material Type: C) 1, 3, 11, 14, 16

KOHLER MIRA LIMITED
Barnett Way, Barnwood,
Gloucester, Gloucestershire, GL4 3RT
Area of Operation: UK & Ireland
Tel: 0870 850 5551 **Fax:** 0870 850 5552
Email: info@kohleruk.com **Web:** www.kohler.com

LECICO PLC
Unit 47a Hobbs Industrial Estate,
Newchapel, Nr Lingfield, Surrey, RH7 6HN
Area of Operation: UK & Ireland
Tel: 01342 834777 **Fax:** 01342 834783
Email: info@lecico.co.uk
Web: www.lecico.co.uk **Product Type:** 1, 3, 4, 5

LONGMEAD GROUP PLC
Millwey Industrial Estate,
Axminster, Devon, EX13 5HU
Area of Operation: Europe
Tel: 01297 32578 **Fax:** 01297 32710
Email: info@longmead-group.co.uk
Web: www.longmead-group.co.uk
Product Type: 1, 3, 4, 6

M & O BATHROOM CENTRE
174-176 Goswell Road,
Clarkenwell, London, EC1V 7DT
Area of Operation: East England, Greater London,
South East England
Tel: 0207 608 0111 **Fax:** 0207 490 3083
Email: mando@lineone.net
Product Type: 1, 2, 3, 4, 5

MEKON PRODUCTS
25 Bessemer Park,
Milkwood Road, London, SE24 0HG
Area of Operation: UK (Excluding Ireland)
Tel: 0207 733 8011 **Fax:** 0207 737 0840
Email: info@mekon.net **Web:** www.mekon.net

MEREWAY CONTRACTS
Unit 1 Wharfdale Road, Tysely,
Birmingham, West Midlands, B11 2DE
Area of Operation: UK (Excluding Ireland)
Tel: 0121 764 7180 **Fax:** 0121 764 7199
Email: info@merewaycontracts.co.uk
Web: www.merewaycontracts.co.uk

MILLER FROM SWEDEN
Unit 18 Thorne Park Business Centre,
Wenman Road, Thame, Oxfordshire, OX9 3XA
Area of Operation: Worldwide
Tel: 01844 264800 **Fax:** 01844 261134
Email: sales@millerbathrooms.co.uk
Web: www.millerbathrooms.co.uk
Product Type: 1, 3, 4, 5, 6 **Material Type:** A) 2, 9

MIRRORKOOL LTD
89 High Street, Earith, Cambridgeshire, PE28 3PN
Area of Operation: Worldwide
Tel: 01487 741300 **Fax:** 08712 367554
Email: sam@mirrorkool.com
Web: www.mirrorkool.com
Product Type: 1 **Other Info:**

**MISCELLANEA DISCONTINUED
BATHROOMWARE**
Churt Place Nurseries, Tilford Road,
Churt, Farnham, Surrey, GU10 2LN
Area of Operation: Worldwide
Tel: 01428 608164 **Fax:** 01428 608165
Email: email@brokenbog.com
Web: www.brokenbog.com **Product Type:** 5, 6

MISTER MIRRORS
Imperial House, Redlands, Coulsdon, Surrey, CR5 2HT
Area of Operation: UK & Ireland
Tel: 0208 668 7016 **Fax:** 0208 660 2384
Email: beourguest@clara.co.uk
Web: www.mister-mirrors.co.uk **Product Type:** 2

NICHOLAS ANTHONY LTD
42-44 Wigmore Street, London, W1U 2RX
Area of Operation: East England, Greater London,
South East England
Tel: 0800 068 3603 **Fax:** 01206 762698
Email: info@nicholas-anthony.co.uk
Web: www.nicholas-anthony.com
Product Type: 1, 3

NO CODE
Larkwhistle Farm Road,
Micheldever, Hampshire, SO21 3BG
Area of Operation: UK & Ireland
Tel: 01962 870078
Fax: 01962 870077
Email: sales@nocode.co.uk
Web: www.nocode.co.uk
Product Type: 1, 3, 4, 5

NORSKE INTERIORS
Estate Road One, South Humberside Industrial
Estate, Grimsby, Lincolnshire, DN31 2TA
Area of Operation: UK (Excluding Ireland)
Tel: 01472 240832
Fax: 01472 360112
Email: sales@norske-int.co.uk
Web: www.norske-int.co.uk **Product Type:** 6

OLD FASHIONED BATHROOMS LTD
Foresters Hall, 52 High Street, Debenham,
Stowmarket, Suffolk, IP14 6QW
Area of Operation: UK (Excluding Ireland)
Tel: 01728 860926
Fax: 01728 860446
Email: ofbshop@yahoo.co.uk
Web: www.oldfashionedbathrooms.co.uk
Product Type: 1, 5, 6
Other Info:
Material Type: A) 10

PARKSIDE TILES
49-51 Highmeres Road, Thurmeston,
Leicester, Leicestershire, LE4 9LZ
Area of Operation: UK (Excluding Ireland)
Tel: 0116 276 2532
Fax: 0116 246 0649
Email: info@parksidetiles.co.uk
Web: www.parksidetiles.co.uk
Product Type: 1

PEPLOW ROBERTS LIMITED
Unit 11 Eden Way, Pages Industrial Park,
Billington Road, Leighton Buzzard,
Bedfordshire, LU7 4TZ
Area of Operation: Worldwide
Tel: 01525 375118
Fax: 01525 852130
Email: info@paperstream.net
Web: www.paperstream.net
Product Type: 3, 6

POLYPIPE KITCHENS & BATHROOMS LTD
Warmsworth, Halt Industrial Estate, Doncaster,
South Yorkshire, DN4 9LS
Area of Operation: Worldwide
Tel: 01709 770990
Fax: 01302 310602
Email: davery@ppbp.com
Web: www.polypipe.com/bk
Product Type: 5

PRETTY SWIFT LTD
Units 7&8, 51 Chancery Lane,
Debenham, Suffolk, IP14 6PJ
Area of Operation: UK (Excluding Ireland)
Tel: 01728 861818
Fax: 01728 861919
Email: prettyswiftltd@yahoo.co.uk

QUALCERAM SHIRES PLC
South Quay, Arklow, Co. Wicklow
Area of Operation: UK & Ireland
Tel: 00353 402 31288
Fax: 00353 402 31292
Email: omoriarty@qualceram-shires.com
Web: www.qualceram-shires.com
Product Type: 1, 2, 3, 4, 5, 6

R&D MARKETING (DEMISTA) LTD
Land House, Anyards Road, Cobham, Surrey, KT11 2LW
Area of Operation: Worldwide
Tel: 01932 866600 **Fax:** 01932 866 688
Email: rd@demista.co.uk
Web: www.demista.co.uk **Product Type:** 2

R&D MARKETING (DEMISTA™) LTD
for steam free mirrors

Area of Operation: Worldwide
Tel: 01932 866600 **Fax:** 01932 866688
Email: rd@demista.co.uk
Web: www.demista.co.uk
Product Type: 2

Eliminate condensation from your mirrors forever with the **Original** *Demista™* heated mirror pads as specified and fitted by hotels and developments worldwide.

• Low Cost • Simple To Fit • Maintenance Free
• International Approvals • Many Sizes
• Saves on cleaning materials and time

REGINOX UK LTD
Radnor Park Trading Estate,
Congleton, Cheshire, CW12 4XJ
Area of Operation: UK & Ireland
Tel: 01260 280033 **Fax:** 01260 298889
Email: sales@reginoxuk.co.uk
Web: www.reginox.com 🔆 **Product Type:** 6

ROSCO COLLECTIONS
Stone Allerton, Axbridge, Somerset, BS26 2NS
Area of Operation: UK & Ireland
Tel: 01934 712299 **Fax:** 01934 713222
Email: jonathan@roscobathrooms.demon.co.uk
Product Type: 1, 2, 3, 4, 5

SAMUEL HEATH
Leopold Street, Birmingham,
West Midlands, B12 0UJ
Area of Operation: Worldwide
Tel: 0121 772 2303 **Fax:** 0121 772 3334
Email: info@samuel-heath.com
Web: www.samuel-heath.com **Product Type:** 1, 3, 4, 6
Material Type: C) 11, 13, 14, 16

SATANA INTERNATIONAL LTD
Unit E Winford Rural Workshops,
Higher Halstock Leigh, Yeovil, Somerset, BA22 9QX
Area of Operation: Worldwide
Tel: 01935 891888 **Fax:** 01935 891819
Email: satanaltd@aol.com
Web: www.heatedmirrors.co.uk 🔆 **Product Type:** 2

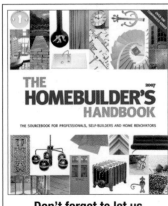

SATANA INTERNATIONAL LTD

Area of Operation: UK, Ireland & International
Tel: 01935 891888
Fax: 01935 891819
Email: satanaltd@aol.com
Web: www.heatedmirrors.co.uk 🔆
Product Type: 2

Steam-Free Mirrors assure a crystal clear view...however hot and steamy your bathroom gets! In addition to our standard range we also make exclusive bespoke mirrors.

SHIRES
Uttoxeter Road, Longton,
Stoke-on-Trent, Staffordshire, ST3 1NA
Area of Operation: UK & Ireland
Tel: 01782 599099
Fax: 01782 599295
Email: hkiddle@qualceram-shires.com
Web: www.shires-bathrooms.com 🔆
Product Type: 1, 4, 5

SHOWERLUX UK LTD
Sibree Road, Coventry, West Midlands, CV3 4FD
Area of Operation: UK & Ireland
Tel: 02476 882515
Fax: 02476 305457
Email: sales@showerlux.co.uk
Web: www.showerlux.com
Product Type: 1, 3, 4

SMART SHOWERS LTD
Unit 11, Woodside Road, South Marston Business Park, Swindon, Wiltshire, SN3 4WA
Area of Operation: UK & Ireland
Tel: 01793 822775
Fax: 01793 823800
Email: enquiries@smartshowers.co.uk
Web: www.smartshowers.co.uk 🔆
Product Type: 1, 4, 5 **Material Type:** D) 5, 6

STIFFKEY BATHROOMS
89 Upper Saint Giles Street,
Norwich, Norfolk, NR2 1AB
Area of Operation: Worldwide
Tel: 01603 627850 **Fax:** 01603 619775
Email: stiffkeybathrooms.norwich@virgin.net
Web: www.stiffkeybathrooms.com
Product Type: 1, 4, 5 **Other Info:** ▽

TAPS SHOP
1 Tristram Road, Ducklington,
Whitney, Oxfordshire, OX29 7XH
Area of Operation: Worldwide
Tel: 0845 4303035 **Fax:** 01993 779653
Email: info@tapsshop.co.uk
Web: www.tapsshop.co.uk 🔆 **Product Type:** 1, 3, 6

TENTERDEN HOUSE INTERIORS
4 West Cross, Tenterden, Kent, TN30 6JL
Area of Operation: Worldwide
Tel: 01580 764481 **Fax:** 01580 765531
Email: tenterdenhouseinteriors@hotmail.com
Product Type: 1, 3

THE HEATED MIRROR COMPANY LTD
Sherston, Wiltshire, SN16 0LW
Area of Operation: UK & Ireland
Tel: 01666 840003 **Fax:** 01666 840856
Email: heated.mirror@virgin.net
Web: www.heated-mirrors.com **Product Type:** 2

THE KITCHEN AND BATHROOM COLLECTION
Nelson House, Nelson Road,
Salisbury, Wiltshire, SP1 3LT
Area of Operation: South West England and South Wales
Tel: 01722 334800 **Fax:** 01722 412252
Email: info@kbc.co.uk **Web:** www.kbc.co.uk
Product Type: 1, 2, 3, 4, 5 **Other Info:** 🔆

THE WATER MONOPOLY
16/18 Lonsdale Road, London, NW6 6RD
Area of Operation: UK (Excluding Ireland)
Tel: 0207 624 2636 **Fax:** 0207 624 2631
Email: enquiries@watermonopoly.com
Web: www.watermonopoly.com

THOMAS CRAPPER & CO. LTD
The Stable Yard, Alscot Park,
Stratford-on-Avon, Warwickshire, CV37 8BL
Area of Operation: Worldwide
Tel: 01789 450522 **Fax:** 01789 450523
Email: wc@thomas-crapper.com
Web: www.thomas-crapper.com 🔆 **Product Type:** 5

TIMELESS BATHROOMS LTD
394 Ringwood Road, Ferndown, Dorset, BH22 9AU
Area of Operation: South East England
Tel: 01202 897110 **Fax:** 01202 892252
Email: bathroom@options394.fsnet.co.uk
Web: www.timelessbathrooms.co.uk
Product Type: 1, 5, 6

TRADEMARK TILES
Tile Store, Somersham Road, St Ives,
Huntingdon, Cambridgeshire, PE27 3WR
Area of Operation: UK (Excluding Ireland)
Tel: 01480 498123
Email: info@tilestoreplus.co.uk
Web: www.tilestoreplus.co.uk 🔆
Product Type: 1, 2, 3, 4, 5

TRITON PLC
Triton Road, Shepperton Business Park,
Caldwell Road, Nuneaton , Warwickshire, CV11 4NR
Area of Operation: UK & Ireland
Tel: 02476 344441 **Fax:** 02476 6349828
Web: www.tritonshowers.co.uk
Product Type: 1, 3, 4

TWYFORD BATHROOMS
Lawton Road, Alsager, Stoke On Trent,
Staffordshire, ST7 2DF
Area of Operation: Worldwide
Tel: 01270 879777
Web: www.twyfordbathrooms.com
Product Type: 3, 5 **Material Type:** D) 2, 4, 5

UK BATHROOM INTERIORS
Units 3-4, The Old Laundry, Fishergreen,
Ripon, North Yorkshire, HG4 1NL
Area of Operation: UK (Excluding Ireland)
Tel: 01765 608822 **Fax:** 01765 608892
Email: mark@ukbathroominteriors.com
Web: www.ukbathroominteriors.com 🔆
Product Type: 1, 2, 3, 4, 6

VICTORIAN BATHROOMS
Victorian Bathrooms , Ings Mill Complex,
Dale Street, Ossett , West Yorkshire, WF5 9HQ
Area of Operation: UK (Excluding Ireland)
Tel: 01924 267736 **Fax:** 01924 261232
Email: sales@vb-bathrooms.com
Web: www.vb-bathrooms.com 🔆
Product Type: 1, 3, 4, 5

WALTON BATHROOMS
The Hersham Centre, The Green, Molesey Road,
Hersham, Walton on Thames, Surrey, KT12 4HL
Area of Operation: UK (Excluding Ireland)
Tel: 01932 224784 **Fax:** 01932 253447
Email: sales@waltonbathrooms.co.uk
Web: www.waltonbathrooms.co.uk 🔆
Product Type: 1

WARM TILES LTD
18 Ernleigh Road, Ipswich, Suffolk, IP4 5LU
Area of Operation: UK & Ireland
Tel: 01473 725743 **Fax:** 01473 725743
Email: barry@warmtiles.co.uk
Web: www.warmtiles.co.uk 🔆 **Product Type:** 2

WARMROOMS
24 Corncroft Lane, St Leonards Park,
Gloucester, Gloucestershire, GL4 6XU
Area of Operation: UK (Excluding Ireland)
Tel: 01452 304460
Fax: 01452 304460
Email: sales@warmrooms.co.uk
Web: www.warmrooms.co.uk 🔆

WATER FRONT
All Worcester Buildings, Birmingham Road,
Redditch, Worcestershire, B97 6DY
Area of Operation: UK & Ireland
Tel: 01527 584244
Fax: 01527 61127
Email: info@waterfrontbathrooms.com
Web: www.waterfrontbathrooms.com
Product Type: 1, 3, 4 **Material Type:** C) 11, 14, 16

WATERPROOFTV.CO.UK
7 Allandale Road, Stoneygate,
Leicester, Leicestershire, LE2 2DA
Area of Operation: Worldwide
Tel: 0116 270 5777 **Fax:** 0116 274 5777
Email: w@terproof.tv
Web: www.waterprooftv.co.uk
Product Type: 6

WHIRLPOOL EXPRESS (UK) LTD
61-62 Lower Dock Street,
Kingsway, Newport, NP20 1EF
Area of Operation: Europe
Tel: 01633 244555
Fax: 01633 244881
Email: reception@whirlpoolexpress.co.uk
Web: www.whirlpoolexpress.co.uk 🔆
Product Type: 1, 3, 4, 6

WILLIAM GARVEY
Leyhill, Payhembury, Honiton, Devon, EX14 3JG
Area of Operation: Worldwide
Tel: 01404 841430
Fax: 01404 841626
Email: webquery@williamgarvey.co.uk
Web: www.williamgarvey.co.uk
Product Type: 1, 4, 5
Other Info: 🔆 **Material Type:** A) 2, 10

DISABILITY & SPECIAL NEEDS EQUIPMENT

KEY
OTHER: ▽ Reclaimed 🔆 On-line shopping
🖉 Bespoke ✋ Hand-made ECO Ecological

AIRBATH APPOLLO LIMITED
Swinnow Lane, Leeds, West Yorkshire, LS13 4TY
Area of Operation: Worldwide
Tel: 0113 255 6666
Fax: 0113 3869176
Email: sales@airbath.co.uk
Web: www.airbath.co.uk

AL CHALLIS LTD
Europower House, Lower Road, Cookham,
Maidenhead, Berkshire, SL6 9EH
Area of Operation: UK & Ireland
Tel: 01628 529024
Fax: 0870 458 0577
Email: chris@alchallis.com
Web: www.alchallis.com

BATHROOM MANUFACTURERS ASSOCIATION
Federation House, Station Road,
Stoke on Trent, Staffordshire, ST4 2RT
Area of Operation: UK & Ireland
Tel: 01782 747123
Fax: 01782 747161
Email: info@bathroom-association.org.uk
Web: www.bathroom-association.org.uk

BATHROOMS PLUS LTD
222 Malmesbury Park Road,
Bournemouth, Dorset, BH8 8PR
Area of Operation: South West England and South Wales
Tel: 01202 294417
Fax: 01202 316425
Email: info@bathrooms-plus.co.uk
Web: www.bathrooms-plus.co.uk

BOUNDARY BATHROOMS
Ainsworth & Dent House,
Regent Street, Colne, Lancashire, BB8 8LD
Area of Operation: UK & Ireland
Tel: 01282 862509
Fax: 01282 871192
Email: sales@boundarybathrooms.co.uk

CARE DESIGN
Moorgate, Ormskirk, Lancashire, L39 4RX
Area of Operation: UK (Excluding Ireland)
Tel: 01695 579061 **Fax:** 01695 570489
Email: caredesign@clara.net
Web: www.caredesign.co.uk

**CHAMBERLAIN & GROVES LTD -
THE DOOR & SECURITY STORE**
101 Boundary Road, Walthamstow, London, E17 8NQ
Area of Operation: UK (Excluding Ireland)
Tel: 0208 520 6776
Fax: 0208 520 2190
Email: ken@secureddoors.co.uk
Web: www.secureddoors.co.uk

CHILTERN INVADEX LTD
Chiltern House, 6 Wedgwood Road,
Bicester, Oxfordshire, OX26 4UL
Area of Operation: Worldwide
Tel: 01869 246470 **Fax:** 01869 247214
Email: sales@chilterninvadex.co.uk
Web: www.chilterninvadex.co.uk

CISTERMISER LTD
Unit 1 Woodley Park Estate, 59-69 Reading Road,
Woodley, Reading, Berkshire, RG5 3AN
Area of Operation: UK & Ireland
Tel: 0118 969 1611 **Fax:** 0118 944 1426
Email: sales@cistermiser.co.uk
Web: www.cistermiser.co.uk

CITY BATHROOMS & KITCHENS
158 Longford Road, Longford,
Coventry, West Midlands, CV6 6DR
Area of Operation: UK & Ireland
Tel: 02476 365877
Fax: 02476 644992
Email: citybathrooms@hotmail.com
Web: www.citybathrooms.co.uk

COASTFORM SYSTEMS LTD.
Unit 18 Dinnington Business Centre, Outgang Lane,
Dinnington, Sheffield, South Yorkshire, S25 3QX
Area of Operation: Worldwide
Tel: 01909 561470 **Fax:** 08700 516793
Email: sales@coastform.co.uk
Web: www.coastform.co.uk

CROSSWATER
Unit 5 Butterly Avenue, Questor,
Dartford, Kent, DA1 1JG
Area of Operation: UK & Ireland
Tel: 01322 628270 **Fax:** 01322 628280
Email: sales@crosswater.co.uk
Web: www.crosswater.co.uk

CYMRU KITCHENS
63 Caerleon Road, Newport, NP19 7BX
Area of Operation: UK (Excluding Ireland)
Tel: 01633 676767 **Fax:** 01633 212512
Email: sales@cymrukitchens.com
Web: www.cymrukitchens.com

DECORLUX LTD
18 Ghyll Industrial Estate, Ghyll Road,
Heathfield, East Sussex, TN21 8AW
Area of Operation: UK (Excluding Ireland)
Tel: 01435 866638 **Fax:** 01435 866641
Email: sales@decorlux.co.uk
Web: www.decorlux.co.uk

DISABILITY ACCESS COMPANY LTD
Access House, 16-18 Chapel Street,
Glossop, Derbyshire, Sk13 8AT
Area of Operation: UK & Ireland
Tel: 01457 868547 **Fax:** 0871 733 5071
Email: sales@disabilityaccessco.com
Web: www.disabilityaccessco.com

DISCONTINUED BATHROOMS
140-142 Pogmoor Road, Pogmoor,
Barnsley, North Yorkshire, S75 2DX
Area of Operation: UK (Excluding Ireland)
Tel: 01226 280200 **Fax:** 01226 733273
Email: sales@discontinuedbathrooms.co.uk
Web: www.discontinuedbathrooms.co.uk

ECOLEC
Sharrocks Street, Wolverhampton, WV1 3RP
Area of Operation: UK & Ireland
Tel: 01902 457575 **Fax:** 01902 457797
Email: sales@ecolec.co.uk
Web: www.ecolec.co.uk

EUROCARE SHOWERS LTD
Unit 19, Doncaster Industry Park, Watch House Lane,
Bentley, Doncaster, South Yorkshire, DN5 9LZ
Tel: 01302 788684 **Fax:** 01302 780010
Email: sales@eurocare-showers.com
Web: www.eurocare-showers.com

GEBERIT LTD
New Hythe Business Park,
New Hythe Lane, Aylesford, Kent, ME20 7PJ
Area of Operation: UK & Ireland
Tel: 01622 717 811 **Fax:** 01622 716 920
Web: www.geberit.co.uk

GO FIX IT LTD
Unit 10 Castle Industrial Estate, Louvain Street, Off
Oldham Road, Failsworth, Manchester, M35 0HB
Area of Operation: UK (Excluding Ireland)
Tel: 0161 681 4109 **Fax:** 0161 681 8169
Email: admin@gofixit.co.uk
Web: www.gofixit.co.uk

GOODWOOD BATHROOMS LTD
Church Road, North Mundham,
Chichester, West Sussex, PO20 1JU
Tel: 01243 532121 **Fax:** 01243 533423
Email: sales@goodwoodbathrooms.co.uk
Web: www.goodwoodbathrooms.co.uk

GROHE UK
1 River Road, Barking, Essex, IG11 0HD
Area of Operation: Worldwide
Tel: 020 8594 7292 **Fax:** 020 8594 8898
Email: info@grohe.co.uk
Web: www.grohe.co.uk

HAROLD MOORE & SON LTD
Rawson Spring Road, Hillsborough,
Sheffield, South Yorkshire, S6 1PD
Area of Operation: UK & Ireland
Tel: 0114 233 6161 **Fax:** 0114 232 6375
Email: admin@haroldmoorebaths.co.uk
Web: www.haroldmoorebaths.co.uk

HERITAGE BATHROOMS
Princess Street, Bedminster, Bristol, BS3 4AG
Area of Operation: UK & Ireland
Tel: 0117 963 3333
Email: marketing@heritagebathrooms.com
Web: www.heritagebathrooms.com

HOUSE ELECTRONIC LTD
97 Francisco Close, Hollyfields Park,
Chafford Hundred, Essex, RM16 6YE
Area of Operation: UK & Ireland
Tel: 01375 483595 **Fax:** 01375 483595
Email: info@houselectronic.co.uk
Web: www.houselectronic.co.uk

INSPIRED BATHROOMS
Unit R4, Innsworth Technology Park, Innsworth Lane,
Gloucester, Gloucestershire, GL3 1DL
Area of Operation: UK & Ireland
Tel: 01452 559121 **Fax:** 01452 530908
Email: sales@inspired-bathrooms.co.uk
Web: www.inspired-bathrooms.co.uk

JAMES GIBBONS FORMAT LTD
Vulcan Road, Bilston, Wolverhampton, WV14 7JG
Area of Operation: Worldwide
Tel: 01902 405500 **Fax:** 01902 385915
Email: info@jgf.co.uk **Web:** www.jgf.co.uk

KENSINGTON STUDIO
13 c & d Kensington Road, Earlsdon,
Coventry, West Midlands, CV5 6GG
Area of Operation: UK (Excluding Ireland)
Tel: 02476 713326 **Fax:** 02476 713136
Email: sales@kensingtonstudio.com
Web: www.kensingtonstudio.com

KERAMAG WAVENEY LTD
London Road, Beccles, Suffolk, NR34 8TS
Area of Operation: UK & Ireland
Tel: 01502 716600 **Fax:** 01502 717767
Email: info@keramagwaveney.co.uk
Web: www.keramag.co.uk

KINGKRAFT LTD
26D Orgreave Crescent, Dore House Industrial
Estate, Sheffield, South Yorkshire, S13 9NQ
Area of Operation: Europe
Tel: 0114 269 0697 **Fax:** 0114 269 5145
Email: info@kingkraft.co.uk
Web: www.kingkraft.co.uk **Other Info:**

LECICO PLC
Unit 47a Hobbs Industrial Estate,
Newchapel, Nr Lingfield, Surrey, RH7 6HN
Area of Operation: UK & Ireland
Tel: 01342 834777 **Fax:** 01342 834783
Email: info@lecico.co.uk **Web:** www.lecico.co.uk

MEREWAY CONTRACTS
Unit 1 Wharfdale Road, Tysely,
Birmingham, West Midlands, B11 2DE
Area of Operation: UK (Excluding Ireland)
Tel: 0121 764 7180 **Fax:** 0121 764 7199
Email: info@merewaycontracts.co.uk
Web: www.merewaycontracts.co.uk

MOBALPA
1 High Street, Halberton, Devon, EX16 7AF
Area of Operation: Worldwide
Tel: 07740 633672 **Fax:** 01884 820828
Email: ploftus@mobalpa.co.uk
Web: www.mobalpa.co.uk

POLYPIPE KITCHENS & BATHROOMS LTD
Warmsworth, Halt Industrial Estate,
Doncaster, South Yorkshire, DN4 9LS
Area of Operation: Worldwide
Tel: 01709 770990 **Fax:** 01302 310602
Email: davery@ppbq.co.uk
Web: www.polypipe.com/bk

ROMAN
Whitworth Avenue, Aycliffe Industrial Estate,
Newton Aycliffe, Durham, DL5 6YN
Area of Operation: Worldwide
Tel: 0845 050 4032 **Fax:** 01325 319889
Email: brochures@roman-showers.com
Web: www.roman-showers.com

RSJ ASSOCIATES LTD
Unit 5, Greenfield Road, Greenfield Farm Industrial
Estate, Congleton, Cheshire, CW12 4TR
Area of Operation: UK & Ireland
Tel: 01260 276188 **Fax:** 01260 280889
Email: info@rsjassociates.co.uk
Web: www.hueppe.com

STEAM DIRECT
187 London Road, Southend-on-Sea, Essex, SS1 1PW
Area of Operation: UK & Ireland
Tel: 01702 433445 **Fax:** 01702 433449
Email: steamdirect@aol.com
Web: www.steam-direct.co.uk

THE KITCHEN AND BATHROOM COLLECTION
Nelson House, Nelson Road,
Salisbury, Wiltshire, SP1 3LT
Area of Operation: South West England and South Wales
Tel: 01722 334800 **Fax:** 01722 412252
Email: info@kbc.co.uk
Web: www.kbc.co.uk **Other Info:**

TWYFORD BATHROOMS
Lawton Road, Alsager,
Stoke On Trent, Staffordshire, ST7 2DF
Area of Operation: Worldwide
Tel: 01270 879777
Web: www.twyfordbathrooms.com

WHIRLPOOL EXPRESS (UK) LTD
61-62 Lower Dock Street,
Kingsway, Newport, NP20 1EF
Area of Operation: Europe
Tel: 01633 244555 **Fax:** 01633 244881
Email: reception@whirlpoolexpress.co.uk
Web: www.whirlpoolexpress.co.uk

COMPLETE BATHROOM SUITES

KEY
OTHER: ▽ Reclaimed   On-line shopping
  Bespoke Hand-made ECO Ecological

ASHLEY BATHROOMS
Duffield Road Industrial Estate,
Little Eaton, Derby, Derbyshire, DE21 5DR
Area of Operation: UK & Ireland
Tel: 01332 830404
Fax: 01332 830202
Email: info@ashleybathrooms.com
Web: www.ashleybathrooms.com

BATHROOM EXPRESS
61-62 Lower Dock Street,
Kingsway, Newport, NP20 1EF
Area of Operation: UK & Ireland
Tel: 0845 130 2000 **Fax:** 01633 244881
Email: sales@bathroomexpress.co.uk
Web: www.bathroomexpress.co.uk

BATHROOM EXPRESS
Area of Operation: UK & Ireland
Tel: 0845 130 2000
Fax: 01633 244881
Email: sales@bathroomexpress.co.uk
Web: www.bathroomexpress.co.uk

Pegasus bathrooms has launched a catalogue aimed firmly at house developers. Simply choose the style of pottery, the size of the bath or shower and the degree of sophistication from a simple plain acrylic bath to a sophisticated 35 jet whirlpool bath enabling the creation of a designer bathroom within any budget coupled with fast nationwide delivery.

BATHROOM MANUFACTURERS ASSOCIATION
Federation House, Station Road,
Stoke on Trent, Staffordshire, ST4 2RT
Area of Operation: UK & Ireland
Tel: 01782 747123
Fax: 01782 747161
Email: info@bathroom-association.org.uk
Web: www.bathroom-association.org.uk

BOUNDARY BATHROOMS
Ainsworth & Dent House,
Regent Street, Colne, Lancashire, BB8 8LD
Area of Operation: UK & Ireland
Tel: 01282 862509 **Fax:** 01282 871192
Email: sales@boundarybathrooms.co.uk

BUILDING & DESIGN SOLUTIONS GERMANY
Auf den Haien 14, 55471 Sargenroth, Germany
Area of Operation: UK (Excluding Ireland)
Tel: 0049 6761 970 871
Email: mail@buildingdesign-germany.eu
Web: www.buildingdesign-germany.eu

CAPLE
Fourth Way, Avonmouth, Bristol, BS11 8DW
Area of Operation: UK (Excluding Ireland)
Tel: 0870 6069606 **Fax:** 0117 938 7449
Email: amandalowe@mlay.co.uk
Web: www.mlay.co.uk

CHADDER & CO.
Blenheim Studio, London Road,
Forest Row, East Sussex, RH18 5EZ
Area of Operation: Worldwide
Tel: 01342 823243 **Fax:** 01342 823097
Web: www.chadder.com

COLOURWASH LTD
165 Chamberlayne Road, London, NW10 3NU
Area of Operation: UK & Ireland
Tel: 0208 830 2992 **Fax:** 0208 830 2317
Email: sales@colourwash.co.uk
Web: www.colourwash.co.uk

COUNTY GRANITE AND MARBLE
Mill Lane, Creech Saint Michael,
Taunton, Somerset, TA3 5PX
Area of Operation: UK (Excluding Ireland)
Tel: 01823 444554 **Fax:** 01823 445013
Web: www.countygranite.co.uk

DIYWETROOM.COM
Oakstone House, Middleton, Youlgrave,
Bakewell, Derbyshire, DE45 1LS
Area of Operation: Worldwide
Tel: 01629 636109 **Fax:** 01629 636109
Email: sales@diywetroom.com
Web: www.diywetroom.com

FIRED EARTH
3 Twyford Mill, Oxford Road,
Adderbury, Banbury, Oxfordshire, OX17 3SX
Area of Operation: Worldwide
Tel: 01295 812088 **Fax:** 01295 810832
Email: enquiries@firedearth.com
Web: www.firedearth.com

JOHN LEWIS OF HUNGERFORD
Grove Technology Park, Downsview Road,
Wantage, Oxfordshire, OX12 9FA
Area of Operation: UK (Excluding Ireland)
Tel: 01235 774300 **Fax:** 01235 769031
Email: park.street@john-lewis.co.uk
Web: www.john-lewis.co.uk

KENLEY KITCHENS
24-26 Godstone Road, Kenley, Surrey, CR8 5JE
Area of Operation: UK (Excluding Ireland)
Tel: 0208 668 7000

**MISCELLANEA DISCONTINUED
BATHROOMWARE**
Churt Place Nurseries, Tilford Road,
Churt, Farnham, Surrey, GU10 2LN
Area of Operation: Worldwide
Tel: 01428 608164 **Fax:** 01428 608165
Email: email@brokenbog.com
Web: www.brokenbog.com

MOODS BATHROOMS
PJH Group, Alder House, Kearsley,
Bolton, Lancashire, BL4 8SL
Area of Operation: UK & Ireland
Tel: 01204 707070 **Fax:** 01204 573140
Email: info@pjh.co.uk
Web: www.bathroom-moods.com

OLD FASHIONED BATHROOMS LTD
Foresters Hall, 52 High Street, Debenham,
Stowmarket, Suffolk, IP14 6QW
Area of Operation: UK (Excluding Ireland)
Tel: 01728 860926 **Fax:** 01728 860446
Email: ofbshop@yahoo.co.uk
Web: www.oldfashionedbathrooms.co.uk

ORIGINAL
3 Festival Units, The Showground,
Bridgwater, Somerset, TA6 6LS
Area of Operation: South West England and South Wales
Tel: 0870 0110808 **Fax:** 0870 011 0606
Email: enquiries@obsc.co.uk
Web: www.obsc.co.uk

QUALCERAM SHIRES PLC
South Quay, Arklow, Co. Wicklow
Area of Operation: UK & Ireland
Tel: 00353 402 31288 **Fax:** 00353 402 31292
Email: omoriarty@qualceram-shires.com
Web: www.qualceram-shires.com

QUANTUM FITTED FURNITURE
2a Poplar Court Parade, Richmond Road,
Twickenham, London, TW1 2DT
Area of Operation: UK (Excluding Ireland)
Tel: 0208 892 6430 **Fax:** 0208 892 6035
Email: info@quantumfittedfurniture.co.uk
Web: www.quantumfittedfurniture.co.uk

RAK CERAMICS
The Tile House , Easebourne Lane,
Easebourne, West Sussex, GU29 9AZ
Area of Operation: Worldwide
Tel: 01730 815507 **Fax:** 01730 815007
Email: info@rakceramics.co.uk
Web: www.rakceramics.co.uk

RICHARD BAKER FURNITURE LTD
Wimbledon Studios, 257 Burlington Road,
New Malden, Surrey, KT3 4NE
Area of Operation: Europe
Tel: 0208 336 1777 **Fax:** 0208 336 1666
Email: richard@richardbakerfurniture.co.uk
Web: www.richardbakerfurniture.co.uk

RIVERBED
Priory Park, Chewton Mendip,
Bath, Somerset, BA3 4NT
Area of Operation: UK & Ireland
Tel: 01761 241133 **Fax:** 01761 241134
Email: sales@riverbed.ltd.uk
Web: www.riverbed.ltd.uk

ROMANYS
Hatch End, Unit 1, Chantry Place,
Headstone Lane, Harrow, Middlesex, HA3 6NY
Area of Operation: UK & Ireland
Tel: 0208 421 6324
Fax: 0208 421 6757
Email: bharat.pindolia@romanys.uk.com
Web: www.romanys.uk.com

ROOTS KITCHENS BEDROOMS BATHROOMS
Vine Farm, Stockers Hill, Boughton under Blean,
Faversham, Kent, ME13 9AB
Area of Operation: South East England
Tel: 01227 751130 **Fax:** 01227 750033
Email: showroom@rootskitchens.co.uk
Web: www.rootskitchens.co.uk

SHIRES
Uttoxeter Road, Longton,
Stoke-on-Trent, Staffordshire, ST3 1NA
Area of Operation: UK & Ireland
Tel: 01782 599099 **Fax:** 01782 599295
Email: hkiddle@qualceram-shires.com
Web: www.shires-bathrooms.com

SIMON TAYLOR FURNITURE LIMITED
Cane End Lane, Bierton, Aylesbury,
Buckinghamshire, HP22 5BH
Area of Operation: UK & Ireland
Tel: 01296 488207
Fax: 01296 398722
Email: information@simon-taylor.co.uk
Web: www.simon-taylor.co.uk **Other Info:** ✎

THOMAS CRAPPER & CO. LTD
The Stable Yard, Alscot Park,
Stratford-on-Avon, Warwickshire, CV37 8BL
Area of Operation: Worldwide
Tel: 01789 450522 **Fax:** 01789 450523
Email: wc@thomas-crapper.com
Web: www.thomas-crapper.com

TWYFORD BATHROOMS
Lawton Road, Alsager,
Stoke On Trent, Staffordshire, ST7 2DF
Area of Operation: Worldwide
Tel: 01270 879777
Web: www.twyfordbathrooms.com
Material Type: C) 2, 3

UK BATHROOM INTERIORS
Units 3-4, The Old Laundry, Fishergreen,
Ripon, North Yorkshire, HG4 1NL
Area of Operation: UK (Excluding Ireland)
Tel: 01765 608822 **Fax:** 01765 608892
Email: mark@ukbathroominteriors.com
Web: www.ukbathroominteriors.com

VICTORIAN BATHROOMS
Ings Mill Complex, Dale Street,
Ossett , West Yorkshire, WF5 9HQ
Area of Operation: UK (Excluding Ireland)
Tel: 01924 267736 **Fax:** 01924 261232
Email: sales@vb-bathrooms.com
Web: www.vb-bathrooms.com

WATTS & WRIGHT (THE JOINERY SHOP)
Watts & Wright, PO Box 4251,
Walsall, West Midlands, WS3 3WY
Area of Operation: Worldwide
Tel: 01922 610800 / 020 70437619
Fax: 0870 7626387
Email: sales@wattsandwright.com
Web: www.wattsandwright.com

NOTES

Company Name ....
....
Address ....
....
....
email ....
Web ....

Company Name ....
....
Address ....
....
....
email ....
Web ....

Company Name ....
....
Address ....
....
....
email ....
Web ....

Company Name ....
....
Address ....
....
....
email ....
Web ....

Company Name ....
....
Address ....
....
....
email ....
Web ....

Image courtesy of William Ball (01375 375151)

SPONSORED BY WILLIAM BALL
Tel 01375 375151 Web www.wball.co.uk

Worktops

The life of the worktop is not an easy one, enduring sharp knives, scalding pans and food and drink stains on a day-to-day basis. We reveal which materials have what it takes to keep your work surfaces in tip top condition.

Touchstone

Your choice of worktop plays a huge role in defining the finished look of your new kitchen. Add to this the fact that the wrong choice of surface could affect the kitchen's performance, and you'll realise how important the decision is. So what are the pros and cons of the most popular surfaces?

WOOD: Wooden work surfaces have never fallen out of favour. Even concerns over hygiene have been discarded, after evidence came to light suggesting that wood actually has inherent properties which destroy bacteria far more effectively than any plastic ever could.

But wood's main attraction is arguably its ability to score highly in the style department. Contemporary kitchens are well suited to richly coloured hardwoods, such as wenge and iroko, whilst traditional schemes will always benefit from the addition of oak. Some of these hardwoods can be quite expensive, but there are plenty of cheaper softwoods on the market, such as beech and maple, which can prove just as effective.

STONE: By far the most popular type of stone for work surfaces is granite, which is remarkably hard-wearing, heat resistant and maintenance free. It is a high-cost option, but is seen as a good investment because of its durability. Granite is available in wide range of colours, from deep inky blacks and blues, through earthy greens and summery yellows, to simple snow white. So, there will certainly be a colour to suit even the most individual of kitchens.

COMPOSITES: Corian is the most well-known brand of this durable surface. Made of resin and stone, it is heat and stain-resistant, and flexible in that it can be moulded with integrated sinks for a one-piece effect. However, it can be a costly option.

STAINLESS STEEL: As far as performance goes you really cannot get much better than stainless steel. As the name suggests, it will not stain, and neither will it burn or chip. If you are seriously considering stainless steel, you should bear in mind its thickness – at depths below 0.9mm it could be prone to bending. But stainless steel's performance is surely backed up by the fact it used in most commercial kitchens and top-class restaurants.

LAMINATE: Still the cheapest option on the market, laminate has come a long way since the days when it was prone to serious peeling, bubbling and scratching – everything you don't want your worktop to do. Today they have reassuring qualities such as 'hot melt seal' and 'drip seal', plus many are now impregnated with antibacterial substances. Laminate also comes in a multitude of colours and finishes, convincingly taking on the guise of wood and stone. The only remaining downside is that laminate is very difficult to repair.

GLASS: Glass isn't the most popular option for a worktop as it can be prone to scratching, but it certainly looks cool and contemporary. It really is a special feature, especially with the 'wow factor' it produces when underlit. Glass can also give the feeling of more space in smaller kitchens.

Top tips

- Check you have enough material for the job. You will need surface cuttings for sinks, taps, hobs, fitting round corners etc. Work out what cuts, and exactly how much, you will need.
- Ask about the porosity of the surface – the less porous, the more durable it is
- Select the thickest worktop you can afford. Thicker worktops are more resistant to damage.
- Think about maintenance. Some wooden surfaces require great care and regular oiling.
- Contrary to opinion, wooden worktops are actually quite hygienic, and are as safe and clean as any other surface. Stainless steel is said to be the most hygienic.
- Consider having your worktop professionally fitted. A skilled tradesperson will disguise joins and fit the surface seamlessly around sinks, pipes etc.
- The type of grouting required depends on your choice of tiles. A coarse grain for wide joints will be needed for handmade tiles to compensate for irregular edges. Consider a contrasting grout on plain white tiles for an attractive, decorative effect.
- With proper care and attention, a correctly installed, good quality ceramic floor tile should give you many years of trouble-free service. Grit is the biggest enemy of any floor material and a mat adjacent to doors is strongly recommended.

COOKER HOODS AND EXTRACTORS

KEY

SEE ALSO: VENTILATION - Extractor Fans
OTHER: ▽ Reclaimed ✈ On-line shopping
✎ Bespoke ✋ Hand-made   ECO Ecological

AMBER KITCHENS OF BISHOP'S STORTFORD
Clarklands House, Parsonage Lane,
Sawbridgeworth, Hertfordshire, CM21 0NG
Area of Operation: East England, Greater London
Tel: 01279 600030   **Fax:** 01279 721528
Email: info@amberkitchens.com
Web: www.amberkitchens.com

ASHFORD & BROOKS
The Old Workshop, Ashtree Barn, Caters Road,
Bredfield, Woodbridge, Suffolk, IP13 6BE
Area of Operation: UK (Excluding Ireland)
Tel: 01473 737764   **Fax:** 01473 277176
Email: ashfordbrooks@mailbox.co.uk
Web: www.ashfordandbrooks.co.uk

BATH KITCHEN COMPANY
22 Hensley Road, Bloomfield,
Bath, Somerset, BA2 2DR
Area of Operation: South West England and South Wales
Tel: 01225 312003   **Fax:** 01225 312003
Email: david@bathkitchencompany.co.uk
Web: www.bathkitchencompany.co.uk

BAUMATIC LTD
Baumatic Buildings,
6 Bennet Road, Berkshire, RG2 0QX
Area of Operation: Europe
Tel: 01189 336900   **Fax:** 01189 310035
Email: sales@baumatic.co.uk
Web: www.baumatic.com

BEAU-PORT LTD
Unit 2, Elhanger Business Park,
Bentworth, Hampshire, GU34 5Q2
Area of Operation: UK & Ireland
Tel: 0845 230 1545   **Fax:** 0870 350 0134
Email: sales@beau-port.co.uk
Web: www.beau-port.co.uk ✈

BELLING
Stoney Lane, Prescot, Merseyside, L35 2XW
Area of Operation: UK & Ireland
Tel: 0870 444 9929   **Fax:** 0870 458 9693
Web: www.belling.co.uk

BRADSHAW APPLIANCES
Kenn Road, Clevedon, Bristol, BS21 6LH
Area of Operation: UK & Ireland
Tel: 01275 343000   **Fax:** 01275 343454
Email: info@bradshaw.co.uk
Web: www.bradshaw.co.uk

BRITANNIA LIVING LTD
Britannia House, 281 Bristol Avenue,
Blackpool, Lancashire, FY2 0JF
Area of Operation: UK & Ireland
Tel: 01253 471111   **Fax:** 01253 471136
Email: enquiry@britannialiving.co.uk
Web: www.britannialiving.co.uk

To recommend a company for inclusion in the next edition of The Homebuilder's Handbook, email
customerservice@centaur.co.uk

BRITANNIA LIVING LTD

Area of Operation: UK & Ireland
Tel: 01253 471111
Fax: 01253 471136
Email: enquiry@britannialiving.co.uk
Web: www.britannialiving.co.uk

Britannia offers a selection of classic and contemporary range cookers, built-in ovens, hobs and hoods, all designed to make cooking a perfect pleasure!

CITY BATHROOMS & KITCHENS
158 Longford Road, Longford,
Coventry, West Midlands, CV6 6DR
Area of Operation: UK & Ireland
Tel: 02476 365877   **Fax:** 02476 644992
Email: citybathrooms@hotmail.com
Web: www.citybathrooms.co.uk

CONNAUGHT KITCHENS
2 Porchester Place, London, W2 2BS
Area of Operation: Greater London
Tel: 0207 706 2210   **Fax:** 0207 706 2209
Email: design@connaughtkitchens.co.uk
Web: www.connaughtkitchens.co.uk

COUNTRY KITCHENS
The Old Farm House, Birmingham Road,
Blackminster, Evesham, Worcestershire, WR11 7TD
Area of Operation: UK (Excluding Ireland)
Tel: 01386 831705   **Fax:** 01386 834051
Web: www.handcraftedkitchens.com
Other Info: ▽ ✎

CRABTREE KITCHENS
17 Station Road, Barnes, Greater London, SW13 0LF
Area of Operation: Greater London, South West England and South Wales
Tel: 0208 392 6955   **Fax:** 0208 392 6944
Email: design@crabtreekitchens.co.uk
Web: www.crabtreekitchens.co.uk

CYMRU KITCHENS
63 Caerleon Road, Newport, NP19 7BX
Area of Operation: UK (Excluding Ireland)
Tel: 01633 676767   **Fax:** 01633 212512
Email: sales@cymrukitchens.com
Web: www.cymrukitchens.com

DESIGNER KITCHENS
37 High Street, Potters Bar, Hertfordshire, EN6 5AJ
Area of Operation: Greater London
Tel: 01707 650565   **Fax:** 01707 663050
Email: info@designer-kitchens.co.uk
Web: www.designer-kitchens.co.uk

DR COOKERHOODS
2 Alpha Road, Aldershot, Hampshire, GU12 4RG
Area of Operation: UK (Excluding Ireland)
Tel: 01252 351111   **Fax:** 01252 311608
Email: lynn@drcookerhoods.co.uk
Web: www.elica.co.uk

ELITE TRADE KITCHENS LTD
90 Willesden Lane, Kilburn, London, NW6 7TA
Area of Operation: UK (Excluding Ireland)
Tel: 0207 328 1234
Fax: 0207 328 1243
Email: sales@elitekitchens.co.uk
Web: www.elitekitchens.co.uk

FALCON APPLIANCES
Clarence Street, Royal Leamington Spa,
Warwickshire, CV31 2AD
Area of Operation: Worldwide
Tel: 0845 634 0070   **Fax:** 01926 311032
Email: consumers@falconappliances.co.uk
Web: www.falconappliances.co.uk

FOURNEAUX DE FRANCE LTD (FDF)
Unit 3, Albion Close, Newtown Business Park,
Poole, Dorset, BH12 3LL
Area of Operation: UK & Ireland
Tel: 01202 733011   **Fax:** 01202 733499
Email: sales@fdef.co.uk   **Web:** www.fdef.co.uk ✈

FRANKE UK LTD
West Park, Manchester International Office,
Styal Road, Manchester, M22 5WB
Area of Operation: UK & Ireland
Tel: 0161 436 6280   **Fax:** 0161 436 2180
Email: info.uk@franke.com
Web: www.franke.co.uk

GORENJE UK
Tuition House, 27-37 St George's Road,
London, SW19 4EU
Area of Operation: UK & Ireland
Tel: 0208 247 3980   **Fax:** 0208 247 3999
Email: reception@gorenjeuk.co.uk
Web: www.gorenje.co.uk

HATT KITCHENS
Hartlebury Trading Estate,
Hartlebury, Worcestershire, DY10 4JB
Area of Operation: UK (Excluding Ireland)
Tel: 01299 251320   **Fax:** 01299 251579
Email: design@hatt.co.uk   **Web:** www.hatt.co.uk

HOOVER CANDY GROUP BUILT-IN DIVISION
New Chester Road, Bromborough, Wirral, CH62 3PE
Area of Operation: Europe
Tel: 0151 334 2781   **Fax:** 0151 334 9056
Web: www.candy-domestic.co.uk

INDESIT
Morley Way, Peterborough, Cambridgeshire, PE2 9JB
Area of Operation: UK & Ireland
Tel: 01733 282800
Email: info@indesitcompany.com
Web: www.indesit.com

IN-TOTO
Shaw Cross Court, Shaw Cross Business Park,
Dewsbury, West Yorkshire, WF12 7RF
Area of Operation: UK (Excluding Ireland)
Tel: 01924 487900   **Fax:** 01924 437305
Email: graham.russell@intoto.co.uk
Web: www.intoto.co.uk

JJO PLC (J&J ORMEROD)
Colonial House, Bacup, Lancashire, OL13 0EA
Area of Operation: UK & Ireland
Tel: 01706 877877   **Fax:** 01706 879827
Email: npeters@jjoplc.com
Web: www.jjoplc.com

JOHN LEWIS OF HUNGERFORD
Grove Technology Park, Downsview Road,
Wantage, Oxfordshire, OX12 9FA
Area of Operation: UK (Excluding Ireland)
Tel: 01235 774300   **Fax:** 01235 769031
Email: park.street@john-lewis.co.uk
Web: www.john-lewis.co.uk   **Other Info:** ✋

KENSINGTON STUDIO
13c/d Kensington Road, Earlsdon,
Coventry, West Midlands, CV5 6GG
Area of Operation: UK (Excluding Ireland)
Tel: 02476 713326   **Fax:** 02476 713136
Email: sales@kensingtonstudio.com
Web: www.kensingtonstudio.com ✈

MARK LEIGH KITCHENS LTD
11 Common Garden Street,
Lancaster, Lancashire, LA1 1XD
Area of Operation: North West England and North Wales
Tel: 01524 63273   **Fax:** 01524 62352
Email: mark@markleigh.co.uk
Web: www.markleigh.co.uk

MAYTAG
2 St. Annes Boulevard, Foxboro Business Park,
Redhill, Surrey, RH1 1AX
Area of Operation: UK & Ireland
Tel: 01737 231000   **Fax:** 01737 778822
Email: ukquery@maytag.com
Web: www.maytag.co.uk

MERCURY APPLIANCES
Whisby Road, Lincoln, Lincolnshire, LN6 3QZ
Area of Operation: Europe
Tel: 01522 881717   **Fax:** 01522 880220
Email: sales@mercury-appliances.co.uk
Web: www.mercury-appliances.co.uk

MEREWAY CONTRACTS
Unit 1 Wharfdale Road, Tysely,
Birmingham, West Midlands, B11 2DE
Area of Operation: UK (Excluding Ireland)
Tel: 0121 764 7180   **Fax:** 0121 764 7199
Email: info@merewaycontracts.co.uk
Web: www.merewaycontracts.co.uk

MOBALPA
1 High Street, Halberton, Devon, EX16 7AF
Area of Operation: Worldwide
Tel: 07740 633672   **Fax:** 01884 820828
Email: ploftus@mobalpa.com
Web: www.mobalpa.co.uk

MONTANA KITCHENS LTD
BIC 1, Studio 2/3 Innova Business Park,
Mollison Avenue, Enfield, Middlesex, EN3 7XU
Area of Operation: Greater London, South East England
Tel: 0800 58 75 628
Email: angie@montanakitchens.com
Web: www.montanakitchens.co.uk   **Other Info:** ✎

NEFF UK
Grand Union House, Old Wolverton Road, Wolverton,
Milton Keynes, Buckinghamshire, MK12 5PT
Area of Operation: UK (Excluding Ireland)
Tel: 01908 328300   **Fax:** 01908 328560
Email: info@neff.co.uk   **Web:** www.neff.co.uk

NEW WORLD
Stoney Lane, Prescot, Merseyside, L35 2XW
Area of Operation: UK & Ireland
Tel: 0870 444 9929   **Fax:** 0870 458 9693
Email: newworld@gdha.com
Web: www.newworldappliances.co.uk

NICHOLAS ANTHONY LTD
42-44 Wigmore Street, London, W1U 2RX
Area of Operation: East England, Greater London, South East England
Tel: 0800 068 3603   **Fax:** 01206 762698
Email: info@nicholas-anthony.co.uk
Web: www.nicholas-anthony.co.uk

NTP KITCHENS & JOINERY LTD
Unit 20/1, West Bowling Green Street,
Edinburgh, EH6 5PE
Area of Operation: Scotland
Tel: 0131 554 8787   **Fax:** 0131 554 9191
Email: sales@ntp-kitchens.co.uk
Web: www.ntp-kitchens.co.uk

PRICE KITCHENS
11 Imperial Way, Croydon, Surrey, CR0 4RR
Area of Operation: South East England
Tel: 0208 686 9006   **Fax:** 0208 686 5958
Email: info@pricekitchens.co.uk
Web: www.pricekitchens.co.uk

PRIMA APPLIANCES
PJH Group, Alder House, Kearsley,
Bolton, Lancashire, BL4 8SL
Area of Operation: UK & Ireland
Tel: 01204 707070   **Fax:** 01204 573140
Email: info@pjh.co.uk   **Web:** www.pjhdistribution.com

RANGE COOKERS
3 Lime Grove, Hoole, Chester, Cheshire, CH2 3HW
Area of Operation: UK & Ireland
Tel: 01244 345888   **Fax:** 01244 400224
Email: enquires@rangecookers.co.uk
Web: www.rangecookers.co.uk ✈

William Ball
Est 1963
Manufacturers of exclusive fitted furniture

Since 1963 the William Ball family has manufactured quality fitted furniture. The third generation are now on the board of directors and the hands on approach by the family ensures you receive professionalism, commitment to quality and attention to detail. William Ball products are made to be enjoyed made to be admired and above all made to last.

Shown here is just a small selection from the full range of 40 Kitchens, 15 Bedrooms, 10 Bathrooms 10 Studies & Open Plan Living.

For more information call us on 01375 375151 or visit our website: www.wball.co.uk

Sorbus
20mm thick solid ash timber with T&G effect centre panel finished in ivory ash with antiquing effect.

William Ball
Contemporary and Traditional Kitchens, Bedrooms, Bathrooms, Studies and Open plan Living. Showrooms Nationwide
Tel: 01375 375151
Email: marketing@wball.co.uk
Web: www.wball.co.uk

Bianca
18mm thick MDF white high gloss vinyl pressed slab style door with tight radius edges.

William Ball
Contemporary and Traditional Kitchens, Bedrooms, Bathrooms, Studies and Open plan Living. Showrooms Nationwide
Tel: 01375 375151
Email: marketing@wball.co.uk
Web: www.wball.co.uk

Firefly
22mm thick MDF fox maple vinyl pressed.

William Ball
Contemporary and Traditional Kitchens, Bedrooms, Bathrooms, Studies and Open plan Living. Showrooms Nationwide
Tel: 01375 375151
Email: marketing@wball.co.uk
Web: www.wball.co.uk

Chalice
23mm thick solid oak timber with T&G effect centre panel finished in light oak with antiquing effect.

William Ball
Contemporary and Traditional Kitchens, Bedrooms, Bathrooms, Studies and Open plan Living. Showrooms Nationwide
Tel: 01375 375151
Email: marketing@wball.co.uk
Web: www.wball.co.uk

Citadel
20mm thick shaker style solid alder frame with veneered centre panel stained to fox maple.

William Ball
Contemporary and Traditional Kitchens, Bedrooms, Bathrooms, Studies and Open plan Living. Showrooms Nationwide
Tel: 01375 375151
Email: marketing@wball.co.uk
Web: www.wball.co.uk

Sophia
22mm thick MDF walnut vinyl pressed.

William Ball
Contemporary and Traditional Kitchens, Bedrooms, Bathrooms, Studies and Open plan Living. Showrooms Nationwide
Tel: 01375 375151
Email: marketing@wball.co.uk
Web: www.wball.co.uk

Merlin
20mm thick solid oak timber with solid centre panel finished in light oak with antiquing effect.

William Ball
Contemporary and Traditional Kitchens, Bedrooms, Bathrooms, Studies and Open plan Living. Showrooms Nationwide
Tel: 01375 375151
Email: marketing@wball.co.uk
Web: www.wball.co.uk

Nero & Claudia Bedroom
Nero high gloss black, **Claudia** chestnut. 18mm thick MDF vinyl pressed.

William Ball
Contemporary and Traditional Kitchens, Bedrooms, Bathrooms, Studies and Open plan Living. Showrooms Nationwide
Tel: 01375 375151
Email: marketing@wball.co.uk
Web: www.wball.co.uk

Helena Bedroom
18mm thick MDF ivory high gloss vinyl pressed slab style door with tight radius edges.

William Ball
Contemporary and Traditional Kitchens, Bedrooms, Bathrooms, Studies and Open plan Living. Showrooms Nationwide
Tel: 01375 375151
Email: marketing@wball.co.uk
Web: www.wball.co.uk

Nero & Claudia Bathroom
Nero high gloss black, **Claudia** chestnut. 18mm thick MDF vinyl pressed.

William Ball
Contemporary and Traditional Kitchens, Bedrooms, Bathrooms, Studies and Open plan Living. Showrooms Nationwide
Tel: 01375 375151
Email: marketing@wball.co.uk
Web: www.wball.co.uk

Helena Bathroom
18mm thick MDF ivory high gloss vinyl pressed slab style door with tight radius edges.

William Ball
Contemporary and Traditional Kitchens, Bedrooms, Bathrooms, Studies and Open plan Living. Showrooms Nationwide
Tel: 01375 375151
Email: marketing@wball.co.uk
Web: www.wball.co.uk

the professional's choice

RANGEMASTER
Clarence Street, Royal Leamington Spa,
Warwickshire, CV31 2AD
Area of Operation: Worldwide
Tel: 01926 457400 **Fax:** 01926 450526
Email: consumers@rangemaster.co.uk
Web: www.rangemaster.co.uk

ROUNDEL DESIGN (UK) LTD
Flishinghurst Orchards, Chalk Lane,
Cranbrook, Kent, TN17 2QA
Area of Operation: South East England
Tel: 01580 712666
Email: homebuild@roundeldesign.co.uk
Web: www.roundeldesign.co.uk

SMEG UK
3 Milton Park, Abingdon, Oxfordshire, OX14 4RY
Area of Operation: UK & Ireland
Tel: 0870 990 9908 **Fax:** 01235 861120
Email: sales@smeguk.com
Web: www.smeguk.com

SPILLERS OF CHARD LTD.
Chard Business Park,
Chard, Somerset, TA20 1FA
Area of Operation: South West England and South Wales
Tel: 01460 67878 **Fax:** 01460 65252
Email: info@cookercentre.com
Web: www.cookercentre.com

STOVES
Stoney Lane, Prescot, Merseyside, L35 2XW
Area of Operation: UK & Ireland
Tel: 0870 458 9663 **Fax:** 0870 458 9693
Web: www.stoves.co.uk

THE AMERICAN APPLIANCE CENTRE
17-19 Mill Lane, Woodford Green, Essex, IG8 0UN
Area of Operation: UK (Excluding Ireland)
Tel: 0208 505 5616 **Fax:** 0208 505 8700
Email: sales@american-appliance.co.uk
Web: www.american-appliance.co.uk

THE CDA GROUP LTD
Harby Road, Langar, Nottingham,
Nottinghamshire, NG13 9HY
Area of Operation: UK & Ireland
Tel: 01949 862000 **Fax:** 01949 8624001
Email: sales@cda-europe.com
Web: www.cda-europe.com

THE KITCHEN AND BATHROOM COLLECTION
Nelson House, Nelson Road,
Salisbury, Wiltshire, SP1 3LT
Area of Operation: South West England and South Wales
Tel: 01722 334800 **Fax:** 01722 412252
Email: info@kbc.co.uk **Web:** www.kbc.co.uk
Other Info:

THE ORIGINAL KITCHEN COMPANY
4 Main Street, Breaston,
Derby, Derbyshire, DE72 3DX
Area of Operation: UK & Ireland
Tel: 01332 873746 **Fax:** 01332 873731
Email: originalkitchens@aol.com

TRADE APPLIANCES LTD
Cathedral Warehouse, Common Road, Huthwaite,
Sutton in Ashfield, Nottinghamshire, NG17 2JL
Area of Operation: UK (Excluding Ireland)
Tel: 0800 195 9596 **Fax:** 01623 445083
Email: info@trade-appliances.co.uk
Web: www.trade-appliances.co.uk

VECTAIRE LTD
Lincoln Road, Cressex Business Park,
High Wycombe, Buckinghamshire, HP12 3RH
Area of Operation: Worldwide
Tel: 01494 522333 **Fax:** 01494 522337
Email: sales@vectaire.co.uk
Web: www.vectaire.co.uk

VECTAIRE LTD
Area of Operation: Worldwide
Tel: 01494 522333
Fax: 01494 522337
Email: sales@vectaire.co.uk
Web: www.vectaire.co.uk

Extractor
"X-Mart" deluxe low profile toilet/
bathroom/kitchen fans finished in stainless steel
or white: in 3 sizes and capacities;
splashproof to IPX4; standard, timer and humidity
control; fixed or automatic opening front cover.

VENT AXIA
Fleming Way, Crawley, West Sussex, RH10 9YX
Area of Operation: UK (Excluding Ireland)
Tel: 01293 526062
Fax: 01293 552375
Email: sales@vent-axia.com
Web: www.vent-axia.com

W.S. WESTIN LTD
Phoenix Mills, Leeds Road,
Huddersfield, West Yorkshire, HD1 6NG
Area of Operation: UK (Excluding Ireland)
Tel: 01484 421585 **Fax:** 01484 432420
Email: sales@westin.co.uk
Web: www.westin.co.uk

W.S. WESTIN LTD
Area of Operation: UK (Excluding Ireland)
Tel: 01484 421585
Fax: 01484 432420
Email: sales@westin.co.uk
Web: www.westin.co.uk

Westin manufacture and supply custom-built
kitchen extraction systems, built-in extraction,
stainless steel cooker hoods, worktops, doors
and splashbacks and also provide expert after-
sales care.

WINNING DESIGNS
Dyke Farm, West Chiltington Road,
Pulborough, West Sussex, RH20 2EE
Area of Operation: UK & Ireland
Tel: 0870 754 4446
Fax: 0700 032 9946
Email: info@winning-designs-uk.com
Web: www.winning-designs-uk.com
Other Info: ▽ ECO

WOODEN HEART WAREHOUSE
Laburnum Road, Chertsey, Surrey, KT16 8BY
Area of Operation: Greater London, South East England
Tel: 01932 568684 **Fax:** 01932 568685
Email: whw@btclick.com

COOKERS AND RANGES

AGA-RAYBURN
Station Road, Ketley, Telford, Shropshire, TF1 5AQ
Area of Operation: Worldwide
Tel: 01952 642000 **Fax:** 01952 243138
Email: jkingsbury-webber@aga-web.co.uk
Web: www.aga-web.co.uk **Product Type:** 2, 3

AMBER KITCHENS OF BISHOP'S STORTFORD
Clarklands House, Parsonage Lane,
Sawbridgeworth, Hertfordshire, CM21 0NG
Area of Operation: East England, Greater London
Tel: 01279 600030
Fax: 01279 721528
Email: info@amberkitchens.com
Web: www.amberkitchens.com
Product Type: 1, 2, 3, 4, 5

ASHFORD & BROOKS
The Old Workshop, Ashtree Barn, Caters Road,
Bredfield, Woodbridge, Suffolk, IP13 6BE
Area of Operation: UK (Excluding Ireland)
Tel: 01473 737764
Fax: 01473 277176
Email: ashfordbrooks@mailbox.co.uk
Web: www.ashfordandbrooks.co.uk
Product Type: 1, 2, 3, 4, 5

BATH KITCHEN COMPANY
22 Hensley Road, Bloomfield, Bath, Somerset, BA2 2DR
Area of Operation: South West England and South Wales
Tel: 01225 312003 **Fax:** 01225 312003
Email: david@bathkitchencompany.co.uk
Web: www.bathkitchencompany.co.uk

BAUMATIC LTD
Baumatic Buildings,
6 Bennet Road, Berkshire, RG2 0QX
Area of Operation: Europe
Tel: 01189 336900 **Fax:** 01189 310035
Email: sales@baumatic.co.uk
Web: www.baumatic.com **Product Type:** 1, 3, 5

BEAU-PORT LTD
Unit 2, Elhanger Business Park,
Bentworth, Hampshire, GU34 5Q2
Area of Operation: UK & Ireland
Tel: 0845 230 1545 **Fax:** 0870 350 0134
Email: sales@beau-port.co.uk
Web: www.beau-port.co.uk
Product Type: 1, 2, 3, 4, 5

BELLING
Stoney Lane, Prescot, Merseyside, L35 2XW
Area of Operation: UK & Ireland
Tel: 0870 444 9929 **Fax:** 0870 458 9693
Web: www.belling.co.uk **Product Type:** 1, 3, 5

BRADSHAW APPLIANCES
Kenn Road, Clevedon, Bristol, Somerset, BS21 6LH
Area of Operation: UK & Ireland
Tel: 01275 343000 **Fax:** 01275 343454
Email: info@bradshaw.co.uk
Web: www.bradshaw.co.uk
Product Type: 1, 2, 3, 5

BRITANNIA LIVING LTD
Britannia House, 281 Bristol Avenue,
Blackpool, Lancashire, FY2 0JF
Area of Operation: UK & Ireland
Tel: 01253 471111
Fax: 01253 471136
Email: enquiry@britannialiving.co.uk
Web: www.britannialiving.co.uk
Product Type: 1, 2, 3, 5

BRITANNIA LIVING LTD
Area of Operation: UK & Ireland
Tel: 01253 471111
Fax: 01253 471136
Email: enquiry@britannialiving.co.uk
Web: www.britannialiving.co.uk

Colourange – The cooker of your dreams in any
colour you can dream of… Take your inspiration
from absolutely anywhere! Please call for your
free brochure or advice.

CHRISTOPHER PETERS ORIGINAL UNFITTED KITCHENS
Lower Farm Barns, Brandon Lane,
Warwickshire, CV3 3GW
Area of Operation: Europe
Tel: 02476 303300
Email: enquiries@christopherpetersantiques.co.uk
Web: www.christopherpetersantiques.co.uk

CITY BATHROOMS & KITCHENS
158 Longford Road, Longford,
Coventry, West Midlands, CV6 6DR
Area of Operation: UK & Ireland
Tel: 02476 365877 **Fax:** 02476 644992
Email: citybathrooms@hotmail.com
Web: www.citybathrooms.co.uk

CONNAUGHT KITCHENS
2 Porchester Place, London, W2 2BS
Area of Operation: Greater London
Tel: 0207 706 2210 **Fax:** 0207 706 2209
Email: design@connaughtkitchens.co.uk
Web: www.connaughtkitchens.co.uk
Product Type: 1, 2, 3, 4, 5

CONQUIRA LTD
2 Central Buildings, Warwick Road,
Coventry, Warwickshire, CV8 1FQ
Area of Operation: Midlands & Mid Wales
Tel: 02476 222255 **Fax:** 02476 552211
Email: gary@conquira.freeserve.co.uk
Web: www.conquira.co.uk **Product Type:** 1, 2, 3, 5

COUNTRY KITCHENS
The Old Farm House, Birmingham Road,
Blackminster, Evesham, Worcestershire, WR11 7TD
Area of Operation: UK (Excluding Ireland)
Tel: 01386 831705
Fax: 01386 834051
Web: www.handcraftedkitchens.com
Product Type: 1, 2, 3, 4, 5

CRABTREE KITCHENS
17 Station Road, Barnes, Greater London, SW13 0LF
Area of Operation: Greater London, South West
England and South Wales
Tel: 0208 392 6955 **Fax:** 0208 392 6944
Email: design@crabtreekitchens.co.uk
Web: www.crabtreekitchens.co.uk
Product Type: 1, 2, 3, 4, 5

CYMRU KITCHENS
63 Caerleon Road, Newport, NP19 7BX
Area of Operation: UK (Excluding Ireland)
Tel: 01633 676767
Fax: 01633 212512
Email: sales@cymrukitchens.com
Web: www.cymrukitchens.com
Product Type: 1, 2, 3, 4, 5

The cooker of your dreams in any colour you can dream of.

DESIGNER KITCHENS
37 High Street, Potters Bar, Hertfordshire, EN6 5AJ
Area of Operation: Greater London
Tel: 01707 650565 **Fax:** 01707 663050
Email: info@designer-kitchens.co.uk
Web: www.designer-kitchens.co.uk
Product Type: 1, 2, 3, 5

DISCOUNT APPLIANCE CENTRE
Cook House, Brunel Drive, Newark,
Nottingham, Nottinghamshire, NG24 2FB
Area of Operation: Worldwide
Tel: 0870 067 1420 **Fax:** 01636 707737
Email: info@thedac.co.uk
Web: www.thedac.co.uk
Product Type: 1, 2, 3, 4, 5

DUNSLEY HEAT LTD
Bridge Mills, Huddersfield Road, Holmfirth,
Huddersfield, West Yorkshire, HD9 3TW
Area of Operation: UK & Ireland
Tel: 01484 682635
Fax: 01484 688428
Email: sales@dunsleyheat.co.uk
Web: www.dunsleyheat.co.uk **Product Type:** 2

ELITE TRADE KITCHENS LTD
90 Willesden Lane, Kilburn, London, NW6 7TA
Area of Operation: UK (Excluding Ireland)
Tel: 0207 328 1234 **Fax:** 0207 328 1243
Email: sales@elitekitchens.co.uk
Web: www.elitekitchens.co.uk
Product Type: 1, 2, 3, 5

EVERHOT COOKERS
Coaley Mill, Coaley, Nr Dursley,
Gloucestershire, GL11 5DS
Area of Operation: UK & Ireland
Tel: 01453 890018 **Fax:** 01453 890958
Email: sales@everhot.co.uk
Web: www.everhot.co.uk
Product Type: 3 **Other Info:**

FALCON APPLIANCES
Clarence Street, Royal Leamington Spa,
Warwickshire, CV31 2AD
Area of Operation: Worldwide
Tel: 0845 634 0070 **Fax:** 01926 311032
Email: consumers@falconappliances.co.uk
Web: www.falconappliances.co.uk
Product Type: 1, 2, 3

FALCON APPLIANCES

Area of Operation: Worldwide
Tel: 0845 634 0070
Fax: 01926 311032
Email: consumers@falconappliances.co.uk
Web: www.falconappliances.co.uk

Falcon range cookers, refrigeration products, sinks and taps combines the build quality and performance expected by the professional chef with the design flair that the modern home enthusiast desires.

FIREPLACE DESIGN CONSULTANCY
Stansley Wood Farm, Dapple Heath,
Rugeley, Staffordshire, WS15 3PH
Tel: 01889 500500 **Fax:** 01889 500500
Email: info@inglenooks.co.uk
Web: www.inglenooks.co.uk

FOURNEAUX DE FRANCE LTD (FDF)
Unit 3, Albion Close,
Newtown Business Park,
Poole, Dorset, BH12 3LL
Area of Operation: UK & Ireland
Tel: 01202 733011 **Fax:** 01202 733499
Email: sales@fdef.co.uk
Web: www.fdef.co.uk
Product Type: 1, 2, 3, 4, 5

GORENJE UK
Tuition House, 27-37 St George's Road,
London, SW19 4EU
Area of Operation: UK & Ireland
Tel: 0208 247 3980 **Fax:** 0208 247 3999
Email: reception@gorenjeuk.co.uk
Web: www.gorenje.co.uk **Product Type:** 1, 5

HATT KITCHENS
Hartlebury Trading Estate,
Hartlebury, Worcestershire, DY10 4JB
Area of Operation: UK (Excluding Ireland)
Tel: 01299 251320 **Fax:** 01299 251579
Email: design@hatt.co.uk
Web: www.hatt.co.uk **Product Type:** 1, 2, 3, 4, 5

HERITAGE RANGE COOKERS
2/3 Miller Business Park, Station Road,
Liskeard, Cornwall, PL14 4DA
Area of Operation: UK & Ireland
Tel: 01579 345680
Fax: 01579 346439
Email: enquiries@heritagecookers.co.uk
Web: www.heritagecookers.co.uk
Product Type: 2, 3

HOOVER CANDY GROUP BUILT-IN DIVISION
New Chester Road, Bromborough, Wirral, CH62 3PE
Area of Operation: Europe
Tel: 0151 334 2781
Fax: 0151 334 9056
Web: www.candy-domestic.co.uk
Product Type: 1, 2, 5

INDESIT
Morley Way, Peterborough, Cambridgeshire, PE2 9JB
Area of Operation: UK & Ireland
Tel: 01733 282800
Email: info@indesitcompany.com
Web: www.indesit.com
Product Type: 1, 2, 3, 5

IN-TOTO
Shaw Cross Court, Shaw Cross Business Park,
Dewsbury, West Yorkshire, WF12 7RF
Area of Operation: UK (Excluding Ireland)
Tel: 01924 487900 **Fax:** 01924 437305
Email: graham.russell@intoto.co.uk
Web: www.intoto.co.uk
Product Type: 1, 2, 3, 5

JJO PLC (J&J ORMEROD)
Colonial House, Bacup, Lancashire, OL13 0EA
Area of Operation: UK & Ireland
Tel: 01706 877877 **Fax:** 01706 879827
Email: npeters@jjoplc.com
Web: www.jjoplc.com **Product Type:** 1, 2, 3, 4, 5

JOHN LEWIS OF HUNGERFORD
Grove Technology Park, Downsview Road,
Wantage, Oxfordshire, OX12 9FA
Area of Operation: UK (Excluding Ireland)
Tel: 01235 774300 **Fax:** 01235 769031
Email: park.street@john-lewis.co.uk
Web: www.john-lewis.co.uk
Product Type: 1, 2, 3, 5

KENSINGTON STUDIO
13 c & d Kensington Road, Earlsdon,
Coventry, West Midlands, CV5 6GG
Area of Operation: UK (Excluding Ireland)
Tel: 02476 713326
Fax: 02476 713136
Email: sales@kensingtonstudio.com
Web: www.kensingtonstudio.com
Product Type: 1, 2, 3, 4, 5

DOMESTIC GOD

Lofty Manhattan-style fridge freezer in stainless steel. Super cool.

DOMESTIC GODDESS

- Makes a hundred ice cubes all in one go. (Cheers.)
- Dispenses up to 6 litres of chilled water at a time (such largesse).
- Never needs to defrost either fridge or freezer, thank heavens.

For a free brochure call 0870 513 3090 www.neff.co.uk

Email: info@neff.co.uk
Website: www.neff.co.uk

Neff is the UK's foremost brand of built-in appliances designed specifically for building in to kitchen furniture. The company is most well known for its award-winning collection of single and double ovens featuring the famous CircoTherm system of forced air cooking, much imitated but never equalled.

Also available to match are hobs & hoods, plus compact appliances such as microwaves, warming drawers and coffee machine. Dishwashers, refrigeration and laundry products complete the coordinated line-up for the modern fitted kitchen.

For the latest Neff brochure & stockist list, call **0870 513 3090** or visit the website at www.neff.co.uk

N7290

The heat will be on if you add one of Neff's two new warming drawers, either for 6 or 12 place settings (as shown), to your new kitchen.

B6774

Combine a multifunction oven with microwave technology to create this compact cooking appliance with 51 automatic programmes.

C7660

Come home to freshly brewed coffee with this stunning built in coffee centre, designed to coordinate with Neff's cooking appliance range

T4593

With a choice of 5 cooking zones including a large 28cm central zone, this new 90cm wide induction hob is a very powerful newcomer to the range.

T27F7

Gas on glass is the perfect combination for those who prefer the speed of gas and the ease of cleaning associated with a ceramic surface.

T1683

There are four cooking zones to choose from on this impressive new Piezo ceramic hob available in both 60cm and 80cm wide versions

T26F1

At 70cm wide, this new top of the range gas hob incorporates high speed & economy burners as well as a wok burner for size and power.

F3470

Be the envy of your neighbours with this majestic new triple cavity range cooker offering total flexibility for professional cooking capabilities.

B1644

Electronic control is just one of the many features of this impressive multifunction single oven with telescopic FlexiRail shelving system. Available in black as well as stainless steel.

U1644

This top-of-the-range double oven boasts electronic control with ClearText for a host of impressive cooking and easy cleaning options. Available in black as well as stainless steel.

U1744

Designed to fit under the worktop, this compact double oven is the answer to all your space requirements. Available in three colourways.

MARK LEIGH KITCHENS LTD
11 Common Garden Street,
Lancaster, Lancashire, LA1 1XD
Area of Operation: North West England and North Wales
Tel: 01524 63273   **Fax:** 01524 62352
Email: mark@markleigh.co.uk
Web: www.markleigh.co.uk
Product Type: 1, 2, 3, 4, 5
Other Info: ✎

MAYTAG
2 St. Annes Boulevard, Foxboro Business Park,
Redhill, Surrey, RH1 1AX
Area of Operation: UK & Ireland
Tel: 01737 231000   **Fax:** 01737 778822
Email: ukquery@maytag.com
Web: www.maytag.co.uk   **Product Type:** 3

MERCURY APPLIANCES
Whisby Road, Lincoln, Lincolnshire, LN6 3QZ
Area of Operation: Europe
Tel: 01522 881717   **Fax:** 01522 880220
Email: sales@mercury-appliances.co.uk
Web: www.mercury-appliances.co.uk
Product Type: 1, 2, 3, 4, 5

MEREWAY CONTRACTS
Unit 1 Wharfdale Road, Tysely,
Birmingham, West Midlands, B11 2DE
Area of Operation: UK (Excluding Ireland)
Tel: 0121 764 7180
Fax: 0121 764 7199
Email: info@merewaycontracts.co.uk
Web: www.merewaycontracts.co.uk

MONTANA KITCHENS LTD
BIC 1, Studio 2/3 Innova Business Park,
Mollison Avenue, Enfield, Middlesex, EN3 7XU
Area of Operation: Greater London, South East England
Tel: 0800 58 75 628
Email: angie@montanakitchens.co.uk
Web: www.montanakitchens.co.uk
Product Type: 1, 2, 3, 4, 5

NEFF UK
Grand Union House, Old Wolverton Road, Wolverton,
Milton Keynes, Buckinghamshire, MK12 5PT
Area of Operation: UK (Excluding Ireland)
Tel: 01908 328300   **Fax:** 01908 328560
Email: info@neff.co.uk
Web: www.neff.co.uk   **Product Type:** 1, 3, 5

NEW WORLD
Stoney Lane, Prescot, Merseyside, L35 2XW
Area of Operation: UK & Ireland
Tel: 0870 444 9929
Fax: 0870 458 9693
Email: newworld@gdha.com
Web: www.newworldappliances.co.uk
Product Type: 1, 2, 3

NICHOLAS ANTHONY LTD
42-44 Wigmore Street, London, W1U 2RX
Area of Operation: East England, Greater London,
South East England
Tel: 0800 068 3603   **Fax:** 01206 762698
Email: info@nicholas-anthony.co.uk
Web: www.nicholas-anthony.co.uk
Product Type: 1, 3, 5

NTP KITCHENS & JOINERY LTD
Unit 20/1, West Bowling Green Street,
Edinburgh, EH6 5PE
Area of Operation: Scotland
Tel: 0131 554 8787   **Fax:** 0131 554 9191
Email: sales@ntp-kitchens.co.uk
Web: www.ntp-kitchens.co.uk
Product Type: 1, 2, 3, 4, 5

PHIL GREEN & SON
Unit 7, Maylite Trading Estate, Berrow Green Road,
Martley, Worcester, Worcestershire, WR6 6PQ
Area of Operation: UK (Excluding Ireland)
Tel: 01885 488936
Fax: 01885 488936
Email: info@philgreenandson.co.uk
Web: www.philgreenandson.co.uk
Product Type: 2

PRICE KITCHENS
11 Imperial Way, Croydon, Surrey, CR0 4RR
Area of Operation: South East England
Tel: 0208 686 9006
Fax: 0208 686 5958
Email: info@pricekitchens.co.uk
Web: www.pricekitchens.co.uk
Product Type: 1, 2, 3, 5

PRIMA APPLIANCES
PJH Group, Alder House, Kearsley,
Bolton, Lancashire, BL4 8SL
Area of Operation: UK & Ireland
Tel: 01204 707070   **Fax:** 01204 573140
Email: info@pjh.co.uk
Web: www.pjhdistribution.com
Product Type: 1, 5

RANGE COOKERS
3 Lime Grove, Hoole, Chester, Cheshire, CH2 3HW
Area of Operation: UK & Ireland
Tel: 01244 345888
Fax: 01244 400224
Email: enquires@rangecookers.co.uk
Web: www.rangecookers.co.uk ✎
Product Type: 1, 2, 3

RANGEMASTER
Clarence Street, Royal Leamington Spa,
Warwickshire, CV31 2AD
Area of Operation: Worldwide
Tel: 01926 457400   **Fax:** 01926 450526
Email: consumers@rangemaster.co.uk
Web: www.rangemaster.co.uk
Product Type: 1, 3, 5

REDFYRE COOKERS
Osprey Road, Sowton Industrial Estate,
Exeter, Devon, EX2 7JG
Area of Operation: UK & Ireland
Tel: 01392 474061   **Fax:** 01392 444804
Email: redfyre@gazco.com
Web: www.redfyrecookers.co.uk   **Product Type:** 2

ROBEYS
Belper, Derbyshire, DE56 1BY
Area of Operation: UK & Ireland
Tel: 01773 820940   **Fax:** 01773 821652
Email: info@robeys.co.uk
Web: www.robeys.co.uk   **Product Type:** 1, 2, 3

ROUNDEL DESIGN (UK) LTD
Flishinghurst Orchards, Chalk Lane,
Cranbrook, Kent, TN17 2QA
Area of Operation: South East England
Tel: 01580 712666
Email: homebuild@roundeldesign.co.uk
Web: www.roundeldesign.co.uk
Product Type: 1, 2, 3, 5

SMEG UK
3 Milton Park, Abingdon, Oxfordshire, OX14 4RY
Area of Operation: UK & Ireland
Tel: 0870 990 9908   **Fax:** 01235 861120
Email: sales@smeguk.com
Web: www.smeguk.com   **Product Type:** 2, 3, 5

SPILLERS OF CHARD LTD.
Chard Business Park, Chard, Somerset, TA20 1FA
Area of Operation: South West England and South Wales
Tel: 01460 67878
Fax: 01460 65252
Email: info@cookercentre.com
Web: www.cookercentre.com
Product Type: 1, 2, 3, 4, 5

STOVES
Stoney Lane, Prescot, Merseyside, L35 2XW
Area of Operation: UK & Ireland
Tel: 0870 458 9663   **Fax:** 0870 458 9693
Web: www.stoves.co.uk   **Product Type:** 1, 3, 5

STOVES ON LINE LTD
Capton, Dartmouth, Devon, TQ6 0JE
Area of Operation: UK (Excluding Ireland)
Tel: 0845 226 5754   **Fax:** 0870 220 0920
Email: info@stovesonline.co.uk
Web: www.stovesonline.co.uk   **Product Type:** 1

THE AMERICAN APPLIANCE CENTRE
17-19 Mill Lane, Woodford Green, Essex, IG8 0UN
Tel: 0208 505 5616   **Fax:** 0208 505 8700
Email: sales@american-appliance.co.uk
Web: www.american-appliance.co.uk 🖑
Product Type: 1, 2, 3, 4, 5

THE CDA GROUP LTD
Harby Road, Langar, Nottingham,
Nottinghamshire, NG13 9HY
Tel: 01949 862000   **Fax:** 01949 8624001
Email: sales@cda-europe.com
Web: www.cda-europe.com   **Product Type:** 1, 2, 3, 5

THE KITCHEN AND BATHROOM COLLECTION
Nelson House, Nelson Road, Salisbury, Wiltshire, SP1 3LT
Area of Operation: South West England and South Wales
Tel: 01722 334800   **Fax:** 01722 412252
Email: info@kbc.co.uk   **Web:** www.kbc.co.uk
Product Type: 1, 2, 3, 4, 5   **Other Info:** ✎

THE ORIGINAL KITCHEN COMPANY
4 Main Street, Breaston,
Derby, Derbyshire, DE72 3DX
Area of Operation: UK & Ireland
Tel: 01332 873746   **Fax:** 01332 873731
Email: originalkitchens@aol.com

THE WESTYE GROUP EUROPE LTD
6B Imprimo Park, Lenthall Road,
Debden, Essex, IG10 3UF
Area of Operation: Europe
Tel: 0208 418 3800   **Email:** gshine@westye.co.uk
Web: www.westye.co.uk   **Product Type:** 1, 2, 5

TRADE APPLIANCES LTD
Cathedral Warehouse, Common Road, Huthwaite,
Sutton in Ashfield, Nottinghamshire, NG17 2JL
Tel: 0800 195 9596   **Fax:** 01623 445083
Email: info@trade-appliances.co.uk
Web: www.trade-appliances.co.uk
Product Type: 1, 2, 3, 4, 5

TWYFORD COOKERS
31/32 Three Elms Trading Estate,
Bakers Lane, Hereford, Herefordshire, HR4 9PU
Area of Operation: Worldwide
Tel: 01432 355924   **Fax:** 01432 272664
Email: md@twyford-cookers.com
Web: www.twyford-cookers.com
Product Type: 1, 2, 3

WATERFORD STANLEY
Unit B8, Whitwood Enterprise Park, Speedwell Road,
Castleford, West Yorkshire, WF105PX
Area of Operation: UK & Ireland
Tel: 01977 603427   **Fax:** 01977 603692
Email: gbsales@waterfordstanley.com
Web: www.waterfordstanley.com
Product Type: 1, 2, 3

WATERFORD STANLEY
Area of Operation: UK & Ireland
Tel: 01977 603427
Fax: 01977 603692
Email: gbsales@waterfordstanley.com
Web: www.waterfordstanley.com
Product Type: 1, 2, 3
The Stanley family is one that stretches back through generations to when the first range cooker was made in Waterford in 1936. Nothing makes a statement like a Stanley range cooker in your home.

WINNING DESIGNS
Dyke Farm, West Chiltington Road,
Pulborough, West Sussex, RH20 2EE
Area of Operation: UK & Ireland
Tel: 0870 754 4446   **Fax:** 0700 032 9946
Email: info@winning-designs.co.uk
Web: www.winning-designs-uk.com
Product Type: 1, 2, 3, 4, 5

APPLIANCES & WHITE GOODS

KEY
PRODUCT TYPES: 1= Fridges   2 = Freezers
3 = Fridge Freezers   4 = Dishwashers
5 = Waste Disposal Units   6 = Washing
Machines   7 = Tumble Dryers   8 = Microwaves

OTHER: ▽ Reclaimed   🖑 On-line shopping
✎ Bespoke   ✋ Hand-made   ECO Ecological

ADMIRAL
2 St Annes Boulevard, Foxboro Business Park,
Redhill, Surrey, RH1 1AX
Area of Operation: UK & Ireland
Tel: 01737 231000   **Fax:** 01737 778822
Email: ukquery@maytag.com
Web: www.maytag.co.uk
Product Type: 1, 2, 3, 6, 7

AMANA
2 St Annes Boulevard, Foxboro Business Park,
Redhill, Surrey, RH1 1AX
Area of Operation: UK & Ireland
Tel: 01737 231000   **Fax:** 01737 778822
Email: info.uk@amana.com
Web: www.amana.co.uk   **Product Type:** 3, 4

AMBER KITCHENS OF BISHOP'S STORTFORD
Clarklands House, Parsonage Lane,
Sawbridgeworth, Hertfordshire, CM21 0NG
Area of Operation: East England, Greater London
Tel: 01279 600030   **Fax:** 01279 721528
Email: info@amberkitchens.com
Web: www.amberkitchens.com
Product Type: 1, 2, 3, 4, 5, 6, 7, 8   **Other Info:** ✎

ASHFORD & BROOKS
The Old Workshop, Ashtree Barn, Caters Road,
Bredfield, Woodbridge, Suffolk, IP13 6BE
Area of Operation: UK (Excluding Ireland)
Tel: 01473 737764
Fax: 01473 277176
Email: ashfordbrooks@mailbox.co.uk
Web: www.ashfordandbrooks.co.uk
Product Type: 1, 2, 3, 4, 5, 6, 7, 8

BATH KITCHEN COMPANY
22 Hensley Road, Bloomfield,
Bath, Somerset, BA2 2DR
Area of Operation: South West England and South Wales
Tel: 01225 312003   **Fax:** 01225 312003
Email: david@bathkitchencompany.co.uk
Web: www.bathkitchencompany.co.uk

BAUMATIC LTD
Baumatic Buildings,
6 Bennet Road, Berkshire, RG2 0QX
Area of Operation: Europe
Tel: 01189 336900   **Fax:** 01189 310035
Email: sales@baumatic.co.uk
Web: www.baumatic.com   **Product Type:** 1, 3, 4, 6

BEAU-PORT LTD
Unit 2, Elhanger Business Park,
Bentworth, Hampshire, GU34 5Q2
Area of Operation: UK & Ireland
Tel: 0845 230 1545   **Fax:** 0870 350 0134
Email: info@beau-port.co.uk
Web: www.beau-port.co.uk 🖑
Product Type: 1, 2, 3, 4, 5, 6, 7, 8

BELLING
Stoney Lane, Prescot, Merseyside, L35 2XW
Area of Operation: UK & Ireland
Tel: 0870 444 9929 **Fax:** 0870 458 9693
Web: www.belling.co.uk
Product Type: 1, 2, 3, 4, 6, 8

BRADSHAW APPLIANCES
Kenn Road, Clevedon, Bristol, Somerset, BS21 6LH
Area of Operation: UK & Ireland
Tel: 01275 343000 **Fax:** 01275 343454
Email: info@bradshaw.co.uk
Web: www.bradshaw.co.uk
Product Type: 1, 2, 3, 4, 8

CARE DESIGN
Moorgate, Ormskirk, Lancashire, L39 4RX
Area of Operation: UK (Excluding Ireland)
Tel: 01695 579061 **Fax:** 01695 570489
Email: caredesign@clara.net
Web: www.caredesign.co.uk
Product Type: 1, 2, 3, 4, 6, 7, 8

CITY BATHROOMS & KITCHENS
158 Longford Road, Longford,
Coventry, West Midlands, CV6 6DR
Area of Operation: UK & Ireland
Tel: 02476 365877 **Fax:** 02476 644992
Email: citybathrooms@hotmail.com
Web: www.citybathrooms.co.uk

CONNAUGHT KITCHENS
2 Porchester Place, London, W2 2BS
Area of Operation: Greater London
Tel: 0207 706 2210 **Fax:** 0207 706 2209
Email: design@connaughtkitchens.co.uk
Web: www.connaughtkitchens.co.uk
Product Type: 1, 2, 3, 4, 5, 6, 7, 8

CORNER FRIDGE COMPANY
Unit 6 Harworth Enterprise Park, Brunel Industrial Esate,
Harworth, Doncaster, South Yorkshire, DN11 8SG
Area of Operation: UK & Ireland
Tel: 01302 759308 **Fax:** 01302 751233
Email: info@cornerfridge.com
Web: www.cornerfridge.com **Product Type:** 1

COUNTRY KITCHENS
The Old Farm House, Birmingham Road,
Blackminster, Evesham, Worcestershire, WR11 7TD
Area of Operation: UK (Excluding Ireland)
Tel: 01386 831705 **Fax:** 01386 834051
Web: www.handcraftedkitchens.com
Product Type: 1, 2, 3, 4, 5, 6, 7, 8

CRABTREE KITCHENS
17 Station Road, Barnes, Greater London, SW13 0LF
Area of Operation: Greater London, South West
England and South Wales
Tel: 0208 392 6955 **Fax:** 0208 392 6944
Email: design@crabtreekitchens.co.uk
Web: www.crabtreekitchens.co.uk
Product Type: 1, 2, 3, 4, 5, 6, 7, 8

CYMRU KITCHENS
63 Caerleon Road, Newport, NP19 7BX
Area of Operation: UK (Excluding Ireland)
Tel: 01633 676767 **Fax:** 01633 212512
Email: sales@cymrukitchens.com
Web: www.cymrukitchens.com
Product Type: 1, 2, 3, 4, 5, 6, 7, 8

DESIGNER KITCHENS
37 High Street, Potters Bar, Hertfordshire, EN6 5AJ
Area of Operation: Greater London
Tel: 01707 650565 **Fax:** 01707 663050
Email: info@designer-kitchens.co.uk
Web: www.designer-kitchens.co.uk
Product Type: 1, 2, 3, 4, 5, 6, 7, 8

DISCOUNT APPLIANCE CENTRE
Cook House, Brunel Drive, Newark,
Nottingham, Nottinghamshire, NG24 2FB
Area of Operation: Worldwide
Tel: 0870 067 1420 **Fax:** 01636 707 737
Email: info@thedac.co.uk
Web: www.thedac.co.uk
Product Type: 1, 2, 3, 4, 5, 6, 7, 8

ELITE TRADE KITCHENS LTD
90 Willesden Lane, Kilburn, London, NW6 7TA
Area of Operation: UK (Excluding Ireland)
Tel: 0207 328 1234 **Fax:** 0207 328 1243
Email: sales@elitekitchens.co.uk
Web: www.elitekitchens.co.uk
Product Type: 1, 2, 3, 4, 6, 8

EUROFLEX
Portman House, Millbrook Road East,
Southampton, Hampshire, SO15 1HN
Area of Operation: UK & Ireland
Tel: 02380 635131 **Fax:** 02380 635303
Email: sales@euroflex.co.uk
Web: www.euroflex.co.uk

FALCON APPLIANCES
Clarence Street, Royal Leamington Spa,
Warwickshire, CV31 2AD
Area of Operation: Worldwide
Tel: 0845 634 0070 **Fax:** 01926 311032
Email: consumers@falconappliances.co.uk
Web: www.falconappliances.co.uk
Product Type: 1, 2

FOURNEAUX DE FRANCE LTD (FDF)
Unit 3, Albion Close, Newtown Business Park,
Poole, Dorset, BH12 3LL
Area of Operation: UK & Ireland
Tel: 01202 733011 **Fax:** 01202 733499
Email: sales@fdef.co.uk
Web: www.fdef.co.uk **Product Type:** 1, 2, 3

FRANKE UK LTD
West Park, Manchester International Office,
Styal Road, Manchester, M22 5WB
Area of Operation: UK & Ireland
Tel: 0161 436 6280 **Fax:** 0161 436 2180
Email: info.uk@franke.com
Web: www.franke.co.uk

GORENJE UK
Tuition House, 27-37 St George's Road,
London, SW19 4EU
Area of Operation: UK & Ireland
Tel: 0208 247 3980 **Fax:** 0208 247 3999
Email: reception@gorenjeuk.co.uk
Web: www.gorenje.co.uk
Product Type: 1, 2, 3, 4, 6, 7, 8

HATT KITCHENS
Hartlebury Trading Estate,
Hartlebury, Worcestershire, DY10 4JB
Area of Operation: UK (Excluding Ireland)
Tel: 01299 251320 **Fax:** 01299 251579
Email: design@hatt.co.uk **Web:** www.hatt.co.uk
Product Type: 1, 2, 3, 4, 5, 6, 7, 8

HOOVER CANDY GROUP BUILT-IN DIVISION
New Chester Road, Bromborough, Wirral, CH62 3PE
Area of Operation: Europe
Tel: 0151 334 2781 **Fax:** 0151 334 9056
Web: www.candy-domestic.co.uk
Product Type: 1, 2, 3, 4, 6, 8

INDESIT
Morley Way, Peterborough, Cambridgeshire, PE2 9JB
Area of Operation: UK & Ireland
Tel: 01733 282800
Email: info@indesitcompany.com
Web: www.indesit.com
Product Type: 1, 2, 3, 4, 6, 7

INSINKERATOR
Emerson Electric UK Ltd, 6 The Courtyards, Croxley
Business Park, Watford, Hertfordshire, WD18 8YH
Area of Operation: Worldwide
Tel: 01923 297880 **Fax:** 01923 800628
Email: insinkeratoruk@insinkerator.com
Web: www.insinkerator.co.uk **Product Type:** 5

IN-TOTO
Shaw Cross Court, Shaw Cross Business Park,
Dewsbury, West Yorkshire, WF12 7RF
Area of Operation: UK (Excluding Ireland)
Tel: 01924 487900 **Fax:** 01924 437305
Email: graham.russell@intoto.co.uk
Web: www.intoto.co.uk
Product Type: 1, 2, 3, 4, 5, 6, 7, 8

J&J ORMEROD PLC
Colonial House, Bacup, Lancashire, OL13 0EA
Area of Operation: UK & Ireland
Tel: 01706 877877 **Fax:** 01706 879827
Email: info@jjoplc.com **Web:** www.jjoplc.com

JJO PLC (J&J ORMEROD)
Colonial House, Bacup, Lancashire, OL13 0EA
Area of Operation: UK & Ireland
Tel: 01706 877877 **Fax:** 01706 879827
Email: npeters@jjoplc.com **Web:** www.jjoplc.com
Product Type: 1, 2, 3, 4, 5, 6, 7, 8

JOHN LEWIS OF HUNGERFORD
Grove Technology Park, Downsview Road,
Wantage, Oxfordshire, OX12 9FA
Area of Operation: UK (Excluding Ireland)
Tel: 01235 774300 **Fax:** 01235 769031
Email: park.street@john-lewis.co.uk
Web: www.john-lewis.co.uk
Product Type: 1, 2, 3, 4, 5, 6, 7, 8

KENSINGTON STUDIO
13 c & d Kensington Road, Earlsdon,
Coventry, West Midlands, CV5 6GG
Area of Operation: UK (Excluding Ireland)
Tel: 02476 713326 **Fax:** 02476 713136
Email: sales@kensingtonstudio.com
Web: www.kensingtonstudio.com
Product Type: 1, 2, 3, 4, 5, 6, 7, 8

KITCHENS BY JULIAN ENGLISH
Ideal Home, Blackbird Road,
Leicester, Leicestershire, LE4 0AH
Area of Operation: Midlands & Mid Wales
Tel: 0116 251 9999 **Fax:** 0116 251 9999
Email: philiphalifax@aol.com
Web: www.kitchens-by-julianenglish.co.uk

LEC REFRIGERATION
Glen Dimplex Home Appliances,
Stoney Lane, Prescot, Merseyside, L35 2XW
Area of Operation: UK & Ireland
Tel: 0870 458 4378 **Web:** www.lec.co.uk
Product Type: 1, 2, 3

LIEBHERR
Coolectric Limited, Interchange Point, Renny Park
Road, Newport Pagnell, Buckinghamshire, MK16 0HA
Area of Operation: UK & Ireland
Tel: 0870 898 5050 **Fax:** 01908 219760
Email: mark.bristow@coolectric.co.uk
Product Type: 1, 3

MARK LEIGH KITCHENS LTD
11 Common Garden Street,
Lancaster, Lancashire, LA1 1XD
Area of Operation: North West England and North Wales
Tel: 01524 63273 **Fax:** 01524 62352
Email: mark@markleigh.co.uk
Web: www.markleigh.co.uk
Product Type: 1, 2, 3, 4, 5, 6, 7, 8 **Other Info:** ✎

MAYTAG
2 St. Annes Boulevard, Foxboro Business Park,
Redhill, Surrey, RH1 1AX
Area of Operation: UK & Ireland
Tel: 01737 231000 **Fax:** 01737 778822
Email: ukquery@maytag.com
Web: www.maytag.co.uk **Product Type:** 3, 4, 6, 7

MEREWAY CONTRACTS
Unit 1 Wharfdale Road, Tysely,
Birmingham, West Midlands, B11 2DE
Area of Operation: UK (Excluding Ireland)
Tel: 0121 764 7180
Fax: 0121 764 7199
Email: info@merewaycontracts.co.uk
Web: www.merewaycontracts.co.uk

MONTANA KITCHENS LTD
BIC 1, Studio 2/3 Innova Business Park,
Mollison Avenue, Enfield, Middlesex, EN3 7XU
Area of Operation: Greater London, South East England
Tel: 0800 58 75 628
Email: angie@montanakitchens.co.uk
Web: www.montanakitchens.co.uk
Product Type: 1, 2, 3, 4, 5, 6, 7, 8

MWD
Clutton Hill Estate, King Lane,
Clutton Hill, Bristol, BS39 5QQ
Area of Operation: Midlands & Mid Wales, South
West England and South Wales
Tel: 0870 033 2288 **Fax:** 0800 197 6593
Email: sales@mwdretail.com
Web: www.mikewalker.co.uk

NEFF UK
Grand Union House, Old Wolverton Road, Wolverton,
Milton Keynes, Buckinghamshire, MK12 5PT
Area of Operation: UK (Excluding Ireland)
Tel: 01908 328300 **Fax:** 01908 328560
Email: info@neff.co.uk **Web:** www.neff.co.uk
Product Type: 1, 2, 3, 6, 7

NEW WORLD
Stoney Lane, Prescot, Merseyside, L35 2XW
Area of Operation: UK & Ireland
Tel: 0870 444 9929 **Fax:** 0870 458 9693
Email: newworld@gdha.com
Web: www.newworldappliances.co.uk
Product Type: 1, 2, 3, 4, 6, 8

NICHOLAS ANTHONY LTD
42-44 Wigmore Street, London, W1U 2RX
Area of Operation: East England, Greater London,
South East England
Tel: 0800 068 3603 **Fax:** 01206 762698
Email: info@nicholas-anthony.co.uk
Web: www.nicholas-anthony.co.uk
Product Type: 1, 2, 3, 4, 5, 6, 7, 8

NTP KITCHENS & JOINERY LTD
Unit 20/1, West Bowling Green Street,
Edinburgh, EH6 5PE
Area of Operation: Scotland
Tel: 0131 554 8787 **Fax:** 0131 554 9191
Email: sales@ntp-kitchens.co.uk
Web: www.ntp-kitchens.co.uk
Product Type: 1, 2, 3, 4, 5, 6, 7, 8

PRICE KITCHENS
11 Imperial Way, Croydon, Surrey, CR0 4RR
Area of Operation: South East England
Tel: 0208 686 9006 **Fax:** 0208 686 5958
Email: info@pricekitchens.co.uk
Web: www.pricekitchens.co.uk
Product Type: 1, 2, 3, 4, 5, 6, 7, 8

PRIMA APPLIANCES
PJH Group, Alder House, Kearsley,
Bolton, Lancashire, BL4 8SL
Tel: 01204 707070 **Fax:** 01204 573140
Email: info@pjh.co.uk **Web:** www.pjhdistribution.com
Product Type: 1, 2, 3, 4, 6, 7, 8

RANGEMASTER
Clarence Street, Royal Leamington Spa,
Warwickshire, CV31 2AD
Area of Operation: Worldwide
Tel: 01926 457400 **Fax:** 01926 450526
Email: consumers@rangemaster.co.uk
Web: www.rangemaster.co.uk **Product Type:** 1, 3

ROBEYS
Belper, Derbyshire, DE56 1BY
Area of Operation: UK & Ireland
Tel: 01773 820940 **Fax:** 01773 821652
Email: info@robeys.co.uk
Web: www.robeys.co.uk **Product Type:** 1, 3

ROUNDEL DESIGN (UK) LTD
Flishinghurst Orchards, Chalk Lane,
Cranbrook, Kent, TN17 2QA
Area of Operation: South East England
Tel: 01580 712666
Email: homebuild@roundeldesign.co.uk
Web: www.roundeldesign.co.uk
Product Type: 1, 2, 3, 4, 5, 6, 7, 8

ROY WARING SOUTH LIMITED
Unit 1, Lodge Lane, Tuxford,
Newark, Nottinghamshire, NG22 0NL
Tel: 01777 872082 **Fax:** 01777 871563
Email: sales@roywaring.co.uk
Web: www.roywaring.co.uk
Product Type: 1, 2, 3, 4, 6, 7, 8

Second Nature
Kitchen Collection

SMEG UK
3 Milton Park, Abingdon, Oxfordshire, OX14 4RY
Area of Operation: UK & Ireland
Tel: 0870 990 9908 **Fax:** 01235 861120
Email: sales@smeguk.com
Web: www.smeguk.com **Product Type:** 1, 4, 6, 7

SPILLERS OF CHARD LTD.
Chard Business Park, Chard, Somerset, TA20 1FA
Area of Operation: South West England and South Wales
Tel: 01460 67878 **Fax:** 01460 65252
Email: info@cookercentre.com
Web: www.cookercentre.com
Product Type: 1, 2, 3, 4, 5, 6, 7, 8

STOVES
Stoney Lane, Prescot, Merseyside, L35 2XW
Area of Operation: UK & Ireland
Tel: 0870 458 9663 **Fax:** 0870 458 9693
Web: www.stoves.co.uk
Product Type: 1, 2, 3, 8

THE AMERICAN APPLIANCE CENTRE
17-19 Mill Lane, Woodford Green, Essex, IG8 0UN
Area of Operation: UK (Excluding Ireland)
Tel: 0208 505 5616 **Fax:** 0208 505 8700
Email: sales@american-appliance.co.uk
Web: www.american-appliance.co.uk ▽
Product Type: 1, 2, 3, 4, 5, 6, 7, 8

THE CDA GROUP LTD
Harby Road, Langar, Nottingham,
Nottinghamshire, NG13 9HY
Area of Operation: UK & Ireland
Tel: 01949 862000 **Fax:** 01949 862001
Email: sales@cda-europe.com
Web: www.cda-europe.com
Product Type: 1, 2, 3, 4, 6, 7, 8

THE HAIGH TWEENY COMPANY LTD
Max Appliances Ltd, Kingfisher House, Wheel Farm
Business Park, Westfield, East Sussex, TN35 4SE
Area of Operation: UK (Excluding Ireland)
Tel: 0700 4893369 **Fax:** 01424 751444
Email: sales@tweeny.co.uk
Web: www.tweeny.co.uk **Product Type:** 5

THE KITCHEN AND BATHROOM COLLECTION
Nelson House, Nelson Road,
Salisbury, Wiltshire, SP1 3LT
Area of Operation: South West England and South Wales
Tel: 01722 334800
Fax: 01722 412252
Email: info@kbc.co.uk **Web:** www.kbc.co.uk
Product Type: 1, 2, 3, 4, 5 **Other Info:** ✎

THE ORIGINAL KITCHEN COMPANY
4 Main Street, Breaston,
Derby, Derbyshire, DE72 3DX
Area of Operation: UK & Ireland
Tel: 01332 873746 **Fax:** 01332 873731
Email: originalkitchens@aol.com

THE WESTYE GROUP EUROPE LTD
6B Imprimo Park, Lenthall Road,
Debden, Essex, IG10 3UF
Area of Operation: Europe
Tel: 0208 418 3800
Email: gshine@westye.co.uk
Web: www.westye.co.uk **Product Type:** 1, 2, 3

TRADE APPLIANCES LTD
Cathedral Warehouse, Common Road, Huthwaite,
Sutton in Ashfield, Nottinghamshire, NG17 2JL
Area of Operation: UK (Excluding Ireland)
Tel: 0800 195 9596
Fax: 01623 445083
Email: info@trade-appliances.co.uk
Web: www.trade-appliances.co.uk
Product Type: 1, 2, 3, 4, 5, 6, 7, 8

WATERPROOFTV.CO.UK
7 Allandale Road, Stoneygate,
Leicester, Leicestershire, LE2 2DA
Area of Operation: Worldwide
Tel: 0116 270 5777 **Fax:** 0116 274 5777
Email: w@terproof.tv
Web: www.waterprooftv.co.uk

WINNING DESIGNS
Dyke Farm, West Chiltington Road,
Pulborough, West Sussex, RH20 2EE
Area of Operation: UK & Ireland
Tel: 0870 754 4446 **Fax:** 0700 032 9946
Email: info@winning-designs-uk.com
Web: www.winning-designs-uk.com
Product Type: 1, 2, 3, 4, 5, 6, 7, 8

WOODEN HEART WAREHOUSE
Laburnum Road, Chertsey, Surrey, KT16 8BY
Area of Operation: Greater London, South East England
Tel: 01932 568684 **Fax:** 01932 568685
Email: whw@btclick.com
Product Type: 1, 2, 3, 4, 5, 6, 7, 8

COMPLETE FITTED KITCHENS

KEY
PRODUCT TYPES: 1= Shaker
2 = Contemporary   3 = Farmhouse
4 = Industrial   5 = Long Island
6 = New England 7 = Period 8 = Minimalist
9 = Other

OTHER: ▽ Reclaimed 📱 On-line shopping
✎ Bespoke ✋ Hand-made ECO Ecological

ALLMILMO UK
Briff Well, Little Lane, Reading, Berkshire, RG7 6QX
Tel: 01635 868181 **Fax:** 01635 869693
Email: allmilmo@aol.com
Web: www.allmilmo.com **Product Type:** 1, 2, 5, 9

AMBER KITCHENS OF BISHOP'S STORTFORD
Clarklands House, Parsonage Lane,
Sawbridgeworth, Hertfordshire, CM21 0NG
Area of Operation: East England, Greater London
Tel: 01279 600030 **Fax:** 01279 721528
Email: info@amberkitchens.com
Web: www.amberkitchens.com
Product Type: 1, 2, 3, 4, 5, 6, 7, 8, 9, 10

ARTICHOKE (KITCHEN AND CABINET MAKERS)
Hortswood, Long Lane, Wrington, Somerset, BS40 5SP
Area of Operation: Worldwide
Tel: 01934 863840 **Fax:** 01934 863841
Email: mail@artichoke-ltd.com
Web: www.artichoke-ltd.com
Product Type: 1, 2, 3, 4, 5, 6, 7, 8, 9

ASHFORD & BROOKS
The Old Workshop, Ashtree Barn, Caters Road,
Bredfield, Woodbridge, Suffolk, IP13 6BE
Tel: 01473 737764 **Fax:** 01473 277176
Email: ashfordbrooks@mailbox.co.uk
Web: www.ashfordandbrooks.co.uk
Product Type: 1, 2, 3, 5, 6, 7, 8, 9, 10

BATH KITCHEN COMPANY
22 Hensley Road, Bloomfield,
Bath, Somerset, BA2 2DR
Area of Operation: South West England and South Wales
Tel: 01225 312003 **Fax:** 01225 312003
Email: david@bathkitchencompany.co.uk
Web: www.bathkitchencompany.co.uk
Product Type: 1, 2, 3, 4, 5, 6, 7, 8, 9 **Other Info:** ✎

BAYFIELD STAIR CO
Unit 4, Praed Road, Trafford Park, Manchester, M17 1PQ
Area of Operation: Worldwide
Tel: 0161 848 0700 **Fax:** 0161 872 2230
Email: sales@bayfieldstairs.co.uk
Web: www.bayfieldstairs.co.uk
Product Type: 1, 2, 3, 4, 5, 6, 7, 8, 9, 10

BLUM UK LTD
Mandeville Drive, Kingston, Milton Keynes, MK10 0AW
Area of Operation: Worldwide
Tel: 01908 285700 **Fax:** 01908 285701
Email: info.uk@blum.com
Web: www.blum.com **Product Type:** 2

BROOKMANS ENGLISH FURNITURE CO LTD
Portland Business Park, Richmond Park Road,
Sheffield, South Yorkshire, S13 8HT
Area of Operation: Worldwide
Tel: 0114 280 0970 **Fax:** 0114 256 1840
Email: jim.brookman@brookmans.co.uk
Web: www.brookmans.co.uk
Product Type: 1, 3, 7, 8

BROOKMANS OF RICKMANSWORTH LTD
1 Moneyhill Parade, Uxbridge Road,
Rickmansworth, Hertfordshire, WD3 7BQ
Area of Operation: Worldwide
Tel: 01923 773906 **Fax:** 01923 896098
Email: celia.warbrick@brookmans.co.uk
Web: www.brookmans.co.uk

BUILDING & DESIGN SOLUTIONS GERMANY
Auf den Haien 14, 55471 Sargenroth, Germany
Area of Operation: UK (Excluding Ireland)
Tel: 0049 6761 970 871
Email: mail@buildingdesign-germany.eu
Web: www.buildingdesign-germany.eu

CAPLE
Fourth Way, Avonmouth, Bristol, BS11 8DW
Area of Operation: UK (Excluding Ireland)
Tel: 0870 6069606 **Fax:** 0117 938 7449
Email: amandalowe@mlay.co.uk
Web: www.mlay.co.uk

CHURCHWOOD DESIGN
Unit 9A & 9B, Whitecross Road Industrial Estate,
Tideswell, Derbyshire, SK17 8PY
Area of Operation: UK (Excluding Ireland)
Tel: 01298 872422 **Fax:** 01298 873068
Web: www.churchwood.co.uk
Product Type: 1, 2, 3, 5, 6, 7, 8, 9

CITY BATHROOMS & KITCHENS
158 Longford Road, Longford,
Coventry, West Midlands, CV6 6DR
Area of Operation: UK & Ireland
Tel: 02476 365877 **Fax:** 02476 644992
Email: citybathrooms@hotmail.com
Web: www.citybathrooms.co.uk

CONNAUGHT KITCHENS
2 Porchester Place, London, W2 2BS
Area of Operation: Greater London
Tel: 0207 706 2210 **Fax:** 0207 706 2209
Email: design@connaughtkitchens.co.uk
Web: www.connaughtkitchens.co.uk
Product Type: 2

CONQUIRA LTD
2 Central Buildings, Warwick Road,
Coventry, Warwickshire, CV8 1FQ
Area of Operation: Midlands & Mid Wales
Tel: 02476 222255 **Fax:** 02476 552211
Email: gary@conquira.freeserve.co.uk
Web: www.conquira.co.uk
Product Type: 1, 2, 3, 5, 6, 7, 8, 9

COTTAGE FARM ANTIQUES
Stratford Road, Aston Sub Edge,
Chipping Campden, Gloucestershire, GL55 6PZ
Area of Operation: Worldwide
Tel: 01386 438263 **Fax:** 01386 438263
Email: info@cottagefarmantiques.co.uk
Web: www.cottagefarmantiques.co.uk ▽
Product Type: 8

COUNTESS(KITCHENS & BEDROOMS) LTD
Mounsey Road, Bamber Bridge,
Preston, Lancashire, PR6 7RA
Area of Operation: North West England and North Wales
Tel: 01772 321218 **Fax:** 01772 316165
Email: sales@countessinteriors.co.uk
Web: www.countessinteriors.co.uk
Product Type: 1, 2, 3, 9, 10 **Other Info:** ✎ ✋

COUNTRY KITCHENS
The Old Farm House, Birmingham Road,
Blackminster, Evesham, Worcestershire, WR11 7TD
Area of Operation: UK (Excluding Ireland)
Tel: 01386 831705 **Fax:** 01386 834051
Web: www.handcraftedkitchens.com
Product Type: 1, 3, 8 **Other Info:** ▽ ✎ ✋

CP HART GROUP
Newnham Terrace, Hercules Road, London, SE1 7DR
Area of Operation: Greater London
Tel: 0845 600 1950 **Fax:** 01322 422101
Email: sales@cphart.co.uk **Web:** www.cphart.co.uk

CRABTREE KITCHENS
17 Station Road, Barnes, Greater London, SW13 0LF
Area of Operation: Greater London, South West
England and South Wales
Tel: 0208 392 6955 **Fax:** 0208 392 6944
Email: design@crabtreekitchens.co.uk
Web: www.crabtreekitchens.co.uk
Product Type: 1, 2, 4, 5, 7, 8, 9, 10

CREATE DESIGN SOLUTIONS LTD
The Wood Yard, Castell Ddu Road,
Waun Gron, Pontarddulais, Swansea, SA4 8DH
Area of Operation: Greater London, Midlands & Mid
Wales, North West England and North Wales, South
East England, South West England and South Wales
Tel: 01792 386677 **Fax:** 01792 386677
Email: mail@createdesignsolutions.co.uk
Web: www.createdesignsolutions.co.uk

CREATE JOINERY
The Wood Yard, Castell Ddu Road,
Waun Gron , Pontarddulais, Swansea, SA4 8DH
Area of Operation: Greater London, Midlands & Mid
Wales, North West England and North Wales, South
East England, South West England and South Wales
Tel: 01792 386677 **Fax:** 01792 386677
Email: mail@create-joinery.co.uk
Web: www.create-joinery.co.uk

CRS AGENCIES LIMITED
Quaint Corners, Petersham Lane,
Gaunts Common, Dorset, BH21 4JS
Area of Operation: UK (Excluding Ireland)
Tel: 01202 880832 **Fax:** 01202 880832
Email: info@crsagencies.co.uk
Web: www.crsagencies.co.uk **Product Type:** 2, 5, 9

CYMRU KITCHENS
63 Caerleon Road, Newport, NP19 7BX
Area of Operation: UK (Excluding Ireland)
Tel: 01633 676767
Fax: 01633 212512
Email: sales@cymrukitchens.com
Web: www.cymrukitchens.com
Product Type: 1, 2, 3, 4, 5, 6, 7, 8, 9, 10

D.A FURNITURE LTD
Woodview Workshop, Pitway Lane,
Farrington Gurney, Bristol, BS39 6TX
Area of Operation: South West England and South Wales
Tel: 01761 453117
Email: enquiries@dafurniture.co.uk
Web: www.dafurniture.co.uk
Product Type: 1, 2, 3, 5 **Other Info:** ✎ ✋

DESIGNER KITCHENS
37 High Street, Potters Bar, Hertfordshire, EN6 5AJ
Area of Operation: Greater London
Tel: 01707 650565
Fax: 01707 663050
Email: info@designer-kitchens.co.uk
Web: www.designer-kitchens.co.uk
Product Type: 1, 2, 3, 5, 6, 7, 8, 9, 10

DREW FORSYTH & CO.
Beehive Mills, Hebble End,
Hebden Bridge, West Yorkshire, HX7 6HJ
Area of Operation: Midlands & Mid Wales, North
East England, North West England and North Wales
Tel: 01422 842206
Fax: 01422 844828
Email: shane_kenyon@hotmail.com
Web: www.drewforsyth.co.uk
Product Type: 1, 2, 3, 5 **Other Info:** ✎ ✋

DUKE CHRISTIE
Hillockhead Farmhouse, Dallas, Forres, Moray, IV36 2SD
Area of Operation: Worldwide
Tel: 01343 890347 **Fax:** 01343 890347
Email: enquiries@dukechristie.com
Web: www.dukechristie.com
Product Type: 2, 3, 8 **Other Info:** ✎ ✋

FINEWOOD INTERIORS

Exquisite hand made interiors and individual items of furniture from design to completion

For further information or to make an appointment call

Head office/showroom, Bentley
01420 23883

Showroom, Farnham
01252 715454

or alternatively visit
www.finewoodinteriors.co.uk

ELITE TRADE KITCHENS LTD
90 Willesden Lane, Kilburn, London, NW6 7TA
Area of Operation: UK (Excluding Ireland)
Tel: 0207 328 1234 **Fax:** 0207 328 1243
Email: sales@elitekitchens.co.uk
Web: www.elitekitchens.co.uk
Product Type: 1, 2, 3, 4, 5, 7, 8, 9, 10

ELLIOTT BROTHERS LTD
Millbank Wharf, Northam,
Southampton, Hampshire, SO14 5AG
Area of Operation: South East England, South West
England and South Wales
Tel: 02380 226852 **Fax:** 02380 638780
Email: laurenh@elliott-brothers.co.uk
Web: www.elliotts.uk.com
Product Type: 1, 2, 3, 5, 7, 8, 9

ENGLISH INTERIORS LTD
Unit 15 Brooklands Way, Basford Lane Industrial
Estate, Leekbrook, Leek, Staffordshire, ST13 7QF
Area of Operation: UK & Ireland
Tel: 01538 399191 **Fax:** 01538 386486
Email: enquiries@englishinteriorsltd.co.uk
Web: www.englishinteriorsltd.co.uk
Product Type: 1, 2, 3, 5, 7, 8

FINEWOOD INTERIORS
Head Office, Blacknest House, Blacknest Business
Park, Near Bentley, Alton, Hampshire, GU34 4PX
Area of Operation: UK (Excluding Ireland)
Tel: 01420 23883 **Fax:** 01420 23883
Email: info@finewoodinteriors.co.uk
Web: www.finewoodinteriors.co.uk

FITZROY JOINERY
Garden Close, Langage Industrial Estate,
Plympton, Plymouth, Devon, PL7 5EU
Area of Operation: UK & Ireland
Tel: 0870 428 9110 **Fax:** 0870 428 9111
Email: admin@fitzroy.co.uk
Web: www.fitzroyjoinery.co.uk

G MIDDLETON LTD
Cross Croft Industrial Estate,
Appleby, Cumbria, CA16 6HX
Area of Operation: Europe
Tel: 01768 352067 **Fax:** 01768 353228
Email: info@graham-middleton.co.uk
Web: www.graham-middleton.co.uk
Product Type: 1, 3, 8

HARVEY JONES
137-139 Essex Road, Islington, London, N1 2NR
Area of Operation: UK (Excluding Ireland)
Tel: 0800 032 6497 **Fax:** 0207 354 1006
Web: www.harveyjones.com

HATT KITCHENS
Hartlebury Trading Estate,
Hartlebury, Worcestershire, DY10 4JB
Area of Operation: UK (Excluding Ireland)
Tel: 01299 251320 **Fax:** 01299 251579
Email: design@hatt.co.uk **Web:** www.hatt.co.uk
Product Type: 1, 2, 3, 4, 5, 6, 7, 8, 9, 10

HITT OAK LTD
10 Park Parade, Gunnersbury Avenue,
London, W3 9BD
Area of Operation: UK (Excluding Ireland)
Tel: 0208 896 1900 **Fax:** 0208 896 1900
Email: zhitas@yahoo.co.uk
Product Type: 3, 5, 7, 8

HOLME TREE LTD
Units 2 and 3 Machins Business Centre, 29 Wood
Street, Asby-de-la-Zouch, Leicestershire, LE65 1EL
Area of Operation: UK (Excluding Ireland)
Tel: 01530 564561 **Fax:** 01530 417986
Email: info@holmetree.co.uk
Web: www.holmetree.co.uk

HYGROVE
152/154 Merton Road,
Wimbledon, London, SW19 1EH
Area of Operation: South East England
Tel: 0208 543 1200 **Fax:** 0208 543 6521
Email: sales@hygrove.fsnet.co.uk
Web: www.hygrovefurniture.co.uk

INDESIGN
Kiran House, 53 Park Royal Road, London, NW10 7LQ
Area of Operation: UK & Ireland
Tel: 0208 963 5841 **Fax:** 0208 965 6261
Email: dhanja.bhudia@akshars.co.uk
Web: www.akshars.co.uk

IN-TOTO
Shaw Cross Court, Shaw Cross Business Park,
Dewsbury, West Yorkshire, WF12 7RF
Tel: 01924 487900 **Fax:** 01924 437305
Email: graham.russell@intoto.co.uk
Web: www.intoto.co.uk **Product Type:** 1, 2, 3, 4, 5

J&J ORMEROD PLC
Colonial House, Bacup, Lancashire, OL13 0EA
Area of Operation: UK & Ireland
Tel: 01706 877877 **Fax:** 01706 879827
Email: info@jjoplc.com **Web:** www.jjoplc.com
Product Type: 1, 2, 3, 5, 6, 7, 8, 9, 10

JAIC LTD
Pattern House, Southwell Business Park,
Portland, Dorset, DT5 2NR
Area of Operation: UK (Excluding Ireland)
Tel: 01305 826991 **Fax:** 01305 823535
Email: info@jaic.co.uk **Web:** www.jaic.co.uk
Product Type: 1, 3, 5

JJO PLC (J&J ORMEROD)
Colonial House, Bacup, Lancashire, OL13 0EA
Area of Operation: UK & Ireland
Tel: 01706 877877 **Fax:** 01706 879827
Email: npeters@jjoplc.com **Web:** www.jjoplc.com
Product Type: 1, 2, 3, 4, 5, 6, 7, 8, 9, 10

JOHN FLEMING & CO LTD
Silverburn Place, Bridge of Don,
Aberdeen, Aberdeenshire, AB23 8EG
Area of Operation: Scotland
Tel: 0800 085 8728 **Fax:** 01224 825377
Email: info@johnfleming.co.uk
Web: www.johnfleming.co.uk

JOHN LADBURY & CO
Unit 11, Alpha Business Park, Travellers Close,
Welham Green, Hertfordshire, AL9 7NT
Area of Operation: Greater London
Tel: 01707 262966 **Fax:** 01707 265400
Email: sales@johnladbury.co.uk
Web: www.johnladbury.co.uk
Product Type: 1, 2, 3, 5, 7, 8, 9 **Other Info:**

JOHN LEWIS OF HUNGERFORD
Grove Technology Park, Downsview Road,
Wantage, Oxfordshire, OX12 9FA
Area of Operation: UK (Excluding Ireland)
Tel: 01235 774300 **Fax:** 01235 769031
Email: park.street@john-lewis.co.uk
Web: www.john-lewis.co.uk **Product Type:** 1, 3, 8

JOHNNY GREY
Fyning Copse , Fyning Lane, Rogate,
Petersfield, Hampshire, GU31 5DH
Area of Operation: Worldwide
Tel: 01730 821424 **Email:** miles@johnnygrey.co.uk
Web: www.johnnygrey.co.uk **Product Type:** 2, 5, 10

KENLEY KITCHENS
24-26 Godstone Road, Kenley, Surrey, CR8 5JE
Area of Operation: UK (Excluding Ireland)
Tel: 0208 668 7000

KENSINGTON STUDIO
13 c & d Kensington Road, Earlsdon,
Coventry, West Midlands, CV5 6GG
Area of Operation: UK (Excluding Ireland)
Tel: 02476 713326 **Fax:** 02476 713136
Email: sales@kensingtonstudio.com
Web: www.kensingtonstudio.com
Product Type: 1, 2, 3, 4, 5, 6, 7, 8, 9, 10

KITCHENS BY JULIAN ENGLISH
Ideal Home, Blackbird Road,
Leicester, Leicestershire, LE4 0AH
Area of Operation: Midlands & Mid Wales
Tel: 0116 251 9999 **Fax:** 0116 251 9999
Email: philiphalifax@aol.com
Web: www.kitchens-by-julianenglish.co.uk

MARK HENRY INTERIORS & BUILDING
Unit 9 Greenway, Harlow Business Park,
Harlow, Essex, CM19 5QB
Area of Operation: UK (Excluding Ireland)
Tel: 01279 444829 **Fax:** 01279 441598
Email: info@markhenryfurniture.co.uk
Web: www.markhenryfurniture.co.uk

MARK LEIGH KITCHENS LTD
11 Common Garden Street,
Lancaster, Lancashire, LA1 1XD
Area of Operation: North West England and North Wales
Tel: 01524 63273 **Fax:** 01524 62352
Email: mark@markleigh.co.uk
Web: www.markleigh.co.uk
Product Type: 1, 2, 5, 9 **Other Info:** ✎

MASTER LTD
30 Station Road, Heacham, Norfolk, PE31 7EX
Area of Operation: Europe
Tel: 01485 572032 **Fax:** 01485 571675
Email: info@masterlimited.co.uk
Web: www.masterlimited.co.uk
Product Type: 1, 3, 4

MEREWAY CONTRACTS
Unit 1 Wharfdale Road, Tysely,
Birmingham, West Midlands, B11 2DE
Area of Operation: UK (Excluding Ireland)
Tel: 0121 764 7180 **Fax:** 0121 764 7199
Email: info@merewaycontracts.co.uk
Web: www.merewaycontracts.co.uk

MOBALPA
1 High Street, Halberton, Devon, EX16 7AF
Area of Operation: Worldwide
Tel: 07740 633672 **Fax:** 01884 820828
Email: ploftus@mobalpa.com
Web: www.mobalpa.co.uk
Product Type: 1, 2, 3, 4, 5, 6, 7, 9, 10

MONTANA KITCHENS LTD
BIC 1 , Studio 2/3 Innova Business Park,
Mollison Avenue, Enfield, Middlesex, EN3 7XU
Area of Operation: Greater London, South East England
Tel: 0800 58 75 628
Email: angie@montanakitchens.co.uk
Web: www.montanakitchens.co.uk
Product Type: 1, 2, 3, 4, 5, 6, 7, 9, 10

MURDOCH TROON KITCHENS
5-5A Emery Lane, Boston, Lincolnshire, PE21 8QA
Area of Operation: UK (Excluding Ireland)
Tel: 01205 364348 **Fax:** 01205 761284
Email: enquires@murdochtroon.co.uk
Web: www.murdochtroon.co.uk
Product Type: 1, 2, 3, 7, 8

NEIL LERNER
487 Finchley Road, London, NW3 6HS
Area of Operation: UK & Ireland
Tel: 0207 433 0705
Email: info@neillerner.com
Web: www.neillerner.com **Product Type:** 5, 9

NEW KITCHEN DIY
9 Priory Road, Stamford, Lincolnshire, PE9 2ES
Area of Operation: UK (Excluding Ireland)
Tel: 01780 766651
Email: sales@newkitchendiy.com
Web: www.newkitchendiy.com ✎
Product Type: 1, 2, 3, 10

NEWARK TRADITIONAL KITCHENS
Newark Stedding, Milton, Crocketford, Dumfries,
Dumfries & Galloway, DG2 8QT
Area of Operation: UK (Excluding Ireland)
Tel: 01556 690544
Email: calumsabey@hotmail.co.uk

NICHOLAS ANTHONY LTD
42-44 Wigmore Street, London, W1U 2RX
Area of Operation: East England, Greater London,
South East England
Tel: 0800 068 3603 **Fax:** 01206 762698
Email: info@nicholas-anthony.co.uk
Web: www.nicholas-anthony.co.uk
Product Type: 2, 5

NOLTE KITCHENS
41 London Road, Sawbridgeworth,
Hertfordshire, CM21 9EH
Area of Operation: UK & Ireland
Tel: 01279 868500 **Fax:** 01279 868802
Email: email@noltekitchens.co.uk
Web: www.nolte-kuechen.de **Product Type:** 2

NOW GROUP PLC (CONTRACTS DIVISION)
Red Scar Business Park, Longridge Road,
Preston, Lancashire, PR2 5NA
Area of Operation: UK & Ireland
Tel: 01772 703838 **Fax:** 01772 705788
Email: sales@nowkitchens.co.uk
Web: www.nowkitchens.co.uk
Product Type: 1, 2, 3, 5, 7, 9

NTP KITCHENS & JOINERY LTD
Unit 20/1, West Bowling Green Street,
Edinburgh, EH6 5PE
Area of Operation: Scotland
Tel: 0131 554 8787 **Fax:** 0131 554 9191
Email: sales@ntp-kitchens.co.uk
Web: www.ntp-kitchens.co.uk
Product Type: 1, 2, 3, 5, 6, 7, 8, 9, 10

OAKWOOD BESPOKE
80 High Street, Camberley, Surrey, GU46 7RN
Area of Operation: Greater London, South East
England, South West England and South Wales
Tel: 01276 708630
Email: enquiries@oakwoodbespokecamberley.co.uk
Web: www.oakwoodbespokecamberley.co.uk
Product Type: 1, 2, 3, 5, 6, 7, 10

ORIGINAL
3 Festival Units, The Showground,
Bridgwater, Somerset, TA6 6LS
Area of Operation: South West England and South Wales
Tel: 0870 011 0808 **Fax:** 0870 011 0606
Email: enquiries@obsc.co.uk **Web:** www.obsc.co.uk

PANELS PLUS
22-24 Mill Place,
Kingston Upon Thames, Surrey, KT1 2RJ
Area of Operation: Greater London
Tel: 0208 399 6343 **Fax:** 0208 399 6343
Email: sales@panelsplusltd.com
Web: www.panelsplusltd.com ✎
Product Type: 1, 2, 3, 4, 5, 6, 7, 10

PARLOUR FARM
Unit 12b, Wilkinson Road, Love Lane Industrial
Estate, Cirencester, Gloucestershire, GL7 1YT
Area of Operation: Europe
Tel: 01285 885336 **Fax:** 01285 643189
Email: info@parlourfarm.com
Web: www.parlourfarm.com

PINELAND FURNITURE LTD
Unit 5 Cleobury Trading Estate,
Cleobury Mortimer, Shropshire, DY14 8DP
Area of Operation: UK (Excluding Ireland)
Tel: 01299 271143 **Fax:** 01299 271166
Email: pineland@onetel.com
Web: www.pineland.co.uk

PLAIN ENGLISH
Stowupland Hall, Stowupland, Suffolk, IP14 4BE
Area of Operation: Worldwide
Tel: 01449 774028 **Fax:** 01449 613519
Email: info@plainenglishdesign.co.uk
Web: www.plainenglishdesign.co.uk
Product Type: 1, 2, 8

POGGENPOHL
477-481 Finchley Road, London, NW3 6HS
Area of Operation: UK & Ireland
Tel: 0800 298 1098 **Fax:** 0207 794 6251
Email: kitchens@poggenpohl-group.co.uk
Web: www.poggenpohl.co.uk **Product Type:** 5, 8, 9

POSH PANTRIES
81 Kelvin Road North, Lenziemill,
Cumbernauld, Lanarkshire, G67 2BD
Area of Operation: UK (Excluding Ireland)
Tel: 01236 453556 **Fax:** 01236 728068
Email: office@poshpantries.co.uk
Web: www.poshpantries.co.uk

PRICE KITCHENS
11 Imperial Way, Croydon, Surrey, CR0 4RR
Area of Operation: South East England
Tel: 0208 686 9006 **Fax:** 0208 686 5958
Email: info@pricekitchens.co.uk
Web: www.pricekitchens.co.uk
Product Type: 1, 2, 3, 4, 5, 6, 7, 8, 9, 10

QUANTUM FITTED FURNITURE
2a Poplar Court Parade, Richmond Road,
Twickenham, London, TW1 2DT
Area of Operation: UK (Excluding Ireland)
Tel: 0208 892 6430 **Fax:** 0208 892 6035
Email: info@quantumfittedfurniture.co.uk
Web: www.quantumfittedfurniture.co.uk
Product Type: 2, 5, 9, 10

RAY PEARS JOINERY LTD
42 Mill Hill Road, Hinckley, Leicestershire, LE10 0AX
Area of Operation: UK (Excluding Ireland)
Tel: 01455 616279
Fax: 01455 891533
Email: sales@peartree.co.uk
Web: www.peartree.co.uk
Product Type: 1, 2, 3, 4, 5, 6, 7, 8, 9

RICHARD BAKER FURNITURE LTD
Wimbledon Studios, 257 Burlington Road,
New Malden, Surrey, KT3 4NE
Area of Operation: Europe
Tel: 0208 336 1777
Fax: 0208 336 1666
Email: richard@richardbakerfurniture.co.uk
Web: www.richardbakerfurniture.co.uk
Product Type: 1, 2, 5, 8, 9

ROBINSON AND CORNISH LTD
St George's House, St George's Road,
Barnstaple, Devon, EX32 7AS
Area of Operation: Europe
Tel: 01271 329300
Fax: 01271 328277
Email: sales@robinsonandcornish.co.uk
Web: www.robinsonandcornish.co.uk
Product Type: 2, 3, 8, 10 **Other Info:** ✎

ROMANYS
Hatch End, Unit 1, Chantry Place,
Headstone Lane, Harrow, Middlesex, HA3 6NY
Area of Operation: UK & Ireland
Tel: 0208 421 6324 **Fax:** 0208 421 6757
Email: bharat.pindolia@romanys.uk.com
Web: www.romanys.uk.com

ROOTS KITCHENS BEDROOMS BATHROOMS
Vine Farm, Stockers Hill, Boughton under Blean,
Faversham, Kent, ME13 9AB
Area of Operation: South East England
Tel: 01227 751130
Fax: 01227 750033
Email: showroom@rootskitchens.co.uk
Web: www.rootskitchens.co.uk ✎
Product Type: 1, 2, 3, 4, 5, 6, 7, 8, 9, 10

ROUNDEL DESIGN (UK) LTD
Flishinghurst Orchards, Chalk Lane,
Cranbrook, Kent, TN17 2QA
Area of Operation: South East England
Tel: 01580 712666
Email: homebuild@roundeldesign.co.uk
Web: www.roundeldesign.co.uk
Product Type: 1, 2, 3, 5, 7, 8, 9

SCHMIDT KITCHENS
Mereworth Business Centre, Hermitage Oast,
Danns Lane, Mereworth, Kent, ME18 5LW
Area of Operation: Worldwide
Tel: 01622 812123
Email: info@schmidt-kitchens.com
Web: www.schmidt-kitchens.com
Product Type: 1, 2, 9

SECOND NATURE KITCHEN COLLECTION
PO Box 20, Station Road, Aycliffe Industrial Park,
Newton Aycliffe, Durham, DL5 6XJ
Area of Operation: UK & Ireland
Tel: 01325 505539
Email: mail@sncollection.co.uk
Web: www.sncollection.co.uk

SECOND NATURE

Area of Operation: UK & Ireland
Tel: 01325 505539
Email: mail@secondnaturecollection.co.uk
Web: www.sncollection.co.uk
Product Type: 1, 2, 3, 4, 5, 6, 7, 8, 9

The Avant Beige range with its beautiful curves is just one design from the exceptional choice of modern kitchens from Second Nature.

SECOND NATURE
Area of Operation: UK & Ireland
Tel: 01325 505539
Email: mail@secondnaturecollection.co.uk
Web: www.sncollection.co.uk
Product Type: 1, 2, 3, 4, 5, 6, 7, 8, 9

Second Nature has an extensive range of classic styled kitchens for timeless appeal. The Eden Sanded range featured above creates a warm and welcoming interior.

SIEMATIC
Osprey House, Primett Road,
Stevenage, Hertfordshire, SG1 3EE
Area of Operation: UK & Ireland
Tel: 01438 369251 **Fax:** 01438 368920
Email: sales@siematic.co.uk
Web: www.siematic.co.uk

SIMON BRAY AT GK DESIGN
Greensbury Farm, Thurleigh Road,
Bolnhurst, Bedfordshire, MK44 2ET
Tel: 01234 376990 **Fax:** 01234 376991
Email: studio@gkdesign.co.uk
Web: www.simon-bray.co.uk **Other Info:** ✎

SIMON TAYLOR FURNITURE LIMITED
Cane End Lane, Bierton, Aylesbury,
Buckinghamshire, HP22 5BH
Tel: 01296 488207 **Fax:** 01296 398722
Email: information@simon-taylor.co.uk
Web: www.simon-taylor.co.uk
Product Type: 1, 2, 3, 5, 8, 10 **Other Info:** ✎ 🖐

SPILLERS OF CHARD LTD.
Spillers of Chard Ltd., Chard Business Park,
Chard, Somerset, TA20 1FA
Area of Operation: South West England and South Wales
Tel: 01460 67878 **Fax:** 01460 65252
Email: info@cookercentre.com
Web: www.cookercentre.com
Product Type: 1, 2, 3, 5, 9, 10

STONEHAM KITCHENS
Powerscroft Road, Footcray, Sidcup, Kent, DA14 5DZ
Area of Operation: UK (Excluding Ireland)
Tel: 0208 300 8181
Fax: 0208 300 8183
Email: kitchens@stoneham.plc.uk
Web: www.stoneham-kitchens.co.uk
Product Type: 1, 2, 3 **Other Info:** ✎

TASKWORTHY
The Old Brickyard, Pontrilas, Herefordshire, HR2 0DJ
Area of Operation: UK (Excluding Ireland)
Tel: 01981 242900 **Fax:** 01981 242901
Email: peter@taskworthy.co.uk
Web: www.taskworthy.co.uk
Product Type: 1, 3, 4, 5, 7, 8, 9, 10

THE DESIGN STUDIO
39 High Street, Reigate, Surrey, RH2 9AE
Area of Operation: South East England
Tel: 01737 248228
Fax: 01737 224180
Email: enq@the-design-studio.co.uk
Web: www.the-design-studio.co.uk ✎
Product Type: 1, 2, 3, 5, 9

THE KITCHEN AND BATHROOM COLLECTION
Nelson House, Nelson Road,
Salisbury, Wiltshire, SP1 3LT
Area of Operation: South West England and South Wales
Tel: 01722 334800 **Fax:** 01722 412252
Email: info@kbc.co.uk **Web:** www.kbc.co.uk
Product Type: 2, 3, 4, 5, 6, 7, 9 **Other Info:** ✎✋

THE MODERN ROOM LTD
54 St.Pauls Road, Luton, Bedfordshire, LU1 3RX
Area of Operation: UK (Excluding Ireland)
Tel: 01582 612070 **Fax:** 01582 612070
Email: laura@themodernroom.com
Web: www.themodernroom.com
Product Type: 2, 5, 9 **Other Info:** ✎✋

THE OLD PINE STORE
Coxons Yard, Off Union Street,
Ashbourne, Derbyshire, DE6 1FG
Area of Operation: Europe
Tel: 01335 344112 **Fax:** 01335 344112
Email: martin@old-pine.co.uk
Web: www.old-pine.co.uk
Product Type: 1, 3, 5 **Other Info:** ▽ ECO ✎✋

THE ORIGINAL KITCHEN COMPANY
4 Main Street, Breaston, Derby, Derbyshire, DE72 3DX
Area of Operation: UK & Ireland
Tel: 01332 873746 **Fax:** 01332 873731
Email: originalkitchens@aol.com

TIM WOOD LIMITED
1 Burland Road, London, SW11 6SA
Area of Operation: Worldwide
Tel: 07041 380030 **Fax:** 08700 548645
Email: homeb@timwood.com
Web: www.timwood.com

TOUCHSTONE - GRANITE, MARBLE & SILESTONE WORKTOPS
Touchstone House, 82 High Street,
Measham, Derbyshire, DE12 7JB
Area of Operation: UK (Excluding Ireland)
Tel: 0845 130 1862 **Fax:** 01530 274271
Email: sales@touchstone-uk.com
Web: www.touchstone-uk.com
Product Type: 1, 2, 3, 4, 6, 7, 9

TRADESTYLE CABINETS LTD
Carmaben Road, Easter Quennslie Industrial Estate,
Glasgow, Lothian, G33 4UN
Area of Operation: UK (Excluding Ireland)
Tel: 0141 781 6800 **Fax:** 0141 781 6801
Email: info@tradestylecabinets.com
Web: www.tradestylecabinets.com

TURNER FURNITURE
The Old Dairy, Manor Farm,
Sipilly Handley, Salisbury, SP5 5NU
Area of Operation: Greater London, South East England, South West England and South Wales
Tel: 01725 516990 **Fax:** 01725 516991
Email: nick@turner-furniture.co.uk
Web: www.turner-furniture.co.uk
Product Type: 1, 3, 5, 7, 9 **Other Info:** ✎

UNICOM
Kingdom House, 219 Gleniffer Road,
Paisley, Renfrewshire, PA2 8UL
Area of Operation: UK & Ireland
Tel: 0845 330 7642 **Fax:** 0845 330 7641
Email: george@unicom-direct.com
Web: www.unicom-direct.com
Product Type: 1, 2, 3, 4, 5, 6, 7, 8, 9, 10

WATTS & WRIGHT (THE JOINERY SHOP)
PO Box 4251, Walsall, West Midlands, WS5 3WY
Area of Operation: Worldwide
Tel: 01922 610800 / 0207 043 7619
Fax: 0870 762 6387
Email: sales@wattsandwright.com
Web: www.wattsandwright.com
Product Type: 1, 2, 3, 4, 5, 7, 8, 10

WICKES
Wickes Customer Services, Wickes House, 120-138 Station Road, Harrow, Middlesex, HA1 2QB
Area of Operation: UK (Excluding Ireland)
Tel: 0870 608 9001 **Fax:** 0208 863 6225
Web: www.wickes.co.uk

WILLIAM BALL
London Road, Grays, Essex, RM20 4WB
Area of Operation: Worldwide
Tel: 01375 375151 **Fax:** 01375 379033
Email: marketing@wball.co.uk
Web: www.wball.co.uk ✎

William Ball
Ultimate House, London Road,
Grays, Essex. RM20 4WB
Area of operation: Worldwide
Tel: 01375 375151
Fax: 01375 379033
Email: marketing@wball.co.uk
Web: www.wball.co.uk

The FIRA Gold award has been awarded for the excellence of William Ball products. Over 100 carcase sizes in 12 finishes and over 40 door designs. Helena shown here 600mm base unit with full height doors £177

WILLIAM GARVEY
Leyhill, Payhembury, Honiton, Devon, EX14 3JG
Area of Operation: Worldwide
Tel: 01404 841430
Fax: 01404 841626
Email: webquery@williamgarvey.co.uk
Web: www.williamgarvey.co.uk
Product Type: 2 **Other Info:** ✎✋

WINNING DESIGNS
Dyke Farm, West Chiltington Road,
Pulborough, West Sussex, RH20 2EE
Area of Operation: UK & Ireland
Tel: 0870 754 4446
Fax: 0700 032 9946
Email: info@winning-designs-uk.com
Web: www.winning-designs-uk.com
Product Type: 1, 2, 3, 4, 5, 6, 7, 8, 9, 10
Other Info: ▽ ECO ✎✋

WOODCHESTER KITCHENS & INTERIORS
Unit 18a Chalford Industrial Estate,
Chalford, Gloucestershire, GL6 8NT
Area of Operation: UK (Excluding Ireland)
Tel: 01453 886411
Fax: 01453 886411
Email: enquires@woodchesterkitchens.co.uk
Web: www.woodchesterkitchens.co.uk
Product Type: 1, 2, 3, 4, 5, 6, 7, 8, 9, 10

WOODEN HEART WAREHOUSE
Laburnum Road, Chertsey, Surrey, KT16 8BY
Area of Operation: Greater London, South East England
Tel: 01932 568684 **Fax:** 01932 568685
Email: whw@btclick.com **Product Type:** 1, 3, 5, 6, 7, 9

WOODSTOCK FURNITURE
17 Park Drive, East Sheen, London, SW14 8RB
Area of Operation: Worldwide
Tel: 020 8876 0131 **Fax:** 020 8876 0131
Email: ask@woodstockfurniture.co.uk
Web: www.woodstockfurniture.co.uk
Product Type: 1, 2, 3, 5, 6, 7, 8, 9, 10
Other Info: ✎✋

ZIMMER KUCHEN
Jenna House, North Crawley Road,
Newport Pagnell, Buckinghamshire, MK16 9QA
Tel: 0870 556 1560 **Fax:** 0800 585531
Email: info@zimmerkuchen.co.uk
Web: www.zimmerkuchen.co.uk
Product Type: 1, 3, 5, 9

KITCHEN FURNITURE, UNFITTED

KEY
PRODUCT TYPES: 1 = Shaker
2 = Contemporary 3 = Farmhouse
4 = Industrial 5 = Long Island 6 = New
England 7 = Period 8 = Minimalist 9 = Other

OTHER: ▽ Reclaimed ✎ On-line shopping
✎ Bespoke ✋ Hand-made ECO Ecological

ALLMILMO UK
Briff Well, Little Lane, Reading, Berkshire, RG7 6QX
Area of Operation: UK & Ireland
Tel: 01635 868181 **Fax:** 01635 869693
Email: allmilmo@aol.com
Web: www.allmilmo.com **Product Type:** 1, 2, 5, 9

ASHFORD & BROOKS
The Old Workshop, Ashtree Barn, Caters Road,
Bredfield, Woodbridge, Suffolk, IP13 6BE
Area of Operation: UK (Excluding Ireland)
Tel: 01473 737764 **Fax:** 01473 277176
Email: ashfordbrooks@mailbox.co.uk
Web: www.ashfordandbrooks.co.uk
Product Type: 1, 2, 3, 5, 6, 7, 8, 9, 10

B ROURKE & CO LTD
Vulcan Works, Accrington Road,
Burnley, Lancashire, BB11 5QD
Area of Operation: Worldwide
Tel: 01282 422841 **Fax:** 01282 458901
Email: info@rourkes.co.uk
Web: www.rourkes.co.uk **Product Type:** 10

BATH KITCHEN COMPANY
22 Hensley Road, Bloomfield,
Bath, Somerset, BA2 2DR
Area of Operation: South West England and South Wales
Tel: 01225 312003
Fax: 01225 312003
Email: david@bathkitchencompany.co.uk
Web: www.bathkitchencompany.co.uk
Product Type: 1, 2, 3, 4, 5, 6, 7, 8, 9
Other Info: ✍

BLUM UK LTD
Mandeville Drive, Kingston, Milton Keynes, MK10 0AW
Area of Operation: Worldwide
Tel: 01908 285700   **Fax:** 01908 285701
Email: info.uk@blum.com
Web: www.blum.com   **Product Type:** 2

BORDERCRAFT
Old Forge, Peterchurch,
Hereford, Herefordshire, HR2 0SD
Area of Operation: UK (Excluding Ireland)
Tel: 01981 550251
Fax: 01981 550552
Email: sales@bordercraft.co.uk
Web: www.bordercraft.co.uk   **Other Info:** ✍ 🖐

BUYDESIGN
Monteviot Nurseries, Ancrum,
Jedburgh, Borders, TD8 6TU
Area of Operation: Scotland
Tel: 01835 830740
Email: enquries@buydesign-furniture.com
Web: www.buydesign-furniture.com
Product Type: 1, 2, 3, 5

CARE DESIGN
Moorgate, Ormskirk, Lancashire, L39 4RX
Area of Operation: UK (Excluding Ireland)
Tel: 01695 579061   **Fax:** 01695 570489
Email: caredesign@clara.net
Web: www.caredesign.co.uk
Product Type: 10

CHANTRY HOUSE OAK LTD
28 North Street, Chichester, West Sussex, PO20 2BT
Area of Operation: South East England
Tel: 01243 776811
Email: shop@chantryhouseoak.co.uk
Web: www.chantryhouseoak.co.uk
Product Type: 1, 3, 5, 7, 9

CHRISTOPHER PETERS ORIGINAL UNFITTED KITCHENS
Lower Farm Barns,
Brandon Lane, Warwickshire, CV3 3GW
Area of Operation: Europe
Tel: 02476 303300
Email: enquiries@christopherpetersantiques.co.uk
Web: www.christopherpetersantiques.co.uk
Product Type: 1, 3, 7, 8, 10   **Other Info:** ✍

CHURCHWOOD DESIGN
Unit 9A & 9B, Whitecross Road Industrial Estate,
Tideswell, Derbyshire, SK17 8PY
Area of Operation: UK (Excluding Ireland)
Tel: 01298 872422
Fax: 01298 873068
Web: www.churchwood.co.uk
Product Type: 1, 2, 3, 5, 6, 7, 8, 9

CITY BATHROOMS & KITCHENS
158 Longford Road, Longford,
Coventry, West Midlands, CV6 6DR
Area of Operation: UK & Ireland
Tel: 02476 365877
Fax: 02476 644992
Email: citybathrooms@hotmail.com
Web: www.citybathrooms.co.uk

CONNAUGHT KITCHENS
2 Porchester Place, London, W2 2BS
Area of Operation: Greater London
Tel: 0207 706 2210
Fax: 0207 706 2209
Email: design@connaughtkitchens.co.uk
Web: www.connaughtkitchens.co.uk
Product Type: 2

CONQUIRA LTD
2 Central Buildings, Warwick Road,
Coventry, Warwickshire, CV8 1FQ
Area of Operation: Midlands & Mid Wales
Tel: 02476 222255   **Fax:** 02476 552211
Email: gary@conquira.freeserve.co.uk
Web: www.conquira.co.uk
Product Type: 1, 2, 3, 5, 6, 7, 8, 9

COTTAGE FARM ANTIQUES
Stratford Road, Aston Sub Edge,
Chipping Campden, Gloucestershire, GL55 6PZ
Area of Operation: Worldwide
Tel: 01386 438263   **Fax:** 01386 438263
Email: info@cottagefarmantiques.co.uk
Web: www.cottagefarmantiques.co.uk 🖐
Product Type: 3, 8, 10

COUNTRY KITCHENS
The Old Farm House, Birmingham Road,
Blackminster, Evesham, Worcestershire, WR11 7TD
Area of Operation: UK (Excluding Ireland)
Tel: 01386 831705   **Fax:** 01386 834051
Web: www.handcraftedkitchens.co.uk
Product Type: 1, 3, 8

CRABTREE KITCHENS
17 Station Road, Barnes, Greater London, SW13 0LF
Area of Operation: Greater London, South West
England and South Wales
Tel: 0208 392 6955   **Fax:** 0208 392 6944
Email: design@crabtreekitchens.co.uk
Web: www.crabtreekitchens.co.uk
Product Type: 1, 2, 4, 5, 7, 8, 9, 10

CRS AGENCIES LIMITED
Quaint Corners, Petersham Lane,
Gaunts Common, Dorset, BH21 4JS
Area of Operation: UK (Excluding Ireland)
Tel: 01202 880832   **Fax:** 01202 880832
Email: info@crsagencies.co.uk
Web: www.crsagencies.co.uk   **Product Type:** 2, 5, 9

CYMRU KITCHENS
63 Caerleon Road, Newport, NP19 7BX
Area of Operation: UK (Excluding Ireland)
Tel: 01633 676767   **Fax:** 01633 212512
Email: sales@cymrukitchens.com
Web: www.cymrukitchens.com   **Other Info:** ✍ 🖐

D.A FURNITURE LTD
Woodview Workshop, Pitway Lane,
Farrington Gurney, Bristol, BS39 6TX
Area of Operation: South West England and South Wales
Tel: 01761 453117
Email: enquiries@dafurniture.co.uk
Web: www.dafurniture.co.uk
Product Type: 1, 2, 3, 5   **Other Info:** ✍ 🖐

DESIGNER KITCHENS
37 High Street, Potters Bar, Hertfordshire, EN6 5AJ
Area of Operation: Greater London
Tel: 01707 650565   **Fax:** 01707 663050
Email: info@designer-kitchens.co.uk
Web: www.designer-kitchens.co.uk
Product Type: 1, 2, 3, 5, 6, 7, 8, 9, 10

DORLUXE LIMITED
30 Pinbush Road, Lowestoft, Suffolk, NR33 7NL
Area of Operation: UK & Ireland
Tel: 01502 567744   **Fax:** 01502 567743
Email: info@dorluxe.co.uk
Web: www.dorluxe.co.uk   **Product Type:** 2, 3, 5, 8

DUKE CHRISTIE
Hillockhead Farmhouse, Dallas, Forres, Moray, IV36 2SD
Area of Operation: Worldwide
Tel: 01343 890347   **Fax:** 01343 890347
Email: enquiries@dukechristie.com
Web: www.dukechristie.com
Product Type: 2, 3, 8   **Other Info:** ✍ 🖐

ELITE TRADE KITCHENS LTD
90 Willesden Lane, Kilburn, London, NW6 7TA
Area of Operation: UK (Excluding Ireland)
Tel: 0207 328 1234   **Fax:** 0207 328 1243
Email: sales@elitekitchens.co.uk
Web: www.elitekitchens.co.uk

ENGLISH INTERIORS LTD
Unit 15 Brooklands Way, Basford Lane Inudustrial
Estate, Leekbrook, Leek, Staffordshire, ST13 7QF
Area of Operation: UK & Ireland
Tel: 01538 399191   **Fax:** 01538 386486
Email: enquiries@englishinteriorsltd.co.uk
Web: www.englishinteriorsltd.co.uk
Product Type: 1, 2, 3, 5, 7, 8

FIRED EARTH
3 Twyford Mill, Oxford Road, Adderbury,
Banbury, Oxfordshire, OX17 3SX
Area of Operation: Worldwide
Tel: 01295 812088   **Fax:** 01295 810832
Email: enquiries@firedearth.com
Web: www.firedearth.com 🖐

G MIDDLETON LTD
Cross Croft Industrial Estate,
Appleby, Cumbria, CA16 6HX
Area of Operation: Europe
Tel: 01768 352067   **Fax:** 01768 353228
Email: info@graham-middleton.co.uk
Web: www.graham-middleton.co.uk 🖐
Product Type: 1, 3, 8

HARVEY JONES
137-139 Essex Road, Islington, London, N1 2NR
Area of Operation: UK (Excluding Ireland)
Tel: 0800 032 6497   **Fax:** 0207 354 1006
Web: www.harveyjones.com

HATT KITCHENS
Hartlebury Trading Estate,
Hartlebury, Worcestershire, DY10 4JB
Area of Operation: UK (Excluding Ireland)
Tel: 01299 251320   **Fax:** 01299 251579
Email: design@hatt.co.uk
Web: www.hatt.co.uk
Product Type: 1, 2, 3, 4, 5, 6, 7, 8, 9, 10

HYGROVE
152/154 Merton Road, Wimbledon, London, SW19 1EH
Area of Operation: South East England
Tel: 0208 543 1200   **Fax:** 0208 543 6521
Email: sales@hygrove.fsnet.co.uk
Web: www.hygrovefurniture.co.uk

IMPORTANT ROOMS LTD
62 High Street, Wargrave,
Berkshire, Reading, Berkshire, RG10 8BY
Area of Operation: Greater London, South East
England, South West England and South Wales
Tel: 0118 940 1266   **Fax:** 0118 940 1667
Email: steve@importantrooms.co.uk
Web: www.importantrooms.co.uk
Product Type: 1, 3, 8

J&J ORMEROD PLC
Colonial House, Bacup, Lancashire, OL13 0EA
Area of Operation: UK & Ireland
Tel: 01706 877877   **Fax:** 01706 879827
Email: info@jjoplc.com   **Web:** www.jjoplc.com

JAIC LTD
Pattern House, Southwell Business Park,
Portland, Dorset, DT5 2NR
Area of Operation: UK (Excluding Ireland)
Tel: 01305 826991   **Fax:** 01305 823535
Email: info@jaic.co.uk   **Web:** www.jaic.co.uk
Product Type: 1, 3, 5

JOHN LADBURY & CO
Unit 11, Alpha Business Park, Travellers Close,
Welham Green, Hertfordshire, AL9 7NT
Area of Operation: Greater London
Tel: 01707 262966   **Fax:** 01707 265400
Email: sales@johnladbury.co.uk
Web: www.johnladbury.co.uk
Other Info: ✍ 🖐

JOHN LEWIS OF HUNGERFORD
Grove Technology Park, Downsview Road,
Wantage, Oxfordshire, OX12 9FA
Area of Operation: UK (Excluding Ireland)
Tel: 01235 774300   **Fax:** 01235 769031
Email: park.street@john-lewis.co.uk
Web: www.john-lewis.co.uk   **Product Type:** 1, 3, 8

JOHN OWEN JOINERY
Unit 1 Hays Bridge Farm, Brickhouse Lane,
South Godstone, Surrey, RH9 8JW
Area of Operation: Greater London, South West
England and South Wales
Tel: 01342 844036   **Fax:** 01342 844036
Email: johnowen.joinery@virgin.net
Web: www.johnowen.co.uk
Product Type: 1, 2, 3, 6, 7, 8

JOHN STRAND (MK) LTD
12-22 Herga Road, Wealdstone,
Harrow, Middlesex, HA3 5AS
Area of Operation: UK & Ireland
Tel: 0208 930 6006   **Fax:** 0208 930 6008
Email: enquiry@johnstrand-mk.co.uk
Web: www.johnstrand-mk.co.uk
Product Type: 5, 10

JOHNNY GREY
Fyning Copse, Fyning Lane, Rogate,
Petersfield, Hampshire, GU31 5DH
Area of Operation: Worldwide
Tel: 01730 821424   **Email:** miles@johnnygrey.co.uk
Web: www.johnnygrey.co.uk   **Product Type:** 2, 5, 10

JONATHAN ELWELL
Bryn Teg Workshop & Tan y Bryn Cottage,
Tanrallt Road, Gwespyr, Flintshire, CH8 9JT
Area of Operation: UK (Excluding Ireland)
Tel: 01745 887766
Email: jonathanelwell@ukonline.co.uk
Web: www.jonathanelwell.co.uk

KENSINGTON STUDIO
13 c & d Kensington Road, Earlsdon,
Coventry, West Midlands, CV5 6GG
Area of Operation: UK (Excluding Ireland)
Tel: 02476 713326   **Fax:** 02476 713136
Email: sales@kensingtonstudio.com
Web: www.kensingtonstudio.com 🖐
Product Type: 1, 2, 3, 4, 5, 6, 7, 8, 9, 10

KITCHEN DOOR SHOP
123 Oldham Road, Middleton, Manchester, M24 1AU
Area of Operation: UK (Excluding Ireland)
Tel: 0845 634 6444   **Fax:** 0870 300 2003
Email: kitchendoors@clara.net
Web: www.kitchendoorsltd.com

KITCHENS BY JULIAN ENGLISH
Ideal Home, Blackbird Road,
Leicester, Leicestershire, LE4 0AH
Area of Operation: Midlands & Mid Wales
Tel: 0116 251 9999   **Fax:** 0116 251 9999
Email: philiphalifax@aol.com
Web: www.kitchens-by-julianenglish.co.uk

MARK HENRY INTERIORS & BUILDING
Unit 9 Greenway, Harlow Business Park,
Harlow, Essex, CM19 5QB
Area of Operation: UK (Excluding Ireland)
Tel: 01279 444829   **Fax:** 01279 441598
Email: info@markhenryfurniture.co.uk
Web: www.markhenryfurniture.co.uk

MASTER LTD
30 Station Road, Heacham, Norfolk, PE31 7EX
Area of Operation: Europe
Tel: 01485 572032   **Fax:** 01485 571675
Email: sales@masterlimited.co.uk
Web: www.masterlimited.co.uk
Product Type: 1, 3, 4

MEREWAY CONTRACTS
Unit 1 Wharfdale Road, Tysely,
Birmingham, West Midlands, B11 2DE
Area of Operation: UK (Excluding Ireland)
Tel: 0121 764 7180   **Fax:** 0121 764 7199
Email: info@merewaycontracts.co.uk
Web: www.merewaycontracts.co.uk

MOBALPA
1 High Street, Halberton, Devon, EX16 7AF
Area of Operation: Worldwide
Tel: 07740 633672   **Fax:** 01884 820828
Email: ploftus@mobalpa.com
Web: www.mobalpa.co.uk
Product Type: 1, 2, 3, 4, 5, 6, 7, 9, 10

MONTANA KITCHENS LTD
BIC 1, Studio 2/3 Innova Business Park,
Mollison Avenue, Enfield, Middlesex, EN3 7XU
Area of Operation: Greater London, South East England
Tel: 0800 58 75 628
Email: angie@montanakitchens.co.uk
Web: www.montanakitchens.co.uk
Product Type: 1, 2, 3, 4, 5, 6, 7, 9, 10

MURDOCH TROON KITCHENS
5-5A Emery Lane, Boston, Lincolnshire, PE21 8QA
Area of Operation: UK (Excluding Ireland)
Tel: 01205 364348 **Fax:** 01205 761284
Email: enquires@murdochtroon.co.uk
Web: www.murdochtroon.co.uk
Product Type: 1, 2, 3, 7, 8

NEIL LERNER
487 Finchley Road, London, NW3 6HS
Area of Operation: UK & Ireland
Tel: 0207 433 0705 **Email:** info@neillerner.com
Web: www.neillerner.com **Product Type:** 5, 9

NICHOLAS ANTHONY LTD
42-44 Wigmore Street, London, W1U 2RX
Area of Operation: East England, Greater London,
South East England
Tel: 0800 068 3603 **Fax:** 01206 762698
Email: info@nicholas-anthony.co.uk
Web: www.nicholas-anthony.co.uk
Product Type: 2, 5

NOW GROUP PLC (CONTRACTS DIVISION)
Red Scar Business Park, Longridge Road,
Preston, Lancashire, PR2 5NA
Area of Operation: UK & Ireland
Tel: 01772 703838 **Fax:** 01772 705788
Email: sales@nowkitchens.co.uk
Web: www.nowkitchens.co.uk
Product Type: 1, 2, 3, 5, 7, 9

NTP KITCHENS & JOINERY LTD
Unit 20/1, West Bowling Green Street,
Edinburgh, EH6 5PE
Area of Operation: Scotland
Tel: 0131 554 8787 **Fax:** 0131 554 9191
Email: sales@ntp-kitchens.co.uk
Web: www.ntp-kitchens.co.uk
Product Type: 1, 2, 3, 5, 6, 7, 8, 9, 10

PANELS PLUS
22-24 Mill Place, Kingston Upon Thames,
Surrey, KT1 2RJ
Area of Operation: Greater London
Tel: 0208 399 6343 **Fax:** 0208 399 6343
Email: sales@panelspluslltd.com
Web: www.panelspluslltd.com
Product Type: 1, 2, 3, 5, 6, 10

PARLOUR FARM
Unit 12b, Wilkinson Road, Love Lane Industrial
Estate, Cirencester, Gloucestershire, GL7 1YT
Area of Operation: Europe
Tel: 01285 885336 **Fax:** 01285 643189
Email: info@parlourfarm.com
Web: www.parlourfarm.com

PLAIN ENGLISH
Stowupland Hall, Stowupland, Suffolk, IP14 4BE
Area of Operation: Worldwide
Tel: 01449 774028 **Fax:** 01449 613519
Email: info@plainenglishdesign.co.uk
Web: www.plainenglishdesign.co.uk
Product Type: 1, 2, 8

POSH PANTRIES
81 Kelvin Road North, Lenziemill,
Cumbernauld, Lanarkshire, G67 2BD
Area of Operation: UK (Excluding Ireland)
Tel: 01236 453556 **Fax:** 01236 728068
Email: office@poshpantries.co.uk
Web: www.poshpantries.co.uk

PRICE KITCHENS
11 Imperial Way, Croydon, Surrey, CR0 4RR
Area of Operation: South East England
Tel: 0208 686 9006 **Fax:** 0208 686 5958
Email: info@pricekitchens.co.uk
Web: www.pricekitchens.co.uk

RICHARD BAKER FURNITURE LTD
Wimbledon Studios, 257 Burlington Road,
New Malden, Surrey, KT3 4NE
Area of Operation: Europe
Tel: 0208 336 1777
Fax: 0208 336 1666
Email: richard@richardbakerfurniture.co.uk
Web: www.richardbakerfurniture.co.uk
Product Type: 1, 2, 5, 8

ROBERT J TURNER & CO
Roe Green, Sandon, Buntingford, Hertfordshire, SG9 0QE
Area of Operation: East England, Greater London
Tel: 01763 288371 **Fax:** 01763 288440
Email: sales@robertjturner.co.uk
Web: www.robertjturner.co.uk
Product Type: 1, 2, 3, 4, 5, 6, 7, 8, 9, 10

ROBINSON AND CORNISH LTD
St George's House, St George's Road,
Barnstaple, Devon, EX32 7AS
Area of Operation: Europe
Tel: 01271 329300
Fax: 01271 328277
Email: sales@robinsonandcornish.co.uk
Web: www.robinsonandcornish.co.uk
Product Type: 2, 3, 8, 10 **Other Info:** ✎

ROUNDEL DESIGN (UK) LTD
Flishinghurst Orchards, Chalk Lane,
Cranbrook, Kent, TN17 2QA
Area of Operation: South East England
Tel: 01580 712666
Email: homebuild@roundeldesign.co.uk
Web: www.roundeldesign.co.uk
Product Type: 1, 2, 3, 5, 7, 8, 9

SAMUEL SCOTT PARTNERSHIP
Surgery House, The Square,
Skillington, Lincolnshire, NG33 5HB
Area of Operation: Europe
Tel: 01476 861806 **Fax:** 01476 861806
Email: samuel_scott@tiscali.co.uk
Web: www.butcherblocks.co.uk **Other Info:** ✎ 🖐

SANDERSON'S FINE FURNITURE
Unit 5 & 6, The Village Workshop, Four Crosses
Business Park, Four Crosses, Powys, SY22 6ST
Area of Operation: UK (Excluding Ireland)
Tel: 01691 830075
Fax: 01691 830075
Email: sales@sandersonsfinefurniture.co.uk
Web: www.sandersonsfinefurniture.co.uk

SECOND NATURE KITCHEN COLLECTION
PO Box 20, Station Road, Aycliffe Industrial Park,
Newton Aycliffe, Durham, DL5 6XJ
Area of Operation: UK & Ireland
Tel: 01325 505539
Email: mail@sncollection.co.uk
Web: www.sncollection.co.uk
Product Type: 1, 3, 4, 5, 6, 7, 8, 9, 10

SIEMATIC
Osprey House, Primett Road,
Stevenage, Hertfordshire, SG1 3EE
Area of Operation: UK & Ireland
Tel: 01438 369251 **Fax:** 01438 368920
Email: sales@siematic.co.uk
Web: www.siematic.co.uk

SIMON BRAY AT GK DESIGN
Greensbury Farm, Thurleigh Road,
Bolnhurst, Bedfordshire, MK44 2ET
Area of Operation: UK (Excluding Ireland)
Tel: 01234 376990
Fax: 01234 376991
Email: studio@gkdesign.co.uk
Web: www.simon-bray.co.uk **Other Info:** ✎

SPILLERS OF CHARD LTD.
Chard Business Park, Chard, Somerset, TA20 1FA
Area of Operation: South West England and South Wales
Tel: 01460 67878
Fax: 01460 65252
Email: info@cookercentre.com
Web: www.cookercentre.com
Product Type: 1, 2, 3, 5, 10

SPRINGWELL DOORS LTD T/A PARAPAN
Thistle House, Thistle Way,
Gildersome Spur, Wakefield Road,
Morley, Leeds, West Yorkshire, LS27 7JZ
Area of Operation: UK (Excluding Ireland)
Tel: 0113 201 2240 **Fax:** 0113 253 0717
Email: info@parapan.co.uk
Web: www.parapan.co.uk **Product Type:** 5, 9

TASKWORTHY
The Old Brickyard, Pontrilas, Herefordshire, HR2 0DJ
Area of Operation: UK (Excluding Ireland)
Tel: 01981 242900 **Fax:** 01981 242901
Email: peter@taskworthy.co.uk
Web: www.taskworthy.co.uk
Product Type: 1, 2, 3, 4, 5, 7, 8, 9, 10

TENTERDEN HOUSE INTERIORS
4 West Cross, Tenterden, Kent, TN30 6JL
Area of Operation: Worldwide
Tel: 01580 764481 **Fax:** 01580 765531
Email: tenterdenhouseinteriors@hotmail.com
Product Type: 2, 3, 8

THE KITCHEN AND BATHROOM COLLECTION
Nelson House, Nelson Road,
Salisbury, Wiltshire, SP1 3LT
Area of Operation: South West England and South Wales
Tel: 01722 334800 **Fax:** 01722 412252
Email: info@kbc.co.uk **Web:** www.kbc.co.uk
Product Type: 2, 3, 4, 5, 6, 7, 9 **Other Info:** ✎ 🖐

THE KITCHEN GROUP
PJH Group, Alder House, Kearsley,
Bolton, Lancashire, BL4 8SL
Area of Operation: UK & Ireland
Tel: 01204 707070 **Fax:** 01204 573140
Email: info@pjh.co.uk
Web: www.kitchengroup.co.uk
Product Type: 1, 2, 3, 6, 7, 8, 9

THE MODERN ROOM LTD
54 St.Pauls Road, Luton, Bedfordshire, LU1 3RX
Area of Operation: UK (Excluding Ireland)
Tel: 01582 612070 **Fax:** 01582 612070
Email: laura@themodernroom.com
Web: www.themodernroom.com
Product Type: 2, 5, 9 **Other Info:** ✎ 🖐

THE OLD CREAMERY
Watercombe Park, Lynx Trading Estate,
Yeovil, Somerset, BA20 2EB
Area of Operation: South West England and South Wales
Tel: 01935 410500 **Fax:** 01935 426908
Email: oldcreamery@hotmail.com
Web: www.oldcreameryfurniture.com
Product Type: 1, 2, 3, 5, 8, 10
Other Info: ▽ ✎ 🖐

THE OLD PINE STORE
Coxons Yard, Off Union Street,
Ashbourne, Derbyshire, DE6 1FG
Area of Operation: Europe
Tel: 01335 344112 **Fax:** 01335 344112
Email: martin@old-pine.co.uk
Web: www.old-pine.co.uk **Product Type:** 3, 5

THE ORIGINAL KITCHEN COMPANY
4 Main Street, Breaston, Derby, Derbyshire, DE72 3DX
Area of Operation: UK & Ireland
Tel: 01332 873746 **Fax:** 01332 873731
Email: originalkitchens@aol.com

TIM WOOD LIMITED
1 Burland Road, London, SW11 6SA
Area of Operation: Worldwide
Tel: 07041 380030 **Fax:** 08700 548645
Email: homeb@timwood.com
Web: www.timwood.com

TOMPKINS LTD
High March Close, Long March Industrial Estate,
Daventry, Northamptonshire, NN11 4EZ
Area of Operation: UK (Excluding Ireland)
Tel: 01327 877187 **Fax:** 01327 310491
Email: info@tompkinswood.co.uk
Web: www.tompkinswood.co.uk
Product Type: 1, 2, 3, 4, 5, 6, 7, 8, 9, 10
Other Info: ✎ 🖐

TRADESTYLE CABINETS LTD
Carmaben Road, Easter Queenslie Industrial Estate,
Glasgow, Lothian, G33 4UN
Area of Operation: UK (Excluding Ireland)
Tel: 0141 781 6800 **Fax:** 0141 781 6801
Email: info@tradestylecabinets.com
Web: www.tradestylecabinets.com

TURNER FURNITURE
The Old Dairy, Manor Farm,
Sipilly Handley, Salisbury, SP5 5NU
Area of Operation: Greater London, South East
England, South West England and South Wales
Tel: 01725 516990 **Fax:** 01725 516991
Email: nick@turner-furniture.co.uk
Web: www.turner-furniture.co.uk
Product Type: 1, 3, 5, 7, 9

UNPAINTED KITCHENS LTD
258 Battersea Park Road, London, SW11 3BP
Area of Operation: UK (Excluding Ireland)
Tel: 0207 223 2017 **Fax:** 01604 722573
Email: unpaintedkss@aol.com
Web: www.unpaintedkitchens.com
Product Type: 1

WATTS & WRIGHT (THE JOINERY SHOP)
PO Box 4251, Walsall, West Midlands, WS5 3WY
Area of Operation: Worldwide
Tel: 01922 610800 / 020 7043 7619
Fax: 0870 762 6387
Email: sales@wattsandwright.com
Web: www.wattsandwright.com
Product Type: 1, 2, 3, 4, 5, 7, 8, 10

WICKES
Wickes Customer Services, Wickes House, 120-138
Station Road, Harrow, Middlesex, HA1 2QB
Area of Operation: UK (Excluding Ireland)
Tel: 0870 608 9001 **Fax:** 0208 863 6225
Web: www.wickes.co.uk

WILLIAM GARVEY
Leyhill, Payhembury, Honiton, Devon, EX14 3JG
Area of Operation: Worldwide
Tel: 01404 841430
Fax: 01404 841626
Email: webquery@williamgarvey.co.uk
Web: www.williamgarvey.co.uk
Product Type: 2 **Other Info:** ✎ 🖐

WINE CORNER LTD
Unit 6 Harworth Enterprise Park, Brunel Industrial Estate,
Harworth, Doncaster, South Yorkshire, DN11 8SG
Area of Operation: Worldwide
Tel: 01302 757047 **Fax:** 01302 751233
Email: elaine@winecorner.co.uk
Web: www.winecorner.co.uk

WINNING DESIGNS
Dyke Farm, West Chiltington Road,
Pulborough, West Sussex, RH20 2EE
Area of Operation: UK & Ireland
Tel: 0870 754 4446
Fax: 0700 032 9946
Email: info@winning-designs-uk.com
Web: www.winning-designs-uk.com
Product Type: 1, 2, 3, 4, 5, 6, 7, 8, 9, 10
Other Info: ▽ ECO ✎ 🖐

WOODCHESTER KITCHENS & INTERIORS
Unit 18a Chalford Industrial Estate,
Chalford, Gloucestershire, GL6 8NT
Area of Operation: UK (Excluding Ireland)
Tel: 01453 886411 **Fax:** 01453 886411
Email: enquires@woodchesterkitchens.co.uk
Web: www.woodchesterkitchens.co.uk
Product Type: 1, 2, 3, 4, 5, 6, 7, 8, 9, 10

WOODSTOCK FURNITURE
17 Park Drive, East Sheen, London, SW14 8RB
Area of Operation: Worldwide
Tel: 020 8876 0131
Fax: 020 8876 0131
Email: ask@woodstockfurniture.co.uk
Web: www.woodstockfurniture.co.uk
Product Type: 1, 2, 3, 4, 5, 6, 7, 8, 9, 10
Other Info: ✎ 🖐

WORKTOPS

KEY

OTHER: ▽ Reclaimed   ⌐𝕆 On-line shopping
✐ Bespoke   ✋ Hand-made   ECO Ecological

AFFORDABLE GRANITE LTD
Unit 5 John Lory Farm, Charlwood Place,
Norwood Hill Road, Charlwwod, Surrey, RH6 0EB
Area of Operation: UK (Excluding Ireland)
Tel: 0845 330 1692   **Fax:** 0845 330 1260
Email: sales@affordablegranite.co.uk
Web: www.affordablegranite.co.uk
Material Type: E) 1

AFFORDABLE GRANITE LTD
Unit 5 Charlwood Place,
Norwood Hill Road, Surrey, RH6 0EB
Area of Operation: UK (Excluding Ireland)
Tel: 0845 330 1692   **Fax:** 0845 330 1260
Email: sales@affordablegranite.co.uk
Web: www.affordablegranite.co.uk
Material Type: E) 1

ALISTAIR MACKINTOSH LTD
Bannerley Road, Garretts Green,
Birmingham, West Midlands, B33 0SL
Area of Operation: UK & Ireland
Tel: 0121 784 6800   **Fax:** 0121 789 7068
Email: info@alistairmackintosh.co.uk
Web: www.alistairmackintosh.co.uk
Material Type: E) 1

ALLMILMO UK
Briff Well, Little Lane, Reading, Berkshire, RG7 6QX
Area of Operation: UK & Ireland
Tel: 01635 868181   **Fax:** 01635 869693
Email: allmilmo@aol.com
Web: www.allmilmo.com   **Material Type:** E) 1

AMBER KITCHENS OF BISHOP'S STORTFORD
Clarklands House, Parsonage Lane,
Sawbridgeworth, Hertfordshire, CM21 0NG
Area of Operation: East England, Greater London
Tel: 01279 600030   **Fax:** 01279 721528
Email: info@amberkitchens.com
Web: www.amberkitchens.com
Material Type: A) 1, 2, 3, 4, 5, 6, 7, 8, 9, 10, 11, 12, 13, 14, 15

ARO MARBLE
18 Minerva Road, London, NW10 6HJ
Area of Operation: UK (Excluding Ireland)
Tel: 020 8965 1144   **Fax:** 020 8965 1818
Email: info@aromarble.com
Web: www.aromarble.com

ASHFORD & BROOKS
The Old Workshop, Ashtree Barn, Caters Road,
Bredfield, Woodbridge, Suffolk, IP13 6BE
Area of Operation: UK (Excluding Ireland)
Tel: 01473 737764   **Fax:** 01473 277176
Email: ashfordbrooks@mailbox.co.uk
Web: www.ashfordandbrooks.co.uk
Material Type: A) 2, 3, 4, 5, 6, 7, 8, 9, 10, 11, 12, 14

ASHLAR MASON
Manor Building, Manor Road, London, W13 0JB
Area of Operation: East England, Greater London,
Midlands & Mid Wales, South East England, South
West England and South Wales
Tel: 0208 997 0002
Fax: 0208 997 0008
Email: enquiries@ashlarmason.co.uk
Web: www.ashlarmason.co.uk
Material Type: E) 1, 2, 3, 4, 5, 8, 9, 11, 12, 13

ASTRACAST PLC
Holden Ing Way, Birstall, West Yorkshire, WF17 9AE
Area of Operation: UK & Ireland
Tel: 01924 477466
Fax: 01924 351297
Email: brochures@astracast.co.uk
Web: www.astracast.co.uk ⌐𝕆

AXIOM BY FORMICA
Formica Ltd, Coast Road,
North Shields, Tyne & Wear, NE29 8RE
Area of Operation: UK & Ireland
Tel: 0191 259 3478   **Fax:** 0191 258 2719
Email: axiom.info@formica.co.uk
Web: www.axiomworktops.com
Material Type: A) 1, 2, 3, 4, 5, 7

AXIOM BY FORMICA
Area of Operation: UK & Ireland
Tel: 0191 259 3478
Fax: 0191 258 2719
Email: axiom.info@formica.co.uk
Web: www.axiomworktops.com

The Axiom by Formica collection contains 85
worktops, 21 splashbacks and 20 upstands,
offering designs and finishes to cater for all tastes.
Axiom® Signature offers a range of premium
worktops including solid surfacing and solid wood.

AZTEC METAL TILES
Bowl Road, Charing, Kent, TN27 0HB
Area of Operation: UK & Ireland
Tel: 01233 712332
Fax: 01233 714994
Email: enquiries@aztecmetaltiles.co.uk
Web: www.aztecmetaltiles.co.uk
Material Type: C) 1, 2, 3, 4, 6, 7, 11, 12

BARNCREST HARDWOOD KITCHEN WORKTOPS
Unit 9, Tregoniggie Industrial Estate,
Falmouth, Cornwall, TR11 4SN
Area of Operation: UK & Ireland
Tel: 01326 375982
Email: enquiries@barncrest.co.uk
Web: www.barncrest.co.uk
Material Type: A) 2, 3, 4, 7

BATH KITCHEN COMPANY
22 Hensley Road, Bloomfield, Bath, Somerset, BA2 2DR
Area of Operation: South West England and South Wales
Tel: 01225 312003
Fax: 01225 312003
Email: david@bathkitchencompany.co.uk
Web: www.bathkitchencompany.co.uk
Material Type: A) 1, 2, 3, 4, 5, 6, 7, 8, 9, 10, 11, 12, 13, 14, 15

BAYFIELD STAIR CO
Unit 4, Praed Road, Trafford Park, Manchester, M17 1PQ
Area of Operation: Worldwide
Tel: 0161 848 0700   **Fax:** 0161 872 2230
Email: sales@bayfieldstairs.co.uk
Web: www.bayfieldstairs.co.uk

BERWYN SLATE QUARRY LTD
The Horseshoe Pass, Llangollen,
Denbighshire, LL20 8DP
Area of Operation: UK (Excluding Ireland)
Tel: 01978 861897   **Fax:** 01978 869292
Email: sales@berwynslate.com
Web: www.berwynslate.com   **Material Type:** E) 3

BORDERCRAFT
Old Forge, Peterchurch, Hereford,
Herefordshire, HR2 0SD
Area of Operation: UK (Excluding Ireland)
Tel: 01981 550251   **Fax:** 01981 550552
Email: sales@bordercraft.co.uk
Web: www.bordercraft.co.uk   **Other Info:** ECO ✐ ✋
Material Type: A) 2, 3, 4, 5, 6, 7

BUSHBOARD LTD
9-29 Rixon Road, Wellingborough,
Northamptonshire, NN8 4BA
Area of Operation: UK & Ireland
Tel: 01933 232200
Email: washrooms@bushboard.co.uk
Web: www.bushboard.co.uk

BUYDESIGN
Monteviot Nurseries, Ancrum,
Jedburgh, Borders, TD8 6TU
Area of Operation: Scotland
Tel: 01835 830740
Email: enquiries@buydesign-furniture.com
Web: www.buydesign-furniture.com
Material Type: A) 1, 2, 3, 4, 5, 6, 8, 9, 11

CARE DESIGN
Moorgate, Ormskirk, Lancashire, L39 4RX
Area of Operation: UK (Excluding Ireland)
Tel: 01695 579061   **Fax:** 01695 570489
Email: caredesign@clara.net
Web: www.caredesign.co.uk

CHRISTOPHER PETERS
ORIGINAL UNFITTED KITCHENS
Lower Farm Barns,
Brandon Lane, Warwickshire, CV3 3GW
Area of Operation: Europe
Tel: 02476 303300
Email: enquiries@christopherpetersantiques.co.uk
Web: www.christopherpetersantiques.co.uk

CHROMA INTERNATIONAL GLASS LTD
Unit 200 Bridgwater Business Park,
Bridgwater, Somerset, TA6 4TB
Area of Operation: Europe
Tel: 01278 426226   **Fax:** 01278 450088
Email: info@chroma-glass.com
Web: www.chroma-glass.com
Material Type: J) 4, 5, 6

CITY BATHROOMS & KITCHENS
158 Longford Road, Longford,
Coventry, West Midlands, CV6 6DR
Area of Operation: UK & Ireland
Tel: 02476 365877   **Fax:** 02476 644992
Email: citybathrooms@hotmail.com
Web: www.citybathrooms.co.uk

CONNAUGHT KITCHENS
2 Porchester Place, London, W2 2BS
Area of Operation: Greater London
Tel: 0207 706 2210   **Fax:** 0207 706 2209
Email: design@connaughtkitchens.co.uk
Web: www.connaughtkitchens.co.uk

CONQUIRA LTD
2 Central Buildings, Warwick Road,
Coventry, Warwickshire, CV8 1FQ
Area of Operation: Midlands & Mid Wales
Tel: 02476 222255   **Fax:** 02476 552211
Email: gary@conquira.freeserve.co.uk
Web: www.conquira.co.uk

COTTAGE FARM ANTIQUES
Stratford Road, Aston Sub Edge,
Chipping Campden, Gloucestershire, GL55 6PZ
Area of Operation: Worldwide
Tel: 01386 438263   **Fax:** 01386 438263
Email: info@cottagefarmantiques.co.uk
Web: www.cottagefarmantiques.co.uk ⌐𝕆
Material Type: A) 4, 5, 6

COUNTRY KITCHENS
The Old Farm House, Birmingham Road,
Blackminster, Evesham, Worcestershire, WR11 7TD
Area of Operation: UK (Excluding Ireland)
Tel: 01386 831705   **Fax:** 01386 834051
Web: www.handcraftedkitchens.com
Material Type: A) 2, 4, 5, 6

COUNTY GRANITE AND MARBLE
Mill Lane, Creech Saint Michael,
Taunton, Somerset, TA3 5PX
Area of Operation: UK (Excluding Ireland)
Tel: 01823 444554   **Fax:** 01823 445013
Web: www.countygranite.co.uk
Material Type: E) 1, 2, 3, 5

COUNTY HARDWOODS
Creech Mill, Mill Lane, Creech Saint Michael,
Taunton, Somerset, TA3 5PX
Area of Operation: UK & Ireland
Tel: 01823 443760   **Fax:** 01823 443940
Email: sales@countyhardwoods.co.uk
Web: www.countyhardwoods.co.uk ⌐𝕆
Material Type: A) 2, 5

CRABTREE KITCHENS
17 Station Road, Barnes, Greater London, SW13 0LF
Area of Operation: Greater London, South West
England and South Wales
Tel: 0208 392 6955   **Fax:** 0208 392 6944
Email: design@crabtreekitchens.co.uk
Web: www.crabtreekitchens.co.uk
Other Info: ✐ ✋

CRAFTSHIP WORKTOPS LTD
Beach Bros Ltd, Western Road,
St Thomas, Exeter, Dorset, EX4 1EQ
Area of Operation: UK (Excluding Ireland)
Tel: 01392 421111   **Fax:** 01392 421212
Email: sales@woodentops.co.uk
Web: www.woodentops.co.uk

CYMRU KITCHENS
63 Caerleon Road, Newport, NP19 7BX
Area of Operation: UK (Excluding Ireland)
Tel: 01633 676767   **Fax:** 01633 212512
Email: sales@cymrukitchens.com
Web: www.cymrukitchens.com

DESIGNER KITCHENS
37 High Street, Potters Bar, Hertfordshire, EN6 5AJ
Area of Operation: Greater London
Tel: 01707 650565   **Fax:** 01707 663050
Email: info@designer-kitchens.co.uk
Web: www.designer-kitchens.co.uk

DEVON STONE LTD
8 Pilot Road, Pierhead, Exmouth, Devon, EX8 1XA
Area of Operation: UK (Excluding Ireland)
Tel: 01395 222525
Email: amy@devonstone.com
Web: www.devonstone.com   **Other Info:** ✐ ✋
Material Type: E) 1, 2, 3

DUPONT CORIAN & ZODIAQ
10 Quarry Court, Pitstone Green Business Park,
Pitstone, Nr. Tring, Buckinghamshire, LU7 9GW
Area of Operation: UK & Ireland
Tel: 01296 663555   **Fax:** 01296 663599
Email: sales@corian.co.uk
Web: www.corian.co.uk

ECO IMPACT LTD
50a Kew Green, Richmond,
Greater London, TW9 3BB
Area of Operation: UK & Ireland
Tel: 0208 940 7072   **Fax:** 0208 332 1218
Email: sales@ecoimpact.co.uk
Web: www.ecoimpact.co.uk   **Other Info:** ECO ✐

EGGER (UK) LIMITED
Anick Grange Road, Hexham,
Northumberland, NE46 4JS
Area of Operation: UK & Ireland
Tel: 01434 602191   **Fax:** 01434 605103
Email: building.uk@egger.com
Web: www.egger.co.uk   **Material Type:** H) 1, 2, 6

ELITE TRADE KITCHENS LTD
90 Willesden Lane, Kilburn, London, NW6 7TA
Area of Operation: UK (Excluding Ireland)
Tel: 0207 328 1234   **Fax:** 0207 328 1243
Email: sales@elitekitchens.co.uk
Web: www.elitekitchens.co.uk

FRANCIS N. LOWE LTD.
The Marble Works, New Road,
Middleton, Matlock, Derbyshire, DE4 4NA
Area of Operation: Europe
Tel: 01629 822216
Fax: 01629 824348
Email: info@lowesmarble.com
Web: www.lowesmarble.com
Material Type: E) 1, 2, 3, 5, 8

G MIDDLETON LTD
Cross Croft Industrial Estate,
Appleby, Cumbria, CA16 6HX
Area of Operation: Europe
Tel: 01768 352067 **Fax:** 01768 353228
Email: info@graham-middleton.co.uk
Web: www.graham-middleton.co.uk

HATT KITCHENS
Hartlebury Trading Estate,
Hartlebury, Worcestershire, DY10 4JB
Area of Operation: UK (Excluding Ireland)
Tel: 01299 251320 **Fax:** 01299 251579
Email: design@hatt.co.uk **Web:** www.hatt.co.uk

HITT OAK LTD
10 Park Parade, Gunnersbury Avenue, London, W3 9BD
Area of Operation: UK (Excluding Ireland)
Tel: 0208 8961900 **Fax:** 0208 8961900
Email: zhitas@yahoo.co.uk

HYGROVE
152/154 Merton Road, Wimbledon, London, SW19 1EH
Area of Operation: South East England
Tel: 0208 543 1200 **Fax:** 0208 543 6521
Email: sales@hygrove.fsnet.co.uk
Web: www.hygrovefurniture.co.uk
Material Type: A) 1, 2, 3, 4, 5, 6, 7, 8, 9, 10, 11, 12, 14

IMPORTANT ROOMS LTD
62 High Street, Wargrave,
Reading, Berkshire, RG10 8BY
Area of Operation: Greater London, South East
England, South West England and South Wales
Tel: 0118 940 1266 **Fax:** 0118 940 1667
Email: steve@importantrooms.co.uk
Web: www.importantrooms.co.uk
Material Type: A) 10

IN-TOTO
Shaw Cross Court, Shaw Cross Business Park,
Dewsbury, West Yorkshire, WF12 7RF
Area of Operation: UK (Excluding Ireland)
Tel: 01924 487900 **Fax:** 01924 437305
Email: graham.russell@intoto.co.uk
Web: www.intoto.co.uk

ISAAC LORD LTD
West End Court, Suffield Road,
High Wycombe, Buckinghamshire, HP11 2JY
Area of Operation: East England, Greater London,
North East England, South East England, South West
England and South Wales
Tel: 01494 462121 **Fax:** 01494 461376
Email: info@isaaclord.co.uk
Web: www.isaaclord.co.uk

J & R MARBLE COMPANY LTD
Unit 9,Period Works, Lammas Road,
Leyton, London, E10 7QT
Area of Operation: UK (Excluding Ireland)
Tel: 0208 539 6471 **Fax:** 0208 539 9264
Email: sales@jrmarble.co.uk
Web: www.jrmarble.co.uk **Other Info:**
Material Type: E) 1, 2, 3, 4, 5, 8, 9, 13, 14

JOHN LEWIS OF HUNGERFORD
Grove Technology Park, Downsview Road,
Wantage, Oxfordshire, OX12 9FA
Area of Operation: UK (Excluding Ireland)
Tel: 01235 774300 **Fax:** 01235 769031
Email: park.street@john-lewis.co.uk
Web: www.john-lewis.co.uk **Material Type:** F) 2

JOHN OWEN JOINERY
Unit 1 Hays Bridge Farm, Brickhouse Lane,
South Godstone, Surrey, RH9 8JW
Area of Operation: Greater London, South West
England and South Wales
Tel: 01342 844036 **Fax:** 01342 844036
Email: johnowen.joinery@virgin.net
Web: www.johnowen.co.uk

JOHN STRAND (MK) LTD
12-22, Herga Road, Wealdstone,
Harrow, Middlesex, HA3 5AS
Area of Operation: UK & Ireland
Tel: 0208 930 6006 **Fax:** 0208 930 6008
Email: enquiry@johnstrand-mk.co.uk
Web: www.johnstrand-mk.co.uk

KENSINGTON STUDIO
13 c & d Kensington Road, Earlsdon,
Coventry, West Midlands, CV5 6GG
Area of Operation: UK (Excluding Ireland)
Tel: 02476 713326 **Fax:** 02476 713136
Email: sales@kensingtonstudio.com
Web: www.kensingtonstudio.com

KIEVEL.KL-CHEMIE (UK) LTD
Lower Farm, Lower Farm Lane,
Ampfield, Romsey, Hampshire, SO51 9BN
Area of Operation: UK & Ireland
Tel: 01794 368865 **Fax:** 01794 368914
Email: info@kievel.com
Web: www.kievel.com **Other Info:**
Material Type: E) 1, 2, 3, 4, 5, 7, 8, 9

KIRK NATURAL STONE
Bridgend, Fyvie, Turriff, Aberdeenshire, AB53 8LL
Area of Operation: Worldwide
Tel: 01651 891891 **Fax:** 01651 891794
Email: info@kirknaturalstone.com
Web: www.kirknaturalstone.com

KIRKSTONE QUARRIES LIMITED
Skelwith Bridge, Ambleside, Cumbria, LA22 9NN
Area of Operation: UK & Ireland
Tel: 01539 433296 **Fax:** 01539 434006
Email: info@kirkstone.com
Web: www.kirkstone.com
Material Type: E) 1, 3, 5

KITCHEN SUPPLIES
East Chesters , North Way, Hillend Industrial Estate,
Dalgety Bay, Fife, KY11 9JA
Area of Operation: UK (Excluding Ireland)
Tel: 01383 824729
Email: sales@kitchensupplies.co.uk
Web: www.kitchensupplies.co.uk

KITCHENS BY JULIAN ENGLISH
Ideal Home, Blackbird Road,
Leicester, Leicestershire, LE4 0AH
Area of Operation: Midlands & Mid Wales
Tel: 0116 251 9999 **Fax:** 0116 251 9999
Email: philiphalifax@aol.com
Web: www.kitchens-by-julianenglish.co.uk

M D STAINLESS DESIGNS
79 Verity Cresent, Poole, Dorset, BH17 8TT
Area of Operation: UK (Excluding Ireland)
Tel: 01202 684998 **Fax:** 01202 684998
Email: stainlessdesigns@onetel.com

MANDARIN
Unit 1 Wonastow Road Industrial Estate,
Monmouth, Monmouthshire, NP25 5JB
Area of Operation: Europe
Tel: 01600 715444 **Fax:** 01600 715494
Email: info@mandarinstone.com
Web: www.mandarinstone.com

MARBLE CLASSICS
Unit 3, Station Approach,
Emsworth, Hampshire, PO10 7PW
Area of Operation: UK & Ireland
Tel: 01243 370011 **Fax:** 01243 371023
Email: info@marbleclassics.co.uk
Web: www.marbleclassics.co.uk
Material Type: E) 1, 2, 3

MARBLE HART.COM
1 Edwin Street, Daybrook, Arnold,
Nottingham, Nottinghamshire, NG5 6AX
Area of Operation: Worldwide
Tel: 0115 920 3159 **Fax:** 0115 952 5752
Email: chris@cghart.com
Web: www.marblehart.com

MARK LEIGH KITCHENS LTD
11 Common Garden Street,
Lancaster, Lancashire, LA1 1XD
Area of Operation: North West England and North Wales
Tel: 01524 63273 **Fax:** 01524 62352
Email: mark@markleigh.co.uk
Web: www.markleigh.co.uk **Other Info:**
Material Type: A) 1, 2, 3, 4, 5, 6, 7, 8, 9, 10, 11, 12, 13, 14

MASTER LTD
30 Station Road, Heacham, Norfolk, PE31 7EX
Area of Operation: Europe
Tel: 01485 572032 **Fax:** 01485 571675
Email: sales@masterlimited.co.uk
Web: www.masterlimited.co.uk
Material Type: A) 2, 3, 4, 5, 11, 15

MEDUSA CREATIONS UK LTD
Unit 2B Lancaster Road, Carnaby Industrial Estate,
Bridlington, East Riding of Yorks, YO15 3QY
Area of Operation: UK (Excluding Ireland)
Tel: 01262 605222
Fax: 01262 605654
Email: info@medusacreationscommercial.co.uk
Web: www.medusacreationscommercial.co.uk

MEREWAY CONTRACTS
Unit 1 Wharfdale Road, Tysely,
Birmingham, West Midlands, B11 2DE
Area of Operation: UK (Excluding Ireland)
Tel: 0121 764 7180
Fax: 0121 764 7199
Email: info@merewaycontracts.co.uk
Web: www.merewaycontracts.co.uk

MIDLAND STONE CENTRE LIMITED
The Old Brick Yard, Orton Road,
Rothwell, Northamptonshire, NN14 6AA
Area of Operation: UK (Excluding Ireland)
Tel: 01536 713020 **Fax:** 01536 713880
Material Type: E) 1, 9

MOBALPA
1 High Street, Halberton, Devon, EX16 7AF
Area of Operation: Worldwide
Tel: 07740 633672 **Fax:** 01884 820828
Email: ploftus@mobalpa.com
Web: www.mobalpa.co.uk

MONTANA KITCHENS LTD
BIC 1, Studio 2/3 Innova Business Park,
Mollison Avenue, Enfield, Middlesex, EN3 7XU
Area of Operation: Greater London, South East England
Tel: 0800 58 75 628
Email: angie@montanakitchens.co.uk
Web: www.montanakitchens.co.uk
Material Type: A) 1, 2, 3, 4, 5, 6, 7, 8, 9, 10, 11, 12, 13, 14

NATURAL IMAGE (GRANITE, MARBLE, STONE)
Station Road, Staplehurst, Kent, TN12 0QD
Area of Operation: UK & Ireland
Tel: 01580 895489 **Fax:** 01580 893720
Web: www.naturalimage.co.uk

NICHOLAS ANTHONY LTD
42-44 Wigmore Street, London, W1U 2RX
Area of Operation: East England, Greater London,
South East England
Tel: 0800 068 3603 **Fax:** 01206 762698
Email: info@nicholas-anthony.co.uk
Web: www.nicholas-anthony.co.uk

NOW GROUP PLC (CONTRACTS DIVISION)
Red Scar Business Park, Longridge Road,
Preston, Lancashire, PR2 5NA
Area of Operation: UK & Ireland
Tel: 01772 703838
Fax: 01772 705788
Email: sales@nowkitchens.co.uk
Web: www.nowkitchens.co.uk

NTP KITCHENS & JOINERY LTD
Unit 20/1, West Bowling Green Street,
Edinburgh, EH6 5PE
Area of Operation: Scotland
Tel: 0131 554 8787
Fax: 0131 554 9191
Email: sales@ntp-kitchens.co.uk
Web: www.ntp-kitchens.co.uk
Material Type: A) 2, 4

ORAMA
Azalea Close, Clover Nook Industrial Estate,
Somercotes, Derbyshire, DE55 4QX
Area of Operation: UK & Ireland
Tel: 01773 520560 **Fax:** 01773 520319
Email: sales@orama.co.uk **Web:** www.orama.co.uk

PANELS PLUS
22-24 Mill Place,
Kingston Upon Thames, Surrey, KT1 2RJ
Area of Operation: Greater London
Tel: 0208 399 6343 **Fax:** 0208 399 6343
Email: sales@panelsplusltd.com
Web: www.panelsplusltd.com
Material Type: H) 2, 5

PFLEIDERER INDUSTRIE LIMITED
Oakfield House, Springwood Way, Tytherington
Business Park, Macclesfield, Cheshire, SK10 2XA
Area of Operation: Worldwide
Tel: 01625 660410 **Fax:** 01625 617301
Email: info@pfleiderer.co.uk
Web: www.pfleiderer.co.uk

PLAIN ENGLISH
Stowupland Hall, Stowupland, Suffolk, IP14 4BE
Area of Operation: Worldwide
Tel: 01449 774028 **Fax:** 01449 613519
Email: info@plainenglishdesign.co.uk
Web: www.plainenglishdesign.co.uk
Material Type: A) 2, 3, 4, 5, 6, 9

POGGENPOHL
477-481 Finchley Road, London, NW3 6HS
Area of Operation: UK & Ireland
Tel: 0800 298 1098 **Fax:** 0207 794 6251
Email: kitchens@poggenpohl-group.co.uk
Web: www.poggenpohl.co.uk
Material Type: A) 1, 2, 3, 4, 5, 7

PRICE KITCHENS
11 Imperial Way, Croydon, Surrey, CR0 4RR
Area of Operation: South East England
Tel: 0208 686 9006 **Fax:** 0208 686 5958
Email: info@pricekitchens.co.uk
Web: www.pricekitchens.co.uk **Other Info:** ✐
Material Type: A) 1, 2, 3, 4, 5, 7, 9

QUINCE STONEWORKS
3 Potton Road, Biggleswade,
Bedfordshire, SG18 0DU
Area of Operation: UK (Excluding Ireland)
Tel: 01767 314180 **Fax:** 01767 600872
Email: sales@qstoneworks.co.uk
Web: www.qstoneworks.co.uk
Other Info: ✐ ✋
Material Type: E) 1, 2, 3, 4, 5

RAK CERAMICS
The Tile House, Easebourne Lane,
Easebourne, West Sussex, GU29 9AZ
Area of Operation: Worldwide
Tel: 01730 815507 **Fax:** 01730 815007
Email: info@rakceramics.co.uk
Web: www.rakceramics.co.uk

RED ROSE PLASTICS (BURNLEY) LTD
Parliament Street, Burnley, Lancashire, BB11 3JT
Area of Operation: East England, North East
England, North West England and North Wales
Tel: 01282 724600 **Fax:** 01282 724644
Email: info@redroseplastics.co.uk
Web: www.redroseplastics.co.uk

REGINOX UK LTD
Radnor Park Trading Estate,
Congleton, Cheshire, CW12 4XJ
Area of Operation: UK & Ireland
Tel: 01260 280033 **Fax:** 01260 298889
Email: sales@reginoxuk.co.uk
Web: www.reginox.com

RICHARD BAKER FURNITURE LTD
Wimbledon Studios, 257 Burlington Road,
New Malden, Surrey, KT3 4NE
Area of Operation: Europe
Tel: 0208 336 1777 **Fax:** 0208 336 1666
Email: richard@richardbakerfurniture.co.uk
Web: www.richardbakerfurniture.co.uk

PLEASE MENTION

THE HOMEBUILDER'S HANDBOOK 2007

WHEN YOU CALL

ROBERT J TURNER & CO
Roe Green, Sandon, Buntingford,
Hertfordshire, SG9 0QE
Area of Operation: East England, Greater London
Tel: 01763 288371 **Fax:** 01763 288440
Email: sales@robertjturner.co.uk
Web: www.robertjturner.co.uk

ROOTS KITCHENS BEDROOMS BATHROOMS
Vine Farm, Stockers Hill, Boughton under Blean,
Faversham, Kent, ME13 9AB
Area of Operation: South East England
Tel: 01227 751130 **Fax:** 01227 750033
Email: showroom@rootskitchens.co.uk
Web: www.rootskitchens.co.uk
Material Type: A) 2, 3, 4, 5, 7

ROUNDEL DESIGN (UK) LTD
Flishinghurst Orchards, Chalk Lane,
Cranbrook, Kent, TN17 2QA
Area of Operation: South East England
Tel: 01580 712666
Email: homebuild@roundeldesign.co.uk
Web: www.roundeldesign.co.uk
Material Type: A) 2, 3, 5, 6, 7, 8

S.L. HARDWOODS
390 Sydenham Road, Croydon, Surrey, CR0 2EA
Area of Operation: UK (Excluding Ireland)
Tel: 0208 683 0292 **Fax:** 0208 683 0404
Email: sales@slhardwoods.co.uk
Web: www.slhardwoods.co.uk

SCHOCK UK LTD
Unit 444 Walton Summit Centre,
Bamber Bridge, Lancashire, PR5 8AT
Area of Operation: UK (Excluding Ireland)
Tel: 01772 332710 **Fax:** 01772 332717
Email: sales@schock.co.uk
Web: www.schock.de **Other Info:** ✐

SECOND NATURE KITCHEN COLLECTION
PO Box 20, Station Road, Aycliffe Industrial Park,
Newton Aycliffe, Durham, DL5 6XJ
Area of Operation: UK & Ireland
Tel: 01325 505539
Email: mail@sncollection.co.uk
Web: www.sncollection.co.uk **Material Type:** C) 3

SECOND NATURE
Area of Operation: UK & Ireland
Tel: 01325 505539
Email: mail@secondnaturecollection.co.uk
Web: www.sncollection.co.uk
Material Type: A E)1 E)13 C)3

Second Nature's bespoke timber worksurface
collection includes 12 species from rubberwood,
bamboo and oak through to rich walnut and
exotic wenge.

SECOND NATURE
Area of Operation: UK & Ireland
Tel: 01325 505539
Email: mail@secondnaturecollection.co.uk
Web: www.sncollection.co.uk
Material Type: A E)1 E)13 C)3

Second Nature offer an extensive and inspiring
range of over 50 granite worksurfaces, with 4
exclusive designs plus a superb selection of
composite stone finishes.

SIEMATIC
Osprey House, Primett Road,
Stevenage, Hertfordshire, SG1 3EE
Area of Operation: UK & Ireland
Tel: 01438 369251 **Fax:** 01438 368920
Email: sales@siematic.co.uk
Web: www.siematic.co.uk

SIMALI STONE FLOORING
40E Wincombe Business Park,
Shaftesbury, Dorset, SP7 9QJ
Area of Operation: Europe
Tel: 01747 852557
Fax: 01747 852557
Email: stonefloors@aol.com
Web: www.stoneflooringonline.com
Material Type: E) 1, 2, 3, 5, 7, 8

SLATE WORLD LTD
Westmoreland Road, Kingsbury, London, NW9 9RN
Area of Operation: Europe
Tel: 0208 204 3444 **Fax:** 0208 204 3311
Email: kingsbury@slateworld.com
Web: www.slateworld.com
Material Type: E) 3, 5

SPILLERS OF CHARD LTD.
Chard Business Park, Chard, Somerset, TA20 1FA
Area of Operation: South West England and South Wales
Tel: 01460 67878 **Fax:** 01460 65252
Email: info@cookercentre.com
Web: www.cookercentre.com

STONELL DIRECT
7 showrooms nationwide - see website for details
Area of Operation: Worldwide
Tel: 08000 832283
Fax: 01283 501098
Email: info@stonelldirect.com
Web: www.stonelldirect.com

STONEVILLE (UK) LTD
Unit 12, Set Star Estate, Transport Avenue, Great
West Road, Brentford, Greater London, TW8 9HF
Area of Operation: Europe
Tel: 0208 560 1000 **Fax:** 0208 560 4060
Email: info@stoneville.co.uk
Web: www.stoneville.co.uk
Material Type: E) 1, 2, 3, 5, 8

STUDIO STONE
The Stone Yard, Alton Lane,
Four Marks, Hampshire, GU34 5AJ
Area of Operation: UK (Excluding Ireland)
Tel: 01420 562500 **Fax:** 01420 563192
Email: sales@studiostone.co.uk
Web: www.studiostone.co.uk
Other Info: ✐
Material Type: E) 1, 2, 3, 5, 8

THE CARPENTRY INSIDER - AIRCOMDIRECT
1 Castleton Crescent,
Skegness, Lincolnshire, PE25 2TJ
Area of Operation: Worldwide
Tel: 01754 767163
Email: aircom8@hotmail.com
Web: www.easycarpentry.com ✐

THE DESIGN STUDIO
39 High Street, Reigate, Surrey, RH2 9AE
Area of Operation: South East England
Tel: 01737 248228 **Fax:** 01737 224180
Email: enq@the-design-studio.co.uk
Web: www.the-design-studio.co.uk ✐

THE GRANITE FACTORY
4 Winchester Drive, Peterlee, Durham, SR8 2RJ
Area of Operation: North East England
Tel: 0191 518 3600 **Fax:** 0191 518 3600
Email: admin@granitefactory.co.uk
Web: www.granitefactory.co.uk ✐
Material Type: E) 1, 2, 3, 4, 5, 7, 8, 9, 11, 13

THE GRANITE WORKSHOP
Church Farm, Stow Longa,
Huntingdon, Cambridgeshire, PE28 0TN
Area of Operation: East England
Tel: 01480 860088 **Fax:** 01480 860089
Email: sales@thegraniteworkshop.co.uk
Web: www.thegraniteworkshop.co.uk
Other Info: ✐ ✋
Material Type: E) 1, 2, 3, 4, 5, 8, 11, 13

THE KITCHEN AND BATHROOM COLLECTION
Nelson House, Nelson Road,
Salisbury, Wiltshire, SP1 3LT
Area of Operation: South West England and South Wales
Tel: 01722 334800 **Fax:** 01722 412252
Email: info@kbc.co.uk **Web:** www.kbc.co.uk
Other Info: ✐ ✋ **Material Type:** A) 1

THE KITCHEN GROUP
PJH Group, Alder House, Kearsley,
Bolton, Lancashire, BL4 8SL
Area of Operation: UK & Ireland
Tel: 01204 707070 **Fax:** 01204 573140
Email: info@pjh.co.uk
Web: www.kitchengroup.co.uk

THE MODERN ROOM LTD
54 St.Pauls Road, Luton, Bedfordshire, LU1 3RX
Area of Operation: UK (Excluding Ireland)
Tel: 01582 612070 **Fax:** 01582 612070
Email: laura@themodernroom.com
Web: www.themodernroom.com
Other Info: ✐ ✋

THE NATURAL WOOD FLOOR COMPANY
Unit 6B, Freshfields Business Park,
Stevenson Road, Brighton, East Sussex, BN2 0DF
Area of Operation: Worldwide
Tel: 01273 605800 **Fax:** 01273 605799
Email: sales@naturalwoodfloor.co.uk
Web: www.naturalwoodfloor.co.uk

**THE NATURAL WOOD
FLOORING COMPANY LTD**
20 Smugglers Way, Wandsworth, London, SW18 1EQ
Area of Operation: Worldwide
Tel: 0208 871 9771 **Fax:** 0208 877 0273
Email: sales@naturalwoodfloor.co.uk
Web: www.naturalwoodfloor.co.uk

THE ORIGINAL KITCHEN COMPANY
4 Main Street, Breaston,
Derby, Derbyshire, DE72 3DX
Area of Operation: UK & Ireland
Tel: 01332 873746 **Fax:** 01332 873731
Email: originalkitchens@aol.com

UNICOM
Kingdom House, 219 Gleniffer Road,
Paisley, Renfrewshire, PA2 8UL
Area of Operation: UK & Ireland
Tel: 0845 330 7642
Fax: 0845 330 7641
Email: george@unicom-direct.com
Web: www.unicom-direct.com ✐

INTERIORS, FIXTURES & FINISHES - Kitchens - Worktops; Sinks

SPONSORED BY: WILLIAM BALL www.wball.co.uk

WARMSWORTH STONE LTD
1-3 Sheffield Road, Warmsworth,
Doncaster, South Yorkshire, DN4 9QH
Area of Operation: UK & Ireland
Tel: 01302 858617 **Fax:** 01302 855844
Email: info@warmsworth-stone.co.uk
Web: www.warmsworth-stone.co.uk
Other Info: ✏ ✋ **Material Type:** E) 1, 2, 4, 5, 8

WILLIAM GARVEY
Leyhill, Payhembury, Honiton, Devon, EX14 3JG
Area of Operation: Worldwide
Tel: 01404 841430 **Fax:** 01404 841626
Email: webquery@williamgarvey.co.uk
Web: www.williamgarvey.co.uk **Other Info:** ✏ ✋
Material Type: A) 2, 3, 4, 10

WINNING DESIGNS
Dyke Farm, West Chiltington Road,
Pulborough, West Sussex, RH20 2EE
Area of Operation: UK & Ireland
Tel: 0870 754 4446 **Fax:** 0700 032 9946
Email: info@winning-designs-uk.com
Web: www.winning-designs-uk.com
Other Info: ▽ ECO ✏ ✋
Material Type: A)1, 2, 3, 4, 5, 6, 7, 8, 9, 10, 11, 12, 13, 14, 15

WOODEN HEART WAREHOUSE
Laburnum Road, Chertsey, Surrey, KT16 8BY
Area of Operation: Greater London, South East England
Tel: 01932 568684 **Fax:** 01932 568685
Email: whw@btclick.com **Material Type:** A) 2, 4, 5

WOODENTOPS
Western Road, Exeter, Devon, EX4 1EQ
Area of Operation: UK (Excluding Ireland)
Tel: 01392 421111 **Fax:** 01392 421212
Email: steve@woodentops.co.uk
Web: www.woodentopsdirect.co.uk ⌁
Material Type: A) 2, 3, 4, 5, 6, 7, 8, 10, 11

WOODSTOCK FURNITURE
17 Park Drive, East Sheen, London, SW14 8RB
Area of Operation: Worldwide
Tel: 020 8876 0131 **Fax:** 020 8876 0131
Email: ask@woodstockfurniture.co.uk
Web: www.woodstockfurniture.co.uk

ZARKA MARBLE
43 Belsize Lane, Hampstead, London, NW3 5AU
Area of Operation: South East England
Tel: 0207 431 3042 **Fax:** 0207 431 3879
Email: enquiries@zarkamarble.co.uk
Web: www.zarkamarble.co.uk
Material Type: E) 1, 2, 3, 5, 8

SINKS

KEY
PRODUCT TYPES: 1= Contemporary
2 = Traditional 3 = Belfast 4 = Double
5 = Other
OTHER: ▽ Reclaimed ⌁ On-line shopping
✏ Bespoke ✋ Hand-made ECO Ecological

AFFORDABLE GRANITE LTD
Unit 5 John Lory Farm, Charlwood Place,
Norwood Hill Road, Charlwwod, Surrey, RH6 0EB
Area of Operation: UK (Excluding Ireland)
Tel: 0845 330 1692
Fax: 0845 330 1260
Email: sales@affordablegranite.co.uk
Web: www.affordablegranite.co.uk

AMBER KITCHENS OF BISHOP'S STORTFORD
Clarklands House, Parsonage Lane,
Sawbridgeworth, Hertfordshire, CM21 0NG
Area of Operation: East England, Greater London
Tel: 01279 600030 **Fax:** 01279 721528
Email: info@amberkitchens.com
Web: www.amberkitchens.com
Product Type: 1, 2, 3, 4, 5

ASHFORD & BROOKS
The Old Workshop, Ashtree Barn, Caters Road,
Bredfield, Woodbridge, Suffolk, IP13 6BE
Area of Operation: UK (Excluding Ireland)
Tel: 01473 737764 **Fax:** 01473 277176
Email: ashfordbrooks@mailbox.co.uk
Web: www.ashfordandbrooks.co.uk
Product Type: 1, 2, 3, 4, 5

ASHLAR MASON
Manor Building, Manor Road, London, W13 0JB
Area of Operation: East England, Greater London,
Midlands & Mid Wales, South East England, South
West England and South Wales
Tel: 0208 997 0002 **Fax:** 0208 997 0008
Email: enquiries@ashlarmason.co.uk
Web: www.ashlarmason.co.uk
Product Type: 1, 2, 3, 4, 5

ASTRACAST PLC
Holden Ing Way, Birstall, West Yorkshire, WF17 9AE
Area of Operation: UK & Ireland
Tel: 01924 477466 **Fax:** 01924 351297
Email: brochures@astracast.co.uk
Web: www.astracast.co.uk ⌁
Product Type: 1, 2, 3, 4, 5

BATH KITCHEN COMPANY
22 Hensley Road, Bloomfield,
Bath, Somerset, BA2 2DR
Area of Operation: South West England and South Wales
Tel: 01225 312003 **Fax:** 01225 312003
Email: david@bathkitchencompany.co.uk
Web: www.bathkitchencompany.co.uk
Product Type: 1, 2, 3, 4

BAUMATIC LTD
Baumatic Buildings, 6 Bennet Road, Berkshire, RG2 0QX
Area of Operation: Europe
Tel: 01189 336900 **Fax:** 01189 310035
Email: sales@baumatic.co.uk
Web: www.baumatic.com **Product Type:** 1

BEAU-PORT LTD
Unit 2, Elhanger Business Park,
Bentworth, Hampshire, GU34 5Q2
Area of Operation: UK & Ireland
Tel: 0845 230 1545 **Fax:** 0870 350 0134
Email: sales@beau-port.co.uk
Web: www.beau-port.co.uk ⌁
Product Type: 1, 2, 3, 4, 5

**BROOK-WATER DESIGNER
BATHROOMS & KITCHENS**
The Downs, Woodhouse Hill,
Uplyme, Lyme Regis, Dorset, DT7 3SL
Area of Operation: Worldwide
Tel: 0870 851 9739 **Email:** sales@brookwater.co.uk
Web: www.brookwater.co.uk ⌁ **Product Type:** 1, 5

CARE DESIGN
Moorgate, Ormskirk, Lancashire, L39 4RX
Area of Operation: UK (Excluding Ireland)
Tel: 01695 579061 **Fax:** 01695 570489
Email: caredesign@clara.net
Web: www.caredesign.co.uk **Product Type:** 5

Don't Forget !

You can use the materials key at the beginning of this Handbook to get much more information from a company's listing.

CARRON PHOENIX
Carron Works, Stenhouse Road, Falkirk, FK2 8DW
Area of Operation: UK & Ireland
Tel: 01324 638321
Fax: 01324 620978
Email: fgp-sales@carron.com
Web: www.carron.com **Product Type:** 1, 2, 3, 4, 5

CARRON PHOENIX
Area of Operation: UK & Ireland
Tel: 01324 638 321 **Fax:** 01324 620 978
Email: fgp-sales@carron.com
Web: www.carron.com
Product Type: 1, 2, 3, 4, 5

Exceptional quality. Exceptional value.
An extensive range of sinks in granite, ceramic
and stainless steel to suit the diversity of today's
kitchen styling.

CASTELLO LUXURY BATHS LTD
Unit 3 Diamond Industrial Centre, Works Road,
Letchworth, Hertfordshire, SG6 4BS
Area of Operation: UK & Ireland
Tel: 01462 483131 **Fax:** 01462 670939
Email: sales@castellobaths.co.uk
Web: www.castellobaths.co.uk **Product Type:** 5

**CHRISTOPHER PETERS
ORIGINAL UNFITTED KITCHENS**
Lower Farm Barns, Brandon Lane,
Warwickshire, CV3 3GW
Area of Operation: Europe
Tel: 02476 303300
Email: enquiries@christopherpetersantiques.co.uk
Web: www.christopherpetersantiques.co.uk
Product Type: 2, 3, 4

CITY BATHROOMS & KITCHENS
158 Longford Road, Longford,
Coventry, West Midlands, CV6 6DR
Area of Operation: UK & Ireland
Tel: 02476 365877 **Fax:** 02476 644992
Email: citybathrooms@hotmail.com
Web: www.citybathrooms.co.uk

CONNAUGHT KITCHENS
2 Porchester Place, London, W2 2BS
Area of Operation: Greater London
Tel: 0207 706 2210 **Fax:** 0207 706 2209
Email: design@connaughtkitchens.co.uk
Web: www.connaughtkitchens.co.uk
Product Type: 1, 2, 3, 4

COTTAGE FARM ANTIQUES
Stratford Road, Aston Sub Edge,
Chipping Campden, Gloucestershire, GL55 6PZ
Area of Operation: Worldwide
Tel: 01386 438263
Fax: 01386 438263
Email: info@cottagefarmantiques.co.uk
Web: www.cottagefarmantiques.co.uk ⌁
Product Type: 2, 3, 5

COUNTRY KITCHENS
The Old Farm House, Birmingham Road,
Blackminster, Evesham, Worcestershire, WR11 7TD
Area of Operation: UK (Excluding Ireland)
Tel: 01386 831705 **Fax:** 01386 834051
Web: www.handcraftedkitchens.com
Product Type: 2, 3, 4

CRABTREE KITCHENS
17 Station Road, Barnes, Greater London, SW13 0LF
Area of Operation: Greater London, South West
England and South Wales
Tel: 0208 392 6955 **Fax:** 0208 392 6944
Email: design@crabtreekitchens.co.uk
Web: www.crabtreekitchens.co.uk
Product Type: 1, 2, 3, 4, 5

CYMRU KITCHENS
63 Caerleon Road, Newport, NP19 7BX
Area of Operation: UK (Excluding Ireland)
Tel: 01633 676767 **Fax:** 01633 212512
Email: sales@cymrukitchens.com
Web: www.cymrukitchens.com
Product Type: 1, 2, 3, 4, 5

DESIGNER KITCHENS
37 High Street, Potters Bar, Hertfordshire, EN6 5AJ
Area of Operation: Greater London
Tel: 01707 650565 **Fax:** 01707 663050
Email: info@designer-kitchens.co.uk
Web: www.designer-kitchens.co.uk
Product Type: 1, 2, 3, 4, 5

DUPONT CORIAN & ZODIAQ
10 Quarry Court, Pitstone Green Business Park,
Pitstone, Nr. Tring, Buckinghamshire, LU7 9GW
Area of Operation: UK & Ireland
Tel: 01296 663555 **Fax:** 01296 663599
Email: sales@corian.co.uk
Web: www.corian.co.uk
Product Type: 1, 2, 4

ELITE TRADE KITCHENS LTD
90 Willesden Lane, Kilburn, London, NW6 7TA
Area of Operation: UK (Excluding Ireland)
Tel: 0207 328 1234 **Fax:** 0207 328 1243
Email: sales@elitekitchens.co.uk
Web: www.elitekitchens.co.uk
Product Type: 1, 2, 3, 4, 5

ELON
12 Silver Road, London, W12 7SG
Area of Operation: UK & Ireland
Tel: 0208 932 3000 **Fax:** 0208 932 3001
Email: marketing@elon.co.uk
Web: www.elon.co.uk ⌁ **Product Type:** 1, 2, 3, 4

FALCON APPLIANCES
Clarence Street, Royal Leamington Spa,
Warwickshire, CV31 2AD
Area of Operation: Worldwide
Tel: 0845 634 0070 **Fax:** 01926 311032
Email: consumers@falconappliances.co.uk
Web: www.falconappliances.co.uk
Product Type: 1, 2, 4

FRANKE UK LTD
West Park, Manchester International Office,
Styal Road, Manchester, M22 5WB
Area of Operation: UK & Ireland
Tel: 0161 436 6280 **Fax:** 0161 436 2180
Email: info.uk@franke.com
Web: www.franke.co.uk **Product Type:** 1, 2, 3, 5

HATT KITCHENS
Hartlebury Trading Estate,
Hartlebury, Worcestershire, DY10 4JB
Area of Operation: UK (Excluding Ireland)
Tel: 01299 251320 **Fax:** 01299 251579
Email: design@hatt.co.uk
Web: www.hatt.co.uk **Product Type:** 1, 2, 3, 4, 5

IN-TOTO
Shaw Cross Court, Shaw Cross Business Park,
Dewsbury, West Yorkshire, WF12 7RF
Area of Operation: UK (Excluding Ireland)
Tel: 01924 487900 **Fax:** 01924 437305
Email: graham.russell@intoto.co.uk
Web: www.intoto.co.uk **Product Type:** 1, 3, 4

J&J ORMEROD PLC
Colonial House, Bacup, Lancashire, OL13 0EA
Area of Operation: UK & Ireland
Tel: 01706 877877 **Fax:** 01706 879827
Email: info@jjoplc.com **Web:** www.jjoplc.com
Product Type: 1, 2, 3, 4, 5

JJO PLC (J&J ORMEROD)
Colonial House, Bacup, Lancashire, OL13 0EA
Area of Operation: UK & Ireland
Tel: 01706 877877 **Fax:** 01706 879827
Email: npeters@jjoplc.com **Web:** www.jjoplc.com

JOHN LEWIS OF HUNGERFORD
Grove Technology Park, Downsview Road,
Wantage, Oxfordshire, OX12 9FA
Area of Operation: UK (Excluding Ireland)
Tel: 01235 774300 **Fax:** 01235 769031
Email: park.street@john-lewis.co.uk
Web: www.john-lewis.co.uk **Product Type:** 2, 3, 4

JOHN STRAND (MK) LTD
12-22, Herga Road, Wealdstone,
Harrow, Middlesex, HA3 5AS
Area of Operation: UK & Ireland
Tel: 0208 930 6006 **Fax:** 0208 930 6008
Email: enquiry@johnstrand-mk.co.uk
Web: www.johnstrand-mk.co.uk **Product Type:** 1

KENSINGTON STUDIO
13 c & d Kensington Road, Earlsdon,
Coventry, West Midlands, CV5 6GG
Area of Operation: UK (Excluding Ireland)
Tel: 02476 713326 **Fax:** 02476 713136
Email: sales@kensingtonstudio.com
Web: www.kensingtonstudio.com
Product Type: 1, 2, 3, 4, 5

KITCHEN SUPPLIES
East Chesters, North Way,
Hillend Industrial Estate, Dalgety Bay, Fife, KY11 9JA
Area of Operation: UK (Excluding Ireland)
Tel: 01383 824729
Email: sales@kitchensupplies.co.uk
Web: www.kitchensupplies.co.uk
Product Type: 1, 2, 3, 4

KITCHENS BY JULIAN ENGLISH
Ideal Home, Blackbird Road,
Leicester, Leicestershire, LE4 0AH
Area of Operation: Midlands & Mid Wales
Tel: 0116 251 9999 **Fax:** 0116 251 9999
Email: philiphalifax@aol.com
Web: www.kitchens-by-julianenglish.co.uk

MARBLE CLASSICS
Unit 3, Station Approach,
Emsworth, Hampshire, PO10 7PW
Area of Operation: UK & Ireland
Tel: 01243 370011 **Fax:** 01243 371023
Email: info@marbleclassics.co.uk
Web: www.marbleclassics.co.uk
Product Type: 1 **Other Info:**

MARK LEIGH KITCHENS LTD
11 Common Garden Street,
Lancaster, Lancashire, LA1 1XD
Area of Operation: North West England and North Wales
Tel: 01524 63273 **Fax:** 01524 62352
Email: mark@markleigh.co.uk
Web: www.markleigh.co.uk
Product Type: 1, 2, 3, 4 **Other Info:**

MASTER LTD
30 Station Road, Heacham, Norfolk, PE31 7EX
Area of Operation: Europe
Tel: 01485 572032 **Fax:** 01485 571675
Email: sales@masterlimited.co.uk
Web: www.masterlimited.co.uk
Product Type: 1, 2, 3, 4, 5

MEREWAY CONTRACTS
Unit 1 Wharfdale Road, Tysely,
Birmingham, West Midlands, B11 2DE
Area of Operation: UK (Excluding Ireland)
Tel: 0121 764 7180 **Fax:** 0121 764 7199
Email: info@merewaycontracts.co.uk
Web: www.merewaycontracts.co.uk

MOBALPA
1 High Street, Halberton, Devon, EX16 7AF
Area of Operation: Worldwide
Tel: 07740 633672 **Fax:** 01884 820828
Email: ploftus@mobalpa.com
Web: www.mobalpa.co.uk
Product Type: 1, 2, 3, 4, 5

MONTANA KITCHENS LTD
BIC 1, Studio 2/3 Innova Business Park,
Mollison Avenue, Enfield, Middlesex, EN3 7XU
Area of Operation: Greater London, South East England
Tel: 0800 58 75 628
Email: angie@montanakitchens.co.uk
Web: www.montanakitchens.co.uk
Product Type: 1, 2, 3, 4, 5

MWD
Clutton Hill Estate, King Lane,
Clutton Hill, Bristol, BS39 5QQ
Area of Operation: Midlands & Mid Wales, South
West England and South Wales
Tel: 0870 033 2288
Fax: 0800 197 6593
Email: sales@mwdretail.co.uk
Web: www.mikewalker.co.uk

NICHOLAS ANTHONY LTD
42-44 Wigmore Street, London, W1U 2RX
Area of Operation: East England, Greater London,
South East England
Tel: 0800 068 3603 **Fax:** 01206 762698
Email: info@nicholas-anthony.co.uk
Web: www.nicholas-anthony.co.uk **Product Type:** 1

NTP KITCHENS & JOINERY LTD
Unit 20/1, West Bowling Green Street,
Edinburgh, EH6 5PE
Area of Operation: Scotland
Tel: 0131 554 8787 **Fax:** 0131 554 9191
Email: sales@ntp-kitchens.co.uk
Web: www.ntp-kitchens.co.uk
Product Type: 1, 2, 3, 4

POGGENPOHL
477-481 Finchley Road, London, NW3 6HS
Area of Operation: UK & Ireland
Tel: 0800 298 1098 **Fax:** 0207 794 6251
Email: kitchens@poggenpohl-group.co.uk
Web: www.poggenpohl.co.uk **Product Type:** 1

PRICE KITCHENS
11 Imperial Way, Croydon, Surrey, CR0 4RR
Area of Operation: South East England
Tel: 0208 686 9006
Fax: 0208 686 5958
Email: info@pricekitchens.co.uk
Web: www.pricekitchens.co.uk
Product Type: 1, 2, 3, 4, 5

PYRAMIS (UK) LTD
Unit 1, Alexandra Way, Ashburch Industrial Estate,
Tewkesbury, Gloucestershire, GL20 8NB
Area of Operation: UK & Ireland
Tel: 01684 298040 **Fax:** 01684 293114
Email: c.grattan@pyramisuk.com
Web: www.pyramisuk.co.uk
Product Type: 1, 4, 5

RAK CERAMICS
The Tile House, Easebourne Lane,
Easebourne, West Sussex, GU29 9AZ
Area of Operation: Worldwide
Tel: 01730 815507
Fax: 01730 815007
Email: info@rakceramics.co.uk
Web: www.rakceramics.co.uk
Product Type: 1, 2, 3, 4

RANGEMASTER
Clarence Street, Royal Leamington Spa,
Warwickshire, CV31 2AD
Area of Operation: Worldwide
Tel: 01926 457400 **Fax:** 01926 450526
Email: consumers@rangemaster.co.uk
Web: www.rangemaster.co.uk
Product Type: 1, 2, 3, 4, 5

REGINOX UK LTD
Radnor Park Trading Estate,
Congleton, Cheshire, CW12 4XJ
Area of Operation: UK & Ireland
Tel: 01260 280033 **Fax:** 01260 298889
Email: sales@reginoxuk.co.uk
Web: www.reginox.com
Product Type: 1, 2, 3, 4, 5

ROUNDEL DESIGN (UK) LTD
Flishinghurst Orchards, Chalk Lane,
Cranbrook, Kent, TN17 2QA
Area of Operation: South East England
Tel: 01580 712666
Email: homebuild@roundeldesign.co.uk
Web: www.roundeldesign.co.uk
Product Type: 1, 2, 3, 4

SCHOCK UK LTD
Unit 444 Walton Summit Centre,
Bamber Bridge, Lancashire, PR5 8AT
Area of Operation: UK & Ireland
Tel: 01772 332710 **Fax:** 01772 332717
Email: sales@schock.co.uk
Web: www.schock.de **Product Type:** 1

SECOND NATURE KITCHEN COLLECTION
PO Box 20, Station Road, Aycliffe Industrial Park,
Newton Aycliffe, Durham, DL5 6XJ
Area of Operation: UK & Ireland
Tel: 01325 505539
Email: mail@sncollection.co.uk
Web: www.sncollection.co.uk

SHAWS
Waterside, Darwen, Lancashire, BB3 3NX
Area of Operation: Worldwide
Tel: 01254 775111 **Fax:** 01254 873462
Email: ecrofts@qualceram-shires.com
Web: www.shawsofdarwen.com
Product Type: 1, 2, 3, 4, 5

SMEG UK
3 Milton Park, Abingdon, Oxfordshire, OX14 4RY
Area of Operation: UK & Ireland
Tel: 0870 990 9908 **Fax:** 01235 861120
Email: sales@smeguk.com
Web: www.smeguk.com

SPILLERS OF CHARD LTD.
Chard Business Park, Chard, Somerset, TA20 1FA
Area of Operation: South West England and South Wales
Tel: 01460 67878 **Fax:** 01460 65252
Email: info@cookercentre.com
Web: www.cookercentre.com **Product Type:** 1,2,3,4

THE CDA GROUP LTD
Harby Road, Langar, Nottingham,
Nottinghamshire, NG13 9HY
Area of Operation: UK & Ireland
Tel: 01949 862000 **Fax:** 01949 8624001
Email: sales@cda-europe.com
Web: www.cda-europe.com **Product Type:** 1, 3, 4

THE DESIGN STUDIO
39 High Street, Reigate, Surrey, RH2 9AE
Area of Operation: South East England
Tel: 01737 248228 **Fax:** 01737 224180
Email: enq@the-design-studio.co.uk
Web: www.the-design-studio.co.uk
Product Type: 1, 2, 3, 4

THE KITCHEN AND BATHROOM COLLECTION
Nelson House, Nelson Road,
Salisbury, Wiltshire, SP1 3LT
Area of Operation: South West England and South Wales
Tel: 01722 334800 **Fax:** 01722 412252
Email: info@kbc.co.uk **Web:** www.kbc.co.uk
Product Type: 1, 2, 3, 4, 5 **Other Info:**

THE KITCHEN GROUP
PJH Group, Alder House, Kearsley,
Bolton, Lancashire, BL4 8SL
Area of Operation: UK & Ireland
Tel: 01204 707070 **Fax:** 01204 573140
Email: info@pjh.co.uk
Web: www.kitchengroup.co.uk
Product Type: 1, 2, 3, 4

THE KITCHEN SINK COMPANY
Unit 10, Evans Place, South Bersted Industrial Estate,
Bognor Regis, West Sussex, PO22 9RY
Area of Operation: UK & Ireland
Tel: 01243 841332 **Fax:** 01243 837294
Email: colin@kitchensinkco.com
Web: www.kitchensinkco.com
Product Type: 1, 2, 3, 4, 5

THE ORIGINAL KITCHEN COMPANY
4 Main Street, Breaston,
Derby, Derbyshire, DE72 3DX
Area of Operation: UK & Ireland
Tel: 01332 873746 **Fax:** 01332 873731
Email: originalkitchens@aol.com

TRADE APPLIANCES LTD
Cathedral Warehouse, Common Road, Huthwaite,
Sutton in Ashfield, Nottinghamshire, NG17 2JL
Area of Operation: UK (Excluding Ireland)
Tel: 0800 195 9596 **Fax:** 01623 445083
Email: info@trade-appliances.co.uk
Web: www.trade-appliances.co.uk
Product Type: 1, 2, 4, 5

UNICOM
Kingdom House, 219 Gleniffer Road,
Paisley, Renfrewshire, PA2 8UL
Area of Operation: UK & Ireland
Tel: 0845 330 7642 **Fax:** 0845 330 7641
Email: george@unicom-direct.com
Web: www.unicom-direct.com
Product Type: 1, 2, 3, 4, 5

WILLIAM GARVEY
Leyhill, Payhembury, Honiton, Devon, EX14 3JG
Area of Operation: Worldwide
Tel: 01404 841430 **Fax:** 01404 841626
Email: webquery@williamgarvey.co.uk
Web: www.williamgarvey.co.uk
Product Type: 1, 3, 4 **Other Info:**

WINNING DESIGNS
Dyke Farm, West Chiltington Road,
Pulborough, West Sussex, RH20 2EE
Area of Operation: UK & Ireland
Tel: 0870 754 4446 **Fax:** 0700 032 9946
Email: info@winning-designs-uk.com
Web: www.winning-designs-uk.com
Product Type: 1, 2, 3, 4, 5
Other Info: ▽ ECO

TAPS

KEY
SEE ALSO: MERCHANTS - Plumbers
Merchants; BATHROOMS - Taps
OTHER: ▽ Reclaimed On-line shopping
Bespoke Hand-made ECO Ecological

ABODE
Unit L Zenith Park, Whaley Road,
Barnsley, South Yorkshire, S75 1HT
Area of Operation: Europe
Tel: 01226 283434
Email: mshaw@abodedesigns.co.uk
Web: www.abode.eu

AL CHALLIS LTD
Europower House, Lower Road,
Cookham, Maidenhead, Berkshire, SL6 9EH
Area of Operation: UK & Ireland
Tel: 01628 529024 **Fax:** 0870 458 0577
Email: chris@alchallis.com
Web: www.alchallis.com

AMBER KITCHENS OF BISHOP'S STORTFORD
Clarklands House, Parsonage Lane,
Sawbridgeworth, Hertfordshire, CM21 0NG
Area of Operation: East England, Greater London
Tel: 01279 600030 **Fax:** 01279 721528
Email: info@amberkitchens.com
Web: www.amberkitchens.com

AQUAAQUA LTD
Melin Maes Dulais, Porthyrhyd,
Carmarthenshire, SA32 8BT
Area of Operation: UK (Excluding Ireland)
Tel: 01267 275255 **Fax:** 01267 275597
Email: jamie@aquaaqua.co.uk
Web: www.aquaaqua.co.uk

ASHFORD & BROOKS
The Old Workshop, Ashtree Barn, Caters Road,
Bredfield, Woodbridge, Suffolk, IP13 6BE
Area of Operation: UK (Excluding Ireland)
Tel: 01473 737764   **Fax:** 01473 277176
Email: ashfordbrooks@mailbox.co.uk
Web: www.ashfordandbrooks.co.uk

ASHLAR MASON
Manor Building, Manor Road, London, W13 0JB
Area of Operation: East England, Greater London,
Midlands & Mid Wales, South East England, South
West England and South Wales
Tel: 0208 997 0002   **Fax:** 0208 997 0008
Email: enquiries@ashlarmason.co.uk
Web: www.ashlarmason.co.uk

ASTRACAST PLC
Holden Ing Way, Birstall, West Yorkshire, WF17 9AE
Area of Operation: UK & Ireland
Tel: 01924 477466   **Fax:** 01924 351297
Email: brochures@astracast.co.uk
Web: www.astracast.co.uk

ASTRACAST PLC
Area of Operation: UK & Ireland
Tel: 01924 477466
Fax: 01924 351297
Email: brochures@astracast.co.uk
Web: www.astracast.co.uk
Astracast is the UK's largest manufacturer of
kitchen sinks and taps with a comprehensive
product portfolio that reflects Astracast's desire
to constantly evolve, adding products and
materials, finishes and colours to meet
ever-changing market needs.

BATH KITCHEN COMPANY
22 Hensley Road, Bloomfield, Bath, Somerset, BA2 2DR
Area of Operation: South West England and South Wales
Tel: 01225 312003   **Fax:** 01225 312003
Email: david@bathkitchencompany.co.uk
Web: www.bathkitchencompany.co.uk

BAUMATIC LTD
Baumatic Buildings, 6 Bennet Road, Berkshire, RG2 0QX
Area of Operation: Europe
Tel: 01189 336900   **Fax:** 01189 310035
Email: sales@baumatic.co.uk
Web: www.baumatic.com

BEAU-PORT LTD
Unit 2, Elhanger Business Park,
Bentworth, Hampshire, GU34 5Q2
Area of Operation: UK & Ireland
Tel: 0845 230 1545   **Fax:** 0870 350 0134
Email: sales@beau-port.co.uk
Web: www.beau-port.co.uk   **Other Info:**

BROOK-WATER DESIGNER BATHROOMS & KITCHENS
The Downs, Woodhouse Hill,
Uplyme, Lyme Regis, Dorset, DT7 3SL
Area of Operation: Worldwide
Tel: 0870 851 9739   **Email:** sales@brookwater.co.uk
Web: www.brookwater.co.uk

CARE DESIGN
Moorgate, Ormskirk, Lancashire, L39 4RX
Area of Operation: UK (Excluding Ireland)
Tel: 01695 579061   **Fax:** 01695 570489
Email: caredesign@clara.net
Web: www.caredesign.co.uk

CARRON PHOENIX
Carron Works, Stenhouse Road, Falkirk, FK2 8DW
Area of Operation: UK (Excluding Ireland)
Tel: 01324 638321   **Fax:** 01324 620978
Email: fgp-sales@carron.com
Web: www.carron.com

CARRON PHOENIX
Area of Operation: UK & Ireland
Tel: 01324 638 321
Fax: 01324 620 978
Email: fgp-sales@carron.com
Web: www.carron.com

Exceptional quality. Exceptional value. Tap styles
to complement the sink collection including
single lever, dual flow and filtration in a choice of
stunning metal or granite finishes.

CHRISTOPHER PETERS ORIGINAL UNFITTED KITCHENS
Lower Farm Barns,
Brandon Lane, Warwickshire, CV3 3GW
Area of Operation: Europe
Tel: 02476 303300
Email: enquiries@christopherpetersantiques.co.uk
Web: www.christopherpetersantiques.co.uk

CIFIAL UK LTD
7 Faraday Court, Park Farm Industrial Estate,
Wellingborough, Northamptonshire, NN8 6XY
Area of Operation: UK & Ireland
Tel: 01933 402008   **Fax:** 01933 402063
Email: sales@cifial.co.uk   **Web:** www.cifial.co.uk

CITY BATHROOMS & KITCHENS
158 Longford Road, Longford,
Coventry, West Midlands, CV6 6DR
Area of Operation: UK & Ireland
Tel: 02476 365877   **Fax:** 02476 644992
Email: citybathrooms@hotmail.com
Web: www.citybathrooms.co.uk

CONNAUGHT KITCHENS
2 Porchester Place, London, W2 2BS
Area of Operation: Greater London
Tel: 0207 706 2210   **Fax:** 0207 706 2209
Email: design@connaughtkitchens.co.uk
Web: www.connaughtkitchens.co.uk

COTTAGE FARM ANTIQUES
Stratford Road, Aston Sub Edge,
Chipping Campden, Gloucestershire, GL55 6PZ
Area of Operation: Worldwide
Tel: 01386 438263   **Fax:** 01386 438263
Email: info@cottagefarmantiques.co.uk
Web: www.cottagefarmantiques.co.uk

COUNTRY KITCHENS
The Old Farm House, Birmingham Road,
Blackminster, Evesham, Worcestershire, WR11 7TD
Area of Operation: UK (Excluding Ireland)
Tel: 01386 831705   **Fax:** 01386 834051
Web: www.handcraftedkitchens.com

CRABTREE KITCHENS
17 Station Road, Barnes, Greater London, SW13 0LF
Area of Operation: Greater London, South West
England and South Wales
Tel: 0208 392 6955   **Fax:** 0208 392 6944
Email: design@crabtreekitchens.co.uk
Web: www.crabtreekitchens.co.uk   **Other Info:**

CYMRU KITCHENS
63 Caerleon Road, Newport, NP19 7BX
Area of Operation: UK (Excluding Ireland)
Tel: 01633 676767
Fax: 01633 212512
Email: sales@cymrukitchens.com
Web: www.cymrukitchens.com

DANICO BRASS LTD
31-35 Winchester Road,
Swiss Cottage, London, NW3 3NR
Area of Operation: Worldwide
Tel: 0207 483 4477   **Fax:** 0207 722 7992
Email: sales@danico.co.uk

DESIGNER KITCHENS
37 High Street, Potters Bar, Hertfordshire, EN6 5AJ
Area of Operation: Greater London
Tel: 01707 650565   **Fax:** 01707 663050
Email: info@designer-kitchens.co.uk
Web: www.designer-kitchens.co.uk

ELITE TRADE KITCHENS LTD
90 Willesden Lane, Kilburn, London, NW6 7TA
Area of Operation: UK (Excluding Ireland)
Tel: 0207 328 1234   **Fax:** 0207 328 1243
Email: sales@elitekitchens.co.uk
Web: www.elitekitchens.co.uk

ELON
12 Silver Road, London, W12 7SG
Area of Operation: UK & Ireland
Tel: 0208 932 3000   **Fax:** 0208 932 3001
Email: marketing@elon.co.uk
Web: www.elon.co.uk

EUROBATH INTERNATIONAL LIMITED
Eurobath House, Wedmore Road,
Cheddar, Somerset, BS27 3EB
Area of Operation: Worldwide
Tel: 01934 744466
Fax: 01934 744345
Email: sales@eurobath.co.uk
Web: www.eurobath.co.uk/www.ilbagno.co.uk

FALCON APPLIANCES
Clarence Street, Royal Leamington Spa,
Warwickshire, CV31 2AD
Area of Operation: Worldwide
Tel: 0845 634 0070   **Fax:** 01926 311032
Email: consumers@falconappliances.co.uk
Web: www.falconappliances.co.uk

FRANKE UK LTD
West Park, Manchester International Office,
Styal Road, Manchester, M22 5WB
Area of Operation: UK & Ireland
Tel: 0161 436 6280   **Fax:** 0161 436 2180
Email: info.uk@franke.com   **Web:** www.franke.co.uk

GROHE UK
1 River Road, Barking, Essex, IG11 0HD
Area of Operation: Worldwide
Tel: 020 8594 7292   **Fax:** 020 8594 8898
Email: info@grohe.co.uk
Web: www.grohe.co.uk

HATT KITCHENS
Hartlebury Trading Estate, Hartlebury,
Worcestershire, DY10 4JB
Area of Operation: UK (Excluding Ireland)
Tel: 01299 251320   **Fax:** 01299 251579
Email: design@hatt.co.uk   **Web:** www.hatt.co.uk

HUDSON REED
Rylands Street, Burnley, Lancashire, BB10 1RG
Area of Operation: Worldwide
Tel: 01282 418000   **Fax:** 01282 428915
Email: info@ultra-group.co.uk
Web: www.hudsonreed.info

IN-TOTO
Shaw Cross Court, Shaw Cross Business Park,
Dewsbury, West Yorkshire, WF12 7RF
Area of Operation: UK (Excluding Ireland)
Tel: 01924 487900   **Fax:** 01924 437305
Email: graham.russell@intoto.co.uk
Web: www.intoto.co.uk

ITFITZ
11-12 Woodlands Farm, Spring Lane,
Cookham Dean, Berkshire, SL6 9PN
Area of Operation: UK (Excluding Ireland)
Tel: 01628 890432   **Fax:** 0870 133 7955
Email: sales@itfitz.co.uk
Web: www.itfitz.co.uk

JOHN LEWIS OF HUNGERFORD
Grove Technology Park, Downsview Road,
Wantage, Oxfordshire, OX12 9FA
Area of Operation: UK (Excluding Ireland)
Tel: 01235 774300   **Fax:** 01235 769031
Email: park.street@john-lewis.co.uk
Web: www.john-lewis.co.uk

JOHN STRAND (MK) LTD
12-22 Herga Road, Wealdstone,
Harrow, Middlesex, HA3 5AS
Area of Operation: UK & Ireland
Tel: 0208 930 6006
Fax: 0208 930 6008
Email: enquiry@johnstrand-mk.co.uk
Web: www.johnstrand-mk.co.uk

KITCHEN SUPPLIES
East Chesters, North Way, Hillend Industrial Estate,
Dalgety Bay, Fife, KY11 9JA
Area of Operation: UK (Excluding Ireland)
Tel: 01383 824729
Email: sales@kitchensupplies.co.uk
Web: www.kitchensupplies.co.uk

KITCHENS BY JULIAN ENGLISH
Ideal Home, Blackbird Road,
Leicester, Leicestershire, LE4 0AH
Area of Operation: Midlands & Mid Wales
Tel: 0116 251 9999   **Fax:** 0116 251 9999
Email: philiphalifax@aol.com
Web: www.kitchens-by-julianenglish.co.uk

MARK LEIGH KITCHENS LTD
11 Common Garden Street,
Lancaster, Lancashire, LA1 1XD
Area of Operation: North West England and North Wales
Tel: 01524 63273
Fax: 01524 62352
Email: mark@markleigh.co.uk
Web: www.markleigh.co.uk   **Other Info:**

MASTER LTD
30 Station Road, Heacham, Norfolk, PE31 7EX
Area of Operation: Europe
Tel: 01485 572032
Fax: 01485 571675
Email: sales@masterlimited.co.uk
Web: www.masterlimited.co.uk   **Other Info:**

MEKON PRODUCTS
25 Bessemer Park,
Milkwood Road, London, SE24 0HG
Area of Operation: UK (Excluding Ireland)
Tel: 0207 733 8011   **Fax:** 0207 737 0840
Email: info@mekon.net   **Web:** www.mekon.net

MEREWAY CONTRACTS
Unit 1 Wharfdale Road, Tysely,
Birmingham, West Midlands, B11 2DE
Area of Operation: UK (Excluding Ireland)
Tel: 0121 764 7180
Fax: 0121 764 7199
Email: info@merewaycontracts.co.uk
Web: www.merewaycontracts.co.uk

MOBALPA
1 High Street, Halberton, Devon, EX16 7AF
Area of Operation: Worldwide
Tel: 07740 633672   **Fax:** 01884 820828
Email: ploftus@mobalpa.com
Web: www.mobalpa.co.uk

MONTANA KITCHENS LTD
BIC 1, Studio 2/3 Innova Business Park,
Mollison Avenue, Enfield, Middlesex, EN3 7XU
Area of Operation: Greater London, South East England
Tel: 0800 58 75 628
Email: angie@montanakitchens.co.uk
Web: www.montanakitchens.co.uk

MWD
Clutton Hill Estate, King Lane,
Clutton Hill, Bristol, BS39 5QQ
Area of Operation: Midlands & Mid Wales, South
West England and South Wales
Tel: 0870 033 2288
Fax: 0800 197 6593
Email: sales@mwdretail.co.uk
Web: www.mikewalker.co.uk

NICHOLAS ANTHONY LTD
42-44 Wigmore Street, London, W1U 2RX
Area of Operation: East England, Greater London,
South East England
Tel: 0800 068 3603   **Fax:** 01206 762698
Email: info@nicholas-anthony.co.uk
Web: www.nicholas-anthony.co.uk

NTP KITCHENS & JOINERY LTD
Unit 20/1, West Bowling Green Street,
Edinburgh, EH6 5PE
Area of Operation: Scotland
Tel: 0131 554 8787   **Fax:** 0131 554 9191
Email: sales@ntp-kitchens.co.uk
Web: www.ntp-kitchens.co.uk
Other Info: ECO 🖊 🖐

PEGLER LIMITED
St Catherine's Avenue,
Doncaster, South Yorkshire, DN4 8DF
Area of Operation: Worldwide
Tel: 0870 120 0281   **Fax:** 01302 560108
Email: uk.sales@pegler.co.uk
Web: www.pegler.co.uk/francis

PERRIN & ROWE
Gateway XIII, Ferry Lane,
Rainham, Essex, RM13 9JY
Area of Operation: Worldwide
Tel: 01708 526361   **Fax:** 01708 550220
Web: www.perrinandrowe.co.uk   **Other Info:** 🖊 🖐

PRICE KITCHENS
11 Imperial Way, Croydon, Surrey, CR0 4RR
Area of Operation: South East England
Tel: 0208 686 9006
Fax: 0208 686 5958
Email: info@pricekitchens.co.uk
Web: www.pricekitchens.co.uk

PYRAMIS (UK) LTD
Unit 1, Alexandra Way, Ashburch Industrial Estate,
Tewkesbury, Gloucestershire, GL20 8NB
Area of Operation: UK & Ireland
Tel: 01684 298040   **Fax:** 01684 293114
Email: c.grattan@pyramisuk.com
Web: www.pyramisuk.co.uk 🖐

QUOOKER
Unit 206, Kings Wharf,
301 Kingsland Road, London, E8 4DS
Area of Operation: UK (Excluding Ireland)
Tel: 0207 923 3355   **Email:** info@quooker.co.uk
Web: www.quooker.co.uk

RANGEMASTER
Clarence Street, Royal Leamington Spa,
Warwickshire, CV31 2AD
Area of Operation: Worldwide
Tel: 01926 457400   **Fax:** 01926 450526
Email: consumers@rangemaster.co.uk
Web: www.rangemaster.co.uk

REGINOX UK LTD
Radnor Park Trading Estate,
Congleton, Cheshire, CW12 4XJ
Area of Operation: UK & Ireland
Tel: 01260 280033   **Fax:** 01260 298889
Email: sales@reginoxuk.co.uk
Web: www.reginox.com 🖐

ROBINSON AND CORNISH LTD
St George's House, St George's Road,
Barnstaple, Devon, EX32 7AS
Area of Operation: Europe
Tel: 01271 329300   **Fax:** 01271 328277
Email: sales@robinsonandcornish.co.uk
Web: www.robinsonandcornish.co.uk

ROOTS KITCHENS BEDROOMS BATHROOMS
Vine Farm, Stockers Hill, Boughton under Blean,
Faversham, Kent, ME13 9AB
Area of Operation: South East England
Tel: 01227 751130   **Fax:** 01227 750033
Email: showroom@rootskitchens.co.uk
Web: www.rootskitchens.co.uk 🖐

ROUNDEL DESIGN (UK) LTD
Flishinghurst Orchards, Chalk Lane,
Cranbrook, Kent, TN17 2QA
Area of Operation: South East England
Tel: 01580 712666
Email: homebuild@roundeldesign.co.uk
Web: www.roundeldesign.co.uk

SCHOCK UK LTD
Unit 444 Walton Summit Centre,
Bamber Bridge, Lancashire, PR5 8AT
Area of Operation: UK (Excluding Ireland)
Tel: 01772 332710   **Fax:** 01772 332717
Email: sales@schock.co.uk   **Web:** www.schock.de

SECOND NATURE KITCHEN COLLECTION
PO Box 20, Station Road, Aycliffe Industrial Park,
Newton Aycliffe, Durham, DL5 6XJ
Area of Operation: UK & Ireland
Tel: 01325 505539   **Email:** mail@sncollection.co.uk
Web: www.sncollection.co.uk

SOGA LTD
41 Mayfield Street, Hull, East Riding of Yorks, HU3 1NT
Area of Operation: Worldwide
Tel: 01482 327025   **Email:** info@soga.co.uk
Web: www.soga.co.uk 🖐

SPILLERS OF CHARD LTD.
Chard Business Park, Chard, Somerset, TA20 1FA
Area of Operation: South West England and South Wales
Tel: 01460 67878   **Fax:** 01460 65252
Email: info@cookercentre.com
Web: www.cookercentre.com

THE CDA GROUP LTD
Harby Road, Langar, Nottingham,
Nottinghamshire, NG13 9HY
Area of Operation: UK & Ireland
Tel: 01949 862000   **Fax:** 01949 8624001
Email: sales@cda-europe.com
Web: www.cda-europe.com

THE KITCHEN AND BATHROOM COLLECTION
Nelson House, Nelson Road,
Salisbury, Wiltshire, SP1 3LT
Area of Operation: South West England and South Wales
Tel: 01722 334800   **Fax:** 01722 412252
Email: info@kbc.co.uk
Web: www.kbc.co.uk   **Other Info:** 🖊

THE KITCHEN GROUP
PJH Group, Alder House, Kearsley,
Bolton, Lancashire, BL4 8SL
Area of Operation: UK & Ireland
Tel: 01204 707070   **Fax:** 01204 573140
Email: info@pjh.co.uk
Web: www.kitchengroup.co.uk

THE KITCHEN SINK COMPANY
Unit 10, Evans Place, South Bersted Industrial Estate,
Bognor Regis, West Sussex, PO22 9RY
Area of Operation: UK & Ireland
Tel: 01243 841332   **Fax:** 01243 837294
Email: colin@kitchensinkco.co.uk
Web: www.kitchensinkco.co.uk

THE ORIGINAL KITCHEN COMPANY
4 Main Street, Breaston,
Derby, Derbyshire, DE72 3DX
Area of Operation: UK & Ireland
Tel: 01332 873746   **Fax:** 01332 873731
Email: originalkitchens@aol.com

TRADE APPLIANCES LTD
Cathedral Warehouse, Common Road, Huthwaite,
Sutton in Ashfield, Nottinghamshire, NG17 2JL
Area of Operation: UK (Excluding Ireland)
Tel: 0800 195 9596   **Fax:** 01623 445083
Email: info@trade-appliances.co.uk
Web: www.trade-appliances.co.uk

UNICOM
Kingdom House, 219 Gleniffer Road,
Paisley, Renfrewshire, PA2 8UL
Area of Operation: UK & Ireland
Tel: 0845 330 7642
Fax: 0845 330 7641
Email: george@unicom-direct.com
Web: www.unicom-direct.com 🖐

WATER FRONT
All Worcester Buildings, Birmingham Road,
Redditch, Worcestershire, B97 6DY
Area of Operation: UK & Ireland
Tel: 01527 584244
Fax: 01527 61127
Email: info@waterfrontbathrooms.com
Web: www.waterfrontbathrooms.com

WHIRLPOOL EXPRESS (UK) LTD
61-62 Lower Dock Street,
Kingsway, Newport, NP20 1EF
Area of Operation: Europe
Tel: 01633 244555   **Fax:** 01633 244881
Email: reception@whirlpoolexpress.co.uk
Web: www.whirlpoolexpress.co.uk 🖐

WINNING DESIGNS
Dyke Farm, West Chiltington Road,
Pulborough, West Sussex, RH20 2EE
Area of Operation: UK & Ireland
Tel: 0870 754 4446
Fax: 0700 032 9946
Email: info@winning-designs-uk.com
Web: www.winning-designs-uk.com

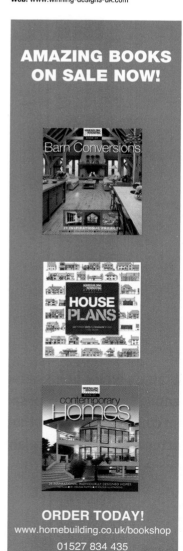
NOTES

Company Name ....
....
Address ....
....
....
email ....
Web ....

Company Name ....
....
Address ....
....
....
email ....
Web ....

Company Name ....
....
Address ....
....
....
email ....
Web ....

Company Name ....
....
Address ....
....
....
email ....
Web ....

Company Name ....
....
Address ....
....
....
email ....
Web ....

www-plotfinder-net

THE UK'S LAND AND RENOVATION DATABASE

Searching for your perfect plot of land – be it one with a fantastic view, one in a country hideaway or one close to a buzzing city – is often an uphill struggle. Endless effort and time can be spent trawling through papers, calling estate agents and going to auctions. Which is where www.plotfinder.net and www.sitefinderireland.com can help you…

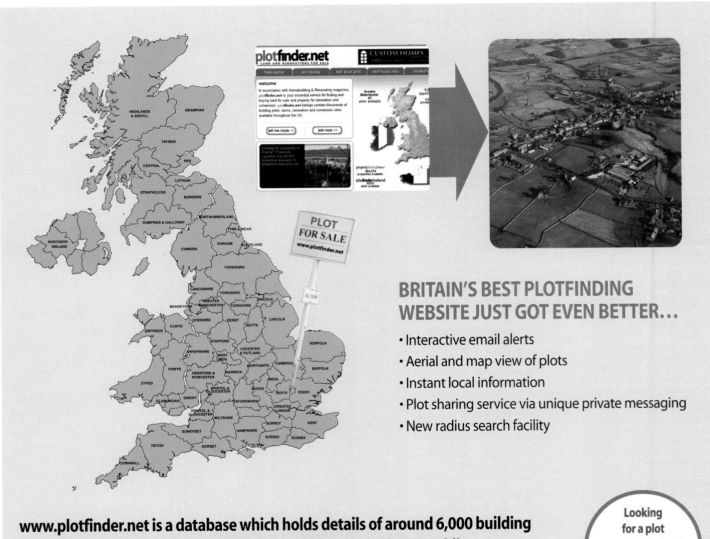

BRITAIN'S BEST PLOTFINDING WEBSITE JUST GOT EVEN BETTER…

- Interactive email alerts
- Aerial and map view of plots
- Instant local information
- Plot sharing service via unique private messaging
- New radius search facility

www.plotfinder.net is a database which holds details of around 6,000 building plots and properties for renovation currently for sale in the UK, whilst www.sitefinderireland.com contains details on thousands of building sites and renovation opportunities for sale in Ireland.

Looking for a plot for sale in Ireland? Visit: www.sitefinder ireland.com

SUBSCRIBE TODAY!
VISIT: www.plotfinder.net

CENTAUR SPECIAL INTEREST MEDIA

FURNITURE & FURNISHINGS

Image courtesy of Bryn Hall (01260 278111)

SPONSORED BY Bryn Hall
Tel: 01260 278111 Web: www.brynhall.co.uk

BRYN HALL

Antiques

Antiques have come back into vogue in recent times with the mixing of old and new furniture – a fad named 'shabby chic', which is popular with the young and old alike.

Much of the trading in antiques today is done on Ebay. The website is good for sellers as it's quick and easy to showcase a whole range of antiques to a wide audience. And the buyer benefits too, as the sheer quantity of antiques on Ebay means there are bargains aplenty to be had by the shrewd antique hunter. Those dabbling in the antiques market should note however, that pieces purchased should match the period of their home.

The surge in popularity in the antiques and architectural salvage market has its downsides, however. Some items are sold in poor condition, making that tricky restoration or conversion too much to bear. It is a matter of weighing up how much the character and value of the new piece could add to your home against the risk involved. You should also use respected dealers, auction houses, or salvage yards where possible. Salvo (www.salvo.co.uk) is an association which lists reputable dealers.

Originals

Original pieces represent a slice of history, full of charm and character. And if you are careful with your purchases they can prove to be much more than just an attractive feature, as they will often retain their value, making good investments. Whilst venturing into the world of antiques can be fraught with pitfalls, if you are armed with knowledge and awareness, there is no reason why you shouldn't go home with your own piece of history, and a bargain in the process.

BELOW: Courtesy of LASSCO

Top tips for buying antiques at auction

- Arrive early to get the best buys – you can be sure antiques dealers and enthusiasts will be there at the crack of dawn, so make sure you are there to compete.

- Always get a receipt from a dealer or trader at a fair, showing their business name and address. If possible, get a written receipt which includes a description of the product – this may help with insurance.

- Be prepared to haggle to get a better price – this may not work so well with the dealers, but it is virtually expected at fairs and car boot sales.

- Ensure your purchases are wrapped carefully – you don't want your treasures to break on the way home.

- Don't be afraid to rummage! Looking behind and under other items can unearth treasures – just make sure you are careful, as breakages could prove costly.

FURNITURE

KEY

SEE ALSO: BATHROOMS - Bathroom Furniture;
KITCHENS - Kitchen Furniture, Fitted; KITCHENS
- Kitchen Furniture, Unfitted; GARDEN
ACCESSORIES AND DECORATIVE FEATURES -
Garden and Patio Furniture

PRODUCT TYPES: 1= General 2 = Bedroom
3 = Home Office 4 = Other

OTHER: ▽ Reclaimed ⌐⌐ On-line shopping
✐ Bespoke ✋ Hand-made ECO Ecological

AACORN JOINERY AND DESIGN LTD
2 Balaclava Place, South Street,
Bridport, Dorset, DT6 3PE
Area of Operation: Europe
Tel: 01308 456217 **Fax:** 01308 424511
Email: info@aacornjoinery.co.uk
Web: www.aacornjoinery.co.uk

ABUNDANCE UK
12 Beauchamp Industrial Estate, Two Gates,
Tamworth, Staffordshire, B77 5BZ
Area of Operation: Europe
Tel: 0800 970 6176
Email: brittaniatrading@aol.com
Web: www.abundanceuk.co.uk ⌐⌐
Product Type: 1, 2 **Material Type:** A) 2

ALEXANDER INTERIORS
Head Office, 10 Woodberry Avenue,
Harrow, Greater London, HA2 6AU
Area of Operation: Worldwide
Tel: 07980 191825 **Fax:** 0208 933 1127
Email: juliana.alexander@talk21.com
Web: www.alexanderinteriors.co.uk

ANDY THORNTON LTD
Ainleys Industrial Estate, Elland,
West Yorkshire, HX5 9JP
Area of Operation: Worldwide
Tel: 01422 375595 **Fax:** 01422 377455
Email: marketing@ataa.com
Web: www.andythornton.com
Product Type: 1, 4 **Other Info:** ▽ ✐ ✋

ANTIQUARIUS ANTIQUES CENTRE
131-141 Kings Road, Chelsea, London, SW3 5EB
Area of Operation: Worldwide
Tel: 0207 351 5353 **Fax:** 0207 969 1639
Email: antique@dial.pipex.com
Web: www.antiquarius.co.uk ⌐⌐
Product Type: 1, 2, 4

ARTICHOKE (KITCHEN AND CABINET MAKERS)
Hortswood, Long Lane,
Wrington, Somerset, BS40 5SP
Area of Operation: Worldwide
Tel: 01934 863840 **Fax:** 01934 863841
Email: mail@artichoke-ltd.com
Web: www.artichoke-ltd.com **Product Type:** 1, 2, 3

ARTISAN GLASS PRODUCTS LTD
Unit 2 Graylaw Trading Estate, Wareing Road,
Aintree, Liverpool, Merseyside, L9 7AU
Area of Operation: UK (Excluding Ireland)
Tel: 0151 525 0220 **Fax:** 0151 524 2152
Email: sue@artisanglassproducts.co.uk
Web: www.artisanglassproducts.co.uk
Product Type: 1, 2, 3, 4
Material Type: J) 2, 4, 6

B ROURKE & CO LTD
Vulcan Works, Accrington Road,
Burnley, Lancashire, BB11 5QD
Area of Operation: Worldwide
Tel: 01282 422841 **Fax:** 01282 458901
Email: info@rourkes.co.uk
Web: www.rourkes.co.uk
Product Type: 1 **Material Type:** C) 1, 4, 5, 6

BADMAN & BADMAN JOINERY LTD
The Drill Hall, Langford Road,
Weston Super Mare, Somerset, BS23 3PQ
Area of Operation: UK (Excluding Ireland)
Tel: 01934 644122 **Fax:** 01934 628189
Email: info@badmanandbadman.fsnet.co.uk
Web: www.badmans.co.uk **Product Type:** 1, 2, 3

BARBE & BALD LTD
112 Tudor Way, Hertford, Hertfordshire, SG14 2DL
Area of Operation: Worldwide
Tel: 01992 552783 **Fax:** 01992 552783
Email: mark@baldsbalm.co.uk
Web: www.baldsbalm.co.uk ⌐⌐
Product Type: 1, 2, 3

BARRY SIMS
11 Bognor Road, Chichester, West Sussex, PO19 7TF
Area of Operation: UK & Ireland
Tel: 07787 987652 **Email:** info@barrysims.biz
Web: www.barrysims.biz **Product Type:** 1
Material Type: A) 2, 4, 6, 9, 12, 15

BATHROOM CITY
Seeleys Road, Tyseley Industrial Estate,
Birmingham, West Midlands, B11 2LQ
Area of Operation: UK & Ireland
Tel: 0121 753 0700 **Fax:** 0121 753 1110
Email: sales@bathroomcity.com
Web: www.bathroomcity.com ⌐⌐ **Product Type:** 4

BAYFIELD STAIR CO
Unit 4, Praed Road, Trafford Park,
Manchester, M17 1PQ
Area of Operation: Worldwide
Tel: 0161 848 0700 **Fax:** 0161 872 2230
Email: sales@bayfieldstairs.co.uk
Web: www.bayfieldstairs.co.uk
Product Type: 1, 2, 3, 4

BEN NEWICK HOME FURNITURE
10 Lower Street, Haslemere, Surrey, GU27 2NX
Area of Operation: UK (Excluding Ireland)
Tel: 01428 664430 **Fax:** 01428 664430
Email: mail@bennewick.com
Web: www.bennewick.com **Product Type:** 1, 2, 3

BOB LANE WOODTURNERS
Unit 1, White House Workshop, Old London Road,
Swinfen, Lichfield, Staffordshire, WS14 9QW
Area of Operation: UK (Excluding Ireland)
Tel: 01543 483148 **Fax:** 01543 481245
Email: sales@theturner.co.uk
Web: www.theturner.co.uk **Product Type:** 4

BORDERCRAFT
Old Forge, Peterchurch, Hereford,
Herefordshire, HR2 0SD
Area of Operation: UK (Excluding Ireland)
Tel: 01981 550251 **Fax:** 01981 550552
Email: sales@bordercraft.co.uk
Web: www.bordercraft.co.uk **Other Info:** ✐ ✋

BRASS FOUNDRY CASTINGS
PO Box 151, Westerham, Kent, TN16 1YF
Area of Operation: Worldwide
Tel: 01959 563863 **Fax:** 01959 561262
Email: info@brasscastings.co.uk
Web: www.brasscastings.co.uk ⌐⌐
Product Type: 1 **Other Info:** ✋
Material Type: C) 7, 11, 12, 13, 14, 15, 16

BROOKMANS ENGLISH FURNITURE CO LTD
Portland Business Park, Richmond Park Road,
Sheffield, South Yorkshire, S13 8HT
Area of Operation: Worldwide
Tel: 0114 280 0970 **Fax:** 0114 256 1840
Email: jim.brookman@brookmans.co.uk
Web: www.brookmans.co.uk
Product Type: 1, 2, 3

BROOKMANS OF RICKMANSWORTH LTD
1 Moneyhill Parade, Uxbridge Road,
Rickmansworth, Hertfordshire, WD3 7BQ
Area of Operation: Worldwide
Tel: 01923 773906 **Fax:** 01923 896098
Email: celia.warbrick@brookmans.co.uk
Web: www.brookmans.co.uk
Product Type: 2, 3

BRYN HALL
Knolton Bryn, Overton-On-Dee, Wrexham, LL13 0LF
Area of Operation: UK (Excluding Ireland)
Tel: 01978 710317 **Fax:** 01978 710027
Email: info@brynhall.co.uk
Web: www.brynhall.co.uk
Product Type: 1, 2, 3

BUILDING & DESIGN SOLUTIONS GERMANY
Auf den Haien 14, 55471 Sargenroth, Germany
Area of Operation: UK (Excluding Ireland)
Tel: 0049 6761 970 871
Email: mail@buildingdesign-germany.eu
Web: www.buildingdesign-germany.eu

BUYDESIGN
Monteviot Nurseries, Ancrum,
Jedburgh, Borders, TD8 6TU
Area of Operation: Scotland
Tel: 01835 830740
Email: enquries@buydesign-furniture.com
Web: www.buydesign-furniture.com
Product Type: 1, 2, 3
Material Type: A) 1, 2, 3, 4, 5, 6, 8, 9, 11

BYLAW (ROSS) LIMITED
The Workshop, Norwich Road,
Lenwade, Norwich, Norfolk, NR9 5SH
Area of Operation: Worldwide
Tel: 01603 308090 **Fax:** 01603 872122
Email: graham@bylaw.co.uk
Web: www.bylaw.co.uk **Product Type:** 1, 2, 3

CADIRA
233-235 Sandycomb Road, Kew,
Richmond, Greater London, TW9 2EW
Area of Operation: UK (Excluding Ireland)
Tel: 0208 334 1086
Email: info@cadira.co.uk
Web: www.cadira.co.uk ⌐⌐ **Product Type:** 1

CAMERON PETERS LTD
The Old Dairy, Home Farm, Ardington,
Wantage, Oxfordshire, OX12 8PD
Area of Operation: Worldwide
Tel: 01235 835000 **Fax:** 01235 835005
Email: info@cameronpeters.co.uk
Web: www.cameronpeters.co.uk
Product Type: 1, 2, 3, 4

CAPLE
Fourth Way, Avonmouth, Bristol, BS11 8DW
Area of Operation: UK (Excluding Ireland)
Tel: 0870 6069606 **Fax:** 0117 938 7449
Email: amandalowe@mlay.co.uk
Web: www.mlay.co.uk **Product Type:** 2

CHANTRY HOUSE OAK LTD
28 North Street, Chichester, West Sussex, PO20 2BT
Area of Operation: South East England
Tel: 01243 776811
Email: shop@chantryhouseoak.co.uk
Web: www.chantryhouseoak.co.uk
Product Type: 1, 2, 3

CHIC SHACK
77 Lower Richmond Road, London, SW15 1ET
Area of Operation: Worldwide
Tel: 0208 785 7777 **Fax:** 0208 789 0444
Email: info@chicshack.net
Web: www.chicshack.net
Product Type: 1, 2, 3, 4

**CHRISTOPHER PETERS
ORIGINAL UNFITTED KITCHENS**
Lower Farm Barns, Brandon Lane,
Warwickshire, CV3 3GW
Area of Operation: Europe
Tel: 02476 303300
Email: enquiries@christopherpetersantiques.co.uk
Web: www.christopherpetersantiques.co.uk

CLOSETMAID UK
Unit 218, 36 Blenheim Grove, London, SE15 4QL
Area of Operation: Worldwide
Tel: 0870 225 7002 **Fax:** 0870 225 7003
Email: ianpurdy@closetmaiduk.com
Web: www.closetmaiduk.com **Product Type:** 2

CLOTH
North Street, Huthwaite, Nottinghamshire, NG17 2PE
Area of Operation: UK & Ireland
Tel: 0870 777 5100 **Fax:** 0870 777 5101
Email: info@clothuk.com **Product Type:** 1, 2

COBALT BLACKSMITHS
The Forge, English Farm, English Lane,
Nuffield, Oxfordshire, RG9 5TH
Tel: 01491 641990 **Fax:** 01491 640909
Email: enquiries@cobalt-blacksmiths.co.uk
Web: www.cobalt-blacksmiths.co.uk
Product Type: 1 **Other Info:** ✐ ✋

COTTAGE FARM ANTIQUES
Stratford Road, Aston Sub Edge,
Chipping Campden, Gloucestershire, GL55 6PZ
Area of Operation: Worldwide
Tel: 01386 438263 **Fax:** 01386 438263
Email: info@cottagefarmantiques.co.uk
Web: www.cottagefarmantiques.co.uk ⌐⌐
Product Type: 1, 2, 3, 4

COUNTESS (KITCHENS & BEDROOMS) LTD
Mounsey Road, Bamber Bridge,
Preston, Lancashire, PR6 7RA
Area of Operation: North West England and North Wales
Tel: 01772 321218 **Fax:** 01772 316165
Email: sales@countessinteriors.co.uk
Web: www.countessinteriors.co.uk
Product Type: 1, 2, 3, 4 **Other Info:** ✐ ✋

CREATE DESIGN SOLUTIONS LTD
The Wood Yard, Castell Ddu Road,
Waun Gron, Pontarddulais, Swansea, SA4 8DH
Area of Operation: Greater London, Midlands & Mid
Wales, North West England and North Wales, South
East England, South West England and South Wales
Tel: 01792 386677 **Fax:** 01792 386677
Email: mail@createdesignsolutions.co.uk
Web: www.createdesignsolutions.co.uk

CREATE JOINERY
The Wood Yard, Castell Ddu Road,
Waun Gron, Pontarddulais, Swansea, SA4 8DH
Area of Operation: Greater London, Midlands & Mid
Wales, North West England and North Wales, South
East England, South West England and South Wales
Tel: 01792 386677 **Fax:** 01792 386677
Email: mail@create-joinery.co.uk
Web: www.create-joinery.co.uk

CUSTOM MADE SHUTTERS
Avalon, Swan Lane, Marlpit Hill,
Eadenbridge, Kent, TN8 6BA
Area of Operation: UK & Ireland
Tel: 01732 863554
Email: info@custommadeshutters.co.uk
Web: www.custommadeshutters.co.uk
Product Type: 1, 2, 3, 4 **Other Info:** ✐ ✋
Material Type: A) 1, 2, 3, 4, 5, 6, 7, 9, 10, 12

D.A. FURNITURE LTD
Woodview Workshop, Pitway Lane,
Farrington Gurney, Bristol, BS39 6TX
Area of Operation: South West England and South Wales
Tel: 01761 453117
Email: enquiries@dafurniture.co.uk
Web: www.dafurniture.co.uk
Product Type: 1, 2, 3, 4 **Other Info:** ✋
Material Type: A) 1, 2, 3, 4, 5, 6, 7, 8, 9, 10, 11, 12, 13, 14, 15

DAR INTERIORS
Arch 11, Miles Street, London, SW8 1RZ
Area of Operation: Worldwide
Tel: 020 7720 9678
Fax: 020 7627 5129
Email: enquiries@darinteriors.com
Web: www.darinteriors.com **Product Type:** 1
Other Info: ✐ ✋ **Material Type:** A) 7, 12

DEBDEN ANTIQUES & INTERIORS
Elder Street, Debden, Saffron Walden, Essex, CB11 3JY
Area of Operation: Worldwide
Tel: 01799 543007
Email: info@debden-antiques.co.uk
Web: www.debden-antiques.co.uk
Product Type: 1, 2

BRYN HALL
AT THE MILL

Bespoke furniture for your lifestyle

40 Holmes Chapel Road
Congleton
Cheshire CW12 4NG

t 01260 278111
m 07801 236342

e mill@brynhall.co.uk
www.brynhall.co.uk

- British made traditional and contemporary bespoke furniture
- Expert advice from an established family business
- We can help with room design and create bespoke, individual or customised pieces to suit your requirements
- Beautiful furniture for every room, plus a complete range of stylish accessories
- Nationwide service or visit our fabulous Cheshire showroom
- On the road - come and meet us at major shows and exhibitions across the UK - see the website for details

NEW COMPREHENSIVE BROCHURE/PRICE LIST AVAILABLE

WINDSOR CHAIR

Stick back Windsor chair C07
Available medium and large

LAMP TABLE

Lamp table with potboard and drawer LT3
W: 46cm D:46cm H:56cm
Available in Cherry or Oak
(can be made to any size)

CHURNTON CABINET

Churnton Hi-Fi/CD Cabinet/Chest of Drawers in
Cherry CCD1A
As shown W:61cm D: 51cm H:109cm
(can be made to any size)

UPHOLSTERED DINING CHAIR

Barton stripe fabric upholstered chair C14
Available in Cherry or Oak. Side chair or carver
Select from a wide range of fabrics

HAMPTON ARMCHAIR

Hampton armchair in check fabric
W: 84cm D:97cm H: 84cm
Select from a wide range of fabrics

GRAND KNOLE SOFA

Grand Knole 3.5 seater with handmade tassels
Available as 2.5, 3, 3.5 or 4 seater
Select from a wide range of fabrics

LLOYD LOOM

'Boston' Chair
Available in 25 colours, with or without arms
W:50cm D:61cm H:99cm

REFECTORY TABLE

Fixed top refectory table T03
Available in various sizes and in Oak or Cherry
Drawleaf version also available

BOOKCASE

Bookcase with drawers.
Ideal for the home office.
Any size available to order

MONTGOMERYSHIRE BASE

4 drawer Montgomeryshire base
Available in 3 or 4 drawer

PAINTED DRESSER

Painted dresser base and rack with pippy oak
shelves
W:122cm D:51cm H:203cm
Ask about our freestanding kitchen pieces

SPONSORED BY: BRYN HALL www.brynhall.co.uk

DISTINCTIVE COUNTRY FURNITURE LIMITED
Parrett Works, Martock, Somerset, TA12 6AE
Area of Operation: Worldwide
Tel: 01935 825800 **Fax:** 01935 825800
Email: Dcfltdinteriors@aol.com
Web: www.distinctivecountryfurniture.co.uk
Other Info: ▽ ✎ ✋ **Material Type:** A) 2, 3, 4, 7, 14

DOVETAIL ENTERPRISES
Dunsinane Avenue, Dunsinane Industrial Estate,
Dundee, Angus, DD2 3QN
Tel: 01382 833890 **Fax:** 01382 814816
Email: sales@dovetailenterprises.co.uk
Web: www.dovetailenterprises.co.uk
Product Type: 1, 2 **Material Type:** A) 1, 2, 3, 4, 6

DREW FORSYTH & CO.
Beehive Mills, Hebble End,
Hebden Bridge, West Yorkshire, HX7 6HJ
Area of Operation: Midlands & Mid Wales, North
East England, North West England and North Wales
Tel: 01422 842206
Fax: 01422 844828
Email: shane_kenyon@hotmail.com
Web: www.drewforsyth.co.uk
Product Type: 2, 3 **Other Info:** ✎ ✋

DUKE CHRISTIE
Hillockhead Farmhouse, Dallas,
Forres, Moray, IV36 2SD
Area of Operation: Worldwide
Tel: 01343 890347 **Fax:** 01343 890347
Email: enquiries@dukechristie.com
Web: www.dukechristie.com
Product Type: 1, 2, 4 **Other Info:** ✎ ✋
Material Type: A) 2, 3, 4, 5, 6, 7, 8, 9, 11, 12, 13, 14

ENCOMPASS FURNITURE & ACCESSORIES
The Pool Room, Stansted House, Stansted Park,
Rowlands Castle, Hampshire, PO9 6DX
Area of Operation: Worldwide
Tel: 02392 410045 **Fax:** 02392 412145
Email: info@encompassco.com
Web: www.encompassco.com **Product Type:** 1, 2

ESPACIO
Chelsea store - 276 King's Road, London SW3 5AW.
West End store - 82 Tottenham Court Road,
London W1T 4TF
Area of Operation: Worldwide
Tel: Chelsea - 0207 376 5088
West End - 0207 637 1932
Fax: Chelsea - 0207 376 5099
West End - 0207 813 1956
Email: johnash1@blueyonder.co.uk
Web: www.espacio.co.uk ✎ **Product Type:** 1, 2, 3

FATBOY
Enterprise D2 Ltd, Unit D2 Enterprise Way,
Vale Park, Evesham, Worcestershire, WR11 1GS
Area of Operation: UK (Excluding Ireland)
Tel: 01386423760 **Email:** leeb@fatboy-uk.com
Web: www.fatboy-uk.com ✋ **Product Type:** 1, 2

FINEWOOD INTERIORS
Head Office, Blacknest House, Blacknest Business
Park, Near Bentley, Alton, Hampshire, GU34 4PX
Area of Operation: UK (Excluding Ireland)
Tel: 01420 23883
Fax: 01420 23883
Email: info@finewoodinteriors.co.uk
Web: www.finewoodinteriors.co.uk **Product Type:** 3

FINISHING TOUCH
The Barn at Hudsons Cottage, 251 Lower Shelton
Road, Upper Shelton, Bedford, Bedfordshire, MK43 0LS
Area of Operation: Worldwide
Tel: 01234 764098 **Fax:** 01234 764098
Email: finishingtouchinteriors@fsmail.net
Web: www.finishingtouchinteriors.co.uk ✎

FITZROY JOINERY
Garden Close, Langage Industrial Estate, Plympton,
Plymouth, Devon, PL7 5EU
Area of Operation: UK & Ireland
Tel: 0870 428 9110 **Fax:** 0870 428 9111
Email: admin@fitzroy.co.uk
Web: www.fitzroyjoinery.co.uk ✎

FORMFOLLOWS
35 Matlock Road, Brighton, East Sussex, BN1 5BS
Area of Operation: Worldwide
Tel: 01273 550180 **Fax:** 01273 823995
Email: sk@formfollows.co.uk
Web: www.formfollows.co.uk ✎
Product Type: 1, 2 **Other Info:** ✋

FUNKY BEDS 'N' STUFF
La Gouitiere, Donnay, Thury-Harcourt, France, 14220
Area of Operation: Europe
Tel: +33 231 780 032
Email: funkybeds@wanadoo.fr
Web: www.funky-beds.co.uk **Product Type:** 2

FURNITURE123.CO.UK
Sandway Business Centre, Shannon Street,
Leeds, West Yorkshire, LS9 8SS
Area of Operation: UK & Ireland
Tel: 0113 248 2233 **Fax:** 0113 248 2266
Email: p.haddock@furniture123.co.uk
Web: www.furniture123.co.uk ✎
Product Type: 1, 2, 3, 4

GRANGEWOOD
Unit 29, Fairways, New River Trading Estate
(Brookfield Centre), Cheshunt,
Waltham Cross, Hertfordshire, EN8 0NL
Area of Operation: East England,
Greater London, South East England
Tel: 01992 623933 **Fax:** 01992 623944
Email: info@grangewood.net
Web: www.grangewood.net **Product Type:** 1, 4
Other Info: ✎ ✋ **Material Type:** A) 4

HADDONCRAFT FORGE
The Forge House, East Haddon,
Northampton, Northamptonshire, NN6 8DB
Area of Operation: UK & Ireland
Tel: 01604 772027
Fax: 01604 770027
Email: info@haddoncraft.co.uk
Web: www.haddoncraft.co.uk
Product Type: 1 **Other Info:** ✎ ✋
Material Type: C) 2, 4

HAMMONDS FURNITURE LTD
Fleming Road, Harrowbrook Industrial Estate,
Hinckley, Leicestershire, LE10 3DU
Area of Operation: UK (Excluding Ireland)
Tel: 0800 251505 **Fax:** 01455 623356
Email: info@hammonds-uk.com
Web: www.hammonds-uk.com **Product Type:** 2, 3

HELBENT DESIGNS
Stonehaven, Wet Lane, Draycott,
Cheddar, Somerset, BS27 3TG
Area of Operation: Worldwide
Tel: 0208 133 1795
Email: enquiries@helbentdesigns.co.uk
Web: www.helbentdesigns.co.uk ✎
Product Type: 2, 4

HIDEAWAY BEDS LTD
Unit 1 Engineering Resource Centre, Bell Close,
Plympton, Plymouth, Devon, PL7 4JH
Area of Operation: Worldwide
Tel: 01752 511111 **Fax:** 01752 511117
Email: knancollis@hideaway.co.uk
Web: www.hideaway.co.uk **Product Type:** 2

HOLME TREE LTD
Units 2 and 3 Machins Business Centre, 29 Wood
Street, Asby-de-la-Zouch, Leicestershire, LE65 1EL
Area of Operation: UK (Excluding Ireland)
Tel: 01530 564561
Fax: 01530 417986
Email: info@holmetree.co.uk
Web: www.holmetree.co.uk **Product Type:** 2, 3

HYGROVE
152/154 Merton Road,
Wimbledon, London, SW19 1EH
Area of Operation: South East England
Tel: 0208 543 1200 **Fax:** 0208 543 6521
Email: sales@hygrove.fsnet.co.uk
Web: www.hygrovefurniture.co.uk
Product Type: 1, 2, 3

IMPORTANT ROOMS LTD
62 High Street, Wargrave, Reading, Berkshire, RG10 8BY
Area of Operation: Greater London, South East
England, South West England and South Wales
Tel: 0118 940 1266 **Fax:** 0118 940 1667
Email: Steve@importantrooms.co.uk
Web: www.importantrooms.co.uk
Product Type: 1, 3 **Material Type:** A) 10

INDESIGN
Kiran House, 53 Park Royal Road, London, NW10 7LQ
Area of Operation: UK & Ireland
Tel: 0208 963 5841 **Fax:** 0208 965 6261
Email: dhanja.bhudia@akshars.co.uk
Web: www.akshars.co.uk **Product Type:** 2

INTERIOR DOOR SYSTEMS LTD
'Hopton House', 3 & 4 Rivington Court, Hardwick
Grange, Warrington, Cheshire, WA1 4RT
Area of Operation: UK & Ireland
Tel: 01925 813100 **Fax:** 01925 814300
Email: cb@interiordoorsystems.co.uk
Web: www.interiordoorsystems.co.uk
Product Type: 2 **Material Type:** J) 6

IRONART OF BATH
Upper Lambridge Street, Larkhall,
Bath, Somerset, BA1 6RY
Area of Operation: UK (Excluding Ireland)
Tel: 01225 311273 **Fax:** 01225 443060
Email: ironart@btinternet.com
Web: www.ironart.co.uk

JALI LTD
Albion Works, Church Lane, Barham, Kent, CT4 6QS
Area of Operation: UK (Excluding Ireland)
Tel: 01227 833333 **Fax:** 01227 831950
Email: sales@jali.co.uk **Web:** www.jali.co.uk ✎
Product Type: 1 **Other Info:** ✎

JARABOSKY
Old Station Road, Exley Lane,
Elland, West Yorkshire, HX5 0SW
Area of Operation: UK & Ireland
Tel: 01422 311922 **Fax:** 01422 374053
Email: sales@jarabosky.co.uk
Web: www.jarabosky.co.uk
Product Type: 1, 4 **Other Info:** ▽

JJO PLC (J&J ORMEROD)
Colonial House, Bacup, Lancashire, OL13 0EA
Area of Operation: UK & Ireland
Tel: 01706 877877 **Fax:** 01706 879827
Email: npeters@jjoplc.com
Web: www.jjoplc.com **Product Type:** 2

JOHN ALAN DESIGNS
129 New Road Side, Horsforth,
Leeds, West Yorkshire, LS18 4QD
Area of Operation: Worldwide
Tel: 0113 258 6596 **Fax:** 0113 281 8069
Email: leeds@johnalandesigns.co.uk
Web: www.johnalandesigns.co.uk
Product Type: 1 **Other Info:** ✎ ✋

JOHN LEIGHTON RETAIL LTD
Swan House, 69- 71 Windmill Road,
Sunbury on Thames, Greater London, TW16 7DT
Tel: 01932 710890 **Fax:** 01932 710711
Email: alexl@storacall.co.uk
Web: www.biedermeier.co.uk
Product Type: 1, 2, 3, 4

JOHN NETHERCOTT & CO
147 Corve Street, Ludlow, Shropshire, SY8 2PG
Tel: 01584 877044 **Fax:** 01547 560255
Email: showroom@johnnethercott.com
Web: www.johnnethercott.com
Product Type: 1, 2, 3, 4 **Other Info:** ✎ ✋
Material Type: A) 2, 3, 4, 5, 6, 7, 8, 9, 11

JOHN OWEN JOINERY
Unit 1 Hays Bridge Farm, Brickhouse Lane,
South Godstone, Surrey, RH9 8JW
Area of Operation: Greater London, South West
England and South Wales
Tel: 01342 844036 **Fax:** 01342 844036
Email: johnowen.joinery@virgin.net
Web: www.johnowen.co.uk **Product Type:** 1, 2, 3

KASPAR SWANKEY
405, Goldhawk Road, Hammersmith,
West London, W6 0SA
Area of Operation: Worldwide
Tel: 020 8746 3586 **Fax:** 020 8746 3586
Email: kaspar@swankeypankey.com
Web: www.swankeypankey.com **Product Type:** 1, 4

KENLEY KITCHENS
24-26 Godstone Road, Kenley, Surrey, CR8 5JE
Area of Operation: UK (Excluding Ireland)
Tel: 0208 668 7000 **Product Type:** 2

KITCHEN DOOR SHOP
123 Oldham Road, Middleton, Manchester, M24 1AU
Area of Operation: UK (Excluding Ireland)
Tel: 0845 634 6444 **Fax:** 0870 300 2003
Email: kitchendoors@clara.net
Web: www.kitchendoorsltd.com
Product Type: 1, 2, 3

LANARKSHIRE HARDWOODS
Girdwoodend Farm, Auchengray,
Carnwath, Lanark, Lanarkshire, ML11 8LL
Area of Operation: Scotland
Tel: 01501 785460
Email: patrickbaxter@girdwoodend.wanadoo.co.uk
Web: www.lanarkshirehardwoods.co.uk
Product Type: 1 **Other Info:** ECO ✎ ✋
Material Type: A) 2, 3, 4, 5, 6, 7, 8, 9, 11

LPD DOORS
Holme Well Road, Leeds, West Yorkshire, LS10 4SL
Area of Operation: UK & Ireland
Tel: 0845 658 5115
Email: sales@lpddoors.co.uk **Product Type:** 1, 2

MALL ANTIQUES ARCADE
359 Upper Street, Islington, London, N1 0PD
Area of Operation: Worldwide
Tel: 0207 351 5353 **Fax:** 0207 969 1639
Email: antique@dial.pipex.com
Web: www.themallantiques.co.uk
Product Type: 1, 2, 3, 4

MARK HENRY INTERIORS & BUILDING
Unit 9 Greenway, Harlow Business Park,
Harlow, Essex, CM19 5QB
Area of Operation: UK (Excluding Ireland)
Tel: 01279 444829 **Fax:** 01279 441598
Email: info@markhenryfurniture.co.uk
Web: www.markhenryfurniture.co.uk

MIRRORKOOL LTD
89 High Street, Earith, Cambridgeshire, PE28 3PN
Area of Operation: Worldwide
Tel: 01487 741300 **Fax:** 08712 367554
Email: sam@mirrorkool.com
Web: www.mirrorkool.com ✎
Product Type: 1, 2, 3, 4

MOBALPA
1 High Street, Halberton, Devon, EX16 7AF
Area of Operation: Worldwide
Tel: 07740 633672 **Fax:** 01884 820828
Email: ploftus@mobalpa.com
Web: www.mobalpa.co.uk
Product Type: 1, 2, 4

MYFLOATINGWORLD.COM LIMITED
3 Hartlepool Court, Galleons Lock,
Royal Docks, London, E16 2RL
Area of Operation: Europe
Tel: 0870 777 0728
Fax: 0870 777 0729
Email: info@myfloatingworld.com
Web: www.myfloatingworld.com ✎
Product Type: 1

N E J STEVENSON LIMITED
Church Lawford Business Centre, Limestone Hall Lane,
Church Lawford, Rugby, Warwickshire, CV23 9HD
Area of Operation: Worldwide
Tel: 024 7654 4662 **Fax:** 024 7654 5345
Email: info@nejstevenson.co.uk
Web: www.nejstevenson.co.uk
Product Type: 1, 2, 3, 4
Other Info: ✎ ✋
Material Type: A) 1, 2, 3, 4, 5, 6, 7, 8, 9, 10, 11, 12, 13, 14, 15

NEVILLE JOHNSON
Broadoak Business Park, Ashburton Road West,
Trafford Park, Manchester, M17 1RW
Tel: 0161 873 8333
Fax: 0161 873 8335
Email: sales@nevillejohnson.co.uk
Web: www.nevillejohnson.co.uk
Product Type: 1, 2, 3, 4

OAKWOOD BESPOKE
80 High Street, Camberley, Surrey, GU46 7RN
Area of Operation: Greater London, South East England, South West England and South Wales
Tel: 01276 708630
Email: enquiries@oakwoodbespokecamberley.co.uk
Web: www.oakwoodbespokecamberley.co.uk
Product Type: 2, 3

OLD GINGER
1b Bridge Studios, 318-326 Wandsworth
Bridge Road, London, SW6 2TZ
Area of Operation: UK & Ireland
Tel: 0207 384 3130 **Fax:** 0207 384 3138
Email: sales@oldginger.com
Web: www.oldginger.com
Product Type: 1, 2, 3, 4
Material Type: A) 10

ORIGINAL
3 Festival Units, The Showground,
Bridgwater, Somerset, TA6 6LS
Area of Operation: South West England and South Wales
Tel: 0870 0110808 **Fax:** 0870 011 0606
Email: enquiries@obsc.co.uk
Web: www.obsc.co.uk

PANELS PLUS
22-24 Mill Place,
Kingston Upon Thames, Surrey, KT1 2RJ
Area of Operation: Greater London
Tel: 0208 399 6343 **Fax:** 0208 399 6343
Email: sales@panelsplusltd.com
Web: www.panelsplusltd.com
Product Type: 2

PARLOUR FARM
Unit 12b, Wilkinson Road, Love Lane Industrial
Estate, Cirencester, Gloucestershire, GL7 1YT
Area of Operation: Europe
Tel: 01285 885336 **Fax:** 01285 643189
Email: info@parlourfarm.com
Web: www.parlourfarm.com

PETER CARLSON INTERIORS
Lower Hillgate, Stockport, Cheshire, SK1 3AW
Area of Operation: North West England and North Wales
Tel: 0161 480 8164 **Fax:** 0161 480 0097
Email: petercarlson@petercarlson.co.uk
Web: www.petercarlson.co.uk
Product Type: 1, 2, 3

PINELAND FURNITURE LTD
Unit 5 Cleobury Trading Estate,
Cleobury Mortimer, Shropshire, DY14 8DP
Area of Operation: UK (Excluding Ireland)
Tel: 01299 271143 **Fax:** 01299 271166
Email: pineland@onetel.com
Web: www.pineland.co.uk
Product Type: 1

POETSTYLE
Unit 1, Bayford Street Industrial Centre,
Hackney, Greater London, E8 3SE
Area of Operation: Worldwide
Tel: 0208 533 0915 **Fax:** 0208 985 2953
Email: sofachairs@aol.com
Web: www.sofachairs.co.uk
Product Type: 1

PORTICO GB LTD
Unit 9 Windmill Avenue, Woolpit Business Park,
Woolpit, Bury St Edmunds, Suffolk, IP30 9UP
Area of Operation: Greater London, South East England
Tel: 01359 244299
Fax: 01359 244232
Email: info@portico-gb.co.uk
Web: www.portico-newbuild.co.uk
Product Type: 2, 4 **Material Type:** H) 5

POSH PANTRIES
81 Kelvin Road North, Lenziemill,
Cumbernauld, Lanarkshire, G67 2BD
Tel: 01236 453556 **Fax:** 01236 728068
Email: office@poshpantries.co.uk
Web: www.poshpantries.co.uk **Product Type:** 2

PS INTERIORS
11 Cecil Road, Hale,
Altrincham, Cheshire, WA15 9NY
Area of Operation: Europe
Tel: 0161 926 9398 **Fax:** 0161 929 0363
Email: sales@ps-interiors.co.uk
Web: www.ps-interiors.co.uk **Product Type:** 1

RADIATING ELEGANCE
32 Main Street, Orton-on-the-Hill,
Warwickshire, CV9 3NN
Area of Operation: UK (Excluding Ireland)
Tel: 08000 280 921
Email: info@radiatingelegance.co.uk
Web: www.radiatingelegance.co.uk
Product Type: 1

RB UK LTD
Element House, Napier Road,
Bedford, Bedfordshire, MK41 0QS
Area of Operation: UK & Ireland
Tel: 01234 272717 **Fax:** 01234 270202
Email: info@rbuk.co.uk **Web:** www.rbuk.co.uk
Product Type: 4 **Material Type:** C) 2

REINDEER ANTIQUES LTD
43 Watling Street, Potterspury,
Northamptonshire, NN12 7QD
Tel: 01908 542407 **Fax:** 01908 542121
Email: sales@reindeerantiques.co.uk
Web: www.reindeerantiques.co.uk
Product Type: 1, 2, 3

RICHARD BAKER FURNITURE LTD
Wimbledon Studios, 257 Burlington Road,
New Malden, Surrey, KT3 4NE
Area of Operation: Europe
Tel: 0208 336 1777 **Fax:** 0208 336 1666
Email: richard@richardbakerfurniture.co.uk
Web: www.richardbakerfurniture.co.uk
Product Type: 1, 2, 3, 4

ROCKINGHAM FENDER SEATS
Grange Farm, Thorney, Peterborough,
Cambridgeshire, PE6 0PJ
Area of Operation: Worldwide
Tel: 01733 270233 **Fax:** 01733 270512
Email: info@fenderseats.com
Web: www.rockingham-fenderseats.com
Product Type: 1 **Material Type:** A) 2

ROLLA-GLIDE HARDWARE LTD
Unit 21 Yardley Business Park,
Luckyn Lane, Basildon, Essex, SS14 3GN
Area of Operation: East England
Tel: 01268 271771 **Fax:** 01268 272665
Email: rolla-glide@tiscali.co.uk
Web: www.rollaglide.co.uk **Product Type:** 2

ROOMS FOR KIDS LTD
Unit 20 Argyle Industrial Estate, Argyle Street South,
Birkenhead, Cheshire, CH41 4HH
Tel: 0151 650 2401 **Fax:** 0151 650 2403
Email: roger@friezeframe.com
Web: www.friezeframe.com **Product Type:** 4

ROOTS KITCHENS BEDROOMS BATHROOMS
Vine Farm, Stockers Hill, Boughton under Blean,
Faversham, Kent, ME13 9AB
Area of Operation: South East England
Tel: 01227 751130 **Fax:** 01227 750033
Email: showroom@rootskitchens.co.uk
Web: www.rootskitchens.co.uk

SANDERSON'S FINE FURNITURE
Unit 5 & 6, The Village Workshop, Four Crosses
Business Park, Four Crosses, Powys, SY22 6ST
Area of Operation: UK (Excluding Ireland)
Tel: 01691 830075 **Fax:** 01691 830075
Email: sales@sandersonsfinefurniture.co.uk
Web: www.sandersonsfinefurniture.co.uk
Product Type: 1, 2, 3

SANDERSONS FINE FURNITURE
Area of Operation: UK (Excluding Ireland)
Tel: 01691 830075
Fax: 01691 830075
Email: sales@sandersonsfinefurniture.co.uk
Web: www.sandersonsfinefurniture.co.uk
Product Type: 1, 2, 3

Traditional manufacturers of quality bespoke oak furniture & joinery. For further information visit our website.

SHARPS BEDROOMS
Albany Park, Camberley, Surrey, GU16 7PU
Area of Operation: UK (Excluding Ireland)
Tel: 01276 802000 **Fax:** 01276 802030
Email: enquiries@sharps.co.uk
Web: www.sharps.co.uk **Product Type:** 2, 3
Other Info: ✎ **Material Type:** A) 2, 4, 5, 9

SHIMU LTD
3C Harrogate Road, Rawdon, Leeds, LS19 6HW
Area of Operation: Worldwide
Tel: 0870 207 1433 **Fax:** 0113 250 8284
Email: info@shimu.co.uk
Web: www.shimu.co.uk **Product Type:** 1, 2, 3

SIMON TAYLOR FURNITURE LIMITED
Cane End Lane, Bierton, Aylesbury,
Buckinghamshire, HP22 5BH
Area of Operation: UK & Ireland
Tel: 01296 488207 **Fax:** 01296 398722
Email: information@simon-taylor.co.uk
Web: www.simon-taylor.co.uk
Product Type: 1, 2, 3, 4 **Other Info:** ✎ ☞

SOFACLASSICS
Suite 4A (West), 350 The Highway,
London, E1W 3HU
Area of Operation: Worldwide
Tel: 0207 790 9001 **Fax:** 0207 790 8014
Email: info@sofaclassics.co.uk
Web: www.sofaclassics.co.uk
Product Type: 1 **Other Info:** ✎ ☞

SOGA LTD
41 Mayfield Street, Hull,
East Riding of Yorks, HU3 1NT
Area of Operation: Worldwide
Tel: 01482 327025 **Email:** info@soga.co.uk
Web: www.soga.co.uk **Product Type:** 4

STROUDS WOODWORKING COMPANY LTD
Ashmansworthy, Woolsery,
Bideford, Devon, EX39 5RE
Area of Operation: South West England and South Wales
Tel: 01409 241624 **Fax:** 01409 241769
Email: enquiries@stroudswoodworking.co.uk
Web: www.stroudswoodworking.co.uk
Product Type: 1, 2, 3 **Other Info:** ✎ ☞

STUART INTERIORS
Barrington Court, Barrington,
Ilminster, Somerset, TA19 0NQ
Area of Operation: Worldwide
Tel: 01460 240349
Fax: 01460 242069
Email: design@stuartinteriors.com
Web: www.stuartinteriors.com
Product Type: 1, 2
Other Info: ✎ ☞
Material Type: A) 2, 7

TASKWORTHY
The Old Brickyard, Pontrilas,
Herefordshire, HR2 0DJ
Area of Operation: UK (Excluding Ireland)
Tel: 01981 242900
Fax: 01981 242901
Email: peter@taskworthy.co.uk
Web: www.taskworthy.co.uk
Product Type: 1, 2, 3, 4

TENTERDEN HOUSE INTERIORS
4 West Cross, Tenterden, Kent, TN30 6JL
Area of Operation: Worldwide
Tel: 01580 764481
Fax: 01580 765531
Email: tenterdenhouseinteriors@hotmail.com
Product Type: 1, 2, 3

THE DESIGN STUDIO
39 High Street, Reigate, Surrey, RH2 9AE
Area of Operation: South East England
Tel: 01737 248228
Fax: 01737 224180
Email: enq@the-design-studio.co.uk
Web: www.the-design-studio.co.uk ☞
Product Type: 1

THE EXPANDED METAL COMPANY LIMITED
PO Box 14, Longhill Industrial Estate (North),
Hartlepool, Durham, TS25 1PR
Area of Operation: Worldwide
Tel: 01429 867388
Fax: 01429 866795
Email: paulb@expamet.co.uk
Web: www.expandedmetalcompany.co.uk

THE FIREPLACE GALLERY (UK) LTD
Clarence Road, Worksops,
Nottinghamshire, S80 1QA
Area of Operation: UK & Ireland
Tel: 01909 500802
Fax: 01909 500810
Email: fireplacegallery@btinternet.com
Web: www.fireplacegallery.co.uk
Product Type: 1, 4
Other Info: ECO ✎ ☞
Material Type: A) 1, 2, 3, 4, 7, 11

THE HOME & GARDEN CENTRE
Benfield ATT Group, Castle Way,
Caldicot, Monmouthshire, NP26 5PR
Area of Operation: UK (Excluding Ireland)
Tel: 01291 437062
Fax: 01291 437051
Email: info@homegardenshop.co.uk
Web: www.home-garden-centre.co.uk ☞
Product Type: 1, 2

THE JRG GROUP
3 Crompton Way, North Newmoor Industrial Estate,
Irvine, Ayrshire, KA11 4HU
Area of Operation: Europe
Tel: 0871 200 8080
Fax: 01294 211 222
Email: chris@jrgfiresurrounds.com
Web: www.jrggroup.com
Product Type: 2

THE MODERN ROOM LTD
54 St.Pauls Road, Luton, Bedfordshire, LU1 3RX
Area of Operation: UK (Excluding Ireland)
Tel: 01582 612070
Fax: 01582 612070
Email: laura@themodernroom.com
Web: www.themodernroom.com
Product Type: 1, 2, 3, 4
Other Info: ✎ ☞
Material Type: C) 1, 3, 14

THE OLD CREAMERY
Watercombe Park, Lynx Trading Estate,
Yeovil, Somerset, BA20 2EB
Area of Operation: South West England and South Wales
Tel: 01935 410500
Fax: 01935 426908
Email: oldcreamery@hotmail.com
Web: www.oldcreameryfurniture.com
Product Type: 1, 2, 3, 4 **Other Info:** ▽ ✎ ☞

SPONSORED BY: BRYN HALL www.brynhall.co.uk

THE OLD PINE STORE
Coxons Yard, Off Union Street,
Ashbourne, Derbyshire, DE6 1FG
Area of Operation: Europe
Tel: 01335 344112 **Fax:** 01335 344112
Email: martin@old-pine.co.uk
Web: www.old-pine.co.uk
Product Type: 1, 2, 3, 4 **Other Info:** ▽ECO ✏ ✋
Material Type: A) 2, 4, 5

THE REAL WOOD FURNITURE CO
London House, 16 Oxford Street,
Woodstock, Oxfordshire, OX20 1TS
Area of Operation: Worldwide
Tel: 01993 813887
Email: info@rwfco.com
Web: www.rwfco.com
Product Type: 1 **Material Type:** A) 2, 3, 6

TIM PEEK WOODCARVING
The Woodcarving Studio, Highfield Avenue,
High Wycombe, Buckinghamshire, HP12 4ET
Area of Operation: UK (Excluding Ireland)
Tel: 01494 439629
Email: timpeekwoodcarving@hotmail.com
Web: www.timpeekwoodcarving.co.uk
Product Type: 1, 2, 3, 4

TIM WOOD LIMITED
1 Burland Road, London, SW11 6SA
Area of Operation: Worldwide
Tel: 07041 380030 **Fax:** 08700 548645
Email: homeb@timwood.com
Web: www.timwood.com
Product Type: 1, 2, 3, 4

TOMPKINS LTD
High March Close, Long March Industrial Estate,
Daventry, Northamptonshire, NN11 4EZ
Area of Operation: UK (Excluding Ireland)
Tel: 01327 877187 **Fax:** 01327 310491
Email: info@tompkinswood.co.uk
Web: www.tompkinswood.co.uk
Product Type: 1, 2, 3 **Other Info:** ✏ ✋

TURNER FURNITURE
The Old Dairy, Manor Farm,
Sipilly Handley, Salisbury, SP5 5NU
Area of Operation: Greater London, South East
England, South West England and South Wales
Tel: 01725 516990 **Fax:** 01725 516991
Email: nick@turner-furniture.co.uk
Web: www.turner-furniture.co.uk
Product Type: 1, 2, 3

VICTORIA HAMMOND INTERIORS
Bury Farm, Church Street, Bovingdon,
Hemel Hempstead, Hertfordshire, HP3 0LU
Area of Operation: UK (Excluding Ireland)
Tel: 01442 831641 **Fax:** 01442 831641
Email: victoria@victoriahammond.com
Web: www.victoriahammond.com
Product Type: 1, 2, 3, 4

WATTS & WRIGHT (THE JOINERY SHOP)
PO Box 4251, Walsall, West Midlands, WS5 3WY
Area of Operation: Worldwide
Tel: 01922 610800 / 0207 043 7619
Fax: 0870 762 6387
Email: sales@wattsandwright.com
Web: www.wattsandwright.com
Product Type: 1, 2

WICKES
Wickes Customer Services, Wickes House,
120-138 Station Road, Harrow, Middlesex, HA1 2QB
Area of Operation: UK (Excluding Ireland)
Tel: 0870 608 9001 **Fax:** 0208 863 6225
Web: www.wickes.co.uk **Product Type:** 2

WILLIAM GARVEY
Leyhill, Payhembury, Honiton, Devon, EX14 3JG
Area of Operation: Worldwide
Tel: 01404 841430 **Fax:** 01404 841626
Email: webquery@williamgarvey.co.uk
Web: www.williamgarvey.co.uk
Product Type: 1, 2, 3, 4 **Other Info:** ✏ ✋
Material Type: A) 2, 3, 4, 6, 7, 8, 9, 10, 11, 12, 15

WOODCHESTER KITCHENS & INTERIORS
Unit 18a Chalford Industrial Estate,
Chalford, Gloucestershire, GL6 8NT
Area of Operation: UK (Excluding Ireland)
Tel: 01453 886411
Fax: 01453 886411
Email: enquires@woodchesterkitchens.co.uk
Web: www.woodchesterkitchens.co.uk
Product Type: 1, 2, 3, 4

WOODSTOCK FURNITURE
17 Park Drive, East Sheen, London, SW14 8RB
Area of Operation: Worldwide
Tel: 020 88760131
Fax: 020 88760131
Email: ask@woodstockfurniture.co.uk
Web: www.woodstockfurniture.co.uk
Product Type: 1, 2, 3, 4

WWW.DIRECT-CANE.CO.UK
123 Richards Street, Cathays, Cardiff, CF24 4DD
Area of Operation: UK & Ireland
Tel: 02920 664600
Email: sales@direct-cane.co.uk
Web: www.direct-cane.co.uk ✓🛒
Product Type: 1, 2, 3 **Other Info:** ✋

SCREENS AND ROOM DIVIDERS

```
KEY
OTHER:   ▽ Reclaimed   ✓🛒 On-line shopping
         ✏ Bespoke   ✋ Hand-made   ECO Ecological
```

ARCHITECTURAL IRONMONGERY LTD
28 Kyrle Street, Ross-on-Wye, Herefordshire, HR9 7DB
Area of Operation: Worldwide
Tel: 01989 567946 **Fax:** 01989 567946
Email: info@arciron.co.uk
Web: www.arciron.com ✓🛒

ASHFIELD TRADITIONAL
119 High Street, Needham Market,
Ipswich, Suffolk, IP6 8DQ
Area of Operation: Europe
Tel: 01449 723601 **Fax:** 01449 723602
Email: mail@limelightgb.com
Web: www.limelightgb.com ✓🛒
Product Type: 7

B ROURKE & CO LTD
Vulcan Works, Accrington Road,
Burnley, Lancashire, BB11 5QD
Area of Operation: Worldwide
Tel: 01282 422841 **Fax:** 01282 458901
Email: info@rourkes.co.uk
Web: www.rourkes.co.uk

BRASS GRILLES UK
Unit 174, 78 Marylebone High Street,
London, W1U 5AP
Area of Operation: UK (Excluding Ireland)
Tel: 07905 292101 / 01923 451600
Fax: 01923 451600
Email: sales@brass-grilles.co.uk
Web: www.brass-grilles.co.uk ✓🛒

BROCKHOUSE MODERNFOLD LIMITED
Aztec House, 137 Molesey Avenue,
West Molesey, Surrey, KT8 2RY
Area of Operation: Worldwide
Tel: 0208 481 7288 **Fax:** 0208 481 7289
Email: neilohalleran@brockhouse.net
Web: www.brockhouse.net

BURNT ASH CEILINGS
228 Burnt Ash Hill, Lee, London, SE12 0QE
Area of Operation: Greater London, South East England
Tel: 0208 857 4856
Fax: 0208 857 7667
Email: info@burntashceilings.co.uk
Web: www.burntashceilings.co.uk

C.I.C. SCREENS
The Metro Centre, St Johns Road,
Isleworth, TW7 6NJ
Area of Operation: Worldwide
Tel: 0208 560 3337 **Fax:** 0208 560 4442
Email: sales@cicscreens.co.uk
Web: cicscreens.co.uk

CHIC SHACK
77 Lower Richmond Road, London, SW15 1ET
Area of Operation: Worldwide
Tel: 0208 785 7777 **Fax:** 0208 789 0444
Email: info@chicshack.net
Web: www.chicshack.net

CUSTOM MADE SHUTTERS
Avalon, Swan Lane, Marlpit Hill,
Eadenbridge, Kent, TN8 6BA
Area of Operation: UK & Ireland
Tel: 01732 863554
Email: info@custommadeshutters.co.uk
Web: www.custommadeshutters.co.uk
Product Type: 5 **Other Info:** ✏ ✋
Material Type: A) 1, 2, 3, 4, 5, 6, 7, 9, 10, 12

DAR INTERIORS
Arch 11, Miles Street, London, SW8 1RZ
Area of Operation: Worldwide
Tel: 020 7720 9678 **Fax:** 020 7627 5129
Email: enquiries@darinteriors.com
Web: www.darinteriors.com

DARTINGTON STEEL DESIGN
Webbers Yard, Dartington Industrial Estate,
Totnes, Devon, TQ9 6JY
Area of Operation: Worldwide
Tel: 01803 868671 **Fax:** 01803 868665
Email: sales@dartington.com
Web: www.dartington.com

DORMA UK LIMITED
Wilbury Way, Hitchin, Hertfordshire, SG4 0AB
Area of Operation: UK & Ireland
Tel: 01462 477600 **Fax:** 01462 477601
Email: info@dorma-uk.co.uk
Web: www.dorma-uk.co.uk

ECLIPSE BLIND SYSTEMS LIMITED
Inchinnan Business Park, Inchinnan,
Renfrew, Renfrewshire, PA4 9RE
Area of Operation: UK & Ireland
Tel: 0141 812 3322 **Fax:** 0141 812 5253
Email: orrd@eclipseblinds.co.uk
Web: www.eclipse-blinds.com
Product Type: 1, 2, 3, 4

EDEN HOUSE LIMITED
Elveden, Kennel Lane,
Windlesham, Surrey, GU20 6AA
Area of Operation: Greater London, South East England
Tel: 01276 470192 **Fax:** 01276 489689
Email: info@internalshutters.co.uk
Web: www.edenhouse.biz
Product Type: 5 **Other Info:** ✏

HAF DESIGNS LTD
HAF House, Mead Lane, Hertford,
Hertfordshire, SG13 7AP
Area of Operation: UK & Ireland
Tel: 0800 389 8821 **Fax:** 01992 505705
Email: info@hafltd.co.uk
Web: www.hafdesigns.co.uk ✓🛒

HANNAH WHITE
Area of Operation: Worldwide
Tel: 01372 806703 **Fax:** 01372 806703
Email: info@hannahwhite.co.uk
Web: www.hannahwhite.co.uk

HOT GLASS DESIGN
Unit 24 Crosby Yard Industrial Estate,
Bridgend, Mid Glamorgan, CF31 1JZ
Area of Operation: Europe
Tel: 01656 659884 **Fax:** 01656 659884
Email: info@hotglassdesign.co.uk
Web: www.hotglassdesign.co.uk

IN DOORS
Beechinwood Farm, Beechinwood Lane,
Platt, Nr. Sevenoaks, Kent, TN15 8QN
Tel: 01732 887445 **Fax:** 01732 887446
Email: info@indoorsltd.co.uk
Web: www.indoorsltd.co.uk

INTERIOR ASSOCIATES
3 Highfield Road, Windsor, Berkshire, SL4 4DN
Area of Operation: UK & Ireland
Tel: 01753 865339 **Fax:** 01753 865339
Email: sales@interiorassociates.fsnet.co.uk
Web: www.interiorassociates.co.uk **Other Info:** ✏

INTERIOR DOOR SYSTEMS LTD
Hopton House, 3 & 4 Rivington Court,
Hardwick Grange, Warrington, Cheshire, WA1 4RT
Area of Operation: UK & Ireland
Tel: 01925 813100 **Fax:** 01925 814300
Email: cb@interiordoorsystems.co.uk
Web: www.interiordoorsystems.co.uk

IRONMONGERY DIRECT
Unit 2-3 Eldon Way Trading Estate,
Eldon Way, Hockley, Essex, SS5 4AD
Area of Operation: Worldwide
Tel: 01702 562770 **Fax:** 01702 562799
Email: sales@ironmongerydirect.com
Web: www.ironmongerydirect.com ✓🛒

ISAAC LORD LTD
West End Court, Suffield Road,
High Wycombe, Buckinghamshire, HP11 2JY
Area of Operation: East England, Greater London,
North East England, South East England, South West
England and South Wales
Tel: 01494 462121 **Fax:** 01494 461376
Email: info@isaaclord.co.uk
Web: www.isaaclord.co.uk ✓🛒

LEVOLUX LTD
1 Forward Drive, Harrow, Middlesex, HA3 8NT
Tel: 0208 863 9111 **Fax:** 0208 863 8760
Email: info@levolux.com
Web: www.levolux.com
Product Type: 1, 2, 3, 4, 6

LPD DOORS
Holme Well Road, Leeds, West Yorkshire, LS10 4SL
Area of Operation: UK & Ireland
Tel: 0845 658 5115 **Email:** sales@lpddoors.co.uk

MBL
55 High Street, Biggleswade, Bedfordshire, SG18 0JH
Area of Operation: UK (Excluding Ireland)
Tel: 01767 318695 **Fax:** 01767 318834
Email: info@mblai.co.uk **Web:** www.mblai.co.uk
Product Type: 5 **Other Info:** ✏

OAKLEAF (GLASGOW)
Birch Court, Doune, Stirlingshire, FK16 6JD
Area of Operation: Scotland
Tel: 01786 842216 **Fax:** 01786 842216
Email: sales@oakleaf.co.uk
Web: www.oakleaf.co.uk

PETER CARLSON INTERIORS
Lower Hillgate, Stockport, Cheshire, SK1 3AW
Area of Operation: North West England and North Wales
Tel: 0161 480 8164 **Fax:** 0161 480 0097
Email: petercarlson@petercarlson.co.uk
Web: www.petercarlson.co.uk

PLANTATION SHUTTERS
131 Putney Bridge Road, London, SW15 2PA
Area of Operation: UK & Ireland
Tel: 0208 871 9222 / 9333
Fax: 0208 871 0041
Email: sales@plantation-shutters.co.uk
Web: www.plantation-shutters.co.uk
Product Type: 2, 5

POLARLIGHT ACRYLIC BLOCK WINDOWS
Unit 4 Townspark Industrial Estate,
Athlone Road, Langford, Ireland
Area of Operation: UK & Ireland
Tel: 00 353 43 45 794 **Fax:** 00 353 43 46 531
Email: info@polarlight.co.uk
Web: www.polarlight.co.uk

PORTICO GB LTD
Unit 9 Windmill Avenue, Woolpit Business Park,
Woolpit, Bury St Edmunds, Suffolk, IP30 9UP
Area of Operation: Greater London, South East England
Tel: 01359 244299 **Fax:** 01359 244232
Email: info@portico-gb.co.uk
Web: www.portico-newbuild.co.uk

SHIMU LTD
3C Harrogate Road, Rawdon, Leeds, LS19 6HW
Area of Operation: Worldwide
Tel: 0870 207 1433 **Fax:** 0113 250 8284
Email: info@shimu.co.uk
Web: www.shimu.co.uk ✏

STROUDS WOODWORKING COMPANY LTD
Ashmansworthy, Woolsery, Bideford, Devon, EX39 5RE
Area of Operation: South West England and South Wales
Tel: 01409 241624 **Fax:** 01409 241769
Email: enquiries@stroudswoodworking.co.uk
Web: www.stroudswoodworking.co.uk
Product Type: 5 **Other Info:** ✏ 🖐

SURFACE MATERIAL DESIGN
17 Skiffington Close, London, SW2 3UL
Area of Operation: Worldwide
Tel: 0208 671 3383
Email: info@surfacematerialdesign.co.uk
Web: www.surfacematerialdesign.co.uk ✏

THE CANE STORE
Wash Dyke Cottage, 1 Witham Road,
Long Bennington, Lincolnshire, NG23 5DS
Area of Operation: Worldwide
Tel: 01400 282271 **Fax:** 01400 281103
Email: jaki@canestore.co.uk
Web: www.canestore.co.uk **Product Type:** 3, 7

THE EXPANDED METAL COMPANY LIMITED
PO Box 14, Longhill Industrial Estate (North),
Hartlepool, Durham, TS25 1PR
Area of Operation: Worldwide
Tel: 01429 867388 **Fax:** 01429 866795
Email: paulb@expamet.co.uk
Web: www.expandedmetalcompany.co.uk

VISTAMATIC LIMITED
51-55 Fowler Road, Hainault Industrial Estate,
Hainault, Essex, IG6 3XE
Area of Operation: Worldwide
Tel: 0208 500 2200 **Fax:** 0208 559 8584
Email: sales@vistamatic.com
Web: www.vistamatic.com **Product Type:** 5

WWW.DIRECT-CANE.CO.UK
123 Richards Street, Cathays, Cardiff, CF24 4DD
Area of Operation: UK & Ireland
Tel: 02920 664600 **Email:** sales@direct-cane.co.uk
Web: www.direct-cane.co.uk ✏

WWW.OPENNSHUT.CO.UK
Forum House, Stirling Road,
Chichester, West Sussex, PO19 7DN
Area of Operation: UK (Excluding Ireland)
Tel: 01243 774 888
Email: shutters@opennshut.co.uk
Web: www.opennshut.co.uk ✏
Product Type: 1, 3, 5

ZERO SEAL SYSTEMS LTD
Unit 6, Ladford Covert, Seighford,
Stafford, Staffordshire, ST18 9QG
Area of Operation: Europe
Tel: 01785 282910 **Fax:** 01785 282498
Email: sales@zeroplus.co.uk
Web: www.zeroplus.co.uk

ANTIQUES

KEY
SEE ALSO: MERCHANTS - Architectural
Antiques and Salvage Yards
OTHER: ▽ Reclaimed ✏ On-line shopping
✏ Bespoke 🖐 Hand-made ECO Ecological

ACADEMY BILLIARD COMPANY
5 Camphill Industrial Estate, Camphill Road,
West Byfleet, Surrey, KT14 6EW
Area of Operation: Worldwide
Tel: 01932 352067 **Fax:** 01932 353904
Email: academygames@fsbdial.co.uk
Web: www.games-room.com

ANTIQUARIUS ANTIQUES CENTRE
131-141 Kings Road, Chelsea, London, SW3 5EB
Area of Operation: Worldwide
Tel: 0207 351 5353 **Fax:** 0207 969 1639
Email: antique@dial.pipex.com
Web: www.antiquarius.co.uk ✏

ARCHITECTURAL TREASURES
The Old Garage, Smarden Road,
Pluckley, Kent, TN27 0RF
Area of Operation: Worldwide
Tel: 01233 840004 **Fax:** 01233 840055
Email: info@architecturaltreasures.co.uk
Web: www.architecturaltreasures.co.uk

BARBE & BALD LTD
112 Tudor Way, Hertford, Hertfordshire, SG14 2DL
Area of Operation: Worldwide
Tel: 01992 552783 **Fax:** 01992 552783
Email: mark@baldsbalm.co.uk
Web: www.baldsbalm.co.uk ✏

BINGLEY ANTIQUES
Springfield Farm Estate, Haworth,
West Yorkshire, BD21 5PT
Area of Operation: UK (Excluding Ireland)
Tel: 01535 646666 **Fax:** 01535 648527
Email: john@bingleyantiques.com
Web: www.bingleyantiques.com ✏

CHIC SHACK
77 Lower Richmond Road, London, SW15 1ET
Area of Operation: Worldwide
Tel: 0208 785 7777 **Fax:** 0208 789 0444
Email: info@chicshack.net
Web: www.chicshack.net

COTTAGE FARM ANTIQUES
Stratford Road, Aston Sub Edge, Chipping Campden,
Gloucestershire, GL55 6PZ
Area of Operation: Worldwide
Tel: 01386 438263 **Fax:** 01386 438263
Email: info@cottagefarmantiques.co.uk
Web: www.cottagefarmantiques.co.uk ✏
Product Type: 3

DEBDEN ANTIQUES & INTERIORS
Elder Street, Debden, Saffron Walden, Essex, CB11 3JY
Area of Operation: Worldwide
Tel: 01799 543007
Email: info@debden-antiques.co.uk
Web: www.debden-antiques.co.uk

DUKE CHRISTIE
Hillockhead Farmhouse, Dallas,
Forres, Moray, IV36 2SD
Area of Operation: Worldwide
Tel: 01343 890347 **Fax:** 01343 890347
Email: enquiries@dukechristie.com
Web: www.dukechristie.com

HICKS SHARP & CO.
Grange Close, Milton Ernest, Bedfordshire, MK44 1RR
Area of Operation: Worldwide
Tel: 01234 822843 **Fax:** 01234 822843
Email: tom@hickssharp.freeserve.co.uk
Web: www.perioddoorfurniture.com ✏

JAIL ANTIQUES
40 Mill Road, Watlington,
King's Lynn, Norfolk, PE33 0HJ
Area of Operation: UK (Excluding Ireland)
Tel: 07773 380880
Email: meljoe43@aol.com
Web: www.jailantiques.com

JOHN ARMISTEAD RESTORATIONS
Malham Cottage, Bellingdon,
Nr. Chesham, Buckinghamshire, HP5 2UR
Area of Operation: Worldwide
Tel: 01494 758209 **Fax:** 01494 758209
Email: j.armistead@ntlworld.com
Web: www.john-armistead-restorations.co.uk

MALL ANTIQUES ARCADE
359 Upper Street, Islington, London, N1 0PD
Area of Operation: Worldwide
Tel: 0207 351 5353 **Fax:** 0207 969 1639
Email: antique@dial.pipex.com
Web: www.themallantiques.co.uk

REINDEER ANTIQUES LTD
43 Watling Street, Potterspury,
Northamptonshire, NN12 7QD
Area of Operation: Worldwide
Tel: 01908 542407 **Fax:** 01908 542121
Email: sales@reindeerantiques.co.uk
Web: www.reindeerantiques.co.uk

SHIMU LTD
3C Harrogate Road, Rawdon, Leeds, LS19 6HW
Area of Operation: Worldwide
Tel: 0870 207 1433 **Fax:** 0113 250 8284
Email: info@shimu.co.uk
Web: www.shimu.co.uk ✏

STUART INTERIORS
Barrington Court, Barrington,
Ilminster, Somerset, TA19 0NQ
Area of Operation: Worldwide
Tel: 01460 240349 **Fax:** 01460 242069
Email: design@stuartinteriors.com
Web: www.stuartinteriors.com

Don't Forget!
You can use the materials key at the beginning of this Handbook to get much more information from a company's listing.

WATTS & WRIGHT (THE JOINERY SHOP)
PO Box 4251, Walsall, West Midlands, WS5 3WY
Area of Operation: Worldwide
Tel: 01922 610800 / 020 70437619
Fax: 0870 7626387
Email: sales@wattsandwright.com
Web: www.wattsandwright.com

PAINTINGS, PHOTOGRAPHY AND SCULPTURE

KEY
OTHER: ▽ Reclaimed ✏ On-line shopping
✏ Bespoke 🖐 Hand-made ECO Ecological

2TECHVISUALS
Unit 11, EuroLink Business Centre,
49 Effra Road, London, SW2 1BZ
Area of Operation: Europe
Tel: 0207 738 6560 **Fax:** 0207 738 6596
Email: annette@2techvisuals.co.uk
Web: www.2techvisuals.co.uk

ABUNDANCE UK
12 Beauchamp Industrial Estate, Two Gates,
Tamworth, Staffordshire, B77 5BZ
Area of Operation: Europe
Tel: 0800 970 6176
Email: brittaniatrading@aol.com
Web: www.abundanceuk.co.uk ✏

ALUMINIUM ARTWORKS
Persistence Works, 21 Brown Street,
Sheffield, S1 2BS
Area of Operation: Worldwide
Tel: 0114 249 4748
Email: info@aluminiumartworks.co.uk
Web: www.aluminiumartworks.co.uk

ANNETTE NIX
150a Camden Street, London, NW1 9PA
Area of Operation: Worldwide
Tel: 07956 451719
Email: annette.n@virgin.net
Web: www.annettenix.com

ANTIQUARIUS ANTIQUES CENTRE
131-141 Kings Road, Chelsea, London, SW3 5EB
Area of Operation: Worldwide
Tel: 0207 351 5353 **Fax:** 0207 969 1639
Email: antique@dial.pipex.com
Web: www.antiquarius.co.uk ✏

ARTPARKS INTERNATIONAL LTD
Sausmarez Manor , St Martin, Guernsey, GY4 6SG
Area of Operation: Worldwide
Tel: 01481 235571 **Fax:** 01481 235572
Email: peter@artparks.co.uk
Web: www.artparks.co.uk

BARRY SIMS
11 Bognor Road, Chichester, West Sussex, PO19 7TF
Area of Operation: UK & Ireland
Tel: 07787 987652
Email: info@barrysims.biz
Web: www.barrysims.biz

BLINK RED CONTEMPORARY ART
40 Maritime Street, Edinburgh, Lothian, EH6 6SA
Area of Operation: UK & Ireland
Tel: 0131 625 0192
Fax: 0131 467 7995
Email: customerservices@blinkred.com
Web: www.blinkred.com ✏

BRIMSTONE DESIGN & PRINT LTD
Centenary Business Centre, Hammond Close,
Nuneaton, Warwickshire, CV11 6RY
Area of Operation: Worldwide
Tel: 024 7637 4663
Email: enquiries@brimstoneprint.co.uk
Web: www.brimstoneprint.co.uk ✏

BUYDESIGN
Monteviot Nurseries, Ancrum,
Jedburgh, Borders, TD8 6TU
Area of Operation: Scotland
Tel: 01835 830740
Email: enquries@buydesign-furniture.com
Web: www.buydesign-furniture.com

CANVAS BY DESIGN
PO Box 238, Hythe, Kent, CT21 5WU
Area of Operation: UK & Ireland
Tel: 01303 264107
Email: info@canvasbydesign.co.uk
Web: www.canvasbydesign.co.uk ⌂

CLOTH
North Street, Huthwaite, Nottinghamshire, NG17 2PE
Area of Operation: UK & Ireland
Tel: 0870 7775100   **Fax:** 0870 7775101
Email: info@clothuk.com

COOLSCAPES LTD - PHOTO ROLLER BLINDS
114a Top Lane, Whitley,
Melksham, Wiltshire, SN12 8QU
Area of Operation: Worldwide
Tel: 01225 702938   **Email:** info@coolscapes.co.uk
Web: www.photorollerblinds.co.uk

DEBDEN ANTIQUES & INTERIORS
Elder Street, Debden, Saffron Walden, Essex, CB11 3JY
Area of Operation: Worldwide
Tel: 01799 543007
Email: info@debden-antiques.co.uk
Web: www.debden-antiques.co.uk

DM4ART.COM
147 Hartington Road, London, SW8 2EY
Area of Operation: Worldwide
Tel: 0207 720 0239
Email: david@dm4art.com   **Web:** dm4art.com ⌂

FIRE AND IRON GALLERY
Oxshott Road, Leatherhead, Surrey, KT22 0EN
Area of Operation: UK & Ireland
Tel: 01372 386453   **Email:** lucy@fireandiron.co.uk
Web: www.fireandiron.co.uk

FOREVER CANVAS LTD
74 Devonshire Business Park, Eldon Street,
Sheffield, South Yorkshire, S1 4GT
Area of Operation: UK (Excluding Ireland)
Tel: 0845 603 6229
Email: sam.joyce@forevercanvas.co.uk
Web: www.forevercanvas.co.uk ⌂

GLASS & LIGHTING STUDIO
56 The Tything, Worcester, Worcestershire, WR1 1JT
Area of Operation: UK & Ireland
Tel: 01905 26285   **Fax:** 01905 26285
Email: Studio@glass-lighting.co.uk
Web: www.glass-lighting.co.uk

HANNAH WHITE
Area of Operation: Worldwide
Tel: 01372 806703   **Fax:** 01372 806703
Email: info@hannahwhite.co.uk
Web: www.hannahwhite.co.uk

ID-WALL LTD
90 New North Road, Huddersfield,
West Yorkshire, HD1 5NE
Area of Operation: Worldwide
Tel: 01484 543210   **Email:** info@id-wall.com
Web: www.id-wall.com ⌂

IMAGE SHED
Penkelly, Bartestree, Hereford, Herefordshire, HR1 4BY
Area of Operation: Worldwide
Tel: 0845 430 8757
Email: info@imageshed.co.uk
Web: www.imageshed.co.uk ⌂

LUCYART
178b Batley Road, Alverthorpe,
Wakefield, West Yorkshire, WF2 0AJ
Area of Operation: Worldwide
Tel: 01924 362009   **Fax:** 0870 122 7055
Email: sales@lucyart.co.uk
Web: www.lucyart.co.uk ⌂

MALL ANTIQUES ARCADE
359 Upper Street, Islington, London, N1 0PD
Tel: 0207 351 5353   **Fax:** 0207 969 1639
Email: antique@dial.pipex.com
Web: www.themallantiques.co.uk

MYFLOATINGWORLD.COM LIMITED
3 Hartlepool Court, Galleons Lock,
Royal Docks, London, E16 2RL
Area of Operation: Europe
Tel: 0870 777 0728   **Fax:** 0870 777 0729
Email: info@myfloatingworld.com
Web: www.myfloatingworld.com ⌂

PETER CARLSON INTERIORS
Lower Hillgate, Stockport, Cheshire, SK1 3AW
Area of Operation: North West England and North Wales
Tel: 0161 480 8164   **Fax:** 0161 480 0097
Email: petercarlson@petercarlson.co.uk
Web: www.petercarlson.co.uk

PHILLIP FLOCKHART
Flat 3/61 Wilton Road, Bexhill on Sea,
East Sussex, TN40 1HX
Area of Operation: Worldwide
Tel: 01424 731807
Email: phillip_flockhart@yahoo.co.uk
Web: www.phil-flockhart-artist.com

POSTERS2FRAME.COM
Alvey & Towers, A37 The Springboard Centre,
Mantle Lane, Coalville, Leicestershire, LE67 3DW
Area of Operation: Worldwide
Tel: 01530 450011   **Web:** www.posters2frame.com

RICEDESIGN
The Barn, Shawbury Lane,
Shustoke, Nr Coleshill, B46 2RR
Area of Operation: Worldwide   **Tel:** 01675 481183
Email: ricedesigns@hotmail.com

TENTERDEN HOUSE INTERIORS
4 West Cross, Tenterden, Kent, TN30 6JL
Area of Operation: Worldwide
Tel: 01580 764481   **Fax:** 01580 765531
Email: tenterdenhouseinteriors@hotmail.com

THE ARTCROWD
Gascoyne House, Upper Borough Walls,
Bath, Somerset, BA1 1RN
Area of Operation: UK & Ireland
Tel: 01225 335842
Email: stevenc@theartcrowd.com
Web: www.theartcrowd.com ⌂

THINK ABSTRACT LTD
P.O.Box 718, Ipswich, Suffolk, IP1 9DT
Area of Operation: Worldwide
Tel: 0870 919 2590   **Email:** matt@thinkabstract.com
Web: www.thinkabstract.com

TIM PEEK WOODCARVING
The Woodcarving Studio, Highfield Avenue,
High Wycombe, Buckinghamshire, HP12 4ET
Area of Operation: UK (Excluding Ireland)
Tel: 01494 439629
Email: timpeekwoodcarving@hotmail.com
Web: www.timpeekwoodcarving.co.uk

LUXURY FITTINGS

KEY

PRODUCT TYPES: 1= Dumb Waiters
2 = Bars   3 = Gym Equipment   4 = Other
OTHER: ▽ Reclaimed   ⌂ On-line shopping
✎ Bespoke   ✋ Hand-made   ECO Ecological

ACADEMY BILLIARD COMPANY
5 Camphill Industrial Estate, Camphill Road,
West Byfleet, Surrey, KT14 6EW
Area of Operation: Worldwide
Tel: 01932 352067   **Fax:** 01932 353904
Email: academygames@fsbdial.co.uk
Web: www.games-room.com   **Product Type:** 4

ACHIEVE FITNESS EQUIPMENT LTD
14 Blackwell Business Park, Blackwell, Near
Shipston-On-Stour, Warwickshire, CV36 4PE
Area of Operation: UK (Excluding Ireland)
Tel: 01608 682191
Email: info@achieve-fitness.co.uk
Web: www.achieve-fitness.co.uk ⌂
Product Type: 3

B ROURKE & CO LTD
Vulcan Works, Accrington Road,
Burnley, Lancashire, BB11 5QD
Area of Operation: Worldwide
Tel: 01282 422841   **Fax:** 01282 458901
Email: info@rourkes.co.uk
Web: www.rourkes.co.uk
Product Type: 2

BROADWAY SPORTS
Units 17/18 HQ Building, 237 Union Street,
Stonehouse, Plymouth, Devon, PL1 3HQ
Area of Operation: UK (Excluding Ireland)
Tel: 01752 601400   **Fax:** 01752 601401
Email: info@thefitnessstore.co.uk
Web: www.thefitnessstore.co.uk
Product Type: 3

CHANTRY HOUSE OAK LTD
28 North Street, Chichester, West Sussex, PO20 2BT
Area of Operation: South East England
Tel: 01243 776811
Email: shop@chantryhouseoak.co.uk
Web: www.chantryhouseoak.co.uk

GRAYDEN ONLINE
16 Church Farm Close, Hoo,
Rochester, Kent, ME3 9AY
Tel: 01634 250483   **Fax:** 01634 250483
Email: gjb@grayden.co.uk
Web: www.grayden.co.uk ⌂
Product Type: 2

HARD ROCK FLOORING
Fleet Marston Farm, Fleet Marston, Aylesbury,
Buckinghamshire, HP18 0PZ
Area of Operation: Europe
Tel: 01296 658755   **Fax:** 01296 655735
Email: paul@hardrockflooring.co.uk
Web: www.hardrockflooring.co.uk
Product Type: 2

HOUSE OF CLOCKS
98 Dunstable Street, Ampthill,
Bedford, Bedfordshire, MK45 2JP
Area of Operation: Worldwide
Tel: 01525 403136
Product Type: 4

KASPAR SWANKEY
405 Goldhawk Road,
Hammersmith, West London, W6 0SA
Area of Operation: Worldwide
Tel: 020 8746 3586   **Fax:** 020 8746 3586
Email: kaspar@swankeypankey.com
Web: www.swankeypankey.com

QUENCH! HOME BARS
The Studio, 29 Woodham Way,
Woking, Surrey, GU21 5SJ
Area of Operation: Worldwide
Tel: 01483 740455   **Fax:** 01483 740244
Email: bars@quench.info   **Web:** www.quench.info
Product Type: 2

VINTAGEVIEW UK
16 Lower Park Road, New Southgate, London, N11 1QD
Tel: 0870 765 9225   **Fax:** 0870 705 2939
Email: info@vintageview.co.uk
Web: www.vintageview.co.uk ⌂
Product Type: 2

WILLIAM GARVEY
Leyhill, Payhembury, Honiton, Devon, EX14 3JG
Area of Operation: Worldwide
Tel: 01404 841430   **Fax:** 01404 841626
Email: webquery@williamgarvey.co.uk
Web: www.williamgarvey.co.uk
Product Type: 2, 4

NOTES

Company Name ....
....
Address ....
....
....
email ....
Web ....

Company Name ....
....
Address ....
....
email ....
Web ....

Company Name ....
....
Address ....
....
email ....
Web ....

Company Name ....
....
Address ....
....
email ....
Web ....

Company Name ....
....
Address ....
....
....
email ....
Web ....

EXTERIOR ARCHITECTURAL DETAIL

Image courtesy of Design & Materials (01909 540123)

EXTERIOR PRODUCTS

Chimneys

Most chimney pot patterns have evolved since their development in the late 18th century due to regional traditions and differing downdraught conditions. Since the last century, people made a feature of their chimneys, opting for grandiose and ornate designs. Fireplaces, and therefore chimneys, went out of fashion for a while, but have been enjoying a renaissance in recent years.

A chimney stack can add balance and detail to a house as well as providing the opportunity for a real fire or decorative gas alternative. Nowadays, chimney pots tend to be made from terracotta or fireclay, with red, buff or blue/black the most popular colours.

The chimney can also add an interesting dimension to your roof, with some people specially commissioning pertinent designs such as dragons or gargoyles, or simply duplicating the architecture of the house itself. It is possible to match chimney pots to ridge tiles and finials, with extremely fancy specials available. Bear in mind, however, that the most effective chimney is one positioned in the centre of a house which is straight and terminates in a straight-sided pot.

Different types of chimney pot or terminal include anti-down draught, square, H-type, octagonal, Scottish, Captain and Bishop. With hundreds of variations on the market it can be tricky choosing the right chimney. You can pay as much as £2,000 for a 6ft chimney but as little as £10 for a chimney from a pottery. Salvage yards can also be a good place to find a bargain. Try the Internet too – www.salvo.co.uk is a leading player in the web-based salvage market, and www.periodliving.co.uk has a useful product directory.

Before opting for you chimney, it would be wise to contact one of the few manufacturers left in the UK which have the technical services departments to help you decide which pot is most suitable for you.

The correct chimney pot or terminal is an essential component of a well constructed chimney system, as it minimises the effect of local turbulence that comes from the bulk of the chimney stack, and therefore reduces the possibility of water ingress.

Fitting

The pot should be built into the chimney stack to give an embedment of not less than 125mm, or one quarter of its length. A straight sided pot or terminal should be butt jointed to the flue liner, whilst a tapered pot

or terminal sits on the stack over the flue liner.

Calculations regarding chimneys, fireplace hearths, flue liners and pots are extremely complex and should be left to the experts – architects, builders and building inspectors. The pitch of the roof, wind pressure and suction patterns, all need to be taken into account, and will ultimately affect the size and shape of the pot you are able to choose.

WEATHERVANES, CLOCKS AND CLOCK TOWERS

KEY

PRODUCT TYPES: 1= Weathervanes
2 = Clocks   3 = Clock Towers

OTHER: ▽ Reclaimed ⌐🖑 On-line shopping

✏ Bespoke 🖑 Hand-made   ECO Ecological

ARCHITECTURAL HERITAGE
Taddington Manor, Taddington, Nr Cutsdean,
Cheltenham, Gloucestershire, GL54 5RY
Area of Operation: Worldwide
Tel: 01386 584414 **Fax:** 01386 584236
Email: puddy@architectural-heritage.co.uk
Web: www.architectural-heritage.co.uk

B ROURKE & CO LTD
Vulcan Works, Accrington Road,
Burnley, Lancashire, BB11 5QD
Area of Operation: Worldwide
Tel: 01282 422841 **Fax:** 01282 458901
Email: info@rourkes.co.uk
Web: www.rourkes.co.uk **Product Type:** 1, 3

C.J.BLACKSMITHS
Yr Eithin, Llangynog, Oswestry, Powys, SY100HA
Area of Operation: Worldwide
Tel: 01691 860750 **Fax:** 01691 860750
Email: sales@cjblacksmiths.co.uk ⌐🖑
Web: www.cjblacksmiths.co.uk/
www.thecastironemporium.co.uk
Product Type: 1 **Other Info:** ▽ ✏ 🖑
Material Type: C) 2, 3, 4, 5, 6, 7, 8, 12, 17

CASTAWAY CAST PRODUCTS AND WOODWARE
Brocklesby Station, Brocklesby Road,
Ulceby, Lincolnshire, DN39 6ST
Area of Operation: Worldwide
Tel: 01469 588995 **Fax:** 01469 588995
Email: castawaycastproducts@btinternet.com
Product Type: 1, 3 **Other Info:** ✏ 🖑
Material Type: C) 1, 2, 4, 5, 6, 7, 11, 12, 16

CHRIS TOPP & COMPANY WROUGHT IRONWORKS
Lyndhurst, Carlton Husthwaite,
Thirsk, North Yorkshire, YO7 2BJ
Area of Operation: Worldwide
Tel: 01845 501415 **Fax:** 01845 501072
Email: enquiry@christopp.co.uk
Web: www.christopp.co.uk
Product Type: 1, 3 **Other Info:** ✏ 🖑
Material Type: C) 2, 3, 4, 5, 6, 7, 11, 12, 17

GLASSWORK
73 Victor Road, Teddington, Middlesex, TW11 8SP
Area of Operation: UK (Excluding Ireland)
Tel: 0208 943 3177
Email: michaelwnewby@yahoo.com
Web: www.glassworkteddington.co.uk
Product Type: 1 **Other Info:** ✏ 🖑
Material Type: C) 8, 11

GOOD DIRECTIONS LTD
8 Bottings Industrial Estate, Hilltons Road,
Botley, Southampton, Hampshire, SO30 2DY
Area of Operation: UK & Ireland
Tel: 01489 797773 **Fax:** 01489 796700
Email: office@good-directions.co.uk
Web: www.good-directions.co.uk
Product Type: 1, 2, 3 **Material Type:** C) 3, 7

GRP STRUCTURES LIMITED
Fitzherbert Road, Farlington,
Portsmouth, Hampshire, PO6 1RU
Area of Operation: East England, Greater London,
Midlands & Mid Wales, South East England, South
West England and South Wales
Tel: 023 9238 4921 **Fax:** 023 9221 0716
Email: david@grpstructures.com
Web: www.grpstructures.com **Product Type:** 1, 2, 3
Other Info: ✏ 🖑 **Material Type:** D) 6

HADDONCRAFT FORGE
The Forge House, East Haddon,
Northampton, Northamptonshire, NN6 8DB
Area of Operation: UK & Ireland
Tel: 01604 772027 **Fax:** 01604 770027
Email: info@haddoncraft.co.uk
Web: www.haddoncraft.co.uk
Product Type: 1 **Other Info:** ✏ 🖑
Material Type: C) 2, 4

HARRISON THOMPSON & CO. LTD (YEOMAN RAINGUARD)
Yeoman House, Whitehall Estate,
Whitehall Road, Leeds, West Yorkshire, LS12 5JB
Area of Operation: UK & Ireland
Tel: 0113 279 5854 **Fax:** 0113 231 0406
Email: info@rainguard.co.uk
Web: www.rainguard.co.uk **Product Type:** 3

HAWKINS CLOCK COMPANY
PO Box 39, Market Deeping,
Peterborough, Cambridgeshire, PE6 8XQ
Area of Operation: Worldwide
Tel: 01733 330222 **Fax:** 01733 333700
Email: sales@hawkinsclocks.co.uk
Web: www.hawkinsclocks.co.uk
Product Type: 1, 2, 3

HAWKINS CLOCK CO

Area of Operation: Worldwide
Tel: 01733 330222 **Fax:** 01733 333700
Email: sales@hawkinsclocks.co.uk
Web: www.hawkinsclocks.co.uk
Product Type: 1, 2, 3 **Other Info:** ⌐🖑

Bespoke or standard clocks, clock towers and
pillar clocks for any building. Design, installation
and renovation service available.

J G S METALWORK
Unit 6, Broomstick Estate, High Street,
Edlesborough, Dunstable, Bedfordshire, LU6 2HS
Area of Operation: UK (Excluding Ireland)
Tel: 01525 220360 **Fax:** 01525 222786
Email: enquiries@jgsmetalwork.co.uk
Web: www.jgsmetalwork.co.uk **Product Type:** 1

JANKOWSKI WEATHERVANES, FOUNTAINS, SIGNS & GARDEN ART
Bryn Melyn, Llanwddyn, Oswestry, Powys, SY10 0LP
Area of Operation: Worldwide
Tel: 01691 870311
Email: stan@panjankowski.co.uk
Web: www.panjankowski.co.uk
Product Type: 1 **Material Type:** C) 7, 11, 12, 16

JGS METALWORK
Unit 6 Broomstick Estate, High Street,
Edlesborough, Dunstable, Bedfordshire, LU6 2HS
Area of Operation: East England
Tel: 01525 220360 **Fax:** 01525 222786
Email: enquiries@jgsmetalwork.co.uk
Web: www.jgsmetalwork.co.uk **Product Type:** 1

ST. GILES WEATHERVANES
Station Approach, Melksham, Wiltshire, SN12 8DB
Area of Operation: UK & Ireland
Tel: 01225 707466 **Fax:** 01225 704241
Email: rphillips@novacast.co.uk
Web: www.stgilesweathervanes.com ⌐🖑
Product Type: 1

WESSEX BUILDING PRODUCTS (MULTITEX)
Dolphin Industrial Estate, Southampton Road,
Salisbury, Wiltshire, SP1 2NB
Area of Operation: UK & Ireland
Tel: 01722 332139
Fax: 01722 338458
Email: sales@wessexbuildingproducts.co.uk
Web: www.wessexbuildingproducts.co.uk
Product Type: 1, 2, 3 **Material Type:** D) 6

TURRETS AND CUPOLAS

KEY

PRODUCT TYPES: 1= Turrets   2 = Cupolas
OTHER: ▽ Reclaimed ⌐🖑 On-line shopping
✏ Bespoke 🖑 Hand-made   ECO Ecological

C.J.BLACKSMITHS
Yr Eithin, Lllangynog, Oswestry, Powys, SY100HA
Area of Operation: Worldwide
Tel: 01691 860750
Fax: 01691 860750
Email: sales@cjblacksmiths.co.uk
Web: www.cjblacksmiths.co.uk/
www.thecastironemporium.co.uk ⌐🖑

CHILSTONE
Victoria Park, Fordcombe Road,
Langton Green, Kent, TN3 0RD
Area of Operation: Worldwide
Tel: 01892 740 866 **Fax:** 01892 740 249
Email: ornaments@chilstone.com
Web: www.chilstone.com ⌐🖑
Material Type: E) 13

GOOD DIRECTIONS LTD
8 Bottings Industrial Estate, Hilltons Road,
Botley, Southampton, Hampshire, SO30 2DY
Area of Operation: UK & Ireland
Tel: 01489 797773
Fax: 01489 796700
Email: office@good-directions.co.uk
Web: www.good-directions.co.uk
Product Type: 1, 2 **Material Type:** D) 6

GRP STRUCTURES LIMITED
Fitzherbert Road, Farlington,
Portsmouth, Hampshire , PO6 1RU
Area of Operation: East England, Greater London,
Midlands & Mid Wales, South East England, South
West England and South Wales
Tel: 023 9238 4921 **Fax:** 023 9221 0716
Email: david@grpstructures.com
Web: www.grpstructures.com **Product Type:** 1, 2
Other Info: ✏ 🖑 **Material Type:** D) 6

HARRISON THOMPSON & CO. LTD (YEOMAN RAINGUARD)
Yeoman House, Whitehall Estate,
Whitehall Road, Leeds, West Yorkshire, LS12 5JB
Area of Operation: UK & Ireland
Tel: 0113 279 5854 **Fax:** 0113 231 0406
Email: info@rainguard.co.uk
Web: www.rainguard.co.uk
Product Type: 1

HAWKINS CLOCK COMPANY
PO Box 39, Market Deeping,
Peterborough, Cambridgeshire, PE6 8XQ
Area of Operation: Worldwide
Tel: 01733 330222
Fax: 01733 333700
Email: sales@hawkinsclocks.co.uk
Web: www.hawkinsclocks.co.uk
Product Type: 1, 2

KIRK NATURAL STONE
Bridgend, Fyvie, Turriff, Aberdeenshire, AB53 8LL
Area of Operation: Worldwide
Tel: 01651 891891
Fax: 01651 891794
Email: info@kirknaturalstone.com
Web: www.kirknaturalstone.com

ORCHARD STONEMASONS
48 West Street, Axbridge, Somerset, BS26 2AD
Area of Operation: UK (Excluding Ireland)
Tel: 01934 732718
Fax: 01934 732718
Email: info@orchardstonemasons.co.uk
Web: www.orchardstonemasons.co.uk

WESSEX BUILDING PRODUCTS (MULTITEX)
Dolphin Industrial Estate, Southampton Road,
Salisbury, Wiltshire, SP1 2NB
Area of Operation: UK & Ireland
Tel: 01722 332139 **Fax:** 01722 338458
Email: sales@wessexbuildingproducts.co.uk
Web: www.wessexbuildingproducts.co.uk
Product Type: 1, 2 **Material Type:** D) 6

PORCHES, PORTICOS, CANOPIES AND AWNINGS

KEY

OTHER: ▽ Reclaimed ⌐🖑 On-line shopping
✏ Bespoke 🖑 Hand-made   ECO Ecological

ARC-COMP
Friedrichstr. 3, 12205 Berlin-Lichterfelde, Germany
Area of Operation: Europe
Tel: +49 (0)308 430 9956
Fax: +49 (0)308 430 9957
Email: jvs@arc-comp.com
Web: www.arc-com.com **Material Type:** C) 1, 3

ARC-COMP (IRISH BRANCH)
Whitefield Cottage, Lugduff,
Tinahely, Co. Wicklow, Republic of Ireland
Area of Operation: Europe
Tel: +353 (0)868 729 945 **Fax:** +353 (0)402 28900
Email: jvs@arc-comp.com
Web: www.arc-comp.com **Material Type:** C) 1, 3

ARUNDEL STONE LTD
62 Aldwick Road, Bognor Regis, West Sussex, PO21 2PE
Area of Operation: Greater London, South East England
Tel: 01243 829151 **Fax:** 01243 860341
Email: sales@arundelstone.co.uk
Web: www.arundelstone.co.uk **Other Info:** ✏ 🖑

ASPECTS OF STONE LTD
Unit 29, Broughton Grounds, Broughton,
Newport Pagnell, Buckinghamshire, MK16 0HZ
Area of Operation: UK (Excluding Ireland)
Tel: 01908 830061 **Fax:** 01908 830062
Email: sales@aspectsofstone.co.uk
Web: www.aspectsofstone.co.uk

ASSOCIATED PLASTIC COMPONENTS
Unit 5, Kingston International Business Park,
Somerdon Road, Hedon Road, Hull,
East Riding of Yorks, HU9 5PE
Area of Operation: UK & Ireland
Tel: 01482 783631 **Fax:** 01482 783292
Email: sales@apcmouldings.co.uk
Web: www.apcmouldings.co.uk

BALMORAL BLINDS
Beresford Close, Frimley Green,
Camberley, Surrey, GU16 6LB
Area of Operation: Greater London, South East England
Tel: 01252 674172
Fax: 0870 132 7683
Email: sales@balmoralblinds.co.uk
Web: www.balmoralblinds.co.uk

BORDER CONCRETE PRODUCTS
Jedburgh Road, Kelso, Borders, TD5 8JG
Area of Operation: North East England, North West
England and North Wales, Scotland
Tel: 01573 224393
Fax: 01573 276360
Email: sales@borderconcrete.co.uk
Web: www.borderconcrete.co.uk
Other Info: ✏ 🖑

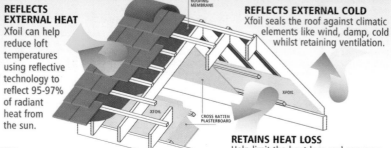

CAMBRIDGE MASONRY LTD
Station Road, Longstanton,
Nr Cambridge, Cambridgeshire, CB4 5FB
Area of Operation: East England, Greater London, Midlands & Mid Wales, South East England, South West England and South Wales
Tel: 01954 261907 **Fax:** 01954 260847
Email: coling@cambridgemasonry.co.uk
Web: www.cambridgemasonry.co.uk
Material Type: E) 5

CANOPIES SOUTH WEST
The Shop, 2 Roman Road, Taunton, Somerset, TA1 2BD
Area of Operation: UK (Excluding Ireland)
Tel: 01823 254843 **Fax:** 01823 254844
Email: sales@canopiessouthwest.co.uk
Web: www.canopiessouthwest.co.uk ⌁

CANOPIES UK
Whipps Mill, Richmond Terrace,
Darwin, Lancashire, BB3 0DR
Area of Operation: Worldwide
Tel: 01254 777002 **Fax:** 01254 775747
Email: info@canopiesuk.co.uk
Web: www.canopiesuk.co.uk

CANOPY PRODUCTS LTD
Paradise Works, Paradise Street,
Ramsbottom, Greater Manchester, BL0 9BS
Area of Operation: Europe
Tel: 01706 822665 **Fax:** 01706 823333
Email: sales@canopyproducts.co.uk
Web: www.canopyproducts.co.uk
Other Info: ⌁ ✋ **Material Type:** B) 8, 10

CHILSTONE
Victoria Park, Fordcombe Road,
Langton Green, Kent, TN3 0RD
Tel: 01892 740 866 **Fax:** 01892 740 249
Email: ornaments@chilstone.com
Web: www.chilstone.com ⌁ **Material Type:** E) 13

FLAMINGO BLINDS & FABRICS
12 Chaseville Parade, Chaseville Park Road,
Winchmore Hill, London, N21 1PG
Area of Operation: East England, Greater London, Midlands & Mid Wales, South East England
Tel: 0870 777 1665 **Fax:** 0208 245 8323
Email: admin@flamingoblinds.co.uk
Web: www.flamingoblinds.co.uk ⌁

GARDEN OASIS LIMITED
Garden Oasis, 3 Caradoc, Glascote,
Tamworth, Staffordshire, B77 2DX
Tel: 01827 706110 **Fax:** 01827 706110
Email: sales@gardenoasis.co.uk
Web: www.gardenoasis.co.uk ⌁

GARDEN REQUISITES
Budleigh House, 307 London Road East,
Batheaston, Bath, Somerset, BA1 7RL
Area of Operation: Worldwide
Tel: 01225 851577 **Fax:** 01225 859908
Email: info@garden-requisites.co.uk
Web: www.garden-requisites.co.uk
Other Info: ⌁ ✋ **Material Type:** C) 2, 3, 4, 7, 9

GEMINI BLINDS & AWNINGS (GLOUCESTER) LTD
Unit 16, St James Trading Estate,
280, Barton Street, Gloucester,
Gloucestershire, GL1 4JJ
Area of Operation: Midlands & Mid Wales
Tel: 01452 546814
Fax: 01452 546814
Email: derek@gemini-blindsawnings.co.uk
Web: www.gemini-blindsawnings.co.uk ⌁

GEORGE WOODS
4D Yeo Vale Industrial Estate,
Lapford, Crediton, Devon, EX17 6YQ
Area of Operation: Worldwide
Tel: 01363 884218
Fax: 01363 884128
Email: georgewoods@tiscali.co.uk
Web: www.georgewoods.co.uk

GLASSWORK
73 Victor Road, Teddington, Middlesex, TW11 8SP
Area of Operation: UK (Excluding Ireland)
Tel: 0208 943 3177
Email: michaelwlnewby@yahoo.com
Web: www.glassworkteddington.co.uk
Other Info: ⌁ ✋
Material Type: J) 1, 3, 4, 5, 6

GRANT MERCER
PO Box 246, Banstead, Surrey, SM7 3LE
Area of Operation: Europe
Tel: 01737 357957
Fax: 01737 373003
Email: grantmercer@shuttersuk.co.uk
Web: www.shuttersuk.com

GRP STRUCTURES LIMITED
Fitzherbert Road, Farlington,
Portsmouth, Hampshire, PO6 1RU
Area of Operation: East England, Greater London, Midlands & Mid Wales, South East England, South West England and South Wales
Tel: 023 9238 4921
Fax: 023 9221 0716
Email: david@grpstructures.com
Web: www.grpstructures.com
Other Info: ⌁ ✋ **Material Type:** D) 6

HADDONSTONE LTD
The Forge House, East Haddon,
Northampton, Northamptonshire, NN6 8DB
Area of Operation: Worldwide
Tel: 01604 770711 **Fax:** 01604 770027
Email: info@haddonstone.co.uk
Web: www.haddonstone.com ⌁

HADDONSTONE
Area of Operation: Worldwide
Tel: 01604 770711 **Fax:** 01604 770027
Email: info@haddonstone.co.uk
Web: www.haddonstone.com
Other Info: ⌁ ✋ ⌁

Haddonstone has an extensive range of columns, half columns, pilasters and entablatures to create porticos, door surrounds and porches to meet individual design requirements.

HICKS SHARP & CO.
Grange Close, Milton Ernest,
Bedfordshire, MK44 1RR
Area of Operation: Worldwide
Tel: 01234 822843
Fax: 01234 822843
Email: tom@hickssharp.freeserve.co.uk
Web: www.perioddoorfurniture.com ⌁

INTERLAND TRADING LTD
9 Eversden Close, Toft, Cambridgeshire, CB3 7RS
Area of Operation: UK & Ireland
Tel: 01223 265598
Fax: 01223 265673
Email: mail@interland-trading.co.uk
Web: www.interland-trading.co.uk

KENT BALUSTERS
1 Gravesend Road, Strood, Kent, ME2 3PH
Area of Operation: UK (Excluding Ireland)
Tel: 01634 711617 **Fax:** 01634 714644
Email: info@kentbalusters.co.uk
Web: www.kentbalusters.co.uk
Other Info: ⌁ ✋ **Material Type:** E) 13

KIRK NATURAL STONE
Bridgend, Fyvie, Turriff, Aberdeenshire, AB53 8LL
Area of Operation: Worldwide
Tel: 01651 891891 **Fax:** 01651 891794
Email: info@kirknaturalstone.com
Web: www.kirknaturalstone.com

MARKILUX (UK) LTD
4 Chantry Court, Sovereign Way,
Chester, Cheshire, CH1 4QN
Area of Operation: Worldwide
Tel: 01244 394 209 **Fax:** 01244 394 210
Email: markilux.uk@markilux.com
Web: www.markilux.com **Other Info:** ⌁

MEADOWSTONE (DERBYSHIRE) LTD
West Way, Somercotes, Derbyshire, DE55 4QJ
Area of Operation: UK & Ireland
Tel: 01773 540707 **Fax:** 01773 527261
Email: info@meadowstone.co.uk
Web: www.meadowstone.co.uk ⌁ **Other Info:** ⌁ ✋

NEW WORLD DEVELOPMENTS LTD
Woodside Road Industrial Estate,
Ballymena, BT42 4HX
Area of Operation: UK & Ireland
Tel: 028256 32200 **Fax:** 028256 59334
Email: linda.tomb@nwd.uk.com
Web: www.nwd.uk.com
Other Info: ⌁ **Material Type:** D) 1, 6

OCTAVEWARD LIMITED
Balle Street, Darwen, Lancashire, BB3 2AZ
Tel: 01254 773300 **Fax:** 01254 773950
Email: info@octaveward.com
Web: www.octaveward.com

OLDE WORLDE OAK JOINERY LTD
Unit 12, Longford Industrial Estate,
Longford Road, Cannock, Staffordshire, WS11 0DG
Area of Operation: Europe
Tel: 01543 469328 **Fax:** 01543 469328
Email: sales@oldeworldeoakjoinery.co.uk
Web: www.oldeworldeoakjoinery.co.uk

ORCHARD STONEMASONS
48 West Street, Axbridge, Somerset, BS26 2AD
Area of Operation: UK (Excluding Ireland)
Tel: 01934 732718 **Fax:** 01934 732718
Email: info@orchardstonemasons.co.uk
Web: www.orchardstonemasons.co.uk

PENNINE STONE LTD
Askern Road, Carcroft, Doncaster, DN6 8DH
Tel: 01302 729277 **Fax:** 01302 729288
Email: info@penninestone.co.uk
Web: www.penninestone.co.uk **Material Type:** G) 1

EXTERIOR PRODUCTS

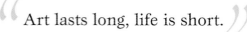

ROUNDWOOD CONSTRUCTION LTD
The Packhouse, Cryals Farm,
Cryals Road, Matfield, Kent, TN12 7HN
Area of Operation: Europe
Tel: 0800 328 3847 **Fax:** 01892 725416
Email: mary@roundwoodconstruction.com
Web: www.roundwoodconstruction.com

SBI LTD
85c Beckenham Lane, Shortlands,
Bromley, Kent, BR2 0DN
Area of Operation: South East England
Tel: 0800 0742 721 **Fax:** 01634 670354
Email: mail@sbiukltd.co.uk
Web: www.sbiukltd.co.uk
Material Type: D) 3, 5, 6

SIMPLY SHUTTERS LTD
Unit 2A Station Way, Brandon, Suffolk, IP27 0BH
Area of Operation: Europe
Tel: 01842 814260 **Fax:** 01842 814460
Email: sales@simplyshutters.co.uk
Web: www.simplyshutters.co.uk
Material Type: D) 1

STEVENSONS OF NORWICH LIMITED
Roundtree Way, Norwich, Norfolk, NR7 8SQ
Area of Operation: Worldwide
Tel: 01603 400824 **Fax:** 01603 405113
Email: info@stevensons-of-norwich.co.uk
Web: www.stevensons-of-norwich.co.uk

SUPERIOR FASCIAS
Adelaide House, Portsmouth Road, Lowford,
Southampton, Hampshire, SO31 8EQ
Area of Operation: South East England, South West
England and South Wales
Tel: 0700 596 4603 **Fax:** 0700 596 4609
Email: info@superiorfascias.co.uk
Web: www.superiorfascias.co.uk

THE HOME & GARDEN CENTRE
Benfield ATT Group, Castle Way,
Caldicot, Monmouthshire, NP26 5PR
Area of Operation: UK (Excluding Ireland)
Tel: 01291 437062
Fax: 01291 437051
Email: info@homegardenshop.co.uk
Web: www.home-garden-centre.co.uk

THE PAST RE-CAST LIMITED
Mere House, Harleston Road,
Dickleburgh, Diss, Kent, IP21 4PD
Area of Operation: UK & Ireland
Tel: 01379 741381
Fax: 01379 741534
Email: sales@thepastrecast.com
Web: www.thepastrecast.com
Material Type: C) 1

UC BLINDS
1150 Stratford Road, Hall Green,
Birmingham, West Midlands, B28 8AF
Area of Operation: UK (Excluding Ireland)
Tel: 0800 026 9394
Fax: 0121 777 3143
Email: ben@ucblinds.co.uk
Web: www.ucblinds.co.uk

UK AWNINGS
8-10 Ruxley Lane, Ewell, Surrey, KT19 0JD
Area of Operation: East England, Greater London,
Midlands & Mid Wales, North East England, North
West England and North Wales, South East England,
South West England and South Wales
Tel: 0800 071 8888
Email: info@uk-awnings.com
Web: www.uk-awnings.com

VOUSTONE DESIGNS LIMITED.
Kingdom Cottage, Tibbs Court Lane,
Brenchley, Nr. Tonbridge, Kent, TN12 7AH
Area of Operation: UK (Excluding Ireland)
Tel: 01892 722449
Fax: 01892 722573
Email: sales@voustone.co.uk
Web: www.voustone.co.uk
Material Type: E) 13

WARMSWORTH STONE LTD
1-3 Sheffield Road, Warmsworth,
Doncaster, South Yorkshire, DN4 9QH
Area of Operation: UK & Ireland
Tel: 01302 858617
Fax: 01302 855844
Email: info@warmsworth-stone.co.uk
Web: www.warmsworth-stone.co.uk
Other Info: ✏ 👜   **Material Type:** E) 4, 5

WESSEX BUILDING PRODUCTS (MULTITEX)
Dolphin Industrial Estate, Southampton Road,
Salisbury, Wiltshire, SP1 2NB
Area of Operation: UK & Ireland
Tel: 01722 332139
Fax: 01722 338458
Email: sales@wessexbuildingproducts.co.uk
Web: www.wessexbuildingproducts.co.uk
Material Type: D) 6

WHITE VILLA LIMITED
23 Orion Business Center,
Surrey Canal Road, London, SE14 5RT
Area of Operation: UK (Excluding Ireland)
Tel: 0207 237 8000 **Fax:** 0207 237 8621
Web: whitevilla@aol.com

CHIMNEYS

KEY
OTHER: ▽ Reclaimed 🖱 On-line shopping
✏ Bespoke ✋ Hand-made ECO Ecological

ANKI CHIMNEY SYSTEMS
Bishops Way, Newport, Isle of Wight, PO30 5WS
Area of Operation: UK (Excluding Ireland)
Tel: 01983 527997 **Fax:** 01983 537788
Email: anki@ajwells.co.uk
Web: www.anki.co.uk

BORDER CONCRETE PRODUCTS
Jedburgh Road, Kelso, Borders, TD5 8JG
Area of Operation: North East England, North West
England and North Wales, Scotland
Tel: 01573 224393 **Fax:** 01573 276360
Email: sales@borderconcrete.co.uk
Web: www.borderconcrete.co.uk
Other Info: ✏ ✋

CAWARDEN BRICK & TILE CO. LTD
Cawarden Springs Farm, Blithbury Road,
Rugeley, Staffordshire, WS15 3HL
Area of Operation: UK (Excluding Ireland)
Tel: 01889 574066 **Fax:** 01889 575695
Email: home-garden@cawardenreclaim.co.uk
Web: www.cawardenreclaim.co.uk

GRP STRUCTURES LIMITED
Fitzherbert Road, Farlington,
Portsmouth, Hampshire, PO6 1RU
Area of Operation: East England, Greater London,
Midlands & Mid Wales, South East England, South
West England and South Wales
Tel: 023 9238 4921 **Fax:** 023 9221 0716
Email: david@grpstructures.com
Web: www.grpstructures.com **Other Info:** ECO ✏ ✋

**HANSON RED BANK
MANUFACTURING COMPANY LIMITED**
Measham, Swadlincote, Derbyshire, DE12 7EL
Area of Operation: UK & Ireland
Tel: 01530 270333 **Fax:** 01530 273667
Email: sales@redbankmfg.co.uk
Web: www.redbankmfg.co.uk

**NUMBER 9 STUDIO UK
ARCHITECTURAL CERAMICS**
Mole Cottage Industries, Mole Cottage, Watertown,
Chittlehamholt, Devon, EX37 9HF
Area of Operation: Worldwide
Tel: 01769 540471 **Fax:** 01769 540471
Email: arch.ceramics@moley.uk.com
Web: www.moley.uk.com

ORCHARD STONEMASONS
48 West Street, Axbridge, Somerset, BS26 2AD
Area of Operation: UK (Excluding Ireland)
Tel: 01934 732718
Fax: 01934 732718
Email: info@orchardstonemasons.co.uk
Web: www.orchardstonemasons.co.uk

ROBERT AAGAARD & CO
Frogmire House, Stockwell Road,
Knaresborough, North Yorkshire, HG5 0JP
Area of Operation: UK (Excluding Ireland)
Tel: 01423 864805 **Fax:** 01423 869356
Email: info@robertaagaard.co.uk
Web: www.robertaagaard.co.uk

ROOFDRAGON.COM
Battlesbridge Antique Centre, Motling Road,
Battlesbridge, Essex, SS11 7RF
Area of Operation: UK & Ireland
Tel: 07717 055530
Email: colin@roofdragon.com
Web: www.roofdragon.com
Other Info: ▽

SCHIEDEL ISOKERN
14 Haviland Road, Ferndown Industrial Estate,
Wimborne, Dorset, BH21 7RF
Area of Operation: UK & Ireland
Tel: 01202 861650 **Fax:** 01202 861632
Email: sales@isokern.co.uk
Web: www.isokern.co.uk

STOVES ON LINE LTD
Capton, Dartmouth, Devon, TQ6 0JE
Area of Operation: UK (Excluding Ireland)
Tel: 0845 226 5754
Fax: 0870 220 0920
Email: info@stovesonline.com
Web: www.stovesonline.co.uk

THE CHIMNEY POT SHOP
Unit 41 Birch Road East Industrial Estate,
Witton, Birmingham, West Midlands, B6 7DA
Area of Operation: Worldwide
Tel: 0121 3277776
Email: info@thechimneypotshop.com
Web: www.thechimneypotshop.com

THE EXPANDED METAL COMPANY LIMITED
PO Box 14, Longhill Industrial Estate (North),
Hartlepool, Durham, TS25 1PR
Area of Operation: Worldwide
Tel: 01429 867388
Fax: 01429 866795
Email: paulb@expamet.co.uk
Web: www.expandedmetalcompany.co.uk

WESSEX BUILDING PRODUCTS (MULTITEX)
Dolphin Industrial Estate, Southampton Road,
Salisbury, Wiltshire, SP1 2NB
Area of Operation: UK & Ireland
Tel: 01722 332139
Fax: 01722 338458
Email: sales@wessexbuildingproducts.co.uk
Web: www.wessexbuildingproducts.co.uk

NOTES

Company Name ....

Address ....

email ....
Web ....

Company Name ....

Address ....

email ....
Web ....

Company Name ....

Address ....

email ....
Web ....

Company Name ....

Address ....

email ....
Web ....

Company Name ....

Address ....

email ....
Web ....

Company Name ....

Address ....

email ....
Web ....

Company Name ....

Address ....

email ....
Web ....

Company Name ....

Address ....

email ....
Web ....

Company Name ....

Address ....

email ....
Web ....

Company Name ....

Address ....

email ....
Web ....

Company Name ....

Address ....

email ....
Web ....

Company Name ....

Address ....

email ....
Web ....

EXTERIOR PRODUCTS

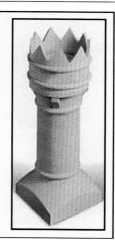

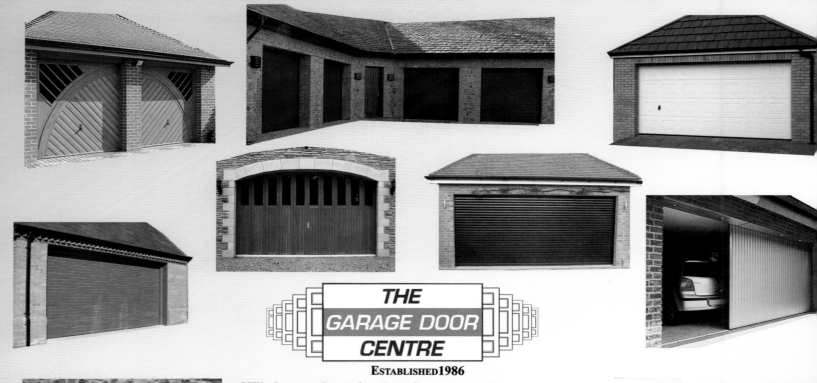

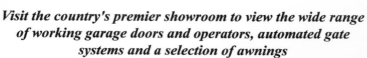

Image courtesy of Gliderol Garage & Industrial Doors (0191 518 0455)

EXTERIOR PRODUCTS

SPONSORED BY GLIDEROL GARAGE & INDUSTRIAL DOORS LTD
Tel 0191 518 0455 Web www.gliderol.co.uk

GLIDEROL
GARAGE &
INDUSTRIAL
DOORS LTD

Garages & Garden Buildings

In designing your overall project, you need to consider what other structures are required besides the main house. Garaging for the car might be top of most people's wish lists and, whilst it is not absolutely necessary, and is a sizeable expense (the structure costing almost as much per m² as the house does), it can often add as much in value to your house price.

The bulk of the cost involved in building a garage, is in many cases, purely aesthetic. The garage is usually located at the front of the property, so the same brick and roof tiles will be used as on the main house, with extra being spent installing an attractive garage door.

However, whereas a commercial developer has to build the garage at the same time as the house, the self-builder can afford to take a more relaxed approach. Provided the details of the garage are included with the original planning consent, you can choose to build the structure in your own good time (although bear in mind that you will not be able to reclaim VAT if you leave it until afterwards.) Against this, many builders actually choose to build their garage first, to provide a secure storage area from which to manage the rest of the project.

With structures such as sheds and summerhouses, you can afford to take a more leisurely approach. The planning regulations allow you to erect any sort of structure without permission (providing it doesn't constitute a separate dwelling), as long as:

• It is no higher than 4m (3m with a flat roof)

• It covers less than 50% of the garden area

• It is further away from the highway than the main building (or at least 20m away).

(Note however, that special rules apply within conservation areas, in the setting of Listed Buildings, or if the Permitted Development Rights have been expressly removed by the planners for any reason).

To bring more structure to your garden, gazebos, summerhouses and pergolas form an attractive feature as well as a focal point to view from the house – essential for a new garden where plants will take time to establish themselves. Beware though, for however attractive these structures may look in their own right, they may well appear out of place in a bare garden. It is far better to go for something that has a practical purpose, and looks good among the plants too.

Garden building – the home office

Already two million of us work from home, and that figure looks set to increase as technology

Image by B&Q

enables us to work remotely. But creating a home office usually means losing a room in your house.

The alternative is to have a designated garden building, which saves interior space and provides a real differentiation between your home and your work space.

A garden office or workshop can also increase the value of your property. But a garden office should never look overbearing and take over your outdoor space. To improve the building's look, you can screen it with trees and shrubs. Also, make sure the building doesn't take up more than a quarter of your garden.

You may also want to consider your neighbours, as they may object if the room blocks their light or overlooks their property. Contact the local planning office for advice – they may request sketches with dimensions, showing the projected location in the garden. The council will usually let you know within two weeks whether you will require planning permission or not.

It is also worth remembering that timber cabins are considered to be temporary structures, and therefore you will not require building regulations approval if you choose to build in this manner. And remember that garden rooms are easy targets for thieves, so always ensure that you adopt appropriate security measures.

Image by Amdega

GARAGES AND CARPORTS

KEY
OTHER: ▽ Reclaimed   ✋ On-line shopping
✎ Bespoke   ✋ Hand-made   ECO Ecological

ACE MINIMIX
Millfields Road, Ettingshall,
Wolverhampton, West Midlands, WV4 6JP
Area of Operation: UK (Excluding Ireland)
Tel: 0121 5855559   **Fax:** 0121 585 5557
Email: info@tarmac.co.uk
Web: www.tarmac.co.uk

ASSOCIATED PLASTIC COMPONENTS
Unit 5, Kingston International Business Park,
Somerdon Road, Hedon Road, Hull,
East Riding of Yorks, HU9 5PE
Area of Operation: UK & Ireland
Tel: 01482 783631
Fax: 01482 783292
Email: sales@apcmouldings.co.uk
Web: www.apcmouldings.co.uk

BEAVER TIMBER COMPANY
Barcaldine, Argyll & Bute, PA37 1SG
Area of Operation: UK (Excluding Ireland)
Tel: 01631 720353   **Fax:** 01631 720430
Email: info@beavertimber.co.uk
Web: www.beavertimber.co.uk ✋

CANOPIES SOUTH WEST
The Shop, 2 Roman Road, Taunton, Somerset, TA1 2BD
Area of Operation: UK (Excluding Ireland)
Tel: 01823 254843
Fax: 01823 254844
Email: sales@canopiessouthwest.co.uk
Web: www.canopiessouthwest.co.uk ✋

CEDAR SELF-BUILD HOMES
Unit A2 , Abbey Close,
Redwither Business Park, Wrexham, LL13 9XG
Area of Operation: Europe
Tel: 01978 664709   **Fax:** 01978 664596
Email: info@cedar-self-build.com
Web: www.cedar-self-build.com

COMPTON BUILDINGS LTD
Station Works, Fenny Compton,
Southam, Warwickshire, CV47 2XB
Area of Operation: UK & Ireland
Tel: 0800 975 8860   **Fax:** 01295 770748
Email: sales@compton-buildings.co.uk
Web: www.comptonbuildings.co.uk **Other Info:** ✎

DENCROFT GARAGES LTD
230 Bradford Road, Batley, West Yorkshire, WF17 6JD
Area of Operation: UK (Excluding Ireland)
Tel: 01924 461996   **Fax:** 01924 465157
Email: phil.denton@btclick.com
Web: www.dencroftgarages.co.uk

EASYGATES
Unit 4 Broadcott Industrial Estate, Station Road,
Cradley Heath, Birmingham, West Midlands, B64 6NT
Area of Operation: Europe
Tel: 0845 054 5070   **Fax:** 0121 561 3395
Email: info@easygates.co.uk
Web: www.easygates.co.uk

ENGLISH HERITAGE BUILDINGS
Coldharbour Farm Estate,
Woods Corner, East Sussex, TN21 9LQ
Area of Operation: Europe
Tel: 01424 838643   **Fax:** 01424 838606
Email: info@ehbp.co.uk   **Web:** www.ehbp.com

GARDEN AFFAIRS LTD
Trowbridge Garden Centre, 288 Frome Road,
Trowbridge, Wiltshire, BA14 0DT
Area of Operation: UK (Excluding Ireland)
Tel: 01225 470372   **Fax:** 01225 442855
Email: sales@gardenaffairs.co.uk
Web: www.gardenaffairs.co.uk

HOUSE - UK
347 Leverington Common, Leverington,
Wisbech, Cambridgeshire, P13 5JR
Area of Operation: UK (Excluding Ireland)
Tel: 01945 410361   **Fax:** 01945 419038
Email: enquiries@house-uk.co.uk
Web: www.house-uk.co.uk

OSMO UK LTD
Unit 24 Anglo Business Park, Smeaton Close,
Aylesbury, Buckinghamshire, HP19 8UP
Area of Operation: UK & Ireland
Tel: 01296 481220   **Fax:** 01296 424090
Email: info@osmouk.com   **Web:** www.osmouk.com

ROUNDWOOD CONSTRUCTION LTD
The Packhouse, Cryals Farm,
Cryals Road, Matfield, Kent, TN12 7HN
Area of Operation: Europe
Tel: 0800 328 3847   **Fax:** 01892 725416
Email: mary@roundwoodconstruction.com
Web: www.roundwoodconstruction.com

SBI LTD
85c Beckenham Lane,
Shortlands, Bromley, Kent, BR2 0DN
Area of Operation: South East England
Tel: 0800 0742 721   **Fax:** 01634 670354
Email: mail@sbiukltd.co.uk
Web: www.sbiukltd.co.uk   **Other Info:** ✎

SCOTTS OF THRAPSTON LTD.
Bridge Street, Thrapston, Northamptonshire, NN14 4LR
Area of Operation: UK & Ireland
Tel: 01832 732366   **Fax:** 01832 733703
Email: julia@scottsofthrapston.co.uk
Web: www.scottsofthrapston.co.uk

THE HOME & GARDEN CENTRE
Benfield ATT Group, Castle Way,
Caldicot, Monmouthshire, NP26 5PR
Area of Operation: UK (Excluding Ireland)
Tel: 01291 437062   **Fax:** 01291 437051
Email: info@homegardenshop.co.uk
Web: www.home-garden-centre.co.uk ✋

THE LOG CABIN COMPANY
Potash Garden Centre, 9 Main Road,
Hockley , Hawkwell, Essex, SS5 4JN
Area of Operation: UK (Excluding Ireland)
Tel: 01702 206012
Email: sales@thelogcabincompany.co.uk
Web: www.thelogcabincompany.co.uk

TOWNSEND TRADITION
Parham Park, Pulborough, West Sussex, RH20 4HS
Area of Operation: UK (Excluding Ireland)
Tel: 01903 745 559
Email: enquiries@townsendtradition.com
Web: www.townsendtradition.com

GARAGE DOORS

KEY
PRODUCT TYPES: 1= Automatic   2 = Roller
3 = Sectional   4 = Barn Style   5 = Other
OTHER: ▽ Reclaimed   ✋ On-line shopping
✎ Bespoke   ✋ Hand-made   ECO Ecological

A.S.K. SUPPLIES LIMITED
5 Stretton Close, Bridgnorth, Shropshire, WV16 5DB
Area of Operation: UK (Excluding Ireland)
Tel: 01746 768164   **Fax:** 01746 766835
Email: sales@asksupplies.co.uk
Web: www.asksupplies.co.uk   **Product Type:** 2

AMOURELLE PRODUCTS LTD
8 Ambleside Close, Woodley,
Reading, Berkshire, RG5 4JJ
Area of Operation: UK & Ireland
Tel: 0118 969 4657   **Fax:** 0118 962 8682
Email: nick@amourelle.co.uk
Web: www.garage-door-automation.co.uk ✋
Product Type: 1

ARRIDGE GARAGE DOORS LTD
68-70 Roft Street, Oswestry, Shropshire, SY11 2EP
Area of Operation: UK (Excluding Ireland)
Tel: 01691 670394
Email: info@garagedoor.uk.com
Web: www.discount-garage-doors.co.uk ✋

ARRIDGE GARAGE DOORS LTD

Area of Operation: UK (Excluding Ireland)
Tel: 01691 670394
Email: info@garagedoor.uk.com
Web: www.discount-garage-doors.co.uk ✋

Arridge Garage Doors Ltd., Est.1989 specialises in the supply only of top brand garage doors and remote controls at big discounts. Nationwide delivery. Clear fitting instructions with all doors and remote control units.

B ROURKE & CO LTD
Vulcan Works, Accrington Road,
Burnley, Lancashire, BB11 5QD
Area of Operation: Worldwide
Tel: 01282 422841   **Fax:** 01282 458901
Email: info@rourkes.co.uk
Web: www.rourkes.co.uk   **Product Type:** 1, 2

CARDALE DOORS LTD
Farm Road, Buckingham Road Industrial Estate,
Brackley, Northamptonshire, NN13 7EA
Area of Operation: Europe
Tel: 01280 703022   **Fax:** 01280 701138
Email: enquiries@cardale.co.uk
Web: www.cardale.com   **Product Type:** 1, 2, 3, 4, 5

CENTURION
Westhill Business Park, Arnhall Business Park,
Westhill, Aberdeen, Aberdeenshire, AB32 6UF
Area of Operation: Scotland
Tel: 01224 744440
Fax: 01224 744819
Email: info@centurion-solutions.co.uk
Web: www.centurion-solutions.co.uk

CLEVELAND UP & OVER DOOR CO.
7 Metcalfe Road, Skippers Lane Industrial Estate,
Middlesbrough, North Yorkshire, TS6 6PT
Area of Operation: North East England
Tel: 01642 440920
Fax: 01642 456106
Email: enquiries@clevelandupover.co.uk
Web: www.clevelandupover.co.uk
Product Type: 1, 2, 3, 5

DISCOUNT GARAGE DOORS LTD
68-70 Roft Street, Oswestry, Shropshire, SY11 2EP
Area of Operation: UK (Excluding Ireland)
Tel: 01691 670394
Email: info@garagedoor.uk.com
Web: www.discount-garage-doors.co.uk ✋
Product Type: 1, 2, 3, 4, 5

DYNASTY DOORS
Unit 3, The Micro Centre,
Gillette Way, Reading, Berkshire, RG2 0LR
Area of Operation: South East England, South West England and South Wales
Tel: 0118 987 4000   **Fax:** 0118 921 2999
Email: info@dynastydoors.co.uk
Web: www.dynastydoors.co.uk
Product Type: 1, 2, 3, 4

ARRIDGE GARAGE DOORS LTD
68-70 Roft Street, Oswestry, Shropshire, SY11 2EP
Area of Operation: UK (Excluding Ireland)
Tel: 01691 670394
Email: info@garagedoor.uk.com
Web: www.discount-garage-doors.co.uk ✋

EASYGATES
Unit 4 Broadcott Industrial Estate, Station Road,
Cradley Heath, Birmingham, West Midlands, B64 6NT
Area of Operation: UK & Ireland
Tel: 0845 054 5070   **Fax:** 0121 561 3395
Email: info@easygates.co.uk
Web: www.easygates.co.uk   **Product Type:** 1

ENGELS WINDOWS & DOORS LTD
1 Kingley Centre, Downs Road, West Stoke,
Chichester, West Sussex, PO18 9HJ
Tel: 01243 576633   **Fax:** 01243 576644
Email: admin@engels.co.uk
Web: www.engels.co.uk

EVEREST LTD
Sopers Road, Cuffley, Hertfordshire, EN6 4SG
Area of Operation: UK & Ireland
Tel: 0800 010123   **Web:** www.everest.co.uk ✋
Product Type: 1, 2

GARADOR LTD
Bunford Lane, Yeovil, Somerset, BA20 2YA
Area of Operation: UK (Excluding Ireland)
Tel: 01935 443700   **Fax:** 01935 443744
Email: sally.howell@garador.co.uk
Web: www.garador.co.uk   **Product Type:** 1, 3, 4

GARAGE DOORS (NORTHERN) LTD
Aspden Street, Bamber Bridge,
Preston, Lancashire, PR5 6TL
Area of Operation: North West England and North Wales
Tel: 01772 334828   **Fax:** 01772 627877
Email: post@garagedoorslancs.co.uk
Web: www.garagedoorslancs.co.uk
Product Type: 1, 2, 3, 4, 5

GLIDEROL GARAGE & INDUSTRIAL DOORS LIMITED
Davy Drive, North West Industrial Estate,
Peterlee, Durham, SR8 2JF
Area of Operation: UK (Excluding Ireland)
Tel: 0191 5180455   **Fax:** 0191 5180548
Email: peternewton@gliderol.co.uk
Web: www.gliderol.co.uk   **Product Type:** 1, 2

GLIDEROL GARAGE & INDUSTRIAL DOORS LTD

Area of Operation: UK (Excluding Ireland)
Tel: 0800 834 250   **Fax:** 0191 518 0548
Email: info@gliderol.co.uk
Web: www.gliderol.co.uk
Product Type: 1, 2

Easy to use, space saving, reliable, quiet, secure, low maintenance, manual and automatic garage doors available in a wide range of colours. Smartens your home and your driveway.

HORMANN (UK) LTD
Gee Road, Coalville, Leicestershire, LE67 4JW
Area of Operation: Europe
Tel: 01530 513 055   **Fax:** 01530 513 051
Email: marketing.lei@hormann.co.uk
Web: www.hormann.co.uk

JELD-WEN
Watch House Lane, Doncaster,
South Yorkshire, DN5 9LR
Area of Operation: UK & Ireland
Tel: 0870 126 0000   **Fax:** 01302 787383
Email: customer-services@jeld-wen.co.uk
Web: www.jeld-wen.co.uk

GLIDEROL
GARAGE & INDUSTRIAL DOORS LTD
GlideRol-a-Door®

it's so easy...
so quiet, and oh, so practical

Easy to use - space saving - reliable - secure
low maintenance - manual & automatic
smartens your home & your driveway

For sales & enquiries contact

Freephone 0800 834 250

Available in a wide range of colours

Gliderol Garage & Industrial Doors Ltd. Davy Drive, North West Ind. Est., Peterlee, Co. Durham SR8 2JF. Fax: 0191 518 0548 • E-Mail: info@gliderol.co.uk

GLIDEROL ... THE SMOOTHEST SOUNDING GARAGE DOORS

MERIDIAN GARAGE DOORS
Building 237, Matchams Lane Entrance,
Bournemouth International Airport,
Christchurch, Dorset, BH23 6NE
Area of Operation: UK (Excluding Ireland)
Tel: 01202 577440 **Fax:** 01202 577449
Email: info@meridian-garage-doors.co.uk
Web: www.meridian-garage-doors.co.uk
Product Type: 1, 3, 5

P C HENDERSON LTD
Durham Road, Bowburn, Durham, DH6 5NG
Area of Operation: UK & Ireland
Tel: 0191 377 0701 **Fax:** 0191 377 0855
Email: marketing@pchenderson.com
Web: www.pchenderson.com **Product Type:** 1, 2, 3

PARAMOUNT GARAGE DOORS NORTH WEST
47 Pelham Street, Guide Bridge,
Ashton Under Lyne, Tameside, Lancashire, OL7 0DT
Area of Operation: North West England and North Wales
Tel: 0800 211 8139 **Fax:** 01613 437964
Email: sales@paramountgaragedoors-nw.co.uk
Web: www.paramountgaragedoors-nw.co.uk
Product Type: 1, 2, 3, 4, 5

PREMIER GARAGE DOORS AND GATES
Unit 7 Sparrowhall Business Park, Leighton Road,
Edlesborough, Dunstable, Bedfordshire, LU6 2ES
Area of Operation: East England, South East England
Tel: 01525 220212 **Fax:** 01525 222201
Email: sales@premiergaragedoors.co.uk
Web: www.premiergaragedoors.co.uk

PROGRESSIVE SYSTEMS UK
The White House, Downfield,
Stroud, Gloucestershire, GL5 4HJ
Area of Operation: UK & Ireland
Tel: 01453 762262 **Fax:** 01453 764693
Email: info@progressive-systems.co.uk
Web: www.progressive-systems.co.uk
Product Type: 1, 2 **Other Info:** ✍

RO-DOR LIMITED
Stevens Drove, Houghton,
Stockbridge, Hampshire, SO20 6LP
Area of Operation: UK & Ireland
Tel: 01794 388080 **Fax:** 01794 388090
Email: info@ro-dor.co.uk **Web:** www.ro-dor.co.uk
Product Type: 1, 2, 3, 5 **Other Info:** ✍ ✋

RUNDUM MEIR
1 Trouthbeck Road, Liverpool, Merseyside, L18 3LF
Area of Operation: UK (Excluding Ireland)
Tel: 0151 280 6626 **Fax:** 0151 737 2504
Email: info@rundum.co.uk
Web: www.rundum.co.uk **Product Type:** 1

SBI LTD
85c Beckenham Lane,
Shortlands, Bromley, Kent, BR2 0DN
Area of Operation: South East England
Tel: 0800 0742 721 **Fax:** 01634 670354
Email: mail@sbiukltd.co.uk
Web: www.sbiukltd.co.uk
Product Type: 1, 2 **Other Info:** ✍

SILVELOX
South Street, Ossett, Wakefield,
West Yorkshire, WF5 8LE
Area of Operation: UK & Ireland
Tel: 0800 915 1019 **Fax:** 01924 277453
Email: pat@silvelox.co.uk **Web:** www.silvelox.co.uk

SWS UK
Claughton, Lancaster, Lancashire, LA2 9LA
Area of Operation: UK & Ireland
Tel: 01524 772400 **Fax:** 01524 772411
Email: info@swsuk.co.uk
Web: www.swsuk.co.uk ⌒ **Product Type:** 1

THE GARAGE DOOR CENTRE
Head Office & Main Showroom,
6-8 Meadow Close, Finedon Road,
Wellingborough, Northamptonshire, NN8 4BH
Area of Operation: UK (Excluding Ireland)
Tel: 0800 525442 **Fax:** 01933 442676
Email: enquiries@dovegroup.co.uk
Web: www.thegaragedoorcentre.co.uk

URBAN FRONT LTD
Design Studio, 1 Little Hill, Heronsgate,
Rickmansworth, Hertfordshire, WD3 5BX
Area of Operation: UK & Ireland
Tel: 0870 609 1525 **Fax:** 0870 609 3564
Email: info@urbanfront.co.uk
Web: www.urbanfront.co.uk

WAYNE-DALTON UK
Unit 17, Redbank Court, Redbank, Manchester, M4 4HF
Area of Operation: UK & Ireland
Tel: 0870 754 1660
Fax: 0870 754 1661
Email: eric@waynedalton.co.uk
Web: www.waynedaltoneurope.com
Product Type: 1, 3, 5 **Other Info:** ECO ✍ ✋

WM SHUTTERS LTD
Unit 4 Springhill Trading Estate,
Aston Street, Shifnal, Telford, Shropshire, TF11 8DR
Area of Operation: UK & Ireland
Tel: 01952 272269 **Fax:** 01952 272331
Email: sales@wmshutters.com
Web: www.wmshutters.com
Product Type: 1, 2, 3, 5 **Other Info:** ECO ✍ ✋

GARDEN BUILDINGS

KEY

PRODUCT TYPES: 1= Gazebos   2 = Pergolas
3 = Summerhouses
OTHER: ▽ Reclaimed   ⌒ On-line shopping
✍ Bespoke   ✋ Hand-made   ECO Ecological

AEGEAN SPAS & HOT TUBS
The Aegean National Spa & Hot Tub Centre, 2 Hale
Lane, Mill Hill, London, NW7 3NX
Area of Operation: UK (Excluding Ireland)
Tel: 0208 959 1529 **Fax:** 0208 906 0511
Web: www.tubstore.com ⌒ **Product Type:** 1

ALTHAM OAK & CARPENTRY LTD
Altham Corn Mill, Burnley Road,
Altham, Accrington, Lancashire, BB5 5UP
Area of Operation: UK & Ireland
Tel: 01282 771618
Fax: 01282 777932
Email: info@oak-beams.co.uk
Web: www.oak-beams.co.uk
Product Type: 1, 2 **Other Info:** ECO ✍ ✋

AMDEGA CONSERVATORIES
Woodside, Church Lane, Bursledon,
Southampton, Hampshire, SO31 8AB
Area of Operation: Worldwide
Tel: 0800 591523 **Product Type:** 3
Web: www.amdega-conservatories.co.uk

ARON GREENWOOD
5 Providence Close, Wetherell Road,
Hackney, London, E9 7DS
Area of Operation: East England, Greater London
Tel: 07790 026539
Email: atullgreenwood@yahoo.co.uk
Web: www.atullgreenwood.co.uk
Product Type: 1, 2

BEAVER TIMBER COMPANY
Barcaldine, Argyll & Bute, PA37 1SG
Area of Operation: UK (Excluding Ireland)
Tel: 01631 720353 **Fax:** 01631 720430
Email: info@beavertimber.co.uk
Web: www.beavertimber.co.uk ⌒
Product Type: 3

CANOPIES SOUTH WEST
The Shop, 2 Roman Road, Taunton, Somerset, TA1 2BD
Area of Operation: UK (Excluding Ireland)
Tel: 01823 254843
Fax: 01823 254844
Email: sales@canopiessouthwest.co.uk
Web: www.canopiessouthwest.co.uk ⌒
Product Type: 1, 2

CEDAR NURSERY
Horsley Road, Cobham, Surrey, KT11 3JX
Area of Operation: UK & Ireland
Tel: 01932 862473 **Fax:** 01932 867152
Email: sales@landscaping.co.uk
Web: www.landscaping.co.uk **Product Type:** 1, 3

CEDAR SELF-BUILD HOMES
Unit A2, Abbey Close,
Redwither Business Park, Wrexham, LL13 9XG
Area of Operation: Europe
Tel: 01978 664709 **Fax:** 01978 664596
Email: info@cedar-self-build.com
Web: www.cedar-self-build.com **Product Type:** 3

CHARLES PEARCE LTD
26 Woodstock Road, London, W4 1UF
Area of Operation: Worldwide
Tel: 0208 995 3333
Email: enquiries@charlespearce.co.uk
Web: www.charlespearce.co.uk

COMPTON BUILDINGS LTD
Station Works, Fenny Compton,
Southam, Warwickshire, CV47 2XB
Area of Operation: UK & Ireland
Tel: 0800 975 8860 **Fax:** 01295 770748
Email: sales@compton-buildings.co.uk
Web: www.comptonbuildings.co.uk
Product Type: 3

EAST OF EDEN PLANTS
38 St Andrews Street, Millbrook,
Torpoint, Cornwall, PL10 1BE
Area of Operation: UK & Ireland
Tel: 01752 822782
Email: info@eastofedenplants.co.uk
Web: www.eastofedenplants.co.uk ⌒
Product Type: 1

ELWELL BUILDINGS LIMITED
Unit 5 Excelsior Industrial Estate, Cakemore Road,
Blackheath, West Midlands, B65 5SR
Area of Operation: UK & Ireland
Tel: 0121 561 5656 **Fax:** 0121 559 0505
Email: paul.clews@elwells.co.uk
Web: www.elwells.co.uk

ENGLISH HERITAGE BUILDINGS
Coldharbour Farm Estate,
Woods Corner, East Sussex, TN21 9LQ
Area of Operation: Europe
Tel: 01424 838643 **Fax:** 01424 838606
Email: info@ehbp.com **Web:** www.ehbp.com
Product Type: 1, 3

FOREST GARDEN
Units 291 & 296, Hartlebury Trading Estate,
Hartlebury, Worcestershire, DY10 4JB
Area of Operation: UK (Excluding Ireland)
Tel: 0870 300 9809 **Fax:** 0870 191 9888
Email: info@forestgarden.co.uk
Web: www.forestgarden.co.uk **Product Type:** 1, 2

G&T EVANS
Dulas Mill, Mochdre Lane, Newtown, Powys, SY16 4JD
Area of Operation: UK & Ireland
Tel: 01686 622 100 **Fax:** 01686 622 220
Email: gtevans1@aol.com
Web: www.gtevans.co.uk

GARDEN AFFAIRS LTD
Trowbridge Garden Centre, 288 Frome Road,
Trowbridge, Wiltshire, BA14 0DT
Area of Operation: UK (Excluding Ireland)
Tel: 01225 470372 **Fax:** 01225 442855
Email: sales@gardenaffairs.co.uk
Web: www.gardenaffairs.co.uk
Product Type: 1, 3, 5

GARDEN OASIS LIMITED
Garden Oasis, 3 Caradoc,
Glascote, Tamworth, Staffordshire, B77 2DX
Area of Operation: UK & Ireland
Tel: 01827 706110 **Fax:** 01827 706110
Email: sales@gardenoasis.co.uk
Web: www.gardenoasis.co.uk ⌒
Product Type: 1, 2, 3, 4

GEORGE BARKER & SONS
Backbarrow, Nr Ulverston, Cumbria, LA12 8TA
Area of Operation: UK (Excluding Ireland)
Tel: 01539 531236 **Fax:** 01539 530801
Web: www.gbs-ltd.co.uk

GREENFINGERS.COM
10 Lindsay Square, Deans Industrial Estate,
Livingston, Lothian, EH54 8RL
Area of Operation: UK (Excluding Ireland)
Tel: 0845 345 0728
Email: customer.services@greenfingers.com
Web: www.greenfingers.com ⌒
Product Type: 1, 2, 3, 4

HLD LTD
The Old Shipyard, Gainsborough, Lincolnshire, DN21 ING
Area of Operation: UK & Ireland
Tel: 01427 611800 **Fax:** 01427 612 867
Email: technical@hld.co.uk
Web: www.hld.co.uk **Product Type:** 1, 2

HOME & OFFICE
9 Mead Lane, Farnham, Surrey, GU9 7DY
Area of Operation: UK (Excluding Ireland)
Tel: 01252 820455
Email: info@homeandoffice.co.uk
Web: www.homeandoffice.co.uk **Product Type:** 5

HONEYSUCKLE BOTTOM SAWMILL LTD
Honeysuckle Bottom, Green Dene,
East Horsley, Leatherhead, Surrey, KT24 5TD
Area of Operation: Greater London, South East England
Tel: 01483 282394 **Fax:** 01483 282394
Email: honeysucklemill@aol.com
Web: www.easisites.co.uk/honeysucklebottomsawmill
Product Type: 1, 2

HOUSE - UK
347 Leverington Common, Leverington,
Wisbech, Cambridgeshire, P13 5JR
Area of Operation: UK (Excluding Ireland)
Tel: 01945 410361 **Fax:** 01945 419038
Email: enquiries@house-uk.co.uk
Web: www.house-uk.co.uk **Product Type:** 1, 3, 4, 5

HUT GARDEN STUDIOS
Unit 8b, Canford Business Park,
Magna Road, Wimborne, Dorset, BH21 3BT
Area of Operation: UK & Ireland
Tel: 01202 574584
Email: jonathan@hutdesign.co.uk
Web: www.hutdesign.co.uk **Product Type:** 5

INSIDEOUT BUILDINGS LTD
The Green, Over Kellet, Carnforth, Lancashire, LA6 1BU
Area of Operation: UK (Excluding Ireland)
Tel: 01524 737999
Email: lynn@iobuild.co.uk **Web:** www.iobuild.co.uk

JACKSONS FENCING
Stowting Common, Ashford, Kent, TN25 6BN
Area of Operation: UK & Ireland
Tel: 01233 750393 **Fax:** 01233 750403
Email: sales@jacksons-fencing.co.uk
Web: www.jacksons-fencing.co.uk
Product Type: 2

KELVA HOMES
Old Brightmoor Farm, Thornborough,
Buckinghamshire, MK18 3EA
Area of Operation: Europe
Tel: 01280 824787 **Fax:** 01280 824288
Email: kelvahomesk@aol.com **Product Type:** 3, 5

LLOYD CHRISTIE
Greystones, Sudbrook Lane, Petersham, TW10 7AT
Area of Operation: Worldwide
Tel: 020 8332 6766 **Fax:** 020 8332 2229
Email: info@lloydchristie.com
Web: www.lloydchristie.com **Product Type:** 1, 3

OSMO UK LTD
Unit 24 Anglo Business Park, Smeaton Close,
Aylesbury, Buckinghamshire, HP19 8UP
Area of Operation: UK & Ireland
Tel: 01296 481220 **Fax:** 01296 424090
Email: info@osmouk.com
Web: www.osmouk.com **Product Type:** 1, 2, 3

WM Shutters Ltd
Premier-roll

Made to measure insulated roller garage doors give space saving vertical operation which releases much needed storage space in the garage roof area, this enables you to park as close as possible to the door when closed. With exceptional thermal and acoustic properties the insulated Aluminium interlocking sections offer great benefits for integral garages.

Suppliers Of insulated Remote Control Garage Door Solutions
Micro-roll

On applications where headroom is at a premium the Micro-roll low headroom door can be installed, requiring only 205mm of headroom the Micro-roll. Utilising a specially roll-formed 55mm insulated profile section which enables the garage door to roll into the smaller headroom.
Available in 10 standard colour finishes with a choice of 3 optional textured foil finishes
Available with all the extended features as the Premier-roll

Contact our sales team for further information or demonstration
Tel: 01952 272269

t: 44 (0) 1952 272 269   e: sales@wmshutters.com
f: 44 (0) 1952 272 331   w: www.wmshutters.com

WM Shutters Ltd, Unit 4&6 Springhill Trading Estate, Aston Street, Shifnal, Shropshire, TF11 8DR

EXTERIOR PRODUCTS

PEPPERS FIREPLACE AND GARDEN CENTRE
70 Avenue Road, Bexley Heath, Kent, DA7 4EG
Area of Operation: UK (Excluding Ireland)
Tel: 0208 303 2195 **Fax:** 0208 301 1012
Email: sales@peppers.uk.com
Web: www.peppers.uk.com

RIVERSIDE DECKING COMPANY
4 Chauntry Mews, Chauntry Road,
Maidenhead, Berkshire, SL6 1TT
Area of Operation: Greater London, South East England
Tel: 01628 626545
Email: mklewis3@ukonline.co.uk
Web: www.riversidedeckingcompany.co.uk
Product Type: 2

ROUNDWOOD CONSTRUCTION LTD
The Packhouse, Cryals Farm,
Cryals Road, Matfield, Kent, TN12 7HN
Area of Operation: Europe
Tel: 0800 328 3847 **Fax:** 01892 725416
Email: mary@roundwoodconstruction.com
Web: www.roundwoodconstruction.com
Product Type: 1, 2, 3, 5

RUSTIC WOODLAND
Canterbury Road, Wingham, Canterbury, Kent, CT3 1NH
Area of Operation: UK (Excluding Ireland)
Tel: 0845 260 0876
Email: info@rusticwoodland.com
Web: www.rusticwoodland.com

SAPPHIRE SPAS HOT TUBS
A1 Rowood Estate, Murdock Road,
Bicester, Nr Oxford, Oxfordshire, OX26 4PP
Area of Operation: Worldwide
Tel: 01869 327698 **Fax:** 01869 369552
Email: info@sapphirespas.co.uk
Web: www.sapphirespas.co.uk **Product Type:** 1, 3

SCOTTS OF THRAPSTON LTD.
Bridge Street, Thrapston, Northamptonshire, NN14 4LR
Area of Operation: UK & Ireland
Tel: 01832 732366 **Fax:** 01832 733703
Email: julia@scottsofthrapston.co.uk
Web: www.scottsofthrapston.co.uk
Product Type: 1, 3 **Other Info:**

THE HOME & GARDEN CENTRE
Benfield ATT Group, Castle Way,
Caldicot, Monmouthshire, NP26 5PR
Area of Operation: UK (Excluding Ireland)
Tel: 01291 437062 **Fax:** 01291 437051
Email: info@homegardenshop.co.uk
Web: www.home-garden-centre.co.uk
Product Type: 1, 2, 3, 4

**THE INCREDIBILY SENSIBLE
GREENHOUSECOMPANY**
Trifford, Plasters Green,
Winford, North Somerset, BS40 8BH
Area of Operation: Europe
Tel: 01761 463102 **Fax:** 01761 463154
Email: enquiries@isgreenhouses.co.uk
Web: www.isgreenhouses.co.uk **Product Type:** 3, 4

THE LOG CABIN COMPANY
Potash Garden Centre, 9 Main Road,
Hockley , Hawkwell, Essex, SS5 4JN
Area of Operation: UK (Excluding Ireland)
Tel: 01702 206012 **Product Type:** 3
Email: sales@thelogcabincompany.co.uk
Web: www.thelogcabincompany.co.uk

THE OUTDOOR DECK COMPANY
Unit 6, Teddington Business Park,
Teddington, TW11 9BQ
Area of Operation: UK (Excluding Ireland)
Tel: 020 8977 0820 **Fax:** 020 8977 0825
Email: sales@outdoordeck.co.uk
Web: www.outdoordeck.co.uk **Product Type:** 1

THE PAST RE-CAST LIMITED
Mere House, Harleston Road,
Dickleburgh, Diss, Kent, IP21 4PD
Area of Operation: UK & Ireland
Tel: 01379 741381 **Fax:** 01379 741534
Email: sales@thepastrecast.com
Web: www.thepastrecast.com **Product Type:** 1, 2

THE TIMBER FRAME CO LTD
The Framing Yard, 7 Broadway,
Charlton Adam, Somerset, TA11 7BB
Area of Operation: Worldwide
Tel: 01458 224463 **Fax:** 01458 224571
Email: admin@thetimberframe.co.uk
Web: www.thetimberframe.co.uk
Product Type: 1, 2, 3 **Other Info:** ECO

TOWNSEND TRADITION
Parham Park, Pulborough, West Sussex, RH20 4HS
Area of Operation: UK (Excluding Ireland)
Tel: 01903 745 559
Web: www.townsendtradition.com
Product Type: 3, 5

TRADE CONSERVATORIES 2 U LTD
36 Temple Way, Maldon, Essex, CM9 4PX
Area of Operation: UK (Excluding Ireland)
Tel: 0845 130 3871 **Fax:** 0845 130 3872
Email: sales@tradeconservatories2u.co.uk
Web: www.tradeconservatories2u.co.uk
Product Type: 1, 2, 3, 5

NOTES

Company Name ....

....

Address ....

....

....

email ....

Web ....

Company Name ....

....

Address ....

....

....

email ....

Web ....

Company Name ....

....

Address ....

....

....

email ....

Web ....

Company Name ....

....

Address ....

....

....

email ....

Web ....

Company Name ....

....

Address ....

....

....

email ....

Web ....

Company Name ....

....

Address ....

....

....

email ....

Web ....

Company Name ....

....

Address ....

....

....

email ....

Web ....

Company Name ....

....

Address ....

....

....

email ....

Web ....

Company Name ....

....

Address ....

....

....

email ....

Web ....

Company Name ....

....

Address ....

....

....

email ....

Web ....

Image courtesy of Black Mountain Quarries Ltd (01981 241541)

EXTERIOR PRODUCTS

Hard Landscaping

Hard landscaping can play a crucial role in enhancing the style of your home. It will often be the visitor's first physical contact with your home, and can contribute to that elusive quality: 'kerb appeal'.

Using different patterns and varying the colour of paver will create interest, and also define areas, when block paving a driveway, patio or path. TOP LEFT by Wickes, and ABOVE by Black Mountain Quarries.
LEFT: Concrete is a relatively inexpensive option for a driveway, but bear in mind that concrete colours tend to fade after a few years. Image by Stonemarket.

Using an inappropriate surfacing material can undermine the character of an otherwise attractive home, and it is important to get a balance between appearance, functionality, cost, durability and maintenance.

Hard landscaped surfaces should be in harmony with the building. For instance, sharp-edged, rectangular paving blocks or flags may look out of keeping with a period-style home, whereas pavers that replicate the appearance of natural stone will complement such a setting. A driveway should also be fit for its intended function – supporting vehicles without spreading, cracking or subsiding.

Gravel and Decorative Stone

An attractive option, gravel is durable, easy to lay and makes a pleasant noise when walked on or driven over – a factor which could even help to deter intruders. However, it can be hard going for wheelchairs and prams, as well as being messy when it migrates to surrounding areas, which may require the installation of upstands to contain the spread. Gravel also has a habit of disappearing, so it may need topping up every few years.

Block Paving

Block paving has experienced phenomenal growth over recent years. It allows the creation of a highly attractive, durable surface, which can be installed by any competent DIY-er and

instantly adds to the perceived quality of a property.

The eye-catching appeal of real block paving is undeniable: its richness and complexity will transform the appearance of any setting. The wide range of colours, textures and shapes give greater scope for varied and interesting effects, and even dressed stone setts, cobbled surfaces and handmade bricks can be matched with ease.

Tarmac

Tarmac has a drab monotonous appearance that does little to enhance a dwelling, especially in winter when planting is less attractive. Maintenance is likely to be costly.

Paths and Patios

When it comes to drives, patios and paths around your home, you can't beat concrete

paving blocks and decorative paving slabs for good looks and real performance. Not only can you choose from a multitude of shapes, colours and finishes but these products can be laid in different patterns to provide just the right look for your home.

Footpaths, patios, steps and pool surrounds can be laid in flagstones, block pavers or a combination. Footpaths may require edge restraints which can be formed by an 80mm thick block laid into a 1:3 cement/sand mortar bed on a concrete haunching. A 10mm mortar joint will also be required between each edge restraint. Decorative flagstones can be mixed with block paving to create striking effects in garden landscaping.

Interpave

Interpave is a trade body comprising the leading manufacturers of precast concrete paving and kerbs. It exists to maintain the highest standards in product quality and to provide a wide range of technical and support services to assist users. It has published a Design Handbook for Precast Paving, a comprehensive 64-page guide which covers design, applications and all relevant British Standards. Website: www.interpave.org

EXTERIOR PRODUCTS

DECKING

KEY
OTHER: ▽ Reclaimed ✋ On-line shopping
🖋 Bespoke 🖐 Hand-made ECO Ecological

ARBORDECK
Lincoln Castle, Lincoln Castle Way, New Holland,
Barrow-upon-Humber, Lincolnshire, DN19 7RR
Area of Operation: UK (Excluding Ireland)
Tel: 0800 169 5275
Fax: 01469 535526
Email: enquiries@arbordeck.co.uk
Web: www.arbordeck.co.uk

ARON GREENWOOD
5 Providence Close, Wetherell Road,
Hackney, London, E9 7DS
Area of Operation: East England, Greater London
Tel: 07790 026539
Email: atullgreenwood@yahoo.co.uk
Web: www.atullgreenwood.co.uk **Other Info:** 🖋 🖐

BEAVER TIMBER COMPANY
Barcaldine, Argyll & Bute, PA37 1SG
Area of Operation: UK (Excluding Ireland)
Tel: 01631 720353 **Fax:** 01631 720430
Email: info@beavertimber.co.uk
Web: www.beavertimber.co.uk ✋

DALSOUPLE
Unit 1 Showground Road,
Bridgwater, Somerset, TA6 6AJ
Area of Operation: Worldwide
Tel: 01278 727733 **Fax:** 01278 727766
Email: info@dalsouple.com
Web: www.dalsouple.com **Other Info:** ▽ ECO 🖋

DECK-IT
Po Box 55, Chislehurst, Kent, BR7 6YE
Area of Operation: Greater London, South East England
Tel: 0208 467 9922 **Email:** michael@deck-it.com
Web: www.deck-it.com **Other Info:** ECO 🖋 🖐
Material Type: A) 12

DECKMASTERS UK LIMITED
The Outdoor Room, 266 Selsdon Road,
South Croydon, Surrey, CR2 7AA
Area of Operation: East England, Greater London,
South East England **Tel:** 08000 323325
Fax: 020 8681 4090
Email: deckmasters_limited@hotmail.com
Web: www.deckmasters.co.uk **Other Info:** 🖋

DECKOR TIMBER LTD
PO Box 296, Harrogate, North Yorkshire, HG1 5WE
Area of Operation: UK (Excluding Ireland)
Tel: 01423 527505 **Fax:** 01423 527505
Email: deckortimber@harrogate.com
Web: www.deckortimber.co.uk

DEVON HARDWOODS LTD
Dotton, Colaton Raleigh, Sidmouth, Devon, EX10 0JH
Area of Operation: South West England and South Wales
Tel: 01395 568991 **Fax:** 01395 567881
Email: sales@devonhardwoods.ltd.uk

ECOCHOICE TIMBER PRODUCTS
18 Charlton Lodge,
Temple Fortune Lane, London, NW11 7TY
Area of Operation: UK & Ireland
Tel: 0845 638 1340 **Fax:** 0870 286 3680
Email: info@ecochoice.co.uk
Web: www.ecochoice.co.uk **Other Info:** ECO 🖋

FOREST GARDEN
Units 291 & 296, Hartlebury Trading Estate,
Hartlebury, Worcestershire, DY10 4JB
Area of Operation: UK (Excluding Ireland)
Tel: 0870 300 9809 **Fax:** 0870 191 9888
Email: info@forestgarden.co.uk
Web: www.forestgarden.co.uk

G&T EVANS
Dulas Mill, Mochdre Lane,
Newtown, Powys, SY16 4JD
Area of Operation: UK & Ireland
Tel: 01686 622 100 **Fax:** 01686 622 220
Email: gtevans1@aol.com
Web: www.gtevans.co.uk

HLD LTD
The Old Shipyard, Gainsborough, Lincolnshire, DN21 ING
Area of Operation: UK & Ireland
Tel: 01427 611800 **Fax:** 01427 612 867
Email: technical@hld.co.uk **Web:** www.hld.co.uk

HONEYSUCKLE BOTTOM SAWMILL LTD
Honeysuckle Bottom, Green Dene,
East Horsley, Leatherhead, Surrey, KT24 5TD
Area of Operation: Greater London, South East England
Tel: 01483 282394 **Fax:** 01483 282394
Email: honeysucklemill@aol.com
Web: www.easisites.co.uk/honeysucklebottomsawmill

HOPPINGS SOFTWOOD PRODUCTS
The Woodyard, Epping Road,
Epping, Essex, CM16 6TT
Area of Operation: South East England
Tel: 01992 578877 **Fax:** 01992 563185
Email: sales@hoppings.co.uk
Web: www.hoppings.co.uk

JACKSONS FENCING
Stowting Common, Ashford, Kent, TN25 6BN
Area of Operation: UK & Ireland
Tel: 01233 750393 **Fax:** 01233 750403
Email: sales@jacksons-fencing.co.uk
Web: www.jacksons-fencing.co.uk

KIRK NATURAL STONE
Bridgend, Fyvie, Turriff, Aberdeenshire, AB53 8LL
Area of Operation: Worldwide
Tel: 01651 891891 **Fax:** 01651 891794
Email: info@kirknaturalstone.com
Web: www.kirknaturalstone.com

LAND SKILL PROPERTY
46 Ledger Lane, Outwood, West Yorkshire, WF1 2PH
Tel: 01924 826836 **Fax:** 01924 835174
Email: andrew@landskill.co.uk
Material Type: B) 10

LLOYD CHRISTIE
Greystones, Sudbrook Lane, Petersham, TW10 7AT
Area of Operation: Worldwide
Tel: 020 8332 6766 **Fax:** 020 8332 2229
Email: info@lloydchristie.com
Web: www.lloydchristie.com

PRIORY HARDWOODS LIMITED
Unit 57 Bowers Mill, Branch Road,
Barkisland, West Yorkshire, HX4 0AD
Area of Operation: UK (Excluding Ireland)
Tel: 01422 311 700 **Fax:** 01422 311 118
Email: info@prioryhardwoods.com
Web: www.prioryhardwoods.com

PRO DECK SOLUTIONS LTD
Deck House, 63 Brays Lane,
Coventry, Warwickshire, CV2 4DT
Area of Operation: UK (Excluding Ireland)
Tel: 024 7627 6563 **Fax:** 0871 661 5859
Email: info@prodecksolutions.co.uk
Web: www.prodecksolutions.co.uk

PURE PROJECTS
Repose Toi, Huberts Lane, Doyle Road,
St Peter Port, Guernsey, GY1 1RG
Area of Operation: Europe
Tel: 01481 730773 **Fax:** 01481 730773
Email: info@pure-projects.co.uk
Web: www.pure-projects.co.uk

RICHARD BURBIDGE LTD
Whittington Road, Oswestry, Shropshire, SY11 1HZ
Area of Operation: UK & Ireland
Tel: 01691 655131 **Fax:** 01691 659091
Email: info@richardburbidge.co.uk
Web: www.richardburbidge.co.uk

RIVERSIDE DECKING COMPANY
4 Chauntry Mews, Chauntry Road,
Maidenhead, Berkshire, SL6 1TT
Area of Operation: Greater London, South East England
Tel: 01628 626545
Email: mklewis3@ukonline.co.uk
Web: www.riversidedeckingcompany.co.uk

S.L. HARDWOODS
390 Sydenham Road, Croydon, Surrey, CR0 2EA
Area of Operation: UK (Excluding Ireland)
Tel: 0208 683 0292 **Fax:** 0208 683 0404
Email: info@slhardwoods.co.uk
Web: www.slhardwoods.co.uk

SASH UK LTD
Ferrymoor Way, Park Springs, Grimethorpe,
Barnsley, South Yorkshire, S72 7BN
Area of Operation: Worldwide
Tel: 01226 715619 **Fax:** 01226 719968
Email: mailbox@sashuk.com
Web: www.sashuk.com

STONES DEVELOPMENT (UK) LTD
Unit 2 Irradion House, Southdown Industrial Estate,
Harpenden, Hertfordshire, AL5 1PW
Area of Operation: Europe
Tel: 0800 121 8320 **Fax:** 01727 862009
Email: info@stonestimber.co.uk
Web: www.stonestimber.co.uk
Other Info: ▽ ECO

SUNNY ASPECTS LTD
36 Udney Park Road, Teddington,
Greater London, TW11 9BG
Area of Operation: Europe
Tel: 0208 977 4149
Email: info@sunnyaspects.co.uk
Web: www.sunnyaspects.com

THE DECKING COMPANY
Unit 7, Fall Bank Industrial Estate, Dodworth,
Barnsley, South Yorkshire, S75 3LS
Area of Operation: Worldwide
Tel: 01226 732555 **Fax:** 01226 732555
Email: metrofloorings@aol.com
Web: www.thedeckingcompany.co.uk
Material Type: B) 8, 13

THE ORIGINAL DECKING COMPANY LIMITED
69 Brieryhurst Road, Rookery, Kidsgrove,
Stoke-on-Trent, Staffordshire, ST7 4RZ
Area of Operation: UK (Excluding Ireland)
Tel: 0800 5874985 **Fax:** 01782 783816
Email: craig@originaldecking.co.uk
Web: www.originaldecking.co.uk
Other Info: 🖋 **Material Type:** A) 12

THE OUTDOOR DECK COMPANY
Unit 6, Teddington Business Park,
Teddington, TW11 9BQ
Area of Operation: UK (Excluding Ireland)
Tel: 020 8977 0820 **Fax:** 020 8977 0825
Email: sales@outdoordeck.co.uk
Web: www.outdoordeck.co.uk

THE ROUNDWOOD TIMBER COMPANY LTD
Roundwood, Newick Lane,
Mayfield, East Sussex, TN20 6RG
Area of Operation: UK & Ireland
Tel: 01435 867072 **Fax:** 01435 864708
Email: sales@roundwoodtimber.com
Web: www.roundwoodtimber.com ✋

TIMBER DECKING ASSOCIATION
5 Flemming Court, Castleford,
West Yorkshire, WF10 5HW
Area of Operation: Europe
Tel: 01977 558147 **Fax:** 01977 558247
Email: info@tda.org.uk **Web:** www.tda.org.uk

TIMELESS TIMBER DECKING
BSW Timber, Cargo, Carlisle, Cumbria, CA6 4BA
Area of Operation: UK (Excluding Ireland)
Tel: 01228 673366
Fax: 01228 673365
Email: timeless-timber@bsw.co.uk
Web: www.timeless-timber.co.uk
Material Type: B) 2

PAVING & DRIVEWAYS

KEY

PRODUCT TYPES: 1 = Paviers 2 = Slabs
3 = Cobbles 4 = Impressed Paving
5 = Gravel 6 = Edgings
OTHER: ▽ Reclaimed 🖱 On-line shopping
✎ Bespoke 🖑 Hand-made ECO Ecological

A D CALVERT ARCHITECTURAL STONE SUPPLIES LTD
Smithy Lane, Grove Square,
Leyburn, North Yorkshire, DL8 5DZ
Area of Operation: UK & Ireland
Tel: 01969 622515
Fax: 01969 624345
Email: stone@calverts.co.uk
Web: www.calverts.co.uk

ACE MINIMIX
Millfields Road, Ettingshall,
Wolverhampton, West Midlands, WV4 6JP
Area of Operation: UK (Excluding Ireland)
Tel: 0121 5855559
Fax: 0121 585 5557
Email: info@tarmac.co.uk
Web: www.tarmac.co.uk

ALISTAIR MACKINTOSH LTD
Bannerley Road, Garretts Green,
Birmingham, West Midlands, B33 0SL
Area of Operation: UK & Ireland
Tel: 0121 784 6800
Fax: 0121 789 7068
Email: info@alistairmackintosh.co.uk
Web: www.alistairmackintosh.co.uk
Product Type: 3, 6 **Material Type:** E) 5

ALLAN HARRIS & SONS LIMITED
Station Road, St. Georges,
Weston-Super-Mare, Somerset, BS22 7XN
Tel: 01934 511166 **Fax:** 01934 513066
Email: allanharrisslate@hotmail.com
Web: www.allanharrisslate.co.uk

ARON GREENWOOD
5 Providence Close, Wetherell Road,
Hackney, London, E9 7DS
Area of Operation: East England, Greater London
Tel: 07790 026539
Email: atullgreenwood@yahoo.co.uk
Web: www.atullgreenwood.co.uk
Product Type: 1, 2, 3, 5, 6 **Other Info:** ✎ 🖑

ART OUTSIDE
PO Box 513, Aylesbury, Buckinghamshire, HP22 6WJ
Area of Operation: Worldwide
Tel: 07813 881480 **Email:** emma@art-outside.com
Web: www.art-outside.com 🖱 **Other Info:** ✎

BAGGERIDGE BRICK
Fir Street, Sedgley, West Midlands, DY3 4AA
Area of Operation: Worldwide
Tel: 01902 880555 **Fax:** 01902 880432
Email: marketing@baggeridge.co.uk
Web: www.baggeridge.co.uk **Product Type:** 1, 3, 6

BINGLEY STONE
Cullingworth Mills, Cullingworth,
West Yorkshire, BD13 5AB
Tel: 01535 273813 **Email:** info@bingleystone.co.uk
Web: www.bingleystone.co.uk
Product Type: 1, 2, 6

BLACK MOUNTAIN QUARRIES LTD
Howton Court, Pontrilas, Herefordshire, HR2 0BG
Tel: 01981 241541
Email: info@blackmountainquarries.com
Web: www.blackmountainquarries.com 🖱
Product Type: 1, 2, 3, 6 **Other Info:** ECO 🖑
Material Type: E) 1, 3, 4, 5, 8

BLANC DE BIERGES
Eastrea Road, Whittlesey, Cambridgeshire, PE7 2AG
Area of Operation: Worldwide
Tel: 01733 202566 **Fax:** 01733 205405
Email: info@blancdebierges.com
Web: www.blancdebierges.com
Product Type: 1, 2, 3, 6 **Other Info:** ✎ 🖑

BLANC DE BIERGES
Area of Operation: Worldwide
Tel: 01733 202566
Fax: 01733 205405
Email: info@blancdebierges.com
Web: www.blancdebierges.com
Product Type: 1, 2, 3, 6
Other Info: ✎ 🖑
An extensive range of handcrafted products for paths, steps, patios, planters, walls, pool edgings etc. The warm natural colour and lively textured surfaces harmonise with any surroundings. We can help you create your own individual design.

BRADSTONE GARDEN
Aggregate Industries UK Ltd, Hulland Ward,
Ashbourne, Derbyshire, DE6 3ET
Tel: 01335 372 222 **Fax:** 01335 370 973
Email: bradstone.garden@aggregate.com
Web: www.bradstone.com
Product Type: 1, 2, 3, 4, 5, 6 **Material Type:** E) 4, 13

BRETT LANDSCAPING LTD .
Salt Lane, Cliffe, Rochester, Kent, ME3 7SZ
Area of Operation: Worldwide
Tel: 01634 222188
Fax: 01634 222186
Email: cliffeenquiries@brett.co.uk
Web: www.brett.co.uk/landscaping
Product Type: 1, 2, 3, 4, 5, 6

BRICKABILITY
South Road, Bridgend Industrial Estate,
Bridgend, CF31 3XG
Area of Operation: UK (Excluding Ireland)
Tel: 01656 645222 **Fax:** 01656 665832
Email: enquiries@brickability.co.uk
Web: www.brickability.co.uk

BRIDGE STREET STONE LTD
The Old Gas Works Yard, Knotts Lane,
Colne, Lancashire, BB8 8AA
Area of Operation: UK & Ireland
Tel: 01282 860571
Fax: 01282 867446
Email: sales@stonepaving.co.uk
Web: www.stonepaving.co.uk

BRITISH TURNTABLE CO. LTD
Emblem Street, Bolton, Lancashire, BL3 5BW
Area of Operation: Worldwide
Tel: 01204 525626
Fax: 01204 382407
Email: info@turntable.co.uk
Web: www.british.turntable.co.uk 🖱

BRS YORK STONE
50 High Green Road, Altofts,
Normanton, Lancashire, WF6 2LQ
Area of Operation: UK (Excluding Ireland)
Tel: 01924 220356
Fax: 01924 220356
Email: john@york-stone.fsnet.co.uk
Web: www.yorkstonepaving.co.uk

EXTERIOR PRODUCTS

CAMBRIDGE MASONRY LTD
Station Road, Longstanton,
Nr Cambridge, Cambridgeshire, CB4 5FB
Area of Operation: East England, Greater London,
Midlands & Mid Wales, South East England, South
West England and South Wales
Tel: 01954 261907
Fax: 01954 260847
Email: coling@cambridgemasonry.co.uk
Web: www.cambridgemasonry.co.uk
Product Type: 2 **Material Type:** E) 4, 5

CAPITAL GROUP (M/CR) LIMITED
Victoria Mills, Highfield Road,
Little Hulton, Manchester, M38 9ST
Area of Operation: Worldwide
Tel: 0161 799 7555 **Fax:** 0161 799 7666
Email: leigh@choosecapital.co.uk
Web: www.choosecapital.co.uk ⌐🖰
Product Type: 1, 2, 3

CED LTD
728 London Road, West Thurrock,
Grays, Essex, RM20 3LU
Area of Operation: UK (Excluding Ireland)
Tel: 01708 867 237 **Email:** sales@ced.ltd.uk
Web: www.ced.ltd.uk **Product Type:** 1, 2, 3, 4, 5, 6
Material Type: E) 1, 2, 3, 4, 5, 6, 8, 9, 13

CEDAR NURSERY
Horsley Road, Cobham, Surrey, KT11 3JX
Area of Operation: Greater London, South East England
Tel: 01932 862473 **Fax:** 01932 867152
Email: sales@nidagravel.co.uk
Web: www.nidagravel.co.uk **Product Type:** 5

CHESHIRE BRICK & SLATE
Brook House Farm, Salters Bridge,
Tarvin Sands, Tarvin, Cheshire, CH3 8NR
Area of Operation: UK (Excluding Ireland)
Tel: 01829 740883
Fax: 01829 740481
Email: enquiries@cheshirebrickandslate.co.uk
Web: www.cheshirebrickandslate.co.uk
Product Type: 1, 2, 3, 5, 6

COLEFORD BRICK & TILE CO LTD
The Royal Forest of Dean Brickworks,
Cinderford, Gloucestershire, GL14 3JJ
Area of Operation: UK & Ireland
Tel: 01594 822160 **Fax:** 01594 826655
Email: sales@colefordbrick.co.uk
Web: www.colefordbrick.co.uk **Product Type:** 1, 6

COMER LANDSCAPES
Allistock Nurseries, Home Chapel Road,
Knutsford, Cheshire, WA16 9JZ
Area of Operation: UK (Excluding Ireland)
Tel: 0845 006 5555 **Fax:** 01565 723938
Email: info@comerlandscapes.co.uk
Web: www.cheshirelawns.co.uk **Product Type:** 5

DALSOUPLE
Unit 1 Showground Road,
Bridgwater, Somerset, TA6 6AJ
Area of Operation: Worldwide
Tel: 01278 727733 **Fax:** 01278 727766
Email: info@dalsouple.com
Web: www.dalsouple.com **Product Type:** 1
Other Info: ▽ ECO ✏

DENBY DALE CAST PRODUCTS LTD
230 Cumberworth Lane, Denby Dale,
Huddersfield, West Yorkshire, HD8 8PR
Area of Operation: UK & Ireland
Tel: 01484 863560
Fax: 01484 865597
Email: mail@denbydalecastproducts.co.uk
Web: www.denbydalecastproducts.co.uk
Product Type: 4, 6

DEVON STONE LTD
8 Pilot Road, Pierhead, Exmouth, Devon, EX8 1XA
Area of Operation: UK (Excluding Ireland)
Tel: 01395 222525
Email: amy@devonstone.com
Web: www.devonstone.com **Product Type:** 1, 2, 3, 6
Other Info: ▽ ✏ **Material Type:** E) 1, 3, 4

EVEREST LTD
Sopers Road, Cuffley, Hertfordshire, EN6 4SG
Area of Operation: UK & Ireland
Tel: 0800 010123 **Web:** www.everest.co.uk ⌐🖰

FARMINGTON NATURAL STONE
Northleach, Cheltenham, Gloucestershire, GL54 3NZ
Area of Operation: UK (Excluding Ireland)
Tel: 01451 860280 **Fax:** 01451 860115
Email: cotswold.stone@farmington.co.uk
Web: www.farmingtonnaturalstone.co.uk
Product Type: 1, 2, 3, 6

FRANCIS N. LOWE LTD.
The Marble Works, New Road,
Middleton, Matlock, Derbyshire, DE4 4NA
Area of Operation: Europe
Tel: 01629 822216 **Fax:** 01629 824348
Email: info@lowesmarble.com
Web: www.lowesmarble.com

FURNESS BRICK & TILE CO
Askam in Furness, Cumbria, LA16 7HF
Area of Operation: Worldwide
Tel: 01229 462411
Fax: 01229 462363
Email: furnessbrick@mac.com
Web: www.furnessbrick.com
Product Type: 1 **Material Type:** F) 1

GWRHYD SPECIALIST STONE QUARRY
Gwrhyd Road, Rhiwfawr, Swansea, Neath, SA9 2SB
Area of Operation: UK & Ireland
Tel: 01639 830743
Fax: 01639 830930
Email: enquiries@specialiststone.com
Web: www.specialiststone.com
Product Type: 1, 2, 3, 6
Other Info: ✏ **Material Type:** E) 4

HADDONSTONE LTD
The Forge House, East Haddon,
Northampton, Northamptonshire, NN6 8DB
Area of Operation: Worldwide
Tel: 01604 770711 **Fax:** 01604 770027
Email: info@haddonstone.co.uk
Web: www.haddonstone.com ⌐🖰

HAURATON LIMITED
Unit 4, Frenchs Avenue,
Dunstable, Bedfordshire, LU6 1BH
Area of Operation: UK & Ireland
Tel: 01582 501380 **Fax:** 01582 501393
Email: tim.connolly@hauraton.co.uk
Web: www.hauraton.co.uk

HYPERION TILES
67 High Street , Ascot, Berkshire, SL5 7HP
Area of Operation: Greater London, South East England
Tel: 01344 620211
Fax: 01344 620100
Email: graham@hyperiontiles.com
Web: www.hyperiontiles.com

IBSTOCK BRICK LTD
Leicester Road, Ibstock,
Leicester, Leicestershire, LE67 6HS
Area of Operation: UK & Ireland
Tel: 01530 261999
Fax: 01530 263478
Email: marketing@ibstock.co.uk
Web: www.ibstock.com **Product Type:** 1

INDIGENOUS LTD
Cheltenham Road, Burford, Oxfordshire, OX18 4JA
Area of Operation: Worldwide
Tel: 01993 824200
Fax: 01993 824300
Email: enquiries@indigenoustiles.com
Web: www.indigenoustiles.com
Product Type: 2 **Material Type:** E) 3, 4, 5, 8

KEYSTONE NATURAL STONE FLOORING
204 Duggins Lane, Tile Hill,
Coventry, West Midlands, CV4 9GP
Area of Operation: Worldwide
Tel: 02476 422580
Fax: 02476 695794

KIRK NATURAL STONE
Bridgend, Fyvie, Turriff, Aberdeenshire, AB53 8LL
Area of Operation: Worldwide
Tel: 01651 891891 **Fax:** 01651 891794
Email: info@kirknaturalstone.com
Web: www.kirknaturalstone.com
Product Type: 1, 2, 3, 5, 6

LAND SKILL PROPERTY
46 Ledger Lane, Outwood, West Yorkshire, WF1 2PH
Tel: 01924 826836 **Fax:** 01924 835174
Email: andrew@landskill.co.uk
Product Type: 1, 2, 3, 5, 6 **Material Type:** E) 4

LLOYD CHRISTIE
Greystones, Sudbrook Lane, Petersham, TW10 7AT
Area of Operation: Worldwide
Tel: 020 8332 6766 **Fax:** 020 8332 2229
Email: info@lloydchristie.com
Web: www.lloydchristie.com

MARSHALLS
Birkby Grange, Birkby Hall Road, Birkby,
Huddersfield, West Yorkshire, HD2 27A
Area of Operation: UK (Excluding Ireland)
Tel: 01422 306400 **Web:** www.marshalls.co.uk

MIDLANDS SLATE & TILE
Units 9-12, Star Industrial Estate,
Chadwell St Mary, Essex, RM16 4LR
Area of Operation: UK & Ireland
Tel: 0871 4743185
Fax: 01375 846478
Email: mark@slate-tile-brick.co.uk
Web: www.slate-tile-brick.co.uk
Product Type: 1, 2, 3 **Material Type:** E) 1, 3, 4, 5

NATURAL IMAGE (GRANITE, MARBLE, STONE)
Station Road, Staplehurst, Kent, TN12 0QD
Area of Operation: UK & Ireland
Tel: 01580 895489 **Fax:** 01580 893720
Web: www.naturalimage.co.uk
Product Type: 1, 2

NICAN STONE LTD
Bank House, School Lane,
Bronington, Shropshire, SY13 3HN
Area of Operation: UK (Excluding Ireland)
Tel: 01948 780670 **Fax:** 01948 780679
Email: enquiries@nicanstone.com
Web: www.nicanstone.com

ORIGINAL STONE PAVING CO
1 Pan-Y-Bryn, Caia Park, Wrexham, LL13 8TL
Area of Operation: UK (Excluding Ireland)
Tel: 07968 582231
Email: sales@the-original-stone-paving-company.co.uk
Web: www.the-original-stone-paving-company.co.uk

PEPPERS FIREPLACE AND GARDEN CENTRE
70 Avenue Road, Bexley Heath, Kent, DA7 4EG
Area of Operation: UK (Excluding Ireland)
Tel: 0208 303 2195 **Fax:** 0208 301 1012
Email: sales@peppers.uk.com
Web: www.peppers.uk.com 🖰

PLASMOR
P.O. Box 44, Womersley Road,
Knottingley, West Yorkshire, WF11 0DN
Area of Operation: UK (Excluding Ireland)
Tel: 01977 673221 **Fax:** 01977 607071
Email: knott@plasmor.co.uk
Web: www.plasmor.co.uk **Material Type:** G) 1

PROTURF LTD
North Carr Farm, North Carr Road, West Stockwith,
Doncaster, South Yorkshire, DN10 4BD
Area of Operation: Europe
Tel: 01427 890797 **Fax:** 01427 891785
Email: info@proturf.co.uk **Web:** www.proturf.co.uk
Product Type: 3, 5 **Material Type:** E) 1, 3, 4, 5, 6

QUINN-LITE
Derrylin, Co Fermanagh, BT92 9AU
Area of Operation: Europe
Tel: 02867 748866 **Fax:** 02867 6774 8800
Email: info@quinn-lite.com
Web: www.quinn-lite.com

RANSFORDS
Drayton Way, Drayton Fields Industrial Estate,
Daventry, Northamptonshire, NN11 8XW
Area of Operation: Worldwide
Tel: 01327 705310 **Fax:** 01327 706831
Email: sales@ransfords.com
Web: www.ransfords.com /
www.stoneflooringandpaving.com
Product Type: 2

RESIN BONDED LTD
Unit 7 Ashdown Court, Vernon Road,
Uckfield, East Sussex, TN22 5DX
Area of Operation: UK & Ireland
Tel: 01825 766186 **Fax:** 01825 766186
Email: info@resinbonded.co.uk
Web: www.resinbonded.co.uk ⌐🖰
Product Type: 5

RIVAR SAND & GRAVEL LTD
Pinchington Lane, Newbury, Berkshire, RG19 8SR
Area of Operation: South East England
Tel: 01635 523524
Fax: 01635 521621
Email: sales@rivarsandandgravel.co.uk
Web: www.rivarsandandgravel.co.uk
Product Type: 1, 2, 3, 5, 6

ROCK UNIQUE LTD
c/o Select Garden and Pet Centre,
Main Road, Sundridge, Kent, TN14 6ED
Area of Operation: Europe
Tel: 01959 565 608
Fax: 01959 569 312
Email: stone@rock-unique.com
Web: www.rock-unique.com
Product Type: 1, 2, 3, 6 **Other Info:** ▽ ECO ✏ 🖰
Material Type: E) 1, 2, 3, 4, 5, 8, 9, 10

RUSTICA LTD
154c Milton Park, Oxfordshire, OX14 4SD
Area of Operation: UK & Ireland
Tel: 01235 834192 **Fax:** 01235 835162
Email: sales@rustica.co.uk
Web: www.rustica.co.uk **Product Type:** 2

SLATE WORLD LTD
Westmoreland Road, Kingsbury,
Greater London, NW9 9RN
Area of Operation: Europe
Tel: 0208 204 3444 **Fax:** 0208 204 3311
Email: kingsbury@slateworld.com
Web: www.slateworld.com ⌐🖰

SLATE WORLD LTD

Area of Operation: Europe
Tel: 0208 204 3444 / 014 8345 9115
Fax: 0208 204 3311 / 014 8345 9117
Email: kingsbury@slateworld.com
Web: www.slateworld.com

Suppliers of the most comprehensive range of
QUARRY-DIRECT, non-slip and low maintenance
natural slate flooring tiles in the UK.

STONE TILES ONLINE
Boxted Farm, Berkhamsted Road,
Hemel Hempstead, Hertfordshire, HP1 2SQ
Tel: 0845 308 1100 **Fax:** 01442 229282
Email: info@stonetilesonline.co.uk
Web: www.stonetilesonline.co.uk ⌐🖰

EXTERIOR PRODUCTS

EXTERIOR PRODUCTS

STONE2YOURHOME
Area of Operation: UK (Excluding Ireland)
Tel: 0871 8732369
Email: info@stone2yourhome.co.uk
Web: www.stone2yourhome.co.uk
Product Type: 1, 2, 5, 6

STONEMARKET LTD
Oxford Road, Ryton on Dunsmore,
Warwickshire, CV8 3EJ
Area of Operation: UK (Excluding Ireland)
Tel: 02476 518700 Fax: 02476 518777
Email: sales@stonemarket.co.uk
Web: www.stonemarket.co.uk
Product Type: 1, 2, 3, 6

STONEWAYS LTD
Railside Works, Marlbrook,
Leominster, Herefordshire, HR6 0PH
Area of Operation: UK (Excluding Ireland)
Tel: 01568 616818 Fax: 01568 620085
Email: stoneways@msn.com
Web: www.stoneways.co.uk
Product Type: 1

SURESET UK LTD
Unit 32 , Deverill Road Trading Estate,
Sutton Veny , Warminster, Wiltshire, BA12 7BZ
Area of Operation: Europe
Tel: 01985 841180 Fax: 01985 841260
Email: mail@sureset.co.uk
Web: www.sureset.co.uk
Material Type: E) 1, 2, 3, 5, 6, 9

TAYLOR MAXWELL & COMPANY LIMITED
4 John Oliver Buildings, 53 Wood Street,
Barnet, Hertfordshire, EN5 4BS
Area of Operation: UK (Excluding Ireland)
Tel: 0208 440 0551 Fax: 0208 440 0552
Email: barnet@taylor.maxwell.co.uk
Web: www.taylor.maxwell.co.uk
Product Type: 1

THE CORNISH LIME COMPANY LTD.
Brims Park, Old Callywith Road,
Bodmin, Cornwall, PL31 2DZ
Area of Operation: UK (Excluding Ireland)
Tel: 01208 79779
Fax: 01208 73744
Email: sales@cornishlime.co.uk
Web: www.cornishlime.co.uk

THE MATCHING BRICK COMPANY
Lockes Yard , Hartcliffe Way,
Bedminster, Bristol, BS3 5RJ
Area of Operation: UK (Excluding Ireland)
Tel: 0117 963 7000
Fax: 0117 966 4612
Email: matchingbrick@btconnect.com
Web: www.matchingbrick.co.uk
Product Type: 1, 3, 6

THE NATURAL SLATE COMPANY LTD
161 Ballards Lane, Finchley, London, N3 1LJ
Area of Operation: Worldwide
Tel: 0845 177 5008 Fax: 0870 429 9891
Email: sales@theslatecompany.net
Web: www.theslatecompany.net
Material Type: E) 3, 4

TRADSTOCKS LTD
Dunaverig, Thornhill, Stirling, Stirlingshire, FK8 3QW
Area of Operation: Scotland
Tel: 01786 850400 Fax: 01786 850404
Email: info@tradstocks.co.uk
Web: www.tradstocks.co.uk Product Type: 2, 3, 6

VOBSTER CAST STONE CO LTD
Newbury Works, Coleford,
Radstock, Somerset, BA3 5RX
Area of Operation: UK (Excluding Ireland)
Tel: 01373 812514
Fax: 01373 813384
Email: tombrewster@caststonemasonry.co.uk
Web: www.caststonemasonry.co.uk

WELSH SLATE
Business Design Centre, Unit 205,
52 Upper Street, London, N1 0QH
Area of Operation: Worldwide
Tel: 0207 354 0306 Fax: 0207 354 8485
Email: enquiries@welshslate.com
Web: www.welshslate.com Material Type: E) 3

WOODKIRK STONE SALES LTD
Britannia Quarries, Rein Road,
Morley, Leeds, West Yorkshire, LS27 0SW
Area of Operation: Europe
Tel: 0113 253 0464 Fax: 0113 252 7520
Email: sales@woodkirkstone.co.uk
Web: www.woodkirkstone.co.uk
Product Type: 1, 2, 3, 6 Material Type: E) 4

YORK HANDMADE BRICK CO LTD
Forest Lane, Alne, York, North Yorkshire, YO61 1TU
Area of Operation: Worldwide
Tel: 01347 838881 Fax: 01347 838885
Email: sales@yorkhandmade.co.uk
Web: www.yorkhandmade.co.uk
Product Type: 1, 3, 6

ZARKA MARBLE
43 Belsize Lane, Hampstead, London, NW3 5AU
Area of Operation: South East England
Tel: 0207 431 3042 Fax: 0207 431 3879
Email: enquiries@zarkamarble.co.uk
Web: www.zarkamarble.co.uk

**Please mention
The Homebuilder's
Handbook
when you call**

GATES, FENCES & RAILINGS

Image courtesy of Architectural Gates (01225 766944)

EXTERIOR PRODUCTS

EXTERIOR PRODUCTS

Gates & Fencing

A gate in front of your new home will set the tone for the entire property, as well as providing some security, so hold back some of your budget and don't skimp on materials or design – it could well be the finishing touch that makes all the difference.

The challenge with gates is to make them not only practical, but also elegant and attractive. You should also try to reflect the nature of the property.

If you live in a more traditional home then a wooden gate should be suitable. In more urban environments, and with large contemporary homes, metal can be a better option as it's both decorative and functional. The main advantage with metal, particularly steel, is that it is possible to achieve the same strength using smaller sections than with timber.

For lightweight gates you should opt for aluminium, and for more sturdy gates wrought iron, bronze or titanium. But be prepared for the accompanying hefty price tag. For a strong and relatively inexpensive option, by far the most popular choice is powder-coated mild steel.

For larger, timber gates hardwood is a sound option. To combat the weight problem, you can go for double gates with timber frames which have metal rods passing through.

Image by Haddonstone.

For much larger gates, it's quite likely that they'll be controlled by automated opening systems. Automated gates are not cheap, especially when combined with a smart entry system, but it is all too easy to overlook these finishing touches when planning your new home. Always factor these expensive extras in at the planning stages to ensure that your budget can accommodate what are seen as modern essentials.

Fencing

If you just want to mark a boundary in your garden or outside your home and are not too bothered about privacy or security, the cheapest permanent option is the sawn timber post-and-rail fence. It shouldn't cost more than £10/lin.m, supplied and erected, although you can vary the specification upwards by going for morticed joints and even riven oak.

If you need to fence in animals or children then you will require longer lengths. Post and rail is fine for this and it can be 'stock proofed' by the addition of some wire mesh. Alternatively, a

chain link fence, although less attractive, is an more secure option.

Chestnut palings, 1.2m high, are another cheapish option (costing around £6/m) which, being vertical, are much harder to get over. They are easily fitted — just insert posts in every 2m or so — but have a temporary air about them which may not appeal to all. The picket or palisade fence is similar in design to palings and has an altogether more permanent look, but costs around £15/m.

If you require privacy and security and can't wait for a hedge to grow, you will have to go for a solid or near solid fence with a height of 1.8m (above head height). The traditional option is to erect something similar to a post-and-rail fence and cover it with vertically fixed, feather edged timber boarding, known as a close-boarded fence. Material costs for close boarded fencing are around £15/lin.m, supply and fix costs around £25/lin.m. It is a little cheaper to use ready-made panels of the type you see in garden centres but the result can often be flimsy.

FENCING

KEY

PRODUCT TYPES: 1= Balustrading
2 = Fencing 3 = Railings
OTHER: ▽ Reclaimed ⬧ On-line shopping
✏ Bespoke ⬧ Hand-made ECO Ecological

ACE MINIMIX
Millfields Road, Ettingshall,
Wolverhampton, West Midlands, WV4 6JP
Tel: 0121 585 5559 **Fax:** 0121 585 5557
Email: info@tarmac.co.uk
Web: www.tarmac.co.uk **Product Type:** 2

ADDSTONE CAST STONE
2 Millers Gate, Stone, Staffordshire, ST15 8ZF
Area of Operation: UK (Excluding Ireland)
Tel: 01785 818810 **Fax:** 01785 819958
Email: sales@addstone.co.uk
Web: www.addstone.co.uk ⬧ **Product Type:** 1
Other Info: ✏ ⬧ **Material Type:** E) 11, 13

ARBORDECK
Lincoln Castle, Lincoln Castle Way, New Holland,
Barrow-upon-Humber, Lincolnshire, DN19 7RR
Tel: 0800 169 5275 **Fax:** 01469 535526
Email: enquiries@arbordeck.co.uk
Web: www.arbordeck.co.uk **Product Type:** 1

ARCHITECTURAL GATES
Mallard, Hoopers Pool, Southwick, Trowbridge,
Wiltshire, BA14 9NG (callers by appointment only)
Area of Operation: Worldwide
Tel: 01225 766944
Email: architectural_gates@yahoo.co.uk
Web: www.architectural-gates.com
Product Type: 1, 2, 3 **Material Type:** C) 1, 6

ATG ACCESS LTD
Automation House, Lowton Business Park,
Newton Road, Lowton, Cheshire, WA3 2AP
Area of Operation: Worldwide
Tel: 01942 685 522 **Fax:** 01942 269 676
Email: marketing@atgaccess.com
Web: www.atgaccess.com ⬧
Product Type: 3 **Other Info:** ✏

B ROURKE & CO LTD
Vulcan Works, Accrington Road,
Burnley, Lancashire, BB11 5QD
Area of Operation: Worldwide
Tel: 01282 422841 **Fax:** 01282 458901
Email: info@rourkes.co.uk
Web: www.rourkes.co.uk **Product Type:** 1, 2

BALCAS TIMBER LTD
Laragh, Enniskillen, Co. Fermanagh, BT94 2FQ
Area of Operation: UK & Ireland
Tel: 0286 632 3003 **Fax:** 0286 632 7924
Email: info@balcas.com
Web: www.balcas.com **Product Type:** 1, 2

BLANC DE BIERGES
Eastrea Road, Whittlesey, Cambridgeshire, PE7 2AG
Area of Operation: Worldwide
Tel: 01733 202566 **Fax:** 01733 205405
Email: info@blancdebierges.com
Web: www.blancdebierges.com
Product Type: 2 **Other Info:** ✏ ⬧

CANNOCK GATES (UK) LTD
Hawks Green, Martindale,
Cannock, Staffordshire, WS11 7XT
Area of Operation: UK (Excluding Ireland)
Tel: 08707 54 18 13
Email: sales@cannockgates.co.uk
Web: www.cannockgates.co.uk ⬧

CHAIRWORKS
47 Weir Road, London, SW19 8UG
Tel: 0208 247 3700 **Fax:** 0208 247 3800
Email: info@chairworks.info
Web: www.chairworks.info **Product Type:** 2

**CHRIS TOPP & COMPANY
WROUGHT IRONWORKS**
Lyndhurst, Carlton Husthwaite,
Thirsk, North Yorkshire, YO7 2BJ
Tel: 01845 501415 **Fax:** 01845 501072
Email: enquiry@christopp.co.uk
Web: www.christopp.co.uk
Product Type: 1, 2, 3 **Other Info:** ✏ ⬧
Material Type: C) 2, 3, 4, 5, 6, 7, 11, 12, 17

COLOURFENCE LTD
Unit 2 Hawthorn Business Park, Puddlebrook Road,
Drybrook, Gloucestershire, GL17 9HP
Area of Operation: UK & Ireland
Tel: 0845 230 6330 **Fax:** 01594 541666
Email: info@colourfence.co.uk
Web: www.colourfence.co.uk
Other Info: ECO ✏

DICTATOR DIRECT
Inga House, Northdown Business Park,
Ashford Road, Lenham, Kent, ME17 2DL
Area of Operation: Worldwide
Tel: 01622 854770 **Fax:** 01622 854771
Email: mail@dictatordirect.com
Web: www.dictatordirect.com

EAST OF EDEN PLANTS
38 St Andrews Street, Millbrook,
Torpoint, Cornwall, PL10 1BE
Area of Operation: UK & Ireland
Tel: 01752 822782
Email: info@eastofedenplants.co.uk
Web: www.eastofedenplants.co.uk ⬧
Product Type: 2, 3

EASYGATES
Unit 4 Broadcott Industrial Estate, Station Road,
Cradley Heath, Birmingham, West Midlands, B64 6NT
Area of Operation: Europe
Tel: 0845 054 5070 **Fax:** 0121 561 3395
Email: info@easygates.co.uk
Web: www.easygates.co.uk
Product Type: 1, 2

ECOCHOICE TIMBER PRODUCTS
18 Charlton Lodge,
Temple Fortune Lane, London, NW11 7TY
Area of Operation: UK & Ireland
Tel: 0845 638 1340 **Fax:** 0870 286 3680
Email: info@ecochoice.co.uk
Web: www.ecochoice.co.uk **Other Info:** ECO ⬧

ERMINE ENGINEERING COMPANY LTD
Francis House, Silver Birch Park, Great Northern
Terrace, Lincoln, Lincolnshire, LN5 8LG
Area of Operation: UK (Excluding Ireland)
Tel: 01522 510977 **Fax:** 01522 510929
Email: info@ermineengineering.co.uk
Web: www.ermineengineering.co.uk
Product Type: 1, 2 **Other Info:** ✏ ⬧
Material Type: C) 1, 2, 3, 4, 18

F.P. IRONWORK
Unit 44, Oswin Road,
Leicester, Leicestershire, LE3 1HR
Area of Operation: UK (Excluding Ireland)
Tel: 0116 255 0455 **Fax:** 0116 255 6096
Email: sales@fpironwork.com
Web: www.fpironwork.com
Product Type: 1, 2, 3 **Other Info:** ✏ ⬧
Material Type: C) 2, 4, 6

FOREST GARDEN
Units 291 & 296, Hartlebury Trading Estate,
Hartlebury, Worcestershire, DY10 4JB
Area of Operation: UK (Excluding Ireland)
Tel: 0870 300 9809 **Fax:** 0870 191 9888
Email: info@forestgarden.co.uk
Web: www.forestgarden.co.uk
Product Type: 2

G&T EVANS
Dulas Mill, Mochdre Lane, Newtown, Powys, SY16 4JD
Area of Operation: UK & Ireland
Tel: 01686 622100 **Fax:** 01686 622220
Email: gtevans1@aol.com
Web: www.gtevans.co.uk

GARDEN REQUISITES
Budleigh House, 307 London Road East,
Batheaston, Bath, Somerset, BA1 7RL
Area of Operation: Worldwide
Tel: 01225 851577 **Fax:** 01225 859908
Email: info@garden-requisites.co.uk
Web: www.garden-requisites.co.uk
Other Info: ✏ ⬧ **Material Type:** C) 2, 4

GATE-A-MATION LTD
Unit 8 Boundary Business Centre,
Boundary Way, Woking, Surrey, GU21 5DH
Area of Operation: East England, Greater London, South
East England, South West England and South Wales
Tel: 01483 747373
Fax: 01483 776688
Email: sales@gate-a-mation.com
Web: www.gate-a-mation.com
Product Type: 2 **Other Info:** ✏ ⬧

GEORGE BARKER & SONS
Backbarrow, Nr. Ulverston, Cumbria, LA12 8TA
Area of Operation: UK (Excluding Ireland)
Tel: 01539 531236 **Fax:** 01539 530801
Web: www.gbs-ltd.co.uk

GREENFINGERS.COM
10 Lindsay Square, Deans Industrial Estate,
Livingston, Lothian, EH54 8RL
Area of Operation: UK (Excluding Ireland)
Tel: 0845 345 0728
Email: customer.services@greenfingers.com
Web: www.greenfingers.com ⬧

HLD LTD
The Old Shipyard, Gainsborough,
Lincolnshire, DN21 ING
Area of Operation: UK & Ireland
Tel: 01427 611800 **Fax:** 01427 612 867
Email: technical@hld.co.uk **Web:** www.hld.co.uk

HONEYSUCKLE BOTTOM SAWMILL LTD
Honeysuckle Bottom, Green Dene,
East Horsley, Leatherhead, Surrey, KT24 5TD
Area of Operation: Greater London, South East England
Tel: 01483 282394 **Fax:** 01483 282394
Email: honeysucklemill@aol.com
Web: www.easisites.co.uk/honeysucklebottomsawmill
Product Type: 2

IRONCRAFT
92 High Street, Earl Shilton,
Leicester, Leicestershire, LE9 7DG
Area of Operation: UK (Excluding Ireland)
Tel: 01455 847548 **Fax:** 01455 842422
Email: office@ironcraft.co.uk
Web: www.ironcraft.co.uk **Product Type:** 2

JACKSONS FENCING
Stowting Common, Ashford, Kent, TN25 6BN
Area of Operation: UK & Ireland
Tel: 01233 750393 **Fax:** 01233 750403
Email: sales@jacksons-fencing.co.uk
Web: www.jacksons-fencing.co.uk **Product Type:** 2

JGS METALWORK
Unit 6 Broomstick Estate, High Street,
Edlesborough, Dunstable, Bedfordshire, LU6 2HS
Area of Operation: East England
Tel: 01525 220360
Fax: 01525 222786
Email: enquiries@jgsmetalwork.co.uk
Web: www.jgsmetalwork.co.uk
Product Type: 1, 2, 3

KEE KLAMP LTD
1 Boulton Road, Reading, Berkshire, RG2 0NH
Area of Operation: Worldwide
Tel: 0118 931 1022 **Fax:** 0118 931 1146
Email: sales@keeklamp.com
Web: www.keeklamp.com **Product Type:** 1, 2

KIRK NATURAL STONE
Bridgend, Fyvie, Turriff, Aberdeenshire, AB53 8LL
Area of Operation: Worldwide
Tel: 01651 891891 **Fax:** 01651 891794
Email: info@kirknaturalstone.com
Web: www.kirknaturalstone.com **Product Type:** 2

LAND SKILL PROPERTY
46 Ledger Lane, Outwood, West Yorkshire, WF1 2PH
Tel: 01924 826836 **Fax:** 01924 835174
Email: andrew@landskill.co.uk **Product Type:** 1, 2

LLOYD CHRISTIE
Greystones, Sudbrook Lane, Petersham, TW10 7AT
Area of Operation: Worldwide
Tel: 020 8332 6766 **Fax:** 020 8332 2229
Email: info@lloydchristie.com
Web: www.lloydchristie.com

METALCRAFT [TOTTENHAM]
6-40 Durnford Street, Tottenham, London, N15 5NQ
Area of Operation: UK (Excluding Ireland)
Tel: 0208 802 1715 **Fax:** 0208 802 1258
Email: sales@makingmetalwork.com
Web: www.makingmetalwork.com
Product Type: 1, 2 **Material Type:** C) 2, 3, 4, 5

NATIONAL PLASTICS
Bridge Street, Abercarn, Gwent, NP11 4SB
Area of Operation: UK (Excluding Ireland)
Tel: 01495 244551 **Fax:** 01495 247990
Email: srholt@nationalplastics.co.uk
Web: www.nationalplastics.co.uk ⬧

OCTAVEWARD LIMITED
Balle Street, Darwen, Lancashire, BB3 2AZ
Area of Operation: UK (Excluding Ireland)
Tel: 01254 773300 **Fax:** 01254 773950
Email: info@octaveward.co.uk
Web: www.octaveward.co.uk

OSMO UK LTD
Unit 24 Anglo Business Park, Smeaton Close,
Aylesbury, Buckinghamshire, HP19 8UP
Area of Operation: UK & Ireland
Tel: 01296 481220 **Fax:** 01296 424090
Email: info@osmouk.com
Web: www.osmouk.com **Product Type:** 2

PREFAB STEEL CO. LTD
114 Brighton Road, Shoreham,
West Sussex, BN43 6RH
Area of Operation: Greater London, South East England
Tel: 01273 597733 **Fax:** 01273 597774
Email: prefabsteel@btinternet.com
Web: www.prefabsteel.co.uk
Product Type: 1, 3 **Material Type:** C) 2

RIVERSIDE DECKING COMPANY
4 Chauntry Mews, Chauntry Road,
Maidenhead, Berkshire, SL6 1TT
Area of Operation: Greater London, South East England
Tel: 01628 626545
Email: mklewis3@ukonline.co.uk
Web: www.riversidedeckingcompany.co.uk
Product Type: 1, 2

ROBERT LONGSTAFF WORKSHOPS
Longstaff Workshops, Appleton Road,
Longworth, Oxfordshire, OX13 5EF
Area of Operation: Worldwide
Tel: 01865 820206 **Email:** robert@longstaff.co.uk
Web: www.longstaff.co.uk ⬧
Other Info: ECO ✏ ⬧

RUSTIC WOODLAND
Canterbury Road, Wingham, Canterbury, Kent, CT3 1NH
Area of Operation: UK (Excluding Ireland)
Tel: 0845 260 0876
Email: info@rusticwoodland.com
Web: www.rusticwoodland.com ⬧

RUTLAND TIMBER LTD
20 Underwood Drive, Stoney Stanton,
Leicester, Leicestershire, LE9 4TA
Area of Operation: UK & Ireland
Tel: 01455 272 860 **Fax:** 01455 271 324
Email: info@rutlandtimber.co.uk
Web: www.rutlandtimber.co.uk **Product Type:** 2

STONES DEVELOPMENT (UK) LTD
Unit 2 Irradion House, Southdown Industrial Estate,
Harpenden, Hertfordshire, AL5 1PW
Tel: 0800 121 8320 **Fax:** 01727 862009
Email: info@stonestimber.co.uk
Web: www.stonestimber.co.uk **Other Info:** ▽ ECO

SUNNY ASPECTS LTD
36 Udney Park Road, Teddington,
Greater London, TW11 9BG
Area of Operation: Europe **Tel:** 0208 977 4149
Email: info@sunnyaspects.co.uk
Web: www.sunnyaspects.com **Material Type:** A) 12

THE CANE STORE
Wash Dyke Cottage, No1 Witham Road,
Long Bennington, Lincolnshire, NG23 5DS
Tel: 01400 282271 **Fax:** 01400 281103
Email: jaki@canestore.co.uk
Web: www.canestore.co.uk **Product Type:** 2

THE EXPANDED METAL COMPANY LIMITED
PO Box 14, Longhill Industrial Estate (North),
Hartlepool, Durham, TS25 1PR
Area of Operation: Worldwide
Tel: 01429 867388 **Fax:** 01429 866795
Email: paulb@expamet.com
Web: www.expandedmetalcompany.co.uk

TIMELESS TIMBER DECKING
BSW Timber, Cargo, Carlisle, Cumbria, CA6 4BA
Area of Operation: UK (Excluding Ireland)
Tel: 01228 673366 **Fax:** 01228 673365
Email: timeless-timber@bsw.co.uk
Web: www.timeless-timber.co.uk **Other Info:** ECO

ZAUN LTD
Steel Drive, Wolverhampton, West Midlands, WV10 9ED
Area of Operation: Europe **Tel:** 01902 796699
Email: dan.sullivan@zaun.co.uk

GATES

KEY

PRODUCT TYPES: 1= Gate Closers
2 = Automatic Gates   3 = Other
OTHER: ▽ Reclaimed   🖐 On-line shopping
✎ Bespoke   🖐 Hand-made   ECO Ecological

AACORN JOINERY AND DESIGN LTD.
2 Balaclava Place, South Street,
Bridport, Dorset, DT6 3PE
Area of Operation: Europe
Tel: 01308 456217 **Fax:** 01308 424511
Email: info@aacornjoinery.co.uk
Web: www.aacornjoinery.co.uk

ANDY THORNTON LTD
Ainleys Industrial Estate,
Elland, West Yorkshire, HX5 9JP
Area of Operation: Worldwide
Tel: 01422 375595 **Fax:** 01422 377455
Email: marketing@ataa.co.uk
Web: www.andythornton.com

ARCHITECTURAL GATES
Mallard, Hoopers Pool, Southwick, Trowbridge,
Wiltshire, BA14 9NG   (callers by appointment only)
Area of Operation: Worldwide
Tel: 01225 766944
Email: architectural_gates@yahoo.co.uk
Web: www.architectural-gates.com
Product Type: 1, 2, 3
Material Type: C) 1, 2, 4, 5, 6, 17, 18

ATLAS GROUP
Design House, 27 Salt Hill Way,
Slough, Berkshire, SL1 3TR
Area of Operation: UK (Excluding Ireland)
Tel: 01753 573573 **Fax:** 01753 552424
Email: info@atlasgroup.co.uk
Web: www.atlasgroup.co.uk **Product Type:** 1, 2, 3
Other Info: ✎   **Material Type:** C) 1, 2, 4, 5, 6

AUTOPA LIMITED
Cottage Leap, Rugby, Warwickshire, CV21 3XP
Area of Operation: Worldwide
Tel: 01788 550556 **Fax:** 01788 550265
Email: info@autopa.co.uk
Web: www.autopa.co.uk **Product Type:** 3

B ROURKE & CO LTD
Vulcan Works, Accrington Road,
Burnley, Lancashire, BB11 5QD
Tel: 01282 422841 **Fax:** 01282 458901
Email: info@rourkes.co.uk
Web: www.rourkes.co.uk **Product Type:** 1, 2, 3

BAYFIELD STAIR CO
Unit 4, Praed Road, Trafford Park,
Manchester, M17 1PQ
Area of Operation: Worldwide
Tel: 0161 848 0700 **Fax:** 0161 872 2230
Email: sales@bayfieldstairs.co.uk
Web: www.bayfieldstairs.co.uk
Product Type: 1, 2, 3

BFT AUTOMATION UK LTD
Unit 8E, Newby Road Industrial Estate,
Hazel Grove, Stockport, Cheshire, SK7 5DA
Tel: 0161 456 0456 **Fax:** 0161 456 9090
Email: info@bftautomation.co.uk
Web: www.bft.co.uk **Product Type:** 1, 2

BPT AUTOMATION LTD
Unit 16, Sovereign Park, Cleveland Way,
Hemel Hempstead, Hertfordshire, HP2 7DA
Area of Operation: UK & Ireland
Tel: 01442 235355 **Fax:** 01442 244729
Email: sales@bpt.co.uk
Web: www.bptautomation.co.uk **Product Type:** 1, 2

C&V CARMICHAEL LTD
Fabrication Facility, Mossmorran,
Cowdenbeath, Fife, KY4 8EP
Tel: 01383 510469 **Fax:** 01383 610515
Email: cvcarmichael@cvcarmichael.com
Web: www.cvcarmichael.com

C.J. BLACKSMITHS
Yr Eithin, Llangynog, Oswestry, Powys, SY10 0HA
Tel: 01691 860750 **Fax:** 01691 860750
Email: sales@cjblacksmiths.co.uk
Web: www.cjblacksmiths.co.uk/
www.thecastironemporium.co.uk ✎🖐
Product Type: 2, 3 **Other Info:** ▽✎🖐

CANNOCK GATES (UK) LTD
Hawks Green, Martindale,
Cannock, Staffordshire, WS11 7XT
Area of Operation: UK (Excluding Ireland)
Tel: 08707 54 18 13
Email: sales@cannockgates.co.uk
Web: www.cannockgates.co.uk 🖐

CENTURION
Westhill Business Park, Arnhall Business Park,
Westhill, Aberdeen, Aberdeenshire, AB32 6UF
Area of Operation: Scotland
Tel: 01224 744440 **Fax:** 01224 744819
Email: info@centurion-solutions.co.uk
Web: www.centurion-solutions.co.uk
Product Type: 1, 2, 3

**CHRIS TOPP & COMPANY
WROUGHT IRONWORKS**
Lyndhurst, Carlton Husthwaite,
Thirsk, North Yorkshire, YO7 2BJ
Area of Operation: Worldwide
Tel: 01845 501415 **Fax:** 01845 501072
Email: enquiry@christopp.co.uk
Web: www.christopp.co.uk
Product Type: 1, 2, 3 **Other Info:** ✎🖐
Material Type: C) 2, 3, 4, 5, 6, 7, 11, 12, 17

COEL AUTOMATE
Starkbridge Farm, Syke House,
Nr Goole, East Riding of Yorks, DN14 9AZ
Tel: 01405 785656 **Fax:** 01405 785300
Email: info@theelectricgateshop.co.uk
Web: www.theelectricgateshop.co.uk 🖐
Product Type: 2

COLOURFENCE LTD
Unit 2 Hawthorn Business Park, Puddlebrook Road,
Drybrook, Gloucestershire, GL17 9HP
Tel: 0845 230 6330 **Fax:** 01594 541666
Email: info@colourfence.co.uk
Web: www.colourfence.co.uk
Other Info: ECO 🖐   **Material Type:** C) 2

DEA GATE AUTOMATION LTD
Sandholes Road, Cookstown, Co. Tyrone, BT80 9AR
Area of Operation: UK & Ireland
Tel: 028 8676 6131 **Fax:** 028 8676 2414
Email: gerard.meenan@deagateautomation.com
Web: www.deagateautomation.com 🖐
Product Type: 2

DICTATOR DIRECT
Inga House, Northdown Business Park,
Ashford Road, Lenham, Kent, ME17 2DL
Area of Operation: Worldwide
Tel: 01622 854770 **Fax:** 01622 854771
Email: mail@dictatordirect.com
Web: www.dictatordirect.com **Product Type:** 1

EASYGATES
Unit 4 Broadcott Industrial Estate, Station Road,
Cradley Heath, Birmingham, West Midlands, B64 6NT
Area of Operation: Europe
Tel: 0845 054 5070 **Fax:** 0121 561 3395
Email: info@easygates.co.uk
Web: www.easygates.co.uk **Product Type:** 1, 2

ECOCHOICE TIMBER PRODUCTS
18 Charlton Lodge,
Temple Fortune Lane, London, NW11 7TY
Area of Operation: UK & Ireland
Tel: 0845 638 1340 **Fax:** 0870 286 3680
Email: info@ecochoice.co.uk
Web: www.ecochoice.co.uk **Other Info:** ECO ✎

ERMINE ENGINEERING COMPANY LTD
Francis House, Silver Birch Park, Great Northern
Terrace, Lincoln, Lincolnshire, LN5 8LG
Area of Operation: UK (Excluding Ireland)
Tel: 01522 510977 **Fax:** 01522 510929
Email: info@ermineengineering.co.uk
Web: www.ermineengineering.co.uk
Product Type: 2, 3 **Other Info:** ✎🖐
Material Type: C) 1, 2, 3, 4, 18

F.P. IRONWORK
Unit 44, Oswin Road,
Leicester, Leicestershire, LE3 1HR
Area of Operation: UK (Excluding Ireland)
Tel: 0116 255 0455 **Fax:** 0116 255 6096
Email: sales@fpironwork.com
Web: www.fpironwork.com **Product Type:** 1, 2, 3
Other Info: ✎🖐   **Material Type:** C) 2, 4, 6

FOREST GARDEN
Units 291 & 296, Hartlebury Trading Estate,
Hartlebury, Worcestershire, DY10 4JB
Area of Operation: UK (Excluding Ireland)
Tel: 0870 300 9809 **Fax:** 0870 191 9888
Email: info@forestgarden.co.uk
Web: www.forestgarden.co.uk
Product Type: 3

GARDEN OASIS LIMITED
Garden Oasis, 3 Caradoc, Glascote,
Tamworth, Staffordshire, B77 2DX
Area of Operation: UK & Ireland
Tel: 01827 706110 **Fax:** 01827 706110
Email: sales@gardenoasis.co.uk
Web: www.gardenoasis.co.uk 🖐
Product Type: 1, 3

GARDEN REQUISITES
Budleigh House, 307 London Road East,
Batheaston, Bath, Somerset, BA1 7RL
Area of Operation: Worldwide
Tel: 01225 851577
Fax: 01225 859908
Email: info@garden-requisites.co.uk
Web: www.garden-requisites.co.uk
Other Info: ✎🖐   **Material Type:** C) 2, 4

GATE-A-MATION LTD
Unit 8 Boundary Business Centre,
Boundary Way, Woking, Surrey, GU21 5DH
Area of Operation: East England, Greater London, South
East England, South West England and South Wales
Tel: 01483 747373 **Fax:** 01483 776688
Email: sales@gate-a-mation.com
Web: www.gate-a-mation.com
Product Type: 1, 2 **Other Info:** ✎🖐
Material Type: A) 1, 2, 3, 4, 5, 6, 7, 8, 9, 10, 11, 12, 13, 14, 15

GEORGE BARKER & SONS
Backbarrow, Nr Ulverston, Cumbria, LA12 8TA
Area of Operation: UK (Excluding Ireland)
Tel: 01539 531236 **Fax:** 01539 530801
Web: www.gbs-ltd.co.uk

HADDONCRAFT FORGE
The Forge House, East Haddon,
Northampton, Northamptonshire, NN6 8DB
Area of Operation: UK & Ireland
Tel: 01604 772027 **Fax:** 01604 770027
Email: info@haddoncraft.co.uk
Web: www.haddoncraft.co.uk **Product Type:** 3
Other Info: ✎🖐   **Material Type:** C) 2, 4

IRONCRAFT
92 High Street, Earl Shilton,
Leicester, Leicestershire, LE9 7DG
Area of Operation: UK (Excluding Ireland)
Tel: 01455 847548 **Fax:** 01455 842422
Email: office@ironcraft.co.uk
Web: www.ironcraft.co.uk
Product Type: 1

JACKSONS FENCING
Stowting Common, Ashford, Kent, TN25 6BN
Area of Operation: UK & Ireland
Tel: 01233 750393 **Fax:** 01233 750403
Email: sales@jacksons-fencing.co.uk
Web: www.jacksons-fencing.co.uk
Product Type: 2, 3

JGS METALWORK
Unit 6 Broomstick Estate, High Street,
Edlesborough, Dunstable, Bedfordshire, LU6 2HS
Area of Operation: East England
Tel: 01525 220360 **Fax:** 01525 222786
Email: enquiries@jgsmetalwork.co.uk
Web: www.jgsmetalwork.co.uk
Product Type: 1, 2, 3 **Material Type:** C) 2, 4

JLC AUTOMATION LTD
The Sussex Barn, New Barn Farm, Hailsham Road,
Stone Cross, East Sussex, BN24 5BT
Area of Operation: East England, Greater London,
South East England
Tel: 01323 741199 **Fax:** 01323 741150
Email: tina@jlcautomation.co.uk
Web: www.jlcautomation.co.uk
Product Type: 2

KIRK NATURAL STONE
Bridgend, Fyvie, Turriff, Aberdeenshire, AB53 8LL
Area of Operation: Worldwide
Tel: 01651 891891 **Fax:** 01651 891794
Email: info@kirknaturalstone.com
Web: www.kirknaturalstone.com

LAND SKILL PROPERTY
46 Ledger Lane, Outwood, West Yorkshire, WF1 2PH
Tel: 01924 826836
Fax: 01924 835174
Email: andrew@landskill.co.uk
Product Type: 1, 3

METALCRAFT [TOTTENHAM]
6-40 Durnford Street, Tottenham, London, N15 5NQ
Area of Operation: UK (Excluding Ireland)
Tel: 0208 802 1715
Fax: 0208 802 1258
Email: sales@makingmetalwork.com
Web: www.makingmetalwork.com
Product Type: 2 **Material Type:** C) 2, 3, 4, 5

NATIONAL PLASTICS
Bridge Street, Abercarn, Gwent, NP11 4SB
Area of Operation: UK & Ireland
Tel: 01495 244551
Fax: 01495 247990
Email: srholt@nationalplastics.co.uk
Web: www.nationalplastics.co.uk 🖐

OCTAVEWARD LIMITED
Balle Street, Darwen, Lancashire, BB3 2AZ
Area of Operation: UK (Excluding Ireland)
Tel: 01254 773300 **Fax:** 01254 773950
Email: info@octaveward.com
Web: www.octaveward.com

OSMO UK LTD
Unit 24 Anglo Business Park, Smeaton Close,
Aylesbury, Buckinghamshire, HP19 8UP
Area of Operation: UK & Ireland
Tel: 01296 481220 **Fax:** 01296 424090
Email: info@osmouk.com
Web: www.osmouk.com
Product Type: 1, 2

PATERSON'S AUTOMATION
25 South Road, Bisley, Woking, Surrey, GU24 9ES
Area of Operation: South East England
Tel: 01483 728276
Email: info@patersonsautomation.co.uk
Web: www.patersonsautomation.co.uk
Product Type: 2 **Material Type:** A) 2

PREFAB STEEL CO. LTD
114 Brighton Road, Shoreham,
West Sussex, BN43 6RH
Area of Operation: Greater London, South East England
Tel: 01273 597733 **Fax:** 01273 597774
Email: prefabsteel@btinternet.com
Web: www.prefabsteel.co.uk
Product Type: 3 **Material Type:** C) 2

PREMIER GARAGE DOORS AND GATES
Unit 7 Sparrowhall Business Park, Leighton Road,
Edlesborough, Dunstable, Bedfordshire, LU6 2ES
Area of Operation: East England, South East England
Tel: 01525 220212
Fax: 01525 222201
Email: sales@premiergaragedoors.co.uk
Web: www.premiergaragedoors.co.uk
Product Type: 1, 2

RUSTIC WOODLAND
Canterbury Road, Wingham,
Canterbury, Kent, CT3 1NH
Area of Operation: UK (Excluding Ireland)
Tel: 0845 260 0876
Email: info@rusticwoodland.com
Web: www.rusticwoodland.com ⌐

SWS UK
Claughton, Lancaster, Lancashire, LA2 9LA
Area of Operation: UK & Ireland
Tel: 01524 772400 **Fax:** 01524 772411
Email: info@swsuk.co.uk
Web: www.swsuk.co.uk ⌐ **Product Type:** 2

THE ELECTRIC GATE SHOP
Elm Tree Farm, Sykehouse, Nr. Goole,
East Riding of Yorks, DN14 9AE
Area of Operation: UK & Ireland **Tel:** 01405 785656
Email: info@theelectricgateshop.co.uk
Web: www.theelectricgateshop.co.uk ⌐
Product Type: 2

THE EXPANDED METAL COMPANY LIMITED
PO Box 14, Longhill Industrial Estate (North),
Hartlepool, Durham, TS25 1PR
Area of Operation: Worldwide
Tel: 01429 867388 **Fax:** 01429 866795
Email: paulb@expamet.com
Web: www.expandedmetalcompany.co.uk

TONY HOOPER
Unit 18 Camelot Court,
Bancombe Trading Estate, Somerton, TA11 6SB
Area of Operation: UK (Excluding Ireland)
Tel: 01458 274221 **Fax:** 01458 274690
Email: tonyhooper1@aol.com
Web: www.tonyhooper.co.uk

ZAUN LTD
Steel Drive, Wolverhampton, West Midlands, WV10 9ED
Area of Operation: Europe
Tel: 01902 796699
Email: dan.sullivan@zaun.co.uk

RAILINGS

KEY
OTHER: ▽ Reclaimed ⌐ On-line shopping
✎ Bespoke ✋ Hand-made ECO Ecological

ANDY THORNTON LTD
Ainleys Industrial Estate,
Elland, West Yorkshire, HX5 9JP
Area of Operation: Worldwide
Tel: 01422 375595 **Fax:** 01422 377455
Email: marketing@ataa.co.uk
Web: www.andythornton.com

ARCHITECTURAL GATES
Mallard, Hoopers Pool, Southwick, Trowbridge,
Wiltshire, BA14 9NG (callers by appointment only)
Area of Operation: Worldwide
Tel: 01225 766944
Email: architectural_gates@yahoo.co.uk
Web: www.architectural-gates.com
Material Type: C) 1, 6

B ROURKE & CO LTD
Vulcan Works, Accrington Road,
Burnley, Lancashire, BB11 5QD
Area of Operation: Worldwide
Tel: 01282 422841 **Fax:** 01282 458901
Email: info@rourkes.co.uk
Web: www.rourkes.co.uk **Material Type:** C) 2, 4, 6

BAYFIELD STAIR CO
Unit 4, Praed Road, Trafford Park,
Manchester, M17 1PQ
Area of Operation: Worldwide
Tel: 0161 848 0700 **Fax:** 0161 872 2230
Email: sales@bayfieldstairs.co.uk
Web: www.bayfieldstairs.co.uk

C&V CARMICHAEL LTD
Fabrication Facility, Mossmorran,
Cowdenbeath, Fife, KY4 8EP
Area of Operation: UK (Excluding Ireland)
Tel: 01383 510469 **Fax:** 01383 610515
Email: cvcarmichael@cvcarmichael.com
Web: www.cvcarmichael.com

C.J. BLACKSMITHS
Yr Eithin, Llangynog, Oswestry, Powys, SY10 0HA
Area of Operation: Worldwide
Tel: 01691 860750 **Fax:** 01691 860750
Email: sales@cjblacksmiths.co.uk
Web: www.cjblacksmiths.co.uk/
www.thecastironemporium.co.uk ⌐
Other Info: ▽ ✎ ✋
Material Type: C) 2, 4, 5, 6, 7, 8, 12

CANNOCK GATES (UK) LTD
Hawks Green, Martindale,
Cannock, Staffordshire, WS11 7XT
Area of Operation: UK (Excluding Ireland)
Tel: 08707 54 18 13
Email: sales@cannockgates.co.uk
Web: www.cannockgates.co.uk ⌐

CASTAWAY CAST PRODUCTS AND WOODWARE
Brocklesby Station, Brocklesby Road,
Ulceby, Lincolnshire, DN39 6ST
Area of Operation: Worldwide
Tel: 01469 588995 **Fax:** 01469 588995
Email: castawaycastproducts@btinternet.com
Other Info: ✎ ✋ **Material Type:** C) 1, 2, 4, 5, 6, 11, 12

**CHRIS TOPP & COMPANY
WROUGHT IRONWORKS**
Lyndhurst, Carlton Husthwaite,
Thirsk, North Yorkshire, YO7 2BJ
Area of Operation: Worldwide
Tel: 01845 501415 **Fax:** 01845 501072
Email: enquiry@christopp.co.uk
Web: www.christopp.co.uk **Other Info:** ✎ ✋

DENBY DALE CAST PRODUCTS LTD
230 Cumberworth Lane, Denby Dale,
Huddersfield, West Yorkshire, HD8 8PR
Area of Operation: UK & Ireland
Tel: 01484 863560 **Fax:** 01484 865597
Email: mail@denbydalecastproducts.co.uk
Web: www.denbydalecastproducts.co.uk

EAST OF EDEN PLANTS
38 St. Andrews Street, Millbrook,
Torpoint, Cornwall, PL10 1BE
Area of Operation: UK & Ireland **Tel:** 01752 822782
Email: info@eastofedenplants.co.uk
Web: www.eastofedenplants.co.uk ⌐

ECOCHOICE TIMBER PRODUCTS
18 Charlton Lodge,
Temple Fortune Lane, London, NW11 7TY
Area of Operation: UK & Ireland
Tel: 0845 638 1340 **Fax:** 0870 286 3680
Email: info@ecochoice.co.uk
Web: www.ecochoice.co.uk **Other Info:** ECO ✎

ERMINE ENGINEERING COMPANY LTD
Francis House, Silver Birch Park, Great Northern
Terrace, Lincoln, Lincolnshire, LN5 8LG
Area of Operation: UK (Excluding Ireland)
Tel: 01522 510977 **Fax:** 01522 510929
Email: info@ermineengineering.co.uk
Web: www.ermineengineering.co.uk
Other Info: ✎ ✋ **Material Type:** C) 1, 2, 3, 4

F.P. IRONWORK
Unit 44, Oswin Road,
Leicester, Leicestershire, LE3 1HR
Area of Operation: UK (Excluding Ireland)
Tel: 0116 255 0455 **Fax:** 0116 255 6096
Email: sales@fpironwork.com
Web: www.fpironwork.com
Material Type: C) 2, 4, 6

FOREST GARDEN
Units 291 & 296, Hartlebury Trading Estate,
Hartlebury, Worcestershire, DY10 4JB
Area of Operation: UK (Excluding Ireland)
Tel: 0870 300 9809
Fax: 0870 191 9888
Email: info@forestgarden.co.uk
Web: www.forestgarden.co.uk

GARDEN REQUISITES
Budleigh House, 307 London Road East,
Batheaston, Bath, Somerset, BA1 7RL
Area of Operation: Worldwide
Tel: 01225 851577 **Fax:** 01225 859908
Email: info@garden-requisites.co.uk
Web: www.garden-requisites.co.uk
Other Info: ✎ ✋ **Material Type:** C) 2, 4

GEORGE BARKER & SONS
Backbarrow, Nr Ulverston, Cumbria, LA12 8TA
Area of Operation: UK (Excluding Ireland)
Tel: 01539 531236 **Fax:** 01539 530801
Web: www.gbs-ltd.co.uk

HADDONCRAFT FORGE
The Forge House, East Haddon,
Northampton, Northamptonshire, NN6 8DB
Area of Operation: UK & Ireland
Tel: 01604 772027
Fax: 01604 770027
Email: info@haddoncraft.co.uk
Web: www.haddoncraft.co.uk
Other Info: ✎ ✋ **Material Type:** C) 2, 4

HLD LTD
The Old Shipyard, Gainsborough,
Lincolnshire, DN21 1NG
Area of Operation: UK & Ireland
Tel: 01427 611800 **Fax:** 01427 612867
Email: technical@hld.co.uk
Web: www.hld.co.uk

IRONCRAFT
92 High Street, Earl Shilton,
Leicester, Leicestershire, LE9 7DG
Area of Operation: UK (Excluding Ireland)
Tel: 01455 847548 **Fax:** 01455 842422
Email: office@ironcraft.co.uk
Web: www.ironcraft.co.uk

JACKSONS FENCING
Stowting Common, Ashford, Kent, TN25 6BN
Area of Operation: UK & Ireland
Tel: 01233 750393 **Fax:** 01233 750403
Email: sales@jacksons-fencing.co.uk
Web: www.jacksons-fencing.co.uk

KIRK NATURAL STONE
Bridgend, Fyvie, Turriff, Aberdeenshire, AB53 8LL
Area of Operation: Worldwide
Tel: 01651 891891 **Fax:** 01651 891794
Email: info@kirknaturalstone.com
Web: www.kirknaturalstone.com

LLOYD CHRISTIE
Greystones, Sudbrook Lane, Petersham, TW10 7AT
Tel: 020 8332 6766 **Fax:** 020 8332 2229
Email: info@lloydchristie.com
Web: www.lloydchristie.com

M D STAINLESS DESIGNS
79 Verity Cresent, Poole, Dorset, BH17 8TT
Area of Operation: UK (Excluding Ireland)
Tel: 01202 684998 **Fax:** 01202 684998
Email: stainlessdesigns@onetel.com
Material Type: C) 2, 3

METALCRAFT [TOTTENHAM]
6-40 Durnford Street, Tottenham, London, N15 5NQ
Tel: 0208 802 1715 **Fax:** 0208 802 1258
Email: sales@makingmetalwork.com
Web: www.makingmetalwork.com

OSMO UK LTD
Unit 24 Anglo Business Park, Smeaton Close,
Aylesbury, Buckinghamshire, HP19 8UP
Area of Operation: UK & Ireland
Tel: 01296 481220 **Fax:** 01296 424090
Email: info@osmouk.com **Web:** www.osmouk.com

RIVERSIDE DECKING COMPANY
4 Chauntry Mews, Chauntry Road,
Maidenhead, Berkshire, SL6 1TT
Area of Operation: Greater London, South East England
Tel: 01628 626545
Email: mklewis3@ukonline.co.uk
Web: www.riversidedeckingcompany.co.uk

STONES DEVELOPMENT (UK) LTD
Unit 2 Irradion House, Southdown Industrial Estate,
Harpenden, Hertfordshire, AL5 1PW
Area of Operation: Europe
Tel: 0800 121 8320 **Fax:** 01727 862009
Email: info@stonestimber.co.uk
Web: www.stonestimber.co.uk **Other Info:** ▽ ECO

THE EXPANDED METAL COMPANY LIMITED
PO Box 14, Longhill Industrial Estate (North),
Hartlepool, Durham, TS25 1PR
Tel: 01429 867388 **Fax:** 01429 866795
Email: paulb@expamet.co.uk
Web: www.expandedmetalcompany.co.uk

TRADSTOCKS LTD
Dunaverig, Thornhill, Stirling, Stirlingshire, FK8 3QW
Area of Operation: Scotland
Tel: 01786 850400 **Fax:** 01786 850404
Email: info@tradstocks.co.uk
Web: www.tradstocks.co.uk

ZAUN LTD
Steel Drive, Wolverhampton, West Midlands, WV10 9ED
Area of Operation: Europe **Tel:** 01902 796699
Email: dan.sullivan@zaun.co.uk

**To recommend a
company for inclusion in
the next edition of
The Homebuilder's
Handbook,
email**

customerservice@centaur.co.uk

EXTERIOR PRODUCTS

SPONSORED BY: How To Create A Jardin Paysan
Tel: 01527 834435 Web: www.renovationfrance.net

CENTAUR SPECIAL
INTEREST MEDIA

Horticulture

Some self-builders are so busy worrying about the construction and financing of their new home that they often overlook one crucial aspect – the garden. Yet your new garden will have a significant effect on the overall appearance of your home and, weather permitting, you'll be spending a lot of time out there. So it's worth putting plenty of care and thought into creating that outside space.

Summer is probably the best time to get out a pencil and paper and sketch out the garden of your dreams. To get an idea of designs, visit other people's gardens, and read magazines and books. But don't forget that your garden should be as much a reaction to your unique building plot as your house is.

It pays to establish your garden plan early on. If your landscaping is submitted as part of the planning application for your whole self-build project, then you will be able to claim back VAT on materials.

- When planning you garden there are lots of factors to take in account: soil type, orientation, required style, paths and patios, planning permission, wall & fences, structural features to name but a few. But one of the most important parts of a traditional garden is of course, the lawn.

The lawn

The position of a lawn needs careful consideration. So that the grass grows well, the soil has to be free-draining but water retentive. Heavy, waterlogged soil can become compacted, while light, sandy soil may dry out, and either condition can lead to weak growth of the grass, which will result in bare patches and allow weeds to become established.

Grass also grows best in an open, sunny position where it can dry out readily, thus reducing the risk of disease. Shade-tolerant grass seed and turf is available, but growth will still be weak where the lawn is overhung by trees or shadowed by tall walls or fences.

When drawing out the shape of the lawn on

your design, avoid creating tapering strips of turf or awkward, narrow sections of border that will be difficult to plant and look after. This is most important where the edge of a lawn runs up at an angle to an area of paving, a wall or a fence.

If you're using CAD software to design your home, then be mindful that only some products include a garden design feature. You can buy specialist CAD packages just for the garden.

BELOW: Image by Rolawn Ltd.

Top tips

- Take your time choosing a suitable framework of plants – it will produce a better garden and give quicker results.

- For the new or bare garden, there are lots of cheap, quick-growing shrubs that will fill some of the space. If funds are really tight, these are easy to propagate by cuttings or seed begged from friends and neighbours.

- Use potted shrubs and plants – they are a cheap way to fill space.

- You can fool the eye by making the garden appear larger than it actually is. To do this, create views through the longest axis of the garden. The longest sightline is often into the furthest corners, so extend the lawn as far into these as possible, and create a greater sense of space by designing wide beds close to the house and in front of the middle of the end of the boundary.

- Another trick is to use large pots or containers close to the house and smaller ones further away, thus fooling the eye into creating distance and perspective.

LAWNS & TURF

KEY
OTHER: ▽ Reclaimed ⌐⊕ On-line shopping
✎ Bespoke ✋ Hand-made ECO Ecological

ACCESS IRRIGATION
15 Yelvertoft Road, Crick,
Northampton, Northamptonshire, NN6 7XS
Area of Operation: UK & Ireland
Tel: 01788 823811 **Fax:** 01788 824256
Email: sales@access-irrigation.co.uk
Web: www.access-irrigation.co.uk ⌐⊕

ARTIFICIAL LAWN COMPANY
Hartshill Nurseries, Thong Lane,
Gravesend, Kent, DA12 4AD
Area of Operation: UK & Ireland
Tel: 08700 500901 **Fax:** 01474 321587
Email: sales@artificiallawn.co.uk
Web: www.artificiallawn.co.uk

COMER LANDSCAPES
Allistock Nurseries, Home Chapel Road,
Knutsford, Cheshire, WA16 9JZ
Area of Operation: UK (Excluding Ireland)
Tel: 0845 006 5555
Fax: 01565 723938
Email: info@comerlandscapes.co.uk
Web: www.cheshirelawns.co.uk

DEACONS NURSERY
Moorview, Godshill, Isle of Wight, PO38 3HW
Area of Operation: UK & Ireland
Tel: 01983 522243 **Fax:** 01983 523575
Email: info@deaconsnurseryfruits.co.uk
Web: www.deaconsnurseryfruits.co.uk ⌐⊕

EARTHSCAPES LANDSCAPING SUPPLIES LTD
Papercourt Farm, Papercourt Lane,
Ripley, Surrey, GU23 6DT
Area of Operation: UK (Excluding Ireland)
Tel: 0845 838 0708
Email: info@earthscapesuk.com
Web: www.earthscapesuk.com

EAST OF EDEN PLANTS
38 St. Andrews Street, Millbrook,
Torpoint, Cornwall, PL10 1BE
Area of Operation: UK & Ireland
Tel: 01752 822782
Email: info@eastofedenplants.co.uk
Web: www.eastofedenplants.co.uk ⌐⊕

EASY LAWN
Thingehill Court, Withington, Herefordshire, HR1 3QG
Area of Operation: UK (Excluding Ireland)
Tel: 01432 850850 **Fax:** 01432 850064
Email: mail@easylawn.co.uk
Web: www.easylawn.co.uk

ENVIROMAT BY Q LAWNS
Corkway Drove, Hockwold, Thetford, Norfolk, IP26 4JR
Area of Operation: UK (Excluding Ireland)
Tel: 01842 828266 **Fax:** 01842 827911
Email: sales@qlawns.co.uk
Web: www.enviromat.co.uk ⌐⊕

FGM CLAYMORE
Waterloo Industrial Estate, Waterloo Road,
Bidford on Avon, Warwickshire, B50 4JH
Area of Operation: UK (Excluding Ireland)
Tel: 01789 490177
Fax: 01789 490170
Email: sales@fgmclaymore.co.uk
Web: www.fgmclaymore.co.uk

GREENSCENE
The Nursery, Gunnersbury Park, London, W3 8LQ
Area of Operation: UK (Excluding Ireland)
Tel: 0845 345 9808 **Fax:** 0845 345 9809
Email: info@greenscene.com
Web: www.greenscene.com

HILLIER LANDSCAPES
Ampfield House, Ampfield,
Romsey, Hampshire, SO51 9PA
Area of Operation: South East England, South West England and South Wales
Tel: 01794 368855 **Fax:** 01794 368866
Email: hillierlandscapes@btinternet.com
Web: www.hillier-landscapes.co.uk **Other Info:** ✎

HYDRO TURF LTD
Papercourt Farm, Papercourt Lane,
Ripley, Surrey, GU23 6DT
Area of Operation: UK & Ireland
Tel: 0845 838 0708
Email: info@hydroturf.co.uk
Web: www.hydroturf.co.uk **Other Info:** ECO

PROTURF LTD
North Carr Farm, North Carr Road, West Stockwith,
Doncaster, South Yorkshire, DN10 4BD
Area of Operation: Europe
Tel: 01427 890797 **Fax:** 01427 891785
Email: info@proturf.co.uk
Web: www.proturf.co.uk **Other Info:** ECO ✎

Q LAWNS
Corkway Drove, Hockwold,
Thetford, Norfolk, IP26 4JR
Area of Operation: UK (Excluding Ireland)
Tel: 01842 828266 **Fax:** 01842 827911
Email: sales@qlawns.co.uk
Web: www.qlawns.co.uk ⌐⊕

RIVAR SAND & GRAVEL LTD
Pinchington Lane, Newbury, Berkshire, RG19 8SR
Area of Operation: South East England
Tel: 01635 523524 **Fax:** 01635 521621
Email: sales@rivarsandandgravel.co.uk
Web: www.rivarsandandgravel.co.uk

ROLAWN LIMITED
Elvington, York, North Yorkshire, YO41 4XR
Area of Operation: UK & Ireland
Tel: 0845 604 6050 **Fax:** 01904 608272
Email: info@rolawn.co.uk
Web: www.rolawn.co.uk/www.topsoil.co.uk ⌐⊕

TEAL TURF CO. LTD
Teal Trading Ltd, Wadborough,
Worcester, Worcestershire, WR8 9HJ
Area of Operation: UK (Excluding Ireland)
Tel: 01905 840279 **Fax:** 01905 841460
Email: enquiries@tealturf.co.uk
Web: www.tealturf.co.uk ⌐⊕

TURF CENTRE
Ham Barn Farm, Farnham Road,
Liss, Hampshire, GU33 6LG
Area of Operation: South East England, South West England and South Wales
Tel: 01420 538188 **Fax:** 01420 538208
Email: turfcentre@btinternet.com
Web: www.turfcentre.co.uk

TREES & SHRUBS

KEY
OTHER: ▽ Reclaimed ⌐⊕ On-line shopping
✎ Bespoke ✋ Hand-made ECO Ecological

BILLY ROOT WATERING SYSTEM
Tricor Services Ltd, 7 Hill Street,
Douglas, Isle of Man, IM1 1EF
Area of Operation: Worldwide
Tel: 0870 446 2888 **Fax:** 0845 280 2582
Email: info@tricolor.co.uk
Web: www.tricolor.co.uk ⌐⊕

CEDAR NURSERY
Horsley Road, Cobham, Surrey, KT11 3JX
Area of Operation: UK & Ireland
Tel: 01932 862473 **Fax:** 01932 867152
Email: sales@landscaping.co.uk
Web: www.landscaping.co.uk

CROWN NURSERY
High Street, Ufford, Ipswich, Suffolk, IP13 6EL
Area of Operation: UK (Excluding Ireland)
Tel: 01394 460755 **Fax:** 01394 460142
Email: enquiries@crown-nursery.co.uk

DEACONS NURSERY
Moorview, Godshill, Isle of Wight, PO38 3HW
Area of Operation: UK & Ireland
Tel: 01983 522243
Fax: 01983 523575
Email: info@deaconsnurseryfruits.co.uk
Web: www.deaconsnurseryfruits.co.uk ⌐⊕

FRUIT TREES AND BUSHES
GROWN BY DEACON'S NURSERY

DEACONS NURSERY
Area of Operation: UK & Ireland
Tel: 01983 522243 **Fax:** 01983 523575
Email: info@deaconsnurseryfruits.co.uk
Web: www.deaconsnurseryfruits.co.uk

Established for forty years, at Deacons Nursery we grow: Apples, Pears, Cherries, Peaches, Plums, Nectarines, Apricots, Medlars, Raspberries, Strawberries, Blackberries, Blackcurrants, Loganberrries, Gooseberries & Hybrid Berries, Grapes, Hops etc.

EAST OF EDEN PLANTS
38 St. Andrews Street, Millbrook,
Torpoint, Cornwall, PL10 1BE
Area of Operation: UK & Ireland **Tel:** 01752 822782
Email: info@eastofedenplants.co.uk
Web: www.eastofedenplants.co.uk ⌐⊕

GARDEN OASIS LIMITED
Garden Oasis, 3 Caradoc, Glascote,
Tamworth, Staffordshire, B77 2DX
Area of Operation: UK & Ireland
Tel: 01827 706110 **Fax:** 01827 706110
Email: sales@gardenoasis.co.uk
Web: www.gardenoasis.co.uk ⌐⊕

GREENSCENE
The Nursery, Gunnersbury Park, London, W3 8LQ
Area of Operation: UK (Excluding Ireland)
Tel: 0845 345 9808 **Fax:** 0845 345 9809
Email: info@greenscene.com
Web: www.greenscene.com

HILLIER LANDSCAPES
Ampfield House, Ampfield,
Romsey, Hampshire, SO51 9PA
Area of Operation: South East England, South West England and South Wales
Tel: 01794 368855 **Fax:** 01794 368866
Email: hillierlandscapes@btinternet.com
Web: www.hillier-landscapes.co.uk **Other Info:** ✎

MAJESTIC TREES
Chequers Meadow, Chequers Hill,
Flamstead, St. Albans, Hertfordshire, AL3 8ET
Area of Operation: UK & Ireland
Tel: 01582 843881 **Fax:** 01582 843882
Email: info@majesticgroup.co.uk
Web: www.majestictrees.co.uk

PREMIERTREES
The Garden House, Southill Park, Southill,
Nr.Biggleswade, Bedfordshire, SG18 9LL
Area of Operation: UK (Excluding Ireland)
Tel: 01462 813390 **Fax:** 01462 813392
Web: www.premiertrees.com

TODD'S BOTANICS
West Street, Coggeshall, Colchester, Essex, CO6 1NT
Area of Operation: UK (Excluding Ireland)
Tel: 01376 561212 **Fax:** 01376 561212
Email: info@toddsbotanics.co.uk
Web: www.toddsbotanics.co.uk ⌐⊕

WEASDALE NURSERIES LTD
Newbiggin on Lune,
Kirkby Stephen, Cumbria, CA17 4LX
Area of Operation: Europe
Tel: 01539 623246 **Fax:** 01539 623277
Email: sales@weasdale.com
Web: www.weasdale.com

WYEVALE NURSERIES LTD
Kings Acre, Hereford, Herefordshire, HR4 7AY
Area of Operation: UK (Excluding Ireland)
Tel: 01432 845200 **Fax:** 01432 845227
Email: info@wyevalenurseries.co.uk
Web: www.wyevalenurseries.co.uk

WATER FEATURES & AQUATICS

KEY
SEE ALSO: GARDEN ACCESSORIES AND DECORATIVE FEATURES - Ornamental Stonework
PRODUCT TYPES: 1= Fountains 2 = Statuary 3 = Pond Liners 4 = Pumps
OTHER: ▽ Reclaimed ⌐⊕ On-line shopping
✎ Bespoke ✋ Hand-made ECO Ecological

ACE MINIMIX
Millfields Road, Ettingshall,
Wolverhampton, West Midlands, WV4 6JP
Area of Operation: UK (Excluding Ireland)
Tel: 0121 5855559 **Fax:** 0121 585 5557
Email: info@tarmac.co.uk **Web:** www.tarmac.co.uk

ARCHITECTURAL HERITAGE
Taddington Manor, Taddington, Nr Cutsdean,
Cheltenham, Gloucestershire, GL54 5RY
Area of Operation: Worldwide
Tel: 01386 584414 **Fax:** 01386 584236
Email: puddy@architectural-heritage.co.uk
Web: www.architectural-heritage.co.uk
Product Type: 1

ART OUTSIDE
PO Box 513, Aylesbury, Buckinghamshire, HP22 6WJ
Area of Operation: Worldwide
Tel: 07813 881480 **Email:** emma@art-outside.com
Web: www.art-outside.com ⌐⊕
Product Type: 1, 2 **Other Info:** ✎

ARTPARKS INTERNATIONAL LTD
Sausmarez Manor, St. Martin, Guernsey, GY4 6SG
Area of Operation: Worldwide
Tel: 01481 235571 **Fax:** 01481 235572
Email: peter@artparks.co.uk
Web: www.artparks.co.uk **Product Type:** 1, 2

BARRY SIMS
11 Bognor Road, Chichester, West Sussex, PO19 7TF
Area of Operation: UK & Ireland
Tel: 07787 987652 **Email:** info@barrysims.biz
Web: www.barrysims.biz **Product Type:** 1

BILLY ROOT WATERING SYSTEM
Tricor Services Ltd, 7 Hill Street,
Douglas, Isle of Man, IM1 1EF
Area of Operation: Worldwide
Tel: 0870 446 2888 **Fax:** 0845 280 2582
Email: info@tricolor.co.uk **Web:** www.tricolor.co.uk ⌐⊕

BLOWZONE HOT STUDIO
The Ruskin Glass Centre, Wollaston Road,
Amblecote, West Midlands, DY8 4HF
Tel: 01384 399464 **Fax:** 01384 377746
Email: sales@blowzone.co.uk
Web: www.blowzone.co.uk **Product Type:** 1

EXTERIOR PRODUCTS

CEDAR NURSERY
Horsley Road, Cobham, Surrey, KT11 3JX
Area of Operation: UK & Ireland
Tel: 01932 862473   **Fax:** 01932 867152
Email: sales@landscaping.co.uk
Web: www.landscaping.co.uk   **Product Type:** 1, 2

CHILSTONE
Victoria Park, Fordcombe Road,
Langton Green, Kent, TN3 0RD
Area of Operation: Worldwide
Tel: 01892 740866   **Fax:** 01892 740249
Email: ornaments@chilstone.com
Web: www.chilstone.com
Product Type: 1, 2   **Material Type:** E) 13

COOLSCAPES LTD - PHOTO ROLLER BLINDS
114a Top Lane, Whitley,
Melksham, Wiltshire, SN12 8QU
Area of Operation: Worldwide
Tel: 01225 702938
Email: info@coolscapes.co.uk
Web: www.photorollerblinds.co.uk

CRESS WATER LTD
18 Forcefield Road, Cullompton, Devon, EX15 1QB
Area of Operation: Europe
Tel: 01884 839000   **Fax:** 01884 839909
Email: info@cresswater.co.uk
Web: www.cresswater.co.uk

DESIGNS IN STAINLESS LTD
Unit 2 Semley Business Park, Station Road,
Semley, Shaftesbury, Dorset, SP7 9AN
Area of Operation: Worldwide
Tel: 01747 855802   **Fax:** 01747 855803
Email: info@designs-in-stainless.co.uk
Web: www.designs-in-stainless.co.uk
Product Type: 1   **Other Info:**
Material Type: C) 3

FOUNTAINHEAD LTD
97-101 North Road, Kew, Richmond, Surrey, TW9 4HJ
Area of Operation: Worldwide
Tel: 0208 876 9595   **Fax:** 0208 876 6655
Email: adam@fountainheadlimited.com
Web: www.fountainheadlimited.com
Product Type: 1, 2, 4   **Other Info:**

GARDEN OASIS LIMITED
Garden Oasis, 3 Caradoc, Glascote,
Tamworth, Staffordshire, B77 2DX
Area of Operation: UK & Ireland
Tel: 01827 706110   **Fax:** 01827 706110
Email: sales@gardenoasis.co.uk
Web: www.gardenoasis.co.uk
Product Type: 1, 2, 3, 4

GREENFINGERS.COM
10 Lindsay Square, Deans Industrial Estate,
Livingston, Lothian, EH54 8RL
Area of Operation: UK (Excluding Ireland)
Tel: 0845 345 0728
Email: customer.services@greenfingers.com
Web: www.greenfingers.com
Product Type: 1, 2

HADDONSTONE LTD
The Forge House, East Haddon,
Northampton, Northamptonshire, NN6 8DB
Area of Operation: Worldwide
Tel: 01604 770711   **Fax:** 01604 770027
Email: info@haddonstone.co.uk
Web: www.haddonstone.com   **Product Type:** 1, 2

HADDONSTONE
Area of Operation: Worldwide
Tel: 01604 770711   **Fax:** 01604 770027
Email: info@haddonstone.co.uk
Web: www.haddonstone.com
Product Type: 1, 2
Other Info:

Haddonstone has an extensive range of cast
stone pool surrounds and fountains including
multi-tiered, figured and self-contained.
Traditional, classical and contemporary styles.

HILLIER LANDSCAPES
Ampfield House, Ampfield,
Romsey, Hampshire, SO51 9PA
Area of Operation: South East England, South West
England and South Wales
Tel: 01794 368855   **Fax:** 01794 368866
Email: hillierlandscapes@btinternet.com
Web: www.hillier-landscapes.co.uk
Other Info:

INSIDE OUT GARDEN ORNAMENTS
High Street, Wallcrouch,
Wadhurst, East Sussex, TN5 7JL
Area of Operation: UK (Excluding Ireland)
Tel: 01580 200399
Email: sales@insideout-ornaments.co.uk
Web: www.insideout-ornaments.co.uk
Product Type: 1, 2

IRIS WATER & DESIGN
Langburn Bank, Castleton,
Whitby, North Yorkshire, YO21 2EU
Area of Operation: Europe
Tel: 01287 660002   **Fax:** 01287 660004
Email: info@iriswater.com
Web: www.iriswater.com
Product Type: 1, 2, 3, 4

JANKOWSKI WEATHERVANES,
FOUNTAINS, SIGNS & GARDEN ART
Bryn Melyn, Llanwddyn, Oswestry, Powys, SY10 0LP
Area of Operation: Worldwide
Tel: 01691 870311
Email: stan@panjankowski.co.uk
Web: www.panjankowski.co.uk   **Product Type:** 1

KIRK NATURAL STONE
Bridgend, Fyvie, Turriff, Aberdeenshire, AB53 8LL
Area of Operation: Worldwide
Tel: 01651 891891   **Fax:** 01651 891794
Email: info@kirknaturalstone.com
Web: www.kirknaturalstone.com
Product Type: 1, 2

POND CREATIONS
19 Bramley Chase, Ipswich, Suffolk, IP4 4LW
Area of Operation: East England, Greater London
Tel: 01473 712430
Fax: 01473 712430
Email: enquiries@pondcreations.co.uk
Web: www.pondcreations.co.uk
Product Type: 1, 3, 4   **Other Info:** ECO

POND GUARD/DAVREN ENTERPRISES
Units 1-1b, Central Industrial Estate, Rear 138/146
Bolton Road, Atherton, Greater Manchester, M46 9LF
Area of Operation: UK (Excluding Ireland)
Tel: 01942 888601   **Fax:** 01942 888601
Email: info@davren.co.uk
Web: www.pondguardonline.co.uk

PROTURF LTD
North Carr Farm, North Carr Road, West Stockwith,
Doncaster, South Yorkshire, DN10 4BD
Area of Operation: Europe
Tel: 01427 890797   **Fax:** 01427 891785
Email: info@proturf.co.uk
Web: www.proturf.co.uk   **Product Type:** 1

RIVAR SAND & GRAVEL LTD
Pinchington Lane, Newbury, Berkshire, RG19 8SR
Area of Operation: South East England
Tel: 01635 523524
Fax: 01635 521621
Email: sales@rivarsandandgravel.co.uk
Web: www.rivarsandandgravel.co.uk
Product Type: 1

THE CANE STORE
Wash Dyke Cottage, No1 Witham Road,
Long Bennington, Lincolnshire, NG23 5DS
Area of Operation: Worldwide
Tel: 01400 282271   **Fax:** 01400 281103
Email: jaki@canestore.co.uk
Web: www.canestore.co.uk   **Product Type:** 2

TITAN ENVIRONMENTAL LIMITED
Barbot Hall Industrial Estate, Mangham Road,
Rotherham, South Yorkshire, S61 4RJ
Area of Operation: Europe
Tel: 01709 538300   **Fax:** 01709 538301
Email: tony.soper@titanenv.com
Web: www.titanenv.com

WATERFEATURES2GO.COM
diy2go Ltd, Aquila, Woodgates Close,
North Ferriby, East Riding of Yorks, HU14 3JS
Area of Operation: Worldwide
Tel: 0845 094 2271   **Fax:** 01482 633334
Email: support@waterfeatures2go.co.uk
Web: www.waterfeatures2go.co.uk
Product Type: 1, 2, 4
Material Type: C) 1, 2, 3, 5, 7, 8

NOTES

Company Name ....
....
Address ....
....
....
email ....
Web ....

Company Name ....
....
Address ....
....
....
email ....
Web ....

Company Name ....
....
Address ....
....
....
email ....
Web ....

Image courtesy of Enviromat by Q Lawns (01842 828266)

EXTERIOR PRODUCTS

Garden Accessories

Simple ornaments and furniture can brighten up the green space behind your home, and transform it from an empty garden into a real conversation topic. A few tasteful accessories, in the right places, can help create an area for entertaining or relaxing in style.

Stylish garden ornaments can accentuate your garden's best features. Choose items which are both elegant and interesting to you – this may be a sundial or an original statue – and you never know, the feature may even impress your visitors too.

No matter where you place your garden ornaments, make sure that they are high quality and blend well with their surroundings. If you have created a specifically styled garden, make sure that you use accessories which adhere to the theme – a Victorian statue will look completely out of place in a minimalist Japanese garden, for example.

It is best to select a few well-appointed garden ornaments, rather than crowding in as many as possible. Simple classic pieces such as sundials or fountains can make an excellent centrepiece, and the addition of some elegant garden furniture will ensure that you have a space for alfresco dining and entertaining.

Creating a sense of space

If you don't have a huge garden, clever use of ornaments and decorative features can help to make the space seem larger than it actually is. Placing a bench or ornament at the end of a long, straight path can create a sense of scale, as well as providing an incentive for you and your friends to walk further into the garden.

Well-positioned mirrors can reflect pathways and make them appear to extend beyond a boundary wall or fence. Similarly, obelisks, arches and statues can provide additional height to beds and borders.

Another trick is to use large pots or containers close to the house and smaller ones further away, thus fooling the eye into creating distance and perspective. Pots can also invigorate a dull, basic patio with some much-needed shape and colour.

This Lunar patio feature from Marshalls was designed by Diarmuid Gavin, and is a prime example of how a few simple accessories can enhance and make full use of your patio space.

ORNAMENTAL STONEWORK

KEY
OTHER: ▽ Reclaimed   ⌐⊖ On-line shopping
✑ Bespoke   ✋ Hand-made   ECO Ecological

A D CALVERT ARCHITECTURAL STONE SUPPLIES LTD
Smithy Lane, Grove Square,
Leyburn, North Yorkshire, DL8 5DZ
Area of Operation: UK & Ireland
Tel: 01969 622515 **Fax:** 01969 624345
Email: stone@calverts.co.uk
Web: www.calverts.co.uk

ARCHITECTURAL HERITAGE
Taddington Manor, Taddington, Nr Cutsdean,
Cheltenham, Gloucestershire, GL54 5RY
Area of Operation: Worldwide
Tel: 01386 584414 **Fax:** 01386 584236
Email: puddy@architectural-heritage.co.uk
Web: www.architectural-heritage.co.uk
Other Info: ▽

ART OUTSIDE
PO Box 513, Aylesbury, Buckinghamshire, HP22 6WJ
Area of Operation: Worldwide
Tel: 07813 881480
Email: emma@art-outside.com
Web: www.art-outside.com ⌐⊖

ARTPARKS INTERNATIONAL LTD
Sausmarez Manor, St. Martin, Guernsey, GY4 6SG
Area of Operation: Worldwide
Tel: 01481 235571 **Fax:** 01481 235572
Email: peter@artparks.co.uk
Web: www.artparks.co.uk **Other Info:** ✑ ✋

ASPECTS OF STONE LTD
Unit 29, Broughton Grounds, Broughton,
Newport Pagnell, Buckinghamshire, MK16 0HZ
Area of Operation: UK (Excluding Ireland)
Tel: 01908 830061 **Fax:** 01908 830062
Email: sales@aspectsofstone.co.uk
Web: www.aspectsofstone.co.uk

BRADSTONE GARDEN
Aggregate Industries UK Ltd, Hulland Ward,
Ashbourne, Derbyshire, DE6 3ET
Area of Operation: UK (Excluding Ireland)
Tel: 01335 372222 **Fax:** 01335 370973
Email: bradstone.garden@aggregate.com
Web: www.bradstone.com

BRS YORK STONE
50 High Green Road, Altofts,
Normanton, Lancashire, WF6 2LQ
Area of Operation: UK (Excluding Ireland)
Tel: 01924 220356 **Fax:** 01924 220356
Email: john@york-stone.fsnet.co.uk
Web: www.yorkstonepaving.co.uk

CHILSTONE
Victoria Park, Fordcombe Road,
Langton Green, Kent, TN3 0RD
Area of Operation: Worldwide
Tel: 01892 740866 **Fax:** 01892 740249
Email: ornaments@chilstone.com
Web: www.chilstone.com ⌐⊖

DENBY DALE CAST PRODUCTS LTD
230 Cumberworth Lane, Denby Dale,
Huddersfield, West Yorkshire, HD8 8PR
Area of Operation: UK & Ireland
Tel: 01484 863560 **Fax:** 01484 865597
Email: mail@denbydalecastproducts.co.uk
Web: www.denbydalecastproducts.co.uk

DEVON STONE LTD
8 Pilot Road, Pierhead, Exmouth, Devon, EX8 1XA
Area of Operation: UK (Excluding Ireland)
Tel: 01395 222525
Email: amy@devonstone.com
Web: www.devonstone.com **Other Info:** ▽ ✑ ✋

HADDONSTONE LTD
The Forge House, East Haddon,
Northampton, Northamptonshire, NN6 8DB
Area of Operation: Worldwide
Tel: 01604 770711 **Fax:** 01604 770027
Email: info@haddonstone.co.uk
Web: www.haddonstone.com ⌐⊖

HADDONSTONE
Area of Operation: Worldwide
Tel: 01604 770711 **Fax:** 01604 770027
Email: info@haddonstone.co.uk
Web: www.haddonstone.com
Other Info: ⌐⊖ ✋ ✑

Haddonstone manufacture garden ornaments and architectural cast stone from porticos, gate piers and balustrading to planters, fountains and fireplaces. Extensive standard range. Custom made also available.

INSIDE OUT GARDEN ORNAMENTS
High Street, Wallcrouch,
Wadhurst, East Sussex, TN5 7JL
Area of Operation: UK (Excluding Ireland)
Tel: 01580 200399 **Other Info:** ✋
Email: sales@insideout-ornaments.co.uk
Web: www.insideout-ornaments.co.uk

KENT BALUSTERS
1 Gravesend Road, Strood, Kent, ME2 3PH
Area of Operation: UK (Excluding Ireland)
Tel: 01634 711617 **Fax:** 01634 714644
Email: info@kentbalusters.co.uk
Web: www.kentbalusters.co.uk **Other Info:** ✑ ✋

KIRK NATURAL STONE
Bridgend, Fyvie, Turriff, Aberdeenshire, AB53 8LL
Area of Operation: Worldwide
Tel: 01651 891891 **Fax:** 01651 891794
Email: info@kirknaturalstone.com
Web: www.kirknaturalstone.com

MEADOWSTONE (DERBYSHIRE) LTD
West Way, Somercotes, Derbyshire, DE55 4QJ
Area of Operation: UK & Ireland
Tel: 01773 540707 **Fax:** 01773 527261
Email: info@meadowstone.co.uk
Web: www.meadowstone.co.uk ⌐⊖ **Other Info:** ✑ ✋

PATTISONS ARCHITECTURAL ANTIQUES
108 London Road, Aston Clinton,
Buckinghamshire, HP22 5HS
Area of Operation: Worldwide
Tel: 01296 632300 **Fax:** 01296 631329
Email: info@ddd-uk.com **Web:** www.ddd-uk.com

PHILLIP FLOCKHART
Flat 3/61 Wilton Road, Bexhill on Sea,
East Sussex, TN40 1HX **Tel:** 01424 731807
Email: phillip_flockhart@yahoo.co.uk
Web: www.phil-flockhart-artist.com
Other Info: ▽ ECO ✑ ✋

PROTURF LTD
North Carr Farm, North Carr Road, West Stockwith,
Doncaster, South Yorkshire, DN10 4BD
Area of Operation: Europe
Tel: 01427 890797
Fax: 01427 891785
Email: info@proturf.co.uk
Web: www.proturf.co.uk
Other Info: ▽

ROCK UNIQUE LTD
c/o Select Garden and Pet Centre,
Main Road, Sundridge, Kent, TN14 6ED
Area of Operation: Europe
Tel: 01959 565608 **Fax:** 01959 569312
Email: stone@rock-unique.com
Web: www.rock-unique.com **Other Info:** ▽ ✑ ✋

THE INDIAN GARDEN CO
The Croft, Kingwood Common,
Nr Henley on Thames, Oxfordshire, RG9 5NB
Area of Operation: Worldwide
Tel: 01491 628584 **Fax:** 01492 628927
Email: info@indiangardencompany.co.uk
Web: www.indiangardencompany.co.uk ⌐⊖
Other Info: ✑ ✋

THE MASON'S YARD
Penhenllan, Cusop, Hay on Wye, Herefordshire, HR3 5TE
Area of Operation: UK (Excluding Ireland)
Tel: 01497 821333
Email: hugh@themasonsyard.co.uk
Web: www.themasonsyard.co.uk

VOUSTONE DESIGNS LIMITED
Kingdom Cottage, Tibbs Court Lane,
Brenchley, Nr. Tonbridge, Kent, TN12 7AH
Area of Operation: UK (Excluding Ireland)
Tel: 01892 722449 **Fax:** 01892 722573
Email: sales@voustone.co.uk **Other Info:** ✑ ✋

WARMSWORTH STONE LTD
1-3 Sheffield Road, Warmsworth,
Doncaster, South Yorkshire, DN4 9QH
Area of Operation: UK & Ireland
Tel: 01302 858617 **Fax:** 01302 855844
Email: info@warmsworth-stone.co.uk
Web: www.warmsworth-stone.co.uk
Other Info: ✑ ✋

WELLS CATHEDRAL STONEMASONS
Brunel Stoneworks, Station Road,
Cheddar, Somerset, BS27 3AH
Area of Operation: Worldwide
Tel: 01934 743544 **Fax:** 01934 744536
Email: wcs@stone-mason.co.uk
Web: www.stone-mason.co.uk

GARDEN AND PATIO FURNITURE

KEY
OTHER: ▽ Reclaimed   ⌐⊖ On-line shopping
✑ Bespoke   ✋ Hand-made   ECO Ecological

ALTHAM OAK & CARPENTRY LTD
Altham Corn Mill, Burnley Road,
Altham, Accrington, Lancashire, BB5 5UP
Area of Operation: UK & Ireland
Tel: 01282 771618 **Fax:** 01282 777932
Email: info@oak-beams.co.uk
Web: www.oak-beams.co.uk **Other Info:** ECO ✑ ✋

ANDY THORNTON LTD
Ainleys Industrial Estate,
Elland, West Yorkshire, HX5 9JP
Area of Operation: Worldwide
Tel: 01422 375595 **Fax:** 01422 377455
Email: marketing@ataa.co.uk
Web: www.andythornton.com

ART OUTSIDE
PO Box 513, Aylesbury, Buckinghamshire, HP22 6WJ
Area of Operation: Worldwide
Tel: 07813 881480
Email: emma@art-outside.com
Web: www.art-outside.com ⌐⊖ **Other Info:** ▽ ✑ ✋

B ROURKE & CO LTD
Vulcan Works, Accrington Road,
Burnley, Lancashire, BB11 5QD
Area of Operation: Worldwide
Tel: 01282 422841 **Fax:** 01282 458901
Email: info@rourkes.co.uk
Web: www.rourkes.co.uk

BEAVER TIMBER COMPANY
Barcaldine, Argyll & Bute, PA37 1SG
Area of Operation: UK (Excluding Ireland)
Tel: 01631 720353 **Fax:** 01631 720430
Email: info@beavertimber.co.uk
Web: www.beavertimber.co.uk ⌐⊖

BUYDESIGN
Monteviot Nurseries, Ancrum,
Jedburgh, Borders, TD8 6TU
Area of Operation: Scotland
Tel: 01835 830740
Email: enquries@buydesign-furniture.com
Web: www.buydesign-furniture.com

C&V CARMICHAEL LTD
Fabrication Facility, Mossmorran,
Cowdenbeath, Fife, KY4 8EP
Area of Operation: UK (Excluding Ireland)
Tel: 01383 510469
Fax: 01383 610515
Email: cvcarmichael@cvcarmichael.com
Web: www.cvcarmichael.com

C.J. BLACKSMITHS
Yr Eithin, Llangynog, Oswestry, Powys, SY10 0HA
Area of Operation: Worldwide
Tel: 01691 860750 **Fax:** 01691 860750
Email: sales@cjblacksmiths.co.uk
Web: www.cjblacksmiths.co.uk/
www.thecastironemporium.co.uk ⌐⊖
Other Info: ▽ ✋

CAMERON PETERS LTD
The Old Dairy, Home Farm, Ardington,
Wantage, Oxfordshire, OX12 8PD
Area of Operation: Worldwide
Tel: 01235 835000 **Fax:** 01235 835005
Email: info@cameronpeters.co.uk
Web: www.cameronpeters.co.uk

CEDAR NURSERY
Horsley Road, Cobham, Surrey, KT11 3JX
Area of Operation: UK & Ireland
Tel: 01932 862473 **Fax:** 01932 867152
Email: sales@landscaping.co.uk
Web: www.landscaping.co.uk

CHAIRWORKS
47 Weir Road, London, SW19 8UG
Area of Operation: UK (Excluding Ireland)
Tel: 0208 247 3700 **Fax:** 0208 247 3800
Email: info@chairworks.info
Web: www.chairworks.info

ENCOMPASS FURNITURE & ACCESSORIES
The Pool Room, Stansted House, Stansted Park,
Rowlands Castle, Hampshire, PO9 6DX
Area of Operation: Worldwide
Tel: 02392 410045 **Fax:** 02392 412145
Email: info@encompassco.com
Web: www.encompassco.com **Other Info:** ✑

FATBOY
Enterprise D2 Ltd, Unit D2 Enterprise Way,
Vale Park, Evesham, Worcestershire, WR11 1GS
Area of Operation: UK (Excluding Ireland)
Tel: 01386 423760
Email: leeb@fatboy-uk.com
Web: www.fatboy-uk.com ⌐⊖

FURNITURE123.CO.UK
Sandway Business Centre,
Shannon Street, Leeds, West Yorkshire, LS9 8SS
Area of Operation: UK & Ireland
Tel: 0113 248 2233
Fax: 0113 248 2266
Email: p.haddock@furniture123.co.uk
Web: www.furniture123.co.uk ⌐⊖

GARDEN OASIS LIMITED
Garden Oasis, 3 Caradoc, Glascote,
Tamworth, Staffordshire, B77 2DX
Area of Operation: UK & Ireland
Tel: 01827 706110
Fax: 01827 706110
Email: sales@gardenoasis.co.uk
Web: www.gardenoasis.co.uk ⌐⊖

EXTERIOR PRODUCTS

GEORGE BARKER & SONS
Backbarrow, Nr Ulverston, Cumbria, LA12 8TA
Area of Operation: UK (Excluding Ireland)
Tel: 01539 531236   **Fax:** 01539 530801
Web: www.gbs-ltd.co.uk

GLASSWORK
73 Victor Road, Teddington, Middlesex, TW11 8SP
Tel: 0208 943 3177
Email: michaelwnewby@yahoo.com
Web: www.glassworkteddington.co.uk
Other Info: ✍ ✋

GREENFINGERS.COM
10 Lindsay Square, Deans Industrial Estate,
Livingston, Lothian, EH54 8RL
Area of Operation: UK (Excluding Ireland)
Tel: 0845 345 0728
Email: customer.services@greenfingers.com
Web: www.greenfingers.com ⌐🛒

HADDONCRAFT FORGE
The Forge House, East Haddon,
Northampton, Northamptonshire, NN6 8DB
Tel: 01604 772027   **Fax:** 01604 770027
Email: info@haddoncraft.co.uk
Web: www.haddoncraft.co.uk
Other Info: ✍ ✋

INSIDE OUT GARDEN ORNAMENTS
High Street, Wallcrouch,
Wadhurst, East Sussex, TN5 7JL
Area of Operation: UK (Excluding Ireland)
Tel: 01580 200399
Email: sales@insideout-ornaments.co.uk
Web: www.insideout-ornaments.co.uk
Other Info: ✋

IRONART OF BATH
Upper Lambridge Street, Larkhall,
Bath, Somerset, BA1 6RY
Tel: 01225 311273   **Fax:** 01225 443060
Email: ironart@btinternet.com
Web: www.ironart.co.uk

LLOYD CHRISTIE
Greystones, Sudbrook Lane, Petersham, TW10 7AT
Area of Operation: Worldwide
Tel: 020 8332 6766
Fax: 020 8332 2229
Email: info@lloydchristie.com
Web: www.lloydchristie.com

MADE ON EARTH LTD
Units A & B, The Coach Works, Kingsfield Lane,
Longwell Green, Bristol, BS30 6DL
Area of Operation: Europe
Tel: 0845 095 6161
Fax: 0845 095 6162
Email: info@made-on-earth.co.uk
Web: www.made-on-earth.co.uk

MIRRORKOOL LTD
89 High Street, Earith, Cambridgeshire, PE28 3PN
Area of Operation: Worldwide
Tel: 01487 741300
Fax: 08712 367554
Email: sam@mirrorkool.com
Web: www.mirrorkool.com ⌐🛒

NUMBER 9 STUDIO UK
ARCHITECTURAL CERAMICS
Mole Cottage Industries, Mole Cottage,
Watertown, Chittlehamholt, Devon, EX37 9HF
Area of Operation: Worldwide
Tel: 01769 540471
Fax: 01769 540471
Email: arch.ceramics@moley.uk.com
Web: www.moley.uk.com

OSMO UK LTD
Unit 24 Anglo Business Park, Smeaton Close,
Aylesbury, Buckinghamshire, HP19 8UP
Area of Operation: UK & Ireland
Tel: 01296 481220
Fax: 01296 424090
Email: info@osmouk.com
Web: www.osmouk.com

ROBERT LONGSTAFF WORKSHOPS
Longstaff Workshops, Appleton Road,
Longworth, Oxfordshire, OX13 5EF
Area of Operation: Worldwide
Tel: 01865 820206
Email: robert@longstaff.co.uk
Web: www.longstaff.co.uk ⌐🛒
Other Info: ECO ✍ ✋

RUSTIC WOODLAND
Canterbury Road, Wingham,
Canterbury, Kent, CT3 1NH
Area of Operation: UK (Excluding Ireland)
Tel: 0845 260 0876
Email: info@rusticwoodland.com
Web: www.rusticwoodland.com ⌐🛒

STONES DEVELOPMENT (UK) LTD
Unit 2 Irradion House, Southdown Industrial Estate,
Harpenden, Hertfordshire, AL5 1PW
Area of Operation: Europe
Tel: 0800 121 8320
Fax: 01727 862009
Email: info@stonestimber.co.uk
Web: www.stonestimber.co.uk

THE GREEN SHOP
Cheltenham Road, Bisley,
Nr. Stroud, Gloucestershire, GL6 7BX
Area of Operation: UK & Ireland
Tel: 01452 770629
Fax: 01452 770104
Email: paint@greenshop.co.uk
Web: www.greenshop.co.uk ⌐🛒

THE INDIAN GARDEN CO
The Croft, Kingwood Common,
Nr. Henley on Thames, Oxfordshire, RG9 5NB
Area of Operation: Worldwide
Tel: 01491 628584   **Fax:** 01492 628927
Email: info@indiangardencompany.co.uk
Web: www.indiangardencompany.co.uk ⌐🛒
Other Info: ▽ ECO ✍ ✋

TITAN ENVIRONMENTAL LIMITED
Barbot Hall Industrial Estate, Mangham Road,
Rotherham, South Yorkshire, S61 4RJ
Area of Operation: Europe
Tel: 01709 538300
Fax: 01709 538301
Email: tony.soper@titanenv.com
Web: www.titanenv.com

WWW.DIRECT-CANE.CO.UK
123 Richards Street, Cathays, Cardiff, CF24 4DD
Area of Operation: UK & Ireland
Tel: 02920 664600
Email: sales@direct-cane.co.uk
Web: www.direct-cane.co.uk ⌐🛒

SIGNS & MAILBOXES

KEY
OTHER: ▽ Reclaimed   ⌐🛒 On-line shopping
✍ Bespoke   ✋ Hand-made   ECO Ecological

ART OUTSIDE
PO Box 513, Aylesbury, Buckinghamshire, HP22 6WJ
Area of Operation: Worldwide
Tel: 07813 881480   **mail:** emma@art-outside.com
Web: www.art-outside.com ⌐🛒
Other Info: ✍ ✋

B ROURKE & CO LTD
Vulcan Works, Accrington Road,
Burnley, Lancashire, BB11 5QD
Area of Operation: Worldwide
Tel: 01282 422841
Fax: 01282 458901
Email: info@rourkes.co.uk
Web: www.rourkes.co.uk

C.J.BLACKSMITHS
Yr Eithin, Lllangynog, Oswestry, Powys, SY100HA
Area of Operation: Worldwide
Tel: 01691 860750 **Fax:** 01691 860750
Email: sales@cjblacksmiths.co.uk
Web: www.cjblacksmiths.co.uk/
www.thecastironemporium.co.uk

CASTAWAY CAST PRODUCTS AND WOODWARE
Brocklesby Station, Brocklesby Road,
Ulceby, Lincolnshire, DN39 6ST
Area of Operation: Worldwide
Tel: 01469 588995 **Fax:** 01469 588995
Email: castawaycastproducts@btinternet.com
Other Info:

DELABOLE SLATE COMPANY
Pengelly, Delabole, Cornwall, PL33 9AZ
Area of Operation: UK & Ireland
Tel: 01840 212242 **Fax:** 01840 212948
Email: sales@delaboleslate.co.uk
Web: www.delaboleslatesigns.co.uk

D-LINE UK
Buckingham Court, Brackley,
Northamptonshire, NN13 7EU
Area of Operation: UK & Ireland
Tel: 01280 841200 **Fax:** 01280 845130
Email: uk@dline.com **Web:** www.dline.com

EMERY ETCHINGS LTD
C7 Laser Quay, Medway City Estate,
Rochester, Kent, ME2 4HU
Area of Operation: UK (Excluding Ireland)
Tel: 01634 719396 **Fax:** 01634 720887
Email: sales@emeryetchings.com
Web: www.signs4houses.co.uk

GIRAFFE MARKETING
10 Duncan Grove, East Acton, London, W3 7NN
Area of Operation: UK (Excluding Ireland)
Tel: 020 8743 0233
Email: charles@giraffemarketing.co.uk
Web: www.hippo-box.co.uk

GLENCALL INTERNATIONAL
One Lomond House, GlenLomond,
Kinross-shire, KY13 9HF
Area of Operation: UK & Ireland
Tel: 01592 840853 **Fax:** 01592 840005
Email: enquiries@glencall.co.uk
Web: www.glencall.co.uk/1gi/pillh.html

HOUSE SIGNS BY TRUDY
32 Rose Gardens, Weston-Super-Mare,
Somerset, BS22 7PX
Area of Operation: UK & Ireland
Tel: 01934 517327
Email: mail@trudysilcox.co.uk
Web: www.trudysilcox.co.uk **Other Info:**

HOUSE SIGNS BY TRUDY

Area of Operation: UK & Ireland
Tel: 01934 517327
Email: mail@trudysilcox.co.uk
Web: www.trudysilcox.co.uk

Stunning bespoke signs each one completely
designed and hand painted. Any design or subject
matter you require. Detailed painting to bring your
subject to life.

**JANKOWSKI WEATHERVANES,
FOUNTAINS, SIGNS & GARDEN ART**
Bryn Melyn, Llanwddyn, Oswestry, Powys, SY10 0LP
Area of Operation: Worldwide
Tel: 01691 870311
Email: stan@panjankowski.co.uk
Web: www.panjankowski.co.uk **Other Info:**

JGS METALWORK
Unit 6 Broomstick Estate, High Street,
Edlesborough, Dunstable, Bedfordshire, LU6 2HS
Area of Operation: East England
Tel: 01525 220360
Fax: 01525 222786
Email: enquiries@jgsmetalwork.co.uk
Web: www.jgsmetalwork.co.uk **Other Info:**

KIRK NATURAL STONE
Bridgend, Fyvie, Turriff, Aberdeenshire, AB53 8LL
Area of Operation: Worldwide
Tel: 01651 891891 **Fax:** 01651 891794
Email: info@kirknaturalstone.com
Web: www.kirknaturalstone.com

MAILBOXES DIRECT
Unit 4, Canalside, North Bridge Road,
Berkhamsted, Hertfordshire, HP4 1EG
Area of Operation: Worldwide
Tel: 01442 878440 **Fax:** 01442 871472
Email: info@mailboxesdirect.co.uk
Web: www.mailboxesdirect.co.uk

MANOR ARCHITECTURAL CERAMICS LTD
16 Charles Street, Warwick,
Warwickshire, CV34 5LE
Area of Operation: Worldwide
Tel: 01926 400946 **Fax:** 01926 400272
Email: mike@manorceramic.co.uk
Web: www.manorceramic.co.uk
Other Info:

MARBLE HART.COM
1 Edwin Street, Daybrook, Arnold,
Nottingham, Nottinghamshire, NG5 6AX
Area of Operation: Worldwide
Tel: 0115 920 3159 **Fax:** 0115 952 5752
Email: chris@cghart.com
Web: www.marblehart.com

RIDGEQUEST LIMITED
Croft Road, Croft, Skegness, Lincolnshire, PE24 4PA
Area of Operation: Worldwide
Tel: 01754 880512 **Fax:** 0870 705 8659
Email: stephen@ridgequest.co.uk
Web: www.ridgequest.co.uk **Other Info:**

SIGNS OF THE TIMES
Wingfield Road, Tebworth,
Leighton Buzzard, Bedfordshire, LU7 9QG
Area of Operation: Worldwide
Tel: 01525 874 185 **Fax:** 01525 875 746
Email: enquiries@sott.co.uk
Web: www.sott.co.uk **Other Info:**

STOCKSIGNS LTD
43 Ormside Way, Redhill, Surrey, RH1 2LG
Area of Operation: Worldwide
Tel: 01737 764764 **Fax:** 01737 763763
Email: info@stocksigns.co.uk
Web: www.stocksigns.co.uk

TOUCHSTONE UK
Touchstone House, 82 High Street,
Measham, Derbyshire, DE12 7JB
Area of Operation: UK (Excluding Ireland)
Tel: 0845 130 1862 **Fax:** 01530 274271
Email: sales@touchstone-uk.com
Web: www.touchstone-uk.com **Other Info:**

VILLAGE GREEN SIGNS
Unit 7 Watford Enterprise Centre, 25 Greenhill
Crescent , Watford, Hertfordshire, WD18 8XU
Area of Operation: Worldwide
Tel: 01923 243777
Fax: 01923 243775
Email: vgsigns@tiscali.co.uk
Web: www.villagegreensigns.co.uk
Other Info:

WWW.HOUSENUMBERS.CO.UK
4 Dairy Field, Salisbury Road,
Blandford Forum, Dorset, DT11 7UP
Area of Operation: Worldwide
Tel: 01258 452826
Email: enquiries@housenumbers.co.uk
Web: www.housenumbers.co.uk **Other Info:**

BARBEQUES & PATIO HEATERS

KEY

OTHER: ▽ Reclaimed On-line shopping
Bespoke Hand-made ECO Ecological

COMPLETE CHIMENEA COMPANY
Casa Dali, 31 Upper East Hayes,
Bath, Somerset, BA1 6LP
Tel: 01225 465280 **Fax:** 01225 471581
Email: da@glo-art.co.uk
Web: www.glo-art.co.uk **Other Info:**

ENCOMPASS FURNITURE & ACCESSORIES
The Pool Room, Stansted House, Stansted Park,
Rowlands Castle, Hampshire, PO9 6DX
Tel: 02392 410045 **Fax:** 02392 412145
Email: info@encompassco.com
Web: www.encompassco.com

GARDEN OASIS LIMITED
Garden Oasis, 3 Caradoc, Glascote,
Tamworth, Staffordshire, B77 2DX
Tel: 01827 706110 **Fax:** 01827 706110
Email: sales@gardenoasis.co.uk
Web: www.gardenoasis.co.uk

GREENFINGERS.COM
10 Lindsay Square, Deans Industrial Estate,
Livingston, Lothian, EH54 8RL
Tel: 0845 345 0728
Email: customer.services@greenfingers.com
Web: www.greenfingers.com

GRENADIER FIRELIGHTERS LIMITED
Unit 3C, Barrowmore Enterprise Estate,
Great Barrow, Chester, Cheshire, CH3 7JS
Tel: 01829 741649 **Fax:** 01829 741659
Email: enquiries@grenadier.co.uk
Web: www.grenadier.co.uk

HEATLINE
16-19 The Manton Centre, Manton Lane,
Bedford, Bedfordshire, MK41 7PX
Tel: 0870 777 8323 **Fax:** 0870 777 8320
Email: info@heatline.co.uk **Web:** www.heatline.co.uk

PATIOHEATERS4U LIMITED
Thor Industrial Estate, Braydon,
Cricklade, Swindon, Wiltshire, SN6 6HQ
Tel: 01793 613900
Email: sales@patioheaters4u.com
Web: www.patioheaters4u.com

ROY WARING SOUTH LIMITED
Unit 1, Lodge Lane, Tuxford,
Newark, Nottinghamshire, NG22 0NL
Tel: 01777 872082 **Fax:** 01777 871563
Email: sales@roywaring.co.uk
Web: www.roywaring.co.uk

TANSUN LIMITED
Spectrum House, Unit 1 Ridgacre Road,
West Bromwich, West Midlands, B71 1BW
Area of Operation: Worldwide
Tel: 0121 580 6200 **Fax:** 0121 580 6222
Email: quartzinfo@tansun.co.uk
Web: www.quartzheat.com

THE HOME & GARDEN CENTRE
Benfield ATT Group, Castle Way,
Caldicot, Monmouthshire, NP26 5PR
Area of Operation: UK (Excluding Ireland)
Tel: 01291 437062 **Fax:** 01291 437051
Email: info@homegardenshop.co.uk
Web: www.home-garden-centre.co.uk

EXTERIOR PRODUCTS

WWW.PLOTFINDER.NET

Area of Operation: UK
Tel: 01527 834436 **Fax:** 01527 837810
Email: customerservice@centaur.co.uk
Web: www.plotfinder.net

Plotfinder is an online database which holds details of around 6,000 building plots and properties in need of renovation or conversion currently for sale throughout the UK.

BOOK OF BARN CONVERSIONS

Area of Operation: UK & Ireland
Tel: 01527 834435 **Fax:** 01527 837810
Email: customerservice@centaur.co.uk
Web: www.homebuilding.co.uk/bookshop

Containing 29 inspirational case studies, ranging from rustic to contemporary, this book is a must for anyone contemplating a barn conversion or restoration, whatever their budget. Each project is fully costed with contact details for suppliers.

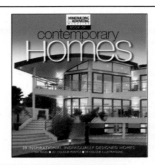

BOOK OF CONTEMPORARY HOMES

Area of Operation: UK & Ireland
Tel: 01527 834435 **Fax:** 01527 837810
Email: customerservice@centaur.co.uk
Web: www.homebuilding.co.uk/bookshop

39 individually designed, contemporary-styled homes, from urban homes to country houses. Each case study includes its floorplan and layout, inspirational pictures, costs for the build and a list of useful contacts.

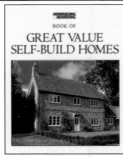

BOOK OF GREAT VALUE SELF-BUILD HOMES

Area of Operation: UK & Ireland
Tel: 01527 834435 **Fax:** 01527 837810
Email: customerservice@centaur.co.uk
Web: www.homebuilding.co.uk/bookshop

Twenty-four homes built for between £32,000 and £150,000. The features show how it is possible to use floor space without sacrificing unique features, and how to achieve maximum style without spending a fortune.

HOMEBUILDING & RENOVATING MAGAZINE

Area of Operation: UK & Ireland
Tel: 01527 834435 **Fax:** 01527 837810
Email: customerservice@centaur.co.uk
Web: www.homebuilding.co.uk

Homebuilding & Renovating, Britain's best selling self-build magazine is an essential read for anyone extending, renovating, converting or building their own home, providing practical advice and inspirational ideas.

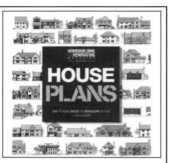

BOOK OF HOUSE PLANS

Area of Operation: UK and Ireland
Tel: 01527 834435 **Fax:** 01527 837810
Email: customerservice@centaur.co.uk
Web: www.homebuilding.co.uk/bookshop

The first colour book of UK House Plans is finally here, packed full of colour illustrations throughout. All beautifully drawn and with ,more plans than ever before.

HOW TO CREATE A JARDIN PAYSAN

Area of Operation: UK & France
Tel: 01527 834435 **Fax:** 01527 837810
Email: customerservice@centaur.co.uk
Web: www.renovationfrance.net

How to create a traditional, rural French-style garden which will have a timeless charm. With plant lists, tips and techniques going back generations, this book shows you how to create an authentic, natural garden.

MOVE OR IMPROVE? MAGAZINE

Area of Operation: UK & Ireland
Tel: 01527 834435 **Fax:** 01527 837810
Email: customerservice@centaur.co.uk
Web: www.moveorimprove.co.uk

Move or Improve? magazine is the Bible for people adding adding space and value to their homes. Includes design guides, practical advice and inspiration on extensions, loft and basement conversions and improving your current home.

PERIOD LIVING MAGAZINE

Area of Operation: UK and Ireland
Tel: 01527 834435 **Fax:** 01527 837810
Email: customerservice@centaur.co.uk
Web: www.periodliving.co.uk

Period Living, Britain's best selling period homes magazine brings you pages of inspirational readers' homes with a wide range of stylish, decorative ideas for your period property.

WWW.PROPERTYFINDERFRANCE.NET

Area of Operation: UK & France
Tel: 01527 834435 **Fax:** 01527 837810
Email: customerservice@centaur.co.uk
Web: www.propertyfinderfrance.net

Looking for a property in France? This fully searchable website contains details of over 50,000 available properties throughout France, To get a 7-day free trial visit:
www.propertyfinderfrance.net.

HOW TO RENOVATE A HOUSE IN FRANCE

Area of Operation: UK & France
Tel: 01527 834435 **Fax:** 01527 837810
Email: customerservice@centaur.co.uk
Web: www.renovationfrance.net

An essential guide to help you turn an old rural property in France into a beautiful home. *How to Renovate* covers the whole process, from assessing and buying a property, through all jobs, large and small, required to get it into shape.

WWW.SITEFINDERIRELAND.COM

Area of Operation: Ireland
Tel: 01527 834435 **Fax:** 01527 837810
Email: customerservice@centaur.co.uk
Web: www.sitefinderireland.com

Whether you are looking for a building site, a property that needs renovating or a building to convert www.sitefinderireland.com can make your search easier; it holds around 2,000 listings currently for sale throughout Ireland.

Image courtesy of Golden Coast Ltd (01271 378100)

EXTERIOR PRODUCTS

Building a Swimming Pool

It is received wisdom in development circles that, while an indoor pool certainly adds value to a property, an outdoor pool can deter potential buyers who might view them as expensive to maintain, unusable for most of the year and a waste of garden space. Your insurance against this – if you decide that an outdoor pool is something you can't live without – is a design proportionate to the size of house and garden, and stylistically in keeping with it.

Indoor pools

A well-designed indoor pool will add considerable value to the right property, and can be used on even the coldest days of the year.

Indoor pools are easier to keep clean than outdoor pools and they are also cheaper to heat. However, building an indoor pool comes with a hefty price tag.

Outdoor pools

A quickly assembled above-ground pool in a small garden is likely to decrease a property's value, with buyers more likely to calculate how much it will cost to remove it than see it as a feature. So design with care, and make your outdoor pool an attractive focal point.

Positioning is also important. Don't build too close to the house and if you can, plant flowers around the area so it blends in well with the garden.

Just because the pool is outside, it doesn't mean you can't take advantage of it all year round – investing in an enclosure over the pool will enable you to enjoy the water at almost any time. There are several options available, ranging from inflatable covers to telescopic enclosures where the heat of the sun warms the pool during colder months.

Planning permission

Planning permission for an outdoor pool isn't generally required, unless you are building in an Area of Outstanding Natural Beauty, or your property is listed. An indoor pool is more likely to require planning permission, and you will always need to apply for Building Regulations approval.

Always check with your local authority to find out if you need planning permission. Further guidance is available from the BSPF (British Swimming Pool Federation) on 01264 356210, or visit the BSPF website at www.bspf.org.uk.

Design and cost

Swimming pools can either be above-ground or partly or fully in-ground. The installation of in-ground pools should generally be left to the professionals, but the competent DIY individual can install an above-ground pool or a self-build pool kit.

If you employ a pool installer, make sure they are suitably experienced by checking that they are a Spatashield member of the Swimming Pool and Allied Trade Association (SPATA). The website is www.spata.co.uk.

- The best time to test the water is in the evening, before adding chemicals. Test it again first thing in the morning to ensure it is suitable for the days bathing.

- If you use the pool a lot, then water tests should be carried out at least three times a day.

- The ideal pH level for pool water is 7.5.

- Strong sunlight can reduce the amount of chlorine in a swimming pool, so monitor levels closely during hot sunny spells.

- The water should generally appear clear blue, any variations, such as cloudiness, may be caused by bacterial or algae growth, suspended matter or other contamination.

- Check water at the return flow to the pool and add any chemicals at this point to ensure effective mixing with filtered water.

- Regularly clean the pool surfaces including the waterline to ensure that build up of sun-oils, body fats, algae, airborne pollution and other dirt is kept to a minimum.

- Pool surround paving slabs should be cleaned with a strong chlorine solution, brushed away from the pool.

VAT

As with a self-built house, it is possible to build a swimming pool largely free of VAT. To do this, it must be constructed at the same time as a new build and attached to the property. Remember that many items of swimming pool equipment, such as diving boards, slides, floating covers and rollers are subject to VAT at the standard rate.

If you are planning to build either an indoor or outdoor pool as an addition to an existing property, you will be subject to VAT.

Maintenance

A common overlooked aspect of owning a pool is its maintenance. Running costs alone are around £500-£1000 a year for heating and chemicals, and you will also have to pay for any damages that may occur.

Some suppliers offer a maintenance service but a few basics will help you along the way to at least keeping your pool clean.

SAUNAS

KEY

OTHER: ▽ Reclaimed ⌐ On-line shopping
✍ Bespoke ✋ Hand-made ECO Ecological

BOUNDARY BATHROOMS
Ainsworth & Dent House, Regent Street,
Colne, Lancashire, BB8 8LD
Area of Operation: UK & Ireland
Tel: 01282 862509   **Fax:** 01282 871192
Email: sales@boundarybathrooms.co.uk

DROM UK LIMITED
Squires Garden Centre, Sixth Cross Road,
Twickenham, Middlesex, TW2 5PA
Area of Operation: UK (Excluding Ireland)
Tel: 0208 977 9900
Fax: 0208 977 9933
Email: twickenham@dromuk.com
Web: www.dromuk.com   **Other Info:** ECO ✍

ENERFOIL MAGNUM LTD
Kenmore Road, Comrie Bridge,
Kenmore, Aberfeldy, Perthshire, PH15 2LS
Area of Operation: Europe
Tel: 01887 822999   **Fax:** 01887 822954
Email: sales@enerfoil.com
Web: www.enerfoil.com ⌐

GEORGE BARKER & SONS
Backbarrow, Nr Ulverston, Cumbria, LA12 8TA
Area of Operation: UK (Excluding Ireland)
Tel: 01539 531236   **Fax:** 01539 530801
Web: www.gbs-ltd.co.uk

GILLINGHAM POOLS
Portinfer Coast Road, Vale, Guernsey, GY6 8LG
Area of Operation: Europe
Tel: 01481 255026   **Fax:** 01481 253626
Email: gillpools@aol.com
Web: www.gillinghampools.co.uk

GOLDEN COAST LTD
Fishleigh Road, Roundswell Commercial Park West,
Barnstaple, Devon, EX31 3UA
Area of Operation: UK & Ireland
Tel: 01271 378100   **Fax:** 01271 371699
Email: swimmer@goldenc.com
Web: www.goldenc.com   **Other Info:** ✍

HIGH TECH HEALTH
PO Box 235, 2 Forest Court,
Egham, Surrey, TW20 9SH
Area of Operation: Worldwide
Tel: 0845 225 5610   **Fax:** 0845 225 5612
Email: info@hightechhealth.net
Web: www.hightechhealth.net ⌐

J W GREEN SWIMMING POOLS LIMITED
Regency House, 88A Great Brickkiln Street,
Graisley, Wolverhampton, West Midlands, WV3 0PU
Area of Operation: Midlands & Mid Wales
Tel: 01902 427709
Email: info@jwgswimming.co.uk
Web: www.jwgswimming.co.uk
Other Info: ✍

**MAGMED LTD -
PHYSIOTHERM INFRARED SAUNAS**
3 Willetts Court, Pottergate, Norwich, Norfolk, NR2 1DG
Area of Operation: UK & Ireland
Tel: 0845 22 55 008   **Fax:** 0870 432 0406
Email: physiotherm@magmed.com
Web: www.4sauna.co.uk

MEDISAUN LIMITED
151 Berengrave Lane, Rainham,
Gillingham, Kent, ME8 7UJ
Area of Operation: UK (Excluding Ireland)
Tel: 0871 423 5975   **Fax:** 0871 423 5974
Email: sales@medisaun.co.uk
Web: www.medisaun.co.uk ⌐

NORDIC
Unit 5, Trading Estate, Holland Road,
Oxted, Surrey, RH8 9BZ
Area of Operation: UK (Excluding Ireland)
Tel: 01883 732400   **Fax:** 01883 716970
Email: info@nordic.co.uk
Web: www.nordic.co.uk

SAUNASHOP.COM
1 Station Road, Kelly Bray,
Callington, Cornwall, PL17 8ES
Area of Operation: UK & Ireland
Tel: 0500 432132   **Fax:** 01579 384333
Email: info@saunashop.com
Web: www.saunashop.co.uk ⌐

SUMMIT LEISURE LTD
Unit 2, Garlands Trading Estate, Cadley Road,
Collingbourne Ducis, Marlborough, Wiltshire, SN8 3EB
Area of Operation: UK & Ireland
Tel: 01264 850001   **Fax:** 01264 850009
Email: office@summitleisure.co.uk
Web: www.summitleisure.co.uk

SVEDBERGS
4E Wilsons Park, Monsall Road,
Newton Heath, Manchester, M40 8WN
Area of Operation: UK & Ireland
Tel: 0161 205 1200   **Fax:** 0161 205 1212
Email: info@svedbergs.co.uk
Web: www.svedbergs.co.uk

THE HOME SAUNA COMPANY LTD
37 Sandhurst Close, Church Hill,
Redditch, Worcestershire, B98 9JY
Area of Operation: UK & Ireland
Tel: 0845 430 3123   **Fax:** 01527 60072
Email: info@homesauna.co.uk
Web: www.homesauna.co.uk

VIKING SAUNAS LTD
108-110 Bradley Hall Trading Estate, Bradley Lane,
Standish, Wigan, Lancashire, WN6 0XQ
Area of Operation: UK & Ireland
Tel: 01257 427019
Fax: 01257 427344
Email: pam@viking-saunas.co.uk
Web: www.viking-saunas.co.uk

ZOKI UK
Zoki Works, 44 Alcester Street,
Birmingham, West Midlands, B12 0PH
Area of Operation: UK & Ireland
Tel: 0121 766 7888   **Fax:** 0121 766 7962
Email: zokiuk@btconnect.com
Web: www.zokiuk.co.uk

SWIMMING POOLS

KEY

PRODUCT TYPES: 1= Swimming Pools
2 = Pool Covers and Enclosures
OTHER: ▽ Reclaimed ⌐ On-line shopping
✍ Bespoke ✋ Hand-made ECO Ecological

AQUAFLEX
1 Edison Road, Churchfields Industrial Estate,
Salisbury, Wiltshire, SP2 7NU
Area of Operation: UK & Ireland
Tel: 01722 328873   **Fax:** 01722 413068
Email: info@aquaflex.co.uk
Web: www.aquaflex.co.uk   **Other Info:** ✍

BECO PRODUCTS LTD
Beco House, 6 Exmoor Avenue,
Scunthorpe, Lincolnshire, DN15 8NJ
Area of Operation: UK & Ireland
Tel: 01724 747576
Fax: 01724 747579
Email: info@becowallform.co.uk
Web: www.becowallform.co.uk
Product Type: 1   **Other Info:** ✍
Material Type: G) 1, K) 11

DOLPHIN LEISURE UK LIMITED
Dolphin House, Unit 15c, No. 4 Lister Road, Highfield
Industrial Estate, Eastbourne, East Sussex, BN23 6PU
Area of Operation: UK (Excluding Ireland)
Tel: 08451 303067   **Fax:** 08451 303067
Email: sales@dolphinpools.co.uk
Web: www.dolphinpools.co.uk ⌐

DRIPOOL
Unit 3, Westwood Court, Brunel Road,
Totton, Southampton, Hampshire, SO40 3WX
Area of Operation: Worldwide
Tel: 02380 663131   **Fax:** 02380 663232
Email: sales@dripool.co.uk
Web: www.dripool.co.uk
Product Type: 2   **Other Info:** ✍

ENDLESS POOLS
200 East Dutton Mill Road,
Aston, Pennsylvania, USA, PA 19014
Area of Operation: Worldwide
Tel: 0800 0281056   **Fax:** 001 610 497 9328
Email: swim@endlesspools.com
Web: www.endlesspools.co.uk/3590

GILLINGHAM POOLS
Portinfer Coast Road, Vale, Guernsey, GY6 8LG
Area of Operation: Europe
Tel: 01481 255026   **Fax:** 01481 253626
Email: gillpools@aol.com
Web: www.gillinghampools.co.uk

GOLDEN COAST LTD
Fishleigh Road, Roundswell Commercial Park West,
Barnstaple, Devon, EX31 3UA
Area of Operation: UK & Ireland
Tel: 01271 378100   **Fax:** 01271 371699
Email: swimmer@goldenc.com
Web: www.goldenc.com   **Product Type:** 1, 2

IAN LEWIS DESIGN
Chapleton, Tulliemet, Pitlochry,
Perth and Kinross, PH9 0PA
Area of Operation: UK (Excluding Ireland)
Tel: 0870 2406356   **Fax:** 01796 482733
Email: irl@pooldesign.co.uk
Web: www.selfbuildpools.co.uk

J W GREEN SWIMMING POOLS LIMITED
Regency House, 88A Great Brickkiln Street, Graisley,
Wolverhampton, West Midlands, WV3 0PU
Area of Operation: Midlands & Mid Wales
Tel: 01902 427709
Email: info@jwgswimming.co.uk
Web: www.jwgswimming.co.uk
Product Type: 1, 2   **Other Info:** ✍

NATIONAL LEISURE
Suite 179, Maritime House, Southwell Business Park,
Portland, Dorset, DT5 2NB
Area of Operation: UK (Excluding Ireland)
Tel: 01305 824610   **Fax:** 01305 824611
Email: pools@national-leisure.com
Web: www.national-leisure.com

PINELOG LTD
Riverside Business Park,
Bakewell, Derbyshire, DE45 1GS
Area of Operation: UK (Excluding Ireland)
Tel: 01629 814481   **Fax:** 01629 814634
Email: admin@pinelog.co.uk
Web: www.pinelog.co.uk   **Product Type:** 1, 2

ROY WARING SOUTH LIMITED
Unit 1, Lodge Lane, Tuxford, Newark,
Nottinghamshire, NG22 0NL
Area of Operation: UK (Excluding Ireland)
Tel: 01777 872 082   **Fax:** 01777 871 563
Email: sales@roywaring.co.uk
Web: www.roywaring.co.uk ⌐

SELFBUILDPOOLS.CO.UK
Chapelton, Tulliemet, Pitlochry,
Perth and Kinross, PH9 0PA
Area of Operation: UK & Ireland
Tel: 0870 240 6356   **Fax:** 01796 482733
Email: irl@selfbuildpools.co.uk
Web: www.selfbuildpools.co.uk   **Product Type:** 1

SUMMIT LEISURE LTD
Unit 2, Garlands Trading Estate, Cadley Road,
Collingbourne Ducis, Marlborough, Wiltshire, SN8 3EB
Area of Operation: UK & Ireland
Tel: 01264 850001   **Fax:** 01264 850009
Email: office@summitleisure.co.uk
Web: www.summitleisure.co.uk
Product Type: 1, 2   **Other Info:** ✍

SUNDANCE POOLS UK LTD
PO Box 284, Milton Keynes,
Buckinghamshire, MK17 0QD
Area of Operation: UK & Ireland
Tel: 01296 715071   **Fax:** 01296 714991
Email: enquiries@sundancepools.com
Web: www.sundancepools.com   **Product Type:** 1, 2

**SWIMMING POOL AND
ALLIED TRADES ASSOCIATION**
4 Eastgate House, East Street,
Andover, Hertfordshire, SP10 1EP
Area of Operation: Worldwide
Tel: 01264 356210   **Fax:** 01264 332628
Email: admin@spata.co.uk   **Web:** www.spata.co.uk

TELESCOPIC POOL ENCLOSURES LTD
Unit 3 Wynford Industrial Park,
Belbins, Romsey, Hampshire, SO51 0PW
Area of Operation: UK & Ireland
Tel: 08000 740872
Email: info@telescopicpoolenclosures.com
Web: www.telescopicpoolenclosures.com
Product Type: 2   **Other Info:** ✍

SPAS AND HOT TUBS

KEY

OTHER: ▽ Reclaimed ⌐ On-line shopping
✍ Bespoke ✋ Hand-made ECO Ecological

AEGEAN SPAS & HOT TUBS
2 Hale Lane, Mill Hill, London, NW7 3NX
Area of Operation: UK (Excluding Ireland)
Tel: 0208 959 1529   **Fax:** 0208 906 0511
Web: www.tubstore.com ⌐

DOLPHIN LEISURE UK LIMITED
Dolphin House, Unit 15c, No. 4 Lister Road, Highfield
Industrial Estate, Eastbourne, East Sussex, BN23 6PU
Area of Operation: UK (Excluding Ireland)
Tel: 08451 303067   **Fax:** 08451 303067
Email: sales@dolphinpools.co.uk
Web: www.dolphinpools.co.uk ⌐

DROM UK LIMITED
Squires Garden Centre, Sixth Cross Road,
Twickenham, Middlesex, TW2 5PA
Area of Operation: UK (Excluding Ireland)
Tel: 0208 977 9900   **Fax:** 0208 977 9933
Email: twickenham@dromuk.com
Web: www.dromuk.com   **Other Info:** ECO

GEORGE BARKER & SONS
Backbarrow, Nr Ulverston, Cumbria, LA12 8TA
Area of Operation: UK (Excluding Ireland)
Tel: 01539 531236   **Fax:** 01539 530801
Web: www.gbs-ltd.co.uk

GILLINGHAM POOLS
Portinfer Coast Road, Vale, Guernsey, GY6 8LG
Area of Operation: Europe
Tel: 01481 255026   **Fax:** 01481 253626
Email: gillpools@aol.com
Web: www.gillinghampools.co.uk

GOLDEN COAST LTD
Fishleigh Road, Roundswell Commercial Park West,
Barnstaple, Devon, EX31 3UA
Area of Operation: UK & Ireland
Tel: 01271 378100
Fax: 01271 371699
Email: swimmer@goldenc.com
Web: www.goldenc.com

EXTERIOR PRODUCTS

J W GREEN SWIMMING POOLS LIMITED
Regency House, 88A Great Brickkiln Street,
Graisley, Wolverhampton, West Midlands, WV3 0PU
Area of Operation: Midlands & Mid Wales
Tel: 01902 427709
Email: info@jwgswimming.co.uk
Web: www.jwgswimming.co.uk

JACUZZI SPA DIVISION
Silverdale Road, Newcastle-under-Lyme,
Staffordshire, ST5 6EL
Area of Operation: UK & Ireland
Tel: 01782 718002   **Fax:** 01782 717245
Email: john.crampton@jacuzziuk.com
Web: www.jacuzzi.co.uk

NATIONAL LEISURE
Suite 179, Maritime House,
Southwell Business Park, Portland, Dorset, DT5 2NB
Area of Operation: UK (Excluding Ireland)
Tel: 01305 824610
Fax: 01305 824611
Email: pools@national-leisure.com
Web: www.national-leisure.com

NORDIC
Unit 5, Trading Estate, Holland Road,
Oxted, Surrey, RH8 9BZ
Area of Operation: UK (Excluding Ireland)
Tel: 01883 732400   **Fax:** 01883 716970
Email: info@nordic.co.uk   **Web:** www.nordic.co.uk

ONEWAY GARDEN LEISURE
18/19 John Samuel Building,
Arthur Drive, Hoo Farm Industrial Estate,
Kidderminster, Worcestershire, DY11 7RA
Area of Operation: UK (Excluding Ireland)
Tel: 01562 750222
Fax: 01562 750222
Email: maureenr18@tiscali.co.uk
Web: www.onewayspas.co.uk

OZTUBS
35 Gladeside, Croydon, Greater London, CR0 7RL
Area of Operation: UK (Excluding Ireland)
Tel: 0845 124 9531   **Email:** sales@oztubs.com
Web: www.oztubs.com

ROY WARING SOUTH LIMITED
Unit 1, Lodge Lane, Tuxford,
Newark, Nottinghamshire, NG22 0NL
Area of Operation: UK (Excluding Ireland)
Tel: 01777 872082
Fax: 01777 871563
Email: sales@roywaring.co.uk
Web: www.roywaring.co.uk

SAPPHIRE SPAS HOT TUBS
A1 Rowood Estate, Murdock Road,
Bicester, Nr Oxford, Oxfordshire, OX26 4PP
Area of Operation: Worldwide
Tel: 01869 327698
Fax: 01869 369552
Email: info@sapphirespas.co.uk
Web: www.sapphirespas.co.uk

SPAFORM UK LIMITED
Spa House, Walton Road, Farlington,
Portsmouth, Hampshire, PO6 1TB
Area of Operation: Worldwide
Tel: 02392 313131   **Fax:** 02392 377597
Email: enquiries@spaform.co.uk
Web: www.spaform.co.uk

SUMMIT LEISURE LTD
Unit 2, Garlands Trading Estate,
Cadley Road, Collingbourne Ducis,
Marlborough, Wiltshire, SN8 3EB
Area of Operation: UK & Ireland
Tel: 01264 850001   **Fax:** 01264 850009
Email: office@summitleisure.co.uk
Web: www.summitleisure.co.uk

SUNDANCE SPAS UK LTD
Unit 8, The Markham Centre, Station Road,
Theal, Reading, Berkshire, RG7 4PE
Area of Operation: UK (Excluding Ireland)
Tel: 0800 146106   **Fax:** 01952 811797
Email: sales@sundance-spas.co.uk
Web: www.sundance-spas.co.uk

SUSSEX SPAS
Area of Operation: Greater London, South East England
Tel: 01403 272878
Email: info@sussexspas.co.uk
Web: www.sussexspas.co.uk

WARDLE SPAS
Horninglow Road, Burton on Trent,
Staffordshire, DE14 2RQ
Area of Operation: UK & Ireland
Tel: 01283 535464   **Fax:** 01283 536893
Email: info@wardlespas.co.uk
Web: www.wardlespas.co.uk

Don't Forget !

You can use the materials key at the beginning of this Handbook to get much more information from a company's listing.

NOTES

Company Name ....

....

Address ....

....

....

email ....

Web ....

Company Name ....

....

Address ....

....

....

email ....

Web ....

Company Name ....

....

Address ....

....

....

email ....

Web ....

Company Name ....

....

Address ....

....

....

email ....

Web ....

Company Name ....

....

Address ....

....

....

email ....

Web ....

Company Name ....

....

Address ....

....

....

email ....

Web ....

Company Name ....

....

Address ....

....

....

email ....

Web ....

Company Name ....

....

Address ....

....

....

email ....

Web ....

Image courtesy of Buildstore (0870 870 9991)

CONSULTANTS, LABOUR & FINANCE

SPONSORED BY BUILDSTORE
Tel 0870 870 9991. Web www.buildstore.co.uk

Finance

Even the taxman can provide help with your self-build project. We outline the financial incentives designed to make the tough task of building your new home a little more manageable.

VAT

To 'level the playing field' for self-builders, the authorities introduced a concession whereby those building a home for their own or their family's occupation can reclaim VAT paid out. Full details are under scheme 719, available from the HM Revenues and Customs.

VAT can be reclaimed on virtually all permanent fixtures in self-build homes. For example, items such as paving and walls will qualify, while a fridge freezer or wardrobe will not.

The sale, purchase or leasing of construction land or domestic residential property does not attract VAT. A person who buys a house from a developer doesn't have to pay VAT on top of the purchase price.

New-Build

If a self-builder uses a VAT-registered builder to construct their new home on a supply-and-fix basis, no VAT should be charged on any of the work or materials. Similarly, if a self-builder employs VAT-registered supply-and-fix tradesmen to work on their new home, or if they are employed on a labour-only basis, then the contract will not attract VAT.

Materials purchased by the self-builder will, however, attract VAT at the standard rate of 17.5% - but most of this can be recovered at the end of the project.

Conversions

Conversions are treated slightly differently. A supply-and-fix builder must charge VAT at the reduced rate of 5% on the full contract value. Labour-only and supply-and-fix contracts with VAT-registered subcontractors will also be subject to VAT at 5%. Material

purchases by the converter will attract VAT at 17.5%. However most, if not all, of the VAT paid out on both labour and materials can be recovered at the end of the project.

Renovations and Extensions

There's not as much help at hand for those renovating and extending. You will have to pay VAT at the full rate of 17.5% on top of the price for all labour and materials.

However, if the property has been unoccupied for more than 10 years, it is treated as a 'conversion', and the rules for the payment and recovery of VAT are as detailed above. Also, if the property has been unoccupied for more than three years, it is possible for a builder to charge VAT at the reduced rate of 5%.

Listed Buildings

Alterations and extensions to listed buildings are not covered by the self-build concession. However, if works come within the criteria

laid down in "Guide to VAT – Free Works to Your Listed Home", a VAT-registered builder may zero-rate the work. This means that you won't pay VAT on top of their bill, but only if they purchase the materials. There is no relief for works to renovate, refurbish or repair a listed building. However, there may be grants available - contact your local authority for details.

Claims

The claim form itself is relatively straightforward to complete but it can take the authorities up to three months to process and refund the claim. The most important thing is to retain all of your VAT invoices. Watch out for paying VAT out to non-registered labour or contractors. Some unscrupulous companies will seek to add it to their bills, but it never gets to HM Revenue and Customs, who won't refund money that has been paid out incorrectly.

What Can't I Reclaim VAT on?

- Professional fees to architects, surveyors etc.
- The purchase or hire of tools and plant, including diggers and scaffolding.
- Outbuildings other than garages.
- Carpets, underlay or carpet tiles.
- White goods such as ovens, fridges, washing machines etc, even if they are built in.
- Fitted wardrobes that are not part of the structure of the house
- Doorbells, electrically operated doors or gates.
- Aerials and satellite dishes

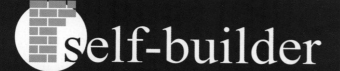

self-builder

Converting, renovating, extending or building your home?

Self-builder insurance provides cover for:

- Contract works - 125% works value

- Site huts and caravans - £30,000 and their contents £5,000

- Owned or hired tools, plant & equipment - £30,000 for each

- Employees' personal tools and effects - £2,000

- Existing structures - 110% of reinstatement value

- Employers Liability - £10 million

- Public Liability - £5 million

(also available is Public Liability only cover for clear, vacant land)

- Personal Accident - £20,000

- Legal Expenses - £50,000

For instant cover, call **0800 018 7660** or visit **www.self-builder.com**

(10% discount with on-line quotes)

INSURANCE

KEY
OTHER: ▽ Reclaimed   🖰 On-line shopping
🖎 Bespoke   ✋ Hand-made   ECO Ecological

BUILDSTORE
Unit 1 Kingsthorne Park, Houstoun Industrial Estate, Livingston, Lothian, EH54 5DB
Area of Operation: UK (Excluding Ireland)
Tel: 0870 870 9991   **Fax:** 0870 870 9992
Email: enquiries@buildstore.co.uk
Web: www.buildstore.co.uk 🖰

BUILDSTORE
Area of Operation: UK (Excluding Ireland)
Tel: 0870 870 9991
Fax: 0870 870 9992
Email: enquiries@buildstore.co.uk
Web: www.buildstore.co.uk

BuildCare site insurance
BuildCare site insurance from the UK's leading self build specialists BuildStore has been developed especially for the self builder and renovator and provides you with the protection you need for your new home. With competitive site insurance benefits call BuildStore for a quote today and receive a free health and safety guide.

CARTEL MARKETING LTD
5th Floor, Building 7, Salford Quays, Exchange Quay, Manchester, M5 3EP
Area of Operation: Worldwide
Tel: 0161 836 4343
Fax: 0161 836 4241
Email: john.agha@cartelgroupholdings.plc.uk
Web: www.cartelgroupholdings.plc.uk

DESIGN AND MATERIALS LTD
Lawn Road, Carlton in Lindrick, Nottinghamshire, S81 9LB
Area of Operation: UK (Excluding Ireland)
Tel: 01909 540123   **Fax:** 01909 730605
Email: enquiries@designandmaterials.uk.com
Web: www.designandmaterials.uk.com 🖰

DMS SERVICES LTD
Orchard House, Sheffield Road, Blyth, Nr. Worksop, Nottinghamshire, S81 8HF
Area of Operation: UK (Excluding Ireland)
Tel: 01909 591652
Fax: 01909 591031
Email: insurance@selfbuildonline.co.uk
Web: www.selfbuildonline.co.uk

FLEXIBLE MORTGAGE.NET
Commerce Way, Edenbridge, Kent, TN8 6ED
Area of Operation: UK (Excluding Ireland)
Tel: 01732 866007
Fax: 01732 866155
Email: Davidc@flexible-mortgage.net
Web: www.flexible-mortgage.net

INTELLIGENT MORTGAGE SERVICES
208 High Road, Leytonstone, London, E11 3HU
Area of Operation: UK & Ireland
Tel: 0208 279 0719   **Fax:** 0208 279 0720
Email: info@intelligentmortgageservices.co.uk
Web: www.intelligentmortgageservices.co.uk 🖰

LAPLAYA LTD
The Stables, Manor Farm, Milton Road, Impington, Cambridge, Cambridgeshire, CB4 9NF
Area of Operation: UK (Excluding Ireland)
Tel: 01223 200650 / 200652
Fax: 01223 237942
Email: liz.hunter@laplaya.co.uk
Web: www.laplaya.co.uk

LIBERTY SYNDICATES
One Minster Court, 5th Floor, Mincing Lane, London, EC3R 7AA
Area of Operation: Worldwide
Tel: 020 7895 0011   **Fax:** 020 7860 8573
Web: www.libertysyndicates.com

MFC MORTGAGE OPTIONS
231 Grimsby Road, Cleethorpes, Lincolnshire, DN35 7HE
Area of Operation: East England, North East England, North West England and North Wales, South East England, South West England and South Wales
Tel: 01472 200664   **Fax:** 01472 200664
Email: markhallam@insurer.com
Web: www.mfcmortgageoptions.co.uk

NHBC
Buildmark House, Chiltern Avenue, Amersham, Buckinghamshire, HP6 5AP
Area of Operation: Worldwide
Tel: 01494 735363   **Web:** www.nhbc.co.uk

PROJECT BUILDER INSURANCE FACILITY
Tower Gate House, St. Edwards Court, London Road, Romford, Essex, RM7 9QD
Area of Operation: UK (Excluding Ireland)
Tel: 01708 777402   **Fax:** 01708 777737
Email: projectbuilder@towergate.co.uk
Web: www.siteinsurance.net

SELF-BUILD ZONE
London House, 77 High Street, Sevenoaks, Kent, TN13 1LD
Area of Operation: UK & Ireland
Tel: 0845 230 9874   **Fax:** 01732 740994
Email: sales@selfbuildzone.com
Web: www.selfbuildzone.com 🖰

SELF-BUILDER.COM
Belmont International, Becket House, Vestry Road, Sevenoaks, Kent, TN14 5EL
Area of Operation: UK & Ireland
Tel: 0800 018 7660   **Fax:** 01732 745499
Email: sales@self-builder.com
Web: www.self-builder.com 🖰

STERLING HAMILTON WRIGHT
Stuards House, St. Edwards Court, London Road, Romford, Essex, RM7 9QD
Area of Operation: UK (Excluding Ireland)
Tel: 0870 3333 810   **Fax:** 01708 756103
Email: projectbuilder@towergate.co.uk
Web: www.siteinsurance.net 🖰

WISEMONEY.COM LTD
24 Charlton Drive, Cheltenham, Gloucestershire, GL53 8ES
Area of Operation: Worldwide
Email: sdye@wisemoney.com
Web: www.wisemoney.com 🖰

ZURICH INSURANCE COMPANY BUILDING GUARANTEE
Southwood Crescent, Farnborough, Hampshire, GU14 0NJ
Area of Operation: UK (Excluding Ireland)
Tel: 01252 377474
Email: building.guarantee@uk.zurich.com
Web: www.zurich.co.uk/buildingguarantee

**Please mention
The Homebuilder's
Handbook
when you call**

CONSULTANTS, LABOUR & FINANCE

www.buildstore.co.uk | 0800 018 5740

Every year more and more people across the UK are choosing to self build, renovate or make their own home improvements. And what's most stressful about these projects is not having the funds when you need them most. That's where BuildStore can help. Our unique Accelerator mortgage will provide the money at the start of each build stage, so you can stay in complete control throughout. It's quicker, cheaper, easier and safer with Accelerator, and has already helped thousands of people turn their dream into a reality. So when it comes to building your future, BuildStore is only a call or a click away.

Call us or click online for unrivalled advice

With money readily available, build your new home faster with Accelerator.

Build Store
FINANCIAL SERVICES

www.buildstore.co.uk | 0800 018 5740

Every year more and more people across the UK are choosing to self build, renovate or make their own home improvements. And what's most stressful about these projects is not having the funds when you need them most. That's where BuildStore can help. Our unique Accelerator mortgage will provide the money at the start of each build stage, so you can stay in complete control throughout. It's quicker, cheaper, easier and safer with Accelerator, and has already helped thousands of people turn their dream into a reality. So when it comes to building your future, BuildStore is only a call or a click away.

Call us or click online for unrivalled advice

The Accelerator mortgage.
Get the money you need up-front and leave stress behind.

Build Store
FINANCIAL SERVICES

CONSULTANTS, LABOUR & FINANCE

MORTGAGE PROVIDERS

KEY

OTHER: ▽ Reclaimed 🛒 On-line shopping
✎ Bespoke 🤚 Hand-made ECO Ecological

ADVANCED FLEXIBLE SELF BUILD MORTGAGE
Unit 61-62, Alloa Business Centre, Alloa Business Park,
Whins Road, Alloa, Clackmannanshire, FK10 3SA
Area of Operation: UK & Ireland
Tel: 01259 726650 **Fax:** 01259 726651
Email: info@afsbm.co.uk
Web: www.afsbm.co.uk

BISHOPSGATE FUNDING LTD
Tower Business Centre, Portland Tower,
Portland Street, Manchester, M1 3LF
Area of Operation: UK (Excluding Ireland)
Tel: 0845 601 2654 **Fax:** 0845 601 2657
Email: enquiries@bishopsgatefunding.com
Web: www.bishopsgatefunding.com

Don't Forget!

You can use the materials key at the beginning of this Handbook to get much more information from a company's listing.

BUILDSTORE
Unit 1 Kingsthorne Park, Houstoun Industrial Estate,
Livingston, Lothian, EH54 5DB
Area of Operation: UK (Excluding Ireland)
Tel: 0870 870 9991 **Fax:** 0870 870 9992
Email: enquiries@buildstore.co.uk
Web: www.buildstore.co.uk 🛒

BUILDSTORE

Area of Operation: UK (Excluding Ireland)
Tel: 0870 870 9991
Fax: 0870 870 9992
Email: enquiries@buildstore.co.uk
Web: www.buildstore.co.uk

Financing a renovation project – speak to BuildStore
Since 1997, BuildStore has been dedicated to providing financial support to individuals involved in renovation and home improvement projects. Our exclusive ideal Home Improvement Mortgage lets you borrow up to 95% of the costs of buying the property, 95% of the refurbishment costs and 95% of the end value. It's retention free and even provides the money to you before you carry out the renovation work.

CARTEL MARKETING LTD
5th Floor, Building 7, Salford Quays,
Exchange Quay, Manchester, M5 3EP
Area of Operation: Worldwide
Tel: 0161 836 4343 **Fax:** 0161 836 4241
Email: john.agha@cartelgroupholdings.plc.uk
Web: www.cartelgroupholdings.plc.uk

CREDIT & MERCANTILE PLC
Mercantile House, Lingfield, Surrey, RH7 6NG
Area of Operation: UK (Excluding Ireland)
Tel: 01342 837111 **Fax:** 01342 837901
Email: info@creditmercantile.co.uk
Web: www.creditmercantile.co.uk

ECOLOGY BUILDING SOCIETY
7 Belton Road, Silsden,
Keighley, West Yorkshire, BD20 0EE
Area of Operation: UK (Excluding Ireland)
Tel: 01535 650770 **Fax:** 01535 650790
Email: jbarton@ecology.co.uk
Web: www.ecology.co.uk

FIRST PROPERTY FINANCE PLC
Maple House, High Street,
Potters Bar, Hertfordshire, EN6 5BS
Area of Operation: UK (Excluding Ireland)
Tel: 0845 260 3366 **Fax:** 0845 260 3377
Email: info@firstpropertyfinance.com
Web: www.firstpropertyfinance.com

FLEXIBLE MORTGAGE.NET
Commerce Way, Edenbridge, Kent, TN8 6ED
Area of Operation: UK (Excluding Ireland)
Tel: 01732 866007
Fax: 01732 866155
Email: davidc@flexible-mortgage.net
Web: www.flexible-mortgage.net

INTELLIGENT MORTGAGE SERVICES
208 High Road, Leytonstone, London, E11 3HU
Area of Operation: UK & Ireland
Tel: 0208 279 0719 **Fax:** 0208 279 0720
Email: info@intelligentmortgageservices.co.uk
Web: www.intelligentmortgageservices.co.uk 🛒

KENT RELIANCE BUILDING SOCIETY
Reliance House, Sun Pier, Chatham, Kent, ME4 4ET
Area of Operation: UK & Ireland
Tel: 01634 848 944 **Fax:** 01634 830912
Email: mail@krbs.com **Web:** www.krbs.co.uk

LANCASHIRE MORTGAGE CORPORATION
6th Floor, Bracken House,
Charles Street, Manchester, M1 7BD
Area of Operation: UK (Excluding Ireland)
Tel: 0161 276 2476
Fax: 0161 276 2477
Email: webenquiry@financeyourproperty.co.uk
Web: www.financeyourproperty.co.uk

LLOYDS TSB SCOTLAND
Registered Office, Henry Duncan House,
120 George Street, Edinburgh, EH2 4LH
Area of Operation: Scotland
Tel: 0131 225 4555
Fax: 0131 260 0660
Web: www.lloydstsb.co.uk

MFC MORTGAGE OPTIONS
231 Grimsby Road, Cleethorpes,
Lincolnshire, DN35 7HE
Area of Operation: East England, North East
England, North West England and North Wales, South
East England, South West England and South Wales
Tel: 01472 200664
Fax: 01472 200664
Email: markhallam@insurer.com
Web: www.mfcmortgageoptions.co.uk

MORTGAGE GUARANTEE PLC
26 Church Road, Rainford,
St. Helens, Merseyside, WA11 8HE
Area of Operation: UK (Excluding Ireland)
Tel: 01744 886884
Fax: 01744 886885

PHONE A LOAN
4th Floor, Bracken House,
Charles Street, Manchester, M1 7BD
Area of Operation: UK (Excluding Ireland)
Tel: 0870 112 5011
Fax: 0870 112 5012
Email: brokerageunit@phone-a-loan.co.uk
Web: www.phone-a-loan.co.uk

CONSULTANTS, LABOUR & FINANCE

Self-Build Insurance *made easy!*

Comprehensive cover for your Self-Build, Renovation or Conversion project

SAVE Money Online!
Quotes and cover available at
www.selfbuildzone.com

We can cover:

✓ **New Builds**
✓ **Conversions**
✓ **Renovations**
✓ **Extensions**

Option available to convert unexpired Site Insurance into Buildings cover upon completion.

✓ Site Insurance
✓ 10 Year Structural Warranty
✓ Building Control

The Build-Zone Structural Warranty is also available on **COMPLETED** projects!

Whatever type of home you're building, we've got it covered!

Call **0845 230 9874** or visit
www.selfbuildzone.com

Self-Build Zone is a wholly owned subsidiary of Sennocke International Insurance Services Limited who is authorised and regulated by the Financial Services Authority

---

REGENTSMEAD LIMITED
Russell House, 140 High Street,
Edgware, Middlesex, HA8 7LW
Area of Operation: Greater London, Midlands & Mid Wales, South East England, South West England and South Wales
Tel: 0208 952 1414   **Fax:** 0208 952 2424
Email: info@regentsmead.com
Web: www.regentsmead.com

ROWANBANK MORTGAGES
6 Summer Place, Edinburgh, EH3 5NR
Area of Operation: UK (Excluding Ireland)
Tel: 0131 557 3909
Fax: 0131 558 3601
Email: enquiries@rowanbankmortgages.co.uk
Web: www.rowanbankmortgages.co.uk

WISEMONEY.COM LTD
24 Charlton Drive, Cheltenham,
Gloucestershire, GL53 8ES
Area of Operation: Worldwide
Email: sdye@wisemoney.com
Web: www.wisemoney.com

WARRANTY PROVIDERS

KEY
OTHER: ▽ Reclaimed   On-line shopping
Bespoke   Hand-made   ECO Ecological

BUILDSTORE
Unit 1 Kingsthorne Park, Houstoun Industrial Estate, Livingston, Lothian, EH54 5DB
Area of Operation: UK (Excluding Ireland)
Tel: 0870 870 9991   **Fax:** 0870 870 9992
Email: enquiries@buildstore.co.uk
Web: www.buildstore.co.uk

BuildStore
FINANCIAL SERVICES

BUILDSTORE
Area of Operation: UK (Excluding Ireland)
Tel: 0870 870 9991
Fax: 0870 870 9992
Email: enquiries@buildstore.co.uk
Web: www.buildstore.co.uk

BuildStore Financial Services
At BuildStore our customers are key and we aim to provide you with financial products that are best for you and not what benefits us. Our products and services include:

• Exclusive self build and renovation mortgages
• Protection insurance products - including life insurance
• Remortgage deals to save you money
• Residential development finance for builders and smaller developers

NHBC
Buildmark House, Chiltern Avenue,
Amersham, Buckinghamshire, HP6 5AP
Area of Operation: Worldwide
Tel: 01494 735363
Web: www.nhbc.co.uk

PROJECT BUILDER INSURANCE FACILITY
Tower Gate House, St. Edwards Court,
London Road, Romford, Essex, RM7 9QD
Area of Operation: UK (Excluding Ireland)
Tel: 01708 777402
Fax: 01708 777737
Email: projectbuilder@towergate.co.uk
Web: www.siteinsurance.net

SELF-BUILD ZONE
London House, 77 High Street,
Sevenoaks, Kent, TN13 1LD
Area of Operation: UK & Ireland
Tel: 0845 230 9874   **Fax:** 01732 740994
Email: sales@selfbuildzone.com
Web: www.selfbuildzone.com

ZURICH INSURANCE COMPANY BUILDING GUARANTEE
Southwood Crescent,
Farnborough, Hampshire, GU14 0NJ
Area of Operation: UK (Excluding Ireland)
Tel: 01252 377 474
Email: building.guarantee@uk.zurich.com
Web: www.zurich.co.uk/buildingguarantee

CONSULTANTS, LABOUR & FINANCE

SPONSORED BY PERIOD LIVING MAGAZINE
Tel 01527 834435 Web www.periodliving.co.uk

PERIOD LIVING
TRADITIONAL HOMES, INTERIORS, GARDENS, ANTIQUES & RENOVATION

Restoring a Period Home

To restore or not to restore?
It is wise to look before you leap into any restoration project.

When renovating a period house you risk doing more harm than good if you fail to use appropriate materials and techniques. Any serious restoration work will require the skills of a specialist conservator or restorer, who will use the highest standards to ensure the preservation of original material. For the less challenging tasks there are plenty of courses for the layman, which can provide both hands-on experience and historical background. In addition, there is a wealth of technical advice from a variety of impartial organisations. If nothing else, this can give you an understanding of what a conservator is trying to achieve. But a task is too difficult to tackle yourself, how do you go about finding someone suitable?

A good place to start your search would be The

Conservation Register. This is a database of professional conservation and restoration businesses throughout the UK and Ireland. It is operated by the UK Institute for Conservation (UKIC) (in collaboration with the National Council for Conservation-Restoration (NCCR) and Historic Scotland, which administers a parallel register database for Scottish conservation practices). To be included in the Conservation Register, various stringent criteria have to be met, including seven years of experience, relevant training and qualifications, and references from five projects completed within the last five years. The website, www.conservationregister.com, can help you to find a qualified specialist in your area.

The Society for the Protection of Ancient

Buildings (SPAB) is another excellent source of information. SPAB is the largest, oldest and most technically expert national pressure group, fighting to save old buildings from decay, demolition and damage. Visit the organisation's website, www.spab.org.uk, for help on finding builders, suppliers, craftsmen, surveyors and architects.

There are, of course, many other outlets such as the Internet and the Yellow Pages. These sources will be able to provide contact numbers for skilled labourers, as well as a number of individual trade bodies which will be able to provide you with details of its members in your area. As with all labourers, it is always recommended that your see examples of their work, get references, and if possible, check their qualifications, guarantees and warranties before employing them. With specialist works, it is also worth gaining a bit of background knowledge yourself so that you can understand what work needs doing and the best way of doing it. This way you can ensure that your project and your craftsman are compatible, and that the materials and techniques employed, are appropriate. Also, this knowledge will help to ensure that your project runs smoothly; using an inappropriate product, such as modern cement or concrete, can be totally inappropriate for old buildings, and may serve only to accelerate the rate of its decay.

For renovation and restoration help and advice, look no further than Period Living magazine. Every issue includes a renovation section, focusing different techniques such as restoring period fireplaces and maintaining thatched roofs. The Period Living website – www.periodliving.co.uk – includes features, tips and advice from the magazine.

CONSULTANTS, LABOUR & FINANCE - Specialist Crafts & Services - Blacksmithing; Drystone Walling; Lime Plastering; Thatching

SPONSORED BY: PERIOD LIVING MAGAZINE   www.periodliving.co.uk

BLACKSMITHING & METAL CRAFTS

KEY
OTHER: ▽ Reclaimed ⌂ On-line shopping
✎ Bespoke ✋ Hand-made   ECO Ecological

ALUMINIUM ARTWORKS
Persistence Works, 21 Brown Street, Sheffield, S1 2BS
Area of Operation: Worldwide
Tel: 0114 249 4748
Email: info@aluminiumartworks.co.uk
Web: www.aluminiumartworks.co.uk

ARCHITECTURAL METALWORK CONSERVATION
Unit 19, Hoddesdon Industrial Centre,
Pindar Road, Hoddesdon, Hertfordshire, EN11 0DD
Area of Operation: East England
Tel: 01992 443132   **Fax:** 01992 443132

BRITISH ARTIST BLACKSMITHS ASSOCIATION
Anwick Forge, 62 Main Road, Anwick,
Sleaford, Lincolnshire, NG34 9SU
Area of Operation: UK & Ireland
Tel: 01526 830303
Email: babasecretary@anwickforge.co.uk
Web: www.baba.org.uk

C.J. BLACKSMITHS
Yr Eithin, Llangynog, Oswestry, Powys, SY10 0HA
Area of Operation: Worldwide
Tel: 01691 860750   **Fax:** 01691 860750
Email: sales@cjblacksmiths.co.uk
Web: www.cjblacksmiths.co.uk/
www.thecastironemporium.co.uk ⌂

CHRIS TOPP & COMPANY WROUGHT IRONWORKS
Lyndhurst, Carlton Husthwaite,
Thirsk, North Yorkshire, YO7 2BJ
Area of Operation: Worldwide
Tel: 01845 501415   **Fax:** 01845 501072
Email: enquiry@christopp.co.uk
Web: www.christopp.co.uk

COBALT BLACKSMITHS
The Forge, English Farm, English Lane,
Nuffield, Oxfordshire, RG9 5TH
Tel: 01491 641990   **Fax:** 01491 640909
Email: enquiries@cobalt-blacksmiths.co.uk
Web: www.cobalt-blacksmiths.co.uk

JGS METALWORK
Unit 6 Broomstick Estate, High Street,
Edlesborough, Dunstable, Bedfordshire, LU6 2HS
Area of Operation: East England
Tel: 01525 220360   **Fax:** 01525 222786
Email: enquiries@jgsmetalwork.co.uk
Web: www.jgsmetalwork.co.uk

NIGEL TYAS HANDCRAFTED IRONWORK
Bullhouse Mill, Lee Lane, Millhouse Green,
Penistone, Sheffield, South Yorkshire, S36 6BE
Area of Operation: Worldwide
Tel: 01226 766618
Email: sales@nigeltyas.co.uk
Web: www.nigeltyas.co.uk

DRYSTONE WALLING

KEY
OTHER: ▽ Reclaimed ⌂ On-line shopping
✎ Bespoke ✋ Hand-made   ECO Ecological

ANDREW LOUDON - TRADITIONAL & DECORATIVE STONEWORK
Bowmanstead Cottage, Bowmanstead,
Coniston, Cumbria, LA21 8HB
Area of Operation: UK (Excluding Ireland)
Tel: 01539 441985
Email: info@drystone-walling.co.uk
Web: www.drystone-walling.co.uk

ARON GREENWOOD
5 Providence Close, Wetherell Road,
Hackney, London, E9 7DS
Area of Operation: East England, Greater London
Tel: 07790 026539
Email: atullgreenwood@yahoo.co.uk
Web: www.atullgreenwood.co.uk

ARTISAN STONE WORK
1 Isis Close, Abingdon, Oxfordshire, OX14 3TA
Area of Operation: Europe
Tel: 07789 952007
Email: piersconway@yahoo.com
Web: www.artisanstonework.com

DONALD GUNN
Area of Operation: Worldwide
Tel: 07804 802075
Email: dgunnwalls@hotmail.com
Web: www.drystone-walls.com

DRYSTONE CRAFT TM. LIMITED
Unit 61 Edward Street, Bamber Bridge,
Preston, Lancashire, PR5 6FB
Area of Operation: UK (Excluding Ireland)
Tel: 01772 321369
Email: drystonecraft@btinternet.com
Web: www.drystonecraft.co.uk

HISTORIC BUILDING CONSERVATION
Brabazon House, Scalford Road, Eastwell,
Melton Mowbray, Leicestershire, LE14 4EF
Area of Operation: UK (Excluding Ireland)
Tel: 01949 861333
Fax: 01949 861331
Email: info@historic-buildings.net
Web: www.historic-buildings.net

OLDBUILDERS COMPANY
The Studio, Brendan Street, Birr, Co. Offaly, Ireland
Area of Operation: Ireland Only
Tel: +353 (0)509 21133
Fax: +353 (0)865 8236451
Email: info@oldbuilders.com
Web: www.oldbuilders.com

RICHARD CLEGG DWS
5 Springfield Lane, Kirkburton,
Huddersfield, West Yorkshire, HD8 0NZ
Area of Operation: UK (Excluding Ireland)
Tel: 01484 608357
Email: richardclegg@customnet.co.uk
Web: www.richardclegg.co.uk

LIME PLASTERING AND RENDERING

KEY
OTHER: ▽ Reclaimed ⌂ On-line shopping
✎ Bespoke ✋ Hand-made   ECO Ecological

ARTIKA ORNAMENTAL PLASTERERS
6 The Retreat, Foxcote,
Radstock, Somerset, BA3 5YF
Area of Operation: Worldwide
Tel: 01761 433740   **Email:** mark@artika.f9.co.uk
Web: www.bathbusinessfinder.co.uk/artika/index.php

ARTIZAN.UK.NET
29 Fore Street, Bradninch, Exeter, Devon, EX5 4NN
Area of Operation: South West England and South Wales
Tel: 01392 882165
Email: info@artizan.uk.net
Web: www.artizan.uk.net

CONSERVATRIX
17 Culkerton, Tetbury, Gloucestershire, GL8 8SS
Area of Operation: UK (Excluding Ireland)
Tel: 01285 841540
Email: david@conservatrix.co.uk
Web: www.conservatrix.co.uk

FEDERATION OF MASTER BUILDERS
Gordon Fisher House,
14-15 Great James Street, London, WC1N 3DP
Area of Operation: UK & Ireland
Tel: 0207 242 7583   **Fax:** 0207 404 0296
Email: central@fmb.org.uk
Web: www.findabuilder.co.uk

HISTORIC BUILDING CONSERVATION
Brabazon House, Scalford Road, Eastwell,
Melton Mowbray, Leicestershire, LE14 4EF
Area of Operation: UK (Excluding Ireland)
Tel: 01949 861333   **Fax:** 01949 861331
Email: info@historic-buildings.net
Web: www.historic-buildings.net

J&J SHARPE
Furzedon, Merton, Okehampton, Devon, EX20 3DS
Area of Operation: UK (Excluding Ireland)
Tel: 01805 603587   **Fax:** 01805 603587
Email: mail@jjsharpe.co.uk
Web: www.jjsharpe.co.uk

JEREMY WARD INDEPENDENT BUILDING CONSULTANT
Sootfield Green, Charlton Road,
Preston, Hertfordshire, SG4 7TB
Area of Operation: East England, Greater London,
South East England   **Tel:** 01462 438487
Email: sootfieldgreen@aol.com
Web: www.jwibc.com

KIMBOLTON RESTORATION (BUILDING CLEANING & REPAIRS) LTD
Main Street, Old Weston, Huntingdon,
Cambridgeshire, PE28 5LL
Area of Operation: UK & Ireland
Tel: 01832 293100   **Fax:** 08704 286422
Email: sales@kimrest.co.uk
Web: www.kimrest.co.uk

OLDBUILDERS COMPANY
The Studio, Brendan Street, Birr, Co. Offaly, Ireland
Area of Operation: Ireland Only
Tel: +353 (0)509 21133 **Fax: +353 (0)**865 8236451
Email: info@oldbuilders.com
Web: www.oldbuilders.com

ORNATE INTERIORS LIMITED
534 Broad Lane, Stanningley,
Leeds, West Yorkshire, LS28 6PA
Area of Operation: UK & Ireland
Tel: 0113 236 0864   **Fax:** 0113 236 3706
Email: sales@ornateinteriors.co.uk
Web: www.ornateinteriors.co.uk

PLASTER RESTORATIONS (UK) LTD
Shepherd House, 14 Chestnut Way,
Adel, Leeds, West Yorkshire, LS16 7TN
Area of Operation: Worldwide
Tel: 0113 261 4388
Fax: 0113 261 4388
Email: julian@plasterrestorations.com
Web: www.plasterrestorations.com

SCOTTISH LIME CENTRE TRUST
Charleston Workshop, Rocks Road,
Charlestown, Near Dunfermline, Fife, KY11 3EN
Area of Operation: Scotland
Tel: 01383 872722
Fax: 01383 872744
Email: info@scotlime.org
Web: www.scotlime.org

THATCHING

KEY
OTHER: ▽ Reclaimed ⌂ On-line shopping
✎ Bespoke ✋ Hand-made   ECO Ecological

ARON GREENWOOD
5 Providence Close, Wetherell Road,
Hackney, London, E9 7DS
Area of Operation: East England, Greater London
Tel: 07790 026539
Email: atullgreenwood@yahoo.co.uk
Web: www.atullgreenwood.co.uk

FEDERATION OF MASTER BUILDERS
Gordon Fisher House,
14-15 Great James Street, London, WC1N 3DP
Tel: 0207 242 7583
Fax: 0207 404 0296
Email: central@fmb.org.uk
Web: www.findabuilder.co.uk

HALLSWORTH THATCHING LTD
11 Bynner Street, Belle Vue,
Shrewsbury, Shropshire, SY3 7PB
Area of Operation: UK & Ireland
Tel: 0870 760 2158
Email: info@master-thatcher.co.uk
Web: www.master-thatcher.co.uk

INTHATCH
Higher Whatley, Otterford,
Chard, Somerset, TA20 3QL
Area of Operation: Worldwide
Tel: 01460 234477
Fax: 01460 234127
Email: sales@inthatch.co.uk
Web: www.inthatch.co.uk

MASTER THATCHERS (NORTH) LIMITED
8 Thorsby Road, Timperley,
Altrincham, Cheshire, WA15 7QP
Area of Operation: UK & Ireland
Tel: 0161 941 1986
Email: peter.brugge@thatching.net
Web: www.thatching.net

R V MILLER LTD (THATCHERS & MATERIAL SUPPLIERS)
Belhuish Farm House, Coombe Keynes,
Wareham, Dorset, BH20 5PS
Area of Operation: South West England and South Wales
Tel: 01929 462465
Fax: 01929 462465
Email: info@rodmiller.co.uk
Web: www.rodmiller.co.uk

R.J. BOULTON MASTERTHATCHERS LTD
The Maples, Wantage Road, Eddington,
Hungerford, Berkshire, RG17 0PJ
Area of Operation: Worldwide
Tel: 01488 683000
Email: boultonbob@aol.com
Web: www.rjboulton.co.uk

Don't Forget !

You can use the materials key at the beginning of the Handbook to get much more information from a company's listing.

CONSULTANTS, LABOUR & FINANCE

BUILDING RESTORATION

KEY

OTHER: ▽ Reclaimed ⌂ On-line shopping
🖊 Bespoke ✋ Hand-made ECO Ecological

ARTIKA ORNAMENTAL PLASTERERS
6 The Retreat, Foxcote, Radstock, Somerset, BA3 5YF
Area of Operation: Worldwide
Tel: 01761 433740 **Email:** mark@artika.f9.co.uk
Web: www.bathbusinessfinder.co.uk/artika/index.php

ARTIZAN.UK.NET
29 Fore Street, Bradninch, Exeter, Devon, EX5 4NN
Area of Operation: South West England and South Wales
Tel: 01392 882165 **Email:** info@artizan.uk.net
Web: www.artizan.uk.net

B.WILLIAMSON & DAUGHTERS
Copse Cottage, Ford Manor Road,
Dormansland, Lingfield, Surrey, RH7 6NZ
Area of Operation: Greater London, South East England
Tel: 01342 834829 **Fax:** 01342 834829
Email: bryan.williamson@btclick.com
Web: www.specialistcleaning4me.co.uk

CASTLEWAY CONSTRUCTION
52 St.Francis Road, Salisbury, Wiltshire, SP1 3QS
Area of Operation: South West England and South Wales
Tel: 01722 414544 **Fax:** 01722 339123
Email: enquiries@castleway.co.uk
Web: www.castleway.co.uk

COE STONE LTD
Ty Gwyn, Abernant, Carmarthenshire, SA33 5RR
Area of Operation: UK & Ireland
Tel: 01267 281166 **Fax:** 01267 281166
Email: enquiries@olivercoe.com
Web: www.olivercoe.com

CONSERVATRIX
17 Culkerton, Tetbury, Gloucestershire, GL8 8SS
Area of Operation: UK (Excluding Ireland)
Tel: 01285 841540
Email: david@conservatrix.co.uk
Web: www.conservatrix.co.uk

FEDERATION OF MASTER BUILDERS
Gordon Fisher House,
14-15 Great James Street, London, WC1N 3DP
Area of Operation: UK & Ireland
Tel: 0207 242 7583 **Fax:** 0207 404 0296
Email: central@fmb.org.uk
Web: www.findabuilder.co.uk

HALLSWORTH THATCHING LTD
11 Bynner Street, Belle Vue,
Shrewsbury, Shropshire, SY3 7PB
Area of Operation: UK & Ireland
Tel: 0870 760 2158
Email: info@master-thatcher.co.uk
Web: www.master-thatcher.co.uk

HB INSULATIONS
Unit 3 Falcon Court, Manners Industrial Estate,
Ilkeston, Derbyshire, DE7 8EF
Area of Operation: UK (Excluding Ireland)
Tel: 0115 944 0244 **Fax:** 0115 944 0244
Web: www.hbinsulations.com

HIGHTEX-COATINGS LTD
Unit 14 Chapel Farm, Hanslope Road,
Hartwell, Northamptonshire, NN7 2EU
Tel: 01604 861250 **Fax:** 01604 871116
Email: bob@hightexcoatings.co.uk
Web: www.hightexcoatings.co.uk

HISTORIC BUILDING CONSERVATION
Brabazon House, Scalford Road, Eastwell,
Melton Mowbray, Leicestershire, LE14 4EF
Area of Operation: UK (Excluding Ireland)
Tel: 01949 861333 **Fax:** 01949 861331
Email: info@historic-buildings.net
Web: www.historic-buildings.net

J&J SHARPE
Furzedon, Merton, Okehampton, Devon, EX20 3DS
Area of Operation: UK (Excluding Ireland)
Tel: 01805 603587 **Fax:** 01805 603587
Email: mail@jjsharpe.co.uk
Web: www.jjsharpe.co.uk

**JEREMY WARD INDEPENDENT
BUILDING CONSULTANT**
Sootfield Green, Charlton Road,
Preston, Hertfordshire, SG4 7TB
Area of Operation: East England, Greater London,
South East England **Tel:** 01462 438487
Email: sootfieldgreen@aol.com
Web: www.jwibc.co.uk

KEN NEGUS LTD
90 Garfield Road, Wimbledon, London, SW19 8SB
Area of Operation: Greater London, South East England
Tel: 020 8543 9266 **Fax:** 020 8543 9100
Email: graham@kennegus.co.uk
Web: www.kennegus.co.uk

**KIMBOLTON RESTORATION
(BUILDING CLEANING & REPAIRS) LTD**
Main Street, Old Weston, Huntingdon,
Cambridgeshire, PE28 5LL
Area of Operation: UK & Ireland
Tel: 01832 293100 **Fax:** 08704 286422
Email: sales@kimrest.co.uk
Web: www.kimrest.co.uk

M.B.L
55 High Street, Biggleswade,
Bedfordshire, SG18 0JH
Area of Operation: UK (Excluding Ireland)
Tel: 01767 318695 **Fax:** 01767 318695
Email: info@mblai.co.uk
Web: www.mblai.co.uk

**MALCOLM SMITH -
POWER WASHING & GRAFFITI REMOVAL**
45 Roundponds, Melksham, Wiltshire, SN12 8DW
Area of Operation: Midlands & Mid Wales, South
East England, South West England and South Wales
Tel: 01225 707200
Email: powerwashinguk@aol.com
Web: www.powerwashinguk.co.uk

NIMBUS CONSERVATION LTD
Eastgate, Christchurch Street East,
Frome, Somerset, BA11 1QD
Area of Operation: UK (Excluding Ireland)
Tel: 01373 474646 **Fax:** 01373 474648
Email: enquiries@nimbusconservation.com
Web: www.nimbusconservation.com

NORBURY MOOR BUILDING SERVICES LTD
Gawthorne, Hazel Grove,
Stockport, Cheshire, SK7 5AB
Area of Operation: North West England and North Wales
Tel: 0800 093 5785 **Fax:** 0161 456 1944
Email: paul@norburymoor.co.uk
Web: www.norburymoor.co.uk ⌂

OAKBEAMS.COM
Hunterswood Farm, Alfold Road, Dunsfold,
Godalming, Surrey, GU8 4NP
Area of Operation: Worldwide
Tel: 01483 200477
Email: info@oakbeams.com
Web: www.oakbeams.com

OLDBUILDERS COMPANY
The Studio, Brendan Street, Birr, Co. Offaly, Ireland
Area of Operation: Ireland Only
Tel: 0509 21133 **Fax:** 0865 8236451
Email: info@oldbuilders.com
Web: www.oldbuilders.com

ONE-CALL PROPERTY MAINTENANCE
PO Box 4413, Salisbury House,
Ringwood, Hampshire, BH24 1YR
Area of Operation: Greater London, South East England
Tel: 01202 828715
Fax: 01202 828715
Email: paul@one-callgroup.co.uk
Web: www.one-callgroup.co.uk

ORNATE INTERIORS LIMITED
534 Broad Lane, Stanningley,
Leeds, West Yorkshire, LS28 6PA
Area of Operation: UK & Ireland
Tel: 0113 236 0864 **Fax:** 0113 236 3706
Email: sales@ornateinteriors.co.uk
Web: www.ornateinteriors.co.uk

QUADRIGA CONCEPTS LTD
Gadbrook House, Gadbrook Business Park,
Rudheath, Northwich, Cheshire, CW9 7RG
Area of Operation: UK & Ireland
Tel: 0808 100 3777
Fax: 01606 330777
Email: info@quadrigaltd.com
Web: www.quadrigaltd.com

STONE ESSENTIALS CO LTD
Mount Spring Works, Off Burnley Road East,
Rossendale, Lancashire, BB4 9LA
Area of Operation: UK (Excluding Ireland)
Tel: 01706 210605 **Fax:** 01706 228707
Email: ken.howe@btconnect.com
Web: www.stone-essentials.co.uk

STONEHEALTH LTD
Bowers Court, Broadwell,
Dursley, Gloucestershire, GL11 4JE
Tel: 01453 540600 **Fax:** 01453 540609
Email: info@stonehealth.com
Web: www.stonehealth.com

SUFFOLK BRICK & STONE CLEANING CO. LTD.
Dickens House, Old Stowmarket Road, Woolpit,
Near Bury St. Edmunds, Suffolk, IP30 9QS
Area of Operation: South East England
Tel: 01359 242650 **Fax:** 01359 241211
Email: suffolkbrick@aol.com
Web: www.suffolkbrickandstone.co.uk

**TOUCHSTONE -
GRANITE, MARBLE, SLATE & STONE**
Touchstone House, 82 High Street,
Measham, Derbyshire, DE12 7JB
Area of Operation: UK (Excluding Ireland)
Tel: 0845 130 1862 **Fax:** 01530 274271
Email: sales@touchstone-uk.com
Web: www.touchstone-uk.com

DECORATIVE INTERIOR FEATURES RESTORATION

KEY

OTHER: ▽ Reclaimed ⌂ On-line shopping
🖊 Bespoke ✋ Hand-made ECO Ecological

ARTIKA ORNAMENTAL PLASTERERS
6 The Retreat, Foxcote, Radstock, Somerset, BA3 5YF
Area of Operation: Worldwide
Tel: 01761 433740 **Email:** mark@artika.f9.co.uk
Web: www.bathbusinessfinder.co.uk/artika/index.php

BROWNS FRENCH POLISHING CO LTD
Unit A2 Pixmore Estate, Pixmore Avenue,
Letchworth Garden City, Hertfordshire, SG6 1JJ
Area of Operation: East England, Greater London
Tel: 01462 680241 **Fax:** 01462 482999
Email: info@brownsfrenchpolishing.co.uk
Web: www.brownsfrenchpolishing.co.uk

HERITAGE TILE CONSERVATION LTD
The Studio, 2 Harris Green,
Broseley, Shropshire, TF12 5HJ
Tel: 01746 785025 **Fax:** 01746 785025
Email: heritagetile@msn.com
Web: www.heritagetile.co.uk

HERITAGE TILING DESIGN & RESTORATION CO.
P.O. Box 18 Seaforth Vale,
Seaforth, Liverpool, Merseyside, L21 0EQ
Area of Operation: Worldwide
Tel: 0151 920 7349 **Fax:** 0151 9207349
Email: info@heritagetiling.com **Web:** www.tiling.co.uk

**KIMBOLTON RESTORATION
(BUILDING CLEANING & REPAIRS) LTD.**
Main Street, Old Weston, Huntingdon,
Cambridgeshire, PE28 5LL
Area of Operation: UK & Ireland
Tel: 01832 293100 **Fax:** 08704 286422
Email: sales@kimrest.co.uk
Web: www.kimrest.co.uk

ONE-CALL PROPERTY MAINTENANCE
PO Box 4413, Salisbury House,
Ringwood, Hampshire, BH24 1YR
Area of Operation: Greater London, South East England
Tel: 01202 828715 **Fax:** 0870 127 7642
Email: paul@one-callgroup.co.uk
Web: www.one-callgroup.co.uk

PAXTON RESTORATION LTD
Princess House, 50 Eastcastle Street, London, W1W 8EA
Area of Operation: Greater London
Tel: 0870 027 8424 **Fax:** 0870 127 7642
Email: richard@paxtonrestoration.co.uk
Web: www.paxtonrestoration.co.uk

PLASTER RESTORATIONS (UK) LTD
Shepherd House, 14 Chestnut Way,
Adel, Leeds, West Yorkshire, LS16 7TN
Area of Operation: Worldwide
Tel: 0113 261 4388 **Fax:** 0113 261 4388
Email: julian@plasterrestorations.com
Web: www.plasterrestorations.com

POETSTYLE
Unit 1, Bayford Street Industrial Centre,
Hackney, Greater London, E8 3SE
Area of Operation: Worldwide
Tel: 0208 533 0915 **Fax:** 0208 985 2953
Email: sofachairs@aol.com
Web: www.sofachairs.co.uk

SOUTH WESTERN FLOORING SERVICES
145-147 Park Lane,
Frampton Cotterell, Bristol, BS36 2ES
Area of Operation: UK & Ireland
Tel: 01454 880982
Fax: 01454 880982
Email: mikeflanders@blueyonder.co.uk
Web: www.southwesternflooring.co.uk

STEER LEATHERCARE LTD
Unit 5 Dale Close, Wrecclesham,
Farnham, Surrey, GU10 4PQ
Area of Operation: UK & Ireland
Tel: 0870 787 9550
Email: steer@leatheraftercare.com
Web: www.leatheraftercare.com ⌂

STONEHEALTH LTD
Bowers Court, Broadwell, Dursley,
Gloucestershire, GL11 4JE
Area of Operation: Worldwide
Tel: 01453 540600 **Fax:** 01453 540609
Email: info@stonehealth.com
Web: www.stonehealth.com

SUNRISE STAINED GLASS
58-60 Middle Street, Southsea,
Portsmouth, Hampshire, PO5 4BP
Area of Operation: UK (Excluding Ireland)
Tel: 02392 750512
Fax: 02392 875488
Email: sunrise@stained-windows.co.uk
Web: www.stained-windows.co.uk

THE MOSAIC RESTORATION COMPANY LTD
Verwood House, High Street,
West Haddon, Northamptonshire, NN6 7AP
Area of Operation: UK (Excluding Ireland)
Tel: 01788 510000
Fax: 01788 510222
Email: gary@mosaicrestoration.co.uk
Web: www.mosaicrestoration.co.uk

THE PAINT PRACTICE
18 Hallam Chase, Sandygate,
Sheffield, South Yorkshire, S10 5SW
Area of Operation: Europe
Tel: 0114 230 6828 **Fax:** 0114 230 6828

JOINERY RESTORATION

KEY

OTHER: ▽ Reclaimed ⌐ On-line shopping
◇ Bespoke ✋ Hand-made ECO Ecological

CONSERVATRIX
17 Culkerton, Tetbury, Gloucestershire, GL8 8SS
Area of Operation: UK (Excluding Ireland)
Tel: 01285 841540
Email: david@conservatrix.co.uk
Web: www.conservatrix.co.uk

FEDERATION OF MASTER BUILDERS
Gordon Fisher House,
14-15 Great James Street, London, WC1N 3DP
Area of Operation: UK & Ireland
Tel: 0207 242 7583 **Fax:** 0207 404 0296
Email: central@fmb.org.uk
Web: www.findabuilder.co.uk

HISTORIC BUILDING CONSERVATION
Brabazon House, Scalford Road, Eastwell,
Melton Mowbray, Leicestershire, LE14 4EF
Area of Operation: UK (Excluding Ireland)
Tel: 01949 861333 **Fax:** 01949 861331
Email: info@historic-buildings.net
Web: www.historic-buildings.net

JOHN NETHERCOTT & CO
147 Corve Street, Ludlow, Shropshire, SY8 2PG
Area of Operation: UK (Excluding Ireland)
Tel: 01584 877044 **Fax:** 01547 560255
Email: showroom@johnnethercott.com
Web: www.johnnethercott.com

MH JOINERY SERVICES
25b Camwall Road, Harrogate,
North Yorkshire, HG1 4PT
Area of Operation: North East England
Tel: 01423 888856 **Fax:** 01423 888856
Email: info@mhjoineryservices.co.uk
Web: www.mhjoineryservices.co.uk

NORBURY MOOR BUILDING SERVICES LTD
Gawthorne, Hazel Grove,
Stockport, Cheshire, SK7 5AB
Area of Operation: North West England and North Wales
Tel: 0800 093 5785 **Fax:** 0161 456 1944
Email: paul@norburymoor.co.uk
Web: www.norburymoor.co.uk ⌐

OLDBUILDERS COMPANY
The Studio, Brendan Street, Birr, Co. Offaly, Ireland
Area of Operation: Ireland Only
Tel: 0509 21133 **Fax:** 0865 8236451
Email: info@oldbuilders.com
Web: www.oldbuilders.com

PAXTON RESTORATION LTD
Princess House, 50 Eastcastle Street,
London, W1W 8EA
Area of Operation: Greater London
Tel: 0870 027 8424 **Fax:** 0870 127 7642
Email: richard@paxtonrestoration.co.uk
Web: www.paxtonrestoration.co.uk

QUADRIGA CONCEPTS LTD
Gadbrook House, Gadbrook Business Park,
Rudheath, Northwich, Cheshire, CW9 7RG
Area of Operation: UK & Ireland
Tel: 0808 100 3777 **Fax:** 01606 330777
Email: info@quadrigaltd.com
Web: www.quadrigaltd.com

**Please mention
The Homebuilder's
Handbook
when you call**

REPAIR CARE INTERNATIONAL LIMITED
Unit E, Sawtry Business Park, Glatton Road,
Sawtry, Huntingdon, Cambridgeshire, PE28 5GQ
Area of Operation: UK & Ireland
Tel: 01487 830311
Fax: 01487 832876
Email: salesuk@repair-care.com
Web: www.repair-care.com

TIM PEEK WOODCARVING
The Woodcarving Studio , Highfield Avenue, High
Wycombe, Buckinghamshire, HP12 4ET
Area of Operation: UK (Excluding Ireland)
Tel: 01494 439629
Email: timpeekwoodcarving@hotmail.com
Web: www.timpeekwoodcarving.co.uk

VENTROLLA LTD
11 Hornbeam Square South,
Harrogate, North Yorkshire, HG2 8NB
Area of Operation: UK & Ireland
Tel: 0800 378 278 **Fax:** 01423 859321
Email: info@ventrolla.co.uk
Web: www.ventrolla.co.uk

METALWORK RESTORATION

KEY

OTHER: ▽ Reclaimed ⌐ On-line shopping
◇ Bespoke ✋ Hand-made ECO Ecological

**ARCHITECTURAL
METALWORK CONSERVATION**
Unit 19, Hoddesdon Industrial Centre,
Pindar Road, Hoddesdon, Hertfordshire, EN11 0DD
Area of Operation: East England
Tel: 01992 443132 **Fax:** 01992 443132

B.WILLIAMSON & DAUGHTERS
Copse Cottage, Ford Manor Road,
Dormansland, Lingfield, Surrey, RH7 6NZ
Area of Operation: Greater London, South East England
Tel: 01342 834829
Fax: 01342 834829
Email: bryan.williamson@btclick.com
Web: www.specialistcleaning4me.co.uk

CASTAWAY CAST PRODUCTS AND WOODWARE
Brocklesby Station, Brocklesby Road,
Ulceby, Lincolnshire, DN39 6ST
Area of Operation: Worldwide
Tel: 01469 588995 **Fax:** 01469 588995
Email: castawaycastproducts@btinternet.com

CASTAWAY CAST PRODUCTS & WOODWARE

Area of Operation: Worldwide
Tel: 01469 588995
Fax: 01469 588995
Email: castawaycastproducts@btinternet.com

Cast metal and light fabrication work for the
new build and restoration projects.
Bespoke and standard products. Names and
postboxes/windows/grilles/gates and
railings/balconies/carports and much more.

**CHRIS TOPP & COMPANY
WROUGHT IRONWORKS**
Lyndhurst, Carlton Husthwaite,
Thirsk, North Yorkshire, YO7 2BJ
Tel: 01845 501415 **Fax:** 01845 501072
Email: enquiry@christopp.co.uk
Web: www.christopp.co.uk

COBALT BLACKSMITHS
The Forge, English Farm, English Lane,
Nuffield, Oxfordshire, RG9 5TH
Tel: 01491 641990 **Fax:** 01491 640909
Email: enquiries@cobalt-blacksmiths.co.uk
Web: www.cobalt-blacksmiths.co.uk

MBL
55 High Street, Biggleswade, Bedfordshire, SG18 0JH
Area of Operation: UK (Excluding Ireland)
Tel: 01767 318695 **Fax:** 01767 318834
Email: info@mblai.co.uk **Web:** www.mblai.co.uk

STEEL WINDOW SERVICE AND SUPPLIES LTD
30 Oxford Road, Finsbury Park, London, N4 3EY
Area of Operation: Greater London
Tel: 0207 272 2294 **Fax:** 0207 281 2309
Email: post@steelwindows.co.uk
Web: www.steelwindows.co.uk

STONEHEALTH LTD
Bowers Court, Broadwell, Dursley,
Gloucestershire, GL11 4JE
Area of Operation: Worldwide
Tel: 01453 540600 **Fax:** 01453 540609
Email: info@stonehealth.com
Web: www.stonehealth.com

STONEWORK RESTORATION

KEY

OTHER: ▽ Reclaimed ⌐ On-line shopping
◇ Bespoke ✋ Hand-made ECO Ecological

**A D CALVERT
ARCHITECTURAL STONE SUPPLIES LTD**
Smithy Lane, Grove Square,
Leyburn, North Yorkshire, DL8 5DZ
Tel: 01969 622515 **Fax:** 01969 624345
Email: stone@calverts.co.uk
Web: www.calverts.co.uk

ABBEY MASONRY & RESTORATION
Plot 4 Cross Hands Business Park,
Cross Hands, Carmarthenshire, SA14 6RE
Area of Operation: South West England and South Wales
Tel: 01269 845084 **Fax:** 01269 831774
Email: info@abbeymasonry.com

ALBA MASONRY
17 Borestone Crescent, Stirling, Stirlingshire, FK7 9BQ
Area of Operation: Scotland
Tel: 01786 450459 **Email:** t4lcx@hotmail.com
Web: www.albamasonry.co.uk

ARTISAN STONE WORK
1 Isis Close, Abingdon, Oxfordshire, OX14 3TA
Area of Operation: Europe **Tel:** 07789 952007
Email: piersconway@yahoo.com
Web: www.artisanstonework.com

B.WILLIAMSON & DAUGHTERS
Copse Cottage, Ford Manor Road,
Dormansland, Lingfield, Surrey, RH7 6NZ
Area of Operation: Greater London, South East England
Tel: 01342 834829 **Fax:** 01342 834829
Email: bryan.williamson@btclick.com
Web: www.specialistcleaning4me.co.uk

**BURLEIGH STONE CLEANING &
RESTORATION COMPANY LTD**
The Old Stables, 56 Balliol Road,
Bootle, Merseyside, L20 7EJ
Tel: 0151 922 3366 **Fax:** 0151 922 3377
Email: info@burleighstone.co.uk
Web: www.burleighstone.co.uk

CONSERVATRIX
17 Culkerton, Tetbury, Gloucestershire, GL8 8SS
Area of Operation: UK (Excluding Ireland)
Tel: 01285 841540
Email: david@conservatrix.co.uk
Web: www.conservatrix.co.uk

D F FIXINGS
15 Aldham Gardens, Rayleigh, Essex, SS6 9TB
Area of Operation: UK (Excluding Ireland)
Tel: 07956 674673 **Fax:** 01268 655072

FEDERATION OF MASTER BUILDERS
Gordon Fisher House,
14-15 Great James Street, London, WC1N 3DP
Area of Operation: UK & Ireland
Tel: 0207 242 7583 **Fax:** 0207 404 0296
Email: central@fmb.org.uk
Web: www.findabuilder.co.uk

H W POULTER & SON
279 Fulham Road, Chelsea, London, SW10 9PZ
Tel: 0207 352 7268 **Fax:** 0207 351 0984
Email: hwpoulterandson@btconnect.com
Web: www.hwpoulterandson.co.uk

HADDONSTONE LTD
The Forge House, East Haddon,
Northampton, Northamptonshire, NN6 8DB
Tel: 01604 770711
Fax: 01604 770027
Email: info@haddonstone.co.uk
Web: www.haddonstone.com ⌐

HADDONSTONE

Area of Operation: Worldwide
Tel: 01604 770711 **Fax:** 01604 770027
Email: info@haddonstone.co.uk
Web: www.haddonstone.com
Other Info: ⌐ ✋ ◇

Haddonstone manufacture custom cast stone
designs for restoration projects. The company
also has an extensive range of standard designs
including balustrading, columns, entablatures
and window surrounds.

HERITAGE TILE CONSERVATION LTD
The Studio, 2 Harris Green,
Broseley, Shropshire, TF12 5HJ
Tel: 01746 785025 **Fax:** 01746 785025
Email: heritagetile@msn.com
Web: www.heritagetile.co.uk

HISTORIC BUILDING CONSERVATION
Brabazon House, Scalford Road, Eastwell,
Melton Mowbray, Leicestershire, LE14 4EF
Tel: 01949 861333 **Fax:** 01949 861331
Email: info@historic-buildings.net
Web: www.historic-buildings.net

J & R MARBLE COMPANY LTD
Unit 9,Period Works, Lammas Road,
Leyton, London, E10 7QT
Tel: 0208 539 6471 **Fax:** 0208 539 9264
Email: sales@jrmarble.co.uk
Web: www.jrmarble.co.uk

J&J SHARPE
Furzedon, Merton, Okehampton, Devon, EX20 3DS
Area of Operation: UK (Excluding Ireland)
Tel: 01805 603587 **Fax:** 01805 603587
Email: mail@jjsharpe.co.uk
Web: www.jjsharpe.co.uk

CONSULTANTS, LABOUR & FINANCE - Specialist Crafts & Services - Sandblasting; Frescos, Murals & Trompe l'Oeil; Specialist Joinery Manufacturers

SPONSORED BY: PERIOD LIVING MAGAZINE   www.periodliving.co.uk

KEN NEGUS LTD
90 Garfield Road, Wimbledon, London, SW19 8SB
Area of Operation: Greater London, South East England
Tel: 020 8543 9266   **Fax:** 020 8543 9100
Email: graham@kennegus.co.uk
Web: www.kennegus.co.uk

**KIMBOLTON RESTORATION
(BUILDING CLEANING & REPAIRS) LTD.**
Main Street, Old Weston, Huntingdon,
Cambridgeshire, PE28 5LL
Tel: 01832 293100   **Fax:** 08704 286422
Email: sales@kimrest.co.uk
Web: www.kimrest.co.uk

NIMBUS CONSERVATION LTD
Eastgate, Christchurch Street East,
Frome, Somerset, BA11 1QD
Area of Operation: UK (Excluding Ireland)
Tel: 01373 474646   **Fax:** 01373 474648
Email: enquiries@nimbusconservation.com
Web: www.nimbusconservation.com

OLDBUILDERS COMPANY
The Studio, Brendan Street, Birr, Co. Offaly, Ireland
Area of Operation: Ireland Only
Tel: +353 (0)509 21133   **Fax:** +353 (0)865 8236451
Email: info@oldbuilders.com
Web: www.oldbuilders.com

ONE-CALL PROPERTY MAINTENANCE
PO Box 4413, Salisbury House,
Ringwood, Hampshire, BH24 1YR
Area of Operation: Greater London, South East England
Tel: 01202 828715   **Fax:** 01202 828715
Email: paul@one-callgroup.co.uk
Web: www.one-callgroup.co.uk

QUADRIGA CONCEPTS LTD
Gadbrook House, Gadbrook Business Park,
Rudheath, Northwich, Cheshire, CW9 7RG
Area of Operation: UK & Ireland
Tel: 0808 100 3777   **Fax:** 01606 330777
Email: info@quadrigaltd.com
Web: www.quadrigaltd.com

RESTORE BRICK + STONE CLEANING LTD
6 Greenoak Way, Wimbledon Village,
London, SW19 5EN
Area of Operation: Greater London, South East England
Tel: 0208 286 3579   **Fax:** 0208 947 2622
Email: info@restorebrick.co.uk
Web: www.restorebrick.co.uk

STONE ESSENTIALS CO LTD
Mount Spring Works, Off Burnley Road East,
Rossendale, Lancashire, BB4 9LA
Area of Operation: UK (Excluding Ireland)
Tel: 01706 210605   **Fax:** 01706 228707
Email: ken.howe@btconnect.com
Web: www.stone-essentials.co.uk

STONEHEALTH LTD
Bowers Court, Broadwell, Dursley,
Gloucestershire, GL11 4JE
Area of Operation: Worldwide
Tel: 01453 540600   **Fax:** 01453 540609
Email: info@stonehealth.com
Web: www.stonehealth.com

SANDBLASTING & CLEANING SERVICES

KEY
OTHER: ▽ Reclaimed   ✋🛒 On-line shopping
✎ Bespoke   ✋ Hand-made   ECO Ecological

CLEANWALLS
4 Tythe Barn Close, Hurstead,
Rochdale, Lancashire, OL12 9QR
Area of Operation: North West England and North
Wales, South West England and South Wales
Tel: 01706 868249   **Email:** cleanwalls@hotmail.com

HB INSULATIONS
Unit 3, Falcon Court, Manners Industrial Estate,
Ilkeston, Derbyshire, DE7 8EF
Tel: 0115 944 0244   **Fax:** 0115 944 0244
Email: chris@hbinsulations.com
Web: www.hbinsulations.com

**KIMBOLTON RESTORATION
(BUILDING CLEANING & REPAIRS) LTD.**
Main Street, Old Weston, Huntingdon,
Cambridgeshire, PE28 5LL
Tel: 01832 293100   **Fax:** 08704 286422
Email: sales@kimrest.co.uk
Web: www.kimrest.co.uk

**MALCOLM SMITH -
POWER WASHING & GRAFFITI REMOVAL**
45 Roundponds, Melksham, Wiltshire, SN12 8DW
Area of Operation: Midlands & Mid Wales, South
East England, South West England and South Wales
Tel: 01225 707200
Email: powerwashinguk@aol.com
Web: www.powerwashinguk.com

MJK GROUP
Woodlands, Pannell Close,
East Grinstead, West Sussex, RH19 1DA
Area of Operation: South East England
Tel: 01342 324000
Email: mjkgroup324000@aol.com
Web: www.mjk-group.co.uk

OLDBUILDERS COMPANY
The Studio, Brendan Street, Birr, Co. Offaly, .
Area of Operation: Ireland Only
Tel: +353 (0)509 21133   **Fax:** +353 (0)865 8236451
Email: info@oldbuilders.com
Web: www.oldbuilders.com

RESTORE BRICK + STONE CLEANING LTD
6 Greenoak Way, Wimbledon Village,
London, SW19 5EN
Area of Operation: Greater London, South East England
Tel: 0208 286 3579   **Fax:** 0208 947 2622
Email: info@restorebrick.co.uk
Web: www.restorebrick.co.uk

STEADBLAST
4 Buckland Road, Parkside,
Stafford, Staffordshire, ST16 1TZ
Tel: 01785 603506   **Fax:** 01785 609529
Email: enquiries@steadblast.co.uk
Web: www.steadblast.co.uk

SUFFOLK BRICK & STONE CLEANING CO. LTD.
Dickens House, Old Stowmarket Road, Woolpit,
Near Bury St. Edmunds, Suffolk, IP30 9QS
Area of Operation: South East England
Tel: 01359 242650   **Fax:** 01359 241211
Email: suffolkbrick@aol.com
Web: www.suffolkbrickandstone.co.uk

T.C.SEAMARKS (SHOT & SANDBLASTING) LTD
The Bungalow, Wren Park, Hitchin Road,
Shefford, Bedfordshire, SG17 5JD
Area of Operation: East England, Greater London
Tel: 01462 813254   **Fax:** 01462 813254
Email: tonyseamarks@yahoo.co.uk
Web: www.tcseamarks.co.uk

FRESCOS, MURALS & TROMPE L'OEIL

KEY
OTHER: ▽ Reclaimed   ✋🛒 On-line shopping
✎ Bespoke   ✋ Hand-made   ECO Ecological

BLINK RED CONTEMPORARY ART
40 Maritime Street, Edinburgh, Lothian, EH6 6SA
Area of Operation: UK & Ireland
Tel: 0131 625 0192   **Fax:** 0131 467 7995
Email: customerservices@blinkred.com
Web: www.blinkred.com 🛒

BROGAN ARTS
Woodlands, Templehill Estate,
By Auchenblae, Aberdeenshire, AB30 1UJ
Area of Operation: Worldwide
Tel: 01561 320461   **Email:** sandy@broganarts.com
Web: www.broganarts.com

DROSTLE
40 Strand House, Merbury Close, London, SE28 0LU
Area of Operation: Worldwide
Tel: 020 8316 7734   **Fax:** 020 8316 7734
Email: mosaics@drostle.com
Web: www.drostle.com

HUNTER ART & TILE STUDIO
Craft Courtyard, Harestanes,
Ancrum, Jedburgh, Borders, TD8 6UQ
Area of Operation: UK & Ireland
Tel: 01835 830 328
Email: enquiries@hunterartandtilestudio.co.uk
Web: www.hunterartandtilestudio.co.uk 🛒

RICEDESIGN
The Barn, Shawbury Lane,
Shustoke, Nr Coleshill, B46 2RR
Area of Operation: Worldwide
Tel: 01675 481183
Email: ricedesigns@hotmail.com

SALLY SINGER DESIGNS
Unit 3, Saxon Works, Olive Road,
Hove, East Sussex, BN3 5LE
Area of Operation: UK (Excluding Ireland)
Tel: 01273 773437   **Email:** sallysinger3@aol.com
Web: www.sallysingerdesigns.co.uk

SPECIALIST JOINERY MANUFACTURERS

KEY
OTHER: ▽ Reclaimed   ✋🛒 On-line shopping
✎ Bespoke   ✋ Hand-made   ECO Ecological

AACORN JOINERY AND DESIGN LTD.
2 Balaclava Place, South Street,
Bridport, Dorset, DT6 3PE
Area of Operation: Europe
Tel: 01308 456217
Fax: 01308 424511
Email: info@aacornjoinery.co.uk
Web: www.aacornjoinery.co.uk

ALTHAM OAK & CARPENTRY LTD
Altham Corn Mill, Burnley Road,
Altham, Accrington, Lancashire, BB5 5UP
Area of Operation: UK & Ireland
Tel: 01282 771618   **Fax:** 01282 777932
Email: info@oak-beams.co.uk
Web: www.oak-beams.co.uk

B G H JOINERY CO LTD
Unicorn Business Centre, The Ridgeway,
Chiseldon, Swindon, Wiltshire, SN4 0HT
Area of Operation: UK (Excluding Ireland)
Tel: 01793 741330   **Fax:** 01793 741310
Email: sales@bghjoinery.co.uk
Web: www.bghjoinery.co.uk

BADMAN & BADMAN JOINERY LTD
The Drill Hall, Langford Road,
Weston Super Mare, Somerset, BS23 3PQ
Area of Operation: UK (Excluding Ireland)
Tel: 01934 644122   **Fax:** 01934 628189
Email: info@badmanandbadman.fsnet.co.uk
Web: www.badmans.co.uk

BENCHMARK JOINERY GUISBOROUGH LTD
Unit 3 Morgan Drive, Guisborough,
Cleveland, TS14 7DH
Area of Operation: North East England
Tel: 01287 203317
Email: alan@custom-joinery.com
Web: www.custom-joinery.com

BROADLEAF TIMBER
Llandeilo Road Industrial Estate,
Carms, Carmarthenshire, SA18 3JG
Area of Operation: UK & Ireland
Tel: 01269 851910   **Fax:** 01269 851911
Email: sales@broadleaftimber.com
Web: www.broadleaftimber.com

COLIN BAKER
Timberyard, Crownhill, Halberton,
Tiverton, Devon, EX16 7AY
Tel: 01884 820152
Email: colinbaker@colinbakeroak.co.uk
Web: www.colinbakeroak.co.uk

COUNTY JOINERY (SOUTH EAST) LTD
Tetley House, Marley Lane Business Park,
Marley Lane, Battle, East Sussex, TN33 0RE
Area of Operation: Greater London, South East England
Tel: 01424 871500   **Fax:** 01424 871550
Email: info@countyjoinery.co.uk
Web: www.countyjoinery.co.uk

CREATE JOINERY
The Wood Yard, Castell Ddu Road,
Waun Gron, Pontarddulais, Swansea, SA4 8DH
Area of Operation: Greater London, Midlands & Mid
Wales, North West England and North Wales, South
East England, South West England and South Wales
Tel: 01792 386677   **Fax:** 01792 386677
Email: mail@create-joinery.co.uk
Web: www.create-joinery.co.uk

DOVETAIL COMMERCIAL JOINERY
Gamston Aerodrome Industrial Estate, Gamston,
Nr. Retford, Nottinghamshire, DN22 0QL
Tel: 01777 838138   **Fax:** 01777 839132
Email: info@dovetailcommercial.co.uk
Web: www.dovetailcommercial.co.uk

FLETCHER JOINERY
261 Whessoe Road, Darlington, Durham, DL3 0YL
Area of Operation: North East England
Tel: 01325 357347   **Fax:** 01325 357347
Email: enquiries@fletcherjoinery.co.uk
Web: www.fletcherjoinery.co.uk

J L JOINERY
Cockerton View, Grange Lane,
Preston, Lancashire, PR4 5JE
Area of Operation: UK (Excluding Ireland)
Tel: 01772 616123   **Fax:** 01772 619182
Email: mail@jljoinery.co.uk
Web: www.jljoinery.co.uk

JOHN NETHERCOTT & CO
147 Corve Street, Ludlow, Shropshire, SY8 2PG
Tel: 01584 877044   **Fax:** 01547 560255
Email: showroom@johnnethercott.com
Web: www.johnnethercott.com

Don't Forget !

You can use the materials key at the beginning of this Handbook to get much more information from a company's listing.

MARK HENRY INTERIORS & BUILDING
Unit 9 Greenway, Harlow Business Park,
Harlow, Essex, CM19 5QB
Area of Operation: UK (Excluding Ireland)
Tel: 01279 444829   **Fax:** 01279 441598
Email: info@markhenryfurniture.co.uk
Web: www.markhenryfurniture.co.uk

MARK HENRY INTERIORS & BUILDING

Area of Operation: UK (Excluding Ireland)
Tel: 01279 444829
Fax: 01279 441598
Email: info@markhenryfurniture.co.uk
Web: www.markhenryfurniture.co.uk

We specialise in all aspects of interiors ranging from bespoke joinery and cabinet making, ie. handmade kitchens and bedrooms, to house extensions, refurbishments and loft conversions.

NORBUILD TIMBER FABRICATION & FINE CARPENTRY LTD
Marcassie Farm, Rafford, Forres, Moray, IV36 2RH
Tel: 01309 676865   **Fax:** 01309 676865
Email: norbuild@marcassie.fsnet.co.uk

ORIGINAL OAK
Ashlands, Burwash, East Sussex, TN19 7HS
Tel: 01435 882228   **Fax:** 01435 882228
Web: www.originaloak.co.uk

ROBERT J TURNER & CO
Roe Green, Sandon, Buntingford,
Hertfordshire, SG9 0QE
Area of Operation: East England, Greater London
Tel: 01763 288371   **Fax:** 01763 288440
Email: sales@robertjturner.co.uk
Web: www.robertjturner.co.uk

SANDERSON'S FINE FURNITURE
Unit 5 & 6, The Village Workshop, Four Crosses
Business Park, Four Crosses, Powys, SY22 6ST
Tel: 01691 830075   **Fax:** 01691 830075
Email: sales@sandersonsfinefurniture.co.uk
Web: www.sandersonsfinefurniture.co.uk

SCOTTS OF THRAPSTON LTD.
Bridge Street, Thrapston, Northamptonshire, NN14 4LR
Tel: 01832 732366   **Fax:** 01832 733703
Email: julia@scottsofthrapston.co.uk
Web: www.scottsofthrapston.co.uk

THE ROUNDWOOD TIMBER COMPANY LTD
Roundwood, Newick Lane,
Mayfield, East Sussex, TN20 6RG
Tel: 01435 867072   **Fax:** 01435 864708
Email: sales@roundwoodtimber.com
Web: www.roundwoodtimber.com

TIM PEEK WOODCARVING
The Woodcarving Studio, Highfield Avenue,
High Wycombe, Buckinghamshire, HP12 4ET
Tel: 01494 439629
Email: timpeekwoodcarving@hotmail.com
Web: www.timpeekwoodcarving.co.uk

TIM WOOD LIMITED
1 Burland Road, London, SW11 6SA
Tel: 07041 380030   **Fax:** 08700 548645
Email: homeb@timwood.com
Web: www.timwood.com

TONY HOOPER
Unit 18 Camelot Court,
Bancombe Trading Estate, Somerton, TA11 6SB
Tel: 01458 274221   **Fax:** 01458 274690
Email: tonyhooper1@aol.com
Web: www.tonyhooper.co.uk

WYCLIFFE OF WARWICKSHIRE
14-24 North Street, Upper Stoke,
Coventry, West Midlands, CV2 3FW
Area of Operation: UK (Excluding Ireland)
Tel: 02476 635151

AERIAL PHOTOGRAPHY

KEY
OTHER: ▽ Reclaimed   ⌐ On-line shopping
✎ Bespoke   ✋ Hand-made   ECO Ecological

3D VIRTUAL LTD
Crowell End, Crowell Hill, Chinnor, Oxfordshire, OX39 4BT
Area of Operation: Europe   **Tel:** 01844 214572
Email: chrisparker02@btconnect.com
Web: www.3dvirtual.co.uk

AEROLENS
Unit C16 St.George's Business Park,
Castle Road, Sittingbourne, Kent, ME10 3TB
Area of Operation: Greater London, South East England
Tel: 0845 838 1764   **Email:** sales@aerolens.co.uk
Web: www.aerolens.co.uk

NOTES

Company Name ....
....
Address ....
....
....
email ....
Web ....

Company Name ....
....
Address ....
....
....
email ....
Web ....

Company Name ....
....
Address ....
....
....
email ....
Web ....

Company Name ....
....
Address ....
....
....
email ....
Web ....

Company Name ....
....
Address ....
....
....
email ....
Web ....

Company Name ....
....
Address ....
....
....
email ....
Web ....

Company Name ....
....
Address ....
....
....
email ....
Web ....

Company Name ....
....
Address ....
....
....
email ....
Web ....

CONSULTANTS, LABOUR & FINANCE

BOOKS FROM
HOMEBUILDING & RENOVATING

Britain's Best Selling Self-Build Magazine

HOMEBUILDING & RENOVATING

Unit 2 Sugar Brook Court
Aston Road
Bromsgrove
Worcestershire
B60 3EX

Tel: 01527 834435
Fax: 01527 837810
Email: customerservice@centaur.co.uk
Website: www.homebuilding.co.uk

BARN CONVERSIONS

A brand new selection of barn conversions in one of our most successful books, packed with 29 inspirational projects. An essential read for anyone considering, about to start or in the middle of converting their barn. The appetite for barns with both traditional and contemporary finishes continues unabated.

CONTEMPORARY HOMES

The new edition of *Homebuilding & Renovating*'s best selling book — it's bigger, better and completely re-designed, featuring 351 colour pictures, contact details of designers, builders and key suppliers of equipment and services. Enjoy reading about 29 of the most innovative houses to be built in the UK in the past five years. This book is both coffee table and practical, explaining how the houses were conceived and built.

HOUSEPLANS

The first colour book of UK houseplans is finally here, packed with 334 full colour illustrations. All beautifully drawn and with more plans than ever before, it offers superb value for money and is backed by the UK's biggest selling self-build magazine, *Homebuilding and Renovating*. This book also features an introduction to self-building.

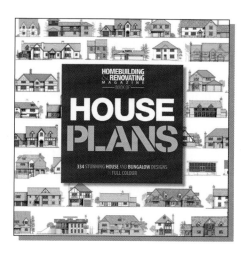

SPONSORED BY HOMEBUILDING & RENOVATING BOOK OF HOUSE PLANS
Tel 01527 834435 Web www.homebuilding.co.uk/bookshop

Britain's Best Selling Self-Build Magazine
HOMEBUILDING
&RENOVATING

House Design

Unless you happen to be highly skilled and confident in dealing with planners and have an expert knowledge of the building regulations, it is likely that you will call in a design professional to help circumnavigate the red tape and bring out the best in your self-build project.

Planning your new home should be the fun part, when all your dreams finally start to become reality, but finding the right designer can prove a trickier task, and there are many important factors you need to consider before taking the plunge. Choose the wrong designer, and the home of your dreams can turn from grand into just plain bland, or end up exceeding your initial budget.

If you are confident about your own building skills, you might simply need someone to prepare a set of drawings for submission to the planning authority. At the other end of the scale you may prefer to employ someone who can help you through the whole process from choosing a site to completion. You can use one design professional, or a combination of people, to produce the same result – an architect could design the initial concept, with the detailed design and specifications drawn up by an architectural technologist and the project overseen by a project manager, quantity surveyor or engineer – with an interior designer brought in at the final stages! This is obviously not the cheapest or easiest of options, as juggling so many professionals can result in a blurring of who is responsible for each aspect of the project. Identify your needs and then match these to the professional who will be best suited to assist you.

Local designers will have experience of the planning authority and are on hand to oversee the project and recommend tradesmen with whom they may have worked before. As with anyone involved in your self-build, make sure you appoint a designer with whom you have a rapport and who has an enthusiasm for the project. Ask to see some recently completed properties of a similar scale to your own. You may even want to ask former clients of their impressions.

Take along your ideas, know your budget and time scale and see how they respond — but always be prepared to keep an open mind as the most outstanding, workable designs tend to result from collaborative discussions. Conversely, never allow your designer to take over the project and dissuade you from features you have set your heart on and can afford. Be prepared to say if you don't like the preliminary sketches and to change designer altogether if you feel unhappy in the early stages. By initially employing a designer on a limited basis, you will be able to monitor progress and your relationship without committing yourself to a full service.

Setting a budget for both the build and design aspects of your project and relating the size of a building to its ultimate cost is essential, whichever design route you choose. Although cutting costs at this stage may prove tempting, it really is a false economy. Your neighbour's father-in-law may offer inexpensive design services, but poor or inadequate drawings will incur additional costs on site and reduce the property's resale value. So it is important not to make too many cutbacks for such a vital part of the project.

ARCHITECTS

KEY
OTHER: ▽ Reclaimed ⬧ On-line shopping
✎ Bespoke ✋ Hand-made ECO Ecological

3S ARCHITECTS LLP
47 High Street, Kingston Upon Thames,
Surrey, KT1 1LQ
Area of Operation: Europe
Tel: 0208 549 2000 **Fax:** 0208 549 3636
Email: info@3sarchitects.com
Web: www.3sarchitects.com

A G N HUGHES
30 Wildwood Court, Hawkhirst Road,
Kenley, Surrey, CR8 5DL
Area of Operation: UK (Excluding Ireland)
Tel: 0208 660 2637 **Fax:** 0208 660 2642
Email: agn.hughes@tiscali.co.uk

A&S DESIGN SERVICES
Cornlands, Sampford Peverell,
Tiverton, Devon, EX16 7UA
Area of Operation: UK (Excluding Ireland)
Tel: 01884 829285 **Fax:** 01884 829285
Email: ascad@aol.com
Web: www.asdesignservices.co.uk

ABBEY ARCHITECTURAL & DESIGN LTD
56 Cheviot Road, London, SE27 0LG
Area of Operation: Greater London
Tel: 0208 676 4393
Email: surveyor@abbeyarch.co.uk
Web: www.abbeyarch.co.uk

AC ARCHITECTS CAMBRIDGE LTD
33-35 Victoria Road, Cambridge,
Cambridgeshire, CB4 3BW
Area of Operation: East England, South East England
Tel: 01223 576315 **Fax:** 01223 576321
Email: info@acarchitects.com
Web: www.acarchitects.com

ACCESS ARCHITECTS LTD
Mortimer House, 49 Church Street,
Theale, Berkshire, RG7 5BX
Area of Operation: South East England, South West England and South Wales
Tel: 0118 930 4440
Email: david@access-architects.co.uk
Web: www.access-architects.co.uk

ALICANTE STONE
Damaso Navarro, 6 Bajo,
03610 Petrer (Alicante), P.O. Box 372, SPAIN
Area of Operation: Europe
Tel: +34 966 31 96 97 **Fax:** +34 966 31 96 98
Email: info@alicantestone.com
Web: www.alicantestone.com

ANDERSON SPARK LTD
Courtyard Studio, Cowley Farm, Aylesbury Road,
Cuddington, Buckinghamshire, HP18 0AD
Area of Operation: Greater London, Midlands & Mid Wales, South East England
Tel: 01296 747121 **Fax:** 01296 747703
Email: info@andersonspark.co.uk
Web: www.andersonspark.co.uk

ANDREW SMITH ASSOCIATES
5 Mount View, Billericay, Essex, CM11 1HB
Area of Operation: East England, Greater London, South East England
Tel: 01277 630310 **Fax:** 01277 651833
Email: architect@andrewsmithassociates.freeserve.co.uk

ANOTHER DIMENSION - ARCHITECTURE AND FENG SHUI
Banff House, 153 Ty Glas Road,
Llanishen, Cardiff, CF14 5EF
Area of Operation: South West England and South Wales
Tel: (029) 2075 5307 **Fax:** (029) 2075 5307
Email: atatchell@madasafish.com

ARCHITECTURAL DESIGN STUDIO LTD
55 Tadorna Drive, Holmer Lake,
Telford, Shropshire, TF3 1QP
Area of Operation: Midlands & Mid Wales
Tel: 01952 592592 **Fax:** 01952 596939
Email: jrbarch@hotmail.com

ARCHITECTURE VERTE LIMITED
10 Glenmore Business Centre,
Hopton Park Industrial Estate, Devizes, SN10 2EQ
Area of Operation: Greater London, Midlands & Mid Wales, South East England, South West England and South Wales
Tel: 01380 739139 **Fax:** 01380 739159
Email: mail@verte.co.uk **Web:** www.verte.co.uk

ARCHTEC DESIGN
41 Gladstone Park Gardens, London, NW2 6LA
Area of Operation: Greater London, South East England, South West England and South Wales
Tel: 0208 208 1262
Email: archtecdesign@hotmail.com
Web: www.archtecdesign.co.uk

ASBA ARCHITECTS LTD
c/o Four Square Design, The Old Surgery,
Crowle Road, Lambourn, Berkshire, RG17 8NT
Area of Operation: UK & Ireland
Tel: 01488 71384
Email: asba@asba-architects.org
Web: www.asba-architects.org

ASBA SCOTLAND
10 Lynedoch Cresent, Glasgow, G3 6EQ
Area of Operation: Scotland
Tel: 0800 731 3405 **Fax:** 0141 331 2751
Email: architects@design-practice.com

BRADBURY BICHARD
40 Corfe Way, Broadstone, Poole, Dorset, BH18 9NE
Area of Operation: South West England and South Wales
Tel: 01202 693988 **Email:** bbcaps@aol.com

BRENNAN & WILSON ARCHITECTS
Belhaven Villa, Edinburgh Road,
Belhaven, Dunbar, Lothian, EH42 1PA
Area of Operation: North East England, Scotland
Tel: 01368 860897 **Fax:** 01368 860897
Email: mail@bwarchitects.co.uk
Web: www.bwarchitects.co.uk

BROWNE SMITH BAKER
11-12 Portland Terrace,
Newcastle upon Tyne, Tyne & Wear, NE2 1QQ
Area of Operation: UK (Excluding Ireland)
Tel: 0191 212 1133 **Fax:** 0191 212 0777
Email: info-n@brownesmithbaker.com
Web: www.brownesmithbaker.com

BUILDINGDOCTORS.CO.UK
96 Farringdon Road, Clerkenwell, London, EC1R 3EA
Area of Operation: East England, Greater London, North West England and North Wales
Tel: 0845 060 0040 **Fax:** 0845 060 0046
Email: architect@building-doctors.co.uk
Web: www.buildingdoctors.co.uk

BURNS ASSOCIATES
32 Market Place, Swaffham, Norfolk, PO37 7QH
Area of Operation: UK (Excluding Ireland)
Tel: 01760 722254 **Fax:** 01760 724424
Email: info@burnsassociates-architects.co.uk
Web: www.burnsassociates-architects.co.uk

CA SUSTAINABLE ARCHITECTURE
83 Old Newtown Road,
Newbury, Berkshire, RG14 7DE
Area of Operation: UK (Excluding Ireland)
Tel: 01635 48363 **Web:** www.ca-sa.co.uk
Email: isabel.carmona@ca-sa.co.uk

CARPENTER OAK LTD & RODERICK JAMES ARCHITECT LTD
The Framing Yard, East Cornworthy,
Totnes, Devon, TQ9 7HF
Area of Operation: Worldwide
Tel: 01803 732900 **Fax:** 01803 732901
Email: enquiries@carpenteroak.com
Web: www.carpenteroak.com

CEDRIC MITCHELL ARCHITECTS
17 South Pallant, Chichester, West Sussex, PO19 1SU
Area of Operation: Europe
Tel: 01243 773166
Email: cedricm@about-architects.com
Web: www.about-architects.com

CHRISTOPHER MAGUIRE ARCHITECT AND GARDEN DESIGNER
15 Harston Road, Newton,
Cambridge, Cambridgeshire, CB2 5PA
Area of Operation: East England
Tel: 01223 872800
Web: www.christophermaguire.co.uk

CONSTRUCTIVE INDIVIDUALS (LONDON) LTD
Trinity Buoy Wharf, 64 Orchard Place, London, E14 0JW
Area of Operation: UK (Excluding Ireland)
Tel: 020 751 59299 **Fax:** 020 751 59737
Email: info@constructiveindividuals.com
Web: www.constructiveindividuals.com

CORK TOFT PARTNERSHIP LTD
Greenbank, Howick Cross Lane,
Penwortham, Preston, Lancashire, PR1 0NS
Area of Operation: North West England and North Wales
Tel: 01772 749014 /5 **Fax:** 01772 749034
Email: mail@corktoft.com

CURTIS WOOD ARCHITECTS LIMITED
23-28 Penn Street, London, N1 5DL
Area of Operation: UK & Ireland
Tel: 0207 684 1400 **Fax:** 0207 729 1411
Email: andrew@curtiswoodarchitects.co.uk
Web: www.curtiswoodarchitects.co.uk

CUTLER ARCHITECTS
43 St. Mary's Street, Wallingford, Oxfordshire, OX10 0EU
Area of Operation: Greater London, South East England
Tel: 01491 838130 **Fax:** 01491 836504
Email: mail@cutlerarch.com
Web: www.cutlerarch.com

DAVID NEILL
Ridge Croft, 37 Dalby Avenue,
Bushby, Leicestershire, LE7 9RE
Area of Operation: East England, Midlands & Mid Wales
Tel: 0116 243 2236 **Fax:** 0116 243 3580
Email: mail@davidneill.net

DESIGN AND MATERIALS LTD
Lawn Road, Carlton in Lindrick,
Nottinghamshire, S81 9LB
Area of Operation: UK (Excluding Ireland)
Tel: 01909 540123 **Fax:** 01909 730605
Email: enquiries@designandmaterials.uk.com
Web: www.designandmaterials.uk.com ⬧

DESIGN FOR HOMES
The Building Centre,
26 Store Street, London, WC1E 7BT
Area of Operation: UK (Excluding Ireland)
Tel: 0870 416 3378 **Fax:** 0207 436 0573
Email: richard@designforhomes.org
Web: www.designforhomes.org

DIL GREEN ARCHITECT
206 Lyham Road, Brixton, Greater London, SW2 5NR
Area of Operation: UK (Excluding Ireland)
Tel: 0208 671 2242 **Fax:** 0208 674 9757
Email: w_info@dilgreenarchitect.co.uk
Web: www.dilgreenarchitect.co.uk

ENGLISHAUS CHARTERED ARCHITECTS LTD
30 Lawrence Road, Hampton, Middlesex, TW12 2RJ
Area of Operation: Greater London, South East England, South West England and South Wales
Tel: 0208 255 0595 **Fax:** 0208 287 3441
Email: enquiries@englishaus.co.uk
Web: www.englishaus.co.uk

FOUR SQUARE DESIGN LTD
The Old Surgery, Crowle Road, Lambourne,
Hungerford, Berkshire, RG17 8NR
Area of Operation: UK (Excluding Ireland)
Tel: 01488 71384 **Fax:** 01488 73207
Email: info@foursquaredesign.co.uk
Web: www.foursquaredesign.co.uk

FRANKLYN NEVARD ASSOCIATES
10 Hamilton Road, Ealing Common, London, W5 2EQ
Area of Operation: Greater London
Tel: 0208 566 2220 **Fax:** 0208 579 4575
Email: projects@franklynnevard.co.uk
Web: www.franklynnevard.co.uk

G.M.MOORE & ASSOCIATES
Old Laughton Sawmills, Park Lane,
Laughton, East Sussex, BN8 6BP
Area of Operation: South East England
Tel: 01323 811689 **Fax:** 01323 811325
Email: sales@gmassociates.co.uk
Web: www.gmassociates.co.uk

GEORGE BLACK ARCHITECT
12 Kingsknowe Crescent, Edinburgh, Lothian, EH14 2JZ
Area of Operation: Scotland
Tel: 0131 443 9898
Email: george@gbarch.abel.co.uk
Web: www.gbarch.abel.co.uk

GLG DESIGN
Beech Studio, 10 Berryhill Road,
Giffnock, Glasgow, Renfrewshire, G46 7NJ
Area of Operation: UK & Ireland
Tel: 0141 621 2050 **Fax:** 0141 638 7017
Email: mail@glgdesign.com

GREENERLIVING HOMES LTD
Sussex Innovation Centre, Science Park Square,
Falmer, Brighton, East Sussex, BN1 9SB
Area of Operation: South East England
Tel: 01273 704509 **Fax:** 01273 704499
Email: info@greenerlivinghomes.co.uk
Web: www.greenerlivinghomes.co.uk

GRINDEY CONSULTING
9 Brook Avenue, Swinton, Manchester, M27 5WG
Area of Operation: North West England and North Wales
Tel: 07773 371488
Email: grindeyconsulting@hotmail.com
Web: www.grindeyconsulting.com

HALLIDAY CLARK LIMITED
Salts Wharf, Ashley Lane, Shipley,
Bradford, West Yorkshire, BD17 7DB
Area of Operation: UK & Ireland
Tel: 01274 589888 **Fax:** 01274 589922
Email: info@hallidayclark.co.uk
Web: www.hallidayclark.co.uk

HINTON COOK ARCHITECTS
214 Upper Fifth Street, Milton Keynes,
Buckinghamshire, MK9 2HR
Area of Operation: South East England
Tel: 01908 235544 **Fax:** 01908 235588
Email: info@hintoncook.co.uk
Web: www.hintoncook.co.uk

HOLDEN + PARTNERS
26 High Street, Wimbledon,
Greater London, SW19 5BY
Area of Operation: Worldwide
Tel: 0208 946 5502 **Fax:** 0208 879 0310
Email: arch@holdenpartners.co.uk
Web: www.holdenpartners.co.uk

HOT ARCHITECTURE
2 Minshull Street, Knutsford, Cheshire, WA16 6HG
Area of Operation: UK (Excluding Ireland)
Tel: 01565 650401
Email: hot@hotarchitecture.com
Web: www.hotarchitecture.com

IBI DESIGN ASSOCIATES
55 Chase Way, Southgate, London, N14 5EA
Area of Operation: Greater London, South East England
Tel: 0208 361 2542 **Fax:** 0208 361 7062
Email: ibides@aol.com

INSCAPE ARCHITECTS
Studio 2 St Andrews Road,
Montpelier, Bristol, BS6 5EH
Area of Operation: UK (Excluding Ireland)
Tel: 0117 923 2305 **Fax:** 0117 944 1006
Email: mail@inscape.uk.com
Web: www.inscape.uk.com

J G HOOD & ASSOCIATES LTD
50 High Street, Bruton, Somerset, BA10 0AN
Area of Operation: Midlands & Mid Wales, South
East England, South West England and South Wales
Tel: 01749 812139   **Fax:** 0870 133 3776
Email: mail@jghood-assoc.co.uk
Web: www.jghood-assoc.co.uk

JIM MORRISON ARCHITECTS
31 Cricklewood Park, Belfast, Co Antrim, BT9 5GW
Area of Operation: UK & Ireland
Tel: (028) 90 660017   **Fax:** (028) 90 201710
Email: jim.morrison@dnet.co.uk
Web: www.jimmorrisonarchitects.co.uk

JNA ARCHITECTS
9 East Park, Southgate,
Crawley, West Sussex, RH10 6AN
Area of Operation: South East England
Tel: 01293 439323   **Fax:** 01293 530160
Email: james@jna-architects.co.uk
Web: www.jna-architects.co.uk

JOHN C. ANGELL
25 Whinfield Lane, Preston, Lancashire, PR2 1NQ
Area of Operation: North West England and North Wales
Tel: 01772 725308
Email: architects@angell.org.uk
Web: www.angell.org.uk

JOHN MOSELEY ARCHITECTS
75 South Street, Bridport, Dorset, DT6 3NZ
Area of Operation: South West England and South Wales
Tel: 01308 424239

JOHN PEATE ARCHITECTURAL SERVICES LTD
6 Newport Road, Shifnal, Shropshire, TF11 8BP
Area of Operation: Midlands & Mid Wales, North
West England and North Wales
Tel: 01952 460175   **Fax:** 01952 460175
Email: info@johnpeate.co.uk
Web: www.johnpeate.co.uk

JOHN SOLOMON DESIGN LIMITED
48 Ham Street, Richmond, Surrey, TW10 7HT
Area of Operation: Worldwide
Tel: 020 8940 2444   **Fax:** 020 8940 1188
Email: mail@jsajsd.com   **Web:** www.jsajsd.com

JPK DESIGN LTD
83 Dimsdale Parade East, Wolstanton,
Newcastle Under Lyme, Staffordshire, ST5 8DP
Area of Operation: Midlands & Mid Wales, North
West England and North Wales
Tel: 01782 622321
Fax: 01782 622323
Email: jason.knight@jpkdesign.co.uk
Web: www.jpkdesign.co.uk

JULIAN OWEN ASSOCIATES ARCHITECTS
6 Cumberland Avenue, Beeston,
Nottingham, Nottinghamshire, NG9 4DH
Area of Operation: Midlands & Mid Wales
Tel: 0115 922 9831
Email: julian@julianowen.co.uk
Web: www.julianowen.co.uk

KORU ARCHITECTS
4a Burton Villas, Hove, East Sussex, BN3 6FN
Area of Operation: South East England
Tel: 01273 204065
Email: map@koruarchitects.co.uk
Web: www.koruarchitects.co.uk

**LEEDS ENVIRONMENTAL DESIGN
ASSOCIATES LTD (LEDA)**
Micklethwaite House, 70 Cross Green Lane,
Leeds, West Yorkshire, LS9 0DG
Area of Operation: North East England
Tel: 0113 200 9380   **Fax:** 0113 200 9381
Email: office@leda.org.uk   **Web:** www.leda.org.uk

LINT DESIGN
2a Bury Lane, Codicote, Hertfordshire, SG4 8XT
Area of Operation: East England, South East England
Tel: 01438 822064   **Fax:** 0870 432 0685
Email: mail@lintdesign.co.uk
Web: www.lintdesign.co.uk

LOREN DESIGN LTD
Unit 6, 51 Derbyshire Street, London, E2 6JQ
Area of Operation: East England, Greater London,
South East England
Tel: 0207 729 4878   **Fax:** 0207 729 6033
Email: lorendes@aol.com

M3 ARCHITECTS
49 Kingsway Place, Sans Walk, London, EC1R 0LU
Area of Operation: East England, Greater London,
Scotland, South East England
Tel: 0207 253 7255   **Fax:** 0207 253 7266
Email: post@m3architects.com
Web: www.m3architects.com

**MALCOLM V LELLIOTT
ARCHITECTS & SURVEYORS**
19 Church Street, Godalming, Surrey, GU7 1EL
Area of Operation: South East England
Tel: 01483 416411
Web: www.mvl-architect.co.uk

MARMOT ASSOCIATES
Higher Tor Farm, Poundsgate,
Newton Abbot, Devon, TQ13 7PD
Area of Operation: South West England and South Wales
Tel: 01364 631566   **Fax:** 01364 631556
Email: marmot-tor@zen.co.uk
Web: www.marmot-tor.com

MEPK ARCHITECTS
10-18 Vestry Street, London, N1 7RE
Area of Operation: UK (Excluding Ireland)
Tel: 0207 251 5573   **Fax:** 0207 251 5574
Email: london@mepk.co.uk   **Web:** www.mepk.co.uk

MJW ARCHITECTS
The Old Chapel, Mendip Road,
Stoke St Michael, Somerset, BA3 5JU
Area of Operation: UK & Ireland
Tel: 01749 840180   **Fax:** 01749 841380
Email: info@mjwarchitects.com
Web: www.mjwarchitects.com

MOLE ARCHITECTS
The Black House, Kingdon Avenue,
Prickwillow, Ely, Cambridgeshire, CB7 4UL
Area of Operation: East England
Tel: 01353 688287   **Fax:** 01353 688287
Email: studio@molearchitects.co.uk
Web: www.molearchitects.co.uk

NARRACOTT OXFORD MILLS ARCHITECTS LTD
13.14 Guinea Street, Bristol, BS1 6SX
Area of Operation: Midlands & Mid Wales, South
East England, South West England and South Wales
Tel: 0117 929 2041   **Fax:** 0117 925 1793
Email: anneli@architect1.co.uk
Web: www.architect1.co.uk

NICHOLAS RAY ASSOCIATES
13-15 Convert Garden,
Cambridge, Cambridgeshire, CB1 2HS
Area of Operation: UK & Ireland
Tel: 01223 464455
Email: design@nray-arch.co.uk
Web: www.nray-arch.co.uk

NICOLAS TYE ARCHITECTS
The Long Barn Studio, Limbersey Lane,
Bedfordshire, MK45 2EA
Area of Operation: UK (Excluding Ireland)
Tel: 01525 406677   **Fax:** 01525 406688
Email: info@nicolastyearchitects.co.uk
Web: www.nicolastyearchitects.co.uk

NINETTE EDWARDS ARCHITECT
12 Alnside, Whittingham, Northumberland, NE66 4SJ
Area of Operation: North East England
Tel: 01655 574733
Email: ninette@alnsideassociates.co.uk
Web: www.alnsideassociates.co.uk

NORDSTROM ASSOCIATES
32 Oswald Road, St Albans, Hertfordshire, AL1 3AQ
Area of Operation: Greater London
Tel: 01727 831971   **Fax:** 01727 752981
Email: gunnar.nordstrom@ntlworld.com

NTARCHITECTS
9 Cumberland Lodge, Cumberland Road,
Brighton, East Sussex, BN1 6ST
Area of Operation: Greater London, South East
England, South West England and South Wales
Tel: 01273 267184
Fax: 01273 267184
Email: nt@nicolathomas.co.uk
Web: www.nicolathomas.co.uk

PAUL A STOWELL
'Sorriso', Farleigh Road, Cliddesden,
Basingstoke, Hampshire, RG25 2JL
Area of Operation: Greater London, South East
England, South West England and South Wales
Tel: 01256 320470
Fax: 01256 320470
Email: paulstowell@constructionplans.co.uk
Web: www.constructionplans.co.uk

PETER BLOCKLEY - CHARTERED ARCHITECT
26 High Street, Worton, Devizes, Wiltshire, SN10 5RU
Area of Operation: Greater London, South West
England and South Wales
Tel: 01380 739394   **Fax:** 01380 739395
Email: peter@pbca.co.uk   **Web:** www.pbca.co.uk

PLANS & DRAWINGS.COM
5 Station Road, Stepps, Glasgow, Lanarkshire, G33 6HB
Area of Operation: Scotland
Tel: 0141 404 0136   **Fax:** 0141 779 5370
Email: info@homecad.org
Web: www.plansanddrawings.com

R E DESIGN
97 Lincoln Avenue, Glasgow, G13 3DH
Area of Operation: Scotland
Tel: 0141 959 1902   **Fax:** 0141 959 3040
Email: mail@r-e-design.co.uk
Web: www.r-e-design.co.uk

RANDELL BURTON ARCHITECTS
The Studio, 7 William Street, Tiverton, Devon, EX16 6BJ
Area of Operation: South West England and South Wales
Tel: 01884 254465   **Fax:** 01884 243451
Email: david@randellburton.co.uk
Web: www.randellburton.co.uk

RICHARD MURPHY ARCHITECTS
The Breakfast Mission,
15 Old Fishmarket Close, Edinburgh, EH1 1RW
Area of Operation: Worldwide
Tel: 0131 220 6125
Fax: 0131 220 6781
Email: mail@richardmurphyarchitects.com
Web: www.richardmurphyarchitects.com

RODERICK JAMES ARCHITECTS LLP
Discovery House, Steamer Quay Road,
Totnes, Devon, TQ9 5AL
Area of Operation: Worldwide
Tel: 01803 722474   **Fax:** 01803 722472
Email: totnes@rjarchitects.co.uk
Web: www.carpenteroak.com

ROMAN PROJECTS LTD
Roman Heights, Llanfair Hill,
Llandovery, Carmarthenshire, SA20 0YF
Area of Operation: South West England and South Wales
Tel: 01550 720533   **Fax:** 01550 720533
Email: romanprojects@aol.com

RUMBALL SEDGWICK
Abbotts House, 198 Lower High Street,
Watford, Hertfordshire, WD17 2FF
Area of Operation: Greater London, South East England
Tel: 01923 224275
Fax: 01923 255005
Email: shaun@w.rumballsedgwick.co.uk
Web: www.rumballsedgwick.co.uk

SARAH ROBERTS ARCHITECTS LTD
3 Church Lane, Bressingham, Diss, Norfolk, IP22 2AE
Area of Operation: UK (Excluding Ireland)
Tel: 01379 688135   **Fax:** 01379 687642
Email: sarah@sr-architects.co.uk
Web: www.sarahrobertsarchitects.co.uk

**SIERRA DESIGNS - ARCHITECTURAL AND
BUILDING CONSULTANTS**
Carfeld House, Pinfold Lane,
Kirk Smeaton, North Yorkshire, WF8 3JT
Area of Operation: UK & Ireland
Tel: 01977 621360   **Fax:** 01977 621365
Email: info@sierradesigns.co.uk
Web: www.sierradesigns.co.uk

SIMON J CUSHING CHARTERED ARCHITECT
28 Wood Lane, Greasby, Wirral, Merseyside, CH49 2PU
Area of Operation: North West England and North Wales
Tel: 0151 677 9188   **Fax:** 0151 677 9188
Email: simonjcushing@btconnect.com

SMC CHARTER ARCHITECTS
St. Mary's House, 15 Cardington Road,
Bedford, Bedfordshire, MK42 0BP
Area of Operation: UK & Ireland
Tel: 01234 342551   **Fax:** 01234 360055
Email: bedford@smccharterarchitects.co.uk
Web: www.smccharterarchitects.co.uk

SNP ASSOCIATES
248 Kingston Road, New Malden, Surrey, KT3 3RN
Area of Operation: Worldwide
Tel: 0208 942 6238
Email: snp@snpassociates.co.uk
Web: www.snpassociates.co.uk

SOUTHPOINT
45 The Dell, Westbury-on-Trym, Bristol, BS9 3UF
Area of Operation: UK (Excluding Ireland)
Tel: 0845 644 6639   **Fax:** 0870 7061866
Email: mail@southpoint.co.uk
Web: www.southpoint.co.uk

TEAM SURVEYS LIMITED
St Austell Bay Business Park,
Par Moor Road, St Austell, Cornwall, PL25 3RF
Area of Operation: Europe
Tel: 01726 816069   **Fax:** 01726 814611
Email: email@teamsurveys.com
Web: www.teamsurveys.com

THOMAS NUGENT ARCHITECTS LIMITED
6 Ramsgate Street, London, E8 2NA
Area of Operation: UK (Excluding Ireland)
Tel: 0207 254 7913   **Fax:** 0207 923 0015
Email: enquiries@tnarchitects.co.uk
Web: www.tnarchitects.co.uk

THOMAS PARRY DESIGN PARTNERSHIP
The Old Sketty Coach House,
21 Gower Road, Sketty, Swansea, SA2 9BX
Area of Operation: UK & Ireland
Tel: 01792 290755   **Fax:** 01792 290527
Email: design@thomasparry.co.uk
Web: www.thomasparry.co.uk

VALERIE HINDE, ARCHITECTS
The Studio, High Bank, River,
Petworth, West Sussex, GU28 9AX
Area of Operation: UK & Ireland
Tel: 01798 860912   **Fax:** 01798 860932
Email: valerie.hinde@virgin.net
Web: www.valerie-hinde.co.uk

WILSON MASON
St James House, 116 Talbot Street,
Nottingham, Nottinghamshire, NG1 5GL
Area of Operation: Europe
Tel: 0115 950 3789   **Fax:** 0115 947 4073
Email: mfindlay@wilsonmason.co.uk
Web: www.wilsonmason.co.uk

ARCHITECTURAL TECHNOLOGISTS

KEY

OTHER: ▽ Reclaimed 🖱 On-line shopping
✍ Bespoke ✋ Hand-made ECO Ecological

3D VIRTUAL LTD
Crowell End, Crowell Hill,
Chinnor, Oxfordshire, OX39 4BT
Area of Operation: Europe
Tel: 01844 214572
Email: chrisparker02@btconnect.com
Web: www.3dvirtual.co.uk

A.W. WELLS, ARCHITECTURAL CONSULTANT
The Granary, The Hem, Shifnal, Shropshire, TF11 9PS
Area of Operation: UK (Excluding Ireland)
Tel: 01952 462244 **Fax:** 01952 463897
Email: awells.architectural@virgin.net

ACROPOLIS DESIGN LTD
13-15, Barstow Square,
Wakefield, West Yorkshire, WF1 2SF
Area of Operation: UK (Excluding Ireland)
Tel: 01924 291963 **Fax:** 0871 7334738
Email: info@acropolisdesign.co.uk
Web: www.acropolisdesign.co.uk

ARCHITECTURE PLUS
5 Dunkery Road, Weston Super Mare,
Somerset, BS23 2TD
Area of Operation: UK (Excluding Ireland)
Tel: 01934 416416
Fax: 01934 622583
Email: office@architecture-plus.co.uk
Web: www.architectureplus.co.uk

ARCHITECTURE VERTE LIMITED
10 Glenmore Business Centre,
Hopton Park Industrial Estate, Devizes, SN10 2EQ
Area of Operation: Greater London,
Midlands & Mid Wales, South East England,
South West England and South Wales
Tel: 01380 739139 **Fax:** 01380 739159
Email: mail@verte.co.uk **Web:** www.verte.co.uk

ASAP- ARCHITECTURAL SERVICES & PLANNING
Howard Buildings, 69-71,
Burpham Lane, Guildford, Surrey, GU4 7LX
Area of Operation: South East England
Tel: 01483 457922
Email: david.haines4@virgin.net
Web: www.asaparchitectural.co.uk

BUILDING PLANS LTD
Unit 10 Beech Avenue, Taverham,
Norwich, Norfolk, NR8 6HW
Area of Operation: UK (Excluding Ireland)
Tel: 01603 868377 **Fax:** 01603 868412
Email: john@constructionhelp.co.uk
Web: www.constructionhelp.co.uk

BUILDINGDOCTORS.CO.UK
96 Farringdon Road, Clerkenwell, London, EC1R 3EA
Area of Operation: East England, Greater London,
North West England and North Wales
Tel: 0845 060 0040
Fax: 0845 060 0046
Email: architect@building-doctors.com
Web: www.buildingdoctors.co.uk

CARPENTER OAK LTD & RODERICK JAMES ARCHITECT LTD
The Framing Yard, East Cornworthy,
Totnes, Devon, TQ9 7HF
Area of Operation: Worldwide
Tel: 01803 732900 **Fax:** 01803 732901
Email: enquiries@carpenteroak.com
Web: www.carpenteroak.com

CHARTERED INSTITUTE OF ARCHITECTURAL TECHNOLOGISTS
397 City Road, Islington, London, EC1V 1NH
Area of Operation: Worldwide
Tel: 0207 278 2206
Email: hugh@ciat.org.uk **Web:** www.ciat.org.uk

COLIN WILLIAMS BUILDING CONSULTANCY
Courtyard Studio, 52A Dereham Road, Mattishall,
Dereham, Norfolk, NR20 3NS
Area of Operation: East England
Tel: 01362 850171 **Fax:** 01362 850171
Email: design@cooptel.net

CO-ORDINATED CONSTRUCTION SERVICES
18 Kiln Road, Crawley Down,
West Sussex, RH10 4JY
Area of Operation: South East England
Tel: 01342 714511 **Fax:** 01342 714511
Email: info@coordsvcs.com
Web: www.coordsvcs.com

DESIGN PLUS (KENT) LTD
59 Marshall Crescent, Broadstairs, Kent, CT10 2HR
Area of Operation: UK (Excluding Ireland)
Tel: 01843 602218
Email: designpluskent@btinternet.com
Web: www.designpluskent.co.uk

DESIGNER HOMES
Pooh Cottage, Minto, Hawick,
Roxburghshire, Borders, TD9 8SB
Area of Operation: UK & Ireland
Tel: 01450 870127 **Fax:** 01450 870127

ECLIPSE DESIGN
Staunton Harold Hall, Staunton Harold,
Leicestershire, LE65 1RT
Area of Operation: UK (Excluding Ireland)
Tel: 0870 4604758
Email: enquiries@eclipsedesignuk.net
Web: www.eclipsedesignuk.net

ENCRAFT
Perseus House, 3 Chapel Court, Holly Walk,
Leamington Spa, Warwickshire, CV32 4YS
Area of Operation: UK & Ireland
Tel: 01926 312159 **Fax:** 01926 772480
Email: enquiries@encraft.co.uk
Web: www.encrafthome.co.uk

FG DESIGN
6 Denmark Drive, Sedbury,
Chepstow, Monmouthshire, NT16 7BD
Area of Operation: South West England and South Wales
Tel: 01291 624366 **Fax:** 01291 624366
Email: frank.fgdesign@virgin.net

GREENERLIVING HOMES LTD
Sussex Innovation Centre, Science Park Square,
Falmer, Brighton, East Sussex, BN1 9SB
Area of Operation: South East England
Tel: 01273 704509 **Fax:** 01273 704499
Email: info@greenerlivinghomes.co.uk
Web: www.greenerlivinghomes.co.uk

J G HOOD & ASSOCIATES LTD
50 High Street, Bruton, Somerset, BA10 0AN
Area of Operation: Midlands & Mid Wales, South
East England, South West England and South Wales
Tel: 01749 812139 **Fax:** 0870 133 3776
Email: mail@jghood-assoc.co.uk
Web: www.jghood-assoc.co.uk

JNA ARCHITECTS
9 East Park, Southgate, Crawley,
West Sussex, RH10 6AN
Area of Operation: South East England
Tel: 01293 439323 **Fax:** 01293 530160
Email: james@jna-architects.co.uk
Web: www.jna-architects.co.uk

JOHN PEATE ARCHITECTURAL SERVICES LTD
6 Newport Rd, Shifnal, Shropshire, TF11 8BP
Area of Operation: Midlands & Mid Wales, North
West England and North Wales
Tel: 01952 460175 **Fax:** 01952 460175
Email: info@johnpeate.co.uk
Web: www.johnpeate.co.uk

JPK DESIGN LTD
83 Dimsdale Parade East, Wolstanton,
Newcastle Under Lyme, Staffordshire, ST5 8DP
Area of Operation: Midlands & Mid Wales, North
West England and North Wales
Tel: 01782 622321 **Fax:** 01782 622323
Email: jason.knight@jpkdesign.co.uk
Web: www.jpkdesign.co.uk

KMD ARCHITECTURAL SERVICES LTD
Second Floor, 1 Station Road,
Whitley Bay, Tyne & Wear, NE26 2QY
Area of Operation: UK (Excluding Ireland)
Tel: 0191 253 7110 **Fax:** 0871 211 0363
Email: info@kmd-limited.co.uk
Web: www.kmd-limited.co.uk 🖱

LARNER SING
The Barn, Rode Hill, Rode, Frome, Somerset, BA11 6PU
Area of Operation: South East England, South West
England and South Wales
Tel: 01373 830527 **Fax:** 01373 830527
Email: ian@larner-sing.co.uk
Web: www.larner-sing.com

M J BRAIN
Kamala House, North Lane, Weston On The Green,
Bicester, Oxfordshire, OX25 3RG
Area of Operation: UK (Excluding Ireland)
Tel: 01869 350771 **Fax:** 01869 351445
Email: malcolmbrain@mjbrain.freeserve.co.uk

MICHAEL D HALL
Studio A, 339 London Road,
Bexhill on Sea, East Sussex, TN39 4AJ
Area of Operation: South East England
Tel: 01424 214541 **Fax:** 01424 731555
Email: bds@michaeldhall.co.uk
Web: www.michaeldhall.co.uk

MORNINGTIDE DEVELOPMENTS LTD
Beauvale, Loamy Hill,
Tolleshunt Major, Essex, CM9 8LS
Area of Operation: UK (Excluding Ireland)
Tel: 01621 815485 **Fax:** 01621 819511
Email: morningtide@fsnet.co.uk
Web: www.morningtide.fsnet.co.uk

NICHOLAS RAY ASSOCIATES
13-15 Convert Garden, Cambridge,
Cambridgeshire, CB1 2HS
Area of Operation: UK & Ireland
Tel: 01223 464455
Email: design@nray-arch.co.uk
Web: www.nray-arch.co.uk

NICHOLSON DESIGN CONSULTANTS
Clematis, Wannock, Polegate, East Sussex, BN26 5JG
Area of Operation: Europe
Tel: 01323 483117
Email: nicholson.design@dial.pipex.com

NOISE.CO.UK LTD
Meadow View, Newnham Grounds, Kings Newnham
Lane, Bretford, Warwickshire, CV23 0JU
Area of Operation: UK & Ireland
Tel: 02476 545397 **Fax:** 02476 545010
Email: dave@noise.co.uk
Web: www.noise.co.uk

OLD MANOR COTTAGES
Turnpike Lane, Ickleford, Hitchin, Hertfordshire, SG5 3UZ
Area of Operation: UK & Ireland
Tel: 01462 456033 **Fax:** 01462 456033
Email: oldmanorco@aol.com

PLANS & DRAWINGS.COM
5 Station Road, Stepps, Glasgow, Lanarkshire, G33 6HB
Area of Operation: Scotland
Tel: 0141 404 0136 **Fax:** 0141 779 5370
Email: info@homecad.org
Web: www.plansanddrawings.com

R E DESIGN
97 Lincoln Avenue, Glasgow, G13 3DH
Area of Operation: Scotland
Tel: 0141 959 1902 **Fax:** 0141 959 3040
Email: mail@r-e-design.co.uk
Web: www.r-e-design.co.uk

SIERRA DESIGNS - ARCHITECTURAL AND BUILDING CONSULTANTS
Carfeld House, Pinfold Lane,
Kirk Smeaton, North Yorkshire, WF8 3JT
Area of Operation: UK & Ireland
Tel: 01977 621360
Fax: 01977 621365
Email: info@sierradesigns.co.uk
Web: www.sierradesigns.co.uk

STATS LIMITED
Porterswood House, Porters Wood,
St Albans, Hertfordshire, AL3 6PQ
Area of Operation: Worldwide
Tel: 01727 833261 **Fax:** 01727 835682
Email: info@stats.co.uk
Web: www.stats.co.uk

THE STEVEN BARLOW PARTNERSHIP
81 Manor Road, Kingston,
Portsmouth, Hampshire, PO1 5LB
Area of Operation: Europe
Tel: 07786 577416
Email: info@tsbp-architecture.co.uk
Web: www.tsbp-architecture.co.uk

XSPACE
99 Woodlands Avenue, Poole, Dorset, BH15 4EG
Area of Operation: South East England, South West
England and South Wales
Tel: 01202 665387 **Fax:** 01202 380235
Email: design@xspace.biz **Web:** www.xspace.biz

BUILDING SURVEYORS

KEY

OTHER: ▽ Reclaimed 🖱 On-line shopping
✍ Bespoke ✋ Hand-made ECO Ecological

BROWNE SMITH BAKER
11-12 Portland Terrace,
Newcastle upon Tyne, Tyne & Wear, NE2 1QQ
Area of Operation: UK (Excluding Ireland)
Tel: 0191 212 1133
Fax: 0191 212 0777
Email: info-n@brownesmithbaker.com
Web: www.brownesmithbaker.com

BUILDING PLANS LTD
Unit 10 Beech Avenue, Taverham,
Norwich, Norfolk, NR8 6HW
Area of Operation: UK (Excluding Ireland)
Tel: 01603 868377
Fax: 01603 868412
Email: john@constructionhelp.co.uk
Web: www.constructionhelp.co.uk

BUILDINGDOCTORS.CO.UK
96 Farringdon Road, Clerkenwell, London, EC1R 3EA
Area of Operation: East England, Greater London,
North West England and North Wales
Tel: 0845 060 0040
Fax: 0845 060 0046
Email: architect@building-doctors.com
Web: www.buildingdoctors.co.uk

CMCR LIMITED
Glenbervie Business Centre, Glenbervie Business
Park, Larbert, Stirlingshire, FK5 4RB
Area of Operation: Europe
Tel: 01324 682200 **Fax:** 01324 682201
Email: david.corfield@cmcr.biz
Web: www.cmcr.biz

CONSTRUCTION COST SOLUTIONS
September Cottage, 1A Wigwam Close,
Poynton, Stockport, Cheshire, SK12 1XF
Area of Operation: Midlands & Mid Wales, North
East England, North West England and North Wales
Tel: 01625 875488
Email: david@constructioncostsolutions.co.uk
Web: www.constructioncostsolutions.co.uk

CONSULTANTS, LABOUR & FINANCE - **Professional Services** - Building Surveyors; Structural Engineers; Environmental Consultants

SPONSORED BY: HOMEBUILDING & RENOVATING BOOK OF HOUSE PLANS www.homebuilding.co.uk/bookshop

FG DESIGN
6 Denmark Drive, Sedbury,
Chepstow, Monmouthshire, NT16 7BD
Area of Operation: South West England and South Wales
Tel: 01291 624366 **Fax:** 01291 624366
Email: frank.fgdesign@virgin.net

GEO THERM LTD
Riverside Business Park, Riverside Road,
Lowestoft, Suffolk, NR33 0TQ
Area of Operation: Europe
Tel: 01502 515707 **Fax:** 01502 530275
Email: info@geothermltd.co.uk
Web: www.geothermltd.co.uk

GRAHAM G BISHOP - CHARTERED SURVEYORS
9 Church Lane Drive, Coulsdon, Surrey, CR5 3RG
Area of Operation: Greater London, South East England
Tel: 01737 558473 **Fax:** 01737 558473
Email: graham@grahamgbishop.co.uk
Web: www.grahamgbishop.co.uk

GRINDEY CONSULTING
9 Brook Avenue, Swinton, Manchester, M27 5WG
Area of Operation: North West England and North Wales
Tel: 07773 371488
Email: grindeyconsulting@hotmail.com
Web: www.grindeyconsulting.com

**HUTTON+ROSTRON
ENVIRONMENTAL INVESTIGATIONS LTD**
Netley House, Gomshall, Guildford, Surrey, GU5 9QA
Area of Operation: UK & Ireland
Tel: 01483 203221 **Fax:** 01483 202911
Email: ei@handr.co.uk **Web:** www.handr.co.uk

J.S. BUILDING CONSULTANCY
53 Hawthorn Road, Yeadon,
Leeds, West Yorkshire, LS19 7UT
Area of Operation: UK (Excluding Ireland)
Tel: 0113 250 1303
Email: jsharples@ricsonline.org
Web: www.ukbuildingconsultancy.co.uk

LARNER SING
The Barn, Rode Hill, Rode, Frome, Somerset, BA11 6PU
Area of Operation: South East England, South West England and South Wales
Tel: 01373 830527 **Fax:** 01373 830527
Email: ian@larner-sing.co.uk
Web: www.larner-sing.com

M J BRAIN
Kamala House, North Lane, Weston On The Green,
Bicester, Oxfordshire, OX25 3RG
Area of Operation: UK (Excluding Ireland)
Tel: 01869 350771 **Fax:** 01869 351445
Email: malcolmbrain@mjbrain.freeserve.co.uk

**MALCOLM V LELLIOTT
ARCHITECTS & SURVEYORS**
19 Church Street, Godalming, Surrey, GU7 1EL
Area of Operation: South East England
Tel: 01483 416411 **Web:** www.mvl-architect.co.uk

MWS ASSOCIATES
Ascot House, 62 Falmouth Avenue,
Normanton, West Yorkshire, WF6 2EB
Area of Operation: North East England, North West England and North Wales
Tel: 0800 083 5638 **Fax:** 0870 762 0723
Email: matthew@mwsa.co.uk
Web: www.mwsa.co.uk

PAUL A STOWELL
'Sorriso', Farleigh Road, Cliddesden,
Basingstoke, Hampshire, RG25 2JL
Area of Operation: Greater London, South East England, South West England and South Wales
Tel: 01256 320470 **Fax:** 01256 320470
Email: paulstowell@constructionplans.co.uk
Web: www.constructionplans.co.uk

PLANS & DRAWINGS.COM
5 Station Road, Stepps, Glasgow, Lanarkshire, G33 6HB
Area of Operation: Scotland
Tel: 0141 404 0136 **Fax:** 0141 779 5370
Email: info@homecad.org
Web: www.plansanddrawings.com

PROPERTYPORTAL.COM
Brookfield House, Ford Lane, Frilford,
Abingdon, Oxfordshire, OX13 5NT
Area of Operation: UK (Excluding Ireland)
Tel: 0870 380 0520 **Fax:** 0870 380 0521
Email: info@propertyportal.com
Web: www.propertyportal.com

RUMBALL SEDGWICK
Abbotts House, 198 Lower High Street,
Watford, Hertfordshire, WD17 2FF
Area of Operation: Greater London, South East England
Tel: 01923 224275
Fax: 01923 255005
Email: shaun@w.rumballsedgwick.co.uk
Web: www.rumballsedgwick.co.uk

SELF BUILD PRO
Belmont Business Centre, Brook Lane,
Endon, Staffordshire, ST9 9EZ
Area of Operation: Worldwide
Tel: 01782 503322 **Fax:** 01782 505127
Email: enquiries@self-build-pro.com
Web: www.self-build-pro.com ⌐↻

**SIERRA DESIGNS - ARCHITECTURAL
AND BUILDING CONSULTANTS**
Carfeld House, Pinfold Lane,
Kirk Smeaton, North Yorkshire, WF8 3JT
Area of Operation: UK & Ireland
Tel: 01977 621360 **Fax:** 01977 621365
Email: info@sierradesigns.co.uk
Web: www.sierradesigns.co.uk

TEAM SURVEYS LIMITED
St Austell Bay Business Park,
Par Moor Road, St Austell, Cornwall, PL25 3RF
Area of Operation: Europe
Tel: 01726 816069 **Fax:** 01726 814611
Email: email@teamsurveys.com
Web: www.teamsurveys.com

THOMAS PARRY DESIGN PARTNERSHIP
The Old Sketty Coach House,
21 Gower Road, Sketty, Swansea, SA2 9BX
Area of Operation: UK & Ireland
Tel: 01792 290755
Fax: 01792 290527
Email: design@thomasparry.co.uk
Web: www.thomasparry.co.uk

TIMBERWISE (UK) LTD
1 Drake Mews, Gadbrook Park,
Northwich, Cheshire, CW9 7XF
Area of Operation: UK (Excluding Ireland)
Tel: 0800 991100
Email: hq@timberwise.co.uk
Web: www.timberwise.co.uk

STRUCTURAL AND CIVIL ENGINEERS

KEY
OTHER: ▽ Reclaimed ⌐↻ On-line shopping
🖋 Bespoke ✋ Hand-made ECO Ecological

ASSOCIATION OF BUILDING ENGINEERS
Lutyens House, Billing Brook Road,
Northampton, Northamptonshire, NN3 8NW
Area of Operation: Worldwide
Tel: 01604 404121
Fax: 01604 784220
Email: building.engineers@abe.org.uk
Web: www.abe.org.uk ↻

BARRON & PARTNERS
382 Winchester Road,
Southampton, Hampshire, SO16 7DH
Area of Operation: South East England
Tel: 023 8070 5155 **Fax:** 023 8070 4333
Email: admin@barron-and-partners.co.uk
Web: www.barron-and-partners.co.uk

BILLINGTON CONSULTANCY LTD
Unit 2a, Station Yard, Station Road,
Sandbach, Cheshire, CW11 3JG
Area of Operation: UK (Excluding Ireland)
Tel: 07774 203117 **Email:** chrisb@billington.co.uk
Web: www.billington.co.uk

BROWNE SMITH BAKER
11-12 Portland Terrace,
Newcastle upon Tyne, Tyne & Wear, NE2 1QQ
Area of Operation: UK (Excluding Ireland)
Tel: 0191 212 1133 **Fax:** 0191 212 0777
Email: info-n@brownesmithbaker.com
Web: www.brownesmithbaker.com

BUILDINGDOCTORS.CO.UK
96 Farringdon Road, Clerkenwell, London, EC1R 3EA
Area of Operation: East England, Greater London, North West England and North Wales
Tel: 0845 060 0040 **Fax:** 0845 060 0046
Email: architect@building-doctors.com
Web: www.buildingdoctors.co.uk

CO-ORDINATED CONSTRUCTION SERVICES
18 Kiln Road, Crawley Down,
West Sussex, RH10 4JY
Area of Operation: South East England
Tel: 01342 714511 **Fax:** 01342 714511
Email: info@coordsvcs.com
Web: www.coordsvcs.com

EDGBASTON DESIGN LIMITED
24 Stirling Road, Birmingham,
West Midlands, B16 9BG
Area of Operation: Midlands & Mid Wales
Tel: 07775 580404
Email: rannett@constructionplus.net
Web: www.edgbastondesign.co.uk

FINDANENGINEER.COM
11 Upper Belgrave Street, London, SW1X 8BH
Area of Operation: UK (Excluding Ireland)
Tel: 0207 235 4535
Fax: 0207 201 9109
Email: veillas@istructe.org.uk
Web: www.findanengineer.com

GRINDEY CONSULTING
9 Brook Avenue, Swinton, Manchester, M27 5WG
Area of Operation: North West England and North Wales
Tel: 07773 371488
Email: grindeyconsulting@hotmail.com
Web: www.grindeyconsulting.com

ISTRUCTE
Institution of Structural Engineers,
11 Upper Belgrave Street, London, SW1X 8BH
Area of Operation: UK (Excluding Ireland)
Tel: 0207 235 4535 **Fax:** 0207 235 4294
Web: www.findanengineer.com

JNA ARCHITECTS
9 East Park, Southgate, Crawley, West Sussex, RH10 6AN
Area of Operation: South East England
Tel: 01293 439323 **Fax:** 01293 530160
Email: james@jna-architects.co.uk
Web: www.jna-architects.co.uk

R E DESIGN
97 Lincoln Avenue, Glasgow, G13 3DH
Area of Operation: Scotland
Tel: 0141 959 1902 **Fax:** 0141 959 3040
Email: mail@r-e-design.co.uk
Web: www.r-e-design.co.uk

ROCKBOURNE ENVIRONMENTAL
6 Silver Business Park, Airfield Way,
Christchurch, Dorset, BH23 3TA
Area of Operation: UK & Ireland
Tel: 01202 480980 **Fax:** 01202 490590
Email: info@rockbourne.net
Web: www.rockbourne.net

SELF BUILD PRO
Belmont Business Centre, Brook Lane,
Endon, Staffordshire, ST9 9EZ
Area of Operation: Worldwide
Tel: 01782 503322 **Fax:** 01782 505127
Email: enquiries@self-build-pro.com
Web: www.self-build-pro.com ⌐↻

SILKCROSS DEVELOPMENTS LTD
54 Potters Lane, Wednesbury,
West Midlands, WS10 0AT
Area of Operation: UK (Excluding Ireland)
Tel: 0121 505 6778 **Fax:** 0121 505 6779
Email: info@silkcross.co.uk
Web: www.silkcross.co.uk

STATS LIMITED
Porterswood House, Porters Wood,
St Albans, Hertfordshire, AL3 6PQ
Area of Operation: Worldwide
Tel: 01727 833261 **Fax:** 01727 835682
Email: info@stats.co.uk
Web: www.stats.co.uk

STRUCTURAL SURVEYS DIRECT
1-2 Aire House, Richmond Business Park, Sidings
Court, Doncaster, South Yorkshire, DN4 5NL
Tel: 08081 448899 **Fax:** 08081 448898
Email: info@structuralsurveysdirect.co.uk
Web: www.structuralsurveysdirect.co.uk

TILLMAN & TSOUKKAS
8 The Broadway, London, SW19 1RF
Area of Operation: Greater London
Tel: 0208 944 7575 **Fax:** 0208 944 7676
Email: tillman_tsoukkas@btinternet.com
Web: www.tillmantsoukkas.co.uk

ENVIRONMENTAL CONSULTANTS

KEY
OTHER: ▽ Reclaimed ⌐↻ On-line shopping
🖋 Bespoke ✋ Hand-made ECO Ecological

ANDERSON SPARK LTD
Courtyard Studio, Cowley Farm, Aylesbury Road,
Cuddington, Buckinghamshire, HP18 0AD
Area of Operation: Greater London, Midlands & Mid Wales, South East England
Tel: 01296 747121 **Fax:** 01296 747703
Email: info@andersonspark.co.uk
Web: www.andersonspark.co.uk

BRENNAN & WILSON ARCHITECTS
Belhaven Villa, Edinburgh Road,
Belhaven, Dunbar, Lothian, EH42 1PA
Area of Operation: North East England, Scotland
Tel: 01368 860897 **Fax:** 01368 860897
Email: mail@bwarchitects.co.uk
Web: www.bwarchitects.co.uk

CONSULTANTS, LABOUR & FINANCE - Professional Services - Environmental Consultants; Financial Advisors; House Designers

SPONSORED BY: HOMEBUILDING & RENOVATING BOOK OF HOUSE PLANS www.homebuilding.co.uk/bookshop

**BRISTOL & SOMERSET RENEWABLE
ENERGY ADVICE SERVICE**
The Create Centre, Smeaton Road, Bristol, BS1 6XN
Area of Operation: South West England and South Wales
Tel: 0800 512012 **Fax:** 0117 929 9114
Email: info@cse.org.uk
Web: www.cse.org.uk/renewables

CA SUSTAINABLE ARCHITECTURE
83 Old Newtown Road, Newbury, Berkshire, RG14 7DE
Area of Operation: UK (Excluding Ireland)
Tel: 01635 48363
Email: isabel.carmona@ca-sa.co.uk
Web: www.ca-sa.co.uk

CENTRE FOR ALTERNATIVE TECHNOLOGY
Llwyngweren Quarry, Machynlleth, Powys, SY20 9AZ
Area of Operation: Worldwide
Tel: 01654 705950 **Fax:** 01654 702782
Email: lucy.stone@cat.org.uk
Web: www.cat.org.uk

CHILTERN DYNAMICS
Chiltern House , Stocking Lane , Hughenden Valley ,
High Wycombe, Buckinghamshire, HP14 4ND
Area of Operation: UK & Ireland
Tel: 01494 569800
Fax: 01494 564895
Email: cd@chilterndynamics.co.uk
Web: www.chilternfire.co.uk

ENCRAFT LTD
Perseus House, 3 Chapel Court, Holly Walk,
Leamington Spa, Warwickshire, CV32 4YS
Area of Operation: UK & Ireland
Tel: 01926 312159 **Fax:** 01926 882636
Email: enquiries@encraft.co.uk
Web: www.encraft.co.uk

ENERGY CHECK LTD
Unit 28 Torfaen Business Centre,
Blaenavon, Torfaen, NP4 RL
Area of Operation: UK (Excluding Ireland)
Tel: 01495 791406 **Fax:** 01495 791406
Email: office@sap-rating.com
Web: www.sap-rating.com

ENERGY MASTER
Keltic Business Park, Unit 1,
Clieveragh Industrial Estate, Listowel, Ireland
Area of Operation: Ireland Only
Tel: 00353 (0)68 23864 **Fax:** 00353 (0)68 24533
Email: info@energymaster.ie
Web: www.energymaster.ie

FREERAIN
Millennium Green Business Centre, Rio Drive,
Collingham, Nottinghamshire, NG23 7NB
Area of Operation: UK & Ireland
Tel: 01636 894900 **Fax:** 01636 894909
Email: info@freerain.co.uk
Web: www.freerain.co.uk

GEO THERM LTD
Riverside Business Park, Riverside Road,
Lowestoft, Suffolk, NR33 0TQ
Area of Operation: Europe
Tel: 01502 515707
Fax: 01502 530275
Email: info@geothermltd.co.uk
Web: www.geothermltd.co.uk

GREENER HOMES & BUILDINGS
Unit 7, Dyfi Eco Parc, Machynlleth, Powys, SY20 8AX
Area of Operation: Midlands & Mid Wales, North
West England and North Wales, South West England
and South Wales
Tel: 08454 585973 **Fax:** 01654 703117
Email: info@greenerhomesandbuildings.co.uk
Web: www.ghb.org.uk

GREENERLIVING HOMES LTD
Sussex Innovation Centre, Science Park Square,
Falmer, Brighton, East Sussex, BN1 9SB
Area of Operation: South East England
Tel: 01273 704509
Fax: 01273 704499
Email: info@greenerlivinghomes.co.uk
Web: www.greenerlivinghomes.co.uk

HB INSULATIONS
Unit 3, Falcon Court, Manners Industrial Estate,
Ilkeston, Derbyshire, DE7 8EF
Area of Operation: UK (Excluding Ireland)
Tel: 0115 944 0244 **Fax:** 0115 944 0244
Email: chris@hbinsulations.com
Web: www.hbinsulations.com

**HUTTON+ROSTRON
ENVIRONMENTAL INVESTIGATIONS LTD**
Netley House, Gomshall, Guildford, Surrey, GU5 9QA
Area of Operation: UK & Ireland
Tel: 01483 203221 **Fax:** 01483 202911
Email: ei@handr.co.uk **Web:** www.handr.co.uk

JOHN SHORE AA DIPL
16 Popes Lane, Rockwell Green,
Wellington, Somerset, TA21 9DQ
Area of Operation: UK & Ireland
Tel: 01823 666177 **Fax:** 01823 666177
Email: shorepower@ukonline.co.uk

**LEEDS ENVIRONMENTAL
DESIGN ASSOCIATES LTD (LEDA)**
Micklethwaite House, 70 Cross Green Lane,
Leeds, West Yorkshire, LS9 0DG
Area of Operation: North East England
Tel: 0113 200 9380 **Fax:** 0113 200 9381
Email: office@leda.org.uk **Web:** www.leda.org.uk

LOW-IMPACT LIVING INITIATIVE
Redfield Community, Buckingham Road,
Winslow, Buckinghamshire, MK18 3LZ
Area of Operation: UK (Excluding Ireland)
Tel: 01296 714184 **Fax:** 01296 714184
Email: lili@lowimpact.org
Web: www.lowimpact.org

MELIN ENERGY CONSULTANTS
Melin Maes Dulais, Porthyrhyd,
Carmarthenshire, SA32 8BT
Area of Operation: UK (Excluding Ireland)
Tel: 01267 275472 **Fax:** 01267 275597
Email: mel@melinenergy.co.uk

MINI SOIL SURVEYS LTD
Viking House, Manchester Road,
Bolton, Lancashire, BL2 1DU
Area of Operation: UK & Ireland
Tel: 01204 386661
Fax: 01204 386611
Email: peter@minisoils.co.uk
Web: www.minisoils.co.uk

NEAR ZERO CO2 LIMITED
Suite 2.9 Howard House, Howard Street,
North Shields, Tyne & Wear, NE30 1AR
Area of Operation: UK (Excluding Ireland)
Tel: 0191 272 8228
Email: enquiry@nearzero.co.uk
Web: www.nearzero.co.uk

NOISE.CO.UK LTD
Meadow View, Newnham Grounds, Kings Newnham
Lane, Bretford, Warwickshire, CV23 0JU
Area of Operation: UK & Ireland
Tel: 02476 545397 **Fax:** 02476 545010
Email: dave@noise.co.uk **Web:** www.noise.co.uk

ROCKBOURNE ENVIRONMENTAL
6 Silver Business Park, Airfield Way,
Christchurch, Dorset, BH23 3TA
Area of Operation: UK & Ireland
Tel: 01202 480980
Fax: 01202 490590
Email: info@rockbourne.net
Web: www.rockbourne.net

**SEVENOAKS ENVIRONMENTAL
CONSULTANCY LTD**
19 Gimble Way, Pembury,
Tunbridge Wells, Kent, TN2 4BX
Area of Operation: East England, Greater London,
Midlands & Mid Wales, North East England, North
West England and North Wales, South East England,
South West England and South Wales
Tel: 01892 822999 **Fax:** 01892 822992
Email: enquires@sevenoaksenvironmental.co.uk
Web: www.sevenoaksenvironmental.co.uk

STATS LIMITED
Porterswood House, Porters Wood,
St Albans, Hertfordshire, AL3 6PQ
Area of Operation: Worldwide
Tel: 01727 833261 **Fax:** 01727 835682
Email: info@stats.co.uk **Web:** www.stats.co.uk

TERRAIN AERATION SERVICES
Aeration House, 20 Mill Fields,
Haughley, Stowmarket, Suffolk, IP14 3PU
Area of Operation: Europe
Tel: 01449 673783 **Fax:** 01449 614564
Email: terrainaeration@aol.com
Web: www.terrainaeration.co.uk

THE NATIONAL ENERGY FOUNDATION
The National Energy Centre, Davy Avenue, Knowlhill,
Milton Keynes, Buckinghamshire, MK5 8NG
Area of Operation: UK (Excluding Ireland)
Tel: 01908 665555 **Fax:** 01908 665577
Email: info@nef.org.uk **Web:** www.nef.org.uk

WOOD FOR GOOD
211 High Road, London, N2 8AN
Area of Operation: UK (Excluding Ireland)
Tel: 0800 279 0016 **Fax:** 0208 883 6700
Email: info@woodforgood.com
Web: www.woodforgood.com

FINANCIAL ADVISORS & VAT SPECIALISTS

BNB TAX CONSULTANTS
Union Chambers, 63 Temple Row,
Birmingham, West Midlands, B2 5LS
Area of Operation: Europe
Tel: 0121 483 6850 **Fax:** 0121 483 6851
Email: steve.botham@bnbtax.com
Web: www.bnbtax.com

HIGHMEAD VAT
Barrons Cuckoo, Portfield Gate,
Haverfordwest, Pembrokeshire, SA62 3LL
Tel: 01437 762278 **Fax:** 01437 769124
Email: vatconcern@btinternet.com

J. M. DANIEL BUSINESS SERVICES LTD
The Old Mission, 22 Hardfield Street,
Heywood, Lancashire, OL10 1DG
Area of Operation: UK (Excluding Ireland)
Tel: 01706 622125
Fax: 01706 622125
Email: j.m.daniel@accamail.com
Web: www.vatrepayments.co.uk

You can use the
materials key at the
beginning of this
Handbook to get
much more information
from a company's
listing.

J. M. DANIEL BUSINESS SERVICES LTD

Area of Operation: UK (Excluding Ireland)
Tel: 01706 622125
Fax: 01706 622125
Email: j.m.daniel@accamail.com
Web: www.vatrepayments.co.uk

VAT Repayments
Professional, efficient and helpful Vat refund
service for DIY Builders and Converters. Together
we can maximise the refund you are eligible to
receive.

MICHAEL J. FLINT VAT SPECIALIST
16 Paynsbridge Way, Horam,
Heathfield, East Sussex, TN21 0HQ
Area of Operation: UK (Excluding Ireland)
Tel: 01435 813360
Fax: 01435 813360
Email: mjfvat@btinternet.com
Web: www.vat-selfbuild.co.uk

NCB ASSOCIATES LTD
Gate House, Fretheren Road,
Welwyn Garden City, Hertfordshire, AL8 6NS
Area of Operation: UK (Excluding Ireland)
Tel: 0845 230 9897
Email: enquiry@ncbassociates.co.uk
Web: www.ncbassociates.co.uk

THE VAT CONSULTANCY
Laurel House, Station Approach,
Alresford, Hampshire, SO24 9JH
Area of Operation: UK (Excluding Ireland)
Tel: 01962 735350
Fax: 01962 735352
Email: vat@thevatconsultancy.com
Web: www.thevatconsultancy.com

HOUSE DESIGNERS

3D VIRTUAL LTD
Crowell End, Crowell Hill,
Chinnor, Oxfordshire, OX39 4BT
Area of Operation: Europe **Tel:** 01844 214572
Email: chrisparker02@btconnect.com
Web: www.3dvirtual.co.uk

ABBEY ARCHITECTURAL & DESIGN LTD
56 Cheviot Road, London, SE27 0LG
Area of Operation: Greater London
Tel: 0208 676 4393
Email: surveyor@abbeyarch.co.uk
Web: www.abbeyarch.co.uk

ACCESS ARCHITECTS LTD
Mortimer House, 49 Church Street,
Theale, Berkshire, RG7 5BX
Area of Operation: South East England, South West
England and South Wales
Tel: 0118 930 4440
Email: david@access-architects.co.uk
Web: www.access-architects.co.uk

ACROPOLIS DESIGN LTD
13-15, Barstow Square, Wakefield,
West Yorkshire, WF1 2SF
Area of Operation: UK (Excluding Ireland)
Tel: 01924 291963 **Fax:** 0871 733 4738
Email: info@acropolisdesign.co.uk
Web: www.acropolisdesign.co.uk

ADS UK LTD
30 Wild Wood Court, Hawkhirst Road,
Kenley, Surrey, CR8 5DL
Area of Operation: Worldwide
Tel: 0208 660 2637 **Fax:** 0208 660 2642
Email: agn.hughes@virgin.net

ANDERSON SPARK LTD
Courtyard Studio, Cowley Farm, Aylesbury Road,
Cuddington, Buckinghamshire, HP18 0AD
Area of Operation: Greater London, Midlands & Mid
Wales, South East England
Tel: 01296 747121 **Fax:** 01296 747703
Email: info@andersonspark.co.uk
Web: www.andersonspark.co.uk

ARCHITECTURAL DESIGN STUDIO LTD
55 Tadorna Drive, Holmer Lake,
Telford, Shropshire, TF3 1QP
Area of Operation: Midlands & Mid Wales
Tel: 01952 592592 **Fax:** 01952 596939
Email: jrbarch@hotmail.com

ARCHITECTURE PLUS
5 Dunkery Road, Weston Super Mare,
Somerset, BS23 2TD
Area of Operation: UK (Excluding Ireland)
Tel: 01934 416416 **Fax:** 01934 622583
Email: office@architecture-plus.co.uk
Web: www.architectureplus.co.uk

ARCHITECTURE VERTE LIMITED
10 Glenmore Business Centre,
Hopton Park Industrial Estate, Devizes, SN10 2EQ
Area of Operation: Greater London, Midlands & Mid
Wales, South East England, South West England and
South Wales
Tel: 01380 739139 **Fax:** 01380 739159
Email: mail@verte.co.uk **Web:** www.verte.co.uk

**ASAP - ARCHITECTURAL
SERVICES & PLANNING**
Howard Buildings, 69-71Burpham Lane,
Guildford, Surrey, GU4 7LX
Area of Operation: South East England
Tel: 01483 457922
Email: david.haines4@virgin.net
Web: www.asaparchitectural.co.uk

ASBA SCOTLAND
10 Lynedoch Cresent, Glasgow, G3 6EQ
Area of Operation: Scotland
Tel: 0800 731 3405 **Fax:** 0141 331 2751
Email: architects@design-practice.com

BACK TO FRONT EXTERIOR DESIGN
37 West Street, Farnham, Surrey, GU9 7DR
Area of Operation: UK & Ireland

Tel: 01252 820984 **Fax:** 01252 821907
Email: design@backtofrontexteriordesign.com
Web: www.backtofrontexteriordesign.com

BILLINGTON CONSULTANCY LTD
Unit 2a, Station Yard, Station Road,
Sandbach, Cheshire, CW11 3JG
Area of Operation: UK (Excluding Ireland)
Tel: 07774 203117
Email: chrisb@billington.co.uk
Web: www.billington.co.uk

BRENNAN & WILSON ARCHITECTS
Belhaven Villa, Edinburgh Road,
Belhaven, Dunbar, Lothian, EH42 1PA
Area of Operation: North East England, Scotland
Tel: 01368 860897 **Fax:** 01368 860897
Email: mail@bwarchitects.co.uk
Web: www.bwarchitects.co.uk

BUILDING PLANS LTD
Unit 10 Beech Avenue, Taverham,
Norwich, Norfolk, NR8 6HW
Area of Operation: UK (Excluding Ireland)
Tel: 01603 868377 **Fax:** 01603 868412
Email: john@constructionhelp.co.uk
Web: www.constructionhelp.co.uk

BUILDINGDOCTORS.CO.UK
96 Farringdon Road, Clerkenwell, London, EC1R 3EA
Area of Operation: East England, Greater London,
North West England and North Wales
Tel: 0845 060 0040 **Fax:** 0845 060 0046
Email: architect@building-doctors.com
Web: www.buildingdoctors.co.uk

CA SUSTAINABLE ARCHITECTURE
83 Old Newtown Road,
Newbury, Berkshire, RG14 7DE
Area of Operation: UK (Excluding Ireland)
Tel: 01635 48363
Email: isabel.carmona@ca-sa.co.uk
Web: www.ca-sa.co.uk

CENTRE FOR ALTERNATIVE TECHNOLOGY
Llwyngwreren Quarry, Machynlleth, Powys, SY20 9AZ
Area of Operation: Worldwide
Tel: 01654 705 950 **Fax:** 01654 702 782
Email: lucy.stone@cat.org.uk **Web:** www.cat.org.uk

**CHRISTOPHER MAGUIRE ARCHITECT
AND GARDEN DESIGNER**
15 Harston Road, Newton,
Cambridge, Cambridgeshire, CB2 5PA
Area of Operation: East England
Tel: 01223 872800
Web: www.christophermaguire.co.uk

COLIN WILLIAMS BUILDING CONSULTANCY
Courtyard Studio, 52A Dereham Road,
Mattishall, Dereham, Norfolk, NR20 3NS
Area of Operation: East England
Tel: 01362 850171 **Fax:** 01362 850171
Email: design@cooptel.net

CONSTRUCTIVE INDIVIDUALS (LONDON) LTD

Trinity Buoy Wharf, 64 Orchard Place, London, E14 0JW
Area of Operation: UK (Excluding Ireland)
Tel: 020 751 59299 **Fax:** 020 751 59737
Email: info@constructiveindividuals.com
Web: www.constructiveindividuals.com

CO-ORDINATED CONSTRUCTION SERVICES
18 Kiln Road, Crawley Down,
West Sussex, RH10 4JY
Area of Operation: South East England
Tel: 01342 714511 **Fax:** 01342 714511
Email: info@coordsvcs.com
Web: www.coordsvcs.com

DESIGN AND MATERIALS LTD
Lawn Road, Carlton in Lindrick,
Nottinghamshire, S81 9LB
Area of Operation: UK (Excluding Ireland)
Tel: 01909 540123 **Fax:** 01909 730605
Email: enquiries@designandmaterials.uk.com
Web: www.designandmaterials.uk.com

DESIGNER HOMES
Pooh Cottage, Minto, Hawick,
Roxburghshire, Borders, TD9 8SB
Area of Operation: UK & Ireland
Tel: 01450 870127 **Fax:** 01450 870127

ECLIPSE DESIGN
Staunton Harold Hall, Staunton Harold,
Leicestershire, LE65 1RT
Area of Operation: UK (Excluding Ireland)
Tel: 0870 460 4758
Email: enquiries@eclipsedesignuk.net
Web: www.eclipsedesignuk.net

ENGLISHAUS CHARTERED ARCHITECTS LTD
30 Lawrence Road, Hampton, Middlesex, TW12 2RJ
Area of Operation: Greater London, South East
England, South West England and South Wales
Tel: 0208 255 0595 **Fax:** 0208 287 3441
Email: enquiries@englishaus.co.uk
Web: www.englishaus.co.uk

FG DESIGN
6 Denmark Drive, Sedbury,
Chepstow, Monmouthshire, NT16 7BD
Area of Operation: South West England and South Wales
Tel: 01291 624366 **Fax:** 01291 624366
Email: frank.fgdesign@virgin.net

GEORGE BLACK ARCHITECT
12 Kingsknowe Crescent,
Edinburgh, Lothian, EH14 2JZ
Area of Operation: Scotland
Tel: 0131 443 9898
Email: george@gbarch.abel.co.uk
Web: www.gbarch.abel.co.uk

GRAHAM G BISHOP - CHARTERED SURVEYORS
9 Church Lane Drive, Coulsdon, Surrey, CR5 3RG
Area of Operation: Greater London, South East England
Tel: 01737 558473 **Fax:** 01737 558473
Email: graham@grahamgbishop.co.uk
Web: www.grahamgbishop.co.uk

GREENERLIVING HOMES LTD
Sussex Innovation Centre, Science Park Square,
Falmer, Brighton, East Sussex, BN1 9SB
Area of Operation: South East England
Tel: 01273 704509 **Fax:** 01273 704499
Email: info@greenerlivinghomes.co.uk
Web: www.greenerlivinghomes.co.uk

GRINDEY CONSULTING
9 Brook Avenue, Swinton, Manchester, M27 5WG
Area of Operation: North West England and North Wales
Tel: 07773 371488
Email: grindeyconsulting@hotmail.com
Web: www.grindeyconsulting.com

HEMPHAB PRODUCTS
Rusheens, Ballygriffen, Kenmare, Kerry, Ireland
Area of Operation: Ireland Only
Tel: +353 644 1747
Email: hempbuilding@eircom.net
Web: www.hempbuilding.com

J G HOOD & ASSOCIATES LTD
50 High Street, Bruton, Somerset, BA10 0AN
Area of Operation: Midlands & Mid Wales, South
East England, South West England and South Wales
Tel: 01749 812139 **Fax:** 0870 133 3776
Email: mail@jghood-assoc.co.uk
Web: www.jghood-assoc.co.uk

J.S. BUILDING CONSULTANCY
53 Hawthorn Road, Yeadon,
Leeds, West Yorkshire, LS19 7UT
Area of Operation: UK (Excluding Ireland)
Tel: 0113 250 1303 **Email:** jsharples@ricsonline.org
Web: www.ukbuildingconsultancy.co.uk

JEREMY RAWLINGS PERIOD HOMES
Coombe Lee, Blackborough,
Cullompton, Devon, EX15 2HJ
Area of Operation: UK & Ireland
Tel: 01884 266444 **Fax:** 01884 266758
Email: jeremy.rawlings@btinternet.com
Web: www.periodhome.net

JNA ARCHITECTS
9 East Park, Southgate, Crawley, West Sussex, RH10 6AN
Area of Operation: South East England
Tel: 01293 439323 **Fax:** 01293 530160
Email: james@jna-architects.co.uk
Web: www.jna-architects.co.uk

JOHN PEATE ARCHITECTURAL SERVICES LTD
6 Newport Road, Shifnal, Shropshire, TF11 8BP
Area of Operation: Midlands & Mid Wales, North
West England and North Wales
Tel: 01952 460175 **Fax:** 01952 460175
Email: info@johnpeate.co.uk
Web: www.johnpeate.co.uk

JONES NASH ECO HOMES
12 Lee Street, Louth, Lincolnshire, LN11 9HJ
Area of Operation: UK (Excluding Ireland)
Tel: 01507 609637 **Fax:** 01507 609637
Email: sd@jones-nash.co.uk
Web: www.eco-houses.co.uk

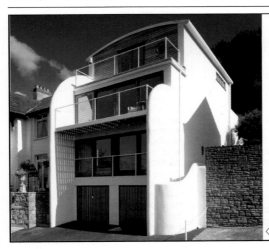

JPK DESIGN LTD
83 Dimsdale Parade East, Wolstanton,
Newcastle Under Lyme, Staffordshire, ST5 8DP
Area of Operation: Midlands & Mid Wales, North
West England and North Wales
Tel: 01782 622321 **Fax:** 01782 622323
Email: jason.knight@jpkdesign.co.uk
Web: www.jpkdesign.co.uk

KMD ARCHITECTURAL SERVICES LTD
Second Floor, 1 Station Road,
Whitley Bay, Tyne & Wear, NE26 2QY
Area of Operation: UK (Excluding Ireland)
Tel: 0191 253 7110 **Fax:** 0871 211 0363
Email: info@kmd-limited.co.uk
Web: www.kmd-limited.co.uk

LARNER SING
The Barn, Rode Hill, Rode, Frome, Somerset, BA11 6PU
Area of Operation: South East England, South West
England and South Wales
Tel: 01373 830527 **Fax:** 01373 830527
Email: ian@larner-sing.co.uk
Web: www.larner-sing.com

M J BRAIN
Kamala House, North Lane, Weston On The Green,
Bicester, Oxfordshire, OX25 3RG
Tel: 01869 350771 **Fax:** 01869 351445
Email: malcolmbrain@mjbrain.freeserve.co.uk

M3 ARCHITECTS
49 Kingsway Place, Sans Walk, London, EC1R 0LU
Area of Operation: East England, Greater London,
Scotland, South East England
Tel: 0207 253 7255 **Fax:** 0207 253 7266
Email: post@m3architects.com
Web: www.m3architects.com

MICHAEL D HALL
Studio A, 339 London Road,
Bexhill on Sea, East Sussex, TN39 4AJ
Area of Operation: South East England
Tel: 01424 214541 **Fax:** 01424 731555
Email: bds@michaeldhall.co.uk
Web: www.michaeldhall.co.uk

NEAR ZERO CO2 LIMITED
Suite 2.9 Howard House, Howard Street,
North Shields, Tyne & Wear, NE30 1AR
Area of Operation: UK (Excluding Ireland)
Tel: 0191 272 8228
Email: enquiry@nearzero.co.uk
Web: www.nearzero.co.uk

NICHOLAS RAY ASSOCIATES
13-15 Convert Garden, Cambridge,
Cambridgeshire, CB1 2HS
Tel: 01223 464455 **Email:** design@nray-arch.co.uk
Web: www.nray-arch.co.uk

NICOLAS TYE ARCHITECTS
The Long Barn Studio,
Limbersey Lane, Bedfordshire, MK45 2EA
Tel: 01525 406677 **Fax:** 01525 406688
Email: info@nicolastyearchitects.co.uk
Web: www.nicolastyearchitects.co.uk

NORDSTROM ASSOCIATES
32 Oswald Road, St Albans, Hertfordshire, AL1 3AQ
Area of Operation: Greater London
Tel: 01727 831971 **Fax:** 01727 752981
Email: gunnar.nordstrom@ntlworld.com

**O'EVE DON INTERIORS &
THE KITCHEN PLANNER**
9 Maple Drive, Castle Park, Mallow, Co Cork, Ireland
Area of Operation: Ireland Only
Tel: 022 20858 **Fax:** 022 20858
Email: oevedoninteriors@eircom.net

PAUL A STOWELL
'Sorriso', Farleigh Road, Cliddesden,
Basingstoke, Hampshire, RG25 2JL
Area of Operation: Greater London, South East
England, South West England and South Wales
Tel: 01256 320470 **Fax:** 01256 320470
Email: paulstowell@constructionplans.co.uk
Web: www.constructionplans.co.uk

PLANS & DRAWINGS.COM
5 Station Road, Stepps,
Glasgow, Lanarkshire, G33 6HB
Area of Operation: Scotland
Tel: 0141 404 0136 **Fax:** 0141 779 5370
Email: info@homecad.org
Web: www.plansanddrawings.com

R E DESIGN
97 Lincoln Avenue, Glasgow, G13 3DH
Area of Operation: Scotland
Tel: 0141 959 1902 **Fax:** 0141 959 3040
Email: mail@r-e-design.co.uk
Web: www.r-e-design.co.uk

RUMBALL SEDGWICK
Abbotts House, 198 Lower High Street,
Watford, Hertfordshire, WD17 2FF
Area of Operation: Greater London, South East England
Tel: 01923 224275 **Fax:** 01923 255005
Email: shaun@w.rumballsedgwick.co.uk
Web: www.rumballsedgwick.co.uk

SELF BUILD PRO
Belmont Business Centre, Brook Lane,
Endon, Staffordshire, ST9 9EZ
Area of Operation: Worldwide
Tel: 01782 503322 **Fax:** 01782 505127
Email: enquiries@self-build-pro.com
Web: www.self-build-pro.com

SELFBUILD-GROUP.CO.UK
Area of Operation: UK & Ireland
Email: enquiries@selfbuild-group.co.uk
Web: www.selfbuild-group.co.uk

**SIERRA DESIGNS - ARCHITECTURAL
AND BUILDING CONSULTANTS**
Carfeld House, Pinfold Lane,
Kirk Smeaton, North Yorkshire, WF8 3JT
Area of Operation: UK & Ireland
Tel: 01977 621360 **Fax:** 01977 621365
Email: info@sierradesigns.co.uk
Web: www.sierradesigns.co.uk

SNP ASSOCIATES
248 Kingston Road, New Malden, Surrey, KT3 3RN
Area of Operation: Worldwide
Tel: 0208 942 6238
Email: snp@snpassociates.co.uk
Web: www.snpassociates.co.uk

ST DESIGN CONSULTANTS
Othona House, Waterside, Bradwell on Sea,
Southminster, Essex, CM0 7QT
Area of Operation: UK (Excluding Ireland)
Tel: 01621 776736 **Fax:** 01621 776736
Email: info@stdesignconsultants.co.uk
Web: www.stdesignconsultants.co.uk

STRAWBALE BUILDING COMPANY UK
34 Rosebery Way, Tring, Hertfordshire, HP23 5DS
Area of Operation: Europe
Tel: 01442 825421
Email: chug@strawbale-building.co.uk
Web: www.strawbale-building.co.uk

T J CRUMP OAKWRIGHTS LIMITED
The Lakes, Swainhill, Hereford, Herefordshire, HR4 7PU
Area of Operation: Worldwide
Tel: 01432 353353 **Fax:** 01432 357733
Email: nick@oakwrights.co.uk
Web: www.oakwrights.co.uk

THE BORDER DESIGN CENTRE
Harelaw Moor, Greenlaw, Borders, TD10 6XT
Area of Operation: UK (Excluding Ireland)
Tel: 01578 740218 **Fax:** 01578 740218
Email: borderdesign@btconnect.com
Web: www.borderdesign.co.uk

**TROTMAN & TAYLOR
ARCHITECTURAL CONSULTANTS**
40 Deer Park, Ivybridge, Devon, PL21 0HY
Area of Operation: UK (Excluding Ireland)
Tel: 01752 698410 **Fax:** 01752 698410
Email: enquiries@trotmantaylor.com
Web: www.trotmantaylor.com

VICTORIA HAMMOND INTERIORS
Bury Farm, Church Street, Bovingdon,
Hemel Hempstead, Hertfordshire, HP3 0LU
Area of Operation: UK (Excluding Ireland)
Tel: 01442 831641 **Fax:** 01442 831641
Email: victoria@victoriahammond.com
Web: www.victoriahammond.com

VIRTUAL-LIVING
11 Mornington Road, Cheadle, Cheshire, SK8 1NJ
Area of Operation: Worldwide
Tel: 01614911162
Email: info@virtual-living.co.uk
Web: www.virtual-living.co.uk

WM DESIGN PARTNERSHIP
First Floor, 14 Bridge Street,
Menai Bridge, Anglesey, LL59 5DW
Area of Operation: UK (Excluding Ireland)
Tel: 01248 717230 **Fax:** 01248 714930
Email: info@wmdesign.co.uk
Web: www.wmdesign.co.uk

XSPACE
99 Woodlands Avenue, Poole, Dorset, BH15 4EG
Area of Operation: South East England, South West
England and South Wales
Tel: 01202 665387 **Fax:** 01202 380235
Email: design@xspace.biz **Web:** www.xspace.biz

INTERIOR DESIGNERS

KEY
OTHER: ▽ Reclaimed 🖰 On-line shopping
📎 Bespoke ✋ Hand-made ECO Ecological

ABOUT PROPERTY PRESENTATION
71 New Road, Brentford, Greater London, TW8 0NU
Area of Operation: UK (Excluding Ireland)
Tel: 0208 580 5592 **Fax:** 0208 580 5592
Email: marie@applondon.co.uk
Web: www.applondon.co.uk

ACROPOLIS DESIGN LTD
13-15, Barstow Square,
Wakefield, West Yorkshire, WF1 2SF
Area of Operation: UK (Excluding Ireland)
Tel: 01924 291963
Fax: 0871 733 4738
Email: info@acropolisdesign.co.uk
Web: www.acropolisdesign.co.uk

ADRIENNE CHINN DESIGN COMPANY LTD
C216 Trident Business Centre,
89 Bickersteth Road, London, SW17 9SH
Area of Operation: UK (Excluding Ireland)
Tel: 0208 516 7783
Fax: 0208 516 7785
Email: info@adriennechinn.co.uk
Web: www.adriennechinn.co.uk

ARCHITECTURE VERTE LIMITED
10 Glenmore Business Centre, Hopton Park Industrial
Estate, Devizes, SN10 2EQ
Area of Operation: Greater London, Midlands & Mid
Wales, South East England, South West England and
South Wales
Tel: 01380 739139 **Fax:** 01380 739159
Email: mail@verte.co.uk **Web:** www.verte.co.uk

ASBA SCOTLAND
10 Lynedoch Cresent, Glasgow, G3 6EQ
Area of Operation: Scotland
Tel: 0800 731 3405 **Fax:** 0141 331 2751
Email: architects@design-practice.com

BROWNE SMITH BAKER
11-12 Portland Terrace,
Newcastle upon Tyne, Tyne & Wear, NE2 1QQ
Area of Operation: UK (Excluding Ireland)
Tel: 0191 212 1133 **Fax:** 0191 212 0777
Email: info-n@brownesmithbaker.com
Web: www.brownesmithbaker.com

BUILDINGDOCTORS.CO.UK
96 Farringdon Road, Clerkenwell, London, EC1R 3EA
Area of Operation: East England, Greater London,
North West England and North Wales
Tel: 0845 060 0040 **Fax:** 0845 060 0046
Email: architect@building-doctors.com
Web: www.buildingdoctors.co.uk

CA SUSTAINABLE ARCHITECTURE
83 Old Newtown Road,
Newbury, Berkshire, RG14 7DE
Area of Operation: UK (Excluding Ireland)
Tel: 01635 48363
Email: isabel.carmona@ca-sa.co.uk
Web: www.ca-sa.co.uk

CANNING & SHERIDAN INTERIORS
718 The Alaska Buildings,
61 Grange Road, London, SE1 3BD
Area of Operation: Greater London
Tel: 0207 740 2117
Email: info@canning-sheridan.co.uk
Web: www.canning-sheridan.co.uk

CHRISTOPHER COOK DESIGNS LTD
29-33 Creek Road, Hampton Court,
East Molesey, Surrey, KT8 9BE
Area of Operation: Worldwide
Tel: 0208 941 9135 **Fax:** 0208 941 7282
Email: contact@christophercook.co.uk
Web: www.christophercook.co.uk

CO-ORDINATED CONSTRUCTION SERVICES
18 Kiln Road, Crawley Down, West Sussex, RH10 4JY
Area of Operation: South East England
Tel: 01342 714511 **Fax:** 01342 714511
Email: info@coordsvcs.com
Web: www.coordsvcs.com

DEBBIE NEAL INTERIORS
32 Clifton Road, Crouch End, London, N8 8JA
Area of Operation: Greater London
Tel: 0208 340 0046
Email: info@debbienealinteriors.co.uk
Web: www.debbienealinteriors.co.uk

DNA DESIGN
43 View Road, Cliffe Woods, Rochester, Kent, ME3 8UE
Area of Operation: South East England
Tel: 01634 222266 **Fax:** 01634 222868
Email: interiors@dna-design.co.uk
Web: dna-design.co.uk

GLG DESIGN
Beech Studio, 10 Berryhill Road,
Giffnock, Glasgow, Renfrewshire, G46 7NJ
Area of Operation: UK & Ireland
Tel: 0141 621 2050 **Fax:** 0141 638 7017
Email: mail@glgdesign.com

INNER SPACE DESIGNS
6 Norfolk Road, Newport, Newport, NP19 7SL
Area of Operation: South West England and South Wales
Tel: 01633 782505 **Fax:** 01633 782506
Email: info@innerspacedesigns.co.uk
Web: www.innerspacedesigns.co.uk

JNA ARCHITECTS
9 East Park, Southgate,
Crawley, West Sussex, RH10 6AN
Area of Operation: South East England
Tel: 01293 439323 **Fax:** 01293 530160
Email: james@jna-architects.co.uk
Web: www.jna-architects.co.uk

JOHN SOLOMON DESIGN LIMITED
48 Ham Street, Richmond, Surrey, TW10 7HT
Area of Operation: Worldwide
Tel: 020 8940 2444 **Fax:** 020 8940 1188
Email: mail@jsajsd.com
Web: www.jsajsd.com

LIGHT IQ LTD
1 Rylett Studios, 77 Rylett Crescent, London, W12 9RP
Area of Operation: Europe
Tel: 020 874 91900 **Fax:** 020 874 91999
Email: philip@lightiq.com
Web: www.lightiq.com

M3 ARCHITECTS
49 Kingsway Place, Sans Walk, London, EC1R 0LU
Area of Operation: East England, Greater London, Scotland, South East England
Tel: 0207 253 7255 **Fax:** 0207 253 7266
Email: post@m3architects.com
Web: www.m3architects.com

MARMOT ASSOCIATES
Higher Tor Farm, Poundsgate,
Newton Abbot, Devon, TQ13 7PD
Area of Operation: South West England and South Wales
Tel: 01364 631566
Fax: 01364 631556
Email: marmot-tor@zen.co.uk
Web: www.marmot-tor.com

NEVILLE JOHNSON
Broadoak Business Park, Ashburton Road West,
Trafford Park, Manchester, M17 1RW
Tel: 0161 873 8333
Fax: 0161 873 8335
Email: sales@nevillejohnson.co.uk
Web: www.nevillejohnson.co.uk

NICOLAS TYE ARCHITECTS
The Long Barn Studio, Limbersey Lane,
Bedfordshire, MK45 2EA
Area of Operation: UK (Excluding Ireland)
Tel: 01525 406677
Fax: 01525 406688
Email: info@nicolastyearchitects.co.uk
Web: www.nicolastyearchitects.co.uk

**O'EVE DON INTERIORS &
THE KITCHEN PLANNER**
9 Maple Drive, Castle Park,
Mallow, Co Cork, Ireland
Area of Operation: Ireland Only
Tel: +353 (0)22 20858 **Fax:** +353 (0)22 20858
Email: oevedoninteriors@eircom.net

PROPERTYPORTAL.COM
Brookfield House, Ford Lane, Frilford,
Abingdon, Oxfordshire, OX13 5NT
Area of Operation: UK (Excluding Ireland)
Tel: 0870 380 0520 **Fax:** 0870 380 0521
Email: info@propertyportal.com
Web: www.propertyportal.com

SALLY DERNIE INTERIOR DESIGN
4/29 Sisters Avenue, London, SW11 5SR
Area of Operation: Worldwide
Tel: 0207 738 1628
Fax: 020 773 89981
Email: info@sallydernie.com
Web: www.sallydernie.com

SIMON KNIGHT DESIGN
44 Langton Road, Bishops Waltham,
Winchester, Hampshire, SO32 1GF
Area of Operation: Europe
Tel: 07900 194744 **Fax:** 01489 894511
Email: enquiries@simonknightdesign.co.uk
Web: www.simonknightinteriors.com

STUART INTERIORS
Barrington Court, Barrington,
Ilminster, Somerset, TA19 0NQ
Area of Operation: Worldwide
Tel: 01460 240349 **Fax:** 01460 242069
Email: design@stuartinteriors.com
Web: www.stuartinteriors.com

THE DESIGN STUDIO
39 High Street, Reigate, Surrey, RH2 9AE
Area of Operation: South East England
Tel: 01737 248228
Fax: 01737 224180
Email: enq@the-design-studio.co.uk
Web: www.the-design-studio.co.uk

THOMAS PARRY DESIGN PARTNERSHIP
The Old Sketty Coach House,
21 Gower Road, Sketty, Swansea, SA2 9BX
Tel: 01792 290755 **Fax:** 01792 290527
Email: design@thomasparry.co.uk
Web: www.thomasparry.co.uk

VICTORIA HAMMOND INTERIORS
Bury Farm, Church Street, Bovingdon,
Hemel Hempstead, Hertfordshire, HP3 0LU
Area of Operation: UK (Excluding Ireland)
Tel: 01442 831641
Fax: 01442 831641
Email: victoria@victoriahammond.com
Web: www.victoriahammond.com

VIRTUAL-LIVING
11 Mornington Road, Cheadle, Cheshire, SK8 1NJ
Area of Operation: Worldwide
Tel: 0161 491 1162
Email: info@virtual-living.co.uk
Web: www.virtual-living.co.uk

WHITEMORE AND THWAYTES
Foxton House, Lowther Street,
Penrith, Cumbria, CA11 7UW
Area of Operation: UK & Ireland
Tel: 01768 863895
Fax: 01768 862459
Email: enquiries@whitemoreandthwaytes.co.uk
Web: www.whitemoreandthwaytes ▽

WILSON MASON
St James House, 116 Talbot Street,
Nottingham, Nottinghamshire, NG1 5GL
Area of Operation: Europe
Tel: 0115 950 3789
Fax: 0115 947 4073
Email: mfindlay@wilsonmason.co.uk
Web: www.wilsonmason.co.uk

WOOLS OF NEW ZEALAND
International Development Centre,
Little Lane, Ilkley, West Yorkshire, LS29 8UG
Area of Operation: Worldwide
Tel: 01943 603888
Fax: 01943 817083
Email: info.uk@canesis.co.uk
Web: www.woolcarpet.com

PLANNING CONSULTANTS

KEY
OTHER: ▽ Reclaimed 🛒 On-line shopping
✎ Bespoke ✋ Hand-made ECO Ecological

ANDERSON SPARK LTD
Courtyard Studio, Cowley Farm, Aylesbury Road,
Cuddington, Buckinghamshire, HP18 0AD
Area of Operation: Greater London, Midlands & Mid Wales, South East England
Tel: 01296 747121
Fax: 01296 747703
Email: info@andersonspark.co.uk
Web: www.andersonspark.co.uk

ARCHITECTURAL DESIGN STUDIO LTD
55 Tadorna Drive, Holmer Lake,
Telford, Shropshire, TF3 1QP
Area of Operation: Midlands & Mid Wales
Tel: 01952 592592
Fax: 01952 596939
Email: jrbarch@hotmail.com

ARCHTEC DESIGN
41 Gladstone Park Gardens, London, NW2 6LA
Area of Operation: Greater London, South East England, South West England and South Wales
Tel: 0208 208 1262
Email: archtecdesign@hotmail.com
Web: www.archtecdesign.co.uk

**ASAP -
ARCHITECTURAL SERVICES & PLANNING**
Howard Buildings, 69-71 Burpham Lane,
Guildford, Surrey, GU4 7LX
Area of Operation: South East England
Tel: 01483 457922
Email: david.haines4@virgin.net
Web: www.asaparchitectural.co.uk

BILLINGTON CONSULTANCY LTD
Unit 2a, Station Yard, Station Road,
Sandbach, Cheshire, CW11 3JG
Area of Operation: UK (Excluding Ireland)
Tel: 07774 203117
Email: chrisb@billington.co.uk
Web: www.billington.co.uk

BROWNE SMITH BAKER
11-12 Portland Terrace,
Newcastle Upon Tyne, Tyne & Wear, NE2 1QQ
Area of Operation: UK (Excluding Ireland)
Tel: 0191 212 1133 **Fax:** 0191 212 0777
Email: info-n@brownesmithbaker.com
Web: www.brownesmithbaker.com

CO-ORDINATED CONSTRUCTION SERVICES
18 Kiln Road, Crawley Down, West Sussex, RH10 4JY
Area of Operation: South East England
Tel: 01342 714511 **Fax:** 01342 714511
Email: info@coordsvcs.com
Web: www.coordsvcs.com

CORK TOFT PARTNERSHIP LTD
Greenbank, Howick Cross Lane,
Penwortham, Preston, Lancashire, PR1 0NS
Area of Operation: North West England and North Wales
Tel: 01772 749014 /5 **Fax:** 01772 749034
Email: mail@corktoft.com

DESIGN PLUS (KENT) LTD
59 Marshall Crescent, Broadstairs, Kent, CT10 2HR
Area of Operation: UK (Excluding Ireland)
Tel: 01843 602218
Email: designpluskent@btinternet.com
Web: www.designpluskent.co.uk

DMH STALLARD PLANNING
100 Queens Road, Brighton, East Sussex, BN1 3YB
Area of Operation: UK (Excluding Ireland)
Tel: 01273 744450 **Fax:** 01273 744455
Email: tony.allen@dmhstallard.com
Web: www.dmhstallard.com

ENGLISHAUS CHARTERED ARCHITECTS LTD
30 Lawrence Road, Hampton, Middlesex, TW12 2RJ
Area of Operation: Greater London, South East England, South West England and South Wales
Tel: 0208 255 0595 **Fax:** 0208 287 3441
Email: enquiries@englishaus.co.uk
Web: www.englishaus.co.uk

FG DESIGN
6 Denmark Drive, Sedbury,
Chepstow, Monmouthshire, NT16 7BD
Area of Operation: South West England and South Wales
Tel: 01291 624366 **Fax:** 01291 624366
Email: frank.fgdesign@virgin.net

G.M.MOORE & ASSOCIATES
Old Laughton Sawmills, Park Lane,
Laughton, East Sussex, BN8 6BP
Area of Operation: South East England
Tel: 01323 811689 **Fax:** 01323 811325
Email: sales@gmassociates.co.uk
Web: www.gmassociates.co.uk

GRINDEY CONSULTING
9 Brook Avenue, Swinton, Manchester, M27 5WG
Area of Operation: North West England and North Wales
Tel: 07773 371488
Email: grindeyconsulting@hotmail.com
Web: www.grindeyconsulting.com

J G HOOD & ASSOCIATES LTD
50 High Street, Bruton, Somerset, BA10 0AN
Area of Operation: Midlands & Mid Wales, South East England, South West England and South Wales
Tel: 01749 812139 **Fax:** 0870 133 3776
Email: mail@jghood-assoc.co.uk
Web: www.jghood-assoc.co.uk

J.S. BUILDING CONSULTANCY
53 Hawthorn Road, Yeadon,
Leeds, West Yorkshire, LS19 7UT
Area of Operation: UK (Excluding Ireland)
Tel: 0113 250 1303
Email: jsharples@ricsonline.org
Web: www.ukbuildingconsultancy.co.uk

**JEREMY WARD INDEPENDENT
BUILDING CONSULTANT**
Sootfield Green, Charlton Road,
Preston, Hertfordshire, SG4 7TB
Area of Operation: East England, Greater London, South East England
Tel: 01462 438487 **Email:** sootfieldgreen@aol.com
Web: www.jwibc.co.uk

JNA ARCHITECTS
9 East Park, Southgate,
Crawley, West Sussex, RH10 6AN
Area of Operation: South East England
Tel: 01293 439323 **Fax:** 01293 530160
Email: james@jna-architects.co.uk
Web: www.jna-architects.co.uk

JOSEPH R NIXON PROJECT MANAGEMENT
Brookview 52a Foxcotte Road,
Charlton, Andover, Hampshire , SP10 4AT
Area of Operation: Greater London, South East England, South West England and South Wales
Tel: 01264 364232 **Fax:** 01264 364232
Email: jrn-pm@tiscali.co.uk

JPK DESIGN LTD
83 Dimsdale Parade East, Wolstanton,
Newcastle Under Lyme, Staffordshire, ST5 8DP
Area of Operation: Midlands & Mid Wales, North West England and North Wales
Tel: 01782 622321 **Fax:** 01782 622323
Email: jason.knight@jpkdesign.com
Web: www.jpkdesign.com

LARNER SING
The Barn, Rode Hill, Rode,
Frome, Somerset, BA11 6PU
Area of Operation: South East England, South West England and South Wales
Tel: 01373 830527 **Fax:** 01373 830527
Email: ian@larner-sing.co.uk
Web: www.larner-sing.com

LEIGH & GLENNIE LTD
6 All Souls Road, Ascot, Berkshire, SL5 9EA
Area of Operation: East England, Greater London, South East England
Tel: 01344 297094
Email: mail@christianleigh.co.uk
Web: www.christianleigh.co.uk

M3 ARCHITECTS
49 Kingsway Place, Sans Walk, London, EC1R 0LU
Area of Operation: East England, Greater London, Scotland, South East England
Tel: 0207 253 7255 **Fax:** 0207 253 7266
Email: post@m3architects.com
Web: www.m3architects.com

NCB ASSOCIATES LTD
Gate House, Fretheren Road,
Welwyn Garden City, Hertfordshire, AL8 6NS
Area of Operation: UK (Excluding Ireland)
Tel: 0845 230 9897
Email: enquiry@ncbassociates.co.uk
Web: www.ncbassociates.co.uk

PAUL A STOWELL
'Sorriso', Farleigh Road, Cliddesden,
Basingstoke, Hampshire , RG25 2JL
Area of Operation: Greater London, South East England, South West England and South Wales
Tel: 01256 320470 **Fax:** 01256 320470
Email: paulstowell@constructionplans.co.uk
Web: www.constructionplans.co.uk

PLANNING & DEVELOPMENT SOLUTIONS LTD.
3 Albion Place, Leeds, West Yorkshire, LS1 6JL
Area of Operation: UK (Excluding Ireland)
Tel: 0113 383 3735 **Fax:** 0870 224 9334
Email: info@pds.uk.com **Web:** www.pds.uk.com

PROPERTYPORTAL.COM
Brookfield House, Ford Lane, Frilford,
Abingdon, Oxfordshire, OX13 5NT
Area of Operation: UK (Excluding Ireland)
Tel: 0870 380 0520 **Fax:** 0870 380 0521
Email: info@propertyportal.com
Web: www.propertyportal.com

RUMBALL SEDGWICK
Abbotts House, 198 Lower High Street,
Watford, Hertfordshire, WD17 2FF
Area of Operation: Greater London, South East England
Tel: 01923 224275
Fax: 01923 255005
Email: shaun@w.rumballsedgwick.co.uk
Web: www.rumballsedgwick.co.uk

**SIERRA DESIGNS - ARCHITECTURAL
AND BUILDING CONSULTANTS**
Carfeld House, Pinfold Lane,
Kirk Smeaton, North Yorkshire, WF8 3JT
Area of Operation: UK & Ireland
Tel: 01977 621360
Fax: 01977 621365
Email: info@sierradesigns.co.uk
Web: www.sierradesigns.co.uk

SNP ASSOCIATES
248 Kingston Road, New Malden, Surrey, KT3 3RN
Area of Operation: Worldwide
Tel: 0208 942 6238
Email: snp@snpassociates.co.uk
Web: www.snpassociates.co.uk

SPEER DADE PLANNING CONSULTANTS
10 Stonepound Road,
Hassocks, West Sussex, BN6 8PP
Area of Operation: UK (Excluding Ireland)
Tel: 01273 843737 **Fax:** 01273 842155
Email: Roy@stonepound.co.uk
Web: www.stonepound.co.uk

**TROTMAN & TAYLOR
ARCHITECTURAL CONSULTANTS**
40 Deer Park, Ivybridge, Devon, PL21 0HY
Area of Operation: UK (Excluding Ireland)
Tel: 01752 698410
Fax: 01752 698410
Email: enquiries@trotmantaylor.com
Web: www.trotmantaylor.com

WHEATMAN PLANNING LIMITED
The Gables, Church Lane,
Haddiscoe, Norwich, Norfolk, NR14 6PB
Area of Operation: East England
Tel: 01502 677636 **Fax:** 01502 677636
Email: simon@wheatmanplanning.co.uk
Web: www.wheatmanplanning.co.uk

PROJECT MANAGERS

KEY
OTHER: ▽ Reclaimed ⌂ On-line shopping
✏ Bespoke ✋ Hand-made ECO Ecological

ACCESS ARCHITECTS LTD
Mortimer House, 49 Church Street,
Theale, Berkshire, RG7 5BX
Area of Operation: South East England, South West England and South Wales
Tel: 0118 930 4440
Email: david@access-architects.co.uk
Web: www.access-architects.co.uk

ANDERSON SPARK LTD
Courtyard Studio, Cowley Farm, Aylesbury Road,
Cuddington, Buckinghamshire, HP18 0AD
Area of Operation: Greater London, Midlands & Mid Wales, South East England
Tel: 01296 747121 **Fax:** 01296 747703
Email: info@andersonspark.co.uk
Web: www.andersonspark.co.uk

ARCHITECTURE VERTE LIMITED
10 Glenmore Business Centre,
Hopton Park Industrial Estate, Devizes, SN10 2EQ
Area of Operation: Greater London, Midlands & Mid Wales, South East England, South West England and South Wales
Tel: 01380 739139 **Fax:** 01380 739159
Email: mail@verte.co.uk **Web:** www.verte.co.uk

BARRON & PARTNERS
382 Winchester Road,
Southampton, Hampshire, SO16 7DH
Area of Operation: South East England
Tel: 023 8070 5155 **Fax:** 023 8070 4333
Email: admin@barron-and-partners.co.uk
Web: www.barron-and-partners.co.uk

BILLINGTON CONSULTANCY LTD
Unit 2a, Station Yard, Station Road,
Sandbach, Cheshire, CW11 3JG
Area of Operation: UK (Excluding Ireland)
Tel: 07774 203117 **Email:** chrisb@billington.co.uk
Web: www.billington.co.uk

BROWNE SMITH BAKER
11-12 Portland Terrace,
Newcastle upon Tyne, Tyne & Wear, NE2 1QQ
Area of Operation: UK (Excluding Ireland)
Tel: 0191 212 1133 **Fax:** 0191 212 0777
Email: info-n@brownesmithbaker.com
Web: www.brownesmithbaker.com

BUILDING PLANS LTD
Unit 10 Beech Avenue, Taverham,
Norwich, Norfolk, NR8 6HW
Area of Operation: UK (Excluding Ireland)
Tel: 01603 868377 **Fax:** 01603 868412
Email: john@constructionhelp.co.uk
Web: www.constructionhelp.co.uk

BUILDINGDOCTORS.CO.UK
96 Farringdon Road, Clerkenwell, London, EC1R 3EA
Area of Operation: East England, Greater London, North West England and North Wales
Tel: 0845 060 0040 **Fax:** 0845 060 0046
Email: architect@building-doctors.com
Web: www.buildingdoctors.co.uk

CDL PROJECT SERVICES LTD
The Studio, Mill Cottage, Sedgeberrow,
Worcester, Worcestershire, WR11 7UA
Area of Operation: UK (Excluding Ireland)
Tel: 0870 062 0018 **Fax:** 01386 882217

CO-ORDINATED CONSTRUCTION SERVICES
18 Kiln Road, Crawley Down, West Sussex, RH10 4JY
Area of Operation: South East England
Tel: 01342 714511 **Fax:** 01342 714511
Email: info@coordsvcs.com
Web: www.coordsvcs.com

DESIGN AND MATERIALS LTD
Lawn Road, Carlton in Lindrick,
Nottinghamshire, S81 9LB
Area of Operation: UK (Excluding Ireland)
Tel: 01909 540123 **Fax:** 01909 730605
Email: enquiries@designandmaterials.uk.com
Web: www.designandmaterials.uk.com ⌂

DESIGN PLUS (KENT) LTD
59 Marshall Crescent, Broadstairs, Kent, CT10 2HR
Area of Operation: UK (Excluding Ireland)
Tel: 01843 602218
Email: designpluskent@btinternet.com
Web: www.designpluskent.co.uk

DIL GREEN ARCHITECT
206 Lyham Road, Brixton, Greater London, SW2 5NR
Area of Operation: UK (Excluding Ireland)
Tel: 0208 671 2242 **Fax:** 0208 674 9757
Email: w_dilgreenarchitect.co.uk
Web: www.dilgreenarchitect.co.uk

ENCRAFT LTD
Perseus House, 3 Chapel Court, Holly Walk,
Leamington Spa, Warwickshire, CV32 4YS
Area of Operation: UK & Ireland
Tel: 01926 312159 **Fax:** 01926 882636
Email: enquiries@encraft.co.uk
Web: www.encraft.co.uk ⌂

ENGLISHAUS CHARTERED ARCHITECTS LTD
30 Lawrence Road, Hampton, Middlesex, TW12 2RJ
Area of Operation: Greater London, South East England, South West England and South Wales
Tel: 0208 255 0595 **Fax:** 0208 287 3441
Email: enquiries@englishaus.co.uk
Web: www.englishaus.co.uk

G.M.MOORE & ASSOCIATES
Old Laughton Sawmills, Park Lane,
Laughton, East Sussex, BN8 6BP
Area of Operation: South East England
Tel: 01323 811689 **Fax:** 01323 811325
Email: sales@gmassociates.co.uk
Web: www.gmassociates.co.uk

GEORGE BLACK ARCHITECT
12 Kingsknowe Crescent,
Edinburgh, Lothian, EH14 2JZ
Area of Operation: Scotland
Tel: 0131 443 9898
Email: george@gbarch.abel.co.uk
Web: www.gbarch.abel.co.uk

GRAHAM G BISHOP - CHARTERED SURVEYORS
9 Church Lane Drive, Coulsdon, Surrey, CR5 3RG
Area of Operation: Greater London, South East England
Tel: 01737 558473 **Fax:** 01737 558473
Email: graham@grahamgbishop.co.uk
Web: www.grahamgbishop.co.uk

GRINDEY CONSULTING
9 Brook Avenue, Swinton, Manchester, M27 5WG
Area of Operation: North West England and North Wales
Tel: 07773 371488
Email: grindeyconsulting@hotmail.com
Web: www.grindeyconsulting.com

HALLIDAY CLARK LIMITED
Salts Wharf, Ashley Lane, Shipley,
Bradford, West Yorkshire, BD17 7DB
Area of Operation: UK & Ireland
Tel: 01274 589888 **Fax:** 01274 589922
Email: info@hallidayclark.co.uk
Web: www.hallidayclark.co.uk

HCT CONSTRUCTION CONSULTANTS LTD
Mercury House, The Court Yard,
Roman Way, Coleshill, Warwickshire, B46 1HQ
Area of Operation: UK (Excluding Ireland)
Tel: 01675 466010 **Fax:** 01675 464543
Email: jamie.timmins@hctcc.co.uk
Web: www.hctcc.co.uk

HORIZON CONSTRUCTION MANAGEMENT
884 The Crescent, Colchester Business Park,
Colchester, Essex, CO4 9YQ
Area of Operation: UK (Excluding Ireland)
Tel: 01206 755415 **Fax:** 01206 755425
Email: info@horizonconstruction.co.uk
Web: www.horizonconstruction.co.uk

J G HOOD & ASSOCIATES LTD
50 High Street, Bruton, Somerset, BA10 0AN
Area of Operation: Midlands & Mid Wales, South East England, South West England and South Wales
Tel: 01749 812139
Fax: 0870 133 3776
Email: mail@jghood-assoc.co.uk
Web: www.jghood-assoc.co.uk

J.S. BUILDING CONSULTANCY
53 Hawthorn Road, Yeadon,
Leeds, West Yorkshire, LS19 7UT
Area of Operation: UK (Excluding Ireland)
Tel: 0113 250 1303
Email: jsharples@ricsonline.org
Web: www.ukbuildingconsultancy.co.uk

**JEREMY WARD INDEPENDENT
BUILDING CONSULTANT**
Sootfield Green, Charlton Road,
Preston, Hertfordshire, SG4 7TB
Area of Operation: East England, Greater London, South East England
Tel: 01462 438487
Email: sootfieldgreen@aol.com
Web: www.jwibc.co.uk

JNA ARCHITECTS
9 East Park, Southgate,
Crawley, West Sussex, RH10 6AN
Area of Operation: South East England
Tel: 01293 439323 **Fax:** 01293 530160
Email: james@jna-architects.co.uk
Web: www.jna-architects.co.uk

JOSEPH R NIXON PROJECT MANAGEMENT
Brookview 52a Foxcotte Road, Charlton,
Andover, Hampshire, SP10 4AT
Area of Operation: Greater London, South East England, South West England and South Wales
Tel: 01264 364232 **Fax:** 01264 364232
Email: jrn-pm@tiscali.co.uk

KMD ARCHITECTURAL SERVICES LTD
Second Floor, 1 Station Road,
Whitley Bay, Tyne & Wear, NE26 2QY
Area of Operation: UK (Excluding Ireland)
Tel: 0191 253 7110
Fax: 0871 211 0363
Email: info@kmd-limited.co.uk
Web: www.kmd-limited.co.uk ⌂

LARNER SING
The Barn, Rode Hill, Rode,
Frome, Somerset, BA11 6PU
Area of Operation: South East England, South West England and South Wales
Tel: 01373 830527
Fax: 01373 830527
Email: ian@larner-sing.co.uk
Web: www.larner-sing.com

MARMOT ASSOCIATES
Higher Tor Farm, Poundsgate,
Newton Abbot, Devon, TQ13 7PD
Area of Operation: South West England and South Wales
Tel: 01364 631566 **Fax:** 01364 631556
Email: marmot-tor@zen.co.uk
Web: www.marmot-tor.com

NCB ASSOCIATES LTD
Gate House, Fretheron Road,
Welwyn Garden City, Hertfordshire, AL8 6NS
Area of Operation: UK (Excluding Ireland)
Tel: 0845 230 9897
Email: enquiry@ncbassociates.co.uk
Web: www.ncbassociates.co.uk

NEAR ZERO CO2 LIMITED
Suite 2.9 Howard House, Howard Street,
North Shields, Tyne & Wear, NE30 1AR
Area of Operation: UK (Excluding Ireland)
Tel: 0191 272 8228
Email: enquiry@nearzero.co.uk
Web: www.nearzero.co.uk ⌂

NICHOLAS RAY ASSOCIATES
13-15 Convert Garden, Cambridge,
Cambridgeshire, CB1 2HS
Area of Operation: UK & Ireland
Tel: 01223 464455
Email: design@nray-arch.co.uk
Web: www.nray-arch.co.uk

**O'EVE DON INTERIORS &
THE KITCHEN PLANNER**
9 Maple Drive, Castle Park, Mallow, Co Cork, Ireland
Area of Operation: Ireland Only
Tel: +353 (0)22 20858 **Fax:** +353 (0)22 20858
Email: oevedoninteriors@eircom.net

OTT PROJECTS LTD
2 Whitney Drive, Stevenage, Hertfordshire, SG1 4BG
Area of Operation: East England, Greater London, South East England
Tel: 01438 223333 **Fax:** 01438 359594
Email: info@ott-projects.co.uk
Web: www.ott-projects.co.uk

PLANS & DRAWINGS.COM
5 Station Road, Stepps,
Glasgow, Lanarkshire, G33 6HB
Area of Operation: Scotland
Tel: 0141 404 0136 **Fax:** 0141 779 5370
Email: info@homecad.co.uk
Web: www.plansanddrawings.com

PROPERTYPORTAL.COM
Brookfield House, Ford Lane, Frilford,
Abingdon, Oxfordshire, OX13 5NT
Area of Operation: UK (Excluding Ireland)
Tel: 0870 380 0520 **Fax:** 0870 380 0521
Email: info@propertyportal.com
Web: www.propertyportal.com

ROMAN PROJECTS LTD
Roman Heights, Llanfair Hill,
Llandovery, Carmarthenshire, SA20 0YF
Area of Operation: South West England and South Wales
Tel: 01550 720533 **Fax:** 01550 720 533
Email: romanprojects@aol.com

SELF BUILD PRO
Belmont Business Centre, Brook Lane,
Endon, Staffordshire, ST9 9EZ
Area of Operation: Worldwide
Tel: 01782 503322
Fax: 01782 505127
Email: enquiries@self-build-pro.com
Web: www.self-build-pro.com

SELFBUILD-GROUP.CO.UK
Area of Operation: UK & Ireland
Email: enquiries@selfbuild-group.co.uk
Web: www.selfbuild-group.co.uk

SIERRA DESIGNS - ARCHITECTURAL AND BUILDING CONSULTANTS
Carfeld House, Pinfold Lane,
Kirk Smeaton, North Yorkshire, WF8 3JT
Area of Operation: UK & Ireland
Tel: 01977 621360
Fax: 01977 621365
Email: info@sierradesigns.co.uk
Web: www.sierradesigns.co.uk

SIMON J CUSHING CHARTERED ARCHITECT
28 Wood Lane, Greasby, Wirral, Merseyside, CH49 2PU
Area of Operation: North West England and North Wales
Tel: 0151 677 9188
Fax: 0151 677 9188
Email: simonjcushing@btconnect.com

SNP ASSOCIATES
248 Kingston Road, New Malden, Surrey, KT3 3RN
Area of Operation: Worldwide
Tel: 0208 942 6238
Email: snp@snpassociates.co.uk
Web: www.snpassociates.co.uk

ST DESIGN CONSULTANTS
Othona House, Waterside, Bradwell on Sea,
Southminster, Essex, CM0 7QT
Area of Operation: UK (Excluding Ireland)
Tel: 01621 776736
Fax: 01621 776736
Email: info@stdesignconsultants.co.uk
Web: www.stdesignconsultants.co.uk

STRAWBALE BUILDING COMPANY UK
34 Rosebery Way, Tring, Hertfordshire, HP23 5DS
Area of Operation: Europe
Tel: 01442 825421
Email: chug@strawbale-building.co.uk
Web: www.strawbale-building.co.uk

TEAM SURVEYS LIMITED
St Austell Bay Business Park, Par Moor Road,
St Austell, Cornwall, PL25 3RF
Area of Operation: Europe
Tel: 01726 816069
Fax: 01726 814611
Email: email@teamsurveys.com
Web: www.teamsurveys.com

XSPACE
99 Woodlands Avenue, Poole, Dorset, BH15 4EG
Area of Operation: South East England, South West England and South Wales
Tel: 01202 665387 **Fax:** 01202 380235
Email: design@xspace.biz
Web: www.xspace.biz

Please mention The Homebuilder's Handbook when you call

QUANTITY SURVEYORS

KEY
OTHER: ▽ Reclaimed 🛒 On-line shopping
🖐 Bespoke 🤚 Hand-made ECO Ecological

BILLINGTON CONSULTANCY LTD
Unit 2a, Station Yard, Station Road,
Sandbach, Cheshire, CW11 3JG
Area of Operation: UK (Excluding Ireland)
Tel: 07774 203117
Email: chrisb@billington.co.uk
Web: www.billington.co.uk

BUILDINGDOCTORS.CO.UK
96 Farringdon Road, Clerkenwell, London, EC1R 3EA
Area of Operation: East England, Greater London, North West England and North Wales
Tel: 0845 060 0040 **Fax:** 0845 060 0046
Email: architect@building-doctors.com
Web: www.buildingdoctors.co.uk

CONSTRUCTION COST SOLUTIONS
September Cottage, 1A Wigwam Close,
Poynton, Stockport, Cheshire, SK12 1XF
Area of Operation: Midlands & Mid Wales, North East England, North West England and North Wales
Tel: 01625 875488
Email: david@constructioncostsolutions.co.uk
Web: www.constructioncostsolutions.co.uk

DEREK GOUGH ASSOCIATES
Toft Smithy, Toft Road,
Knutsford, Cheshire, WA16 9PA
Area of Operation: UK (Excluding Ireland)
Tel: 01565 751500 **Fax:** 01565 751330
Email: derekgough@dgough.co.uk
Web: www.dgough.co.uk

HCT CONSTRUCTION CONSULTANTS LTD
Mercury House, The Court Yard,
Roman Way, Coleshill, Warwickshire, B46 1HQ
Area of Operation: UK (Excluding Ireland)
Tel: 01675 466010 **Fax:** 01675 464543
Email: jamie.timmins@hctcc.co.uk
Web: www.hctcc.co.uk

JOSEPH R NIXON PROJECT MANAGEMENT
Brookview 52a Foxcotte Road,
Charlton, Andover, Hampshire, SP10 4AT
Area of Operation: Greater London, South East England, South West England and South Wales
Tel: 01264 364232 **Fax:** 01264 364232
Email: jrn-pm@tiscali.co.uk

MARMOT ASSOCIATES
Higher Tor Farm, Poundsgate,
Newton Abbot, Devon, TQ13 7PD
Area of Operation: South West England and South Wales
Tel: 01364 631566 **Fax:** 01364 631556
Email: marmot-tor@zen.co.uk
Web: www.marmot-tor.com

PAUL A STOWELL
'Sorriso', Farleigh Road, Cliddesden,
Basingstoke, Hampshire, RG25 2JL
Area of Operation: Greater London, South East England, South West England and South Wales
Tel: 01256 320470 **Fax:** 01256 320470
Email: paulstowell@constructionplans.co.uk
Web: www.constructionplans.co.uk

QUANTI-QUOTE
Trewint, Main Street, Shap, Penrith, Cumbria, CA10 3NH
Area of Operation: UK & Ireland
Tel: 01931 716810 **Email:** peter@quantiquote.co.uk
Web: www.quantiquote.co.uk

RED FIELD PROPERTY CONSULTANTS LTD
23 Pound Field, Stoke Gabriel, Totnes, Devon, TQ9 6QA
Area of Operation: UK (Excluding Ireland)
Tel: 01803 782019 **Fax:** 01803 782019
Email: info@red-field.co.uk
Web: www.red-field.co.uk

SELF BUILD PRO
Belmont Business Centre, Brook Lane,
Endon, Staffordshire, ST9 9EZ
Area of Operation: Worldwide
Tel: 01782 503322
Fax: 01782 505127
Email: enquiries@self-build-pro.com
Web: www.self-build-pro.com

SIERRA DESIGNS - ARCHITECTURAL AND BUILDING CONSULTANTS
Carfeld House, Pinfold Lane,
Kirk Smeaton, North Yorkshire, WF8 3JT
Area of Operation: UK & Ireland
Tel: 01977 621360
Fax: 01977 621365
Email: info@sierradesigns.co.uk
Web: www.sierradesigns.co.uk

LANDSCAPE & GARDEN DESIGNERS

KEY
OTHER: ▽ Reclaimed 🛒 On-line shopping
🖐 Bespoke 🤚 Hand-made ECO Ecological

ACRES WILD LTD
1 Helm Cottages, Nuthurst,
Horsham, West Sussex, RH13 6RG
Area of Operation: UK & Ireland
Tel: 01403 891084 **Fax:** 01403 891084
Email: enquiries@acreswild.co.uk
Web: www.acreswild.co.uk

ALICE BOWE - ENGLISH LANDSCAPE & GARDEN DESIGN (LONDON)
9a Welldon Crescent, London, HA1 1QU
Area of Operation: UK (Excluding Ireland)
Tel: 0845 838 2649
Email: alice@alicebowe.co.uk
Web: www.alicebowe.co.uk

ALICE BOWE - ENGLISH LANDSCAPE & GARDEN DESIGN (NOTTINGHAM)
1 Briar Gate, Nottingham, Nottinghamshire, NG10 4BN
Area of Operation: Greater London, Midlands & Mid Wales, South East England
Tel: 0845 838 2649
Email: alice@alicebowe.co.uk
Web: www.alicebowe.co.uk

BRADSTONE GARDEN
Aggregate Industries UK Ltd, Hulland Ward,
Ashbourne, Derbyshire, DE6 3ET
Area of Operation: UK (Excluding Ireland)
Tel: 01335 372222 **Fax:** 01335 370973
Email: bradstone.garden@aggregate.com
Web: www.bradstone.com

CATHERINE HEATHERINGTON DESIGNS
9 Cecil Road, London, N10 2BU
Area of Operation: UK (Excluding Ireland)
Tel: 0208 374 2321
Email: gardens@chdesigns.co.uk
Web: www.chdesigns.co.uk

CATHERINE THOMAS LANDSCAPE AND GARDEN DESIGN
Fisherton Mill, 108 Fisherton Street,
Salisbury, Wiltshire, SP2 7QY
Area of Operation: UK & Ireland
Tel: 01722 339936
Fax: 01722 339936
Email: catherines_gardens@hotmail.com
Web: www.catherinethomas.co.uk

CHARLESWORTH DESIGN
21 Derbyshire Road, Sale, Cheshire, M33 3EB
Area of Operation: North West England and North Wales
Tel: 0161 905 3871
Email: robertsfrier@hotmail.com
Web: www.charlesworthdesign.com

CHERRY MILLS GARDEN DESIGN
Flora Cottage, The Drive,
Godalming, Surrey, GU7 1PH
Area of Operation: South East England
Tel: 01483 421499 **Fax:** 01483 418678
Email: cmills@cmgardendesign.com
Web: www.cmgardendesign.com

CHRISTOPHER MAGUIRE ARCHITECT AND GARDEN DESIGNER
15 Harston Road, Newton,
Cambridge, Cambridgeshire, CB2 5PA
Area of Operation: East England
Tel: 01223 872800
Web: www.christophermaguire.co.uk

CORK TOFT PARTNERSHIP LTD
Greenbank, Howick Cross Lane,
Penwortham, Preston, Lancashire, PR1 0NS
Area of Operation: North West England and North Wales
Tel: 01772 749014 /5 **Fax:** 01772 749034
Email: mail@corktoft.com

COURTYARD GARDEN DESIGN
The Workshop, 32 Broadway Avenue,
East Twickenham, Greater London, TW1 1RH
Area of Operation: Worldwide
Tel: 0208 892 0118
Fax: 0208 892 0118/0024
Email: sally.cgd@btconnect.com
Web: www.courtyardgardendesign.co.uk

DESIGN AND MATERIALS LTD
Lawn Road, Carlton in Lindrick,
Nottinghamshire, S81 9LB
Area of Operation: UK (Excluding Ireland)
Tel: 01909 540123
Fax: 01909 730605
Email: enquiries@designandmaterials.uk.com
Web: www.designandmaterials.uk.com

DIZZY SHOEMARK (UK) LIMITED
Lingmell Crescent, Seascale, Cumbria, CA20 1JX
Area of Operation: North East England, North West England and North Wales
Tel: 01946 721767
Fax: 01946 721618
Email: aspects@dizzyshoemark.com
Web: www.dizzyshoemark.com

EAST OF EDEN PLANTS
38 St Andrews Street, Millbrook,
Torpoint, Cornwall, PL10 1BE
Area of Operation: UK & Ireland
Tel: 01752 822782
Email: info@eastofedenplants.co.uk
Web: www.eastofedenplants.co.uk

ENGLISH GARDEN DESIGN ASSOCIATES LTD
The Annexe, Ponchydown Farm, Blackborough,
Cullompton, Devon, Exeter, Devon, EX15 2HQ
Area of Operation: South West England and South Wales
Tel: 01884 266188 **Fax:** 01884 266188
Email: hugh.oconnell@btopenworld.com
Web: www.ukgardendesigner.com

ENGLISHAUS CHARTERED ARCHITECTS LTD
30 Lawrence Road, Hampton, Middlesex, TW12 2RJ
Area of Operation: Greater London, South East England, South West England and South Wales
Tel: 0208 255 0595 **Fax:** 0208 287 3441
Email: enquiries@englishaus.co.uk
Web: www.englishaus.co.uk

FISHER TOMLIN
74 Sydney Road, Wimbledon, London, SW20 8EF
Area of Operation: Europe
Tel: 0208 542 0683
Email: info@fishertomlin.com
Web: www.fishertomlin.com

GILLIAN TEMPLE ASSOCIATES
Capel House, Capel Road, Orlestone,
Hamstreet, Ashford, Kent, TN26 2EH
Area of Operation: UK (Excluding Ireland)
Tel: 01233 733073
Email: gillian@gilliantemple.co.uk
Web: www.gilliantemple.co.uk

HILLIER LANDSCAPES
Ampfield House, Ampfield,
Romsey, Hampshire, SO51 9PA
Area of Operation: South East England, South West
England and South Wales
Tel: 01794 368855 **Fax:** 01794 368866
Email: hillierlandscapes@btinternet.com
Web: www.hillier-landscapes.co.uk

HONLEY GARDEN DESIGN LTD
8 Well Hill, Honley, Holmfirth,
West Yorkshire, HD9 6JF
Area of Operation: Europe
Tel: 01484 660783
Email: barrykellington@aol.com
Web: www.lifestylegardens.co.uk

JANE FOLLIS GARDEN DESIGN
71 Eythrope Road, Stone,
Buckinghamshire, HP17 8PH
Area of Operation: South East England
Tel: 01296 747775 **Fax:** 01296 747775
Email: jfgdndesign@aol.com
Web: www.jfgardendesign.co.uk

JANO WILLIAMS GARDEN DESIGN
54 Berkeley Road, Westbury Park, Bristol, BS6 7PL
Area of Operation: Worldwide
Tel: 0117 914 1078
Email: janowilliams@blueyonder.co.uk
Web: www.janowilliams.com

JILL FENWICK
53 Hampstead Road, Dorking, Surrey, RH4 3AE
Area of Operation: Greater London, Midlands & Mid
Wales, South East England
Tel: 01306 889465 **Fax:** 01306 889465
Email: jill.fenwick@gmail.com
Web: www.privategardendesign.co.uk

JOHN NASH ASSOCIATES
19 Cannon Street, St. Albans, Hertfordshire, AL3 5JR
Area of Operation: Greater London, South East England
Tel: 01727 869989
Fax: 01727 869491
Email: jnassoc@globalnet.co.uk
Web: www.johnnashassociates.co.uk

JOHN SOLOMON DESIGN LIMITED
48 Ham Street, Richmond, Surrey, TW10 7HT
Area of Operation: Worldwide
Tel: 020 8940 2444
Fax: 020 8940 1188
Email: mail@jsajsd.com
Web: www.jsajsd.com

JONATHAN PRINGLE GARDEN DESIGN
Chestnut Cottage, Mill Lane, Stradishall,
New Market, Suffolk, CB8 8PZ
Area of Operation: East England, Greater London,
Midlands & Mid Wales
Tel: 01279 303367 **Fax:** 01279 303367
Email: jonathan.pringle@ntlworld.com

JULIET SARGEANT
GARDENS & PRIVATE LANDSCAPES
39 Falmer Road, Rottingdean,
Brighton, East Sussex, BN2 7DA
Area of Operation: UK & Ireland
Tel: 01273 300587
Email: julietdesigns@supanet.com
Web: www.julietdesigns.co.uk

KEITH PULLAN GARDEN DESIGN
1 Amotherby Close, Amotherby,
Malton, North Yorkshire, YO17 6TG
Area of Operation: Midlands & Mid Wales, North
East England, North West England and North Wales
Tel: 01653 693885
Email: keithpullan@fastmail.fm
Web: www.keithpullan.co.uk

KEY GARDEN DESIGN
Hydra, West Wickham Road,
Horseheath, Cambridge, Cambridgeshire, CB1 6QA
Area of Operation: East England
Tel: 01223 893437 **Fax:** 01223 894212
Email: kim.wendelken@btinternet.com

LAURENCE MAUNDER
GARDEN DESIGN & CONSULTANCY
Newton Cottage, Fitzhead,
Taunton, Somerset, TA4 3JW
Area of Operation: South West England and South Wales
Tel: 01823 401208 **Fax:** 01823 401208
Email: info@laurencemaunder.co.uk
Web: www.laurencemaunder.co.uk

MICHAEL DAY GARDEN DESIGN
The Chalet, Marston Meysey,
Swindon, Wiltshire, SN6 6LQ
Area of Operation: Midlands & Mid Wales, South
West England and South Wales
Tel: 01285 810486 **Fax:** 01285 810970
Email: info@michaeldaygardendesign.co.uk
Web: www.michaeldaygardendesign.co.uk

MIRIAM BOOK GARDEN DESIGNS
50 Hill Drive, Hove, East Sussex, BN3 6QL
Area of Operation: Greater London, South East England
Tel: 01273 541600 **Fax:** 01273 541600
Email: miriam@gardenbook.co.uk
Web: www.gardenbook.co.uk

PETER THOMAS ASSOCIATES GARDEN DESIGN
113 High Street, Codicote, Hertfordshire, SG4 8UA
Area of Operation: East England, Greater London,
Midlands & Mid Wales, South East England, South
West England and South Wales
Tel: 01438 821408 **Email:** info@ptadesign.com
Web: www.ptadesign.com

PICKARD GARDEN & LANDSCAPE DESIGN
45 Business Village, Dyson Way, Staffordshire
Technology Park, Beaconside, Stafford, ST18 0TW
Area of Operation: Europe
Tel: 01785 850240 **Email:** admin@pickardsgd.com
Web: www.pickardsgd.com

SAM MCGOWAN DESIGN
26 Dunrobin Place, Edinburgh, EH3 5HZ
Area of Operation: Worldwide
Tel: 0131 343 6536
Email: sammcg.edinburgh@virgin.net
Web: www.sam-mcgowan.co.uk

THE PARSONS GARDEN LTD
2 Walter's Yard, West Stockwell Street,
Colchester, Essex, CO1 1HD
Area of Operation: UK (Excluding Ireland)
Tel: 01206 570440 **Fax:** 01206 561091
Email: design@theparsonsgarden.co.uk
Web: www.theparsonsgarden.co.uk

UP THE GARDEN PATH
10 Paget Drive, Burntwood, Staffordshire, WS7 1HP
Area of Operation: Midlands & Mid Wales, North
West England and North Wales
Tel: 01543 670342 **Fax:** 01543 670342
Email: david@upthegardenpath.net
Web: www.upthegardenpath.net

WIZARD GARDENS
The Hassdocks, Ipswich Road,
Stratford St Mary, Colchester, Essex, CO7 6PG
Area of Operation: Europe
Tel: 01473 311117 **Fax:** 01473 311970
Email: wizard.gardens@virgin.net
Web: www.wizardgardens.co.uk

WIZARD GARDENS
The Hassocks, Ipswich Road,
Stratford St Mary, Colchester, Essex, CO7 6PG
Area of Operation: UK & Ireland
Tel: 01473 311117 **Fax:** 01473 311970
Email: wizard.gardens@virgin.net
Web: www.wizardgardens.co.uk

NOTES

Company Name ....

Address ....

email ....
Web ....

Company Name ....

Address ....

email ....
Web ....

Company Name ....

Address ....

email ....
Web ....

Company Name ....

Address ....

email ....
Web ....

Company Name ....

Address ....

email ....
Web ....

Company Name ....

Address ....

email ....
Web ....

Company Name ....

Address ....

email ....
Web ....

Company Name ....

Address ....

email ....
Web ....

Company Name ....

Address ....

email ....
Web ....

Company Name ....

Address ....

email ....
Web ....

CONSULTANTS, LABOUR & FINANCE

ALL THE PRACTICAL ADVICE AND TIPS YOU NEED TO ADD SPACE AND VALUE TO YOUR HOME

Move or improve? magazine, your bible to help guide you through the process of extending or remodelling to create your dream home

FEATURES:

Design Master Class:
Making efficient use of space.

The Design Doctor:
Design expert Michael Holmes helps two readers find solutions to their improving dilemmas

The Guide:
A complete guide to renovating and extending your home, with advice on planning, building regulations, finance, etc…

Renovation Price Book:
Full estimated costings for different aspects of remodelling

Special features, for example:
Loft conversion guide; how to buy replacement windows; build, buy or renovate?; Wooden floors – complete design guide.

Real life Projects:
Inspiring and practical readers' case studies including cellar conversions, luxurious new sunrooms, kitchen extensions and perfect side extensions.

On sale now in all good newsagents and supermarkets

Image courtesy of www.plotfinder.net

SPONSORED BY PLOTFINDER.NET AND SITEFINDERIRELAND.COM
Tel 01527 834436 Web www.plotfinder.net / www.sitefinderireland.com

www.plotfinder.net
THE UK'S LAND AND RENOVATION DATABASE

www.sitefinderireland.com

Finding a Reputable Tradesman

There may be a lot of them around, but finding a tradesman who is both reputable and reliable can be a tricky business.

Perhaps the best way to find a good tradesman is old fashioned word-of-mouth. If a plumber, window fitter or electrician has done a good job at people's homes you know in your area, then it's fairly safe to say he or she will do the same for you.

Tradespeople can say what they like in their advertising, but nothing that can beat a good, honest recommendation from an impartial friend or associate. Even if someone comes with a glowing recommendation, it's still worth making sure they are fully qualified and registered to carry out the work. For example, electricians should be Part P registered and plumbers installing central heating should be Corgi registered. You should also ask for examples or written recommendations of a tradesman's work.

If you don't have a personal recommendation to go on, then a reliable place to start your search is speaking to an appropriate trade association.

> Iain Macdonald of the UK Trades Confederation provides some helpful pointers and explains why tradesmen need to be 'competent' to carry out works on a domestic property.

It shouldn't be a guessing game as to whether a tradesperson is reputable or not. There are numerous trade associations and vetting schemes in place to protect consumers.

Most trade associations have a directory of vetted professionals who have agreed to follow a code of conduct. To become a member of an association, a tradesperson will normally have to provide references and financial information. Once a tradesperson has been vetted, he or she will be able to display a logo on their website, van or business stationery, as proof of their credibility. But even if a tradesperson is displaying a logo, it's a good idea to contact the association

to confirm the membership is valid.

If you don't have access to the Internet, a good place to start your search for a trade association is the Yellow Pages. Once you have found the association, check it is reputable by making sure it has:

• a strict joining criteria

• a code of conduct

• a complaints procedure

• a protective scheme, for example a homeowner's contract

A good trade association will advise on new regulations affecting the trade. The most recent changes within the construction industry have been for electricians and window installers.

Check your electrician is Part P registered, as you'll need a certificate, provided by the electrician, showing the installation is compliant with the law. Tradesmen installing double glazing should be FENSA registered.

If you use a professional who isn't compliant, then you will have to ask a building inspector to certify the work, leaving a chance that the work may not meet the Building Regulations.

UK Trades Confederation bio

Membership of the UK Trades Confederation provides businesses with a recognised accreditation and customers with the peace of mind of knowing that you are dealing with a company that cares about its image and standards.

For further information contact The UK Trades Confederation on 0800 018 4442, email mail@uktc.org or visit www.uktc.org

Finally, most professional tradespeople should have a contract. If they don't, then a reputable trade association will be able to provide you with a JCT (Joint Contracts Tribunal) or a similar homeowner's contract.

Trading Standards receive over 100,000 complaints each year about building tradesmen, a statistic that highlights the need for trade associations. Such organisations are in place to protect consumers and separate the rogues from the real professionals.

TRADE, REGULATORY BODIES AND ASSOCIATIONS

KEY

OTHER: ▽ Reclaimed ⌐ On-line shopping
◇ Bespoke ✋ Hand-made ECO Ecological

AMERICAN SOFTWOODS
25 Castle Street, High Wycombe,
Buckinghamshire, HP13 6RU
Area of Operation: Europe
Tel: 01494 451000 **Fax:** 01494 451100
Email: info@americansoftwoods.com
Web: www.americansoftwoods.com

ASSOCIATION OF BUILDING ENGINEERS
Lutyens House, Billing Brook Road,
Northampton, Northamptonshire, NN3 8NW
Area of Operation: Worldwide
Tel: 01604 404121
Fax: 01604 784220
Email: building.engineers@abe.org.uk
Web: www.abe.org.uk ⌐

ASSOCIATION OF PLUMBING & HEATING CONTRACTORS (APHC)
14 Ensign House, Ensign Business Centre,
Westwood Way, Coventry, West Midlands, CV4 8JA
Area of Operation: UK (Excluding Ireland)
Tel: 02476 470626 **Fax:** 02476 470942
Email: enquiries@aphc.co.uk
Web: www.aphc.co.uk

ASSOCIATION OF SCOTTISH HARDWOOD SAWMILLERS
Area of Operation: Scotland
Web: www.ashs.co.uk

BASEMENT INFORMATION CENTRE
Riverside House, 4 Meadows Business Park, Station
Approach, Blackwater, Camberley, Surrey, GU17 9AB
Area of Operation: UK (Excluding Ireland)
Tel: 01276 33155 **Fax:** 01276 606801
Email: info@tbic.org.uk
Web: www.tbic.org.uk / www.basements.org.uk

BATHROOM MANUFACTURERS ASSOCIATION
Federation House, Station Road,
Stoke on Trent, Staffordshire, ST4 2RT
Area of Operation: UK & Ireland
Tel: 01782 747123
Fax: 01782 747161
Email: info@bathroom-association.org.uk
Web: www.bathroom-association.org.uk

BRISTOL & SOMERSET RENEWABLE ENERGY ADVICE SERVICE
The Create Centre, Smeaton Road, Bristol, BS1 6XN
Area of Operation: South West England and South Wales
Tel: 0800 512012 **Fax:** 0117 929 9114
Email: info@cse.org.uk
Web: www.cse.org.uk/renewables

BRISTOL & SOMERSET ENERGY EFFICIENCY ADVICE CENTRE
The CREATE Centre, Smeaton Road, Bristol, BS1 6XN
Area of Operation: South West England and South Wales
Tel: 0800 512 012 **Fax:** 0117 929 9114
Email: advice@cse.org.uk
Web: www.cse.org.uk/energyadvice
Product Type: 1, 3

BRITISH ARTIST BLACKSMITHS ASSOCIATION
Anwick Forge, 62 Main Road, Anwick,
Sleaford, Lincolnshire, NG34 9SU
Area of Operation: UK & Ireland
Tel: 01526 830303
Email: babasecretary@anwickforge.co.uk
Web: www.baba.org.uk

BRITISH BLIND AND SHUTTER ASSOCIATION
42 Heath Street, Tamworth, Staffordshire, B79 7JH
Area of Operation: UK & Ireland
Tel: 01827 52337
Fax: 01827 310827
Email: info@bbsa.org.uk
Web: www.bbsa.org.uk

BRITISH CEMENT ASSOCIATION
The concrete Centre, Riverside House,
4 Meadows Business Park, Station Approach,
Blackwater, Camberley, Surrey, GU17 9AB
Area of Operation: UK (Excluding Ireland)
Tel: 01276 608700 **Fax:** 01276 608701
Email: enquiries@concretecentre.com
Web: www.concretecentre.com

BRITISH URETHANE FOAM CONTRACTORS ASSOCIATION
PO Box 12, Haslemere, Surrey, GU27 3AH
Area of Operation: UK (Excluding Ireland)
Tel: 01428 654011 **Fax:** 01428 651401
Email: info@bufca.co.uk **Web:** www.bufca.co.uk

USEFUL INFORMATION

Transform your home with tiles

TTA Members' Retail Showrooms

Avon
Bristol Tile Co Ltd
01179 658000
Ceramic Tile Distributors
01454 326980
Direct Tile Outlet
0117 968403
Exclusive Tile Studio
0117 9428599
N & C Tilestyle
0117 980 3970
Tile & Flooring Centre
01225 310561

Bedford
Ceramics/Discount Tiles
01234 364002

Berkshire
Caversham Tiles Ltd
0118 947 8853
Ceramic Tile Distributors
01635 521 197
Just Tiles Ltd
0118 969 7774
Pavigres-Wich Ltd
01488 674500
Pipers Tiles
01635 871000
QPC Ceramics Ltd
0118 959 4066

Buckinghamshire
Adhesives4tiles
01494 715472
Compass Flooring Ltd
01494 437279
The Ceramic Tile Co Ltd
01494 474736

Cambridgeshire
Eastern Glazed Ceramics
01954 781 010
01733 324 074
Global Tiles
01480 458845

Tile Store Peterborough
01733 566700
Tile Store St. Ives
01487 840471
Trademark Tiles Ltd
01487 825300

Channel Islands
Channel Islands Ceramics
01481 234000

Cheshire
Ceramic Collections Ltd
01244 377755
Profile Contract Interiors
Ltd
01925 721000
Tile Trend Ltd
01244 682440
Tiles UK (Warrington)
01925 419370

Cornwall
Gateway Tile & Slate Ltd
01566 773020
Intertile
01872 553713
Newquay Tile Centre
01637 877741
Tileambitions
01208 814480
Tilewest Ltd
01579 362264
West Country Tile Centre
Ltd
01209 711992

County Durham
Ceramic Tile Distributors
01325 483 414

Coventry
Tubs & Tiles
024 7670 5310

Cumbria
Ceramic Collections Ltd
01228 511714
01539 741155

Ceramic Tile Distributors
01228 536 601
Cumbria Tile Supplies
Ltd
01228 536601
Tile Merchants
01228 631777

Derbyshire
Country Tiles
01773 857184
Nationwide Ceramics Ltd
01773 745797
Simply Tiles Ltd
01332 758828
Stone Emporium
08707 773022
Terra Firma Tiles
01246 456099
01332 755533

Devon
Teign Tile & Stone
01626 879691
International Tiles
01803 527834
N&C Nicobond
01752 339724

Dorset
A & C Dunkley Ltd
01202 526206
Ceramic Tile Distributors
01752 670 278
CSW Tiling Ltd
01202 675836
Leafcutter Design Ltd
01202 716969
New Image Tile Studio
Ltd
01305 781709

East Sussex
Master Tiles
01273 695208

Essex
Ceramic Collections Ltd
01274 531313
Colchester Tile Supplies
Ltd
01206 844161
Eastern Glazed Ceramics
01206 577104
Mastertiler
01708 630638
N & C Tilestyle
01708 680180
01279 621980
N&C Nicobond
020 8586 4600
Pentagon Tile
Distributors Ltd
01279 626662
Tile Centre Ltd
01376 340724
Tile Town Ltd
01206 390096
Tilebase
01992 560565

Gloucester
Ceramic Tile Distributors
01452 527098

Greater London
Bernard J Arnull & Co
Ltd
020 8965 6094
Boyden & Co Ltd
020 8683 6000
European Heritage
Limited
020 7381 6063
Island Stone Natural
Advantage Ltd
0800 083 9351
London Tile Company
0208 847 0441
N&C Tilestyle
020 8269 5960
020 8361 6050

Olympus Tiles Ltd
020 7511 6210
Original Features
(Restorations) Ltd
020 8348 5155
Reed Harris
020 7736 7511
Simmy Ceramics
020 8208 0416
Stonehouse Tiles
London Ltd
020 7237 5375
Swedecor Ltd
0207 554 9700
Tilebase
020 8665 0525
Tileland Limited
020 8965 7773
Walton Ceramics of
Knightsbridge
020 7589 7386
Worlds End Tiles
020 7819 2100
020 7554 9700

Greater Manchester
Ceramic Tile Distributors
01204 707425
Tiles UK Ltd
0161 872 5155

Hampshire
Atlas Ceramics Ltd
01425 621173
Ceramic Tile Distributors
02392 678 338
02380 741307
Colourama Ceramics
Limited
01489 480001
Discount Tiles Limited
01264 359714
DTW Ceramics Ltd
02392 799 007

HTW Tile Distribution
01252 333333
023 8063 9977
KDP Tiles Ltd
023 80270775
N&C Nicobond
01489 779700
On The Tiles
02380 322300
Panache Ceramics Ltd
01489 577043
The Tile Source
01252 333333
01489 797077
023 8063 9977
Tileasy Limited
023 9222 0077
Tileclick Ltd
0870 8519144
Vectis Tile & Stone
01983 810400

Herefordshire
The Bath & Beyond
01432 353053

Hertfordshire
AG Ceramics Ltd
01438 315400
Checkalow Ltd
020 8441 7070
Décor Tiles & Floors Ltd
01923 248531
Fine Ceramics Ltd
01438 315400
Ionic Stone
01727 800 200
Just Tiles
01727 866566
Tile Store Ltd (Tims
Tiles)
01279 813333
Tile Store Ltd
0845 2 60 60 25
Wilton Studios
01472 210820

Humberside
Swedecor Ltd
01482 329 691

Isle of Man
Pacesetter (1981) Ltd
01624 622045
Riverside Ceramics Ltd
01624 619539
The Tile Gallery Ltd
01624 829228

Kent
Bellegrove Ceramics Plc
01322 277877
Ceramic Tile Distributors
01233 650480
01622 757 161
Cerface Construction
Products Ltd
01634 571000
Decoramic Tile Centre
01634 710083
Discount Tile Supplies
01474 351560
Interior Creations Ltd
020 8650 9730
PGA Ceramic Tile
Agency
01622 683375
Sidcup Tile King
020 8309 0482
Tile Magic Plc
01474 369600
Tiles of Tonbridge Ltd
01732 363236

Lancashire
East Lancs Tile Centre
Ltd
01254 57567
Northern Wall & Floor
Ltd
0161 626 3366
Rockform Ltd
01995 643455

Shackerley (Holdings)
Group Ltd
01257 273114
Siramics Ltd
01706 351122
The Discount Tile Trade
Warehouse Ltd
01253 292726
Tile Mart Ltd
01772 258998

Leicestershire
Parkside Tiles
0116 2762532

Lincolnshire
Tile Store Stamford
01780 481900
Tile Trend Ltd
01522 537299

Merseyside
E O Cottam & Sons
01744 23476
Tile Trend Ltd
0151 647 4268
Tile World
0151 650 1443

Middlesex
Ceramic Tile Distributors
020 8941 9781
Middlesex Tile Centre
020 8848 7391
Romanys
020 8421 6324
Tile Store Crews Hill
020 8366 4411
Tileshapes
020 8429 0222

Newcastle-upon-Tyne
Ceramic Tile Distributors
- Factory Tile Shop
0191 265 9359
Ceramic Tile Distributors
0191 276 1506
Lifestile
0191 286 4236

The Tile Association represents all aspects of the wall and floor tile industry in the UK

Tiles will add value to your home and last a lifetime so make sure you get the very best advice. The Tile Association represents all aspects of the wall and floor tile industry in the UK, from manufacture to installation. The Tile Association checks out any tile retailer, fixer or tile fixing company wishing to join their ranks. It checks their experience, abilities, track record and financial health.

If you are buying tiles go to your nearest TTA retailer and buy with confidence.

Tiles are not just a wall and floor covering: they are a fashion statement for your home. Although tiles can last a lifetime, UK home owners are now treating tiles as the Spanish and Italians do – they are changing them every three to four years to keep right up to date with the very latest in interior fashion.

Brighten up that tired kitchen with bright, shiny wall tiles. For heavy foot traffic areas why not tile the floor. Kitchen floors that are tiled are hygienic and trouble free and a hall or porch with a tiled floor won't be damaged by dripping brollies, dribbling wellies and muddy dogs.

With visitors, bathrooms and cloakrooms are also hard to keep fresh. Tiled floors (with under-tile heating if you wish) are easy to keep clean, very smart looking and you don't need to worry if they don't quite shut the shower door! Yes; you can put floor tiles on most suspended wooden floors.

Listed below are retail showroom members of The Tile Association as at 1st September 2006.
For more information and for details of fixers go to

www.tiles.org.uk

or phone 020 8663 0946

Norfolk
Eastern Glazed Ceramics
01328 853 722
All Tile Limited
01263 511888
Eastern Glazed Ceramics
01603 423 391

Northamptonshire
Eurostone Tiles
01933 270352
Walls & Floors Ltd
01536 410484

Northumberland
Tile North East Ltd
01670 716767

Nottinghamshire
Beeston Ceramic Tile Company
0115 922 1743
Bridgford Tiles
0115 981 3804
East Midlands Ceramics Ltd
0115 977 0155
Studio Ceramics Ltd
01636 673527
The Tile Warehouse
0115 9390209
Tile Trend Ltd
0115 948 4241
Trent Ceramics Ltd
01623 636501

Oxfordshire
Rustica Ltd
01235 834192
Minoli
01865 778225

Shropshire
Craven Dunnill & Co Ltd
01746 761611

Somerset
Ceramic Tile Distributors
01823 352773
01934 628378

Wellington Tile Company
01823 667242
Weston Tile Warehouse Ltd
01934 625437
Yeovil Tile Market
01935 433331

Staffordshire
Alton Tiles
01538 703658
Amason Tile Company Ltd
01827 286248
Ceramic Concepts Ltd
01538 372500
Creative Walls and Floors
01782 717633
Creta Ceramica Ltd
01785 852860
N&C Nicobond
01782 575727
ProCeramica/Toms Tiles
01782 822478
Rainbow Decors Ltd
01782 411500

Suffolk
Tile Store Martlesham Heath
01473 630330

Sunderland
Ceramic Tile Distributors
0191 5671333

Surrey
All Tile Ceramics
0208 647 4576
Barge Tiles
01342 833470
Bisazza UK Ltd
0208 640 7994
Ceramic Tile Distributors
01252 721 624
020 8668 3236
01483 766 456

County Tiles Ltd
01483 451303
Domus Tiles Ltd
020 8481 9500
Focus Ceramics Ltd
01932 854881
Square Foot Ceramics Ltd
020 8397 6284
Strata Tiles Ltd
0870 608 8878
Tilebase
020 8763 9837
01306 886026
Tileco Ltd
020 8481 9500
Tiletec Limited
01932 355456
Wokingham Tiles
0118 977 9900

Sussex
Ceramic Tile Distributors
01243 787 664

Teeside
Ceramic Tile Distributors
01642 613 130

Tyne & Wear
Ceramic Tile Distributors
0191 487 8484
Rogers Ceramics
01293 612057
Tyne Tees Ceramics Ltd
0191 491 0555

Warwickshire
Earthwork
01926 411101
Miles of Tiles Ltd
01926 312777
Quali-Tile Contractors Ltd
02476 350824
Stratford Tile Warehouse Ltd
01789 299445

The Tile and Bathroom Gallery
01789 763332
Trinity Tiles & Bathrooms
01926 420825
Weddington Tile Studio Ltd
02476 354818

West Midlands
Tiles UK Ltd
0121 520 8151
Albert & Michael Heath Ltd
024 7670 5300
Novatile Ltd
01384 270786
Tilebase
01213 844 881
Solus Ceramics Ltd
0121 753 0777
Tile Trend Ltd
01384 397722
Mindon Tiling Ltd
01384 442424
Ceramic Tile Distributors
01384 480 456
Euro Ceramic Centre Ltd
0121 706 3639
Architectural Ceramics (UK) Ltd
0121 706 6456

West Sussex
HTW Tile Distribution
01273 597070
RAK Ceramics UK Ltd
01730 815507
Sussex Wall & Floor Tiling Ltd
01273 235550
The Tile Source
01273 597070
Tilebase
01293 565757

Wiltshire
Tile Centre Ltd
01225 777185
Classical Flagstones Ltd
0117 937 1960
Tile Trend Ltd
01743 465691

Worcestershire
Style in Tiles Limited
01905 613873
Tile Trend Ltd
01905 25285

Yorkshire
Alcora Tiles Ltd
01226 786891
Brooke Ceramics Ltd
01482 585888
Caesars Ceramics
01924 366365
Ceramic Tile Distributors
01423 888 092
01484 514440
01132 389 500
Groundwork (Terracotta & Stone) Ltd
01482 877320
Leeds Tile Depot
01132 761166
Majestyk Properties & Interiors
01423 705462
Naturelli Stone
0870 116 3377
Pure Adhesion Ltd
01423 528866
R J Stokes & Co Ltd
0114 2754124
Romana Tile Company
01132 444050
Sheffield Ceramics
0114 2333919
Sheffield Tile Depot
0114 2619898

Specialist Tiling Products Ltd
01423 522259
Terra Firma Tiles
0114 2730250
Terzetto Natural Stone Tiling
01423 358855
The Yorkshire Tile Company Ltd
0114 2731133
Tile Agents Yorkshire Ltd
01427 874242
Tile Depot
01302 554036
Tile in Style (UK) Ltd
0113 294 6833
Tiles UK Ltd
0113 231 1102
W Fisher & Sons (Tilers) Ltd
01484 532182

Northern Ireland
ADL Group
028 37 525839
Armatile Ltd
028 37 527007
Ceramica
028 912 71227
Eurotile Marketing Ltd
028 9260 3000

Lomac Tiles Ltd
02838 322395
Portadown Tiles
02838 330323
Regan Tile Design Ltd
028 7136 0502
028 7964 5121
028 9023 2009

North Wales
Alan Lancaster & Co.
01745 825482
Tile Trend Ltd
01492 874424
Tilestile
01248 352569

South Wales
Ceramiks Ltd
01792 798989
Harris Slate & Stone (UK) Ltd
01267 233824
Mandarin
01600 715444
N&C Nicobond
029 2039 0146
N&C Tilestyle
01792 797337
Taylor Design & Tools Ltd
Taylor Tiles Holdings Ltd
01792 797712

Tiles Ahead Limited
01633 290008
01633 875003

Scotland
Aberdeen Tile Distributors
01224 582332
Ceramic Tile Distributors
01224 649 315
0131 229 7694
0131 657 9911
0141 221 4591
0141 352 9746
01738 633 433
Cosmo Ceramics Ltd
0141 420 1122
N&C Nicobond
0141 880 1200
Tile Boutique
01592 265235

Eire
TileStyle
00 353 1 855 5200
Sealux Ltd
0870 8760121
National Tile Ltd
00 353 42 933 7678
Regan Tile Design Ltd
003531 280 0921

THE TILE ASSOCIATION
buy with confidence

BRITISH WOODWORKING FEDERATION
55 Tufton Street, Westminster, London, SW1P 3QL
Area of Operation: UK & Ireland
Tel: 0870 458 6939   **Fax:** 0870 458 6949
Email: bwf@bwf.org.uk   **Web:** www.bwf.org.uk

**BWF - CERTIFIRE
FIRE DOOR & DOORSET SCHEME**
Area of Operation: UK
Tel: 0870 458 6939   **Fax:** 0870 458 6949
Email: firedoors@bwf.org.uk
Web: www.bwf.org.uk/firedoors

The BWF-CERTIFIRE Fire Door & Doorset Scheme can help you find the right fire door and correct, compatible components to suit your needs. Contact for members' details.

THE BRITISH WOODWORKING FEDERATION
Area of Operation: UK
Tel: 0870 458 6939   **Fax:** 0870 458 6949
Email: bwf@bwf.org.uk
Web: www.bwf.org.uk

As the UK woodworking and joinery industry's leading representative body, our 500+ members produce a variety of timber products and comply with a comprehensive Code of Conduct.

To recommend a company for inclusion in the next edition of The Homebuilder's Handbook, email

customerservice@centaur.co.uk

TWA SCHEME
Area of Operation: UK
Tel: 0870 458 6939   **Fax:** 0870 458 6949
Email: windows@bwf.org.uk
Web: www.bwf.org.uk/windows

In partnership with the British Standards Institute, TWA Scheme members' high quality timber windows & doorsets are rigorously tested and audited. Contact for members' details.

BUILDERS MERCHANTS FEDERATION
15 Soho Square, London, W1D 3HL
Area of Operation: UK (Excluding Ireland)
Tel: 0207 439 1753   **Fax:** 0207 734 2766
Email: info@bmf.org.uk
Web: www.bmf.org.uk

BUILDING PRODUCTS INDEX LTD
Acorn Centre, 30 Gorst Road, London, NW10 6LE
Area of Operation: Worldwide
Tel: 0208 838 1904   **Fax:** 0208 838 1905
Email: info@bpindex.co.uk
Web: www.bpindex.co.uk

BWF - TWA SCHEME
55 Tufton Street, London, SW1P 3QL
Area of Operation: UK (Excluding Ireland)
Tel: 0870 458 6939
Fax: 0870 458 6949
Email: ruth.soundarajah@bwf.org.uk
Web: www.bwf.org.uk/about_the_scheme_twa.cfm

CEDIA UK LTD
Unit 2, Phoenix Park, St Neots,
Cambridgeshire, PE19 8EP
Area of Operation: Worldwide
Tel: 01480 213744   **Fax:** 01480 213469
Email: info@cedia.co.uk   **Web:** www.cedia.co.uk

CENTRE FOR SUSTAINABLE ENERGY
The Create Centre, Smeaton Road, Bristol, BS1 6XN
Area of Operation: UK (Excluding Ireland)
Tel: 0800 512012
Fax: 0117 929 9114
Email: info@cse.org.uk
Web: www.cse.org.uk   **Product Type:** 3

CERAM
Queens Road, Penkhull,
Stoke-on-Trent, Staffordshire, ST4 7LQ
Area of Operation: Worldwide
Tel: 01782 764444   **Fax:** 01782 412331
Email: enquiries@ceram.com
Web: www.ceram.com

**CHARTERED INSTITUTE OF
ARCHITECTURAL TECHNOLOGISTS**
397 City Road, Islington, London, EC1V 1NH
Area of Operation: Worldwide
Tel: 0207 278 2206
Email: hugh@ciat.org.uk   **Web:** www.ciat.org.uk

CONSERVATION REGISTER
c/o Institute of Conservation, 3rd Floor, Downstream Building, 1 London Bridge, London, SE1 9BG
Area of Operation: UK & Ireland
Tel: 0207 785 3804
Email: info@conservationregister.com
Web: www.conservationregister.com

CORGI
1 Elmwood, Chineham Park, Crockford Lane, Chineham, Hampshire, RG24 8WG
Area of Operation: UK & Ireland
Tel: 0870 401 2200
Email: enquiries@corgi-group.com
Web: www.corgi-group.com

DRAUGHT PROOFING ADVISORY ASSOCIATION
PO Box 12, Haslemere, Surrey, GU27 3AH
Area of Operation: UK (Excluding Ireland)
Tel: 01428 654011   **Fax:** 01428 651401
Email: dpaaassociation@aol.com
Web: www.dpaa-association.org.uk

**EARTHA: EAST ANGLIA
TELLURIC HOUSES ASSOCIATION**
Ivy Green, London Road,
Wymondham, Norfolk, NR18 9JD
Area of Operation: East England
Tel: 01953 601701   **Email:** dirkbouwens@aol.com
Web: www.eartha.org.uk

ELECSA LTD
44-48 Borough High Street, London, SE1 1XB
Tel: 0870 749 0080   **Fax:** 0870 749 0085
Email: enquiries@elecsa.org.uk
Web: www.elecsa.org.uk

FAIRTRADES
Quadrant House, The Quadrant,
Hoylake, Wirral, CH47 2EE
Area of Operation: UK & Ireland
Tel: 0870 738 4858   **Fax:** 0870 738 4868
Web: www.fairtrades.co.uk

FEDERATION OF MASTER BUILDERS
Gordon Fisher House,
14-15 Great James Street, London, WC1N 3DP
Area of Operation: UK & Ireland
Tel: 0207 242 7583   **Fax:** 0207 404 0296
Email: central@fmb.org.uk
Web: www.findabuilder.co.uk

FENSA LTD
44-48 Borough High Street, London, SE1 1XB
Tel: 0870 780 2028   **Fax:** 0870 780 2029
Email: enquiries@fensa.org.uk
Web: www.fensa.co.uk

FERFA THE RESIN FLOORING ASSOCIATION
Association House, 99 West Street,
Farnham, Surrey, GU9 7EN
Area of Operation: Worldwide
Tel: 01252 739149   **Fax:** 01252 739140
Email: ferfa@associationhouse.org.uk
Web: www.ferfa.org.uk

**FOREST STEWARDSHIP
COUNCIL UK WORKING GROUP**
11-13 Great Oak Street, Llanidloes, Powys, SY18 6BU
Area of Operation: UK (Excluding Ireland)
Tel: 01686 413916   **Fax:** 01686 412176
Email: info@fsc-uk.org   **Web:** www.fsc-uk.org

GLASS AND GLAZING FEDERATION
44-48 Borough High Street, London, SE1 1XB
Area of Operation: UK (Excluding Ireland)
Tel: 0845 257 7956   **Fax:** 0870 042 4266
Email: info@ggf.org.uk
Web: www.ggf.org.uk

**GRANT AIDED HEATING
INSTALLERS' NETWORK**
PO Box 12, Haslemere, Surrey, GU27 3AH
Area of Operation: UK (Excluding Ireland)
Tel: 01428 654011   **Fax:** 01428 651401
Email: gainassociation@aol.com
Web: www.gainassociation.org.uk

HISTORIC SCOTLAND
Longmore House, Salisbury Place,
Edinburgh, Lothian, EH9 1SH
Area of Operation: Worldwide
Tel: 0131 668 8668
Fax: 0131 668 8669
Email: hs.conservation.bureau@scotland.gsi.gov.uk
Web: www.historic-scotland.gov.uk

HOMEPRO LTD
Quadrant House, The Quadrant,
Hoylake, Wirral, CH47 2EE
Area of Operation: UK & Ireland
Tel: 0870 734 4344   **Fax:** 0870 738 4868
Web: www.homepro.com

ICON, THE INSTITUTE OF CONSERVATION
3rd Floor, Downstream Building,
1 London Bridge, London, SE1 9BG
Area of Operation: Worldwide   **Tel:** 020 7785 3805
Email: admin@icon.org.uk   **Web:** www.icon.org.uk

**INSULATED RENDER &
CLADDING ASSOCIATION**
PO Box 12, Haslemere, Surrey, GU27 3AH
Area of Operation: UK (Excluding Ireland)
Tel: 01428 654011   **Fax:** 01428 651401
Email: incaassociation@aol.com
Web: www.inca-ltd.org.uk

**INSULATING CONCRETE
FORMWORK ASSOCIATION**
PO Box 72, Billingshurst, West Sussex, RH14 0FD
Area of Operation: UK & Ireland
Tel: 01403 701167   **Fax:** 01403 701169
Email: enquiries@icfinfo.org.uk
Web: www.icfinfo.org.uk

ISTRUCTE
Institution of Structural Engineers,
11 Upper Belgrave Street, London, SW1X 8BH
Area of Operation: UK (Excluding Ireland)
Tel: 0207 235 4535   **Fax:** 0207 235 4294
Web: www.findanengineer.com

KBSA
12 Top Barn Business Centre,
Holt Heath, Worcester, Worcestershire, WR6 6NH
Area of Operation: UK (Excluding Ireland)
Tel: 01905 621787   **Fax:** 01905 621887
Email: info@kbsa.co.uk   **Web:** www.kbsa.co.uk

MFC MORTGAGE OPTIONS
231 Grimsby Road, Cleethorpes, Lincolnshire, DN35 7HE
Area of Operation: East England, North East England, North West England and North Wales, South East England, South West England and South Wales
Tel: 01472 200664   **Fax:** 01472 200664
Email: markhallam@insurer.com
Web: www.mfcmortgageoptions.co.uk

NATIONAL FIREPLACE ASSOCIATION
6th Floor, McLaren Building, 35 Dale End,
Birmingham, West Midlands, B4 7LN
Area of Operation: UK & Ireland
Tel: 0121 200 1310   **Fax:** 0121 200 1306
Email: enquiries@nfa.org.uk   **Web:** www.nfa.org.uk

NATIONAL HOME IMPROVEMENT COUNCIL
Carlyle House, 235 Vauxhall Bridge Road,
London, SW1V 1EJ
Area of Operation: UK (Excluding Ireland)
Tel: 0207 828 8230   **Fax:** 0207 828 0667
Email: info@nhic.org.uk
Web: www.nhic.org.uk

NATIONAL PLANT HIRE GUIDE
CM Brough Publishing, Unit 101,
140 Wales Road, London, W3 6UG
Area of Operation: UK (Excluding Ireland)
Tel: 0870 737 4040
Fax: 0870 737 6060
Email: info@planthireguide.co.uk
Web: www.planthireguide.co.uk

PRECAST FLOORING FEDERATION
60 Charles Street, Leicester, Leicestershire, LE1 1FB
Area of Operation: UK (Excluding Ireland)
Tel: 0116 253 6161   **Fax:** 0116 251 4568
Email: info@precastfloors.info
Web: www.pff.org.uk

SOCIETY OF GARDEN DESIGNERS
Katepwa, Ashfield Park Avenue,
Ross on Wye, Herefordshire, HR9 5AX
Tel: 01989 566695   **Fax:** 01989 567676
Email: info@sgd.org.uk   **Web:** www.sgd.org.uk

USEFUL INFORMATION - Trade Associations; Building Plots, Renovation & Conversion Opportunities; Caravans & Static Homes

SPONSORED BY: PLOTFINDER.NET & SITEFINDERIRELAND.COM www.plotfinder.net/www.sitefinderireland.com

SOLID FUEL ASSOCIATION LTD (SFA)
7 Swanwick Court, Alfreton, Derbyshire, DE55 7AS
Tel: 0845 601 4406 **Fax:** 01773 834351
Email: sfa@solidfuel.co.uk
Web: www.solidfuel.co.uk

THE SOLID FUEL ASSOCIATION

Area of Operation: UK (Excluding Ireland)
Tel: 0845 6014406
Email: sfa@solidfuel.co.uk
Web: www.solidfuel.co.uk

Source of independent advice on all aspects of solid fuel and wood fuel heating for residential properties. We publish a range of helpful guides.

STRAW BALE BUILDING ASSOCIATION
Holinroyd Farm, Butts Lane,
Todmorden, West Yorkshire, OL14 8RJ
Tel: 01706 814696
Email: info@strawbalebuildingassociation.org.uk
Web: www.strawbalebuildingassociation.org.uk

SWIMMING POOL AND ALLIED TRADES ASSOCIATION
4 Eastgate House, East Street,
Andover, Hertfordshire, SP10 1EP
Tel: 01264 356210 **Fax:** 01264 332628
Email: admin@spata.co.uk **Web:** www.spata.co.uk

THE ASSOCIATION FOR PROJECT SAFETY
Stanhope House, 12 Stanhope Place,
Edinburgh, Lothian, EH12 5HH
Tel: 08456 121290 **Fax:** 08456 121291
Email: info@aps.org.uk **Web:** www.aps.org.uk

THE BRICK DEVELOPMENT ASSOCIATION LTD.
Woodside House, Winkfield,
Windsor, Berkshire, SL4 2DX
Tel: 01344 885651 **Fax:** 01344 890129
Email: brick@brick.org.uk **Web:** www.brick.org.uk

BRICK DEVELOPMENT ASSOCIATION
Area of Operation: UK (Excluding   Ireland)
Tel: 01344 885651 **Fax:** 01344 890129
Email: brick@brick.org.uk
Web: www.brick.org.uk

The BDA is dedicated to promoting the use of brick in architectural, engineering, landscape and general building applications. Technical information is available free of charge.

THE CHARTERED INSTITUTE OF ARCHITECTURAL TECHNOLOGISTS
397 City Road, London, EC1V 1NH
Area of Operation: Worldwide
Tel: 0207 278 2206 **Fax:** 0207 837 3194
Email: info@ciat.org.uk **Web:** www.ciat.org.uk

THE CHIEF FIRE OFFICERS ASSOCIATION (CFOA)
9-11 Pebble Close, Amington,
Tamworth, Staffordshire, B77 4RD
Area of Operation: UK & Ireland
Tel: 01827 302300 **Fax:** 01827 302399
Email: info@cfoa.org.uk
Web: www.cfoa.org.uk

THE GUILD OF BUILDERS AND CONTRACTORS
Crest House, 102-104 Church Road,
Teddington, Middlesex, TW11 8PY
Area of Operation: Worldwide
Tel: 0208 977 1105 **Fax:** 0208 943 3151
Email: info@buildersguild.co.uk
Web: www.buildersguild.co.uk

THE LISTED PROPERTY OWNERS CLUB
Lower Dane, Hartlip, Sittingbourne, Kent, ME9 7TE
Area of Operation: Worldwide
Tel: 01795 844939 **Fax:** 01795 844862
Email: info@lpoc.co.uk **Web:** www.lpoc.co.uk

THE NATIONAL ENERGY FOUNDATION
The National Energy Centre, Davy Avenue, Knowlhill,
Milton Keynes, Buckinghamshire, MK5 8NG
Area of Operation: UK (Excluding Ireland)
Tel: 01908 665555 **Fax:** 01908 665577
Email: info@nef.org.uk **Web:** www.nef.org.uk

THE NATIONAL FEDERATION OF ROOFING CONTRACTORS
24 Weymouth St, Greater London, W1G 7LX
Area of Operation: UK (Excluding Ireland)
Tel: 0207 436 0387 **Fax:** 0207 637 5215
Email: info@nfrc.co.uk **Web:** www.nfrc.co.uk

THE NATIONAL FEDERATION OF
ROOFING CONTRACTORS LIMITED

THE NATIONAL FEDERATION OF ROOFING CONTRACTORS

Area of Operation: UK (Excluding Ireland)
Tel: 0207 436 0387
Fax: 0207 637 5215
Email: info@nfrc.co.uk
Web: www.nfrc.co.uk

The NFRC (National Federation of Roofing Contractors) promotes the high standards of its members to improve the roofing industry's reputation and drive out rogue traders.

THE SOLAR TRADE ASSOCIATION
The National Energy Centre, Davy Avenue, Knowlhill,
Milton Keynes, Buckinghamshire, MK5 8NG
Area of Operation: UK (Excluding Ireland)
Tel: 01908 442290 **Fax:** 01908 665577
Email: enquiries@solartradeassociation.org.uk
Web: www.solartradeassociation.org.uk

THE TILE ASSOCIATION
Forum Court, 83 Copers Cope Road,
Beckenham, Kent, BR3 1NR
Area of Operation: UK & Ireland
Tel: 020 8663 0946 **Fax:** 0208 663 0949
Email: info@tiles.org.uk
Web: www.tiles.org.uk

THE UK TRADES CONFEDERATION
Tong Hall, Tong, West Yorkshire, BD4 0RR
Area of Operation: UK & Ireland
Tel: 0870 922 0442 **Fax:** 0870 922 0441
Email: membership@uktc.org **Web:** www.uktc.com

THE WELSH TIMBER FORUM
Boughrood House, 97 The Struet,
Brecon, Powys, LD3 7LS
Area of Operation: Midlands & Mid Wales,
North West England and North Wales,
South West England and South Wales
Tel: 0845 456 0342 **Fax:** 01874 625965
Email: welshtimber@lineone.net
Web: www.welshtimberforum.co.uk

THE WOOD SHOP LIMITED
15 Spinney Way, Needingworth,
St Ives, Cambridgeshire, PE27 4SR
Area of Operation: Worldwide
Tel: 01480 469367 **Fax:** 01480 469366
Email: consultancy@thewoodshop.biz
Web: www.thewoodshop.biz

TIMBER DECKING ASSOCIATION
5 Flemming Court, Castleford,
West Yorkshire, WF10 5HW
Area of Operation: Europe
Tel: 01977 558147 **Fax:** 01977 558247
Email: info@tda.org.uk **Web:** www.tda.org.uk

TRADA TECHNOLOGY
Stocking Lane, Hughenden Valley,
High Wycombe, Buckinghamshire, HP14 4ND
Tel: 01494 569600 **Fax:** 01494 565487
Email: rscott@trada.co.uk
Web: www.trada.co.uk

TRADITIONAL HOUSING BUREAU
4th Floor, 60 Charles Street,
Leicester, Leicestershire, LE1 1FB
Area of Operation: UK (Excluding Ireland)
Tel: 0116 253 6161 **Fax:** 0116 251 4568
Email: info@housebuilder.org.uk
Web: www.housebuilder.org.uk

UK CAST STONE ASSOCIATION
15 Stone Hill Court, The Arbours,
Northampton, Northamptonshire, NN3 3RA
Area of Operation: UK & Ireland
Tel: 01604 405666 **Fax:** 01604 405666
Email: info@ukcsa.co.uk **Web:** www.ukcsa.co.uk

UK TIMBER FRAME ASSOCIATION
The E Centre, Cooperage Way Business Village,
Alloa, Clackmannanshire, FK10 3LP
Area of Operation: UK (Excluding Ireland)
Tel: 01259 272140 **Fax:** 01259 272141
Email: info@timber-frame.org
Web: www.timber-frame.org

BUILDING PLOTS, RENOVATION & CONVERSION OPPORTUNITIES

KEY
OTHER: ▽ Reclaimed ✌ On-line shopping
✏ Bespoke ✋Hand-made ECO Ecological

BUILDSTORE
Unit 1 Kingsthorne Park, Houstoun Industrial Estate,
Livingston, Lothian, EH54 5DB
Area of Operation: UK (Excluding Ireland)
Tel: 0870 870 9991 **Fax:** 0870 870 9992
Email: enquiries@buildstore.co.uk
Web: www.buildstore.co.uk

FRENCH PROPERTY SHOP
Elwick Club, Church Road, Ashford, Kent, TN32 5HP
Area of Operation: Europe
Tel: 01233 666902
Email: sales@frenchpropertyshop.com
Web: www.frenchpropertyshop.com

PLOTFINDER.NET
2 Sugar Brook Court, Aston Road,
Bromsgrove, Worcestershire, B60 3EX
Area of Operation: UK & Ireland
Tel: 01527 834428 **Fax:** 01527 837810
Email: customerservice@centaur.co.uk
Web: www.plotfinder.net

PROPERTYFINDERFRANCE.NET
2 Sugar Brook Court, Aston Road,
Bromsgrove, Worcestershire, B60 3EX
Area of Operation: Europe
Email: customerservice@centaur.co.uk
Web: www.propertyfinderfrance.net

PROPERTYPORTAL.COM
Brookfield House, Ford Lane, Frilford,
Abingdon, Oxfordshire, OX13 5NT
Tel: 0870 380 0520 **Fax:** 0870 380 0521
Email: info@propertyportal.com
Web: www.propertyportal.com

SITEFINDERIRELAND.COM
2 Sugar Brook Court, Aston Road,
Bromsgrove, Worcestershire, B60 3EX
Area of Operation: Ireland
Tel: 01527 834428 **Fax:** 01527 837810
Email: customerservice@centaur.co.uk
Web: www.sitefinderireland.com

CARAVANS & STATIC HOMES

KEY
PRODUCT TYPES: 1= Caravans
2 = Static Homes 3 = Modular Buildings
OTHER: ▽ Reclaimed ✌ On-line shopping
✏ Bespoke ✋Hand-made ECO Ecological

AMBER LEISURE
Flag Hill, Great Bentley, Colchester, Essex, CO7 8RF
Area of Operation: South East England
Tel: 01255 821817 **Fax:** 01255 821909
Email: bentley@amberleisure.com
Web: www.amberleisure.com **Product Type:** 1

ATLAS CARAVAN COMPANY LTD
Wykeland Industrial Estate, Wiltshire Road,
Hull, East Riding of Yorks, HU4 6PD
Area of Operation: North East England
Tel: 01482 562101 **Fax:** 01482 566033
Email: info@atlas-caravans.co.uk
Web: www.atlas-caravans.co.uk **Product Type:** 1

C. JENKIN & SON LTD
East Mascalls Farm, East Mascalls Lane,
Lindfield, Haywards Heath, West Sussex, RH16 2QN
Tel: 01444 482333 **Fax:** 01444 484580
Email: info@jenkinmobilehomes.com
Web: www.jenkinmobilehomes.com
Product Type: 1, 2, 3

CARA-SALES
Newspace Site, Catfoss Lane Industrial Estate,
Brandesburton, Hull, East Riding of Yorks, YO25 8EJ
Tel: 01964 542266 **Fax:** 01964 542277
Email: info@cara-sales.com **Product Type:** 1, 2

CARAVAN HIRE UK
Glanyrafon Industrial Estate,
Aberystwyth, Ceredigion, SY23 3JQ
Area of Operation: UK (Excluding Ireland)
Tel: 01970 626920 **Fax:** 01970 611922
Email: info@caravanhireuk.co.uk
Web: www.caravanhireuk.co.uk **Product Type:** 1, 2

GLOSSOP CARAVANS
Main A57, Brookfield, Glossop,
Derbyshire, Derbyshire, SK13 6JF
Area of Operation: UK (Excluding Ireland)
Tel: 01457 868011 **Fax:** 01457 890700
Email: info@glossopcaravans.co.uk
Web: www.glossopcaravans.co.uk
Product Type: 1

USEFUL INFORMATION

Self-Build Accommodation for new build-homes and extensions

Joal Leisure is the leading supplier of pre-owned static caravans in the UK. These quality homes can be used for additional accommodation, agricultural units for staff accommodation, fruit farm lodgings, and site offices. We also supply parks throughout the UK and Europe.

Many people have discovered the benefits of self-build or project managing the building of a new home. Considerable savings which often translate to large profits and the chance to get exactly what you want being just a few of the advantages. As featured on programmes such as 'Grand Designs', living in a caravan on site during a self-build has many attractions:

- Far less expensive than renting
- You'll always have a roof over your head, even if the build over-runs.
- Living on site is a motivational force for the builders
- You're always on hand to give instant decisions
- The security of your building materials is virtually guaranteed

Our static caravans are checked to a very high 36-point quality standard before release, are fully guaranteed and benefit from speedy after-sales service if required. What's more, our maintenance staff are so good that they are insurance company 'approved repairers'.

You can even buy a caravan from our website for total ease and convenience. And if you are in a real hurry, ask for details of our special Preference Scheme which will get you a caravan in double quick time.

We can not only help with the choice of caravan but our experienced transport staff can also advise on delivery and siting.

For more details on how to solve your self-build accommodation problems, please phone us on

01376 501011

JOAL LEISURE
holiday caravan & mobile home dealers

Joal Leisure Ltd, 1 Avenue Road, Witham, Essex, CM8 2DT
Fax: 01376 501701
e-mail: info@joalleisure.com

Please visit us at www.joalleisure.com

IAN JAMES CARAVANS
Yellowsands Holiday Park,
Coast Road, Brean, Somerset, TA8 2RH
Tel: 01278 751349 **Fax:** 01278 751666
Email: icj@breanbeach.co.uk
Web: www.ianjamescaravans.co.uk
Product Type: 1, 2

JOAL LEISURE
1 Avenue Road, Witham, Essex, CM8 2DT
Area of Operation: Worldwide
Tel: 01376 501011 **Fax:** 01376 501701
Email: info@joalleisure.com
Web: www.joalleisure.com
Product Type: 1, 2, 3

KESTREL CARAVANS
Windy Ridge, Warkton Lane,
Kettering, Northamptonshire, NN16 9XG
Area of Operation: Europe
Tel: 01536 514301 **Fax:** 01536 514301
Email: sales@kestrelcaravans.fsnet.co.uk
Web: www.kestrelcaravans.co.uk **Product Type:** 1, 2

OUTSOURCE SITE SERVICES
UK Control Centre, Bradford Street,
Shifnal, Shropshire, TF11 8AU
Area of Operation: UK & Ireland
Tel: 0870 701 9963 **Fax:** 0870 701 9964
Email: roger@out-source.biz
Web: www.out-source.biz **Product Type:** 3

ROUNDSTONE CARAVANS
Worthing Road, Southwater,
Horsham, West Sussex, RH13 9JG
Tel: 01403 730218 **Fax:** 01403 732828
Email: sales@roundstonecaravans.com
Web: www.roundstonecaravans.com
Product Type: 1

SAMBECK CARAVANS LTD
Woodlands Business Park, Tenpenny Hill,
Thorrington, Essex, CO7 8JD
Area of Operation: UK (Excluding Ireland)
Tel: 01206 255223 **Fax:** 01206 257391
Email: info@sambeckcaravans.co.uk
Web: www.sambeckcaravans.co.uk **Product Type:** 1, 2

SQUARE DEAL CARAVANS
Gundrymor Trading Estate, Collingwood Road,
West Moors, Dorset, BH21 6QW
Area of Operation: South East England, South West
England and South Wales
Tel: 01202 892710 **Fax:** 01202 894511
Email: sqdealcaravans@aol.com
Web: www.squaredealcaravans.com
Product Type: 1, 2

SURF BAY LEISURE
The Airfield, Winkleigh, Devon, EX19 8DW
Area of Operation: UK & Ireland
Tel: 01837 680100 **Fax:** 01837 680200
Email: info@surfbay.dircon.co.uk
Web: www.surfbayleisure.co.uk **Product Type:** 1, 2

WORCESTERSHIRE CARAVAN SALES
Nelson Road, Sandy Lane Industrial Estate,
Stourport-on-Severn, Worcestershire, DY13 9QB
Area of Operation: UK (Excluding Ireland)
Tel: 01299 878872 **Fax:** 01299 879988
Email: enquiries@worcestershire-caravan-sales.com
Web: www.worcestershire-caravan-sales.com
Product Type: 1

REMOVALS, STORAGE, AND CHANGE OF ADDRESS SERVICES

KEY

PRODUCT TYPES: 1= Removal Services
2 = Storage Facilities
3 = Change of Address Services
OTHER: ▽ Reclaimed   On-line shopping
 Bespoke   Hand-made   ECO Ecological

A & L REMOVALS
151 West Barnes Lane,
New Malden, Surrey, KT3 6HR
Area of Operation: Greater London, South East England
Tel: 0208 949 8286 **Fax:** 0208 949 8286
Email: sales@removals.ws
Web: www.removals.ws **Product Type:** 1

A££ORDABLE REMOVALS
2 Damon Avenue, Bradford, West Yorkshire, BD10 0LJ
Area of Operation: Europe
Tel: 07836 375024 **Fax:** 07092 286991
Email: mrvanman32000@yahoo.com
Web: www.affordable-removals.co.uk
Product Type: 1, 2, 4

ALLIANCE REMOVALS AND STORAGE LTD
Unit 1, 57 North Street, Portslade,
Brighton, East Sussex, BN41 1EH
Tel: 01273 771741
Email: info@allianceremovals.co.uk
Web: www.allianceremovals.co.uk
Product Type: 1, 2

CAPITAL REMOVAL SERVICE
3 Bowland Road, Woodford Green, Essex, IG8 7LX
Tel: 0208 505 7287
Email: capitalremovalservice@btinternet.com
Web: www.capitalremovalservice.co.uk
Product Type: 1

EASTEND REMOVALS
20 Salisbury Road, London, E10 5RG
Area of Operation: UK (Excluding Ireland)
Tel: 0845 838 1528
Email: eastendremovals@hotmail.com
Web: www.eastendremovals.co.uk
Product Type: 1, 2

HELP I AM MOVING.COM
Unit 3a, Engine Shed Lane,
Skipton, North Yorkshire, BD23 1UP
Area of Operation: Worldwide
Web: www.helpiammoving.com
Product Type: 1, 2, 3

HUGHES REMOVALS & STORAGE LTD
Stonelea, Station Road, Shipton by Beningbrough,
York, North Yorkshire, YO30 1BS
Area of Operation: Europe
Tel: 01904 471471 **Fax:** 01904 471245
Email: enquiries@hughesremovals.co.uk
Web: www.hughesremovals.co.uk
Product Type: 1, 2

I AM MOVING.COM
Tel: 0845 090 0198
Email: customersupport@iammoving.com
Web: www.iammoving.com **Product Type:** 3

LO-COST MOVES
5 Newlands Avenue, Rochdale, Lancashire, OL12 0BN
Area of Operation: UK (Excluding Ireland)
Tel: 0800 043 9014 **Fax:** 01706 673869
Email: pete@lo-costremovals.co.uk
Web: www.lo-costremovals.co.uk
Product Type: 1, 2

PAUL MATTHEWS AND SON LTD
Unit 21, Heol Ffaldau,
Brackla Industrial Estate, Bridgend, CF31 2AJ
Area of Operation: UK (Excluding Ireland)
Tel: 01656 655466 **Fax:** 01656 655466
Email: removals.joanne@virgin.net
Product Type: 1, 2

SINGER'S REMOVALS & STORAGE
Windsor House, 5a King Street,
Newcastle-Under-Lyme,
Stoke-on-Trent, Staffordshire, ST5 1EH
Area of Operation: Midlands & Mid Wales
Tel: 01782 557296
Fax: 01782 557297
Email: info@singersremovals.co.uk
Web: www.singersremovals.co.uk
Product Type: 1, 2, 4

SPACES PERSONAL STORAGE
88 Bushey Road, Raynes Park, London, SW20 0JH
Area of Operation: UK (Excluding Ireland)
Tel: 0800 622244
Fax: 0208 947 9952
Email: enquiries@spacestore.co.uk
Web: www.spacestore.co.uk **Product Type:** 2, 3

TOWN & GOWN REMOVALS
1 James Wolfe Road, Cowley,
Oxford, Oxfordshire, OX4 2PY
Area of Operation: Greater London, South East England
Tel: 0800 027 5695
Fax: 01865 436499
Email: townandgown@gmail.com
Web: www.townngown.co.uk **Product Type:** 1, 2, 4

WHITE AND COMPANY
International House, Britanna Road, London, EN8 7PF
Area of Operation: Worldwide
Tel: 0800 801999 **Fax:** 0208 441 0206
Email: melvyn.neal@whiteandcompanyyes.co.uk
Web: www.whiteandcompany.co.uk
Product Type: 1, 2, 3

AREA CHECKS AND ADVICE

KEY

PRODUCT TYPES:
1 = Environmental Information
2 = Facilities Information 3 = Other
OTHER: ▽ Reclaimed   On-line shopping
 Bespoke   Hand-made   ECO Ecological

NATIONAL MAP CENTRE
11 Hertfordshire Business Centre, Alexander Road,
London Colney, St Albans, Hertfordshire, AL2 1JG
Area of Operation: UK (Excluding Ireland)
Tel: 0845 606 1060 **Fax:** 01727 827 256
Email: enquiries@mapsnmc.co.uk
Web: www.planningmaps.co.uk
Product Type: 3

**SEVENOAKS ENVIRONMENTAL
CONSULTANCY LTD**
19 Gimble Way, Pembury,
Tunbridge Wells, Kent, TN2 4BX
Tel: 01892 822999 **Fax:** 01892 822992
Email: enquiries@sevenoaksenvironmental.co.uk
Web: www.sevenoaksenvironmental.co.uk
Product Type: 1

STATS LIMITED
Porterswood House, Porters Wood,
St Albans, Hertfordshire, AL3 6PQ
Area of Operation: Worldwide
Tel: 01727 833261 **Fax:** 01727 835682
Email: info@stats.co.uk
Web: www.stats.co.uk **Product Type:** 1, 2, 3

UKVILLAGES LTD
48 Mill Way, Cambridgeshire, CB3 9NB
Area of Operation: UK & Ireland
Tel: 0845 634 3243
Email: info@ukvillages.co.uk
Web: www.ukvillages.co.uk **Product Type:** 2

UP MY STREET
10th Floor, Portland House, Stag Place,
London, Greater London, SW1E 5BH
Area of Operation: UK & Ireland
Tel: 020 7802 2992 **Fax:** 020 7233 5933
Email: pr@upmystreet.com
Web: www.upmystreet.com
Product Type: 2

COMPUTER SOFTWARE

KEY

PRODUCT TYPES: 1= CAD Software
2 = Estimating Software   3 = Project
Management Software

OTHER: ▽ Reclaimed   On-line shopping
   Bespoke   Hand-made   ECO Ecological

**ADVANCED COMPUTER
SOLUTIONS LTD (CADDIE)**
Unit 1, Home Farm Business Centre,
Cardington, Bedfordshire, MK44 3SN
Area of Operation: Worldwide
Tel: 01234 834920 **Fax:** 01234 832601
Email: sales@caddie.co.uk
Web: www.caddiesoftware.com **Product Type:** 1

AUTODESK
Unit 8, Thame 40, Jane Morbey Road,
Thame, Oxfordshire, OX9 3RR
Tel: 01844 261872 **Fax:** 01844 216737
Email: sales@manandmachine.co.uk
Web: www.manandmachine.co.uk **Product Type:** 1

AVANQUEST UK
Sheridan House, 40-43 Jewry Street,
Winchester, Hampshire, SO33 8RY
Area of Operation: Worldwide
Tel: 01962 835081
Email: ptracey@avanquest.co.uk
Web: www.avanquest.co.uk   **Product Type:** 1

TurboCAD Professional 12

- Draw plans in 2D then convert to 3D
- 20 stock Door types with 7 different shapes for each
- 15 stock Window types with 14 different shapes for each
- Doors and Windows snap to position in walls
- Roof drawing tool
- Save in all main file formats and easily convert to PDF
- Audio Visual CD explaining all aspects of architectural drawing

For all sales and enquiries call Paul Tracey at Avanquest on 01962 835081
ptracey@avanquest.co.uk   Avanquest

EASY PRICE PRO LTD
The Software Centre, Wattisfield, Norfolk, IP22 1NX
Area of Operation: UK & Ireland
Tel: 0845 612 4747 **Fax:** 0845 612 4748
Email: enquiries@easypricepro.com
Web: www.easypricepro.com
Product Type: 2, 3

ELECO SOFTWARE LIMITED
Christy Estate, Ivy Road,
Aldershot, Hampshire, GU12 4XG
Area of Operation: Worldwide
Tel: 01252 334695 **Fax:** 01252 332287
Email: esales@online-warehouse.co.uk
Web: www.eleco.com/store
Product Type: 1

ESTIMATORS LIMITED
12A High Street, Cheadle, Stockport, Cheshire, SK8 1AL
Area of Operation: UK (Excluding Ireland)
Tel: 0161 286 8601 **Fax:** 0161 428 5788
Email: mail@estimators-online.com
Web: www.estimators-online.com **Product Type:** 2

HBXL
Citypoint, Temple Gate, Bristol, BS1 6PL
Area of Operation: UK & Ireland
Tel: 0870 8502444 **Fax:** 0870 850 2555
Email: sales@hbxl.co.uk
Web: www.hbxl.co.uk
Product Type: 2

HOUSEBUILDER XL
Citypoint, Temple Gate, Bristol, Bristol, BS1 6PL
Area of Operation: UK & Ireland
Tel: 0870 850 2444 **Fax:** 0870 850 2555
Email: sales@hbxl.co.uk
Web: www.hbxl.co.uk
Product Type: 2

QUANTI-QUOTE
Trewint, Main Street, Shap,
Penrith, Cumbria, CA10 3NH
Area of Operation: UK & Ireland
Tel: 01931 716810
Email: peter@quantiquote.co.uk
Web: www.quantiquote.co.uk **Product Type:** 2

SOFTCOVER INTERNATIONAL LIMITED
364 Milton Road, Cambridge,
Cambridgeshire, CB4 1LW
Area of Operation: Worldwide
Tel: 01223 424342
Email: marketing@softcover.com
Web: www.softcover.com   **Product Type:** 1

VIXEN SOFTWARE SOLUTIONS LTD
Market House, 21 Lenten Street,
Alton, Hampshire, GU34 1HG
Tel: 01420 89898 **Fax:** 01420 544195
Email: sales@vixensoft.co.uk
Web: www.vixensoft.co.uk
Product Type: 2

BOOKS AND OTHER LITERATURE

KEY

PRODUCT TYPES: 1= Books
2 = Magazines   3 = Information Websites
4 = Other

OTHER: ▽ Reclaimed   On-line shopping
   Bespoke   Hand-made   ECO Ecological

BASEMENT INFORMATION CENTRE
Riverside House, 4 Meadows Business Park, Station
Approach, Blackwater, Camberley, Surrey, GU17 9AB
Area of Operation: UK (Excluding Ireland)
Tel: 01276 33155 **Fax:** 01276 606801
Email: info@tbic.org.uk
Web: www.tbic.org.uk / www.basements.org.uk
Product Type: 3

BLACKBERRY BOOKS
8 Newport Road, Godshill, Isle of Wight, PO38 3HR
Area of Operation: UK & Ireland
Tel: 01983 840310 **Fax:** 01983 840310
Email: info@blackberry-books.co.uk
Web: www.blackberry-books.co.uk
Product Type: 1

BRICKS AND BRASS
2 Aldermary Road, Bromley, Kent, BR1 3PH
Area of Operation: UK & Ireland
Tel: 0208 290 1488
Email: contact@bricksandbrass.co.uk
Web: www.bricksandbrass.co.uk
Product Type: 3

CENTRE FOR ALTERNATIVE TECHNOLOGY
Llwyngweren Quarry, Machynlleth, Powys, SY20 9AZ
Area of Operation: Worldwide
Tel: 01654 705950 **Fax:** 01654 702782
Email: lucy.stone@cat.org.uk
Web: www.cat.org.uk
Product Type: 1, 2

CHILTERN DYNAMICS
Chiltern House, Stocking Lane, Hughenden Valley,
High Wycombe, Buckinghamshire, HP14 4ND
Area of Operation: UK & Ireland
Tel: 01494 569800 **Fax:** 01494 564895
Email: cd@chilterndynamics.co.uk
Web: www.chilternfire.co.uk
Product Type: 1, 3

COPPERJOB LTD
PO Box 110, Plymouth, Devon, PL7 2ZS
Area of Operation: UK & Ireland
Email: info@copperjob.com
Web: www.centralheatingrepair.co.uk
Product Type: 1

DIYDOCTOR
FTSC, Badgers Hill, Frome, Somerset, BA11 2EH
Tel: 01373 303930 **Fax:** 01373 301438
Email: office@diydoctor.org.uk
Web: www.diydoctor.org.uk   **Product Type:** 1, 4

GOTO PLUMBING
Email: sales@gotoplumbing.co.uk
Web: www.gotoplumbing.co.uk
Product Type: 3

GREENER HOMES & BUILDINGS
Unit 7, Dyfi Eco Parc, Machynlleth, Powys, SY20 8AX
Area of Operation: Midlands & Mid Wales,
North West England and North Wales,
South West England and South Wales
Tel: 08454 585973 **Fax:** 01654 703117
Email: info@greenerhomesandbuildings.co.uk
Web: www.ghb.org.uk **Product Type:** 3

HIDDENWIRES.CO.UK
Great Brownings, College Road, London, SE21 7HP
Area of Operation: Europe **Tel:** 0208 761 1042
Email: info@hiddenwires.co.uk
Web: www.hiddenwires.co.uk **Product Type:** 3, 4

**HOMEBUILDING & RENOVATING
BOOK OF BARN CONVERSIONS**
2 Sugar Brook Court, Aston Road,
Bromsgrove, Worcestershire, B60 3EX
Area of Operation: Worldwide
Tel: 01527 834435 **Fax:** 01527 837810
Email: customerservice@centaur.co.uk
Web: www.homebuilding.co.uk/bookshop
Product Type: 1

**HOMEBUILDING & RENOVATING
BOOK OF CONTEMPORARY HOMES**
2 Sugar Brook Court, Aston Road,
Bromsgrove, Worcestershire, B60 3EX
Area of Operation: Worldwide
Tel: 01527 834435 **Fax:** 01527 837810
Email: customerservice@centaur.co.uk
Web: www.homebuilding.co.uk/bookshop
Product Type: 1

**HOMEBUILDING & RENOVATING
BOOK OF GREAT VALUE SELF-BUILD HOMES**
2 Sugar Brook Court, Aston Road,
Bromsgrove, Worcestershire, B60 3EX
Area of Operation: Worldwide
Tel: 01527 834435 **Fax:** 01527 837810
Email: customerservice@centaur.co.uk
Web: www.homebuilding.co.uk/bookshop
Product Type: 1

**HOMEBUILDING & RENOVATING
BOOK OF HOUSE PLANS**
2 Sugar Brook Court, Aston Road,
Bromsgrove, Worcestershire, B60 3EX
Area of Operation: Worldwide
Tel: 01527 834435 **Fax:** 01527 837810
Email: customerservice@centaur.co.uk
Web: www.homebuilding.co.uk/bookshop
Product Type: 1

USEFUL INFORMATION

HOMEBUILDING & RENOVATING MAGAZINE
Ascent Publishing Ltd, 2 Sugar Brook Court,
Aston Road, Bromsgrove, Worcestershire, B60 3EX
Area of Operation: Worldwide
Tel: 01527 834400 **Fax:** 01527 834497
Email: customerservice@centaur.co.uk
Web: www.homebuilding.co.uk
Product Type: 2, 3

HOMEBUILDING & RENOVATING MAGAZINE ARCHIVE CD ROM
2 Sugar Brook Court, Aston Road,
Bromsgrove, Worcestershire, B60 3EX
Area of Operation: Worldwide
Tel: 01527 834435 **Fax:** 01527 837810
Email: customerservice@centaur.co.uk
Web: www.homebuilding.co.uk
Product Type: 4

HOUSE MOUSE
Hills Farm, Lawshall,
Bury St. Edmunds, Suffolk, IP29 4PJ
Area of Operation: UK (Excluding Ireland)
Tel: 01284 830492 **Fax:** 01284 830495
Email: bpharber@aol.com **Product Type:** 1

HOW TO CREATE A JARDIN PAYSAN
2 Sugar Brook Court, Aston Road,
Bromsgrove, Worcestershire, B60 3EX
Area of Operation: Worldwide
Tel: 01527 834435 **Fax:** 01527 837810
Email: customerservice@centaur.co.uk
Web: www.homebuilding.co.uk/bookshop
Product Type: 1

HOW TO RENOVATE A HOUSE IN FRANCE
2 Sugar Brook Court, Aston Road,
Bromsgrove, Worcestershire, B60 3EX
Area of Operation: Worldwide
Tel: 01527 834435 **Fax:** 01527 837810
Email: customerservice@centaur.co.uk
Web: www.homebuilding.co.uk/bookshop
Product Type: 1

LAURENCE KING PUBLISHING
71 Great Russell Street, London, WC1B 3BP
Area of Operation: UK (Excluding Ireland)
Tel: 0207 430 8850 **Fax:** 0207 430 8880
Email: enquiries@laurenceking.co.uk
Web: www.laurenceking.co.uk
Product Type: 1

LOW-IMPACT LIVING INITIATIVE
Redfield Community, Buckingham Road,
Winslow, Buckinghamshire, MK18 3LZ
Area of Operation: UK (Excluding Ireland)
Tel: 01296 714184 **Fax:** 01296 714184
Email: lili@lowimpact.org
Web: www.lowimpact.org
Product Type: 3, 4

MODELROOMS
12 Clarinda Park East,
Dun Laoghaire, Co Dublin, Ireland
Area of Operation: UK & Ireland
Tel: 0845 456 5886
Email: info@modelrooms.com
Web: www.modelrooms.com
Product Type: 4

MOVE OR IMPROVE? MAGAZINE
2 Sugar Brook Court, Aston Road,
Bromsgrove, Worcestershire, B60 3EX
Area of Operation: Worldwide
Tel: 01527 834435 **Fax:** 01527 837810
Email: customerservice@centaur.co.uk
Web: www.moveorimprove.co.uk
Product Type: 2, 3

OVOLO PUBLISHING LTD
1 The Granary, Brook Farm,
Ellington, Cambridgeshire, PE28 0AE
Area of Operation: Worldwide
Tel: 01480 891777
Fax: 01480 891595
Email: info@ovolopublishing.co.uk
Web: www.ovolopublishing.co.uk
Product Type: 1

PERIOD LIVING MAGAZINE
2 Sugar Brook Court, Aston Road,
Bromsgrove, Worcestershire, B60 3EX
Area of Operation: Worldwide
Tel: 01527 834435 **Fax:** 01527 837810
Email: customerservice@centaur.co.uk
Web: www.periodliving.co.uk **Product Type:** 2, 3

RENOVATIONFRANCE.NET
2 Sugar Brook Court, Aston Road,
Bromsgrove, Worcestershire, B60 3EX
Area of Operation: Worldwide
Email: customerservice@centaur.co.uk
Web: www.renovationfrance.net **Product Type:** 3

RIBA BOOKSHOPS
15 Bonhill Street, London, EC2P 2EA
Area of Operation: Worldwide
Tel: 0207 256 7222 **Fax:** 0207 374 2737
Email: marketing@ribabooks.com
Web: www.ribabookshops.com
Product Type: 1, 2, 4

SANDED FLOORS
7 Pleydell Avenue, Upper Norwood, London, SE19 2LN
Area of Operation: UK (Excluding Ireland)
Tel: 0208 653 6283
Email: peter-weller@sandedfloors.co.uk
Web: www.sandedfloors.co.uk **Product Type:** 3

SELF BUILD IRELAND LTD
119 Cahard Road, Saintfield, Co Down, BT24 7LA
Area of Operation: Ireland Only
Tel: (028) 9751 0570 **Fax:** (028) 9751 0576
Email: info@selfbuild.ie **Web:** www.selfbuild.ie
Product Type: 2

SELF BUILD PRO
Belmont Business Centre, Brook Lane,
Endon, Staffordshire, ST9 9EZ
Area of Operation: Worldwide
Tel: 01782 503322 **Fax:** 01782 505127
Email: enquiries@self-build-pro.com
Web: www.self-build-pro.com **Product Type:** 1

SELFBUILDGUIDES.CO.UK
Area of Operation: UK & Ireland
Email: enquiries@selfbuildguides.co.uk
Web: www.selfbuildguides.co.uk **Product Type:** 3

STOBART DAVIES LIMITED
Stobart House, Pontyclerc, Penybanc Road,
Ammanford, Carmarthenshire, SA18 3HP
Area of Operation: Worldwide
Tel: 01269 593100 **Fax:** 01269 596116
Email: sales@stobartdavies.com
Web: www.stobartdavies.com **Product Type:** 1

STRAWBALE BUILDING COMPANY UK
34 Rosebery Way, Tring, Hertfordshire, HP23 5DS
Area of Operation: Europe
Tel: 01442 825421
Email: chug@strawbale-building.co.uk
Web: www.strawbale-building.co.uk **Product Type:** 1

THE BUILDING CENTRE
26 Store Street, off Tottenham Court Road,
London, WC1E 7BT
Area of Operation: Worldwide
Tel: 020 7692 4000 **Fax:** 020 7631 0329
Email: information@buildingcentre.co.uk
Web: www.buildingcentre.co.uk
Product Type: 1, 2, 4

THE HOUSEBUILDER'S BIBLE 6TH EDITION.
Ovolo Publishing Ltd, 1 The Granary, Brook Farm,
Ellington, Cambridge, Cambridgeshire, PE28 0AE
Area of Operation: Worldwide
Tel: 01480 891595 (24 Hours) **Fax:** 01480 893836
Email: info@ovolopublishing.co.uk
Web: www.ovolopublishing.co.uk **Product Type:** 1

TRADITIONAL HOUSING BUREAU
4th Floor, 60 Charles Street,
Leicester, Leicestershire, LE1 1FB
Area of Operation: UK (Excluding Ireland)
Tel: 0116 253 6161 **Fax:** 0116 251 4568
Email: info@housebuilder.org.uk
Web: www.housebuilder.org.uk **Product Type:** 2, 4

EXHIBITIONS, COURSES AND EVENTS

KEY
OTHER: ▽ Reclaimed ⌐ On-line shopping
✎ Bespoke ✋ Hand-made ECO Ecological

ABLE SKILLS
Unit K5 Riverside Industrial Estate,
Riverside Way, Dartford, Kent, DA1 5 BS
Area of Operation: Europe
Tel: 01322 280202 **Fax:** 01322 280301
Email: chris @ableskills.co.uk
Web: www.ableskills.co.uk

CENTRE FOR ALTERNATIVE TECHNOLOGY
Llwyngweren Quarry, Machynlleth, Powys, SY20 9AZ
Area of Operation: Worldwide
Tel: 01654 705 950 **Fax:** 01654 702 782
Email: lucy.stone@cat.org.uk **Web:** www.cat.org.uk

CHILTERN DYNAMICS
Chiltern House, Stocking Lane, Hughenden Valley,
High Wycombe, Buckinghamshire, HP14 4ND
Tel: 01494 569800 **Fax:** 01494 564895
Email: cd@chilterndynamics.co.uk
Web: www.chilternfire.co.uk

FEDERATION OF MASTER BUILDERS
Gordon Fisher House,
14-15 Great James Street, London, WC1N 3DP
Tel: 0207 242 7583 **Fax:** 0207 404 0296
Email: central@fmb.org.uk
Web: www.findabuilder.co.uk

INSIDE TRACK SEMINARS LTD
3rd Floor Surrey House, 34 Eden Street,
Kingston-Upon-Thames, Surrey, KT1 1ER
Tel: 0208 541 2900 **Web:** www.insidetrack.co.uk

KLC SCHOOL OF DESIGN
503 The Chambers, Chelsea Harbour, London, SW10 0XF
Tel: 020 737 63377 **Fax:** 020 737 67807
Email: info@klc.co.uk **Web:** www.klc.co.uk

LOW-IMPACT LIVING INITIATIVE
Redfield Community, Buckingham Road,
Winslow, Buckinghamshire, MK18 3LZ
Tel: 01296 714184 **Fax:** 01296 714184
Email: lili@lowimpact.org **Web:** www.lowimpact.org

OLCI PRACTICAL TRAINING
9-11 Kings Mews, London, WC1N 2JB
Tel: 0800 0582848 **Email:** info@olcipt.info
Web: www.olcipt.info

SELF BUILD IRELAND LTD
119 Cahard Road, Saintfield, Co. Down, BT24 7LA
Area of Operation: Ireland Only
Tel: (028) 9751 0570 **Fax:** (028) 9751 0576
Email: info@selfbuild.ie **Web:** www.selfbuild.ie

STRAWBALE BUILDING COMPANY UK
34 Rosebery Way, Tring, Hertfordshire, HP23 5DS
Area of Operation: Europe **Tel:** 01442 825421
Email: chug@strawbale-building.co.uk
Web: www.strawbale-building.co.uk

THE PLUMBSKILL CENTRE LTD
High Lea, Witchampton,
Wimborne, Dorset, BH21 5AAd
Tel: 01258 841441 **Fax:** 01258 841441
Email: plumbskill@btconnect.com
Web: www.plumbskill.co.uk

TRADESKILLS4U LTD
Unit 3 Metana House, Priestley Way,
Crawley, West Sussex, RH10 9NT
Tel: 01293 529777 **Fax:** 01293 525007
Email: carl@tradeskills4u.co.uk
Web: www.tradeskills4u.co.uk

USEFUL INFORMATION

"Inside Track showed me how to go from buy-to-let amateur to property millionaire."

"*I knew I could make money in property, I just didn't know where to start. Inside Track taught me everything I needed to get started and make some serious money.*"

Inside Track delegate, SEPTEMBER 2005

Learn the secrets of successful property investing

Inside Track seminars will give you the knowledge you need to build your own property portfolio quickly, confidently and profitably. We are the UK's No.1 provider of specialist education for private property investors. Since 2001, **we've helped over 200 people like you to build £1million property portfolios**. And every one of them started by attending one of our free introductory workshops. **Places are limited, so book yours today.**

Our FREE 2 hour introductory workshop will start to show you how to:

- **make money** from property in eight different ways
- buy direct from the developer **saving up to 20%**
- secure property with **minimal deposits**
- **avoid the pitfalls** amateur buy-to-let landlords fall into
- look forward to a **secure financial future**

Winner of the BUSINESS BRITAIN magazine award for 'PROPERTY INVESTMENT SPECIALIST OF THE YEAR' 2004/2005.

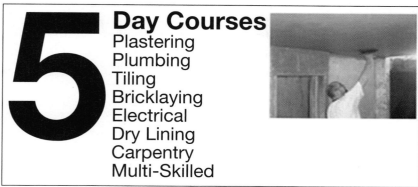

Image courtesy of Able Skils (0808 100 3245°

5 Day Courses
Plastering
Plumbing
Tiling
Bricklaying
Electrical
Dry Lining
Carpentry
Multi-Skilled

SPONSORED BY ABLE SKILLS
Tel 0808 100 3245 Web www.ableskills.co.uk

Able Skills

USEFUL INFORMATION

FEBRUARY

3-4 February
London Weekend Homeowners' Course
£150
Society for the Protection of Ancient Buildings, 37 Spital Square, London E1 6DY.
Tel: 0207 377 1644   Web: www.spab.org.uk
Taking place at the Artworkers Guild in Bloomsbury, this course is designed for anyone who has taken on the challenge of owning an older or period property, and who wants to find out more about the most suitable and sympathetic ways to repair and care for it. SPAB's Weekend Homeowners' Courses are always great fun as well as being informative and educational. Led by experts, including TV's Marianne Suhr of the Restoration series, they give period property owners the chance to meet like minded fellow period house enthusiasts whose own trials and tribulations provide a fascinating backdrop to the course. Cost includes lunch and refreshments but not accommodation.

Other Homeowners' Weekends (usually 5-6 each year), led by Marianne Suhr, take place at different locations throughout the country throughout the year and subjects covered often have a regional emphasis. SPAB also run  a range of other courses, covering a wide variety of subjects which are aimed at building professionals, homeowners and enthusiasts More information is available from www.spab.org.uk, or by calling 0207 377 1644. Alternatively you can write to them at 37 Spital Square, London, E1 6DY.

5 February
Green Architecture
£95
Weald & Downland Open Air Museum, Singleton, Chichester, West Sussex PO18 0EU   Tel: 01243 811464
Email: courses@wealddown.co.uk Web: www.wealddown.co.uk
Reduce the environmental impact of building at design stage. A design school for architects an designers concerned with sustainability issues in new-build and refurbishment.

5-7 February
Brick, Terracotta & Tiles
£285 inclusive of coffee, lunch and tea in the King's Manor Refectory (50% student discount available)
Dept of Archaeology, University of York, The King's Manor, York, YO1 7EP.   Tel: 01904 433963
Email: pab11@york.ac.uk   Web: www.york.ac.uk/depts/arch
Aims to present the rich and varied historic use of burnt clay in building cultures; to explore the decay mechanisms, and appropriate methodology and techniques for conservation and repair; to investigate the use of ceramic building materials in York itself.

5-8 February
Specifying Conservation Works
From £524 (Fully Residential Fee), £410 (Non-residential fee)
West Dean College, West Dean, Chichester, West Sussex, PO18 0QZ.
Tel: 01243 818219/811301   Fax: 01243 811343
Email: bcm@westdean.org.uk   Web: www.westdean.org.uk
The course will cover specifying conservation works from inception to final account and post-contract debrief. John Ashurst will cover the compilation of specifications accurately tailored to the individual building: pre-contract trials; assessing the quality of the specified works. Ian Constantinides will cover the role and requirements in specifying the conservation contractor; preparation for and compilation of a clear unambiguous tender document that minimises risk. The course offers comprehensive coverage of this critical subject from different professional angles, using discussion topics and consideration of case studies, focussing on all that is required to 'make it work in practice'.

12-14 February
The Study & Conservation of Metals and Glass in Architecture
£285 inclusive of coffee, lunch and tea in the King's Manor Refectory (50% student discount available)
Dept of Archaeology, University of York, The King's Manor, York, YO1 7EP.   Tel: 01904 433963
Email: pab11@york.ac.uk   Web: www.york.ac.uk/depts/arch
Aims to introduce the rich cultural history of the use of diverse metals in architecture, and the technology of the manufacture of the principal ones; to introduce the methodology and principles of repair and conservation of metals (especially cast and wrought iron, lead, aluminium, steel); and to visit workshops where outstanding work is still being done in the Yorkshire Region.

12-16 February
Timber Framing From Scratch
£450
Weald & Downland Open Air Museum, Singleton, Chichester, West Sussex PO18 0EU Tel: 01243 811464
Email: courses@wealddown.co.uk Web: www.wealddown.co.uk
A superb opportunity to gain hands-on experience of timber framing. A 5 day practical course introducing students to the historic use of structural oak framing, tools and techniques. The posts, cills, plates and tie beams of a 10' square timber frame are prefabricated during the course using only traditional tools and techniques, and the frame is erected on the final afternoon.

19-21 February
Modern Materials: particular challenges in conserving them.
£285 inclusive of coffee, lunch and tea in the King's Manor Refectory (50% student discount available)
Dept of Archaeology, University of York, The King's Manor, York, YO1 7EP.   Tel: 01904 433963
Aims to introduce the special problems which arise in repairing or conserving buildings of the mid to late twentieth century made of a variety of materials which often respond particularly badly to water penetration or other forms of neglect.

23-25 February
Heating With Wood: Logs, pellets or chips - which one for me?
£320 high-waged; £230 waged; £175 student / unwaged
Centre for Alternative Technology, Machynlleth, Powys, SY20 9AZ
Tel: 01654 705981
Email: courses@cat.org.uk   www.cat.org.uk/courses
This course provides an introduction to using wood to heat homes and small businesses with either wood logs, pellets, chips or briquettes. Participants will be shown working examples of various types of heating equipment including boilers and stoves. A hands-on practical demonstration of calculating moisture content will be given along with examples of log preparation and stacking. Theory sessions will include how best to buy wood for heating, how to burn it cleanly and calculating how much is needed to heat a home.

27 February
Construction & Repair of Timber Framed Buildings
£95
Weald & Downland Open Air Museum, Singleton, Chichester, West Sussex PO18 0EU Tel: 01243 811464
Email: courses@wealddown.co.uk Web: www.wealddown.co.uk
Exploration of the background to timber-framed buildings; dating techniques; structural problems; sympathetic remedial methods.

MARCH

5-8 March
Conservation & Repair of Architectural Metalwork
From £524 (Fully Residential Fee), £410 (Non-residential fee)
West Dean College, West Dean, Chichester, West Sussex, PO18 0QZ.
Tel: 01243 818219/811301   Fax: 01243 811343
Email: bcm@westdean.org.uk   Web: www.westdean.org.uk
This course deals with structural metalwork, as well as purely decorative features and statuary. Non-ferrous as well as ferrous metals are covered. Condition assessments and analyses are included, as well as guidance on remedial techniques, specifications and selected repair methods. Latest developments in the techniques of cleaning using lasers will be demonstrated, along with the use of cathodic protection as a remedial solution to rusting cramps.

7 March
An Introduction to Dating Timber Framed Buildings
£95
Weald & Downland Open Air Museum, Singleton, Chichester, West Sussex PO18 0EU Tel: 01243 811464
Email: courses@wealddown.co.uk Web: www.wealddown.co.uk
The roof timbers often provide the best evidence for the period of construction. Learn to spot the differences between a crown post and a king post, see how radically different the medieval roof is to the Georgian roof, watch the purlins appear and disappear over the centuries and marvel at the skill of the carpenters. A wonderful opportunity to observe and be guided around so many varieties of roof all within easy walking distance of each other.

9-11 March
The Whole House: Ecological Building From New
£320 high-waged; £230 waged; £175 student / unwaged
Centre for Alternative Technology, Machynlleth, Powys, SY20 9AZ
Tel: 01654 705981
Email: courses@cat.org.uk   www.cat.org.uk/courses
Pat Borer and Cindy Harris, authors of 'The Whole House Book', will run this topical course. The course will cover ecological building design for low energy consumption, green building technologies, healthier habitats, the use of environmentally friendly building materials and water efficiency, conservation and sanitation.

12 March
Wattle & Daub
£100
Weald & Downland Open Air Museum, Singleton, Chichester, West Sussex PO18 0EU Tel: 01243 811464
Email: courses@wealddown.co.uk Web: www.wealddown.co.uk
Insights in to the historic use of wattle and daub, and its repair and conservation today. A morning of touring the Museum's examples followed by an afternoon of 'hands on' practical exercise applying wattles and daubing them.

19-22 March
Conservation & Repair of Brick
From £524 (Fully Residential Fee), £410 (Non-residential fee)
West Dean College, West Dean, Chichester, West Sussex, PO18 0QZ.
Tel: 01243 818219/811301   Fax: 01243 811343
Email: bcm@westdean.org.uk   Web: www.westdean.org.uk
This course provides an understanding of, and basic skills in, the conservation and repair of traditional brick and terracotta masonry and flint buildings. The starting point for brick and terracotta is an understanding of the raw materials and their characteristics when fired. A range of buildings will be studied to illustrate methods of construction, common failures and decay processes. Methods of repair, joint treatments and cleaning relevant to brick will be discussed and form part of the practical sessions. For flint buildings the course will cover: origins and characteristics of flint; regional variations in method and style of building; and strengths and weaknesses of flint construction in different contexts. This part of the course aims to establish an appreciation of the importance and quality of flint as a masonry material, and to show how to assess the condition of flint walls, prepare the repair schedule and specification, and carry out remedial treatments to high standard.

19-23 March
Wind Power
Parts 1 & 2: £595 high-waged, £460 waged, £275 student/ unwaged (Part 1 or Part 2 only, £320 / £230 / £175)
Centre for Alternative Technology, Machynlleth, Powys, SY20 9AZ
Tel: 01654 705981
Email: courses@cat.org.uk   www.cat.org.uk/courses
Part 1 of this course covers all the basic requirements for choosing and installing a wind energy system, and is suitable for those thinking of buying or building their own system, as well as those with a general interest in the subject. There will be a visit to a local wind farm. Part 2 consists of detailed workshops on the design of wind machines.

23 March
Energy Conservation in Traditional Buildings
£95
Weald & Downland Open Air Museum, Singleton, Chichester, West Sussex PO18 0EU Tel: 01243 811464
Email: courses@wealddown.co.uk Web: www.wealddown.co.uk
Looks at the implications of improving energy efficiency for traditional buildings, plus a review of relevant regulations and guidance, case studies, and a practical session of carrying out an air pressure test.

23 March
Lath-making Workshop
£75
Weald & Downland Open Air Museum, Singleton, Chichester, West Sussex PO18 0EU Tel: 01243 811464
Email: courses@wealddown.co.uk Web: www.wealddown.co.uk
Learn how to split oak, ash and hazel to form laths for plastering and daubing. Students will make a panel to take home.

23-25 March
Self-build Solar Hot Water
£1695 including system, £150 excluding system (Food and accommodation included).
Low-Impact Living Initiative, Redfield Community, Winslow, Bucks, MK18 3LZ Tel/Fax: 01296 714184
Email: lili@lowimpact.org.uk Web: www.lowimpact.org.uk
Participants can leave with their entire system, tailored to their needs, plus a manual explaining how the system works and how to install it. (It is also possible to attend the course without purchasing a system - this system is not suitable if you have a mains pressure hot water cylinder or a combi boiler). The course begins with a theory session explaining solar water heating and the system in detail. You will then build and pressure test your own pump & control set, expansion vessel kit and air separator. No plumbing experience is needed - this will build confidence in cutting and soldering copper, using expansion joints and fixing leaks. There are also sessions on installing and maintaining your system, including fixing the panels to your roof and how to replace a cylinder. No specialist skills are needed to participate.

30 March
Lime Day Workshop
£70 including VAT & lunch
Tel: 01805 603587
Email: mail@jjsharpe.co.uk Web: www.jjsharpe.co.uk
The aim of the workshops is to give course members knowledge and understanding of uses of lime in building. This will enable people to either undertake work themselves or to instruct contractors with confidence. The lime days are a mix of practical instruction and hands-on experience, including slaking lime, mixing mortar and limewash. We also cover pointing, plastering and rendering. The workshops attract a range of people from professional builders, homeowners and those who wish to self-build. We supply all tools, equipment and materials.

APRIL

6-8 April
Straw Bale Building
£180 high-waged; £150 waged; £120 student / unwaged
Low-Impact Living Initiative, Redfield Community, Winslow, Bucks, MK18 3LZ Tel/Fax: 01296 714184
Email: lili@lowimpact.org.uk Web: www.lowimpact.org.uk
This is a practical building project, aiming to leave a permanent structure on the site - this will involve some carpentry and general building as well as handling straw bales. We will try to avoid power tools and people of all abilities are welcome. You will also learn about the environmental and practical benefits of constructing buildings using straw bales. The course will be run by 'Chug' Tugby, one of the leading straw-bale builders in Britain today. During the weekend you will: build straw-bale walls; learn how to work with straw bales, including cutting and tying; erect at least part of the roof structure; plaster with natural finishes; see a slide show of straw-bale buildings & techniques; examine existing straw-bale buildings, built using different methods.

10-13 April
Energy Awareness (City & Guilds 6176)
£650
Centre for Alternative Technology, Machynlleth, Powys, SY20 9AZ
Tel: 01654 705981
Email: courses@cat.org.uk www.cat.org.uk/courses
This course, developed by NEA and taught by the NEA Cymru Training and Development Officer, leads to a City and Guilds award. It is aimed at those who provide energy advice, or for those wishing to gain knowledge of domestic energy efficiency. It covers heating and hot water systems, heating controls, interpreting fuel cost data, working out fuel costs, improving energy efficiency, grant aid and avoiding condensation and dampness.

13 April
Cob Day Workshop
£70 including VAT & lunch
Tel: 01805 603587
Email: mail@jjsharpe.co.uk Web: www.jjsharpe.co.uk
The aim of the workshops is to provide knowledge and understanding of cob building and repair. to enable people to undertake work themselves, or to instruct contractors with confidence. The cob days are a mix of practical instruction and hands-on experience, covering aspects of build and repair; for example, mixing cob, making blocks and building with mass cob, as well as repair techniques. The workshops attract a range of people from professional builders, homeowners and self-builders.

13-15 April
Wind & Solar Electricity
£180 high-waged; £150 waged; £120 student / unwaged
Low-Impact Living Initiative, Redfield Community, Winslow, Bucks, MK18 3LZ Tel/Fax: 01296 714184
Email: lili@lowimpact.org.uk Web: www.lowimpact.org.uk
Course provides an overview of the basic principles and technology of solar and wind electrical systems, offering participants the theoretical knowledge and practical experience needed to design and install small renewable energy systems. Aimed at anyone requiring an introduction to renewable energy electrical technology, as well as those wishing to install renewable energy systems. The emphasis will be on how things work and what it is practicable to do. Participants will have the opportunity to discuss their own projects. No previous electrical knowledge necessary.

16-17 April
Flint Walling: A Practical Course
£180
Weald & Downland Open Air Museum, Singleton, Chichester, West Sussex PO18 0EU Tel: 01243 811464
Email: courses@wealddown.co.uk Web: www.wealddown.co.uk
A two day course covering the sorting, selection, preparation and knapping of flints. Experience of different styles of laying flints and the use of lime mortars.

16-20 April
Timber Framing From Scratch
£450
Weald & Downland Open Air Museum, Singleton, Chichester, West Sussex PO18 0EU Tel: 01243 811464
Email: courses@wealddown.co.uk Web: www.wealddown.co.uk
A superb opportunity to gain hands-on experience of timber framing. A 5 day practical course introducing students to the historic use of structural oak framing, tools and techniques. The posts, cills, plates and tie beams of a 10' square timber frame are prefabricated during the course using only traditional tools and techniques, and the frame is erected on the final afternoon.

23-26 April
Building With Hemp
400 euros
Anam Cré Studio, County Kerry, Ireland.
Tel : 00 353 64 41747
Email: hempbuilding@eircom.net Web: www.hempbuilding.com
This 4 day course, run by Steve Allin, author of the book 'Building with Hemp' will consist of an introduction to the materials, method and use of hemp/lime in design and construction. The course will cover design and framework aspects of hempbuilding, with an element of hands-on experience in mixing and applying hemp cast walls on site. Hemp plastering, hemp finishes & lime paints will also be covered. Included with the course price is accommodation (2 person per room sharing), self-service breakfast & light lunch.

27 April
Lime Day Workshop
£70 including VAT & lunch
Tel: 01805 603587
Email: mail@jjsharpe.co.uk Web: www.jjsharpe.co.uk
Workshop aimed at giving course members knowledge and understanding of uses of lime in building, enabling them to either undertake work themselves, or to instruct contractors with confidence. The lime days are a mix of practical instruction and hands-on experience, including slaking lime, mixing mortar and limewash. We also cover pointing, plastering and rendering. The workshops attract a range of people from professional builders, homeowners and those who wish to self-build.

MAY

1 May
As Good as New: In Situ Repairs to Historic Timber Structures
£95
Weald & Downland Open Air Museum, Singleton, Chichester, West Sussex PO18 0EU Tel: 01243 811464
Email: courses@wealddown.co.uk Web: www.wealddown.co.uk
Course for architects, engineers and surveyors offering a step-by-step approach to the specification of remedial work to historic timber structures. The course covers stresses and strains: frame behaviour under load, as well as the criteria for repair, the conservation view point , repair forms, and case studies.

4-6 May
Introduction to Solar Electric Systems
£320 high-waged; £230 waged; £175 student / unwaged
Centre for Alternative Technology, Machynlleth, Powys, SY20 9AZ
Tel: 01654 705981
Email: courses@cat.org.uk www.cat.org.uk/courses
Participants learn about photovoltaic principles & systems and undertake practical sessions on system design and basic PV circuits. The CAT site has several grid-connected and stand-alone PV systems, which will be demonstrated. The course is an introduction to photovoltaics and is not suitable for installers.

7-11 May
Sewage Solutions
£595 high-waged, £460 waged, £275 student/ unwaged
Centre for Alternative Technology, Machynlleth, Powys, SY20 9AZ
Tel: 01654 705981
Email: courses@cat.org.uk www.cat.org.uk/courses
CAT is a leading UK centre in the field of natural sewage recycling and treatment, and has several systems in operation. This course is suitable for those looking for an alternative to a septic tank. The first part of the course covers dry sewage systems and examines the theoretical and practical information needed to install a compost toilet system that you would be happy to have in your bathroom; as well as waterless urinals. The second part looks at aquatic plant treatment / reed bed systems and how plants can be used to absorb nutrients and purify polluted water without using chemicals, machinery or extra sources of energy.

10 May
Repair of Timber Framed Buildings
£95
Weald & Downland Open Air Museum, Singleton, Chichester, West Sussex PO18 0EU Tel: 01243 811464
Email: courses@wealddown.co.uk Web: www.wealddown.co.uk
Day school including a lecture on the repair of timber framed buildings by Richard Harris, a workshop session with Roger Champion and a critical examination of repairs executed at the Museum over 30 years.

11 May
Lime Day Workshop
£70 including VAT & lunch
Tel: 01805 603587
Email: mail@jjsharpe.co.uk Web: www.jjsharpe.co.uk
The aim of the workshops is to give course members knowledge and understanding of uses of lime in building. This will enable people to either undertake work themselves or to instruct contractors with confidence. The lime days are a mix of practical instruction and hands-on experience, including slaking lime, mixing mortar and limewash. We also cover pointing, plastering and rendering. The workshops attract a range of people from professional builders, homeowners and those who wish to self-build. We supply all tools, equipment and materials.

11-13 May
Sustainable Water & Sewage
£180 high-waged; £150 waged; £120 student / unwaged
Low-Impact Living Initiative, Redfield Community, Winslow, Bucks, MK18 3LZ Tel/Fax: 01296 714184
Email: lili@lowimpact.org.uk Web: www.lowimpact.org.uk
This course is about the collection, conservation and recycling of water, as well as sustainable ways of dealing with sewage. Water shortages are becoming a serious problem all over the world, and there are financial implications too, now that water meters are becoming the norm. The course covers: ecological sewage treatment; septic tanks to sewage gardens; an appropriate approach to sewage treatment; water efficiency; rainwater harvesting and greywater recycling; and compost toilets.

11-13 May
Community Renewable Energy Schemes
£320 high-waged; £230 waged; £175 student / unwaged
Centre for Alternative Technology, Machynlleth, Powys, SY20 9AZ
Tel: 01654 705981
Email: courses@cat.org.uk www.cat.org.uk/courses
Community ownership of renewable energy is new to the UK, but growing in popularity. This course is ideal for those interested in developing such projects. Sessions will cover: the benefits of community ownership, the mechanics of developing such a venture and case studies from existing schemes in the UK, including our own 75kW Community Wind Turbine.

12-13 May
Homebuilding & Renovating Show - SECC Glasgow
£8 on door, £5 in advance, free to H&R magazine subscribers.
Tickets - Tel:0870 010 9031 (Subscribers: 0870 010 0218)
Web: www.homebuildingshow.co.uk
Visitor Enquiries - Tel: 0207 970 4249
Email: showenquiries@centaur.co.uk

HOMEBUILDING & RENOVATING SHOW
SECC GLASGOW 12 - 13 MAY 2007

From the initial stages of planning to the actual process of converting, renovating, remodeling, building from scratch or extending your home, the Homebuilding & Renovating Shows provides the self-builder and renovator with all the inspiration, solutions, products and services needed to build their dream home. Each event creates an exciting and stimulating place where you can meet hundreds of exhibitors, gain free one-to-one advice from the Homebuilding & Renovating Magazine and local experts, attend free seminar programmes, discover the latest products and services, learn about the best financial packages and find your dream plot of land ready for development.

ABLE SKILLS

Able Skills is a well established and reputable Construction Training Centre.

Able Skills has been specifically set up to help you learn your chosen construction skill in a friendly and spacious environment. No previous experience is required in order to take part in any of our courses; these courses are open to anyone, regardless of gender, age or status.

Whether you are looking for a change in career, looking to do a DIY project or are looking to gain a qualification, Able Skills can accommodate you. Our aim is that you have the confidence and ability to carry out your chosen skill once you have completed your course and left the Centre.

We pride ourselves in the quality of training we deliver, so much so that we have now obtained City & Guilds and NPTC approval which enables us to provide qualifications for those seeking to further their education and career. In addition, we have also obtained accreditation from EAL and NICEIC, enabling us to deliver our Electrical Course to people in order for them to obtain the essential PART P Domestic Installers Certificate, which has become a legal requirement when carrying out electrical installation in the UK.

Unit K5 Riverside Industrial Estate,
Riverside Way,
Dartford,
Kent,
DA1 5 BS
Area of Operation: Europe
Tel: 01322 280202
Fax: 01322 280301
Email: chris@ableskills.co.uk
Web: www.ableskills.co.uk

5 Day Courses

Plastering
Plumbing
Tiling
Bricklaying
Electrical
Dry Lining
Carpentry
Multi-Skilled

Carpentry
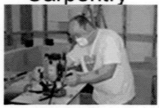

Dry lining

Plumbing

Tiling

Part P Electrical

Plastering

Bricklaying

Kitchen Fitting

14-18 May
Intermediate Timber Framing - Roof Framing
£450
Weald & Downland Open Air Museum, Singleton, Chichester, West Sussex PO18 0EU
Tel: 01243 811464
Email: courses@wealddown.co.uk Web: www.wealddown.co.uk
A 5-day practical course for students who have previously attended our "Timber Framing From Scratch" course. The common principal, hip and jack rafters are marked, cut and fitted to a timber frame that was made on the "Timber Framing From Scratch" course. All the completed roof members are pitched on the last afternoon.

21-25 May
Renewable Energy Systems
£595 high-waged; £460 waged; £275 student / unwaged
Centre for Alternative Technology, Machynlleth, Powys, SY20 9AZ
Tel: 01654 705981
Email: courses@cat.org.uk www.cat.org.uk/courses
This course, led by CAT engineers, will look at the potential for generating your own electricity from wind, water and solar power and also at the possibilities for reducing energy consumption. There will be practical sessions in solar, wind and water and tours of CAT's renewable displays.

21-25 May
Timber Frame Dismantling and Re-erection
£450
Weald & Downland Open Air Museum, Singleton, Chichester, West Sussex PO18 0EU
Tel: 01243 811464
Email: courses@wealddown.co.uk Web: www.wealddown.co.uk
Ever wondered how to dismantle a timber frame building? On this course you will learn how to survey, number, dismantle, move and re-erect a timber frame building.We will be moving the Woodland exhibition cattle shelter, or "lewin" from its current position in the woodland at the top of the site to the Museum's wood yard site above Pendean.

25-27 May
Cob Building
£180 high-waged; £150 waged; £120 student / unwaged
Low-Impact Living Initiative, Redfield Community, Winslow, Bucks, MK18 3LZ Tel/Fax: 01296 714184
Email: lili@lowimpact.org.uk Web: www.lowimpact.org.uk
The course will introduce methods of earth / cob building, and will include theory and practice with short demonstrations, but the emphasis will be on hands-on learning. Participants should leave feeling confident in their ability to build with cob and to make and apply an earthen plaster. During the weekend you will: explore the advantages of building with earth in general; learn the essential aspects of building with, as well as ways of sculpting and finishing cob; learn how to make and apply an earthen plaster, which will include some cob bas relief sculpture; learn about materials, where to locate them and how to test them; learn about relevant tools; learn about earth ovens, including building, firing and cooking; see a slide-show which will give you some inspiring ideas for your own cob structures; and learn more about the possibilities that this versatile material has to offer

29 May - 1 June
Conservation & Repair of Plasters & Renders
From £524 (Fully Residential Fee), £410 (Non-residential fee)
West Dean College, West Dean, Chichester, West Sussex, PO18 0QZ.
Tel: 01243 818219/811301 Fax: 01243 811343
Email: bcm@westdean.org.uk Web: www.westdean.org.uk
Rendered and plastered masonry and timber-framed buildings with rendered infill panels form a very important part of our historic and traditional building stock; repair and maintenance can be a major problem and remedial work and specification is often of poor quality. This unique course covers history, documentation, condition survey, repair options, specifications, execution and quality control of remedial works to lime, gypsum and cement-based internal and external wall plasters and renders, from roughcast to stucco and including plain, moulded, modelled and cast work, with practical workshop exercises.

JUNE

6 June
Cob Walling: History, Theory & Practice
£95
Weald & Downland Open Air Museum, Singleton, Chichester, West Sussex PO18 0EU Tel: 01243 811464
Email: courses@wealddown.co.uk Web: www.wealddown.co.uk
The day school will explore the various types and methods of cob wall construction in the region. It will also examine causes of failure, repair strategies and problems relating to alterations to cob structures. Some hands-on practice.

11-14 June
The Ecological Management of Historic Buildings & Sites
From £524 (Fully Residential Fee), £410 (Non-residential fee)
West Dean College, West Dean, Chichester, West Sussex, PO18 0QZ.
Tel: 01243 818219/811301 Fax: 01243 811343
Email: bcm@westdean.org.uk Web: www.westdean.org.uk
The last decade has seen renewed interest in the ecological importance of historic sites, and there is a growing acceptance of the need to integrate care of plants and animals into the conservation of historic sites and landscapes. This course looks at key habitats involved and their management, with particular focus on recent examples, and implications of wildlife legislation.

15 June
Cob Day Workshop
£70 including VAT & lunch
Tel: 01805 603587
Email: mail@jjsharpe.co.uk Web: www.jjsharpe.co.uk
These workshops aim to provide knowledge and understanding of cob building and repair, enabling people to undertake work themselves, or to instruct contractors with confidence. The cob days are a mix of instruction and hands-on experience, covering aspects of build and repair; for example, mixing cob, making blocks, and building with mass cob, as well as repair techniques. Suitable for professional builders, homeowners and self-builders.

18-20 June
Repair of Traditionally Constructed Brickwork
£285
Weald & Downland Open Air Museum, Singleton, Chichester, West Sussex PO18 0EU Tel: 01243 811464
Email: courses@wealddown.co.uk Web: www.wealddown.co.uk
Causes of failure and decay, and selection of methods of repair. Practical sessions include cutting out bricks, removing defective joints, stitch repairs and re-inforcement, and patch pointing.

18-21 June
Building With Hemp
400 euros
Anam Cré Studio, County Kerry, Ireland. Tel : 00 353 64 41747
Email: hempbuilding@eircom.net Web: www.hempbuilding.com
A 4 day course, run by Steve Allin, author of the book 'Building with Hemp' consists of an introduction to the materials, method and use of hemp/lime in design and construction. The course will cover design and framework aspects of hempbuilding, with an element of hands-on experience in mixing and applying hemp cast walls on site. Hemp plastering, hemp finishes & lime paints will also be covered. Included with the course is accommodation (2 person per room sharing), self-service breakfast & light lunch.

18-22 June
Straw Bale Building
£595 high-waged; £460 waged; £275 student / unwaged
Centre for Alternative Technology, Machynlleth, Powys, SY20 9AZ
Tel: 01654 705981
Email: courses@cat.org.uk www.cat.org.uk/courses
This course will look at the history and use of straw bale buildings, different techniques, planning considerations and how to build. There will be practical workshops on the load bearing method, plaster and render preparation and lime and earth finishes.

18-21 June
Cleaning Masonry Buildings
From £524 (Fully Residential Fee), £410 (Non-residential fee)
West Dean College, West Dean, Chichester, West Sussex, PO18 0QZ.
Tel: 01243 818219/811301 Fax: 01243 811343
Email: bcm@westdean.org.uk Web: www.westdean.org.uk
A comprehensive course for practitioners and specifiers, covering complex aesthetic, technical, practical, and health and safety issues involved in the cleaning of stone, brick and terracotta buildings. With opportunity to try a range of techniques.

18-22 June
Intermediate Timber Framing - Wall Framing
£450
Weald & Downland Open Air Museum, Singleton, Chichester, West Sussex PO18 0EU Tel: 01243 811464
Email: courses@wealddown.co.uk Web: www.wealddown.co.uk
A five day practical course for students who have attended our "Timber Framing From Scratch" course. The studs and braces of wall frames are marked, cut and fitted into a timber frame, that was constructed on the "Timber Framing From Scratch" course.

21 June
Lime Mortars for Traditional Brickwork
£95
Weald & Downland Open Air Museum, Singleton, Chichester, West Sussex PO18 0EU Tel: 01243 811464
Email: courses@wealddown.co.uk Web: www.wealddown.co.uk
Lectures and practical demonstrations on the traditional preparation and uses of limes and lime mortars and the modern misconceptions about them.

22-24 June
Organic Gardening Weekend
£320 high-waged; £230 waged; £175 student / unwaged
Centre for Alternative Technology, Machynlleth, Powys, SY20 9AZ
Tel: 01654 705981
Email: courses@cat.org.uk www.cat.org.uk/courses
Join our organic experts for an inspirational weekend. CAT has over 25 years experience of gardening organically. The course will cover a blend of useful, recreational and ecological organic gardening with sessions on soil fertility, pest and weed control, compost making, growing vegetables and gardening for wildlife.

25 June
Damp in Historic Buildings
£100 inclusive of coffee, lunch and tea in the King's Manor Refectory (50% student discount available)
Dept of Archaeology, University of York, The King's Manor, York, YO1 7EP. Tel: 01904 433963
Email: pab11@york.ac.uk Web: www.york.ac.uk/depts/arch
Aims to critically examine the standardised approaches used in more recent construction technology and discuss how these methods, when applied in an unthinking way to traditional buildings, can often hasten the deterioration of historic fabric.

23-24 June
Homebuilding & Renovating Show - Newbury Showground
£8 on door, £5 in advance, free to H&R magazine subscribers.
Tickets - Tel:0870 010 9031 (Subscribers: 0870 010 0218)
Web: www.homebuildingshow.co.uk
Visitor Enquiries - Tel: 0207 970 4249
Email: showenquiries@centaur.co.uk

From the initial stages of planning to the actual process of converting, renovating, remodeling, building from scratch or extending your home, the Homebuilding & Renovating Shows provides the self-builder and renovator with all the inspiration, solutions, products and services needed to build their dream home. Each event creates an exciting and stimulating place where you can meet hundreds of exhibitors, gain free one-to-one advice from the Homebuilding & Renovating Magazine and local experts, attend free seminar programmes, discover the latest products and services, learn about the best financial packages and find your dream plot of land ready for development.

25-26 June
Traditional Lime Plasters & Renders
£190
Weald & Downland Open Air Museum, Singleton, Chichester, West Sussex PO18 0EU
Tel: 01243 811464
Email: courses@wealddown.co.uk Web: www.wealddown.co.uk
A practically based two day course covering the fundamentals of lime plastering from the simplest renders to the finest ornamental work. Lectures followed by practical demonstrations, hands-on experience and opportunity for discussion.

29 June - 1 July
Domestic Solar Water Heating Systems
£320 high-waged; £230 waged; £175 student / unwaged
Centre for Alternative Technology, Machynlleth, Powys, SY20 9AZ
Tel: 01654 705981
Email: courses@cat.org.uk www.cat.org.uk/courses
A course ideal for those who want to understand the theory and practice of solar water heating systems. Sessions will cover types of collector, energy storage, plumbing and controls. There will be hands-on practicals for constructing a simple collector and a working solar system. Theory sessions include how to choose a solar water heating system, safety considerations and a guide to the regulations. This is not a course for Installers.

JULY

2-6 July
Traditional Roofing Methods
£95 per day (all five days = £425)
Weald & Downland Open Air Museum, Singleton, Chichester, West Sussex PO18 0EU Tel: 01243 811464
Email: courses@wealddown.co.uk Web: www.wealddown.co.uk
Five linked days exploring the traditions, methods and materials used in the roofing industries.
Day one: Thatch, lectures and practical thatch demonstrations.
Day two: Tile, the history of hand-made clay peg tiles and their refinements.
Day three: Slate, conservation and repair of slate roofs and regional variations. Stone, conservation, repair and the use of new local stone slabs.
Day four: Shingles
Day five: Leadwork, theory, repair & replication.

6-8 July
Rammed Earth Building
£180 high-waged; £150 waged; £120 student / unwaged
Low-Impact Living Initiative, Redfield Community, Winslow, Bucks, MK18 3LZ Tel/Fax: 01296 714184
Email: lili@lowimpact.org.uk Web: www.lowimpact.org.uk
Build your own low impact dwelling from cheap, sustainable, easily available materials. Course covers: what is rammed earth?; why build with earth - what are the benefits? ; finding the right earth; choosing a formwork system; different construction methods; design detailing from damp proof course to roof plate; tools; some different design approaches; how to build wall sections including corners; how to build an arch; how to build in electrical services.

13-15 July
Straw Bale Building
£180 high-waged; £150 waged; £120 student / unwaged
Low-Impact Living Initiative, Redfield Community, Winslow, Bucks, MK18 3LZ Tel/Fax: 01296 714184
Email: lili@lowimpact.org.uk Web: www.lowimpact.org.uk
A practical building project, aiming to leave a permanent structure on the site - this will involve some carpentry and general building as well as handling straw bales. We will try to avoid power tools and people of all abilities are welcome. You will also learn about the environmental and practical benefits of constructing buildings using straw bales. The course will be run by 'Chug' Tugby, one of the leading straw-bale builders in Britain today. During the weekend you will: build straw-bale walls; learn how to work with straw bales, including cutting and tying; erect at least part of the roof structure; plaster with natural finishes; see a slide show of straw-bale buildings & techniques; examine existing straw-bale buildings, built using different methods.

16-20 July
Alternative Building Methods
£595 high-waged; £460 waged; £275 student / unwaged
Centre for Alternative Technology, Machynlleth, Powys, SY20 9AZ
Tel: 01654 705981
Email: courses@cat.org.uk www.cat.org.uk/courses
Led by Maurice Mitchell, an architect and lecturer at CAT for over 20 years, daily lectures will cover earth building, ferro-cement, building using a wide range of timbers, and emergency shelters. The bulk of the course will involve the design and construction of a small structure using locally available materials. The course is suitable for building and architecture students, those going to work overseas and anyone who would like to take a broader approach.

20-22 July
Natural Paints & Lime
£180 high-waged; £150 waged; £120 student / unwaged
Low-Impact Living Initiative, Redfield Community, Winslow, Bucks, MK18 3LZ Tel/Fax: 01296 714184
Email: lili@lowimpact.org.uk Web: www.lowimpact.org.uk
How to maintain a property combining the best of traditional and modern techniques and materials to ensure long-lasting protection, and at the same time safeguard your health and that of the environment. Includes theory on the environmental effects of paints, lime and cements, and practical sessions on using various paints and finishes, lime washing, rendering and slaking.

27 July
Lime Day Workshop
£70 including VAT & lunch Tel: 01805 603587
Email: mail@jjsharpe.co.uk Web: www.jjsharpe.co.uk
The aim of the workshops is to give course members knowledge and understanding of uses of lime in building. This will enable people to either undertake work themselves or to instruct contractors with confidence. The lime days are a mix of practical instruction and hands-on experience, including slaking lime, mixing mortar and limewash. We also cover pointing, plastering and rendering. The workshops attract a range of people from professional builders, homeowners and those who wish to self-build. We supply all tools, equipment and materials.

AUGUST

24-26 August
Roofing
£180 high-waged; £150 waged; £120 student / unwaged
Low-Impact Living Initiative, Redfield Community, Winslow, Bucks, MK18 3LZ Tel/Fax: 01296 714184
Email: lili@lowimpact.org.uk Web: www.lowimpact.org.uk
Whether you have a straw-bale house, a rammed earth house or a conventional building, you'll need a roof! This course is for you if you are considering building a new roof, or repairing or insulating an existing one. Whether employing a builder or doing the work yourself, it will help you understand more about how a house works. Course covers: roofing materials, and some environmental and sustainability issues involved; ventilation, insulation, moisture, vents, vermin, and rot; holes in roofs (skylights, vents, chimneys etc); gutters; adding solar hot water and photovoltaic tiles; loft conversions; employing a builder; and DIY practical work.

24-26 August
Round Wood Timber Framing
£180 high-waged; £150 waged; £120 student / unwaged
Low-Impact Living Initiative, Redfield Community, Winslow, Bucks, MK18 3LZ Tel/Fax: 01296 714184
Email: lili@lowimpact.org.uk Web: www.lowimpact.org.uk
A course is for anyone interested in constructing rustic buildings on their site using local coppice wood. We will be using green wood timber framing techniques and freshly felled trees to create an unusual outdoor structure. 'Round' wood is young coppiced trees, not sawn or squared, sometimes with the bark still on. The design we will be following can be put together by a small team of people in a few days; we will be using traditional hand tools. You will also learn how to read trees, their different characteristics and uses, how to get the best from your woodworking tools, how to work with the grain, and elegant ways to join wood.

31st August
Cob Day Workshop
£70 including VAT & lunch Tel: 01805 603587
Email: mail@jjsharpe.co.uk Web: www.jjsharpe.co.uk
Course aims to give course members knowledge and understanding of cob building and cob repair. This will enable people to either undertake work themselves or to instruct contractors with confidence. Cob days are a mix of practical instruction and hands-on experience, covering aspects of build and repair, such as mixing cob, making blocks and building with mass cob as well as repair techniques. The workshops attract a range of people from professional builders, homeowners and self-builders.

SEPTEMBER

3-4 September
Flint Walling: A Practical Course
£180
Weald & Downland Open Air Museum, Singleton, Chichester, West Sussex PO18 0EU Tel: 01243 811464
Email: courses@wealddown.co.uk Web: www.wealddown.co.uk
Sorting, selection, preparation and knapping of flints. Provides experience of various styles of laying flints and use of lime mortar.

7 September
Lime Day Workshop
£70 including VAT & lunch Tel: 01805 603587
Email: mail@jjsharpe.co.uk Web: www.jjsharpe.co.uk
Workshop to give course members knowledge and understanding of uses of lime in building. This will enable people to either undertake work themselves or to instruct contractors with confidence. The lime days are a mix of practical instruction and hands-on experience, including slaking lime, mixing mortar and limewash. We also cover pointing, plastering and rendering. The workshops attract a range of people from professional builders, homeowners and those who wish to self-build.

7-9 September
Building With Earth
£320 high-waged; £230 waged; £175 student / unwaged
Centre for Alternative Technology, Machynlleth, Powys, SY20 9AZ
Tel: 01654 705981
Email: courses@cat.org.uk www.cat.org.uk/courses
CAT has an Information Centre and Shop with beautiful rammed earth internal pillars. Earth blocks were used in the construction of new toilet facilities. This course will cover basic methods and construction techniques, soil analysis and practical sessions in block making and rammed earth techniques.

7-9 September
Natural Rendering: Clay Plaster
£320 high-waged; £230 waged; £175 student / unwaged
Centre for Alternative Technology, Machynlleth, Powys, SY20 9AZ
Tel: 01654 705981
Email: courses@cat.org.uk www.cat.org.uk/courses
This course examines the use of clay as a natural rendering material. Participants will look at preparation of plaster bases, producing mixtures, colour finishes, decorative coats and external and internal finishes.

14-16 September
Domestic Solar Water Heating Systems
£320 high-waged; £230 waged; £175 student / unwaged
Centre for Alternative Technology, Machynlleth, Powys, SY20 9AZ
Tel: 01654 705981
Email: courses@cat.org.uk www.cat.org.uk/courses
This course is ideal for those who want to understand both theory and practice of solar water heating systems. Sessions will cover types of collector, energy storage, plumbing and controls. There will be hands-on practicals for constructing a simple collector and a working solar system. Theory sessions include how to choose a solar water heating system, safety considerations and a guide to the regulations. Examples of working systems are shown as part of a tour of CAT's many solar systems. It is not a course for Installers.

17-21 September
Timber Framing From Scratch
£450
Weald & Downland Open Air Museum, Singleton, Chichester, West Sussex PO18 0EU Tel: 01243 811464
Email: courses@wealddown.co.uk Web: www.wealddown.co.uk
A superb opportunity to gain hands-on experience of timber framing. A 5 day practical course introducing students to the historic use of structural oak framing, tools and techniques. The posts, cills, plates and tie beams of a 10' square timber frame are prefabricated during the course using only traditional tools and techniques, and the frame is erected on the final afternoon.

21-23 September
Straw Bale Building
£180 high-waged; £150 waged; £120 student / unwaged
Low-Impact Living Initiative, Redfield Community, Winslow, Bucks, MK18 3LZ Tel/Fax: 01296 714184
Email: lili@lowimpact.org.uk Web: www.lowimpact.org.uk
A practical building project aiming to leave a permanent structure on the site, involving some carpentry and general building as well as handling straw bales. We will try to avoid power tools - people of all abilities are welcome. You will also learn the environmental and practical benefits of constructing buildings using straw bales. The course is run by 'Chug' Tugby, one of the leading straw-bale builders in Britain today. During the weekend you will: build straw-bale walls; learn how to work with straw bales, including cutting and tying; erect at least part of the roof structure; plaster with natural finishes; see a slide show of straw-bale buildings & techniques; and examine existing straw-bale buildings.

21-23 September
Homebuilding & Renovating Show - ExCeL London
£12 on door, £8 in advance, free to H&R magazine subscribers
Tickets - Tel:0870 010 9031 (Subscribers: 0870 010 0218)
Web: www.homebuildingshow.co.uk
Visitor Enquiries - Tel: 0207 970 4249
Email: showenquiries@centaur.co.uk

From the initial stages of planning to the actual process of converting, renovating, remodeling, building from scratch or extending your home, the Homebuilding & Renovating Shows provides the self-builder and renovator with all the inspiration, solutions, products and services needed to build their dream home. Each event creates an exciting and stimulating place where you can meet hundreds of exhibitors, gain free one-to-one advice from the Homebuilding & Renovating Magazine and local experts, attend free seminar programmes, discover the latest products and services, learn about the best financial packages and find your dream plot of land ready for development. Also includes the Smart Home Zone - see www.smarthomeshow.co.uk for more information.

24-28 September
Building Integrated Renewable Systems
£595 high-waged; £460 waged; £275 student / unwaged
Centre for Alternative Technology, Machynlleth, Powys, SY20 9AZ
Tel: 01654 705981
Email: courses@cat.org.uk www.cat.org.uk/courses
This course will cover the whole range of building integrated renewable energy systems, providing sufficient technical and economic/ financial detail to allow architects, planning control officers and other key decision and policy makers to enable maximum take-up of appropriate systems and best practice.

30 September - 5 October
Build Your Own Wind Turbine
£650 high-waged; £500 waged; £350 student / unwaged
Centre for Alternative Technology, Machynlleth, Powys, SY20 9AZ
Tel: 01654 705981
Email: courses@cat.org.uk www.cat.org.uk/courses
Hugh Piggott, author of 'Wind Power Workshop' and 'Brakedrum Windmill Plans' leads this popular practical course. Participants will be led through the design and build stages, which will cover all the information needed to construct a small aerogenerator.

OCTOBER

5-7 October
Introduction to Solar Electric Systems
£320 high-waged; £230 waged; £175 student / unwaged
Centre for Alternative Technology, Machynlleth, Powys, SY20 9AZ
Tel: 01654 705981
Email: courses@cat.org.uk www.cat.org.uk/courses
Participants will learn about photovoltaic principles & systems and undertake practical sessions on system design and basic PV circuits. The CAT site has several grid-connected and stand-alone PV systems, incorporating roof-integrated, above-roof and free-standing arrays, which will be demonstrated. The course is an introduction to photovoltaics and is not suitable for installers.

5-7 October
DIY for Beginners
£180 high-waged; £150 waged; £120 student / unwaged
Low-Impact Living Initiative, Redfield Community,
Winslow, Bucks, MK18 3LZ
Tel/Fax: 01296 714184
Email: lili@lowimpact.org.uk Web: www.lowimpact.org.uk
If you want to install photovoltaics, solar hot water, compost
toilets or any environmentally-friendly facilities, you'll need to
have some basic DIY skills. This course de-mystifies many
practical skills, explains environmentally-friendly ways to carry
out common DIY tasks, and covers suppliers / buying materials,
fixings and timber.

8-12 October
Timber Frame Self-build
£595 high-waged; £460 waged; £275 student / unwaged
Centre for Alternative Technology, Machynlleth, Powys, SY20 9AZ
Tel: 01654 705981
Email: courses@cat.org.uk www.cat.org.uk/courses
Using the expertise of Self-Build architects and builders who have
designed and built timber frame homes, participants are guided
in theoretical and practical sessions through the basic principles.
A series of frames will be made and erected in the practical
sessions and classroom sessions will cover the timber frame
method, ecological building methods, design for low energy
sustainable housing and appropriate services for low energy
buildings.

12-14 October
Introduction to Heat Pumps
£320 high-waged; £230 waged; £175 student / unwaged
Centre for Alternative Technology,
Machynlleth, Powys, SY20 9AZ
Tel: 01654 705981
Email: courses@cat.org.uk www.cat.org.uk/courses
Of the new low carbon technologies, heat pumps are possibly the
most perplexing. This course will introduce participants to the
complexities of heat pump systems, covering how the heat pump
works, how heat is captured from the ground (or air) and how the
heat is then best distributed around the building. It will also cover
energy needs for different types of building's such that participants
can make an informed decision as to whether a heat pump
installation is (or is not) appropriate.

15-19 October
Timber Framing From Scratch
£450
Weald & Downland Open Air Museum, Singleton, Chichester,
West Sussex PO18 0EU   Tel: 01243 811464
Email: courses@wealddown.co.uk Web: www.wealddown.co.uk
A superb opportunity to gain hands-on experience of timber
framing. A 5 day practical course introducing students to the
historic use of structural oak framing, tools and techniques. The
posts, cills, plates and tie beams of a 10' square timber frame
are prefabricated during the course using only traditional tools
and techniques, and the frame is erected on the final afternoon.

26-28 October
Hydro Electric Power Systems
£320 high-waged; £230 waged; £175 student / unwaged
Centre for Alternative Technology,
Machynlleth, Powys, SY20 9AZ
Tel: 01654 705981
Email: courses@cat.org.uk www.cat.org.uk/courses
CAT has years of experience of installing and running small scale
HEP systems. This course will help you assess your site's
potential, choose the correct equipment and give you the
information you need to install and maintain the system

26-28 October
Self-build Solar Hot Water
£1695 including system, £150 excluding system
(Food and accommodation included).
Low-Impact Living Initiative, Redfield Community, Winslow, Bucks,
MK18 3LZ   Tel/Fax: 01296 714184
Email: lili@lowimpact.org.uk Web: www.lowimpact.org.uk
Participants leave with their entire system, tailored to their needs,
plus a manual explaining how the system works and how to
install it. (Attendees do not have to buy a system - it is not
suitable if you have a mains pressure hot water cylinder or combi
boiler). Course begins with a theory session explaining solar
water heating and the system in detail. You then build and
pressure test your pump & control set, expansion vessel kit and air
separator. No plumbing experience needed - this will build
confidence in cutting and soldering copper, using expansion joints
and fixing leaks. Additional sessions on installing/ maintaining your
system, including fixing the panels to your roof, and replacing a
cylinder.

29 October - 2 November
Eco Design & Construction
£595 high-waged; £460 waged; £275 student / unwaged
Centre for Alternative Technology, Machynlleth, Powys, SY20 9AZ
Tel: 01654 705981
Email: courses@cat.org.uk www.cat.org.uk/courses
This course is suitable for builders, architects and those who
want to investigate aspects of eco-design and construction that
are outside the current mainstream training and education in
architecture and building. A holistic approach to eco design will
be outlined, aimed at producing low energy, sustainable buildings
with a minimal environmental footprint.

NOVEMBER

9-11 November
Domestic Wind Power Systems
£320 high-waged; £230 waged; £175 student / unwaged
Centre for Alternative Technology,
Machynlleth, Powys, SY20 9AZ
Tel: 01654 705981
Email: courses@cat.org.uk www.cat.org.uk/courses
This course is suitable for those interested in buying and
installing an aerogenerator as well as those with a general
interest in the subject. Sessions will cover wind energy, stand-
alone systems, siting of machines and grid-linked systems.

9-11 November
**Homebuilding & Renovating Show - Harrogate International
Centre**
£8 on door, £5 in advance, free to H&R magazine subscribers.
Tickets - Tel:0870 010 9031 (Subscribers: 0870 010 0218)
Web: www.homebuildingshow.co.uk
Visitor Enquiries - Tel: 0207 970 4249
Email: showenquiries@centaur.co.uk
From the initial stages of planning to the
actual process of converting, renovating,
remodeling, building from scratch or
extending your home, the Homebuilding & Renovating Shows
provides the self-builder and renovator with all the inspiration,
solutions, products and services needed to build their dream
home. Each event creates an exciting and stimulating place
where you can meet hundreds of exhibitors, gain free one-to-one
advice from the Homebuilding & Renovating Magazine and local
experts, attend free seminar programmes, discover the latest
products and services, learn about the best financial packages
and find your dream plot of land ready for development.

23-25 November
Building with Timber
£180 high-waged; £150 waged; £120 student / unwaged
Low-Impact Living Initiative, Redfield Community, Winslow, Bucks,
MK18 3LZ   Tel/Fax: 01296 714184
Email: lili@lowimpact.org.uk Web: www.lowimpact.org.uk
Participants will leave equipped with the know-how and
confidence to complete a timber building project. The course is
particularly aimed at those wishing to start building their own low-
impact home or similar structure. Topics covered are: location;
design; planning and grants; building control; footings; materials
specification; sourcing / recycling; local timber procurement;
materials quality control; base construction; wall structures,
insulation and windows; external cladding and roofing; heating,
water and electrics; flooring, steps and ramps.

24-25 November
Homebuilding & Renovating Show - Bath & West Showground
£8 on door, £5 in advance, free to H&R magazine subscribers.
Tickets - Tel:0870 010 9031 (Subscribers: 0870 010 0218)
Web: www.homebuildingshow.co.uk
Visitor Enquiries - Tel: 0207 970 4249
Email: showenquiries@centaur.co.uk
From the initial stages of planning to the
actual process of converting, renovating,
remodeling, building from scratch or extending your home, the
Homebuilding & Renovating Shows provides the self-builder and
renovator with all the inspiration, solutions, products and
services needed to build their dream home. Each event creates
an exciting and stimulating place where you can meet hundreds
of exhibitors, gain free one-to-one advice from the Homebuilding
& Renovating Magazine and local experts, attend free seminar
programmes, discover the latest products and services, learn
about the best financial packages and find your dream plot of
land ready for development.

26-30 November
Renewable Energy Heating Systems
£595 high-waged; £460 waged; £275 student / unwaged
Centre for Alternative Technology, Machynlleth, Powys, SY20 9AZ
Tel: 01654 705981
Email: courses@cat.org.uk www.cat.org.uk/courses
Various technologies will be examined, including, solar water
heating, biomass, heat pumps, domestic CHP and gas condensing
boilers. Advice will be given on making an informed choice, costs,
environmental benefits, installation and ongoing maintenance.

30 November - 2 December
Wind & Solar Electricity
£180 high-waged; £150 waged; £120 student / unwaged
Low-Impact Living Initiative, Redfield Community, Winslow, Bucks,
MK18 3LZ   Tel/Fax: 01296 714184
Email: lili@lowimpact.org.uk Web: www.lowimpact.org.uk
Run your household appliances with the power of the wind and the
sun. Course provides an overview of the basic principles and the
technology of solar and wind electrical systems offering
participants the theoretical knowledge and practical experience
required to design and install small renewable energy systems. It
is aimed at the general public, those in the business, non-profit,
public and academic sectors who wish to get an introduction to
renewable energy electrical technology in general, as well as those
wishing to install renewable energy systems. The emphasis will be
on how things work and what it is practicable to do, and
participants will have the opportunity to discuss their own projects.
No previous electrical knowledge necessary.

When's the next Homebuilding & Renovating Show?

● **National**	NEC, Birmingham 22 - 25 March 2007	NEXT SHOW
● **Glasgow**	SECC 12 - 13 May 2007	
● **Thames Valley**	Newbury Showground 23 - 24 June 2007	
● **London**	ExCeL 21 - 23 September 2007	
● **Harrogate**	Harrogate International Centre 9 - 11 November 2007	
● **Somerset**	The Bath & West Showground 24 - 25 November 2007	

Photos kindly supplied by: Nigel Rigden, Jeremy Phillips, Border Oak, Andrew Lee

HOMEBUILDING & RENOVATING SHOW

The UK's leading self-build and renovating shows

Organised by

In association with the magazine

For more information and to save £'s on advance tickets visit